Network
Synthesis

New York · John Wiley & Sons, Inc.
London · Chapman & Hall, Ltd.

Network Synthesis

VOLUME I

David F. Tuttle, Jr.

Professor of Electrical Engineering
Stanford University

Preface

Here, in this book, is an attempt to present in readable form the most important ideas used in the synthesis of those electric circuits that are called networks. It supposes a reasonable background in circuit analysis and some familiarity with the complex frequency variable. But some of these matters are reviewed in the first chapters.

The work is based chiefly on standard network theory, for the sources of which consult the bibliography. There are, however, occasional new proofs and points of view, especially in the discussion of approximation; to these the potential analogy contributes greatly.

The book has evolved from the teaching of a graduate course in Network Synthesis over a number of years. An expansion has occurred in the process with the addition of material intended to make the work complete, in the sense that nearly all subjects discussed are supported by demonstrations or proofs. It is incomplete in that not all known network-synthesis methods are presented, but it does give a thorough discussion of those most important. These have been drawn primarily from the wide literature of the subject and from experience. In this the author's students in the course, and students engaged in thesis work, have been of tremendous assistance.

How the book is arranged and what is in it the Table of Contents shows. How the book may be used as a text for a course of reasonable length requires some explanation. It is possible to discuss at least the major ideas in this volume, devoted to the two-terminal (one-port) network or one-terminal pair, in a one-quarter (three-month) course. This necessitates that certain lengthy demonstrations be omitted and that some matters receive only passing attention. It requires the guidance of a careful teacher—or a very discriminating attitude in the independent student. In such a course one must pass rapidly over the first three chapters, on the assumption that they are primarily review.

Chapter 4 is one of several chapters in which it is easy to lose sight of the forest in examining the trees. Its essential contribution is the notion of *positive reality* based solely on the assumed passive character of networks; the rest is detail of demonstration, which should be examined to an extent determined by the time available and one's need for detail of derivation.

The first part of Chapter 5 is important, for it discusses general properties; so also are its last six sections, but here again there are important ideas (the principles of the testing) together with derivation detail that may well be passed over.

In Chapter 6 the first synthesis occurs, and this should not be slighted. In Chapter 7 a similar case is treated, and here one can economize on time by omitting all but the parallelism, which is enough.

Chapter 8 returns to general properties, and discusses them at a length not necessary in a short course. The teacher should consider how the integral developments of the first nine sections can be abridged. Of the remaining material perhaps Sections 8.11 and 8.17 will suffice as illustrations. The conclusions of Section 8.16 should not be overlooked.

Chapters 9 and 10 deal with synthesis once more, in detail that again is very likely to obscure the forest. In Chapter 9 one may generally read lightly through the proofs and developments, but must study at least the results: what the Brune and Darlington methods accomplish, a general picture of their mechanics, and above all the basic points they make (that positive reality is sufficient for realization, and that one resistor is the most one needs, if so minded). There are many interesting matters in Chapter 10, but a general appreciation of these methods is enough, although Sections 10.06, 10.07, and 10.08 should receive some attention.

Chapters 11 and 12 provide an interlude of easier reading, for they have no proofs, but discuss how networks are used and some of the difficulties that arise in practical application of the theory of the previous chapters. They do not require lengthy discussion.

In Chapters 13 and 14 we return to mathematical matters, and again in detail unnecessary for a short course. The first five and the last five sections of Chapter 13 should be studied; the two intermediate sections that develop Taylor approximation in detail may be discussed briefly by an instructor who is careful to stress the essential ideas. The first eleven sections of the treatment in Chapter 14 contain the important ideas of the potential analogy. Here again one must be discriminating, if in a hurry, for there is much detail that can be skipped. But the *raison d'être* of this chapter, the utility of the analogy, the rôle of the conductor, and the quantization process should be understood.

Chapter 15 attempts to tie together the various threads spun in the preceding chapters. Benefit will be gained in proportion to the time spent in following through the details of the illustrative syntheses that make it up. The same applies, of course, to *all* the work done, and problems are provided for the necessary practice. These are numerous, and of a wide range of difficulty, from mere exercises to proposals for exploring interesting byways and extensions of the text; selection should be made, in accordance with the time available, to suit the material chosen for study. Here again the guidance of a good teacher is extremely helpful, but the discriminating student will also be able to choose for himself.

In a longer course the student can naturally pause for digestion of ideas and can consider the formal developments omitted in the shorter course. The student with a strong interest may spend considerable time in completely assimilating the book. It provides material for such advanced study and may also serve as a reference book for engineers engaged in the application of network theory.

A text or reference book carries an author's name, but of course it is not solely the work of that man. It is actually the work of many people, organized and coordinated by the nominal author—that is his job, and in doing it he adds whatever freshness and originality he can. I cannot make an accurate listing of my debts here. But I wish specifically to acknowledge indebtedness to the teaching of E. A. Guillemin (at the Massachusetts Institute of Technology), to A. J. Grossman and others at the Bell Telephone Laboratories, and to my colleagues and especially my students at Stanford University, whose criticism has been invaluable.

DAVID F. TUTTLE, JR.

Stanford, California
November, 1957

Contents

1. Introduction 1

   1.01   The aim of this book   1
   1.02   Variables   2
   1.03   Some restrictions on network form   3
   1.04   Summary   5

2. Network Elements and How They Behave . . . 6

   2.01   The elements   6
   2.02   Network analysis   9
   2.03   The loop method of analysis   11
   2.04   The node method of analysis   12
   2.05   Remarks   14
   2.06   Duality   15
   2.07   The sinusoidal steady state   15
   2.08   Immittance   18
   2.09   Circuit theorems   19
   2.10   Summary   22
   2.11   References   22

3. The Complex Frequency Variable 24

   3.01   Shorthand   24
   3.02   The Laplace-transformation approach   25
   3.03   A straightforward alternative approach   26
   3.04   Still another approach   27
   3.05   The complex frequency variable   28
   3.06   The nature of network functions   30
   3.07   Tools   32
   3.08   Complex numbers and the complex variable   32
   3.09   Functional notions   34

3.10   The derivative   36
3.11   Interesting points   38
3.12   Integration   40
3.13   Taylor series   42
3.14   Laurent series   46
3.15   Singularities   48
3.16   Classification of functions   50
3.17   Partial-fraction expansion   50
3.18   Laurent series and partial fractions   52
3.19   Expansion in partial fractions   53
3.20   Contour integration   58
3.21   Evaluation of residues   61
3.22   Another theorem of Cauchy   64
3.23   Some consequences of Cauchy's theorem   65
3.24   Mapping   70
3.25   An application of conformal mapping   77
3.26   A formulary   81
3.27   Infinite products   84
3.28   Summary   87
3.29   References   88
       Problems   88

4. A Consideration of Energy, with Some Remarkable Conclusions   107

4.01   Energy and power   107
4.02   Power in the passive one-terminal pair   108
4.03   Energy in the passive one-terminal pair   112
4.04   Equivalence between conditions   116
4.05   Discussion   121
4.06   Further discussion   123
4.07   Power and energy functions   125
4.08   Magnetic stored energy   129
4.09   Electric stored energy   133
4.10   Dissipated energy   134
4.11   Quadratic forms   134
4.12   The utility of these functions   139
4.13   Positive-real functions   143
4.14   Positive-real functions, continued   145
4.15   Summary   153
4.16   References   154
       Problems   154

5. Properties of Driving-Point Immittance Functions—I   163

5.01   A corollary   163
5.02   First property   164
5.03   Second property   164
5.04   Third property   166

5.05 Fourth property   167
5.06 Fifth property   168
5.07 Sixth property   171
5.08 Seventh property   172
5.09 Eighth property   173
5.10 Even and odd parts   173
5.11 Ninth property   176
5.12 Hurwitz polynomials   177
5.13 A test for positive reality   179
5.14 A test for pole location   183
5.15 Tests for sign of $\mathbf{Re}\, F(j\omega)$ 197
5.16 Discussion   216
5.17 Conclusion   220
5.18 References   220
      Problems   220

6. The Nondissipative (L-C) One-Terminal Pair . . 231

6.01 The L-C case   232
6.02 Zeros and poles   232
6.03 Reactance (susceptance) slope and the separation property   235
6.04 The formal nature of a reactance function   238
6.05 Partial fractions and synthesis   240
6.06 The reactance proper   250
6.07 The frequency pattern   252
6.08 Element values   253
6.09 Biformity   258
6.10 The nonuniqueness of synthesis   261
6.11 Another point of view   265
6.12 Canonic forms   271
6.13 Alternative forms   273
6.14 Examples   276
6.15 Summary   287
6.16 References   289
      Problems   289

7. The R-C and R-L One-Terminal Pairs . . . 302

7.01 The R-C case   302
7.02 Zeros and poles   303
7.03 The slope and separation properties   304
7.04 The formal nature of an R-C impedance function   309
7.05 The partial-fraction expansion   311
7.06 Elements   317
7.07 Corollaries   319
7.08 A second canonic realization   321
7.09 Discussion   326
7.10 Another canonic R-C network   328

7.11 The fourth canonic *R-C* network 335
7.12 *R-C* realization 339
7.13 Examples 342
7.14 *R-L* networks 351
7.15 Summary 355
7.16 References 357
Problems 357

8. Properties of Driving-Point Immitance Functions—II 368

8.01 The concept of minimum reactance and minimum susceptance 368
8.02 The concept of minimum resistance and minimum conductance 373
8.03 Minimum immittance functions 380
8.04 The relation between resistance and reactance (conductance and susceptance) 381
8.05 Additional forms of the relations 387
8.06 The reactance and resistance integral theorems 391
8.07 The relation between magnitude and angle 393
8.08 Summary 398
8.09 An application of the integral relations 398
8.10 Interlude 409
8.11 The Brune-Gewertz method: from resistance (conductance) to immittance function 410
8.12 The Brune-Gewertz method: from reactance (susceptance) to immittance function 422
8.13 From magnitude to immittance function 430
8.14 From angle to immittance function 437
8.15 Interlude 456
8.16 Necessary and sufficient properties of parts of immittance functions 457
8.17 Bode's method: from resistance (conductance) to immittance function 458
8.18 Bode's method: from reactance (susceptance) to immittance function 465
8.19 Review 470
8.20 References 471
Problems 471

9. The *R-L-C* One-Terminal Pair—I 503

9.01 An inventory 504
9.02 Brune's realization 504
9.03 Generalization 513
9.04 Pseudo-p-r functions 514
9.05 Brune's realization, continued 526
9.06 Variations of the Brune procedure 534
9.07 A new point of view 539

9.08   A further variation of the Brune process   543
9.09   The Brune method in retrospect; Darlington's extension
       549
9.10   The zeros of **Ev** $Z(p)$ 551
9.11   The ladder-network point of view   556
9.12   Pseudo-p-r functions again   564
9.13   One-resistor realization   568
9.14   Recapitulation   583
9.15   References   587
       Problems   587

10. The *R-L-C* One-Terminal Pair—II   607

10.01   Realization without mutual inductance   607
10.02   Another point of view   618
10.03   Separation without surplus factors   627
10.04   Separation with surplus factors   632
10.05   But the end is not yet   638
10.06   Realization of the general one-terminal *R-L-C* pair   646
10.07   Equivalent and inverse networks   647
10.08   Constant-resistance networks   650
10.09   Conclusion   655
10.10   References   655
        Problems   656

11. Some Applications   678

11.01   Uses of one-terminal pairs   678
11.02   Distortion correction   679
11.03   Impedance correction and simulation   684
11.04   One-resistor realizations   685
11.05   Interstage and feedback networks   687
11.06   Conclusion   689
11.07   References   689
        Problems   690

12. Some Practical Matters   702

12.01   Actual element behavior   702
12.02   Parasitic dissipation   706
12.03   Predistortion   709
12.04 Q and resonance   712
12.05   Miscellaneous matters   720
12.06   Summary   722
12.07   References   722
        Problems   722

13. Approximation 741

13.01   Approximation   741
13.02   Error   744
13.03   A very straightforward method   746
13.04   Least-mean-square-error approximation   756
13.05   Taylor approximation   760
13.06   Taylor approximation, continued   772
13.07   The Padé table   777
13.08   Chebyshev approximation   782
13.09   Weighted approximation   786
13.10   Some special cases   787
13.11   In retrospect   802
13.12   References   803
        Problems   803

14. The Potential Analogy 832

14.01   Origins of the analogy   832
14.02   Electrostatics in two dimensions   833
14.03   Analogies   844
14.04   The rôle of the conductor   851
14.05   Approximation of a constant   855
14.06   The complex-potential plane   861
14.07   Charge and potential in the w plane   872
14.08   Approximation of a constant, continued   879
14.09   The transformation $p = \sinh w$ 884
14.10   Approximation of a constant, continued   891
14.11   Recapitulation   896
14.12   Arbitrary zeros   899
14.13   High bands and frequency transformations   930
14.14   Internal bands   935
14.15   Taylor and Chebyshev approximation   951
14.16   Constant magnitude of immittance   960
14.17   Odd-function approximation of a constant—I   975
14.18   Odd-function approximation of a constant—II   984
14.19   Recapitulation   1009
14.20   Analog computation   1010
14.21   References   1011
        Problems   1012

15. Illustrations 1051

15.01   Looking back   1051
15.02   Illustration I   1052
15.03   Illustration II   1062
15.04   Illustration III   1084
15.05   Conclusion   1099
        Problems   1099

Appendix A   Computation   1103

A.1   Introduction   1103
A.2   Complex-number computations   1103
A.3   Evaluation of rational functions   1104
A.4   Simultaneous linear equations   1108
A.5   Root finding   1111
A.6   Approximate roots   1112
A.7   Root improvement   1118
A.8   Checking the roots   1124
A.9   Polynomial splitting   1124
A.10 References   1134

Appendix B   The Function $F_0(\omega/\omega_0)$ of § 8.09   .   .   1135

Discussion and tables

Appendix C   Bibliography   1151

Index   1165

1.

Introduction

Begin at the beginning, and go on
till you come to the end; then stop.
—The King of Hearts

1.01 The aim of this book

The purpose of the book is to present the principles of synthesis of electric networks in which steady-state behavior as a function of frequency is all-important. It is only an introduction because there exists much more material than we can cover in a reasonable time.

Samuel Johnson is said to have once defined a network as "anything reticulated or decussated at equal distances with interstices between the intersections." Modern dictionary (and Standards) definitions, although less sesquipedalian, still do not give the precise meaning in which we shall use the word. For us the word *network* will mean a passive electric circuit composed of lumped, linear, constant elements with the three fundamental properties: resistance, inductance, and elastance. We shall find it more convenient at times to describe elements of these types by inverse nomenclature: conductance, reciprocal inductance, and capacitance. In addition, mutual inductance may occur.

These are our building blocks. We shall chiefly investigate how to choose proper values of these elements and how to interconnect them to obtain networks which have desired (preassigned) properties; i.e., we shall investigate how to *synthesize* or *design* networks—that is our aim.

Before we can hope to accomplish anything in putting these blocks together, we must, naturally, have a sound knowledge of how these elements behave. To this end, we shall first review the methods of *analysis* of networks and then proceed to investigate the properties of simple combinations of elements before going on to complicated structures. With knowledge of these properties we shall be in a position to decide just what networks *can* do, and what they *cannot* do—for there are very definite limitations on their behavior. Any overambitious

1

synthesis aims will have to be simplified to reasonable goals before proceeding further. Then, with a reasonable end in view, we can set out toward it.

Concisely, what we have just said indicates three things we must do:

1. obtain a working knowledge of the properties of networks;
2. investigate ways of approximating behavior which may be desired, but which the results of step 1 indicate is not realizable;
3. carry out the actual synthesis (realization) of networks to achieve such attainable ends.

These three steps we shall take in everything we do. Steps 2 and 3, we shall find, do not necessarily lead to *unique* results; in strong contrast to analysis, synthesis may produce *many* "answers."

1.02 Variables

The general laws of behavior which we have are "lumped" (approximate) forms of Maxwell's equations and Ohm's law; they express the instantaneous behavior of elements as functions of time. So in general the synthesis problem is to achieve a desired network response as a function of time. This problem is not only general; it is also very complicated—and it is not yet completely solved. Yet there is a restricted (but very important) synthesis problem which has been investigated over many years and has very practical solutions. This is the problem of synthesis for prescribed characteristics when operating in the a-c steady state, i.e., when all currents and voltages in the network vary sinusoidally with time. It is a condition which obtains when a (single-frequency) sinusoidal generator has been connected and enough time has elapsed for the transients to decay, so that the steady state exists. We shall discuss in detail only this steady a-c state. [The points of view of synthesis for prescribed behavior as a function of time, or considerations of statistical behavior in time, or of information (communication) theory, we do not pretend to consider in this book.]

A logical question at this point is: if time variation (other than sinusoidal variation) is excluded, what of interest then is left? The answer is, networks whose steady-state behavior for one frequency of alternation is different from that for another frequency, networks whose performance is described in terms of steady-state a-c operation but whose performance *varies with frequency*—these are left, and they can be very interesting indeed, and very important. Radically different behavior for different frequencies and over different ranges of frequency may be an extremely useful characteristic, and it is this we shall investigate. Transient effects as the frequency is changed are out of our province, but the steady-state behavior at each of various frequencies, or over various continuous ranges of frequency—this is our territory.

The independent variable of our problem is then going to be *frequency*, the frequency of the sinusoidal (steady-state) alternations taking place in all the currents and voltages of our networks. We shall not immediately abandon time as the independent variable, but shall in these early chapters first establish some fundamental relations leading to the most important properties of networks.

1.03 Some restrictions on network form

Communication and control systems, which are the chief users of networks (Chapter 11), are usually two-wire in nature. They associate the terminals of apparatus in pairs, and in these systems this is the most important (but not the only) manner of using networks. For example, a simple telephone circuit, symbolically, is shown in Fig. 1.03–A, in which

Fig. 1.03–A

two wires connect the two stations. However complicated the system may get, whatever the nature of the apparatus used, this two-wire basis is usually kept, and we'll stick to it. Hence we have a *pair* of conductors as a rule.

A piece of apparatus placed somewhere in a communication system will have then a two-wire input and a two-wire output, as illustrated in Fig. 1.03–B. Networks are no exception, and we often think of networks

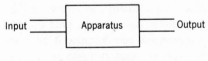

Fig. 1.03–B

as boxes with one pair of input terminals and another pair of output terminals. In general, of course, they may have any number of terminals, and these need not be associated in pairs—but usually they are, so we might as well recognize the fact and limit ourselves to such networks.

If the piece of apparatus is at a terminal of a system, it may look like

Fig. 1.03–C, i.e., a pair of wires go in, but there is no (electric) output. If the piece of apparatus is intermediate in the system, it may look like Fig. 1.03–B, or if it is at a junction point, perhaps it looks like Fig. 1.03–D or 1.03–E.

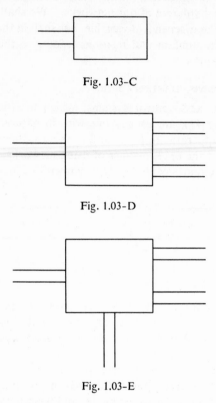

Fig. 1.03–C

Fig. 1.03–D

Fig. 1.03–E

We now generalize our word for two wires, *pair*, and call these boxes (networks) *pairs* also. Specifically, the box in Fig. 1.03–C we call a *one-terminal pair* because it has but one pair of terminals; that in Fig. 1.03–B we call a *two-terminal pair* because it has two pairs of terminals, etc. The adjectives *one-port* and *two-port*, etc., are also used for such networks. The two-terminal pair is often called a *transducer* because it leads signals from one system or circuit (the input) across to another system or circuit (the output). But the term transducer is not, and logically ought not to be, limited to networks, as your imagination can tell you.

We have now defined an alternative name for a two-terminal network, *one-terminal pair*. A *two-terminal pair* is a four-terminal network whose four terminals are associated in pairs. Whether the names with the word *pair*, or those with the word *network*, are used is unimportant, but the "pair" or "port" system is convenient, and emphasizes our restriction to "two-wire-system" networks.

Common sense indicates we should start with the simplest, or one-terminal pair. Once mastered, it will help us with the two-terminal pair. And once we know about two-terminal pairs, we'll be in a better position to tackle three-terminal pairs, etc. Because of space limitations only the first and second of these will be discussed, but they are far and away the most important. Especially is the two-terminal pair interesting and useful, but to understand it we need a prior knowledge of the one-terminal pair; the more complicated networks are nothing but combinations of one-terminal pairs.

1.04 Summary

Here then is the immediate question: What are the properties of the basic network elements, interconnected to form a one-terminal pair, in the steady a-c state, as functions of frequency?

To answer this and to use the results in the synthesis of one-terminal pairs will occupy us for all of the present volume. Only with the knowledge given by this answer can we study the two-terminal pair, which will occupy Volume II.

2.

Network Elements
and How They Behave

What are you able to build with your blocks?
Castles and palaces, temples and docks.
—R. L. S.

Since we are to study first the *properties* of networks, i.e., what they do
after they have been constructed, we start by reviewing the principles of
network analysis. The material of this chapter is condensed, because it
is intended purely as review; it is given only to make sure that we build
on a firm foundation. (Almost any book on a-c circuits or networks
gives these ideas in detail, and there is a list of references at the end of the
chapter.) We are concerned here, then, with *analysis*; specifically, with
the questions: What are the elements of networks, and how do they
behave in combination?

2.01 The elements

We defined the term *element* by implication, in § 1.01; it is a lumped,
linear, constant (with time) resistor, inductor, or capacitor. Our network
elements are of course only idealizations or models of real elements.
But the real elements behave closely as the idealizations do, over usefully
wide frequency ranges, and the idealizations are *much* easier to work
with. Hence we deal with idealized networks (models), but still with
networks which can be closely approximated in practice (of which more
later).

The fundamental network elements obey laws which are derived from
Maxwell's equations and the constitutive equations, including Ohm's law,
on the assumptions of linearity, constancy with time, and lumped (rather
than distributed) nature. Table 2.01–A exhibits these laws, and the
symbols, names, and units we shall use for the elements and their numerical
values. Table 2.01–B exhibits the inverse forms. The inconsistencies in

6

Table 2.01–A

Name (and Property)	Unit	Symbols	Law Governing Behavior
Resistor (resistance)	Ohm (Ω)		$v = Ri$
Inductor or coil (inductance)	Henry (h)		$v = L\dfrac{di}{dt}$
Capacitor or condenser (elastance)	Daraf		$v = S\int i\, dt + \text{constant}$ $= Sq$

Table 2.01–B

Name (and Property)	Unit	Symbols	Law Governing Behavior
Resistor (conductance)	Mho		$i = Gv$
Inductor or coil (reciprocal inductance)			$i = \Gamma\int v\, dt + \text{constant}$ $= \Gamma\psi$
Capacitor or condenser (capacitance)	Farad (f)		$i = C\dfrac{dv}{dt}$

the names of the elements are due to the manner in which circuit analysis developed historically (for it did not initially adopt both viewpoints). For any one element, $RG = 1$, $L\Gamma = 1$, or $SC = 1$. For the variable quantities here the notation is

$i = i(t) = $ instantaneous value of current,

$v = v(t) = $ instantaneous value of voltage (potential difference),

$q = q(t) = $ instantaneous value of charge,

$\psi = \psi(t) = $ instantaneous value of flux linkage.

The arrows and $+$, $-$ signs indicate the assumed directions for flow of (positive) current and voltage rise. Later we shall also use the symbol $e = e(t)$ for the instantaneous value of voltage.

Resistors and capacitors, we assume, have no external fields and hence do not "couple" to one another. We shall permit our coils to have external fields, when desirable, however, so that coupling *may* exist between inductors. This gives us, not another element type, but the supplementary notion of *mutual inductance.*

Name: Coupled inductors or mutual inductance
Property: Mutual inductance
Unit: Henry (h)
Symbols: Shown in Fig. 2.01–A. (The self inductances of the coils are not shown, nor are the voltages due to self inductance.)

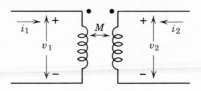

Fig. 2.01–A

Laws governing behavior:

The component of v_2 due to the mutual-inductance effect $= M \dfrac{di_1}{dt}$

(this is the whole of v_2 when $i_2 = 0$)

The component of v_1 due to the mutual-inductance effect $= M \dfrac{di_2}{dt}$

(this is the whole of v_1 when $i_1 = 0$)

The signs to be attached to these terms are determined by the dots on the schematic diagram according to the usual convention. These dots indicate the physical mutual orientation of the coils, and if either *one* were placed at the opposite end of its coil, both mutual-inductance voltages would receive minus signs (equivalent to changing the sign of M) instead of the plus signs in Fig. 2.01–A.

Corollary to mutual inductance is the *transformer,* together with its additional properties (which are necessary and sufficient for its physical existence). (Resistance and capacitance effects in actual transformers are represented by separate elements, if they are to be considered.)

Name: Transformer
Symbols: Shown in Fig. 2.01–B
Properties: Self and mutual inductance
$L_p =$ primary self inductance > 0
$L_s =$ secondary self inductance > 0
$M =$ mutual inductance (may be positive or negative)
$k = \dfrac{|M|}{\sqrt{L_p L_s}} =$ coupling coefficient, $0 \leq k \leq 1$

It is often advantageous in network theory to use the concept of an

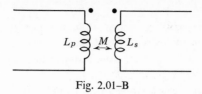

Fig. 2.01–B

ideal transformer. Such a transformer is one for which $k = 1$ and all three inductances become infinite in such fashion that (in the notation of Fig. 2.01–A)

$$\frac{v_2}{v_1} = -\frac{i_1}{i_2} = a, \qquad (2.01\text{--}1)$$

where a represents the ratio of transformation of the ideal transformer. Except for transforming voltage and current thus, the ideal transformer has no effect.

When we interconnect an arbitrary number of these elements, of various values, we form a *network*. It is *passive* because no energy is supplied from within the network; all the energy that may be in the network comes from external sources. Some such current or voltage sources (generators) are needed, of course, to excite the *circuit* [as we may call the combination of network and source(s)] if anything interesting is to happen. (A current source is an idealized device that forces the current at its terminals to have prescribed values as a function of time; a voltage source similarly forces the voltage at its terminals to have prescribed values.) Vacuum tubes and transistors operating in linear regions of their characteristics amount only to combinations of the elements above and sources, but with certain interrelations between the sources and network currents and voltages. We shall not use them enough to warrant extension of our theory to include them; theirs is the domain of *active* networks into which we shall not go.

Most of the time we shall be concerned with networks made up of a finite number of the elements described above. But we shall also have occasion to use our imagination and consider networks composed of a limitless number of elements, i.e., to extend our thinking to what happens when the number of network elements becomes infinite. These infinite "networks" have much in common with systems in which the elements are distributed rather than lumped, e.g., transmission lines. We shall not press the point, however, for such systems should be investigated in terms of their own (partial differential) equations.

2.02 Network analysis

Let us now review briefly the principles of *analysis* of such networks, i.e., of calculation of their behavior when excited by sources.

We use the names

component for a resistor, capacitor, inductor, current, or voltage source (note that sources as well as elements are included in the list—whence the need for a new name—and that mutual inductance does not count as a separate component),

branch for a purely series connection of one or more components,

node for a terminal of a component,

loop for a closed path via one or (usually) several branches,

separate part for a section of a circuit, isolated except possibly for mutual-inductance coupling, i.e., one with no current-carrying (capacitive or resistive or purely self-inductive) connection with the other parts of the circuit

and the symbols

$$e = \text{number of components,}$$
$$N = \text{number of nodes,}$$
$$s = \text{number of separate parts,}$$
$$l = \text{number of } \textit{independent} \text{ loops,}$$
$$n = \text{number of } \textit{independent} \text{ node pairs.}$$

The word *independent* here means roughly that as we mark the loops (node pairs) of a circuit in the process of analysis, the loop (node pair) in question cannot be traced out or formed by combinations of other loops (node pairs) which have already been considered; more precisely, the associated equation of analysis is not equivalent to a linear combination of equations previously written; if it were, it would be superfluous to the analysis.

From topology we get the relations, due originally to Kirchhoff (KI 2)* in this application,

$$l = e - N + s,$$
$$n = N - s, \tag{2.02-1}$$

which tell us how many *independent* loops and node pairs there are, i.e., how many unknowns there really are in the circuit. In complicated cases it may not be easy to find *l* by inspection.

For a circuit, i.e., for interconnected components, the two Kirchhoff laws (KI 3)

$$\Sigma v = 0 \text{ around a loop,}$$
$$\Sigma i = 0 \text{ at a node,} \tag{2.02-2}$$

---

* All such references are to the bibliography. This is not complete—to make it so would be impracticable—but it does give those who are interested a start on further reading. The reference notation used is due to Gardner and Barnes (GA 1).

provide the remaining tools necessary for analysis of circuits. Such analysis can proceed by either of two outstanding methods (or by modifications appropriate to special cases).

2.03 The loop method of analysis

Analysis on the loop basis uses the first Kirchhoff law in (2.02–2), written explicitly for each of l independent loops in the circuit, to set up the network equations. Assuming for the moment that no current sources are present, the equation for loop 1 will have:

(*a*) terms corresponding to the voltage sources on the loop;

(*b*) "self" terms like Ri_1, $L\,di_1/dt$, $S\int i_1\,dt$, containing i_1, the loop current of loop 1;

(*c*) "mutual" terms like Ri_3, $L\,di_2/dt$, $S\int i_4\,dt$, etc., due to elements common to loop 1 and to other loops—as well as terms like $M\,di_2/dt$ due to mutual inductance.

The signs to be attached to the mutual terms depend on the relative directions of flow (through the common element) assumed for the loop currents. We assume the loops so chosen that only two loop currents flow in a common element. We also assume the reference directions for all the loop currents to be chosen in the same (say clockwise) sense, so that the reference directions for the two loop currents flowing in a common element are there opposite. This is usually (but not always) possible; in the exceptional cases the only difference is a disturbance in the symmetry of signs to which these assumptions lead.

The equations for the other $(l - 1)$ loops will have similar form. In brief notation, with

L_{11} = total self inductance on loop 1,

R_{11} = total resistance on loop 1,

S_{11} = total elastance on loop 1,

L_{12} = total self and mutual inductance (with appropriate sign) common to loops 1 and 2,

R_{12} = total resistance common to loops 1 and 2,

S_{12} = total elastance common to loops 1 and 2,

etc.,

and with

$$R_{11}i_1 + L_{11}\frac{di_1}{dt} + S_{11}\int i_1\,dt = a_{11}i_1,$$

$$- R_{12}i_2 - L_{12}\frac{di_2}{dt} - S_{12}\int i_2\,dt = a_{12}i_2,$$

etc.

as definitions of self and mutual operators a_{11}, a_{12}, $\cdots$, we have the set of l equations in this form:

$$a_{11}i_1 + a_{12}i_2 + \cdots = v_1,$$
$$a_{21}i_1 + a_{22}i_2 + \cdots = v_2,$$
$$\cdots \cdots \cdots \cdots \cdots$$
$$a_{l1}i_1 + a_{l2}i_2 + \cdots = v_l,$$

$$(2.03\text{--}1)$$

in which there are l equations and l unknowns. More compactly,

$$\sum_{k=1}^{l} a_{jk}i_k = v_j, \qquad j = 1, 2, 3, \cdots, l, \qquad (2.03\text{--}2)$$

in which the v's represent the *net* driving voltages on the respective loops. It is sometimes convenient to write the third item in each a in terms of loop charge, defined by $q_r = \int i_r \, dt$. If there is a capacitor on the loop in question (loop r), then q_r is actually the part of its charge contributed by i_r; in any case q_r represents the integrated or net charge flowing past a point, due to i_r.

With the assumptions previously mentioned, the use of the minus signs in the mutual operator definitions above results in a neat formulation with all signs positive in (2.03–1). In the numerical equations all self terms will have positive coefficients, and all mutual terms will have negative coefficients. Exceptions may occur when mutual inductance is present; and in some unusual networks, which are not planar, the assumptions are violated, and there will be mixed signs in the mutual terms.

These l equations contain l unknowns, and can be solved for the loop currents. The complete solution may be laborious, but theoretically it can always be carried out.

2.04 The node method of analysis

Analysis on the node basis uses the second Kirchhoff law in (2.02–2), written explicitly for each of n nodes in the circuit, to set up the network equations. On the assumption (for the moment) that no voltage sources are present, the equation for node 1 will have

(*a*) terms corresponding to the current sources attached to the node;

(*b*) "self" terms like Gv_1, $C\,dv_1/dt$, $\Gamma\int v_1\,dt$, containing v_1, the voltage (with respect to a reference node) of node 1;

(*c*) "mutual" terms like Gv_2, $C\,dv_3/dt$, $\Gamma\int v_4\,dt$, etc., due to elements common to node 1 and other nodes.

Mutual inductance complicates the analysis on the node basis; it can be handled (GA 1, GU 5), but when it is present the loop basis may be preferable. The signs to be attached to these mutual terms depend on the relative reference directions assumed for potential rise, with respect to the reference node. We take all node voltages as rises (say) from the reference node.

The equations for the other $(n - 1)$ nodes will have similar form. In brief notation, with

C_{11} = total capacitance attached to node 1,

G_{11} = total conductance attached to node 1,

Γ_{11} = total reciprocal self inductance attached to node 1,

C_{12} = total capacitance common to nodes 1 and 2,

G_{12} = total conductance common to nodes 1 and 2,

Γ_{12} = total reciprocal self inductance common to nodes 1 and 2,

etc.,

and with

$$C_{11} \frac{dv_1}{dt} + G_{11}v_1 + \Gamma_{11} \int v_1 \, dt = b_{11}v_1,$$

$$- C_{12} \frac{dv_2}{dt} - G_{12}v_2 - \Gamma_{12} \int v_2 \, dt = b_{12}v_2,$$

etc.

as definitions of self and mutual operators b_{11}, b_{12}, $\cdot \cdot \cdot$, we have the set of n equations in this form:

$$b_{11}v_1 + b_{12}v_2 + \cdot \cdot \cdot = i_1,$$
$$b_{21}v_1 + b_{22}v_2 + \cdot \cdot \cdot = i_2,$$
$$\cdot \quad \cdot \quad \cdot \quad \cdot \quad \cdot \quad \cdot \quad \cdot \quad \cdot$$
$$b_{n1}v_1 + b_{n2}v_2 + \cdot \cdot \cdot = i_n,$$

$$(2.04\text{--}1)$$

in which there are n equations and n unknowns. More compactly,

$$\sum_{k=1}^{n} b_{jk}v_k = i_j, \qquad j = 1, 2, 3, \cdot \cdot \cdot, n, \qquad (2.04\text{--}2)$$

where the i's represent the net driving currents at the respective nodes.

It is sometimes convenient to write the third item in each b in terms of node "flux linkage," defined by $\psi_r = \int v_r \, dt$. If there is an inductor connected to the node in question (node r), then ψ_r is actually the part of its flux linkage contributed by v_r; in any case ψ_r represents the integrated voltage.

With the reference directions assumed, the use of the minus signs in the mutual operator definitions above results in a neat formulation with all signs positive in (2.04–1). In the numerical equations all self terms will have positive coefficients, and all mutual terms will have negative coefficients. (But for networks with mutual inductance, there may be mixed signs among the mutual terms.)

These n equations contain n unknowns and can be solved for the node voltages. The complete solution may be laborious, but theoretically it can always be carried out.

It will later, in Volume II, be advantageous to modify the analysis above by taking, as unknowns, node-pair voltages which do not all have one node in common. This amounts to abandoning the single reference node and replacing the unknown v_j above by n independent linear combinations thereof, which is perfectly legitimate.

2.05 Remarks

Our choice of method, as between the loop method and the node method, depends on which requires the least work. The numbers l and n may be different, indicating that one approach involves fewer equations. Again, we may want to consider whether it is a loop current or a node voltage that we actually want, and how this affects the total amount of work. In general, if n is less than l, we shall want to use the node method, and vice versa.

If current sources are present, and if the loop method is used, the loop currents for loops containing current sources are immediately known (forced)—or some interrelation is known—and the number of unknowns is reduced. If voltage sources are present, and the node method is used, the node voltages for nodes to which voltage sources are attached are immediately known (forced)—or some interrelation is known—and the number of unknowns is reduced. Or (what is usually the same thing) we may wish to exchange current sources for voltage sources in the first case, or voltage sources for current sources in the second case, according to known laws, before writing the equations.

In the loop method it is possible to use other currents as unknowns, if they are suitable linear combinations of the geometrical loop currents used above; they may then not represent actual currents (but merely combinations thereof) so that a different name ought then to be given the method. Similarly the node method can be modified (as suggested in § 2.04). A general treatment of network analysis (GU 5) would consider these transformations in detail, but this is neither necessary nor appropriate here.

2.06 Duality

The evident parallelism between the two formulations of Tables 2.01–A and 2.01–B, and between the loop and node methods, is closely connected with the concept of *duality* (GA 1, GA 5, DU 2, RU 1). To a mathematician, the sets of simultaneous equations in the two methods are of like form, since the physical meaning of the letters is of no consequence to him. It may well happen, in fact, that the loop-basis equations of one circuit and the node-basis equations of another circuit are identical in number and form of equations, except for numerical values (including signs) and dimensions of coefficients. Then the two circuits are called *duals*, and have identical mathematics, except for numerical values and for these changes in physical interpretations of quantities:

$$R \leftrightarrow G, \qquad S \leftrightarrow \Gamma, \qquad q \leftrightarrow \psi.$$
$$L \leftrightarrow C, \qquad v \leftrightarrow i,$$

Methods of finding dual networks (if they exist) are known, and the utility of dual networks will later develop quite naturally.

We shall for convenience extend the meaning of duality to include not only circuits and networks but also processes, methods of analysis, and the like. Then the loop basis and the node basis are duals; these two bases for analysis procedures lead to dual methods of analysis. Many examples of two alternative, dual ideas or methods of doing a job will come up as we go along. In each case the mathematics will be identical for the two alternatives and hence need be developed but once; a simple change of symbols then gives the dual result, with no additional work.

2.07 The sinusoidal steady state

Since our interest is in the a-c (sinusoidal) steady state, we need not discuss the *complete* solution of (2.03–1) or (2.04–1). When sufficient time has elapsed after a sine-wave generator is connected, all currents and voltages will vary sinusoidally with time, and at the frequency of the source. There are special, idealized networks (without resistance), to be sure, in which other natural sinusoidal currents and voltages, of frequencies characteristic of the network, also exist in theory. Our sinusoidal steady-state analysis and synthesis will ignore these natural currents and voltages and consider only the forced, same-frequency-as-source effects. Since no actual network is resistance-free, these special natural currents and voltages do not really exist in the steady state in practice, and hence cause no trouble.

With the notation

f = frequency in cycles per second,

$\omega = 2\pi f =$ corresponding angular velocity, or frequency in radians per second,

we have

$$v = V_m \cos{(\omega t + \beta_v)},$$
$$i = I_m \cos{(\omega t + \beta_i)},$$

as typical mathematical expressions for voltage and current, in which the zero-time phase angles β will of course be different for different currents and voltages. Much network literature uses the symbol e rather than v for voltage, and we shall also, in this, the steady state. The network voltage and current functions are then

$$e_1 = E_{1m} \cos{(\omega t + \beta_{e1})},$$
$$e_2 = E_{2m} \cos{(\omega t + \beta_{e2})},$$
$$\cdot \quad \cdot \quad \cdot \quad \cdot \quad \cdot \quad \cdot \quad \cdot$$
$$i_1 = I_{1m} \cos{(\omega t + \beta_{i1})},$$
$$i_2 = I_{2m} \cos{(\omega t + \beta_{i2})},$$
$$\cdot \quad \cdot \quad \cdot \quad \cdot \quad \cdot \quad \cdot \quad \cdot$$

As one learns early in a-c circuit theory, the use of complex numbers simplifies the analysis, so we let

$$e_1 = E_{1m} \cos{(\omega t + \beta_{e1})} = \mathbf{Re}\, E_{1m} e^{j(\omega t + \beta_{e1})}$$
$$= \mathbf{Re}\, E_1 e^{j\omega t},$$

in which

$$E_1 = E_{1m} e^{j\beta_{e1}},$$

and we let

$$i_1 = I_{1m} \cos{(\omega t + \beta_{i1})} = \mathbf{Re}\, I_{1m} e^{j(\omega t + \beta_{i1})}$$
$$= \mathbf{Re}\, I_1 e^{j\omega t},$$

in which $I_1 = I_{1m} e^{j\beta_{i1}}$, etc. When these forms are substituted in the equations, i and v or e no longer appear. Since the operators $\mathbf{Re}$, d/dt, and $\int dt$ obey commutative and distributive laws, the symbol $\mathbf{Re}$ need be written but once, at the beginning of each equation, and indeed it may justifiably be omitted entirely. Differentiation becomes merely multiplication by $j\omega$, integration becomes merely division by $j\omega$, and the common $e^{j\omega t}$ may be divided out, as usual. The equations then become

$$Z_{11}I_1 + Z_{12}I_2 + \cdots = E_1,$$
$$Z_{21}I_1 + Z_{22}I_2 + \cdots = E_2,$$
$$\cdot \quad \cdot \quad \cdot \quad \cdot \quad \cdot \quad \cdot \quad \cdot \quad \cdot \quad \cdot$$
$$Z_{l1}I_1 + Z_{l2}I_2 + \cdots = E_l,$$

$$(2.07\text{--}1)$$

and

$$Y_{11}E_1 + Y_{12}E_2 + \cdots = I_1,$$
$$Y_{21}E_1 + Y_{22}E_2 + \cdots = I_2,$$

$$\cdot \quad \cdot \quad \cdot \quad \cdot \quad \cdot \quad \cdot \quad \cdot \quad \cdot \quad \cdot \quad \cdot$$ (2.07-2)

$$Y_{n1}E_1 + Y_{n2}E_2 + \cdots = I_n,$$

in which

$$Z_{11} = L_{11}j\omega + R_{11} + S_{11}/j\omega \qquad (2.07\text{-}3)$$

and replaces a_{11},

$$Z_{12} = -L_{12}j\omega - R_{12} - S_{12}/j\omega \qquad (2.07\text{-}4)$$

and replaces a_{12}, etc., and

$$Y_{11} = C_{11}j\omega + G_{11} + \Gamma_{11}/j\omega \qquad (2.07\text{-}5)$$

and replaces b_{11},

$$Y_{12} = -C_{12}j\omega - G_{12} - \Gamma_{12}/j\omega \qquad (2.07\text{-}6)$$

and replaces b_{12}, etc.   That is,

Z_{11} = total *impedance* on loop 1,

Z_{12} = impedance common to loops 1 and 2, with signs (usually) reversed,

Y_{11} = total *admittance* connected to node 1,

Y_{12} = admittance common to nodes 1 and 2, with signs (usually) reversed,

etc.

These Z's can be written by inspection of the circuit diagram and are called the *self* and *mutual impedances* of the circuit analyzed on the loop basis.   The Y's can also be written by inspection and are called the *self* and *mutual admittances* of the circuit analyzed on the node basis.   Mathematically, they are better called impedance and admittance *functions*, since we shall be interested in how they vary with frequency; for brevity we shall often omit "function."

The equations are now purely *algebraic*; no derivatives or integrals appear.   Their solution (by determinants or otherwise) is a straightforward, though possibly lengthy, operation.   Symbolically written (in determinant notation for brevity), the solutions are

$$I_1 = \frac{\Delta_{11}}{\Delta} E_1 + \frac{\Delta_{21}}{\Delta} E_2 + \cdots + \frac{\Delta_{l1}}{\Delta} E_l,$$

(2.07-7)

$$I_2 = \frac{\Delta_{12}}{\Delta} E_1 + \frac{\Delta_{22}}{\Delta} E_2 + \cdots + \frac{\Delta_{l2}}{\Delta} E_l,$$

etc.

and

$$E_1 = \frac{\Delta_{11}}{\Delta} I_1 + \frac{\Delta_{21}}{\Delta} I_2 + \cdots + \frac{\Delta_{n1}}{\Delta} I_n,$$

$$E_2 = \frac{\Delta_{12}}{\Delta} I_1 + \frac{\Delta_{22}}{\Delta} I_2 + \cdots + \frac{\Delta_{n2}}{\Delta} I_n,$$

$$(2.07\text{--}8)$$

etc.

in which Δ denotes the determinant of the appropriate set of equations, called the *system* (*circuit*) *determinant*; for most circuits, it is not the same for the two bases of analysis. Δ_{12}, Δ_{13}, and the like represent the appropriate cofactors, used in the solution of the sets of equations. Note that the first subscript refers to the cause (to a row in the array of original equations), and the second to the effect (to a column in the array). There are processes for evaluating these determinants if the need arises (GU 3), or it may be preferable to solve the equations by elimination rather than to use determinants. In any event we have above a formal solution to the analysis problem in the a-c steady state.

2.08 Immittance

It seems reasonable to expect from the parallelism in the foregoing that impedance and admittance are about the same sort of animal. They form an example of a pair of concepts which are dual, in fact. Bode (BO 3) uses the word *immittance* (meaning "either impedance or admittance") in discussing general properties which apply to both, and this is a handy word, which we shall use. These immittance functions are old friends, and have a standard nomenclature and symbolism,

$$\begin{aligned}(\text{impedance}) &= (\text{resistance}) \; + j\,(\text{reactance}),\\ Z \qquad &= \qquad R \qquad + jX,\end{aligned}$$

and

$$\begin{aligned}(\text{admittance}) &= (\text{conductance}) + j\,(\text{susceptance}),\\ Y \qquad &= \qquad G \qquad + jB.\end{aligned}$$

Remember that immittances are complex numbers, with both real and imaginary parts in general; the names and symbols are given above. The following interrelations hold, if Y and Z refer to the *same* driving (measuring) point:

$$Y = \frac{1}{Z} = \frac{1}{R + jX} = \frac{R - jX}{R^2 + X^2} = G + jB,$$

$$(2.08\text{--}1)$$

$$G = \frac{R}{R^2 + X^2}, \qquad B = \frac{-X}{R^2 + X^2}.$$

$$Z = \frac{1}{Y} = \frac{1}{G + jB} = \frac{G - jB}{G^2 + B^2} = R + jX,$$

$$R = \frac{G}{G^2 + B^2}, \qquad X = \frac{-B}{G^2 + B^2}.$$

(2.08-2)

2.09 Circuit theorems

Of the many theorems of network analysis, we state only the few which we may have occasion to use—and those quite briefly, on the assumption that they have been proved elsewhere.

Superposition. Since we have assumed linearity throughout, the "behavior" of a circuit when two or more driving forces are applied is the sum of the individual "behaviors" when the forces are separately applied.

Reciprocity. So long as only "bilateral" elements are used (those that behave the same in both directions, like the inductor, capacitor, and resistor) we find $Z_{12} = Z_{21}$, and similarly for all mutual immittances. Our elements are all "bilateral"; hence this will hold for all our networks. From another point of view, we can say (perfectly generally, not just for the steady state) that an interchange of driving and observing (measuring) points and apparatus in a circuit will not affect the measurements.

Equivalent source theorems (stated here for the steady state).

(a) *Equivalent voltage source.* As far as external effects go, any circuit with two terminals may be replaced by an impedance and voltage source in series: the impedance is to be that seen when one is looking into the original circuit (with voltage sources short-circuited and current sources open-circuited, but with any associated impedances left in the circuit); the voltage source is to have the value of the voltage existing across the (open) terminals of the original circuit.

(b) *Equivalent current source.* The dual theorem states that the circuit may equally well be replaced, as far as external effects go, by an impedance of the same value as in (a), in parallel with a current source which is to have the value of the current which flows between the (short-circuited) terminals of the original circuit.

(c) *Interchange of current and voltage sources.* By the use of these two theorems we can replace voltage sources associated with impedances by current sources associated with admittances, and vice versa.

Theorem (a) is usually called Thévenin's theorem (TH 2). It were better named for Helmholtz who seems to have given the first concrete statement of it, though in a restricted case (HE 1, HO 1). The dual form (b) is often called Norton's theorem (WI 2). It follows from (a) directly, by duality.

Maximum power transfer. In the steady state, the maximum possible power transfer at a point in a two-wire system occurs when the impedance looking in the load direction at that point, and the impedance looking toward the source(s) [the equivalent impedance in (*a*) above] at the same point, are complex conjugates. The assumption here is that the impedance looking toward the load is variable, the circuit toward the generators (sources) is fixed, and maximum power toward the load is desired.

Normalization. This is not really a theorem, but merely an extremely useful trick, the use of changes in scale. In practice, inductance values are frequently measured in millihenrys or microhenrys, capacitance values in microfarads or micromicrofarads, resistance values in kilohms or megohms, and frequencies in kilocycles or megacycles per second. The attendant powers of ten can usually be eliminated from most of the calculations by these changes of scale, which are of two kinds.

(*a*) *Impedance scale.* A consistent change in the units of the Z's or Y's in the equations of § 2.07 will affect the E's or I's by the same factor. If this change is made in all elements of the network, it is thus easy to correct for its effect in the last step of the work, and this change may simplify the intermediate calculations. The change is convenient in both analysis and synthesis and does not destroy the generality of the work. Taking some convenient reference value, say R_0 ohms, we shall often use, instead of L, R, S (actual element values), the *normalized* element values

$$\frac{L}{R_0}, \qquad \frac{R}{R_0}, \qquad \frac{S}{R_0} \qquad (2.09-1)$$

or (from the dual point of view) instead of C, G, Γ (actual element values) the normalized element values

$$CR_0, \qquad GR_0, \qquad \Gamma R_0. \qquad (2.09-2)$$

We may temporarily consider these normalized element values to be the actual values; if R_0 represents some actual resistance in the network, the normalized value of that resistance is unity and we can say this normalized network is designed (or analyzed) on a "one-ohm" basis (referring to that resistor). When the work is completed (if it is a synthesis problem), we need only multiply all inductance and resistance values by R_0, and divide all capacitance values by R_0, to obtain the actual desired level of impedance. (Notice the lack of symmetry in the process, caused by the conventional measurement of capacitor values in terms of capacitance rather than elastance.) This restores the appropriate dimensions to the element values, whose dimensions in the normalized network are time (seconds) for L, none for R, and time^{-1} for S, although it is convenient to think of the normalized elements as measured in ohms, henrys, and farads.

(*b*) *Frequency scale.* Normalization of element values with respect to some reference resistance R_0 is usually not sufficient to remove the annoying powers of ten in the values of inductance and capacitance. Since the reactance and susceptance of inductors and capacitors depend on frequency, however, we can also utilize a change in the scale of frequency. We write

$$\text{inductor reactance} = L\omega = (L\omega_0)(\omega/\omega_0) = L'\Omega,$$
$$\text{capacitor susceptance} = C\omega = (C\omega_0)(\omega/\omega_0) = C'\Omega, \quad (2.09\text{–}3)$$

in which

$$\Omega = \omega/\omega_0 \qquad (2.09\text{–}4)$$

is the *normalized* frequency variable, and

$$L' = \omega_0 L,$$
$$C' = \omega_0 C \qquad (2.09\text{–}5)$$

are element values appropriate for use with such a normalized frequency scale. Again there is no loss of generality, and ω_0 can usually be chosen so that L' and C' are numbers of the order of the resistance (conductance) values in the network, without the annoying powers of ten. The new element values of (2.09–5) are simply the reactance and susceptance of the actual element values at the reference frequency ω_0. Again it may be convenient to consider these, temporarily, as the element values in a normalized network, designed on a "one-radian-per-second" basis (ω_0 being the reference frequency). The normalized frequency variable Ω also takes on convenient values, for the interesting region is presumably near $\Omega = 1$. When the work is completed, we need only divide all inductance and capacitance values by ω_0 to obtain the actual desired frequency behavior. This restores the appropriate dimensions to the element values, which have dimensions of reactance (ohms) and susceptance (mhos), respectively, in the normalized network, although it is convenient to consider them as measured in henrys and farads.

(*c*) *Simultaneous impedance and frequency normalization.* The impedance scale change (*a*) in effect reduces the resistance values to convenient numbers, while the frequency scale change (*b*) brings the inductance and elastance values up (down) to the order of the original resistance values. For maximum convenience we need to use both scale changes simultaneously.   When this is done, the normalized network contains elements whose values are related to the actual element values by

$$L_{\text{normalized}} = \frac{\omega_0}{R_0} \times L_{\text{actual}},$$

$$R_{\text{normalized}} = \frac{R_{\text{actual}}}{R_0}, \qquad\qquad (2.09\text{--}6)$$

$$C_{\text{normalized}} = \omega_0 R_0 \times C_{\text{actual}}.$$

These are convenient numbers, and the appropriate "frequency" $\Omega = \omega/\omega_0$ is also of convenient size in the important range of frequencies. The arithmetic of analysis and synthesis is simplified a great deal by this device, since the work proceeds on a "one-ohm" and "one-radian-per-second" basis.   When the analysis or synthesis is complete, the actual scales must be restored.   In synthesis this means the actual element values are obtained from the normalized values by

$$L_{\text{actual}} = L_{\text{normalized}} \times \frac{R_0}{\omega_0},$$

$$R_{\text{actual}} = R_{\text{normalized}} \times R_0, \qquad\qquad (2.09\text{--}7)$$

$$C_{\text{actual}} = C_{\text{normalized}} \times \frac{1}{\omega_0 R_0}.$$

Source impedances.   The following statement is not a theorem, but rather a convenient idealization or assumption: that voltage sources, since they maintain the voltage across their terminals at prescribed values regardless of the current drawn from them, have *zero internal impedance*. In dual fashion current sources maintain their terminal currents, regardless of the terminal voltages developed, and have *zero internal admittance*.

2.10 Summary

This is the apparatus of *analysis*.   With it we can find out how any given network will respond to any given excitation.   For the general case we have but set up the equations; for the sinusoidal steady state we have formally completed the solution.   Now we turn (as planned in Chapter 1) to a deeper analysis of what goes on inside a network, in our search for those network properties which will later help us in our real struggle— to *synthesize* networks.

2.11 References

In the bibliography at the end of this book, there is a long (but not complete) list of original sources and helpful commentaries and redactions.

Appropriate references from these will be selected and listed at the end of each chapter, as well as at appropriate points in the text, as guides for further reading.   It is not necessary to read any of these, but at least an occasional study of sources, particularly original papers, is entertaining, instructive, and helpful in obtaining perspective.

Network elements and laws: CA 4, GU 2, MA 3, RA 2, SC 1, WE 7.
Network analysis: BO 3, GA 1, GU 1, GU 5, MA 3, SY 1, VA 1, VA 6.
Duality: FO 2, GA 1, GU 2, GU 5, MA 3, RU 1, WE 2.

3.

The Complex
Frequency Variable

Πρόσεχε τῷ ὑποκειμένῳ . . .
—Marcus Aurelius

We have decided that the independent variable we want to use is *frequency* (rather than time), since we shall consider the steady a-c state only.   It behooves us then to examine f and ω to see what generalizations are possible and useful and what the essential nature of frequency is.   We start with a closer look at the conventional representations of a-c circuit analysis in the steady state (cf. § 2.07).

3.01 Shorthand

In the usual a-c steady-state analysis, the use of complex numbers enormously simplifies the mathematics of complicated circuits.   We write, for example,

$$I = \frac{E}{Z} = \frac{E}{R_1 + L_1 j\omega + S_1/j\omega} \tag{3.01–1}$$

to express the current flowing in the circuit of Fig. 3.01–A.   (Such a sketch is called a *schematic diagram*, or simply *schematic*.)

What we really mean by this is

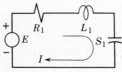

Fig. 3.01–A

$$i(t) = \mathbf{Re}\, Ie^{j\omega t} = \mathbf{Re}\, \frac{Ee^{j\omega t}}{Z}$$

$$= \mathbf{Re}\, \frac{(E_m e^{j\phi})e^{j\omega t}}{R_1 + L_1 j\omega + S_1/j\omega}, \tag{3.01–2}$$

in which i denotes the actual instantaneous value of the current and the voltage source has been taken to have amplitude E_m and zero-time phase ϕ, i.e., the time variation $E_m \cos(\omega t + \phi)$.

24

Now (3.01–2) is still a "shorthand" notation; when it is expanded, the current is given in detail by

$$i(t) = \text{Re} \frac{E_m[\cos(\omega t + \phi) + j \sin(\omega t + \phi)]}{R_1 + j(L_1\omega - S_1/\omega)}$$

$$= \frac{E_m[R_1 \cos(\omega t + \phi) + (\omega L_1 - S_1/\omega)\sin(\omega t + \phi)]}{R_1^2 + (L_1\omega - S_1/\omega)^2},$$

$$(3.01–3)$$

which is fairly messy in comparison with (3.01–1). The advantage of this standard usage of $j\omega$ and of complex numbers representing voltages, currents, impedances, and admittances is not just conciseness. With some generalization, this use of frequency and complex numbers opens up another approach to network theory which simplifies our work; not only that, without this device it would be practically impossible to obtain the results of modern network theory. This generalization is our immediate task. It can be approached in several ways, which we outline below.

3.02 The Laplace-transformation approach

This is perhaps the most satisfactory approach, but requires, of course, that one spend some time studying the Laplace transformation, or the generalized Fourier-integral transformation (which is equivalent). We assume this done. In network analysis by this method we find *impedance functions* and *admittance functions* which formally look exactly like the a-c impedances and admittances of Chapter 2, except that the $j\omega$ is everywhere replaced by a variable s, say, which is complex. In fact, the a-c steady state is merely a special part of the general analysis, in which s is replaced by $j\omega$ and is purely imaginary. Thus the current $i(t)$ flowing in the circuit of Fig. 3.01–A, on the assumption that $E_m \cos(\omega_1 t + \phi)$ represents the driving voltage, is found from

$$I(s) = \frac{E_m[(s\cos\phi - \omega_1\sin\phi)/(s^2 + \omega_1^2)]}{R_1 + L_1 s + S_1/s}. \qquad (3.02–1)$$

This assumes that the circuit is initially at rest, but if we are interested only in the steady state, it makes no difference what the initial conditions are. In actually finding the current, the values of s for which $I(s)$ becomes infinite are very important, and they are in general complex. Since s replaced $j\omega$ in formulating the impedance, this suggests a generalization of our frequency variable ω.

When the theory of the Laplace (or generalized Fourier) transformation is developed, it turns out that this complex variable s is in fact a generalized frequency,

$$s = \sigma + j\omega, \qquad (3.02–2)$$

in which the imaginary part ω is frequency (measured in radians per second) as the word is usually understood. With such a development comes also a knowledge of the meaning of this new, generalized variable and an interpretation of its (complex) values.

In our work we shall use this complex frequency variable a great deal. We shall, however, give it a different symbol, p, to conform to much of network-synthesis literature. The symbol λ, as well as s, is also in use.

3.03 A straightforward alternative approach

Consider Fig. 3.01–A again. The impedance used in calculating the a-c steady-state current is (with the subscript 1 omitted)

$$Z = R + Lj\omega + S/j\omega. \tag{3.03-1}$$

In this, and in any impedance or admittance, ω never appears without j in front of it. In the interests of economy, then, we set

$$p = j\omega \tag{3.03-2}$$

and let one symbol do the work of two. The symbol p here implies nothing more than ω, except that it incorporates the j. In terms of p the impedance is

$$Z = R + Lp + S/p, \tag{3.03-3}$$

which can also be written as

$$Z = \frac{Rp + Lp^2 + S}{p} = L\frac{p^2 + (R/L)p + (S/L)}{p}. \tag{3.03-4}$$

Now let us for a moment look on this as a simple function of the variable p, and factor it, thus:

$$Z = L\frac{(p - p_1)(p - p_2)}{p} \tag{3.03-5}$$

where

$$p_1, p_2 = -(R/2L) \pm \sqrt{(R/2L)^2 - (S/L)}. \tag{3.03-6}$$

In order that p_1 and p_2 (the values of p for which $Z = 0$) be purely imaginary, we must give R the special value zero. So in general p_1 and p_2 are complex and have nonzero, negative, real parts: hence they do not fit into our thinking, in which p is merely $j\omega$. And yet (3.03–3) is neater than (3.03–1), and so we'd like to use p.

We can straighten all this out if we retain our definition of p as $j\omega$ and start thinking of a *generalized* frequency ω which can be *complex*.

In the absence of resistance (i.e., when $R = 0$), we know the impedance is zero for a frequency

$$\omega = \sqrt{S/L} \tag{3.03-7}$$

at which resonance occurs. Evidently when there *is* resistance, the impedance is zero for

$$p = p_1 \quad \text{or} \quad p = p_2, \tag{3.03–8}$$

i.e. for

$$\omega = p/j = j(R/2L) \mp j\sqrt{(R/2L)^2 - (S/L)}. \tag{3.03–9}$$

These values of ω may be purely imaginary (for a highly damped circuit) or complex, but they are never purely real if any resistance is present— they represent values of *complex frequency* for which the circuit is resonant.

It is more convenient not to use this generalized ω but rather to stick to p, which represents the product of j and "complex frequency." The values of p which seem to be characteristic of the circuit, p_1 and p_2, are indeed all-important. They determine the natural behavior of the circuit when shock-excited, as by an impulse voltage, and they are very important in determining its transient response to *any* voltage driving force. Analysis shows that the transient response will contain terms

$$Ae^{p_1 t} \quad \text{and} \quad Be^{p_2 t} \tag{3.03–10}$$

which are called the *natural modes* of the system. Discussion of this is in the province of analysis, so we say no more here, except to recapitulate what we have done. We have, in this example,

(*a*) let $p = j\omega$;

(*b*) written impedance in terms of p, and observed that we get simpler forms, which vanish for certain *complex* values of p;

(*c*) generalized our notion of frequency to the use of this new variable p which we now allow to become complex. Particular values of p which make the impedance vanish are not meaningless, but are closely related to the circuit's transient behavior.

The process is similar for *any* circuit, or for this or other circuits analyzed on the dual basis.

3.04 Still another approach

Suppose the circuit of Fig. 3.01–A is driven by a voltage

$$e = E_m e^{\sigma t} \cos (\omega t + \phi). \tag{3.04–1}$$

The notation

$$e = \mathbf{Re} \, E e^{pt} \tag{3.04–2}$$

in which

$$E = E_m e^{j\phi}, \tag{3.04–3}$$
$$p = \sigma + j\omega,$$

is equally valid. Since the differential equation involved is linear, with constant coefficients, the forced component of the resultant current (the particular integral) is probably of the form

$$i = \mathbf{Re}\, Ie^{pt}, \tag{3.04-4}$$

in which I is as yet unknown. Substitute these expressions in the equation

$$(Ld/dt + R + S\int dt)i = e. \tag{3.04-5}$$

The result, after some manipulation, which exactly parallels the usual treatment of the a-c steady state, is

$$(Lp + R + S/p)I = E, \tag{3.04-6}$$

from which

$$I = \frac{E}{Lp + R + S/p} = \frac{pE}{L[p^2 + (R/L)p + S/L]}. \tag{3.04-7}$$

With this value of I the equation is satisfied, hence

$$i(t) = \mathbf{Re}\, \frac{pEe^{pt}}{L[p^2 + (R/L)p + S/L]} \tag{3.04-8}$$

is the particular integral, corresponding to the steady-state solution when such exists. When $\sigma = 0$ this is the alternating current flowing in the steady state. But in general the current is a positively or negatively damped sinusoid, and the change of amplitude with time is determined by the real part of p.

Generalizing from (3.04-2) and (3.04-8), we call p a generalized frequency variable and observe that the functions we use are obtained simply by replacing $j\omega$ by p, which in turn may become complex. When $\mathbf{Re}\, p < 0$ the current is a damped sinusoid, and when $\mathbf{Re}\, p > 0$ the current is a sinusoid of exponentially increasing amplitude. This p is the same p as that in § 3.02 and § 3.03.

3.05 The complex frequency variable

These three approaches, of which that of § 3.02 is perhaps the most satisfactory, though the others will do, all lead us to a new variable, p. It replaces $j\omega$ in the familiar immittance functions of steady-state a-c circuit theory, but it may become complex. When it does so we seem to be in the domain of transients, and we said that only the a-c steady state would be our concern here. But it will turn out that even in the sinusoidal a-c steady state the use of this generalized variable is not only helpful but almost essential to our purposes. This p is closely connected with (steady-state) frequency, so we refer to it as a "frequency variable."

Since it may become complex, its full name will be the *complex frequency variable*.

Before we go on, let us write down what our generalization from ordinary frequency is.

(*a*) We replace $j\omega$ by p.

(*b*) p may be complex, so we write explicitly

$$p = \sigma + j\omega. \qquad (3.05\text{-}1)$$

(When $\sigma = 0$ we are back where we started, so the use of the same symbol, ω, here is justified.)

Notice that p is not really "complex frequency"; rather

$$p/j = \omega - j\sigma$$

were better called *complex frequency*, for it clearly shows real (conventional) frequency with an added imaginary part. (Some workers prefer this variable; their work differs from ours, of course, by the factor j, or a 90° rotation.) But p is better suited to our purposes, and it we shall use.

We now have to think in terms of a complex plane, the plane of p (Fig. 3.05-A). By our convention, the origin on such planes, the intersection

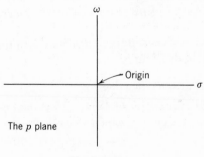

Fig. 3.05-A

of the axes, will usually *not* be marked O, in order to avoid confusion with a similar symbol to be used later. On this plane, *real* frequency corresponds to points on the *imaginary* axis ($\sigma = 0$); hence the imaginary axis is associated with the sinusoidal steady state. Purely *imaginary* frequency corresponds to points on the *real* axis ($\omega = 0$); hence the real axis is associated with transients of the form $e^{\sigma t}$, in which σ is real. This confused nomenclature is unfortunate, but the mathematics behind it has been used so much that it seems best to retain it. With a little practice you should have no trouble with these notions. One might think of *physically* real frequency as corresponding to *mathematically* imaginary frequency, and of physically imaginary frequency as corresponding to mathematically real frequency, but it is probably much clearer to refer only to physical frequency, with the orientation above. All of this is a review of what occurs naturally in the development of analysis procedures with the use of the Laplace transformation, or in any method that employs complex frequency.

Evidently both positive and negative frequencies appear here, even in the steady state. Negative frequency, however, is nothing new. Since

$$\cos(-\omega t + \phi) = \cos(\omega t - \phi), \qquad (3.05\text{-}2)$$

a sinusoid of negative frequency is the same as one of positive frequency except for a change in the sign of the zero-time phase. And in Euler's exponential formulation both kinds appear. This suggests that the upper and lower halves of the plane are symmetrically related; that this is true we shall see later.

Both positive and negative values of σ appear, also, and here there *is* a distinction between the two (left and right) halves of the plane. Transients of decaying amplitude are evidently associated with the left half plane, and transients of exponentially increasing amplitude with the right half plane. The latter have no place in passive systems (unless forced), so that the *left* half plane seems somehow to be the region characterizing passive networks. This is indeed true, and a fact of such fundamental importance that we shall encounter it again and again. The details of the story will develop in due course.

3.06 The nature of network functions

When we analyze the circuit of Fig. 3.01–A, the really important thing is the impedance of the circuit, which we now write

$$Lp + R + S/p. \qquad (3.06\text{-}1)$$

It is a *function* of p in the usual mathematical sense and is intimately associated with the *R-L-S* network; hence we call it *a network function*. Generally, we use *impedance functions* or *admittance functions* in finding currents and voltages, just as in this simple case. In the equations of § 2.07 there are more complicated impedances and admittances, which we now view as *functions of p* ($j\omega$ being replaced by p, if you will), and these we also call *network functions*. Note that these are all ratios of (transformed) voltages and currents and hence are independent of the driving force and are characteristic of the network proper. We may want, later on, to talk about other voltage ratios, or current ratios, such as E_2/E_7 or I_5/I_1, etc.—these ratios, too, we place in the category of network functions. With this definition of *network functions* (impedances and admittances appearing in the equations of analysis, current ratios, voltage ratios), let us see what we can, even now, say about their nature.

All of these network functions come from simple impedances and admittances, combined in determinants, and in multiplication and division of determinants. Now the impedances and admittances of the individual basic elements have, in terms of p, the functional forms shown in Table 3.06–A. Mutual inductance, if present, gives terms Mp to mutual impedances on the loop basis (and corresponding terms if the analysis is made on the node basis); it adds no new *form* of immittance to the catalog in Table 3.06–A.

Table 3.06–A

Impedance	Element	Admittance
	—⟋⟍⟋⟍—	
Lp	$L = 1/\Gamma$	Γ/p
	—⟋⟍—	
R	$R = 1/G$	G
	—⊣⊢—	
S/p	$S = 1/C$	Cp

The operations of adding, subtracting, multiplying, and dividing terms like these—and these are the only operations performed in constructing network functions—can result only in fractions which, when simplified, are merely quotients of two polynomials in p. Such a function, the ratio of two polynomials in p in form, as

$$\frac{a_n p^n + a_{n-1} p^{n-1} + \cdots + a_1 p + a_0}{b_m p^m + b_{m-1} p^{m-1} + \cdots + b_1 p + b_0}, \tag{3.06–2}$$

is called a *rational function* of p.

Evidently network functions are rational functions of p. The impedance of the circuit of Fig. 3.01–A,

$$Z(p) = Lp + R + S/p = L\frac{[p^2 + (R/L)p + S/L]}{p}, \tag{3.06–3}$$

is the quotient of the polynomials $L[p^2 + (R/L)p + S/L]$ and p. Any network function, of even the most complicated network, is always rational, as a consequence of our stipulation that the elements be lumped, constant, and linear. Here we have tacitly assumed the number of elements to be finite; later we shall see what can be said when the number of elements is infinite, and whether such a notion is valuable, and to what extent it will be convenient to extend our definition of network functions.

One more thing we can say immediately. By a fundamental theorem of algebra, the equation

$$c_n p^n + c_{n-1} p^{n-1} + \cdots + c_1 p + c_0 = 0 \qquad (3.06\text{-}4)$$

has n roots; it follows that our network functions can be written in factored form, as

$$\frac{a_n(p - p_1)(p - p_2) \cdots (p - p_n)}{b_m(p - p_1')(p - p_2') \cdots (p - p_m')}, \qquad (3.06\text{-}5)$$

in which the p_i and p_i' are in general complex numbers, and need not all be distinct, either in numerator or in denominator. These complex numbers, together with the multiplier a_n/b_m, completely determine the rational function, and are extremely important. Those of the numerator correspond to values of p for which the network function vanishes and are called *zeros*; those of the denominator correspond to values of p for which the network function becomes infinite and are called *poles*. We shall often find them useful in characterizing networks.

We are tempted to say further that for passive networks these p_i and p_i' must all lie in the left half plane, but we shall postpone any further remarks on the nature of network functions until we are better equipped. The tempting restriction above does not always hold, in fact, but the locations of these zeros and poles will invariably be important.

3.07 Tools

Our immediate aim, remember, is to gain a deeper knowledge of network properties than conventional a-c circuit theory gives us. With this we can pass judgment on the realizability of proposed network characteristics. We have already started toward this goal in introducing p.

Since p is a complex variable, and since network functions are functions of p, it seems likely that a knowledge of the theory of functions of a complex variable will be helpful, if not necessary, for further progress. This is a fact, and it will pay us, right now, to forget networks entirely for a brief time and to look into that branch of mathematics which deals with the properties and behavior of functions of a complex variable. We shall get tools well worth the time spent.

3.08 Complex numbers and the complex variable

Let us first review some already familiar concepts of complex numbers. Neither here, nor anywhere else in this chapter, shall we attempt to give rigorous proofs of the validity of all we do; rather we shall just refresh our memories on things once learned, or merely sketch proofs or validity arguments. For rigor, consult pure mathematics, the veritable foundation of all we do.

The number $\sqrt{-1}$ is called *imaginary* and we symbolize it by j. It acts as the unit of measure among imaginary numbers.

A *complex* number is a number containing both a real number and an imaginary number, as

$$1 + j1, \qquad 17 - j10, \qquad -9 - j15, \qquad \text{etc.}$$

Such (complex) numbers can be expressed in *rectangular* form, as above, or in *polar* form in terms of *magnitude* (absolute value, modulus) and *angle* (amplitude, argument, phase, arc), thus:

$$\underbrace{a + jb}_{\substack{\text{rectangular} \\ \text{form}}} = \underbrace{re^{j\theta}}_{\substack{\text{polar} \\ \text{form}}}.$$

The names are associated with the graphical representation of such numbers on the complex-number plane, Fig. 3.08–A. The *point P*

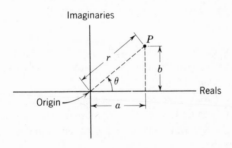

Fig. 3.08–A

represents the complex number $a + jb = re^{j\theta}$. The real numbers a, b, and θ may be either positive or negative, but we require r to be positive (or zero). These two forms of the complex number and the graphical representation emphasize the *two-dimensional* character of a complex number; it is really two (real) numbers. The radius vector from the origin is another convenient representation of a complex number; the difference between two complex numbers is represented by the vector or directed line joining the two representative points.

The two real numbers appearing in the rectangular form are called the *real part*, as a, and the *imaginary part*, as b. (The latter were better called the *coefficient* of the imaginary part, for it is jb which is really the imaginary part; the definition first given above is such common usage, however, that we shall retain it.)

For brevity we shall use the following symbols to indicate the operations of extracting the parts of a complex number.

Rectangular form:

Real part: **Re**, as **Re** $(a + jb) = a$.

Imaginary part: **Im**, as **Im** $(a + jb) = b$.

Polar form:

Magnitude: vertical bars, $|\quad|$, as $|(a + jb)| = r = \sqrt{a^2 + b^2}$.

Angle: horizontal bars, $\overline{}$, as $\overline{(a + jb)} = \theta = \tan^{-1} b/a$.

The complex number whose representation is the mirror image in the real axis of some given complex number is called the (complex) *conjugate* of that number. Given $a + jb = re^{j\theta}$, the conjugate is $a - jb = re^{-j\theta}$.

Complex numbers obey the following laws:

the ordinary laws of algebra, with $j^2 = -1$;

sums, differences, products, and quotients of complex numbers are in turn complex;

two complex numbers are equal when, and only when, their real and imaginary parts are respectively equal; hence $(a + jb) = 0$ when, and only when, $a = 0$ and $b = 0$.

Addition and subtraction are usually most conveniently performed in the rectangular form; multiplication, division, involution, and evolution most easily in the polar form.

Our complex variable $p = \sigma + j\omega$ is such a definite complex number whenever it has a specified value. In general it is a variable, and its real and imaginary parts are not fixed. Nevertheless, p is a number possessed of all the characteristics above.

3.09 Functional notions

Function we define as in real-variable theory: if $F(p)$ is defined when p has a value, then $F(p)$ is a function of p. Since p is complex, $F(p)$ is generally complex also, and hence all the remarks of § 3.08 apply also to functions of p.

Since $p = \sigma + j\omega$, and $F(p) = x + jy$ (x and y being the real and imaginary parts of F) is a function of p, then x and y are separately (real) functions of σ and ω:

$$F = F(p) = x + jy, \qquad p = \sigma + j\omega,$$
$$x = x(\sigma, \omega), \qquad\qquad y = y(\sigma, \omega). \tag{3.09–1}$$

Functional relations are defined by expressions such as

$$w = e^p, \quad p^2, \quad (17p^3 + 46p), \quad (-\sin p), \quad \frac{p + 2}{p^2 + 6p - 10},$$

and the like, or, generally,

$$w = F(p).$$

If we look on this as a relation defining w in terms of p, i.e., as an equation, it can in theory be solved for p in terms of w (though the solution in practice may not be easy). The result is to express p as a function of w, and we call this the *inverse* function (inverse to F), thus:

$$w = F(p) \quad \text{leads to} \quad p = F^{-1}(w). \tag{3.09-2}$$

Even fairly simple inversions can lead to difficulties of multiple values, as we shall see.

Since the act of conjugating p amounts to changing the sign of j in p, a function of $\bar{p}$ (the superscript bar denotes "conjugate") is often the conjugate of that same function of p:

$$F(\bar{p}) = \overline{F(p)}. \tag{3.09-3}$$

The condition that makes this true is essentially that $F(p)$ be real when p is real (CH 3). For example, the following functions are reflected in the real axis (conjugated) when p is conjugated:

$$p + 3, \quad \frac{p}{p^2 + 3}, \quad \frac{p^2 + 1}{(p + 3)(p + 4)} + 6, \quad e^{\pi p}, \quad \cos(jp).$$

In contrast, the following functions, which are generally not real when p is real, do not obey (3.09-3):

$$jp + 3, \quad \frac{p}{p^2 + j3}, \quad \frac{p^2 + 1}{(p + 3)(p + 4)} + j6, \quad e^{j\pi p}, \quad \cos(jp + 2).$$

Continuity we define by generalizing the definition of real-variable theory. There we have the function $y(x)$ defined as continuous at $x = x_1$ if

$$\lim_{x \to x_1} [y(x)] = \lim_{x \to x_1} [y(x)] = y(x_1). \tag{3.09-4}$$

In the complex world we define $F(p)$ as continuous at p_1 if

$$\lim_{p \to p_1} [F(p)] = F(p_1), \tag{3.09-5}$$

no matter what the direction in which p approaches p_1 on the complex plane may be.

3.10 The derivative

We consider now the process of *differentiation*. Suppose we have a function of p, $F(p)$. We define the derivative of F with respect to p at the point p_1 by

$$F'(p)\bigg]_{p=p_1} = F'(p_1) = dF/dp\bigg]_{p=p_1} = \lim_{p \to p_1} \frac{F(p) - F(p_1)}{p - p_1}. \quad (3.10\text{--}1)$$

Two questions immediately arise: does $F'(p_1)$ exist, and is it unique (i.e., does its value depend on the direction of approach)? On the answers to these questions hangs the utility of the derivative in the complex world.

Let us proceed formally as follows.

$$F = F(p) = x + jy, \qquad p = \sigma + j\omega,$$

$$x = x(\sigma, \omega), \qquad\qquad y = y(\sigma, \omega).$$

$$\frac{dF}{dp} = \frac{dx + j\,dy}{d\sigma + j\,d\omega} = \frac{\dfrac{\partial x}{\partial \sigma}\,d\sigma + \dfrac{\partial x}{\partial \omega}\,d\omega + j\dfrac{\partial y}{\partial \sigma}\,d\sigma + j\dfrac{\partial y}{\partial \omega}\,d\omega}{d\sigma + j\,d\omega}$$

$$= \frac{\left(\dfrac{\partial x}{\partial \sigma} + j\dfrac{\partial y}{\partial \sigma}\right) d\sigma + \left(\dfrac{\partial x}{\partial \omega} + j\dfrac{\partial y}{\partial \omega}\right) d\omega}{d\sigma + j\,d\omega}$$

$$= \left(\frac{\partial x}{\partial \sigma} + j\frac{\partial y}{\partial \sigma}\right)\left(\frac{d\sigma + R\,d\omega}{d\sigma + j\,d\omega}\right), \quad (3.10\text{--}2)$$

in which

$$R = \frac{\dfrac{\partial x}{\partial \omega} + j\dfrac{\partial y}{\partial \omega}}{\dfrac{\partial x}{\partial \sigma} + j\dfrac{\partial y}{\partial \sigma}}. \quad (3.10\text{--}3)$$

This expression will be independent of the direction of approach, i.e., of $d\omega/d\sigma$, only if the second parenthesis in (3.10–2) is constant—for it is there and only there that the "path" appears. This requires $R = j$, or

$$\frac{\partial x}{\partial \omega} + j\frac{\partial y}{\partial \omega} = j\frac{\partial x}{\partial \sigma} - \frac{\partial y}{\partial \sigma}$$

or

$$\frac{\partial x}{\partial \omega} = -\frac{\partial y}{\partial \sigma} \quad \text{and} \quad \frac{\partial y}{\partial \omega} = \frac{\partial x}{\partial \sigma}. \quad (3.10\text{--}4)$$

When (3.10–4) is fulfilled,

$$F'(p) = \frac{\partial x}{\partial \sigma} + j\frac{\partial y}{\partial \sigma} = \frac{\partial y}{\partial \omega} - j\frac{\partial x}{\partial \omega} = \frac{\partial x}{\partial(j\omega)} + j\frac{\partial y}{\partial(j\omega)}, \quad (3.10\text{–}5)$$

and is independent of the direction (path) of approach. Equations (3.10–4) are the celebrated Cauchy-Riemann equations; it is both necessary and sufficient for uniqueness of the derivative that they be satisfied.

The Cauchy–Riemann equations (3.10–4) take care of the second question; they tell us when the derivative of a given function is independent of the path of approach, i.e., when the derivative is unique. As to the first question (Does the derivative exist?), evaluation of the formula for the particular function in hand answers that.

Those functions that are well-behaved—i.e., are uniform (single-valued) and continuous, and possess definite, *unique*, continuous derivatives—are very important. To such functions we give the name *analytic* functions, or *regular* functions. (Other adjectives used are holomorphic and monogenic.) Essentially the test for analyticity is to test for satisfaction of the Cauchy–Riemann equations. Whether the other requirements are also met is usually obvious. When a function is analytic, its (unique) derivative is calculated by the same rules as in real-variable theory, the complex nature of p being ignored, e.g.,

$$\frac{d}{dp}(\cos p) = -\sin p.$$

Functions may be analytic (regular) in some regions of the plane of the variable and not in others; in particular, there may be (many) isolated points at which a function is not analytic, though the same function is analytic at all other points. A point at which (and in the immediate neighborhood of which) a function a is analytic we call a regular (analytic) point.

The Cauchy–Riemann equations are so important that we repeat them here where they can stand out.

$$F(p) = x + jy, \qquad p = \sigma + j\omega,$$

$$\frac{\partial x}{\partial \sigma} = \frac{\partial y}{\partial \omega},$$

$$\frac{\partial x}{\partial \omega} = -\frac{\partial y}{\partial \sigma}. \qquad (3.10\text{–}6)$$

From the Cauchy–Riemann equations (3.10–6) you can establish, by differentiation, that the real and imaginary parts of any (analytic) function of a complex variable satisfy Laplace's equation. Hence they are harmonic functions and of great use in solving potential and other physical problems in two dimensions.

3.11 Interesting points

We shall be dealing with network functions, usually with rational functions of the form (3.06–2) or (3.06–5). Evidently the values of p (i.e., the *points* in the p plane) which are most characteristic of such functions are those placed in evidence by (3.06–5), the points at which the function vanishes (becomes zero) or approaches infinity. To such points we give special names (not restricted to rational functions).

A regular point at which $F(p)$ *vanishes*, so that

$$F(p) = 0 \qquad\qquad (3.11–1)$$

is called a *zero* of $F(p)$. Thus p_1, p_2, etc., are zeros of (3.06–5). If the factor $(p - p_1)$ is raised to the power n, as $(p - p_1)^n$, which happens when n of the p_i coincide, we say further that the zero is one *of order n*; a first-order ($n = 1$) zero is called a *simple* zero. Ordinarily n here is a positive integer. If it is positive, but not integral, then the function is no longer rational, nor is it regular at p_1: a different term (branch point) is used, and the situation is more complicated. We do not at present need to consider this case, but shall worry about it when we encounter it.

Points at which functions are not analytic we call *singular* points or *singularities*. Generally the function "blows up" or becomes infinite at such points, e.g., at p_1', p_2', $\cdots$ of (3.06–5). In the case of the rational function, these singularities are called *poles*. The *order* of the pole is the exponent of the factor $(p - p_1')$ if several of the p_i' coincide; if the order is one, the pole is a *simple* pole. If the exponent is not integral, the singularity is again a branch point of the (irrational) function—of which more later.

The same terms (pole and zero) are applied to functions that are not rational. In such cases a more precise definition is necessary, to follow later. For rational functions, the form (3.06–5) immediately places the poles and zeros in evidence, together with their orders (when like factors are grouped together). The poles are the only points at which such functions are not regular.

Our complex plane gives a very convenient representation, by geometrical points, of all values of p for which $|p|$ is finite. What happens when $|p|$ increases without limit, i.e., when $p \to \infty$, will turn out often to be very important, so it would be nice if ∞ were represented on our plane. That is not directly possible, but there is a very convenient device for imagining a point called infinity (∞).

Visualize a sphere resting on the complex plane, tangent to it at the origin. Draw the diameter of the sphere through this tangent point and call its other end N. Figure 3.11–A shows this in perspective. Now suppose the plane of p mapped on the surface of this sphere, point by point, by simply drawing lines from points in the plane to N. Figure 3.11–B shows a cross section through O, P, and N, P being a point to be

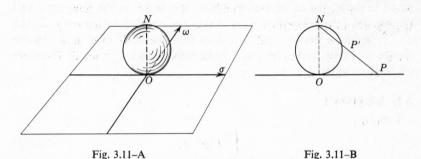

Fig. 3.11–A   Fig. 3.11–B

mapped; we say it maps to P', determined by the intersection of PN and the surface of the sphere. Now every finite point on the P plane maps into some point on the sphere's surface. And as $p \to \infty$, no matter what the direction of motion of p, P' approaches N. Hence we say that ∞ maps into N—and we shall hereafter, whenever convenient, speak of *infinity* as a *point*, a single point (the "point at infinity"), visualizing it with the aid of this mapping.

Note how it, as well as any other point in the p plane, can be approached from any direction. For study or calculations at infinity, such as the application of tests for analytic character, it is often convenient to substitute for p a new variable defined by

$$p' = \frac{1}{p} \quad \text{or} \quad p = \frac{1}{p'}. \tag{3.11–2}$$

The behavior of the new function for $p' = 0$ represents the behavior of the original function at infinity.

Notice that the point at infinity may perfectly well be a pole or zero, too. In the general rational function (3.06–5),

if $n > m$, infinity is a pole of order $n - m$;

if $n = m$, infinity is an ordinary (regular) point, at which the function does not vanish;

if $n < m$, infinity is a zero of order $m - n$.

By counting up in each case the total number of zeros and poles, counting an rth-order zero (pole) as r zeros (poles), and including the behavior at infinity, it is easy to show that

the total number of zeros of a rational function is always equal to the total number of poles.   (3.11–3)

Verify this yourself, for it is important. The number of poles (or of zeros) we call the *order* of the rational function. Note that the order is equal to the higher of the two numbers, the degree of the numerator and the degree of the denominator (or, if they are equal, to either one). Some very interesting nonrational functions that we shall meet have infinite numbers of zeros and poles and may be considered as "rational" functions of "infinite order."

3.12 Integration

Consider

$$\int_{p_1}^{p_2} F(p)\, dp, \tag{3.12–1}$$

and assume it to be defined by extension of real-integral theory. The question now arises: Is the integral independent of the path of integration, the route that p takes in going from p_1 to p_2? If it is not, we anticipate chaos, or at least headaches from multiple values of integrals. There are several ways of discovering the conditions under which it *is* independent of the path of integration.

We may write, for example,

$$F(p) = x(\sigma, \omega) + jy(\sigma, \omega), \qquad p = \sigma + j\omega,$$

$$\int_{p_1}^{p_2} F(p)\, dp = \int_{p_1}^{p_2} (x + jy)(d\sigma + j\, d\omega)$$

$$= \int_{p_1}^{p_2} (x\, d\sigma - y\, d\omega) + j \int_{p_1}^{p_2} (y\, d\sigma + x\, d\omega). \tag{3.12–2}$$

Now observe that independence of (3.12–1) of the path of integration is equivalent to

$$\int_C F(p)\, dp = 0, \tag{3.12–3}$$

in which $\int_C$ means the integral of $F(p)$ around the closed contour C (Fig. 3.12–A). Here a and b are two possible paths. For if (3.12–3) is true, the integral can be split into

$$\int_{a\,p_1}^{p_2} \quad \text{and} \quad \int_{b\,p_2}^{p_1}$$

which then add up to zero, or

$$\int_{a}^{p_2}{}_{p_1} = -\int_{b}^{p_1}{}_{p_2} = \int_{b}^{p_2}{}_{p_1}, \qquad (3.12\text{--}4)$$

so that the integrals along different paths are equal. The converse also holds.

Some conditions under which the two real line integrals in the expanded form of (3.12–3) are independent of the path of integration are (from real-variable theory, by an analysis which we omit)

$$\frac{\partial x}{\partial \omega} = -\frac{\partial y}{\partial \sigma} \quad \text{and} \quad \frac{\partial y}{\partial \omega} = \frac{\partial x}{\partial \sigma}, \qquad (3.12\text{--}5)$$

on and *within* the contour C (in addition to uniformity and continuity of x, y, and the derivatives). But these are exactly (3.10–6), the Cauchy–Riemann equations. Hence the value of the integral of a function does not depend upon the path taken by p, when the function is analytic on and within the closed contour formed by the paths in question. When a

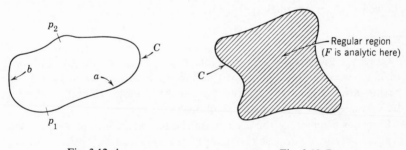

Fig. 3.12–A Fig. 3.12–B

singularity lies on or within C of Fig. 3.12–A, however, then (3.12–3) may not be true.

Another way of looking at this is to break the area enclosed by the two paths down into very small rectangles. The line integral (3.12–3) is equal to the sum of integrals around each rectangle (and pseudorectangles on the periphery). The individual integrals, on examination, lead to the same conclusion, that the integral (3.12–1) is independent of the path when $F(p)$ is analytic on and within the contour formed by the two paths in question.

To sum up, it can be shown that an integral such as (3.12–1) is independent of the path of integration so long as the path of integration remains in a region in which the Cauchy–Riemann equations hold for the integrand. We are going to be more interested in the closed (complete) contour, i.e., in the fact that

$$\int_C F(p)\, dp = 0 \qquad (3.12\text{–}6)$$

if all points within and on the contour (Fig. 3.12–B) are regular. That is, essentially, (3.12–6) holds when $F(p)$ satisfies the Cauchy–Riemann equations on the boundary and within the area. This is *Cauchy's theorem* or *Cauchy's integral law*, and it is of fundamental importance. It makes no difference in which direction the contour C is traversed in the integration. Thus (essentially) satisfaction of the Cauchy–Riemann equations is sufficient for a line integral to be independent of its path—but this is not a necessary condition, as it was for the derivative to be unique. Further discussion of conditions under which (3.12–6) is true will be found in § 3.20.

By extension of this result we can see that the integral (3.12–6) is not changed in value if the contour C (Fig. 3.12–B) is deformed at will, *provided* it remains closed and no points at which $F(p)$ is not analytic are allowed to enter or touch the region enclosed.

3.13 Taylor series

Cauchy's theorem is a remarkable tool. From it, almost otherwise unaided, we can derive most of the important results we need, e.g., the Taylor-series expansion of a function in the complex domain. We first derive some other relations we shall need.

Consider a region of the p plane on the boundary of and within which $F(p)$ is analytic. Suppose the point about which an expansion is desired is within this region (though we shall not use it immediately); in that region draw the path of integration shown in Fig. 3.13–A, in which p_1 is some point in the region. Now we can say, by Cauchy's theorem,

$$\int_{\substack{C = C_1 + C_3 \\ + C_2 + C_4}} F(p) \times \frac{1}{p - p_1}\, dp = 0,$$

for the product of two analytic functions is analytic. (This can be proved by expanding a product, separating real and imaginary parts, and applying the test.) This particular integrand is used simply because prior workers have found it advantageous.

Suppose ϵ is small, and let it approach zero. In the limit, the C_3 and

C_4 integrals cancel, for the integrands have the same values, but the integrations are in opposite directions. Then

$$\int_{C_1} \frac{F(p)}{p - p_1}\, dp + \int_{C_2} \frac{F(p)}{p - p_1}\, dp = 0.$$

Note that the C_1 integral is to be taken in the counterclockwise direction, while the C_2 integral is to be taken clockwise, as shown. Now take the

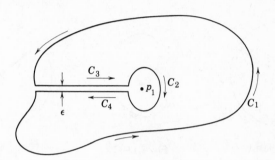

Fig. 3.13–A

following step: let C_2 be deformed to a small circle, centered on p_1 and of radius r, so that when p is on this circle, $(p - p_1)$ may be written in polar form as $re^{j\theta}$ (Fig. 3.13–B). Then

$$\int_{C_1} \frac{F(p)}{p - p_1}\, dp = -\int_{C_2} \frac{F(p)}{p - p_1}\, dp = -\int_{C_2} \frac{F(p)}{re^{j\theta}} re^{j\theta} j\, d\theta = -j \int_{C_2} F(p)\, d\theta.$$

Now let r become vanishingly small. Then the above gives us

$$\int_{C_1} \frac{F(p)}{p - p_1}\, dp = 2\pi j F(p_1).$$

Hence we find, as a result of the additional limit process $r \to 0$, that

$$F(p_1) = \frac{1}{2\pi j} \oint \frac{F(p)\, dp}{p - p_1}, \tag{3.13–1}$$

in which the integral is to be taken on C_1. This means that the counterclockwise line integral indicated is essentially the value of $F(p)$ at the point where the denominator of the integrand vanishes. This is *Cauchy's integral formula*, another important result.

Let us adopt a different notation for the variable of integration, in order to be able to drop the subscript in p_1. After all, p_1 could have been *any* point within the contour, so why use a subscript? Then we have

$$F(p) = \frac{1}{2\pi j} \oint \frac{F(s)\, ds}{s - p},\tag{3.13-2}$$

in which the integral is to be taken counterclockwise around a contour enclosing p, as shown in Fig. 3.13–C.

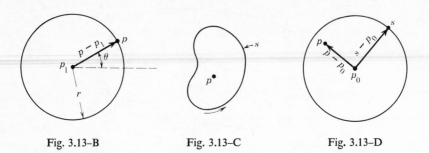

Fig. 3.13–B   Fig. 3.13–C   Fig. 3.13–D

Assuming without proof that we can differentiate under the integral sign (we can), we find

$$\frac{dF}{dp} = \frac{1}{2\pi j} \oint \frac{F(s)\, ds}{(s - p)^2},$$

$$\frac{d^2F}{dp^2} = \frac{2 \times 1}{2\pi j} \oint \frac{F(s)\, ds}{(s - p)^3},\tag{3.13-3}$$

$$\cdots\cdots\cdots\cdots$$

$$\frac{d^nF}{dp^n} = \frac{n!}{2\pi j} \oint \frac{F(s)\, ds}{(s - p)^{n+1}}.$$

So we can say that if $F(p)$ possesses a first derivative, it also possesses all higher derivatives! The notion of regularity is thus not confined to the first derivative.

The formulas above, (3.13–2) and (3.13–3), hold when $F(p)$ is analytic on and within the contour chosen; this contour is to be traversed in the counterclockwise sense. Notice that $n = 0$ gives (3.13–1), Cauchy's integral formula in the original form.

Now let us apply this to our main business here: the finding of the Taylor series. Let p_0 be the point about which we wish to expand, and let us draw a closed contour, a circle centered on p_0, enclosing also the variable (running) point p. Now

$$\frac{1}{s-p} = \frac{1}{(s-p_0)-(p-p_0)} = \frac{1}{s-p_0} \times \frac{1}{1-(p-p_0)/(s-p_0)} \tag{3.13-4}$$

and

$$\left|\frac{p-p_0}{s-p_0}\right| < 1 \tag{3.13-5}$$

for p anywhere within the circle and s on the circle (see Fig. 3.13–D). What we are doing here is forcing a shift of attention (by introducing p_0 thus) to the point about which we wish to expand, i.e., to p_0, which does not appear in $1/(s-p)$. Because of (3.13–5) we assume we can use the familiar series

$$\frac{1}{1-z} = 1 + z + z^2 + \cdots, \tag{3.13-6}$$

an assumption which the theory of infinite series justifies. Then

$$\frac{1}{s-p} = \frac{1}{s-p_0}\left[1 + \left(\frac{p-p_0}{s-p_0}\right) + \left(\frac{p-p_0}{s-p_0}\right)^2 + \cdots\right] \tag{3.13-7}$$

under the same conditions. Hence

$$F(p) = \frac{1}{2\pi j}\oint\frac{F(s)\,ds}{s-p} = \frac{1}{2\pi j}\left[\oint\frac{F(s)\,ds}{s-p_0} + (p-p_0)\oint\frac{F(s)\,ds}{(s-p_0)^2}\right.$$
$$\left. + (p-p_0)^2\oint\frac{F(s)\,ds}{(s-p_0)^3} + \cdots\right], \tag{3.13-8}$$

in which the contour is the circle, traversed in the counterclockwise sense. Hence we can say that

$$F(p) = a_0 + a_1(p-p_0) + a_2(p-p_0)^2 + \cdots \tag{3.13-9}$$

in which

$$a_n = \frac{1}{2\pi j}\oint\frac{F(s)\,ds}{(s-p_0)^{n+1}} = \frac{F^{(n)}(p_0)}{n!}, \tag{3.13-10}$$

by using (3.13–3). The region of validity is the interior of the circle about p_0, and this circle may be increased in radius until the circumference strikes a singularity of $F(p)$; then our assumption of regularity on and within the circle is violated. That particular limiting radius is known as the *radius of convergence*.

By analytic continuation (a process of finding the Taylor series about p_0 and, from that series, the value of the function and of all the derivatives at some other point p_1, about which another expansion is made, whose circle of convergence covers some new ground), the function can usually be calculated even outside the original circle.   The only information necessary to get started is a knowledge of the values of the function and its derivatives at a point (or of the values of the function alone over a small region, which is equivalent).

This section ends up, then, with the old familiar Taylor-series formula, (3.13-9), but valid now for the complex domain.   A rigorous derivation would involve more things—we wish only to show it plausible and shall be content with what we have done.   When $p_0 = 0$ the series is also called a Maclaurin series.

3.14 Laurent series

The Taylor series alone will not get us very far, of course, when there is a singularity near the point about which we wish to expand.   But there is a useful series expansion of a different kind which *will* do so under certain conditions.

Let p_0 be the point of interest, about which we wish to expand $F(p)$. Draw two circles centered on p_0 (C_1 and C_2 of Fig. 3.14-A), between and

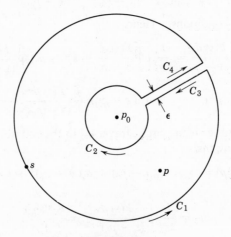

Fig. 3.14-A

on which $F(p)$ is analytic.   That is, we suppose none of $F(p)$'s singularities to be located between C_1 and C_2 (the regions inside C_2 and outside C_1 may contain singularities).   Cut and join the two circles as indicated in Fig. 3.14-A, and apply Cauchy's integral formula (3.13-2) to the composite contour.   Then if we let $\epsilon \to 0$, we find

$$F(p) = \frac{1}{2\pi j} \int_{C_1} \frac{F(s)\, ds}{s - p} + \frac{1}{2\pi j} \int_{C_2} \frac{F(s)\, ds}{s - p}, \qquad (3.14\text{-}1)$$

for the C_3 and C_4 contributions cancel in the limit, just as in § 3.13. We again consider the C_1 integral to be taken in the counterclockwise sense, and the C_2 integral in the clockwise sense.

On C_1 let us use (3.13-7) as before, to obtain a series. On C_2 we need another trick, for there (3.13-5) is not valid. But we can again force a shift of attention to p_0, and obtain a useful development, by reversing the sequence used in (3.13-4). Thus

$$\frac{1}{s - p} = \frac{-1}{(p - p_0) - (s - p_0)}$$

$$= \frac{-1}{p - p_0}\left[1 + \left(\frac{s - p_0}{p - p_0}\right) + \left(\frac{s - p_0}{p - p_0}\right)^2 + \cdots\right] \qquad (3.14\text{-}2)$$

since

$$\left|\frac{s - p_0}{p - p_0}\right| < 1, \qquad (3.14\text{-}3)$$

for p in the annulus and s on C_2. Then from (3.14-1), by using both of these devices, we can get the series we are interested in. For neatness and uniformity, we now take the C_2 integral in the counterclockwise sense (so that all integrals are now to be taken counterclockwise), which cancels the minus sign in (3.14-2). We get

$$F(p) = \frac{1}{2\pi j}\left[\oint \frac{F(s)\, ds}{(s - p_0)} + (p - p_0) \oint \frac{F(s)\, ds}{(s - p_0)^2}\right.$$

$$\left. + (p - p_0)^2 \oint \frac{F(s)\, ds}{(s - p_0)^3} + \cdots\right] + \frac{1}{2\pi j}\left[(p - p_0)^{-1} \oint F(s)\, ds\right.$$

$$+ (p - p_0)^{-2} \oint F(s)(s - p_0)\, ds$$

$$\left. + (p - p_0)^{-3} \oint F(s)(s - p_0)^2\, ds + \cdots\right] \qquad (3.14\text{-}4)$$

$$= b_0 + b_1(p - p_0) + b_2(p - p_0)^2 + \cdots$$
$$+ b_{-1}(p - p_0)^{-1} + b_{-2}(p - p_0)^{-2} + \cdots$$

$$= \cdots + \frac{b_{-2}}{(p - p_0)^2} + \frac{b_{-1}}{(p - p_0)} + b_0 + b_1(p - p_0)$$
$$+ b_2(p - p_0)^2 + \cdots \qquad (3.14\text{-}5)$$

$$= \sum_{n = -\infty}^{+\infty} b_n(p - p_0)^n,$$

in which

$$b_n = \frac{1}{2\pi j} \oint_C \frac{F(s)\,ds}{(s - p_0)^{n+1}}. \qquad (3.14\text{--}6)$$

For $n = \cdots -3,\ -2,\ -1$, C means C_2, and for $n = 0,\ 1,\ 2,\ 3,\ \cdots$, C means C_1, all integrals being taken in the counterclockwise sense. For the purpose of calculating the b's, the coefficients, these contours can be deformed, so long as no singularities are encountered, by Cauchy's theorem. Hence the contours of integration in (3.14–6) can be any closed paths in the region of regularity between the two groups of singularities, and may wander outside C_1 and inside C_2 in part, too—and may all be the same path. (But mark you, this is *not* the way to calculate the b's in practice; there are better ways, to be mentioned later.) This does *not* mean that the new "annulus" (region enclosed by the deformed contours) is a region in which the Laurent series is valid. The region of validity is bounded by the smallest circle C_2 which still encloses all singularities of $F(p)$ in the inner group, and by the largest circle C_1 which still contains no singularities of $F(p)$ in the outer group. We cannot extend the region of convergence, i.e., we cannot deform the annulus to go outside the region bounded by C_1 and C_2, once C_1 has its maximum radius and C_2 its minimum radius; to do so would violate our assumptions (3.13–5) and (3.14–3).

Among all the b_n as defined by (3.14–6), b_{-1} alone has a private name. It is the

$$residue \text{ of } F(s), \qquad (3.14\text{--}7)$$

of which more later.

In (3.14–5) and (3.14–6) we have the *Laurent* series, a sort of generalized Taylor series. It gives us a means of expansion about a point p_0 when nonanalytic points intervene, and even when p_0 is a singularity.

If $F(p)$ has no singularities in the vicinity, then b_{-1}, b_{-2}, etc., all vanish [by Cauchy's theorem, applied to (3.14–6)] and this Laurent series reduces to the ordinary Taylor series. About any given point p_0, for a given allocation of the singularities into two groups, between which lies the annulus of interest (i.e., for a given largest annulus of validity), there is only *one* Laurent series, for the foregoing process can give but one result.

3.15 Singularities

We are now in a position to say a good deal more about those unusual points, the singularities of a function. In the first place, it can be shown that a function with no singularities at all, or a function which is everywhere finite, can be only one thing, a *constant*. As such it is about the most drab and uninteresting function one can think of. Hence the *singularities* are the very heart of a function and the sources from which its lifeblood flows. They are the really interesting things about functions (and this includes network functions).

A little consideration shows that of the two parts of $F(p)$ shown in (3.14-4) or (3.14-5),

that with positive exponents of $(p - p_0)$ is generated by singularities outside C_1, and

that with negative exponents of $(p - p_0)$ is generated by singularities inside C_2.

The first of these two parts is a Taylor series about p_0; the second can be shown to be a Taylor series about "infinity," and hence it is not really much different.

The part with positive exponents of $(p - p_0)$ is called the *ascending branch*. Notice that the ascending branch exhibits the effect of *all* the singularities outside C_1, but that these are all mixed up and cannot readily be individually identified. It is not even apparent, from the series, where these outer singularities are (nor is infinity necessarily a singularity, though it may seem so), because the series is not valid in this region and cannot be used there.

The part with negative exponents of $(p - p_0)$ is called the *descending branch*. Notice that the descending branch exhibits the effect of *all* the singularities inside C_2, but that these are all mixed up and cannot readily be individually identified. The point p_0 itself is not necessarily a singularity, even though the inverse powers of $(p - p_0)$ might suggest this, for the series is not valid near p_0 and reasoning, from the series, that some particular thing happens near p_0 is false.

On the basis of the terms in the descending branch, we can now classify isolated singularities about which the annulus of regularity of § 3.14 can be described. Suppose that p_0 is suspected to be the location of an isolated singularity which we wish to classify. Let the circle C_2 in § 3.14 now be so small in diameter that no singularities (other than the one at p_0 if it exists) lie on or inside C_2. (C_1 may have to be rather small also, but that is irrelevant.) Now if b_{-1}, b_{-2}, b_{-3}, $\cdots$ all vanish, then p_0 is not a singularity at all, but a regular point. But if some or all of the negative-subscript b's are not zero, we have in p_0 a singularity. When the number of terms in the descending branch is finite, i.e., when eventually the b_{-k} vanish for k greater than some definite number, then p_0 is a *pole*. The highest value of k for which b_{-k} is not zero is the *order* of the pole.

Note that if there is a singularity, say p_1, which is not at the *center* of the circle C_2, the Laurent series about the center p_0 will have an infinite number of terms in the descending branch, even though p_1 be but a pole.

(There would be a *finite* number of terms in the expansion about p_1 itself.) The assumptions above that the singularity of interest be at the center of C_2 and that there be no other singularities on or within C_2 are an important part of this classification procedure.

For some functions the descending branch may be an infinite series. Then p_0 is an *essential singularity*. (Singularities which cannot be isolated also exist, and are also called essential.)

The singularities of our rational functions are all *poles*, as we shall see.

We shall occasionally have to consider singularities due to irrationality, as in functions of the form $\sqrt{1 + p^2}$. This function is not uniform (single-valued) and hence does not meet our fundamental requirement of regularity in the annulus. We shall cross this bridge when we come to it.

3.16 Classification of functions

It is now easy to classify functions on the basis of their singularities. We need only a few of the terms used in the classification, and they follow.

Functions which are regular everywhere except at infinity (i.e., have singularities only at infinity) are called *entire* or *integral* functions. If such a function has a *pole* at infinity, it is also *rational*; if the singularity at infinity is *essential*, the function is *transcendental* as well as entire. Rational entire functions have Taylor series with finite numbers of terms —they are simply *polynomials*. Transcendental entire functions have nonterminating Taylor series.

Functions which are quotients of two entire functions are called *meromorphic*. If both entire functions are rational, the quotient is rational; if one or both entire functions are transcendental, the quotient is transcendental. The only singularities which meromorphic functions can have in the finite part of the plane are poles. It is the singularity at infinity which determines whether the meromorphic function is rational or transcendental.

The term *rational* as usually used means "rational meromorphic," i.e., the quotient of two polynomials. This is a more precise definition than that given in § 3.06, but it is the same thing.

3.17 Partial-fraction expansion

Consider a rational function $F(p)$. Let its poles be $p_1, p_2, \cdots, p_l$. Notice that the primes in the notation of (3.06–5) have been dropped; there is no further need for them, as we shall not be discussing zeros for a while. The change ought not to be confusing, and does make for simpler notation. If some poles of (3.06–5) coincide, then l here is different from m there.

Make a Laurent expansion of $F(p)$ about p_1 and choose the annulus so that the expansion will be valid in the immediate vicinity of p_1. That is, make C_2 small enough that $p_2, p_3, \cdots, p_l$ are all *outside* C_1 and do not contribute to the descending branch. The expansion is

$$F(p) = h_1(p) + b_0 + b_1(p - p_1) + \cdots, \qquad (3.17\text{--}1)$$

in which $h_1(p)$ denotes the descending branch. The effect of $p_2, p_3, \cdots$ is bound up in $b_0, b_1, \cdots$; the other poles are disguised, but are implicitly there, so their apparent absence in the expansion is all right.

Now repeat this process at each of the other poles in turn. We get

$$F(p) = h_2(p) + \cdots \quad \text{about } p_2,$$
$$F(p) = h_3(p) + \cdots \quad \text{about } p_3,$$
$$\cdots \cdots \cdots \cdots \cdots \qquad (3.17\text{--}2)$$
$$F(p) = h_l(p) + \cdots \quad \text{about } p_l.$$

Now form

$$F_1(p) = F(p) - h_1(p) = b_0 + b_1(p - p_1) + b_2(p - p_1)^2 + \cdots.$$

We shall not use the infinite-series form of $F_1(p)$, for it is valid only in a limited region near p_1. Rather we shall use the form $F(p) - h_1(p)$ which is closed, compact, and valid everywhere except at $p_2, p_3, \cdots, p_l$ and possibly at infinity. At p_1 this function $F_1(p)$ is regular, as the equation above shows. Now from this form

$$F_2(p) = F_1(p) - h_2(p),$$

which is regular at both p_1 and p_2. Again, $F_2(p)$ is in closed form, and is valid everywhere except at $p_3, p_4, \cdots, p_l$, and possibly infinity. Continue this process, and finally obtain the function

$$G(p) = F(p) - h_1(p) - h_2(p) - h_3(p) - \cdots - h_l(p). \quad (3.17\text{--}3)$$

What we have done here is simply to define $G(p)$ as a function which makes up the difference between $F(p)$ and all the descending branches of the various Laurent series. This $G(p)$ is in closed form [and is *not* to be thought of as obtained by combining the various series in (3.17–2)]. Now $G(p)$ is an entire function, since in it all of the poles have been removed from $F(p)$. It is also, of course, rational. (At infinity, it has, at worst, an ordinary pole.) Hence $G(p)$ is a polynomial.

The form (3.17–3), or, more succinctly,

$$F(p) = \sum_{i=1}^{l} h_i(p) + G(p), \qquad (3.17\text{--}4)$$

is called the *partial-fraction expansion* of $F(p)$. Note that it consists of a number of terms of the form

$$\frac{1}{(p - p_k)^r} \tag{3.17-5}$$

and a polynomial. We shall find frequent use for this expansion.

Decomposition into simple (partial) fractions in this way is frequently possible and useful, even when the function is not rational. The number of terms may then be infinite and we shall later encounter and utilize such "infinite-order," "rational" functions.

3.18 Laurent series and partial fractions

The relation between the Laurent-series expansions and the partial-fraction expansion of a function is a simple one. The Laurent series valid near p_1, say, has the form

$$F(p) = \frac{b_{-r}}{(p - p_1)^r} + \cdots + \frac{b_{-1}}{(p - p_1)} + b_0 + b_1(p - p_1) + \cdots. \tag{3.18-1}$$

and the partial-fraction expansion of $F(p)$, which is valid *everywhere* (except at the poles) is

$$F(p) = \sum_{i=1}^{l} h_i(p) + G(p). \tag{3.18-2}$$

There is no question of convergence or region of validity here, because this is not an infinite series—yet it is still an expansion or development.

The Laurent series (3.18-1) amounts to a juggling of the terms in (3.18-2), for we can write (3.18-2) as

$$F(p) = \underbrace{h_1(p)}_{A} + \underbrace{\sum_{i=2}^{l} h_i(p) + G(p)}_{B}. \tag{3.18-3}$$

Item A is the descending branch of the Laurent series valid near p_1. There item B is regular; its terms can be combined and expanded in a new Taylor series, which is the ascending branch of the same Laurent series. (This holds water, of course, only because p_1 is the center of the circle C_2 and is the only singularity within C_2. All other singularities are outside C_1, as we assumed above.) When p is near p_1, item A becomes very large in magnitude and eclipses item B; hence the name *principal part* is also given to the descending branch of such a series.

One can actually find Laurent expansions by first finding the partial-fraction expansion, setting aside the appropriate $h(p)$, and then expanding the remaining terms of the partial-fraction expansion in a Taylor series. This may seem "the long way round" but may well be the best way.

3.19 Expansion in partial fractions

This section outlines methods of actually *finding* this expansion. The general form of the rational function is

$$F(p) = K \frac{p^n + d_{n-1}p^{n-1} + \cdots + d_0}{(p - p_1)^r(p - p_2)^s \cdots (p - p_l)^t} = K \frac{N(p)}{D(p)}, \quad (3.19\text{–}1)$$

with $r + s + \cdots + t = m$, which form is a potpourri of (3.06–2) and (3.06–5). Note that the denominator has been factored—this is the first step (and a vital one) in finding a partial-fraction expansion—and that all factors due to coincident poles have been grouped together (§ A.5).

Now consider first the pole at p_1 (each pole is to receive exactly the same treatment). Since $(p - p_1)^r F(p)$ remains finite as $p \rightarrow p_1$, from (3.19–1), we can make a Taylor-series expansion of this modified function about p_1. It is

$$H(p) = (p - p_1)^r F(p) = K_{1r} + K_{1, r-1}(p - p_1) + \cdots, \quad (3.19\text{–}2)$$

in which

$$K_{1r} = H(p_1),$$
$$K_{1, r-1} = H'(p_1),$$
$$K_{1, r-2} = H''(p_1)/2!,$$
$$\cdots \cdots \cdots \cdots \quad (3.19\text{–}3)$$
$$K_{11} = \frac{H^{(r-1)}(p_1)}{(r - 1)!}.$$

Then, simply by dividing through by $(p - p_1)^r$, we get

$$F(p) = \frac{K_{1r}}{(p - p_1)^r} + \frac{K_{1, r-1}}{(p - p_1)^{r-1}} + \cdots. \quad (3.19\text{–}4)$$

Hence we see that the principal part of the Laurent series about p_1, valid close by, is

$$\frac{K_{1r}}{(p - p_1)^r} + \frac{K_{1, r-1}}{(p - p_1)^{r-1}} + \cdots + \frac{K_{11}}{(p - p_1)}, \quad (3.19\text{–}5)$$

i.e., it has exactly r terms or the number of terms is equal to the order of the pole. Hence the *total* number of terms in the partial-fraction expansion, excluding the polynomial $G(p)$, is m, the number of zeros of the denominator of $F(p)$. As for $G(p)$, it must be a polynomial of degree $(n - m)$, because for large $|p|$, $F(p) \rightarrow Kp^{n-m}$, and all the $h_i(p) \rightarrow 0$.

[This assumes $n \geqq m$; if $n < m$, then $G(p) = 0$.] These considerations tell us how many terms to expect in the partial-fraction expansion: if $n \geqq m$ there will be $m + (n - m + 1) = n + 1$ terms; if $n < m$, there will be m terms.

Determining $G(p)$. $G(p)$ can be found by various methods. One way is straightforward long division. Symbolically,

$$F(p) = K\frac{N}{D} = \frac{P_1}{P_2} = \cdots + C_3 p^3 + C_2 p^2 + C_1 p + C_0 + \frac{P_3}{P_2}, \qquad (3.19\text{–}6)$$

where the coefficients C are obtained by long division and the last term is a proper fraction. This might well be done before attacking the principal parts, for if $G(p)$ is thus found and subtracted from $F(p)$, then the remainder, P_3/P_2, is a proper fraction and easier to deal with [for its partial-fraction expansion has no polynomial part, $G(p)$]. In the simpler cases it does not much matter whether $G(p)$ is found first and subtracted out, or not; in complicated cases, however, it is usually advantageous to do this.

An alternative is to write $F(p)$ in the form

$$\Sigma\, h_i(p) + C_0 + C_1 p + C_2 p^2 + \cdots + C_{n-m} p^{n-m}, \qquad (3.19\text{–}7)$$

and then to divide through by p^{n-m} to obtain

$$\frac{F(p)}{p^{n-m}} = \frac{\Sigma\, h_i}{p^{n-m}} + \frac{C_0}{p^{n-m}} + \frac{C_1}{p^{n-m-1}} + \cdots + C_{n-m}. \qquad (3.19\text{–}8)$$

Now let $p \to \infty$, which gives C_{n-m}. By differentiating the above, multiplying the result through by p^2, and again letting $p \to \infty$, one can obtain C_{n-m-1}. Further differentiation and the limit process give the other coefficients.

Another method is first to find the K's (i.e., find the fractional parts of the expansion, as discussed below) and then to subtract the sum of the principal parts from $F(p)$, after all the K's have been found.

Still another method, good when $n = m + 1$, is to write, for example,

$$F(p) = \frac{K_{1r}}{(p - p_1)^r} + \cdots + \frac{K_{l1}}{(p - p_l)} + C_0 + C_1 p. \qquad (3.19\text{–}9)$$

After finding the K's (as discussed below) and C_1 (by inspection), then let $p = 0$ and thus obtain an equation which yields C_0. If there are more terms in $G(p)$, an extension of this last method yields simultaneous equations for the coefficients of G, by differentiation of (3.19–9).

Of these various methods, the first (to obtain G by ordinary long division) is the simplest and usually the best. In the special (but very common) case where the degree of the numerator of $F(p)$ exceeds the degree of the denominator of $F(p)$ by unity (or is equal thereto), the last method given is useful.

Determining the K's

(a) *At simple poles*, where there is but one term in the principal part, multiply $F(p)$ by $(p - p_1)$ and evaluate the result at p_1. Take, for instance,

$$F(p) = \frac{(p + 2)}{(p + 1)(p + 3)}. \qquad (3.19\text{--}10)$$

We know the form of the partial-fraction expansion is

$$\frac{K_1}{p + 1} + \frac{K_2}{p + 3} + G(p), \qquad (3.19\text{--}11)$$

in which $G(p) = 0$, since $n < m$. (But if G were not zero, there would be no change whatever in the procedure described here.) The procedure gives

$$(p + 1)F(p) = \frac{p + 2}{p + 3} = K_1 + K_2 \frac{(p + 1)}{(p + 3)}. \qquad (3.19\text{--}12)$$

Now let $p = -1$, and get

$$[(p + 1)F(p)]_{p = -1} = \left[\frac{p + 2}{p + 3}\right]_{p = -1} = \frac{1}{2} = K_1. \qquad (3.19\text{--}13)$$

Similarly,

$$[(p + 3)F(p)]_{p = -3} = \left[\frac{p + 2}{p + 1}\right]_{p = -3} = \frac{-1}{-2} = K_2. \qquad (3.19\text{--}14)$$

Therefore

$$F(p) = \frac{(p + 2)}{(p + 1)(p + 3)} = \frac{\frac{1}{2}}{p + 1} + \frac{\frac{1}{2}}{p + 3}, \qquad (3.19\text{--}15)$$

which can easily be checked by combining the terms over a common denominator.

The general formula is

$$K_j = [(p - p_j)F(p)]_{p = p_j} = \left[\frac{(p - p_j)KN(p)}{D(p)}\right]_{p = p_j} = \frac{KN(p_j)}{D'(p_j)}, \qquad (3.19\text{--}16)$$

in which D' denotes the derivative of the denominator of $F(p)$, easily shown equal (when $p = p_j$) to $D/(p - p_j)$. Alternatively, evaluation of the second bracket in (3.19–16), which is an indeterminate form [since $D(p_j) = 0$] by the usual process, gives

$$K_j = \left\{\frac{(d/dp)[(p - p_j)KN]}{(d/dp)[D]}\right\}_{p = p_j} = \frac{KN(p_j)}{D'(p_j)}. \qquad (3.19\text{--}17)$$

This formula is valuable in cases where $(p - p_j)F(p)$ is not as simple to evaluate as in the illustration above. If the denominator of $F(p)$ is of high degree, it may be easier to evaluate $D'(p_j)$ than to evaluate the product of all the constituent factors of D (the factor $p - p_j$ excepted) at p_j. For example, take the case

$$F(p) = \frac{N}{p^8 + C} = \frac{K_1}{p - p_1} + \cdots + \frac{K_8}{p - p_8}, \quad (3.19\text{--}18)$$

in which N is a polynomial and C a constant. Here

$$K_1 = \left[\frac{(p - p_1)N}{p^8 + C} \right]_{p = p_1} = \frac{N(p_1)}{(p_1 - p_2) \cdots (p_1 - p_8)} = \frac{N(p_1)}{8p_1{}^7}. \quad (3.19\text{--}19)$$

The last form may well be the most practical one to use.

The technique for simple poles should now be clear. In general the poles will not be so conveniently real, and the arithmetic will be more involved, since complex numbers will appear. The *principle*, however, is exactly the same. If two *conjugate* poles appear, their K's will also be conjugate, and but one need be evaluated.

(b) *At multiple poles* there will be several terms corresponding to each pole; the procedure is to multiply through by $(p - p_1)^r$ (for instance) and then to evaluate the result *and its derivatives* at the pole. This amounts to making the Taylor-series expansion (3.19–2). Take, for example,

$$F(p) = \frac{(p + 2)}{(p + 1)^2(p + 3)} = \frac{K_{12}}{(p + 1)^2} + \frac{K_{11}}{(p + 1)} + \frac{K_{21}}{(p + 3)} + G(p),$$

in which $G(p) = 0$. The procedure gives the following.

$$(p + 1)^2 F(p) = \frac{p + 2}{p + 3} = K_{12} + K_{11}(p + 1) + K_{21} \frac{(p + 1)^2}{(p + 3)}.$$

Now let $p = p_1 = -1$; we get

$$\left[\frac{p + 2}{p + 3} \right]_{p = -1} = \frac{1}{2} = K_{12}.$$

Next, by differentiation, we find

$$\frac{d}{dp} \left[\frac{p + 2}{p + 3} \right] = \frac{(p + 3) - (p + 2)}{(p + 3)^2} = \frac{1}{(p + 3)^2}$$

$$= 0 + K_{11} + \frac{d}{dp} \left[K_{21} \frac{(p + 1)^2}{(p + 3)} \right].$$

Now let $p = -1$. The indicated differentiation need not be carried out, for the second-order zero insures that the derivative is zero at $p = -1$. We get

$$K_{11} = \tfrac{1}{4}.$$

Finally, proceeding with the simple pole as in (*a*), we find

$$K_{21} = [(p + 3)F(p)]_{p=-3} = -\tfrac{1}{4}.$$

Therefore

$$F(p) = \frac{(p + 2)}{(p + 1)^2(p + 3)} = \frac{\tfrac{1}{2}}{(p + 1)^2} + \frac{\tfrac{1}{4}}{(p + 1)} + \frac{-\tfrac{1}{4}}{(p + 3)},$$

which should be checked by combination over a common denominator. In general, again, the poles will not be so conveniently real, and the arithmetic will be much more involved because complex numbers will appear. The *principle* is unaffected, however. When two conjugate poles appear, their two sets of K's will also be respectively conjugate and but one set need be evaluated.

A general formula can be written [cf. (3.19–3)], but it is hardly worthwhile to try to remember it; remember the principle above and you can always find the K's easily. (For higher order poles it will be necessary to differentiate several times, of course.)

An alternative method (which may involve less labor when poles are multiple) is to write the expansion in literal terms and then to let p have several suitable values. This gives a set of linear simultaneous equations which may be solved for the unknown K's—and for the coefficients in $G(p)$, too—thereby avoiding the work of differentiation. (This method could of course be used even if all the poles were simple.)

When the expansion has been found, it should be multiplied out and checked against $F(p)$. Alternative checks can be made by evaluating both the expansion and the original $F(p)$ at various (convenient) values of p and making sure that the results agree. You should work enough examples to be sure that you know the technique of making partial-fraction expansions. The procedure, in sum, is to:

1. Determine the factors of the denominator of the given function $F(p)$.
2. Write out the form of the partial-fraction expansion according to the rules above, with literal (unknown) coefficients, for example,

$$F(p) = K \frac{p^6 + d_5 p^5 + \cdots + d_0}{(p - p_1)(p - p_2)^2(p - p_3)}$$

$$= \frac{K_{11}}{p - p_1} + \frac{K_{22}}{(p - p_2)^2} + \frac{K_{21}}{p - p_2} + \frac{K_{31}}{p - p_3} + C_0 + C_1 p + C_2 p^2.$$

3. Determine the coefficients in the polynomial part by one of the methods above (this may be done after step 4 if desired).

4. Determine the coefficients in the principal parts by the rules above.

Complex poles, in network functions, always occur in conjugate pairs, and the corresponding K's are also conjugate and therefore need be calculated only for one pole of the pair. Considerable labor may be necessary for the expansion of complicated functions—but further learning is only by doing. It is worthwhile to check the work by recombining the terms of the partial-fraction expansion and checking that the original $F(p)$ is regained.

3.20 Contour integration

We have been using our complex-variable integration theory to establish developments in series. Now let us turn back to integration itself.

Write (3.14–6), the expression for the coefficients of the Laurent series, for $n = -1$, using p now as the variable of integration, thus:

$$b_{-1} = \frac{1}{2\pi j} \oint F(p)\, dp, \qquad (3.20\text{–}1)$$

which is that one of the Laurent-series coefficients to which the name *residue* has been given. The contour indicated can be any closed path which can be deformed to the circles of § 3.14 and on which $F(p)$ is regular; it is to be traversed in the counterclockwise direction. The choice of contour may, of course, affect the region of validity of the Laurent series. Let us now specialize further and say that within the contour there is only *one* singularity of $F(p)$, say at p_0, as in Fig. 3.20–A. Then b_{-1} is called the *residue of $F(p)$ at the singularity p_0*. The contour can be deformed, so long as it does not strike a singularity of $F(p)$, without altering the value of the integral; hence the value of the residue is a characteristic of the function and does not depend on the contour of integration (except that the contour may not enclose any other singularity).

We can look on (3.20–1) either as an equation giving the residue, or as a way of evaluating the integral when the residue is known—the latter is the useful point of view. By Cauchy's theorem, (3.12–6), we know that the integral in (3.20–1) is zero if $F(p)$ is regular everywhere within the contour, and (3.20–1) checks this, for if $F(p)$ is regular, then the Laurent series has no descending branch, and $b_{-1} = 0$. So we can look on (3.20–1) as a generalized form of Cauchy's theorem, applying even if $F(p)$ is not regular at every point within the contour, and of which (3.12–6) is a special case. Regularity is not *necessary* for the contour integral to vanish, but is *sufficient* therefor.

It is worth taking a moment to obtain (3.20–1) by a slightly different process. Suppose we have $F(p)$ and wish to evaluate

$$\oint F(p)\, dp \qquad (3.20\text{–}2)$$

in accordance with Fig. 3.20–B. We further assume for the moment that there is only one singularity within C, that at p_0. By Cauchy's theorem we can deform this contour as we see fit, without altering the value of the integral, so long as we keep away from singularities in so doing. Let us

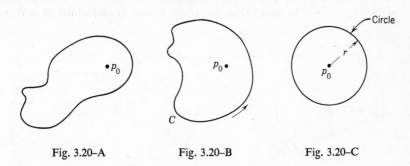

Fig. 3.20–A   Fig. 3.20–B   Fig. 3.20–C

deform C into a circle centered on p_0, as in Fig. 3.20–C. Now let us make use of the Laurent expansion of $F(p)$ about p_0,

$$F(p) = \sum_{n=-\infty}^{\infty} b_n (p - p_0)^n, \qquad (3.20\text{–}3)$$

which is valid on this (circular) contour. Further, let us assume that we can interchange the order of summation and integration, so that

$$\oint F(p)\, dp = \sum_{n=-\infty}^{\infty} b_n \oint (p - p_0)^n\, dp. \qquad (3.20\text{–}4)$$

On this contour C (which is now a circle of radius r),

$$p - p_0 = re^{j\phi}$$

as shown in Fig. 3.20–D (cf. Fig. 3.13–B). Hence

$$dp = re^{j\phi} j\, d\phi. \qquad (3.20\text{–}5)$$

And so we get

$$\oint F(p)\, dp = \sum_{-\infty}^{\infty} b_n \oint r^n e^{jn\phi}\, re^{j\phi} j\, d\phi$$

$$= \sum_{-\infty}^{\infty} jb_n r^{n+1} \oint e^{j(n+1)\phi}\, d\phi. \qquad (3.20\text{–}6)$$

But

$$\oint e^{j(n+1)\phi} \, d\phi = \frac{e^{j(n+1)\phi}}{j(n+1)}\Bigg]_0^{2\pi} = 0, \qquad n \neq -1,$$

$$= 2\pi, \qquad n = -1. \tag{3.20-7}$$

Therefore

$$\oint F(p) \, dp = 2\pi j b_{-1}. \tag{3.20-8}$$

This is the same as (3.20–1) for our restricted case of *one* singularity within C. [Bear in mind that the circle C can be deformed at will, so

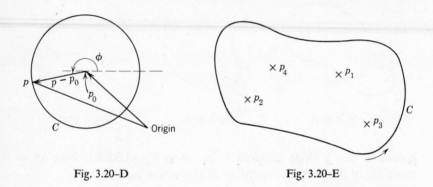

Fig. 3.20–D Fig. 3.20–E

long as singularities are avoided, and hence that C in (3.20–8) is fairly general.]

From either (3.20–1) or (3.20–8) we can say that

the value of a contour integral enclosing one singularity is equal to $2\pi j b_{-1}$, (3.20–9)

in which b_{-1} is the residue of the integrand at this singularity. This result, (3.20–9), is *Cauchy's residue theorem*. Note how all the b's except b_{-1} contribute nothing to the integral; b_{-1} is all that is left, whence its name.

We have still to take care of the more general case in which the contour of integration encloses more than one singularity, as in Fig. 3.20–E, where the small crosses represent singularities. By taking contours constructed in the manner of previous figures, with a small (broken) circle around each singularity and parallel lines joining these circles, it can be shown that the complete contour integral, around the outside path, is equal to the sum of small contour integrals, one around each singularity, all taken counterclockwise. So, if we use a superscript to indicate the singularity at which the residue is taken, i.e., $b_{-1}^{(k)}$ to denote the residue at singularity k, then we get

$$\oint F(p)\,dp = 2\pi j[b_{-1}^{(1)} + b_{-1}^{(2)} + \cdots + b_{-1}^{(l)}], \quad (3.20\text{--}10)$$

in which l is the number of singularities within the contour.   Hence

the value of a contour integral enclosing several singularities is equal
to $2\pi jB$,   (3.20–11)

in which B is the sum of the residues at the singularities enclosed, i.e., the *net* or equivalent residue.   Hence [cf. (3.20–1)] we see that the Laurent-series coefficient b_{-1} is equal to the sum of the residues at all the singularities inside C_2 of Fig. 3.14–A.   At the same time notice that (3.20–11) is not dependent on our ability to deform the contour into the circle C_1 or C_2 of the Laurent-series derivation; the contour may encompass a region in which a Laurent series could not be developed, as in Fig. 3.20–F, yet by the composition suggested above, (3.20–11) is still valid.

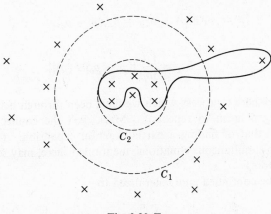

Fig. 3.20–F

These results concerning contour integration are fundamental to complex-variable theory, and we shall find them valuable in network theory.   They are useful for evaluating integrals, and for deriving some surprising results (to come).

3.21 Evaluation of residues

To determine residues by evaluating an integral is not often practicable —and one good use of residues is simply to evaluate integrals.   Hence we need other ways of evaluating residues. Two, applicable to poles, are given below; we need not consider other singularities.

1. From (3.14–5) we see that a singularity may easily be "removed" if it is a *pole*, i.e., if the descending branch of the Laurent series has only a finite number of terms, say r. (The Laurent-series expansion is assumed to be made about the singular point, and C_2 to be small enough that no other singularities are contained within it, just as in § 3.15.) For then, p_0 being the pole,

$$(p - p_0)^r F(p) = b_{-r} + b_{-(r-1)}(p - p_0) + b_{-(r-2)}(p - p_0)^2 + \cdots. \qquad (3.21\text{–}1)$$

In the case of the simple pole, $r = 1$,

$$(p - p_0)F(p) = b_{-1} + b_0(p - p_0) + \cdots,$$

and

$$b_{-1} = \Big[(p - p_0)F(p)\Big]_{p=p_0}. \qquad (3.21\text{–}2)$$

If the pole is second-order,

$$(p - p_0)^2 F(p) = b_{-2} + b_{-1}(p - p_0) + \cdots,$$

and

$$b_{-1} = \left\{\frac{d}{dp}\left[(p - p_0)^2 F(p)\right]\right\}_{p=p_0}. \qquad (3.21\text{–}3)$$

We recognize here a process which we have been through before (§ 3.19), but it does no harm to repeat it. Mark well the connection of this process with that of finding a partial-fraction expansion. (The method of setting up simultaneous equations, mentioned there, may sometimes be useful here too.)

This can be continued and generalized to

$$b_{-1} = \frac{1}{(r - 1)!}\left\{\frac{d^{r-1}}{dp^{r-1}}\left[(p - p_0)^r F(p)\right]\right\}_{p=p_0}, \qquad (3.21\text{–}4)$$

which, however forbidding, is a general formula for finding the residue of $F(p)$ at a pole.

2. Alternatively, we can say that at a pole of $F(p)$, say p_0, $1/[F(p)]$ has a zero, is regular, and can be expanded in a Taylor series about p_0. If we call the reciprocal function $G(p)$, this series is

$$\frac{1}{F(p)} = G(p) = G(p_0) + G'(p_0)(p - p_0) + \cdots. \qquad (3.21\text{–}5)$$

Since $F(p_0)$ is not finite, $G(p_0) = 0$. If the pole is first-order, then $G'(p_0) \neq 0$, and we can say, using (3.13-6) again,

$$F(p) = \frac{1}{G(p)} = \frac{1}{G'(p_0)(p - p_0) + \dfrac{G''(p_0)(p - p_0)^2}{2!} + \cdots}$$

$$= \frac{[G'(p_0)]^{-1}}{p - p_0}\left[1 - \frac{G''(p_0)}{G'(p_0)}\frac{(p - p_0)}{2!} + \cdots\right] \qquad (3.21\text{-}6)$$

which is valid for p sufficiently close to p_0. Hence the residue is given by

$$b_{-1} = \left[\frac{dG}{dp}\right]_{p=p_0}^{-1} = \frac{1}{\left[\dfrac{d(1/F)}{dp}\right]_{p=p_0}}. \qquad (3.21\text{-}7)$$

In particular, if $F(p)$ is in form a quotient, as $N(p)/D(p)$, then by (3.21-7),

$$b_{-1} = \left[\frac{d}{dp}\frac{D}{N}\right]_{p=p_0}^{-1} = \left[\frac{ND' - DN'}{N^2}\right]_{p=p_0}^{-1} = \left[\frac{D'}{N}\right]_{p=p_0}^{-1}$$

$$= \frac{N(p_0)}{D'(p_0)}, \qquad (3.21\text{-}8)$$

for $D(p_0) = 0$ (cf. § 3.19).

For a second-order pole, $G(p_0) = 0$ and also $G'(p_0) = 0$, but $G''(p_0) \neq 0$. Thus

$$F(p) = \frac{1}{\dfrac{G''(p_0)(p - p_0)^2}{2!} + \cdots}$$

$$= \frac{2!}{G''(p_0)} \times \frac{1}{(p - p_0)^2} + \frac{b_{-1}}{(p - p_0)} + \cdots \qquad (3.21\text{-}9)$$

by (3.13-6) again, and b_{-1} is the coefficient of $(p - p_0)^{-1}$ obtained by actually carrying out the division indicated above.

This method becomes more complicated of expression in the general case, but it, or variations on it, may be useful. Sometimes, for example (as above), $F(p)$ may have the form $N(p)/D(p)$ in which the Taylor series for N and for D are easily found. The ideas above then give $1/D$; multiplication by N and collection of all the $(p - p_0)^{-1}$ terms then gives the residue.

The point at infinity requires special attention, and it turns out that there may be a nonzero residue there, even if infinity is a regular point.

Evaluation of integrals "around infinity" requires special care (GU 3), but we shall not need such integrals.

3.22 Another theorem of Cauchy

Cauchy developed analysis (complex-variable theory) much further, and one of his other theorems we shall also need.

Consider the rational function

$$F(p) = K \frac{(p - p_1)^r (p - p_2)^q \cdots (p - p_n)^t}{(p - p_1')^{r'}(p - p_2')^{q'} \cdots (p - p_m')^{t'}}. \qquad (3.22\text{-}1)$$

The change in notation here is necessary, for we are going to find out something about the zeros as well as the poles. Now take the natural logarithm of $F(p)$,

$$G(p) = \ln F(p) = \ln K + r \ln (p - p_1) + q \ln (p - p_2) + \cdots$$
$$- r' \ln (p - p_1') - q' \ln (p - p_2') - \cdots. \qquad (3.22\text{-}2)$$

Then (by differentiation)

$$G'(p) = \frac{F'(p)}{F(p)} = \frac{r}{(p - p_1)} + \frac{q}{(p - p_2)} + \cdots - \frac{r'}{(p - p_1')}$$
$$- \frac{q'}{(p - p_2')} - \cdots. \qquad (3.22\text{-}3)$$

Now suppose $G'(p)$ to be integrated (counterclockwise) around a closed contour large enough to contain all the finite zeros and poles of $F(p)$. We get

$$\frac{1}{2\pi j} \oint \frac{F'(p)}{F(p)} \, dp = (r + q + \cdots + t) - (r' + q' + \cdots + t'). \qquad (3.22\text{-}4)$$

Now let us choose a smaller contour, enclosing only a portion of the zeros and poles. Then those terms of (3.22-3) which correspond to zeros and poles without the contour will contribute nothing to the integral, and the other terms will contribute as before. Hence

the value of a contour integral of the derivative of the logarithm of a function, divided by $2\pi j$, is equal to the net number of zeros within that contour. (3.22-5)

This supposes no zeros or poles on the contour; further, a zero (pole) is to be counted as n zeros (poles) if it is of nth order, and poles are considered to be negative zeros, for convenience.

This theorem is not restricted to rational functions, though our chief interest is in such.   But for utility we have to alter the left side of (3.22–4) to a practical form.   We can say

$$\int \frac{F'(p)}{F(p)}\, dp = \int \frac{d}{dp}\, [\ln F(p)]\, dp = \ln F(p) + \text{constant.} \quad (3.22\text{–}6)$$

The value of the contour (definite) integral in (3.22–4) is then equal to the *change* in $\ln F(p)$ as p traverses the complete contour C and returns to the starting point.   This change is zero, of course, if there are no zeros or poles of $F(p)$ within C.   But if a point p_0 lies within C, then the "vector" $(p - p_0)$ makes one complete (counterclockwise) revolution about the origin as p traverses C.   (Figure 3.20–D has the essentials of the picture here.)   This means that the logarithm of $(p - p_0)$ undergoes no change in its real part [for $(p - p_0)$ returns to its original magnitude], but does increase by $j2\pi$, which corresponds to one positive (counterclockwise) revolution of the vector $(p - p_0)$ about the origin.   Now apply this idea to our function, taking account of the possible multiplicities of zeros, of the fact that poles act here as "negative zeros," and of the coefficient $1/(2\pi j)$ in (3.22–4).   Then (3.22–5) becomes

the net number of zeros of a function $F(p)$ within a closed contour is equal to the net number of revolutions the vector $F(p)$ makes about the origin as p traverses that contour.   (3.22–7)

Here multiplicities of poles and zeros must be considered (as before), poles count as negative zeros, the contour is traversed counterclockwise, and counterclockwise revolutions are considered as positive, clockwise revolutions as negative.   The "net number of zeros" is of course really the number of zeros reduced by the number of poles—and again $F(p)$ is assumed to have no zeros or poles on the contour.   (This restriction is imposed by the derivation, but the presence of such zeros or poles would in any event make the "number of revolutions" meaningless.)

Should we be interested in the net number of zeros (poles) of a function in a certain region, then we can determine it by observing the revolutions which the vector (complex number) corresponding to the function makes as p traces out a contour enclosing that region.   This theorem is useful only when this observation is easier to make than direct calculation of the zeros and poles of the function is.   How this may come about and how we make the observation are questions we shall answer as we use the theorem.

3.23 Some consequences of Cauchy's theorem

Many wonderful things follow as consequences of Cauchy's theorem (3.12–6).   We have already seen a number of them and now we develop

another such corollary.   It happens that the end results of this section
are extremely important in network theory, which makes this all the
happier an excursion.

Consider a function $F(p) = x + jy$, which is a function of our complex
variable, but one somewhat restricted.   Suppose that

> $F(p)$ is analytic everywhere in the right half of the p plane and on the
> imaginary axis, and in particular that $F(\infty)$ is finite and meaningful.

This means that as $p \to \infty$, we assume $F(p) \to F(\infty)$ regardless of the
direction in which p travels out, and this (perhaps complex) number $F(\infty)$
is finite in magnitude.   (Any rational function with no poles in the right
half plane, or on the imaginary axis, or at infinity, obeys these restrictions.)

Now let us apply Cauchy's theorem (3.12–6) not to the function $F(p)$
but rather to the related function

$$G(p) = \frac{F(p)}{p - j\omega_1}, \tag{3.23–1}$$

somewhat in the manner of § 3.13.   Just why we use this integrand will
be clear after the deed is done.   For the path of integration, take one
composed of the imaginary axis, indented to the right around the point
$p = j\omega_1$ (by a small semicircle of radius r), and a large semicircle built on

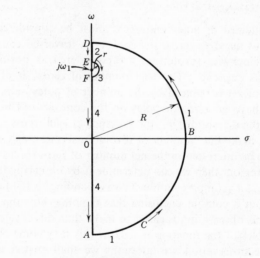

Fig. 3.23–A

the imaginary axis, of radius R, in the manner of Fig. 3.23–A.   (We shall
soon let $R \to \infty$ and $r \to 0$.)   The integrand is to be $G(p)$, so that we have
to avoid the artificial pole at $p = j\omega_1$, to satisfy the condition that the

integrand be regular on and within the contour of integration. Our hypothesis already insures that this is true of $G(p)$ elsewhere on and within C.

With this preliminary work done, the integrand set up and the contour of integration chosen, let us apply (3.12–6). We get

$$\oint G(p)\, dp = 0. \tag{3.23–2}$$

Now take the four parts of the contour (as numbered in Fig. 3.23–A) in turn. We shall evaluate those we can, and thus obtain an expression for the sum of those we cannot, from (3.23–2).

The first part is the large semicircle ABD. On this we have $p = Re^{j\theta}$, say, and

$$\int_1 G(p)\, dp = \int_1 \frac{F(p)}{p - j\omega_1}\, dp = \int_1 \frac{F(Re^{j\theta})}{Re^{j\theta} - j\omega_1} Re^{j\theta} j\, d\theta. \tag{3.23–3}$$

Now let R increase indefinitely, which gives this part of the complete integral the value

$$\int_1 G(p)\, dp = jF(\infty) \int_{-\pi/2}^{\pi/2} d\theta = j\pi F(\infty). \tag{3.23–4}$$

That leaves us with the small semicircle and the whole of the imaginary axis over which to integrate.

On the small semicircle we have $p = j\omega_1 + re^{j\theta}$, say, and

$$\int_3 G(p)\, dp = \int_3 \frac{F(j\omega_1 + re^{j\theta})}{re^{j\theta}} re^{j\theta} j\, d\theta$$

$$= j \int_3 F(j\omega_1 + re^{j\theta})\, d\theta. \tag{3.23–5}$$

The inevitable limit process, $r \to 0$, then gives us

$$\int_3 G(p)\, dp = -j\pi F(j\omega_1). \tag{3.23–6}$$

We now have, substituting the two results above into (3.23–2),

$$j\pi F(\infty) - j\pi F(j\omega_1) + \int_2 G(p)\, dp + \int_4 G(p)\, dp = 0, \tag{3.23–7}$$

in which the two integrals are to be interpreted in the light of the two limit processes, $R \to \infty$ and $r \to 0$. Since these integrals involve only purely imaginary values of p, we can write them in terms of ω. Let us rearrange (3.23–7) into a form for evaluating these integrals, and reverse the direction of integration, so that ω, the new variable, will increase rather than decrease. We get

$$\lim_{r \to 0} \left[\int_{-\infty}^{\omega_1 - r} \frac{F(j\omega)}{\omega - \omega_1} \, d\omega + \int_{\omega_1 + r}^{\infty} \frac{F(j\omega)}{\omega - \omega_1} \, d\omega \right] = j\pi \left[F(\infty) - F(j\omega_1) \right].$$

$$(3.23-8)$$

The sign ∞ implies the limit process $R \to \infty$. The other limit process is specifically indicated above. Now we assume the limits to exist, and for convenience we write the left hand side as a single integral from $-\infty$ to $+\infty$. By this symbol we mean, however, the limit obtained by the process above; this interpretation we must keep in mind, for the integral as written below means little without specification of the manner of passing through the pole of the integrand. Then we have

$$\int_{-\infty}^{\infty} \frac{F(j\omega)}{\omega - \omega_1} \, d\omega = j\pi [F(\infty) - F(j\omega_1)]. \qquad (3.23-9)$$

As a complex-number equation, this is really two real-number equations,

$$\int_{-\infty}^{\infty} \frac{x(\omega)}{\omega - \omega_1} \, d\omega = \pi[y(\omega_1) - y(\infty)],$$

$$(3.23-10)$$

$$\int_{-\infty}^{\infty} \frac{y(\omega)}{\omega - \omega_1} \, d\omega = -\pi[x(\omega_1) - x(\infty)],$$

which evaluate the integrals in terms of the values of $F(p)$ at infinity and at $j\omega_1$. [It is to be understood that $\sigma = 0$ in the expressions $x(\omega)$, $y(\omega)$, $x(\omega_1)$, $y(\omega_1)$.] The utility of these relations, we shall find, is in their expression of the real (or imaginary) part of $F(p)$ at the point $j\omega_1$ (which could be *any* imaginary value of p), in terms of the imaginary (or real) part of $F(p)$ for *all* imaginary values of p. Rewritten to express this, they are

$$x(\omega_1) = x(\infty) - \frac{1}{\pi} \int_{-\infty}^{\infty} \frac{y(\omega)}{\omega - \omega_1} \, d\omega,$$

$$(3.23-11)$$

$$y(\omega_1) = y(\infty) + \frac{1}{\pi} \int_{-\infty}^{\infty} \frac{x(\omega)}{\omega - \omega_1} \, d\omega.$$

Now we can see why the artificial pole was introduced at $j\omega_1$, in $G(p)$ of (3.23–1)! This device is responsible for the appearance of $F(j\omega_1)$, i.e., of $x(\omega_1)$ and $y(\omega_1)$ in the equations—and it is precisely this that makes these relations useful, as we shall see.

One change we shall make here, for clarity later. In (3.23–11) ω is the variable of integration and disappears when the definite integrals are evaluated; any other symbol could equally well be used for it. And $j\omega_1$ is a point on the imaginary axis, which remains fixed during the integration but can be *any* imaginary point. To emphasize these things, we rewrite (3.23–11), using λ for the variable of integration and $j\omega$ for the location of the artificially introduced pole; i.e., we let $\omega = \lambda$ and then (since this frees the symbol ω for other use) we let $\omega_1 = \omega$. We now have the alternate forms

$$x(\omega) = x(\infty) - \frac{1}{\pi} \int_{-\infty}^{\infty} \frac{y(\lambda)}{\lambda - \omega}\, d\lambda,$$

$$y(\omega) = y(\infty) + \frac{1}{\pi} \int_{-\infty}^{\infty} \frac{x(\lambda)}{\lambda - \omega}\, d\lambda.$$

$$(3.23\text{–}12)$$

In (3.23–12) the fact that the location of the artificial pole on the imaginary axis is arbitrary is emphasized in that it is now at $j\omega$—and the value of ω is entirely arbitrary.

Notice again how these equations indicate that, for the restricted kind of function assumed, knowledge of either the real part or the imaginary part alone, and the value at infinity, implies knowledge of the whole function, at least on the imaginary axis. If we know $x(\omega)$, for example, then the function $y(\omega)$ is determined by (3.23–12) within a constant, and this constant is also determined if the value of x at infinity (or some other point, for that matter) is known. This interrelation between the real and imaginary parts may seem novel, but it is not at all unreasonable. After all, we know that the real and imaginary parts of analytic functions are bound by the Cauchy–Riemann equations. These two equations amount to a pair of differential equations which certainly determine x (or y) in terms of y (or x), within some arbitrariness, a well-known property of conjugate harmonic functions. Our main interest here is in this strong relation between the real and imaginary parts of certain functions of a complex variable, which holds at least for imaginary values of p (and it can be extended: cf. Problem 8–48 and GU 3).

Here we have but raised a corner of a curtain, hiding many more such relations. By using weighting factors other than $(p - j\omega_1)^{-1}$, and by varying the integrand in other ways, we could derive a large number of interesting and important relations. We do not do so now, in order to get on to other business. These two equations (3.23–12) are the most important; they typify the many possible integral relations (BO 3, GU 3) and, incidentally, are related to the mathematician's Hilbert transforms (GU 3).

It is very important that we remember how these improper integrals are to be evaluated: in accordance with Fig. 3.23–A and (3.23–8). We shall use these equations, when the time comes, to find some very interesting facts about network functions; for the time being, we merely place them in our tool kit with our other shiny new tools.

3.24 Mapping

When we have a function of a complex variable, as $F(p) = x + jy$, we have in it a rule converting a complex number $p = \sigma + j\omega$ into another complex number $F = x + jy$. If we give to p a series of numerical values lying along a curve of some sort, we then get a series of numerical values of F, which will also lie along some sort of curve, but this new curve will not necessarily resemble the p curve. This is a *transformation* process, by which points of the p plane are converted into different points, the F points. To avoid confusion, let us place the F points on a different set of coordinates, even on a separate plane (Fig. 3.24–A). Then we

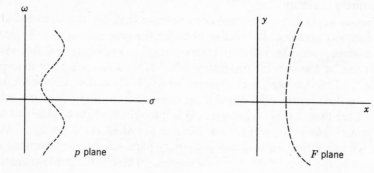

Fig. 3.24–A

have in the definition of F a rule which *maps* points of the p plane onto the F plane (in general, as other, quite different points). By taking enough points in the p plane, close together, to outline a curve, we get enough (image) points in the F plane also to outline a curve, though generally it will be quite a different curve. In the limit, when the points become very close together, we think of the *curve* of the p plane as transformed into the curve of the F plane. This is a process of transformation, or of mapping or representation, which are various names in use.

To be a little more precise, consider what happens when p is near some particular point p_0 at which $F(p)$ is analytic and has the value F_0. We can say (by § 3.13)

$$F = F(p) = F_0 + F'(p_0)(p - p_0) + \cdots \qquad (3.24\text{--}1)$$

for p near p_0 (and consequently F near F_0). Now as p moves slightly away from p_0, we have, to first-order infinitesimals,

$$F = F_0 + F'(p_0)(p - p_0) \tag{3.24-2}$$

or

$$\Delta F = F - F_0 = F'(p_0)\, \Delta p \tag{3.24-3}$$

in which Δ indicates an increment from F_0 (or p_0). This shows that the magnification of infinitesimal elements of curve length in the mapping process is determined by the magnitude of $F'(p_0)$ and hence does not depend on the direction in which p moves out from p_0. (The magnification does vary with the location of p_0, however.) It also shows that if there are two curves in the p plane which intersect at p_0 at an angle ϕ, the two corresponding curves in the F plane intersect (at F_0) at the same angle, ϕ. To see this, consider Fig. 3.24–B. The angle of intersection is

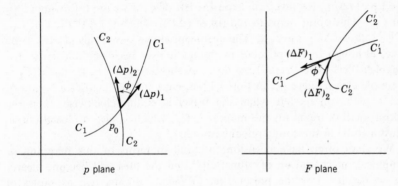

Fig. 3.24–B

the angle of $(\Delta F)_2/(\Delta F)_1$ in the F plane, and is the angle of $(\Delta p)_2/(\Delta p)_1$ in the p plane, and by writing (3.24–3) for each pair and dividing the equations, we see that these ratios of increments along the two pairs of curves are equal. Note that we cannot say this if $F'(p_0) = 0$. For then we have $\Delta F = 0$ for any value of Δp. If $F'(p_0) \to \infty$, we have a similar anomaly: $\Delta p = 0$ corresponds to any value of ΔF. But then $F(p)$ is not analytic, and we would not expect a nice, easily interpreted mapping.

It can be shown with rigor that if

(a) $F(p)$ possesses a unique (finite) derivative, or, better, $F(p)$ is analytic, and furthermore, if

(b) $F'(p)$ does not vanish,

there is a certain correspondence between curves in the two planes. This correspondence is *conformality*, meaning that where two curves intersect (and hence do so in both representations) the angles of intersection are the *same* in the two planes. [The shapes of a small (infinitesimal) figure conform in the two representations, then, and the *form* is conserved, though the scale may change and the figure be translated and rotated.] This applies only at *points*, however, so that there may still be great variation in (noninfinitesimal) *curve shapes* in the two planes. Except for points at which the derivative of $F(p)$ is zero, analytic functions yield conformal transformations. The real reason that $F'(p)$ also cannot vanish is that then the inverse function is not analytic; then $dp/dF \to \infty$ —and the transformation must work equally well both ways, to be useful.

An important corollary property of such a mapping is that the region on one side of a curve (left, or right, defined by our direction of travel) in one plane maps into a region on the *same* side of the mapped curve (traversed in the corresponding direction). In Fig. 3.24–B, the point at the tip of $(\Delta p)_2$, for instance, is on the left of C_1 if we are following $(\Delta p)_1$ on C_1. This point maps to the tip of $(\Delta F)_2$, which is on the left of C_1', if we follow $(\Delta F)_1$ on C_1'. The argument above shows this always to be true, although in complicated mappings it may become difficult to distinguish "left" and "right" regions. A further corollary is that if C_1 is a simple closed curve (as in Fig. 3.12–B, e.g.) and so encloses a region of the p plane on its left when the travel is counterclockwise, then the corresponding travel on the mapping, C_1', which is also a closed curve, must also be in the counterclockwise sense.

We shall often have occasion to think in terms of this mapping or graphical interpretation of "function," and the idea will become clearer as we use it. For the present, let us merely discuss two examples of conformal mapping.

The function

$$F(p) = \frac{ap + b}{cp + d} \tag{3.24–4}$$

gives the so-called *linear fractional* or *bilinear* transformation, named from the form of $F(p)$ or from the equation which results from the clearing of fractions in (3.24–4). It has been thoroughly studied (CH 3, GU 3) and has many interesting properties and applications (as in transmission-line charts). We shall need it only in the specific form

$$F(p) = \frac{1 - p}{1 + p} = x + jy = w. \tag{3.24–5}$$

Now let us study this particular transformation and see what it does. Let us also call the dependent variable w, as above.

Note that the inverse of (3.24–5) is

$$p = F^{-1}(w) = \frac{1 - w}{1 + w},$$ (3.24–6)

hence what goes for one direction of mapping goes also for the other. Notice also that there are no multiple-valued functions here and that the transformation, either way, is single-valued.

Now (3.24–5) is, more explicitly,

$$w = \frac{(1 - \sigma) - j\omega}{(1 + \sigma) + j\omega}.$$ (3.24–7)

Notice first that when p has a value in the right half of the plane, i.e., when $\sigma > 0$, then $|w| < 1$. In words, when p is in the right half plane, w is inside the unit circle (circle of unit radius with center at the origin). When p is in the left half plane, i.e., when $\sigma < 0$, then $|w| > 1$ and w lies outside the unit circle. Thus the right half of the p plane is mapped on the inside of the unit circle in the w plane, and the left half of the p plane is mapped on the outside of the unit circle in the w plane. When p has a purely imaginary value, i.e., when p is on the boundary between the right and left half planes, then $|w| = 1$ and w lies directly on the unit circle. Some specific point-to-point transformations are

p:	0	1	j	$-j$	-1	∞
w:	1	0	$-j$	j	∞	-1

(3.24–8)

All of the above information is summed up in Fig. 3.24–C.

In each part of Fig. 3.24–C the origin is at the intersection of the axes. The light and heavy lines and regions correspond, as do the lettered points. Notice that as we traverse corresponding lines, corresponding regions are on the same side in each case. For example, if we move along the p-plane imaginary axis from D to O to B with the right half of the p plane on our right, the corresponding w motion is along the unit circle from D to O to B, with the (mapped) right half of the p plane still on our right hand. This illustrates the general property of conformal mapping discussed before: except for a scale factor (which may be complex, involving rotation as well as magnitude change), small regions near two corresponding points in the two planes have like internal properties.

A less precise, but very instructive and graphic, interpretation of this transformation is to consider it as a deformation obtained as follows. Suppose the imaginary axis of the p plane is "bent" around to the right into some curved shape, as in Fig. 3.24–D(b). A good imagination can now conceive of the deformation as carried further, to the stage where the point at infinity is brought in and the old (p-plane) imaginary axis

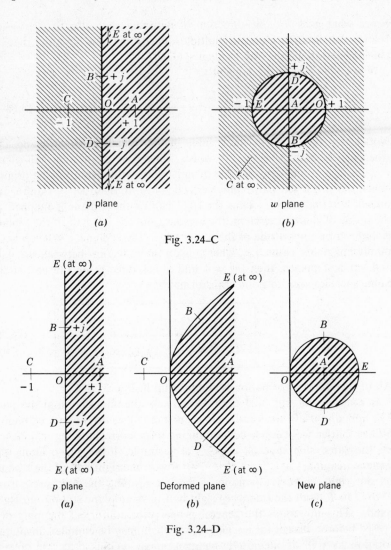

Fig. 3.24–C

Fig. 3.24–D

compressed into a finite closed curve, say a circle as in Fig. 3.24–D(c). The positions of the marked points correspond to the mappings of the similarly marked p-plane points. Compression of the right half of the p plane into the interior of a circle (note how clearly this appears) distorts the left half also, in particular sends the point C to infinity. The mapping of Fig. 3.24–D(c) is almost that of (3.24–5); if the origin is shifted to the right (to lie at A) and the plane is rotated 180°, then the particular form (3.24–5), identical with its inverse, results. To regard a mapping as obtained by continuous deformation, as in this discussion, is often helpful, not only in understanding what a given transformation does but in generating an appropriate transformation to use in a particular situation. (It is necessary, of course, to perform a careful investigation of the detailed properties of the mapping, in addition.) Our second transformation illustrates this even more.

Another very useful transformation is a general one which maps a straight line or series of segments in (say) the p plane into another series or a *polygon* in the w plane, the *Schwartz–Christoffel* transformation (HI 2) which we briefly study now.

Suppose we define $w = F(p)$ in terms of its derivative, dw/dp. We specifically take

$$\frac{dw}{dp} = A(p - p_1)^{a_1}(p - p_2)^{a_2} \cdots . \qquad (3.24\text{–}9)$$

The number of factors is finite (usually 1, 2, 3, or 4 in practical application). How the constants p_1, p_2, $\cdots$ and a_1, a_2, $\cdots$ and A should be determined for the result to be useful we now consider.

Let the points p_1, p_2, $\cdots$ all lie on the straight line of the p plane in which we are interested. Let w_1, w_2, $\cdots$ be the corresponding points in the w plane. Now as p (the variable) traverses the straight line, what happens to w? From (3.24–9) and Fig. 3.24–E we see that w also moves

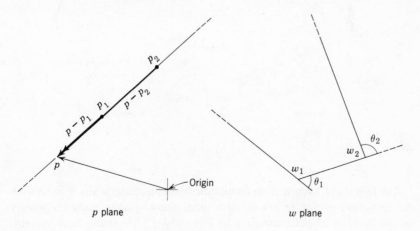

Fig. 3.24–E

along a straight line, since the derivative maintains a constant angle, until one of the points p_1, p_2, $\cdot$ $\cdot$ $\cdot$ is reached; these are the only points at which dw/dp changes in angle, and hence w_1, w_2, $\cdot$ $\cdot$ $\cdot$ are the only points at which the corresponding w curve (set of straight lines) "breaks." Evidently we get a polygon (though some of the lines might cross each other) if the set of lines closes—and it must—of which w_1, w_2, $\cdot$ $\cdot$ $\cdot$ are the corners. It remains to evaluate the effect of a_1, a_2, $\cdot$ $\cdot$ $\cdot$.

Just how much does the angle of the line which w is plotting change as p goes through p_1? From Fig. 3.24–E we see that $(p - p_1)$ changes in angle by 180°; whether it is an increase or a decrease depends on whether the variable point p goes just above p_1 (decrease) or just below p_1 (increase): different transformations result in the two cases. At the same time dw/dp changes in angle by a_1 times as much, i.e., by $a_1\pi$ radians. Hence the angles θ_1, θ_2, $\cdot$ $\cdot$ $\cdot$ are controlled by the a's, which we take to be real. For the point p_1 and the corresponding point w_1, in the case where p goes below p_1, Fig. 3.24–F sums this up.

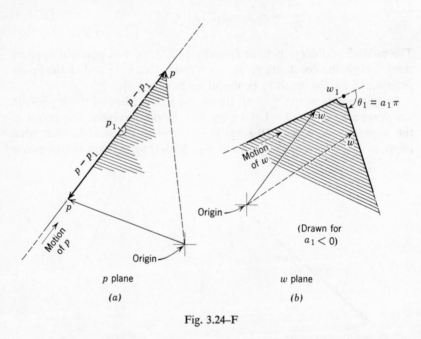

Fig. 3.24–F

The genesis of such a transformation becomes clear when it is viewed as a continuous deformation of the original plane—just as in the discussion of the bilinear transformation. In Fig. 3.24–F, for example, it is very convenient to consider the w plane as obtained simply by bending down the segment of line above and to the right of p_1 in (a) until the figure of (b) is obtained. (The shaded regions correspond in the two parts, and are maps one of the other.) We shall later, in fact, actually set up Schwarz–Christoffel transformations by this heuristic process. The actual details of any such transformation must be carefully and rigorously investigated, to be sure, but this approach is still extremely valuable.

We shall say no more about this transformation until we are ready to use it: then, with specific values, we shall find it much easier to discuss. The above is merely a general description.

3.25 An application of conformal mapping

There is an extremely important theorem which we can develop rapidly by using conformal mapping. It can also be derived analytically (GU 3) if desired, but the graphic clarity of the mapping approach (BO 3) is then lacking.

Suppose the function $F(p)$ to be regular on and within the contour C_1 of Fig. 3.25–A. As the variable p traces out the curve C_1, $F(p)$ takes on values also tracing out a curve, i.e., $F(p)$ maps the curve C_1 into some

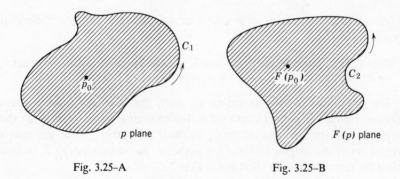

Fig. 3.25–A   Fig. 3.25–B

other curve. Let this curve be C_2, that of Fig. 3.25–B. We have restricted ourselves to analytic functions $F(p)$; in order to avoid twists and turns which produce overlappings and crossings in the curves, let us further restrict ourselves to functions $F(p)$ which yield conformal mappings of the interior of C_1, i.e., $F'(p)$ is also not to vanish for p on and within C_1. We shall not need the extension of our results to remove this restriction (except for one special case to be mentioned shortly), though it can be made. Our assumptions mean that the curve C_2 encloses a reasonable area which corresponds to that enclosed by C_1, and that infinity is not approached so long as p is on or within C_1 (infinity remains outside C_2). Both curves are traversed in (say) the counterclockwise direction, the interiors of the two curves correspond, and there is a point-to-point correspondence between values of p and values of $F(p)$.

Our interest is in the behavior of $F(p)$ as p moves along C_1 and over the area within C_1. There are two (rather different) cases to be considered: that in which the origin in the $F(p)$ plane lies outside the contour C_2, and that in which the contour C_2 encloses or touches the origin, i.e.,

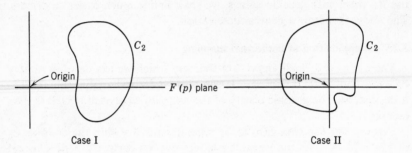

Case I   Case II

Fig. 3.25–C

$F(p)$ vanishes for a value of p within or on C_1. The two are illustrated in Fig. 3.25–C.

Case I: The origin in the $F(p)$ plane is outside the curve C_2, i.e., $F(p)$ has no zeros inside the curve C_1 in the p plane.

Let p explore the region inside C_1 now, and C_1 itself. As p roves around inside the curve C_1 and on it, the changing values of $F(p)$ do the same with respect to the curve C_2 in the $F(p)$ plane. Since the radius vector from the origin, in the $F(p)$ plane, is the value of $F(p)$, it is now clear by mere inspection (is it not?) that

the maximum value of $\quad |F(p)| \quad$ occurs when p is on C_1,

the minimum value of $\quad |F(p)| \quad$ occurs when p is on C_1,

the maximum value of $\quad \overline{F(p)} \quad$ occurs when p is on C_1,

the minimum value of $\quad \overline{F(p)} \quad$ occurs when p is on C_1,

the maximum value of **Re** $F(p)$ occurs when p is on C_1,

the minimum value of **Re** $F(p)$ occurs when p is on C_1,

the maximum value of **Im** $F(p)$ occurs when p is on C_1,

the minimum value of **Im** $F(p)$ occurs when p is on C_1, and none of these maxima and minima occur when p is *inside* C_1. These statements assume, remember, that $F(p)$ is regular on and within C_1, and that our mapping is conformal there.

Case II: The origin in the $F(p)$ plane is inside or on the curve C_2, i.e., $F(p)$ has a zero inside or on the curve C_1 in the p plane.

On inspection of the second part of Fig. 3.25-C, we can say that some but not all of the statements above are still true. Since there is a point inside or on C_2 for which $|F(p)| = 0$, this is now surely the minimum value of the modulus, and this minimum need not occur on the boundary. The statements about the angle of $F(p)$ become difficult to interpret and are not important anyhow. The other five statements stand, and it is only these that we shall use.

We do not need all of these results. Some will be sufficiently important, however, to justify their separate presentation, and these hold in either case. In the first place, if $F(p)$ is regular on and within C_1 and p_0 is some arbitrary point, either within C_1 or on C_1 (cf. Fig. 3.25-A),

the magnitude of $F(p_0)$ is less than, or at most equal to, the largest value that $|F(p)|$ assumes on the boundary C_1. (3.25-1)

This is equivalent to the statement

the maximum value of the modulus of $F(p)$, as p varies over the region bounded by C_1, occurs for a value (or values) of p *on the boundary*, (3.25-2)

which holds in either of the two possible cases. It is known as the *maximum-modulus theorem* or "principle of the maximum modulus." In symbols (p_0 being on or within C_1),

$$|F(p_0)| \leqq |F(p)|_{\substack{\text{maximum.} \\ \text{attained} \\ \text{on } C_1}}$$ (3.25-3)

An important feature of this is that if p_0 is *inside* C_1, then the $=$ sign holds only when $F(p)$ is a constant. For, in the mapping, any maximum of $|F(p)|$ must correspond to a point *on* C_2, since C_2 is the boundary of the region mapped. Hence, if the $=$ sign holds in (3.25-3), then $F(p_0)$ lies on C_2; i.e., p_0 maps to a point on C_2, the boundary. But if p_0 is interior to C_1, it must map to some point in the interior of C_2. Both conditions can be satisfied only if $F(p)$ is a constant, when C_2 degenerates, with its interior, to a single point. To be sure, $F'(p)$ is then zero and the mapping is not conformal, but this is the only way in which the $=$ sign can hold in (3.25-3) when p_0 is *within* C_1. To make this fact stand out, we restate (3.25-3) for the two possible cases.

Let M designate the maximum value which $|F(p)|$ attains as p moves on C_1. Now

if p_0 lies on C_1 [Fig. 3.25–D(a)], then

$$|F(p_0)| \leqq M; \tag{3.25-4}$$

if p_0 lies inside C_1 [Fig. 3.25–D(b)], then

$$|F(p_0)| < M, \tag{3.25-5}$$

except in the special case $F(p) = $ constant, when of course $F(p)$ has the same value wherever p_0 may be.

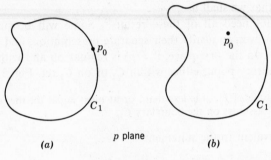

p plane

(a) (b)

Fig. 3.25–D

In either Case I or Case II the real and imaginary parts of $F(p)$ are greatest (and least) for certain values of p on C_1. Hence

the maximum and minimum values of both the real and the imaginary parts of $F(p)$ in a region of regularity occur at points (values of p) on the boundary. (3.25-6)

In particular, the real part (in which we shall have special interest) obeys the relation

$$[\text{Re } F(p)]_{\substack{\text{minimum} \\ \text{attained} \\ \text{on } C_1}} \leqq \text{Re } F(p_0) \leqq [\text{Re } F(p)]_{\substack{\text{maximum} \\ \text{attained} \\ \text{on } C_1}} \tag{3.25-7}$$

in which p_0 is a point on or within C_1. As before, when p_0 is within C_1, the $=$ signs hold only if they hold throughout the region.

To restate this, let $R_{\max}$ and $R_{\min}$ designate, respectively, the maximum and minimum values which $\text{Re } F(p)$ attains as p moves on C_1. Now

if p_0 lies on C_1 [Fig. 3.25–D(a)] then

$$R_{\min} \leqq \text{Re } F(p_0) \leqq R_{\max}; \tag{3.25-8}$$

if p_0 lies inside C_1 [Fig. 3.25–D(b)] then

$$R_{\min} < \mathbf{Re}\, F(p_0) < R_{\max} \qquad (3.25\text{–}9)$$

except in the special case $F(p) = $ constant, when of course $\mathbf{Re}\, F(p)$ has the same value wherever p_0 may be.

We now have in our kit the maximum-modulus theorem (BO 3, GU 3) and its most important relative. There are other implications of the work of this section, but they are not necessary in our work.

3.26 A formulary

Most of the foregoing has been nicely general. For contrast, we now set down (without derivation) some specific formulas for a particular function of a complex variable which (with variations) we shall use a great deal. This is the *exponential function*,

$$F(p) = e^p = \exp(p). \qquad (3.26\text{–}1)$$

The Taylor series for this function, about the origin, is

$$e^p = 1 + p + \frac{p^2}{2!} + \frac{p^3}{3!} + \cdots. \qquad (3.26\text{–}2)$$

We also say

$$e^p = e^{\sigma + j\omega} = e^\sigma \cos \omega + j e^\sigma \sin \omega. \qquad (3.26\text{–}3)$$

Now for $\sigma = 0$, we have

$$e^{j\omega} = 1 + j\omega - \frac{\omega^2}{2!} - j\frac{\omega^3}{3!} + \cdots = \cos \omega + j \sin \omega, \qquad (3.26\text{–}4)$$

$$\sin \omega = \omega - \frac{\omega^3}{3!} + \cdots = \frac{e^{j\omega} - e^{-j\omega}}{2j}, \qquad (3.26\text{–}5)$$

$$\cos \omega = 1 - \frac{\omega^2}{2!} + \cdots = \frac{e^{j\omega} + e^{-j\omega}}{2}. \qquad (3.26\text{–}6)$$

For $\omega = 0$ we have

$$e^\sigma = 1 + \sigma + \frac{\sigma^2}{2!} + \frac{\sigma^3}{3!} + \cdots = \cosh \sigma + \sinh \sigma, \qquad (3.26\text{–}7)$$

$$\sinh \sigma = \sigma + \frac{\sigma^3}{3!} + \cdots = \frac{e^\sigma - e^{-\sigma}}{2}, \qquad (3.26\text{–}8)$$

$$\cosh \sigma = 1 + \frac{\sigma^2}{2!} + \cdots = \frac{e^\sigma + e^{-\sigma}}{2}. \qquad (3.26\text{–}9)$$

The circular and hyperbolic functions of real argument (above) are but natural extensions of the exponential function, if you wish to view them that way. When these functions have *complex* arguments they are a little more complicated, but still are merely variants of the exponential function. Then we have

$$\sin(\sigma + j\omega) = \frac{e^{jp} - e^{-jp}}{2j} = \sin\sigma\cos j\omega + \cos\sigma\sin j\omega$$

$$= \sin\sigma\cosh\omega + j\cos\sigma\sinh\omega, \qquad (3.26\text{-}10)$$

for

$$\cos j\omega = \cosh\omega \qquad (3.26\text{-}11)$$

by (3.26–6) and (3.26–9), and similarly, by (3.26–5) and (3.26–8),

$$\sin j\omega = j\sinh\omega. \qquad (3.26\text{-}12)$$

These last two relations are typical of many similar ones which we shall not write down except as they are needed.

We also have

$$\cos(\sigma + j\omega) = \frac{e^{jp} + e^{-jp}}{2} = \cos\sigma\cos j\omega - \sin\sigma\sin j\omega$$

$$= \cos\sigma\cosh\omega - j\sin\sigma\sinh\omega. \qquad (3.26\text{-}13)$$

Similarly,

$$\sinh(\sigma + j\omega) = \frac{e^{p} - e^{-p}}{2} = \sinh\sigma\cos\omega + j\cosh\sigma\sin\omega, \qquad (3.26\text{-}14)$$

$$\cosh(\sigma + j\omega) = \frac{e^{p} + e^{-p}}{2} = \cosh\sigma\cos\omega + j\sinh\sigma\sin\omega. \qquad (3.26\text{-}15)$$

The functions $\tan p$ and $\tanh p$ and their reciprocals, defined (as usual) as quotients of the functions above, will also be useful to us. They have corresponding expansions.

All of these functions are closely related, for they are merely variants of $\exp(p)$. Notice that the exponential function e^{p} has the period $j2\pi$, for if ω changes by 2π, the value of e^{p} is unchanged. The other functions are periodic too, as you can see from their expansions above.

Another pair of useful formulas is

$$\sinh^{-1}p = \ln(p \pm \sqrt{p^2 + 1}), \qquad (3.26\text{-}16)$$

$$\cosh^{-1}p = \ln(p \pm \sqrt{p^2 - 1}), \qquad (3.26\text{-}17)$$

which can be derived from the exponential definitions (3.26–14) and (3.26–15), with suitable change of notation, by algebra.

Closely related to the exponential function is the (natural) *logarithmic function* $F(p) = \ln p$. If we write

$$w = F(p) = \ln p,$$

then

$$e^w = p. \tag{3.26–18}$$

Let the real and imaginary parts of the logarithm be separated:

$$\ln p = \alpha + j\beta. \tag{3.26–19}$$

Then

$$\alpha = \ln |p| \quad \text{(nepers)},$$
$$\beta = \overline{p} \quad \text{(radians)}. \tag{3.26–20}$$

The units of this (natural, or base-e) logarithm are the *neper* and the *radian*, as indicated.   Nepers are read from a table of natural logarithms entered with the magnitude of the argument of the logarithmic function, and radians are a familiar angular unit.   The imaginary part, β, is arbitrary within any (additive) multiple of 2π, so that $F(p)$ here is not single-valued, unless β is otherwise pinned down.   For this sort of logarithm we shall always use the symbol ln.

It will frequently be helpful to use other units for logarithms, such as the common (base-ten) logarithmic unit, and degrees.   The conversions are given below.   From

$$w = \ln p = \alpha + j\beta, \qquad p = e^w, \tag{3.26–21}$$

$$e^\alpha = |p| = 10^x, \tag{3.26–22}$$

in which x denotes the common (base-ten) logarithm of $|p|$.   The natural logarithm of (3.26–22) gives

$$\alpha = x \ln 10 = 2.303x, \tag{3.26–23}$$

and the common logarithm gives

$$\alpha \log e = x = 0.4343\alpha. \tag{3.26–24}$$

Note that the base-ten logarithm (for which we shall always write log) applies only to the magnitude, and ignores the angle.   For the latter we may take the degree measure of the angle of p for convenience, remembering that $180/\pi = 57.30$ is the degree measure of an angle of 1 radian. (These base-ten logarithms are not decibels, but they may be closely related; just how they are related depends on electrical matters also, so we postpone the discussion of this.)

As we progress in network theory, we shall find the exponential function and its relatives almost as important as rational functions.

3.27 Infinite products

We shall have occasion to deal with the *sin, sinh, cos, cosh,* and similar functions, even though they are not rational functions. That they should appear seems plausible when we take a look at a different manner of representing them, a manner which puts them in the form of rational functions of "infinite order." (Remember that the difference between a rational function and a transcendental function has to do with the finiteness or nonfiniteness of a series expansion; the transcendental function is an "infinite-order" version of the rational function, which may often be reached by a limiting process.)

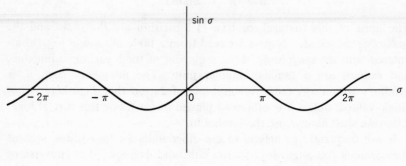

Fig. 3.27–A

Consider first the *sin* function. Its behavior as a function of a real variable is shown in Fig. 3.27–A. The presence of all these zeros (at $\sigma = 0, \pm\pi, \pm 2\pi, \cdot\cdot\cdot$) suggests that

$$[\cdot\cdot\cdot (\sigma + 2\pi)(\sigma + \pi)\sigma(\sigma - \pi)(\sigma - 2\pi) \cdot\cdot\cdot] \times \text{constant} \quad (3.27\text{--}1)$$

may be an approximation to the *sin* function. At least if this product (3.27–1) is finite, it is a function which agrees with *sin* σ at the vanishing points and presumably can be made to agree more closely by taking more and more factors. On the other hand, as we take more and more factors, the constant will have to be made smaller and smaller, because the slope of (3.27–1) at the origin will be

$$[\cdot\cdot\cdot (2\pi)(\pi)(-\pi)(-2\pi) \cdot\cdot\cdot] \times \text{constant}, \quad (3.27\text{--}2)$$

and unless the constant is made smaller, this will surely diverge. It requires detailed analysis, but this manner of representing the *sin* function is at least plausible.

Another approach might be to take the Taylor series for *sin* σ, (3.26–5), and cut it off with some finite number of terms. This will give a poly-nomial, which can be factored into a form resembling (3.27–1), but with different zeros. As the number of terms taken is increased, we expect these zeros to approach the multiples of π, however. In any event, this also leads to the same sort of thing, a polynomial of limitless degree.

Either of these approaches suggests that the function *sin σ* can be represented by a factored form, which displays the zeros very clearly, but which must be "infinite" in order to be an exact representation. Detailed analysis shows that just such a representation *is* possible, but that it must take the form

$$\sin \sigma = \sigma \left(1 - \frac{\sigma^2}{\pi^2}\right) \left(1 - \frac{\sigma^2}{4\pi^2}\right) \cdots$$

$$= \sigma \prod_{k=1}^{\infty} \left(1 - \frac{\sigma^2}{k^2\pi^2}\right), \tag{3.27–3}$$

which is an *infinite product*. Notice the compact notation of the mathe-matician, and how clearly it shows where the zeros of *sin σ* are. Notice also how it fits in with the "infinite-order rational function" idea.

We assume (it can be proved) that if the argument of the *sin* function is complex rather than real, the infinite-product representation is still valid, and

$$\sin p = p \prod_{k=1}^{\infty} \left(1 - \frac{p^2}{k^2\pi^2}\right). \tag{3.27–4}$$

This indicates that the zeros of *sin p* are those real values of p we already know about, and *only* those—and (3.26–10), on examination, will confirm this.

A similar analysis of the *cos* function gives

$$\cos \sigma = \prod_{k=1}^{\infty} \left\{1 - \frac{\sigma^2}{[(2k-1)\pi/2]^2}\right\} \tag{3.27–5}$$

and

$$\cos p = \prod_{k=1}^{\infty} \left\{1 - \frac{p^2}{[(2k-1)\pi/2]^2}\right\}. \tag{3.27–6}$$

Notice again that the zeros are all at real values of p, the well-known points, and there are no others.

From (3.26–6) and (3.26–9), and from (3.26–5) and (3.26–8), we get

$$\cos jp = \cosh p,$$
$$\sin jp = j \sinh p, \tag{3.27–7}$$

and when these are placed in (3.27–4) and (3.27–6) we get

$$\sinh p = p \prod_{k=1}^{\infty} \left(1 + \frac{p^2}{k^2\pi^2} \right), \tag{3.27–8}$$

$$\cosh p = \prod_{k=1}^{\infty} \left\{ 1 + \frac{p^2}{[(2k-1)\pi/2]^2} \right\}. \tag{3.27–9}$$

These last two expressions show that the zeros of the sinh and cosh functions are all at purely imaginary points—a fact which we should have

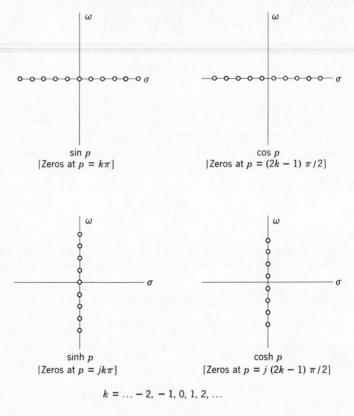

sin p
[Zeros at $p = k\pi$]

cos p
[Zeros at $p = (2k-1)\ \pi/2$]

sinh p
[Zeros at $p = jk\pi$]

cosh p
[Zeros at $p = j\ (2k-1)\ \pi/2$]

$k = \ldots -2, -1, 0, 1, 2, \ldots$

Fig. 3.27–B

expected from the relations in § 3.26 and from the sin and cos infinite products: there is simply a 90° rotation of axes involved. Equations (3.26–14) and (3.26–15) also check this fact.

Pictorially, we can sum this all up in Fig. 3.27–B, in which the small circles represent zeros. These illustrations of the p plane show the locations of all the zeros of these four functions. They have no poles, but do have essential singularities at infinity. Another point of view is to regard the total number of poles as still equal to the total number of zeros, as for rational functions [cf. (3.11–3)]; but since the number of zeros is infinite, so also then is the number of poles—and the poles are all at infinity and form the essential singularity there.

The circular and hyperbolic tangent and cotangent functions are quotients of the functions illustrated in Fig. 3.27–B. Corresponding illustrations for them will consequently have single rows, not of zeros alone, but of alternate zeros and poles. At infinity the singularity is still essential.

Thus the circular and hyperbolic functions are, in a sense, rational; they can be thought of as rational functions of infinite order. This concept will be useful later on. An obvious extension here is to consider functions whose pole-zero plans have not one but a larger number of rows of zeros or poles or both. Some of these are elliptic functions, of considerable importance in network theory, but we shall postpone discussion of these until they are needed.

3.28 Summary

This has been a lengthy chapter. Much of it should already be familiar, but probably some of its ideas are novel. It started by generalizing the usual variable of a-c circuit analysis, ω, to a complex variable, $p = \sigma + j\omega$. The latter is the usual complex variable of the Laplace transformation, and hence not really new. Since we shall use it throughout our work, we have to be familiar with some of the mathematics of complex variables —and that is what the balance of this chapter dealt with. Condensed and concentrated, it may have been confusing. But it is only a kit of tools, and we should not expect to have to use all of them at once, or even in the next few chapters. We need not worry much about them now, but can come back and get them whenever they are needed.

We have now finished our excursion into the wonderland of function theory. Remember we got into it because our analysis led to the use of a complex variable, p, and we thought it well to stop and find out about the behavior of such things before going further. What we want to take out with us is (1) a general familiarity with the notions of function theory, and (2) some specific tools (theorems, procedures, etc.) which we shall use as the need arises. Knowledge of the derivations of these things is important in this book only as it shows their limitations. We are interested in *using* these tools, not in admiring their theory or digging deeper into it, except as we really need to.

So now we turn back to networks. We go all the way back, in fact, and start to think a little more about *analysis*.

3.29 References

For the material of §§ 3.01–3.07, suitable references are BO 1, GA 1, GU 5, VA 1, WE 7.

The literature of function theory is enormous. For most of the material of §§ 3.08–3.26 a good reference is GU 3; another is CH 3; and there are many, many more, some of which are GA 1, BO 3, KN 1, RO 1, PH 1, WO 1.

Infinite products require elaborate analysis for rigorous justification, simple though the idea is. They are usually treated only in fairly advanced works, such as HU 1, MA 1, WH 1.

PROBLEMS

3-1. Calculate the impedance Z in the network shown, as a function of Z_1, Z_2, and a. Explain the physical action of the circuit and the meaning of the

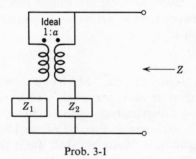

Prob. 3-1

result for $a = 1, 0$, and -1. Plot, versus a, the impedance Z (in appropriate units) for these cases: (*a*) $Z_1 = 0$; (*b*) $Z_2 = 0$; (*c*) $Z_1 = Z_2 = R$; (*d*) $Z_1 = 2Z_2 = R$.

3-2. Write the impedance function for this network as a function of p, taking $\omega_0 = (LC)^{-1/2}$ as the normalization unit for frequency, and $(L/C)^{1/2}$ as that for

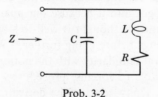

Prob. 3-2

impedance, in terms of the parameter $k = R(L/C)^{-1/2}$. Give also the factored form, and show on the complex plane the locations of the zeros and poles for several different values of k (enough to show all the interesting possibilities). What is the relation between the parameter k and the "quality factor" Q of the L-R combination, defined by $Q = \omega_0 L/R$? What are the loci of the zeros and poles as k varies?

For $k = 0.3$ sketch a curve of the magnitude of the impedance as a function of frequency, using only sketches of the complex plane that show the factors of numerator and denominator at various frequencies (as vectors or phasors) to guide you. Explain how the relative positions of zeros and poles enter into the phenomenon of resonance, and how this changes when k is large.

3-3. Find the impedance that the voltage generator faces in this network. (The element values are in normalized ohms, henrys, and farads.) On a sketch of the p plane mark the locations of the zeros and poles of this function. For a

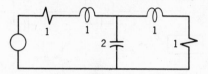

Prob. 3-3

typical real frequency, show on your sketch the vectors (phasors) that enter the numerator and denominator; from a consideration of this sketch for various frequencies, drawn an approximate curve showing how the magnitude and angle of this impedance vary with frequency.

3-4. The accompanying "double-tuned" network connects two pentode vacuum tubes; the function of interest is accordingly the ratio E/I. The two individual tuned circuits are identical, with a 10% coupling coefficient between the two inductors. The elements have the values $3500\,\Omega$, $(0.0028\pi)^{-1}\,\mu\mu\mathrm{f}$, $175/\pi\,\mu\mathrm{h}$.

Choose resistance and frequency units of normalization so that unit normalized frequency corresponds to the actual resonant frequency of either tuned circuit alone, and at this frequency either normalized inductor alone has

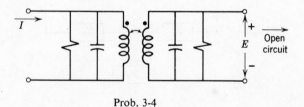

Prob. 3-4

unit reactance. Determine the ratio E/I as a function of the (normalized) complex frequency variable. Calculate and plot its zeros and poles, explaining why it is possible here to avoid factoring of any polynomial of degree greater than two. Does the number of zeros equal the number of poles? What relation is there between these numbers and the number of reactive elements in the network?

By drawing the appropriate lines (vectors or phasors) that represent the factors of numerator and denominator of E/I for a typical real frequency, on a complex-plane sketch that shows its zeros and poles, determine the general nature of, and plot, $|E/I|$ as a function of frequency. Point out interesting characteristics and explain their origin in the relative positions of zeros, poles, and axes of the plane. Repeat with a coupling coefficient of 20% and explain the changes.

3-5. Give in schematic form the network dual to that shown, (*a*) when Z_x is a short circuit, (*b*) when Z_x is an open circuit. What impedance in the dual network is dual to Z_1?

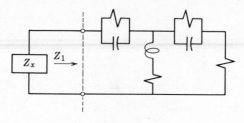

Prob. 3-5

Calculate $Z_1(p)$, taking unit values for all the elements. Where are its zeros and poles? Give the partial-fraction expansion of $Z_1(p)$. What meaning does this function have in the dual network? What relation is there between these zeros and poles, and zeros and poles of the corresponding impedance in the dual network?

3-6. A form of network in wide use in telephone systems is the *bridged-T* network shown. Each box represents an impedance as indicated. The network

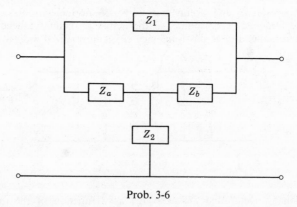

Prob. 3-6

is fed from a voltage generator of internal impedance R_G on the left and is terminated in a load R_L on the right, both purely resistive. (*a*) Determine the current flowing in the load and the voltage across it, using the loop basis of analysis. (*b*) Repeat (*a*) on the node basis. Which basis do you prefer? (*c*) Suppose the boxes contain impedances related by the equations

$$Z_a = Z_b = R_0 \text{ (purely resistive)}, \qquad Z_1 Z_2 = R_0^2, \qquad R_L = R_0.$$

Express the ratio of the load voltage to the (internal) generator voltage as simply as possible. Under these conditions, what is the impedance seen by the generator, i.e., what is the input impedance of the terminated network? What current flows in Z_a?; in Z_b? Explain.

3-7. The circuit shown contains a useful form of network known, from its configuration, as a "symmetrical lattice," as well as a generator of voltage E_0 and a load Z_L. (*a*) Analyze the circuit and calculate I_L as a function of E_0 and the Z's. (*b*) Calculate the ratio E_L/E_0 in the limiting case of operation into

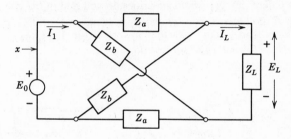

Prob. 3-7

an open circuit. (*c*) For the special case where $Z_a Z_b = R^2$ and $Z_L = R$, R being a pure resistance, what is the simplest form of the voltage ratio E_L/E_0? What then is the value of I_1? What then is the value of the network's input impedance, i.e., of $Z_1 = E_0/I_1$? How does this impedance vary with frequency? How does the ratio E_L/E_0 change if a resistance R is added in series with the generator at the point x? (*d*) Show that the case in which Z_a is the parallel combination of R and Z_c, Z_b is the series combination of R and Z_d, and $Z_c Z_d = R^2$, $Z_L = R$, is a special case of (*c*) and answer the same question about E_L/E_0.

3-8. (*a*) The network in question is that of Prob. 3-7 whose results may be helpful. Here take Z_a to be the parallel combination of L_1 and C_1, Z_b the series combination of L_2 and C_2, Z_L to be R, and assume $L_1/C_2 = L_2/C_1 = R^2$. Let $\sqrt{L_1/C_1} = 2kR$ for simplicity. (All the symbols L, C, and R have their conventional meanings.)

Write, in the simplest possible form, the voltage ratio E_L/E_0 as a function of p. [Normalization of the frequency scale to unit value at the actual frequency $(L_1 C_1)^{-1/2}$ radians per sec is convenient.] Calculate and plot on the p plane the zeros and poles of this ratio, for several different values of k, enough to illustrate the various possibilities.

For a value of k small enough to make the zeros and poles complex, draw in on a p-plane sketch the complex-number lines (vectors or phasors) that represent the factors of the numerator and denominator of the voltage ratio at several real frequencies. By considering this diagram, sketch the approximate shape of the magnitude and phase angle curves of this voltage ratio, as functions of frequency.

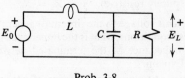

Prob. 3-8

(b) Repeat the above analysis for the network shown here, taking $(LC)^{-1/2}$ as the unit of frequency, and defining k by $(L/C)^{1/2} = 2kR$.

(c) What differences and what similarities do you find in the two analyses?

3-9. Find E_2 in terms of Z in (a) and E_2 in terms of Y in (b). E_{20} is defined in (c); it is the load voltage with the network Z (or Y) removed. Find also E_{20}/E_2 in each of the two cases (a) and (b).

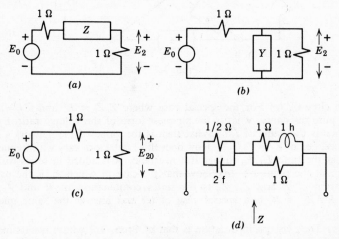

Prob. 3-9

Suppose that Z in (a) has the form shown in (d). On a sketch of the p plane show the locations and numerical values of the zeros and poles of $Z(p)$ and of E_{20}/E_2 in (a). Give the residues of $Z(p)$ at each of its poles. Give the partial-fraction expansion of $Z(p)$. What would the admittance function $Y(p)$ in (b) have to be if E_{20}/E_2 for this case were to be the same as E_{20}/E_2 in (a)? Show the locations of the zeros and poles of this admittance $Y(p)$ on a sketch of the p plane.

3-10. How many finite zeros does $Y(p)$ have? See the accompanying figure. How many finite poles? What is the nature of the behavior of $Y(p)$ at infinity?

Give the partial-fraction expansion of $Y(p)$. Give the complete literal *form* of the partial-fraction expansion of $Z(p) = 1/Y(p)$, on the assumption that all of its poles are simple. Determine the numerical values.

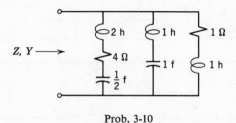

Prob. 3-10

3-11. Show, from the differential equations of Fig. 2.01–B, that a transformer (neglecting all resistive and capacitive effects and considering only primary, secondary, and mutual inductance, L_p, L_s, and M respectively) can be represented by either of the two equivalents shown. What assumption is implied with regard to the manner in which the four terminals are to be grouped? Determine the values of L_1, L_2, L_3 and of L_a, L_b, L_c in terms of L_p, L_s, M. Which equivalent is more useful in Prob. 3-4? When might the other be more useful?

Prob. 3-11

Which of these six inductances may be negative? What is the physical significance of such a negative inductance? In the case of perfect (100%) coupling, what relations exist between the inductances in each equivalent? Explain why an ideal transformer cannot be so represented.

Show how, with the addition of an ideal transformer, any "level" of current or voltage or impedance may be introduced, in place of the actual values, at either end.

3-12. In the analysis of ladder networks (those of the general form shown), a useful method is to assume a convenient value of voltage or current at the load (right) end, and then to work back to the input to determine the voltage or current source required there to give the assumed condition. (This requires only the application of Ohm's law to each box in turn.) For what reason will current and voltage *ratios* retain the values found in this analysis when other sources are used?

If all the "series" boxes (Z_2, Z_4, $\cdots$) contain only inductance, and all the "shunt" boxes (Z_1, Z_3, $\cdots$) contain only capacitance, what form will the ratios

E_L/E_0, E_L/I_0, take? Where (as closely as they can be pinned down) are the zeros and poles of these network functions?

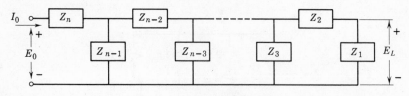

Prob. 3-12

Interchange "inductance" and "capacitance" above, and repeat.

In each of the two cases make Z_1 a resistor, all other Z's being unaltered, and repeat.

3-13. Write the input admittance function $Y(p)$ as a sum of four simple rational functions of p on the assumption that no special relations exist among the element values. How does this sum differ from the partial-fraction expansion of $Y(p)$? Make the necessary changes and obtain this expansion. What is the number of finite poles of $Y(p)$? Show their positions on a sketch of the p plane,

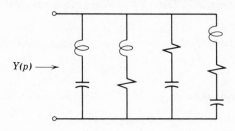

Prob. 3-13

giving the various possibilities where ambiguity exists. What is the behavior of $Y(p)$ at infinity, (a) as obtained by physical reasoning and (b) as obtained from examination of the mathematical function $Y(p)$? What is the number of finite zeros of $Y(p)$?

Discuss the possibilities of changes in your answers in special cases where special relations may exist among the element values.

Draw the schematic diagram of the network dual to this and point out what each of your answers means in this new network.

3-14. An impedance function $Z(p)$ has the value $0.5\,\Omega$ at zero frequency and only the following finite zeros and poles, all of first order.

Poles	Zeros
$-2 + j0$	$-0.34 + j0$
$-4 + j0$	$-3.33 + j0.80$
	$-3.33 - j0.80$

Construct the function $Z(p)$. What is its behavior at infinity? If zero or pole, give its order; if neither, give its value. Calculate the partial-fraction expansion of $Z(p)$. Determine the value of the integral of $Z(p)\,dp$ around a circle of radius r, centered on the origin, as a function of r.

Repeat for an admittance function $Y(p)$ that has the value 9 mhos at the origin and only the following finite zeros and poles, all simple.

$$
\begin{array}{cc}
Poles & Zeros \\
-2 + j0 & -5.305 + j0 \\
-5 + j0 & -1.695 + j0
\end{array}
$$

3-15. For the general three-node network, one of the nodes being taken as a common reference point, the standard form of the equations of analysis on the node basis, (2.07–2), is

$$Y_{11}E_1 + Y_{12}E_2 = I_1,$$
$$Y_{21}E_1 + Y_{22}E_2 = I_2,$$

in which the Y's are network parameters; the E's represent node voltages, and the I's current sources. Evaluate, for this network, the four Y coefficients as functions of p, and relate I_1 and I_2 to the source shown. Evaluate the network function $F(p) = E_2/I_0$.

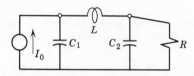

Prob. 3-15

How many finite zeros does $F(p)$ have? How many finite poles? What is the behavior of $F(p)$ at infinity? If zero or pole, give its order; if neither, give its value. On a sketch of the p plane show all possible combinations of types of locations (real, imaginary, complex) of the finite poles of $F(p)$.

Suppose that $F(0) = 1\,\Omega$, that the high-frequency behavior of $|F|$ is as ω^{-3}, and that $F(p)$ has a third-order pole at $p = -1$. Calculate the values of the four elements. Give the partial-fraction expansion of $F(p)$. Determine the residue of $F(p)$ at its pole.

3-16. Calculate the network function $F(p) = E_0/E_2$. (The element values shown are normalized ohms, henrys, farads.) Show on the p plane the loci

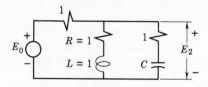

Prob. 3-16

of its zeros and poles as C varies. For the specific value $C = 1$ f, determine
the zeros and poles and express $F(p)$ in the simplest possible form.
Examination of the schematic shows that $F(p)$ has a pole at $p = -R/L$. What
is the residue of $F(p)$ at this pole, both in general and for $C = 1$ f?
If the combination of four elements across which E_2 is measured is now
replaced by a single resistor, how many zeros and poles does the function
$F(p)$ have? Could such a resistor be designed to be the equivalent of the
original network, as far as the ratio $F(p)$ is concerned, when C is arbitrary?
when $C = 1$ f?

3-17. Evaluate the functions $Z(p)$ and $Y(p)$ in the accompanying figure and
plot their zeros and poles on the p plane. Find the Laurent series for $Z(p)$ about
$p = -2$ and that for $Y(p)$ about $p = +j1$. Find the residues of each function

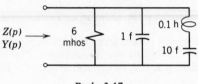

Prob. 3-17

at its various finite poles. Find the partial-fraction expansions of both functions.
Evaluate the integral of each function about a rectangular contour of sides
a and $3a$, centered on the origin, as functions of a.

3-18. Calculate $Z(p)$, the input impedance at the terminals shown. Plot the
zeros and poles of $Z(p)$ on the p plane and describe the behavior of $Z(p)$ at
infinity. Calculate the partial-fraction expansion of $Z(p)$. Evaluate the integral

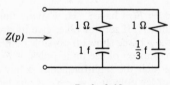

Prob. 3-18

of $Z(p)$ around a circle of unit radius centered on the origin, around a similar
circle centered on the point $-2 + j0$, and around a circle of radius 4 centered
on the point $-1 + j0$.
Calculate the Laurent series for $Z(p)$ valid in an annulus bounded by two
circles centered on the origin, of radii 0.1 and 1.9. Obtain a series for $Z(p)$
in powers of p that is valid outside the circle of radius 3 centered on the origin.

3-19. In the figure shown, calculate $Y(p)$, the input admittance function, and
expand it in partial fractions. Combine the conjugate-complex terms in this
expansion, thus eliminating complex coefficients from it. Now identify each
term in this modified expansion of $Y(p)$ with a simple network (of one or two
elements); combine these networks to obtain a new one-terminal pair whose

impedance function is identical with that of the original network, but whose schematic is different; give this schematic, with element values. Notice how this

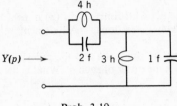

Prob. 3-19

shows a good use for partial-fraction expansion, and how it points out the nonuniqueness of synthesis in general.

3-20. This network is sometimes used as an interstage network in vacuum-tube amplifiers (VA 1, p. 75); if driven by a pentode, the stage voltage ratio is

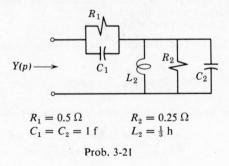

$$C_1 = 0.22C \qquad C = 1\,f$$
$$L_1 = 0.35R^2C \qquad R = 1\,\Omega$$

Prob. 3-20

closely proportional to Z, so that the impedance function is of interest. Calculate this function, $Z(p)$, and find and plot its zeros and poles. Give its partial-fraction expansion. For each term in the expansion, separately, find a small network which has that single term for its impedance function, if possible; if not possible, explain why not.

3-21. This network also has use as an interstage network (SH 4). Calculate the admittance function $Y(p)$; find and plot its zeros and poles. What physical

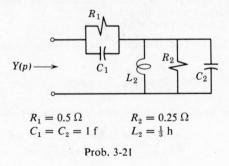

$$R_1 = 0.5\,\Omega \qquad R_2 = 0.25\,\Omega$$
$$C_1 = C_2 = 1\,f \qquad L_2 = \tfrac{1}{3}\,h$$

Prob. 3-21

property of the network, visible on the schematic, makes it unnecessary to solve a cubic equation here (in contrast to Prob. 3-20)? Find the partial-fraction expansion of $Y(p)$. Identify each term with a small network, if possible; if not possible, explain why.

3-22. For each of the network functions, $Z(p)$ in (a), $Y(p)$ in (b), $F(p) = E/I$ in (c), answer the following questions. (All element values are ohms, henrys, or farads.)

Where, in the p plane, are the zeros and the poles? Give numerical answers where possible. What is the order of each? What is the total number of zeros?

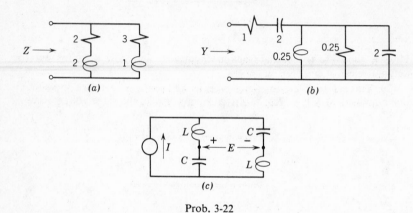

(a)   (b)

(c)

Prob. 3-22

of poles? What are the singularities of the function? What are the residues at each pole? What is the partial-fraction expansion? What is the behavior at infinity? (Answer both by examination of the function, and by purely physical reasoning from the schematic.)

3-23. Consider the function $F(p) = 2(p + 1)^{-1}$. Find the simplest series expansion that meets each of the following requirements, and delimit the region in which it is valid:

(a) An expansion in powers of p valid at and near the origin;
(b) a series expansion about the point $0 + j2$;
(c) an expansion in powers of p valid at and near the point $0 + j2$;
(d) a series expansion about the point $-1 + j0$.
What do series (c) and (d) have in common?

3-24. What is the residue of each of the following functions at each of its poles?

$$(a)\ \frac{p + 3}{p + 2} \qquad (b)\ (\sin p)^{-1} \qquad (c)\ \cos p \qquad (d)\ \frac{p^2 + 13p + 5}{p + 4}$$

$$(e)\ p^n\ (n = -3, -2, -1, 0, 1, 2, 3) \qquad (f)\ (p + 2)^{-3}$$

$$(g)\ \frac{p^4 + 6p^3 + 3p^2 + 7p + 2}{p(p^2 + 1)(p^2 + 2p + 1)}$$

3-25. Obtain, and verify, the partial-fraction expansions of these functions:

(a) $\dfrac{p(p+1)}{(p^2+1)(p+6)}$ (b) $\dfrac{p(p+3)(p+5)}{(p+2)(p+4)}$ (c) $\dfrac{p+1}{(p^2+2p+4)(p+2)}$

(d) $\dfrac{(p^2+1)(p^2+25)}{p(p^2+4)}$ (e) $\dfrac{p^2+2}{p^2+6}$ (f) $\dfrac{p(p+3)}{(p+1)(p+10)}$

(g) $\dfrac{p^6+17p^5+4p^4+3p^3+10p^2+8p}{p^3+4p^2+2p+2}$ (h) $\dfrac{1}{p^2+1}$ (i) $\dfrac{3p^2+13p+13}{(p+2)^2(p+1)}$

3-26. Where are the singularities of the function $(1+p^2)^{1/2}$? Obtain Taylor-series expansions (if possible) about each of these points:

$$(0,0) \qquad (1,0) \qquad (-1,0) \qquad (0,1) \qquad (0,-1)$$

and give the regions of validity. Obtain also a series in powers of p that is valid at infinity, and state its region of validity. Calculate the value of the function at the point $(0, 4)$ to six significant figures from the series, and compare with the actual value.

3-27. If interest is confined to a circle, the Laurent series made about the center of that circle, and valid thereon, becomes a Fourier series in the central angle. Verify this by (a) writing in literal form the Laurent series about the origin (i.e., in powers of $p = re^{j\theta}$) for a function which has no singularities in the annulus $r_1 < r < r_2$; (b) converting this to a trigonometric series in θ, valid on a circle of radius r, centered on the origin and lying in the annulus.

3-28. (a) Discuss the advantages, in the case of a pair of conjugate-complex simple poles, of calculating the K's in the second form given below, rather than those of the first (standard) form, in making the partial-fraction expansion of $F(p)$. How might those of the second form be calculated? (Rational character, and real coefficients, are to be assumed of F.)

$$F(p) = \frac{K}{p - p_1} + \frac{\bar{K}}{p - \bar{p}_1} + \cdots$$

$$= \frac{K_a p + K_b}{p^2 + ap + b} + \cdots, \qquad (p - p_1)(p - \bar{p}_1) = p^2 + ap + b.$$

(b) Discuss the following method of making a partial-fraction expansion, particularly from the labor-saving point of view. Illustrate with examples of the expansion of rational, real-coefficient functions, made both this way and by the standard method of calculating each coefficient in the expansion individually. Write the literal form of the partial-fraction expansion and equate it to the given function. Multiply through by the denominator of the latter, thus obtaining an equation, both sides of which are polynomials. Collect terms on each side, equate coefficients of corresponding powers of p, and solve these simultaneously for the unknown coefficients.

3-29. Find the power-series expansion of $F(p) = \operatorname{sech} p$ about the origin, (a) by evaluating $F(0)$, $F'(0)$, $F''(0)$, . . . ; (b) by writing the (known) series for $G(p) = \cosh p$ and then performing the appropriate division. Compare the two methods.

3-30. The integral $\displaystyle\oint \frac{F(p)\,dp}{p - p_0}$ around a closed contour that encloses p_0, but no singularities of $F(p)$, is to be evaluated. Obtain its value (a) by expanding $F(p)$ in a Taylor series about p_0 and showing that one term alone contributes to the integral; (b) by recognizing the value of the integral immediately, in terms of $F(p)$, from the appropriate formula. What, in general, is the residue of such an integrand at p_0, a regular point of $F(p)$? Illustrate the discussion by evaluating, around a circle of radius 3 centered on the origin,

$$(1) \ \oint \frac{\cos p}{p^3}\, dp, \qquad (2) \ \oint \frac{\sin p}{p^3}\, dp, \qquad (3) \ \oint \frac{e^p}{p^3}\, dp.$$

What relation exists between the three results? Explain it.

3-31. Calculate the input immittance functions of this network. (The element values are ohms, henrys, farads.) Do these functions have zeros or

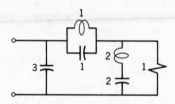

Prob. 3-31

poles at the points $p = \pm j1$, $p = \pm j0.5$? If so, explain the physical reasons therefor; if not so, do they have some other characteristic there of physical interest? Explain. Make the partial-fraction expansion of each function.

3-32. List and classify the singularities of the functions below, and of their reciprocals. Obtain the partial-fraction expansion of each of the rational functions, and of its reciprocal.

(a) p^n \qquad (b) $\dfrac{(p + 1)(p + 3)(p + 5)}{(p + 2)(p + 4)}$ \qquad (c) $\dfrac{1}{(p + 2)^3}$ \qquad (d) $\dfrac{p + 7}{(p^2 + 1)(p^2 + 2)}$

(e) $\dfrac{p^6}{(p + 1)(p + 2)^2(p + 3)^3}$ \qquad (f) $p^{-2.5}$ \qquad (g) $\dfrac{e^{7p}}{p^3 + 1}$ \qquad (h) $\sqrt{p^2 + 1}$

(i) $\tanh p$

3-33. Prove that the product of two analytic functions is again analytic. What can be said, in a similar vein, about the quotient of two analytic functions?

3-34. Let $F(p) = N(p)/D(p)$ be a rational function. Expand both numerator $N(p)$ and denominator $D(p)$ in Taylor series about a point p_0, in literal terms. By considering the important terms in each series, in each of the following cases, determine the value of the first nonzero derivative, or of the residue, as the case may be, in terms of derivatives of $N(p)$ and $D(p)$ individually.

(a) p_0 is a zero of $F(p)$ of order three;
(b) p_0 is a zero of $F(p)$ of order two;
(c) p_0 is a zero of $F(p)$ of order one;
(d) p_0 is a regular point of $F(p)$, not a zero;

(e) p_0 is a pole of $F(p)$ of order one;

(f) p_0 is a pole of $F(p)$ of order two;

(g) p_0 is a pole of $F(p)$ of order three.

3-35. Consider the integral of a function $F(p)$ around a very small circle, or a part thereof, centered on a singularity of $F(p)$, in the limit as the radius of the circle becomes indefinitely small. How does the integral completely around the circle compare in value with the integral taken only halfway around the circle, (a) in the case of a simple pole, (b) in the case of a double pole, (c) in the case of a third-order pole?

3-36. Consider the integral of a function $F(p)$ around a large circle, so large that all the finite singularities of $F(p)$ are inside the circle. What is its value in terms of the residues of $F(p)$ at these singularities? What is the value of the integral when the circle is traversed in the opposite direction? If the function has a singularity at infinity, what is a logical definition for its residue thereat? Would you say that if infinity is not a singularity, $F(p)$ may still have a residue at infinity? Illustrate with simple rational functions that have simple poles at infinity without residues, and residues at infinity without poles. In the function

$$F(p) = H\frac{p^n + a_{n-1}p^{n-1} + \cdots}{p^{n+1} + b_n p^n + \cdots}$$

discuss the relation between the constant H and the residue of $F(p)$ at infinity.

3-37. Calculate the value of $\int_{-\infty}^{\infty} Z(j\omega)\, d\omega$ by use of contour integration and express it in terms of the network element values. You may assume $Z(p)$ to be analytic in the right half plane and on the imaginary axis. If you are given the additional data that in $Z(j\omega) = R(\omega) + jX(\omega)$, $R(\omega)$ is even and $X(\omega)$ is odd, i.e., that $R(-\omega) = R(\omega)$ and $X(-\omega) = -X(\omega)$, what is the value of $\int_0^{\infty} R(\omega)\, d\omega$ and of $\int_0^{\infty} X(\omega)\, d\omega$? Which of the four network elements do and which do not affect the values of these integrals? (See the figure.)

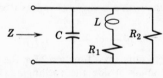

Prob. 3-37

Calculate also the value of $\int_0^{\infty} \frac{X(\omega)}{\omega}\, d\omega$ and determine on which elements it depends.

3-38. Prove that a contour integral is not changed in value if the (closed) contour is deformed, provided it remains closed and no singularities of the integrand are allowed to enter or leave the region enclosed in the process. If some enter, or some leave, does it necessarily follow that the value of the integral is altered? By how much will it change, if it does? Discuss and illustrate with examples.

3-39. Evaluate the integral of each of the functions below around a circle centered on the origin, of radius r, as a function of r.

(a) $\dfrac{13}{(p+1)^3}$ (b) $\dfrac{p}{(p^2+3)(p^2+5)}$ (c) $\dfrac{p(p^2+4)}{(p^2+3)(p^2+5)}$ (d) $\dfrac{p^2+6}{p^2+8}$

(e) $\dfrac{p^3+6p^2+8p+9}{p(p+3)(p^2+6)}$ (f) $\dfrac{p^2+1}{p^4+1}$ (g) $\dfrac{p^3+6p^2+p}{(p^2+p+1)(p^2+2p+1)}$

(h) $\dfrac{p^3+6}{(p^2+2p+4)^2}$

3-40. Discuss briefly the difficulties encountered in evaluating the two integrals below around a circle centered on the origin, for various radii. Point out the differences between the two.

(a) $\oint \sqrt{p+1}\,dp$ (b) $\oint \sqrt{p}\,dp$

3-41. By using § 3.22, determine:

(a) the total number of zeros of a polynomial of degree n (use a large circle);

(b) the division, as between right half plane and left half plane, of the zeros of a polynomial with real coefficients,

$$Q(p) = a_0 + a_1 p + a_2 p^2 + \cdots + a_n p^n$$

such that **Re** $Q(j\omega) > 0$ for all ω,

(1) when n is even,   (2) when n is odd

(use the imaginary axis and a large semicircle constructed thereon);

(c) the division, as in (b), when the property is **Re** $Q(j\omega) < 0$;

(d) the division, as between right half plane and left half plane, of the zeros of the polynomial $Q(p) = p^2 + ap + b$, in which a and b are real, for each of the four possible cases as to signs of a and b, neither being zero;

(e) the total number of roots of $F(p) = K$, in which $F(p)$ is a rational function of order N and K is a constant.

3-42. Use the theorem (3.22-7) to find the number of zeros each of the following polynomials has within a circle of radius r centered on the origin, as functions of r.

(a) $p^4 + 1$ (b) $p^4 + p^2 + 1$ (c) p^8 (d) $(p+1)^3$

By the same means determine, as a function of a, the number of zeros of each of the following polynomials inside the rectangle whose corners are $(0, a)$, $(-a, a)$, $(-a, -a)$, $(0, -a)$.

(e) $p^3 + 6p^2 + 2p + 1$ (f) $p^8 + 1$ (g) $p^3 + p^2 + 2p + 8$

(h) $p^4 - 2p^3 + 3p^2 - 2p + 1$

3-43. By using a contour composed of a large semicircle in the right half plane, closed by the imaginary axis, determine how many zeros each of the polynomials in Prob. 3-42 has in each half plane (left and right). What difficulty arises when zeros lie on the imaginary axis? How may it be resolved?

3-44. In Fig. 3.23–A suppose the contour to follow a small circle around $p = j\omega_1$ in the *left* half plane, instead of in the right half plane as there shown. To what formulas does the development now lead?

3-45. Show from the results of § 3.23 that, apart perhaps from the constants $x(\infty)$ and $y(\infty)$, if $x(\omega)$ is an *even* function, then $y(\omega)$ is an *odd* function, and that if y is *odd*, then x is *even*.

3-46. Indicate how the relations between real and imaginary parts, (3.23–12), may be extended to give relations between magnitude and angle, by taking for the function $F(p)$ the logarithm of the function in question, $G(p)$, i.e., $F(p) = \ln G(p)$. In what way are the restrictions on $G(p)$ then more severe than those on $F(p)$ in the original treatment?

3-47. Apply the results of § 3.23 to one-terminal-pair network theory, to determine reactance (susceptance) given resistance (conductance), or resistance (conductance) given reactance (susceptance), in the cases shown (pp. 104–5). The immittance functions involved may be assumed regular in the right half plane, on the imaginary axis, and at infinity. (There are certain singularities on the imaginary axis, to be sure, but they do not affect the validity of the apparatus of § 3.23—why?) In each case all that is known is the component shown, which has symmetry about the origin, and is resistance (conductance) in (a)—(g) inclusive, reactance (susceptance) in (h)—(m) inclusive. The other component is to be found analytically and plotted against frequency. What arbitrariness is there in your result? (*Note:* Exercise care in taking the limit as $r \to 0$ and be sure that your result is meaningful.)

3-48. The relations developed in § 3.23 determine the whole of $F(j\omega)$ when only the real or imaginary part is given (for all frequencies). Derive formulas under the same assumptions for the determination of the unknown parts of $F(j\omega)$ when the real part is known in the range $0 < \omega < \omega_a$ and the imaginary part in the range $\omega_a < \omega$. The real part may be assumed to have even symmetry about the origin and the imaginary part odd symmetry. Is there any arbitrariness in your results?

Repeat for the case in which it is the imaginary part that is known in $0 < \omega < \omega_a$ and the real part in $\omega_a < \omega$.

[*Suggestion:* For integrand, use $G(p) = \dfrac{F(p)}{(p - j\omega_1)\sqrt{p^2 + \omega_a{}^2}}$; indent the contour to the right of all three singularities, and use only one of the two square roots, so that $G(p)$ is single-valued.]

3-49. By introducing an appropriate additional square-root factor in the denominator (Prob. 3-48), derive formulas for the computation of the unknown parts of $F(j\omega)$, under the same general assumptions, when (a) the real part is known in $0 < \omega < \omega_a$ and in $\omega_b < \omega$, the imaginary part is known in $\omega_a < \omega < \omega_b$; (b) the imaginary part is known in $0 < \omega < \omega_a$ and in $\omega_b < \omega$, the real part is known in $\omega_a < \omega < \omega_b$.

3-50. Discuss the mapping of the p plane given by each of the following functions.

(a) e^p (b) $\ln p$ (c) p^2 (d) $(p^2 + 1)^{-1}$ (e) $p^2 + 3p + 2$ (f) $\sin p$

Where is the mapping conformal? How are parts of the p plane mapped (such as the unit circle, the axes, lines parallel to the axes)? What interesting features does each have? Which mappings are *univalent* as well as conformal, i.e., are also one-to-one in mapping from the new plane back to the p plane?

3-51. Find a bilinear transformation that maps the point $(-1, 0)$ to the point $(0, 0)$, the point $(0, 0)$ to infinity, and the point $(0, 1)$ to $(0, 1)$. Sketch the mapping.

3-52. Let p traverse the unit circle centered on the origin in the p plane, as curve C_1. Draw the corresponding curve C_2 in the F plane for each $F(p)$ given below and indicate how the parts of the p plane map. Considering all values taken by $F(p)$ as p moves over the region within the unit circle and on

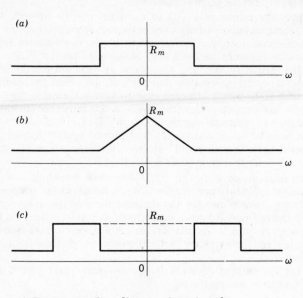

(a)

(b)

(c)

(d) The function $\{R_m - [\text{function shown in } (a)]\}$

(e) The function $\{R_m - [\text{function shown in } (b)]\}$

(f) The function $\{R_m - [\text{function shown in } (c)]\}$

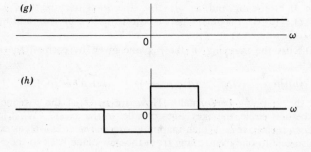

(g)

(h)

Prob. 3-47

that circle, in which cases do the maximum, and the minimum, values of the magnitude of F, the angle of F, its real part, and its imaginary part occur on C_2? Explain.

(a) K (a constant, real and positive)   (b) Kp (c) p^{-1} (d) $(p - 2)^{-1}$

(e) $(p + 2)^{-1}$ (f) $\sqrt{p}$ (g) $\sqrt{p^2 + 1}$

3-53. Derive and tabulate the formulas that relate the circular functions (*sin, cos, tan, cot, sec, csc*) of imaginary argument $j\omega$, to hyperbolic functions of

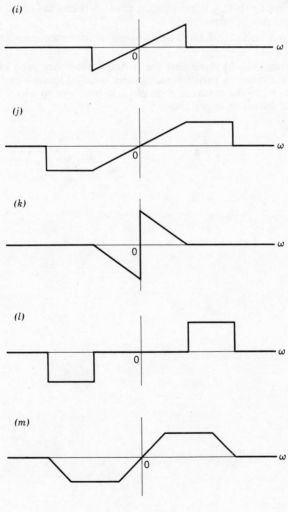

Prob. 3-47 (cont.)

real argument ω. Construct a similar table for hyperbolic functions of imaginary argument, expressing them in terms of circular functions of real argument.

3-54. Derive (3.26–16) and (3.26–17) and explain the meaning of the $\pm$ sign. How should a choice be made? Obtain similar formulas for the circular functions sin^{-1} and cos^{-1}. Obtain corresponding formulas (in logarithmic terms) for the functions $tanh^{-1}$ and tan^{-1}.

3-55. Express the functions tan, cot, $tanh$, and $coth$ in terms of exponentials. Round out Fig. 3.27–B with diagrams of the finite pole and zero locations of the functions tan, cot, $tanh$, $coth$, sec, csc, $sech$, $csch$, all with argument p. What is the nature of the singularity of each at infinity?

3-56. Prove (3.11–3). What relation exists between the order of a rational function and that of its reciprocal?

3-57. Prove (3.20–11) in the manner suggested in connection with Fig. 3.20–E (cf. Fig. 3.13–A).

3-58. From (3.10–6) prove that the real and imaginary parts of an analytic function of a complex variable individually satisfy Laplace's equation in two dimensions. List the more common physical problems to which this equation applies and discuss its importance.

4.

A Consideration of Energy,
with Some
Remarkable Conclusions

· · · a situation born of power and energy
—Edmund Burke

In order to maintain perspective, we ought now to review Chapter 1, especially the three steps indicated at the end of § 1.01. We are concerned for the present with the one-terminal pair (§ 1.03), and have started to take step 1 of the three: to obtain a working knowledge of the properties of networks with but one pair of terminals. In Chapter 2 we reviewed the conventional methods of analysis of networks, particularly in the steady a-c state; in Chapter 3 we found that a generalization of the variable $j\omega$ seemed to simplify things, and we set up such a generalized, complex frequency variable, and we called it p. This suggested that we equip ourselves with some of the apparatus of the theory of functions of a complex variable—and for some time we have been acquiring such tools. We shall not immediately use all of these. But we can now return, well equipped with tools, to networks proper, and when in the course of our investigations using p we need one of these tools, we have only to take it from Chapter 3. So we now go back to the *analysis* of networks.

4.01 Energy and power

It is appropriate to approach the specification of the fundamental properties of one-terminal pairs through an analysis of energy and power in such networks. That fact is by no means obvious, but has been found to be true by various investigators. This particular phase of network theory is an elegant one, and leads to many beautiful relations which are not without values other than beauty. It places network behavior where it can be viewed in the light of mechanics, for instance, by using Lagrange's equations and discussing not voltages and currents but rather energy functions. So we should be acquainted with this approach and its implications. A jump into this subject is apt to tie us down for some time, so many and interesting are the possibilities. When we finally emerge from it, however, to go on with the main problem, we shall find that very little of the energy-based analysis is really directly applicable to the synthesis problem. And the efficient use of our limited time is an important factor. Another ·effect to be considered is that the energy analysis, beautiful though it is, often bores a student. The subject might be omitted entirely in a book like this were it not for one thing: although we shall forget the subject of energy, for the most part, once we are through with this chapter, we shall find that one or two extremely important *properties* of networks come out of this energy study. These properties are vital, and although perhaps they can be derived in other ways, the energy approach is convenient, so we shall use it.

There are, in this chapter, two rather different developments. One, which we shall take up second, discusses the power and energy functions of networks; the other, which we take up first, is an examination of the analysis process, with emphasis on the fact that a passive network cannot be a source of energy, to see what more we can find out about network properties. We shall talk about *energy* in the usual physical sense of the word (measured by *work*) and about *power* which is, of course, the time derivative of energy or work. Instantaneous power is the product of instantaneous voltage and instantaneous current (in the a-c steady state power can be written in terms of the complex numbers we use to represent voltage and current, provided we talk about *average* power).

4.02 Power in the passive one-terminal pair

Let us now retrace the original path of analysis that Brune took in discovering these properties. (His paper, BR 1, is one of the historically more important ones and well worth reading.) We assume a *passive* one-terminal pair—and it is marvellous indeed how much can be discovered with this one assumption of passivity, as we shall see. About such a general passive network the only thing we can definitely say is that it cannot generate or furnish energy (unless stored from previous experience), for it has no internal sources. We are going to excite the system and by analysis determine whatever we can about its properties, using this fact of passiveness. Our first job, then, is to determine some expression for energy to which we can apply the fact. This in turn requires some knowledge of energy flow, or power, and calls for analysis. To our passive network we connect a source, and restrict our attention to the two terminals to which that source is connected. Let it be a voltage source for the present. The situation is shown in Fig. 4.02–A.

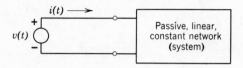

Fig. 4.02–A

We are again dealing with the actual, instantaneous values, as functions of time, of currents and voltages. In order to find the function $i(t)$ we might set up the full set of (say) loop-basis equations for the network, eliminate the currents in which we are not interested, and thus obtain one equation for $i(t)$, in which we *are* interested. This would be a differential equation, probably of rather high order. A simpler way is to perform the work of elimination in the Laplace-transform world, in which only algebra is involved. The end result of this will be a system function $Y(p)$ which relates the resulting current $i(t)$ to the causative voltage $v(t)$, but in terms, of course, of transforms. To simplify matters (we lose nothing by it), we shall say that the condition of the network at time $t = 0$ is one of rest, and there are then no currents flowing, no voltages present, no energy stored anywhere within the network; we shall see what happens for $t > 0$. Then we have the transform equation

$$I(p) = Y(p)V(p), \qquad (4.02\text{–}1)$$

in which the capital letters I and V refer to the transforms of the time functions represented by the corresponding lower-case letters. The system function $Y(p)$ is the ordinary, steady-state a-c admittance at the driving point, with $j\omega$ replaced by p, as Laplace analysis tells us. We can be fairly general here, incidentally, and do not need to require that the network contain only lumped elements, or even that it be finite; it need merely be a system such that a system function $Y(p)$ can be written—and hence $Y(p)$ may not be rational. We shall actually have occasion to consider only one departure from our limitation to a finite number of linear, lumped, constant elements—which is to remove the restriction that the number of elements be finite. This we shall in time find convenient, even in designing finite networks, but enough of that for now.

To get the results we want, we need to be specific about the form of the driving voltage function $v(t)$. For this we take

$$v(t) = e^{\alpha t} \sin(\beta t + \psi). \qquad (4.02\text{–}2)$$

This is reasonably simple, yet general enough. In order to avoid any question of impulsive response in the network (with attendant annoyances), let us make $v(0) = 0$, i.e., take $\psi = 0$. Then we have

$$v(t) = e^{\alpha t} \sin \beta t, \qquad (4.02\text{-}3)$$

$$V(p) = \mathcal{L}[v(t)] = \frac{\beta}{(p - \alpha)^2 + \beta^2}, \qquad (4.02\text{-}4)$$

and so

$$I(p) = Y(p)V(p) = \frac{\beta Y(p)}{(p - \alpha)^2 + \beta^2}. \qquad (4.02\text{-}5)$$

Since the network is passive, $Y(p)$ will have no poles in the right half of the p plane; if one or more were there, the response to any voltage driving force, even a slight, passing disturbance, would contain terms increasing exponentially in magnitude (envelope) with time, which a passive network certainly cannot support. [If $Y(p)$ is not rational, we can still be sure that the response must decay with time, or at most remain of the same order of magnitude, though perhaps something more than poles will be involved.] The dual statement, that $Y(p)$ will have no zeros in the right half of the p plane, is equally true, as can be seen by imagining a current disturbance to be the driving force. To be completely general, we ought to include the possibility that the network of Fig. 4.02–A be merely a short circuit, or an open circuit, which are certainly instances of physical passive networks, and might be considered violations of the statements above. These are trivial cases, however, and we shall ignore them here. When they are necessary in synthesis, common sense alone can handle them.

We now take the rather peculiar step of choosing for α a positive value. This is not unreasonable; it is just novel. The reason for it is that, if we do so, the forced (driven) part of the response will increase in magnitude as time goes on and hence be easy to separate from the natural part of the solution, a step we want to take. It calls for a husky generator, perhaps, but this we can set up on paper. This places the poles of $V(p)$ in the right half of the p plane, of course, as in Fig. 4.02–B, and we make the following definition:

$$p_1 = \alpha + j\beta = |p_1| e^{j\theta_1}. \qquad (4.02\text{-}6)$$

With the preliminaries out of the way, let us now calculate $i(t)$ in the usual manner. We have, for $t > 0$,

$$i(t) = \mathcal{L}^{-1}[I(p)]$$

$$= \mathcal{L}^{-1}\left[\frac{\beta Y(p)}{(p - \alpha)^2 + \beta^2} \right], \qquad (4.02\text{-}7)$$

in which the $=$ sign is to be interpreted in the usual Laplace-transform-analysis sense.

The evaluation of this inverse transform will yield two sorts of terms. One sort will come from the two poles of $V(p)$ and will have the same general form as (4.02–2), when the two terms are combined. This we shall calculate specifically. The other sort of terms in $i(t)$ comes from the poles of the system function, i.e., these are *natural*-response terms (as opposed to forced-response terms). As such, they must decay or at most remain bounded in amplitude (magnitude, envelope), and we need not

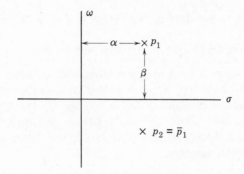

Fig. 4.02–B

bother specifically to compute them. We shall find that the first of these, the term like (4.02–2), the driven or forced component, will eventually become large enough to mask the natural components for our purposes. Let us denote the sum of the natural terms by N. Then we have

$$i(t) = 2 \, \mathbf{Re} \left[\frac{\beta Y(\alpha + j\beta)}{2j\beta} \, e^{(\alpha + j\beta)t} \right] + N$$

$$= \mathbf{Re} \, [Y(\alpha + j\beta)e^{\alpha t} \, e^{j(\beta t - \pi/2)}] + N. \qquad (4.02\text{–}8)$$

To simplify matters, let the polar form of the system function, evaluated at p_1, be

$$Y_1 = Y(p_1) = Y(\alpha + j\beta) = |Y_1| \, e^{j\phi_1}. \qquad (4.02\text{–}9)$$

Then we have

$$i(t) = |Y_1| \, e^{\alpha t} \cos \left(\beta t - \frac{\pi}{2} + \phi_1 \right) + N$$

$$= |Y_1| \, e^{\alpha t} \sin (\beta t + \phi_1) + N. \qquad (4.02\text{–}10)$$

Our next step is to compute the power taken by the network from the source, which is, of course, the instantaneous rate at which energy is being supplied to the network; it is

$$vi = (e^{\alpha t} \sin \beta t)[|Y_1| e^{\alpha t} \sin (\beta t + \phi_1) + N]$$

$$= e^{2\alpha t}|Y_1| \sin \beta t \sin (\beta t + \phi_1) + N e^{\alpha t} \sin \beta t. \qquad (4.02\text{–}11)$$

From trigonometry we take the relation

$$\sin x \sin y = \tfrac{1}{2}[\cos (x - y) - \cos (x + y)] \qquad (4.02\text{–}12)$$

and use it to get rid of the product of sines in (4.02–11). This gives

$$vi = \frac{e^{2\alpha t}|Y_1|}{2} [\cos \phi_1 - \cos (2\beta t + \phi_1)] + N e^{\alpha t} \sin \beta t$$

$$= \tfrac{1}{2} \operatorname{Re} [Y_1(e^{2\alpha t} - e^{2p_1 t})] + N e^{\alpha t} \sin \beta t. \qquad (4.02\text{–}13)$$

Note that we are now back in complex-number notation; the reason we had to drop it temporarily was that power involves the *product* of current and voltage (actual quantities) and is not simply the product of transforms, or the like. Once the multiplication is carried out, we find ourselves with a double-frequency sinusoid, and hence can easily drop back into complex numbers.

4.03 Energy in the passive one-terminal pair

Our next manipulation is to convert (4.02–13) into something about which we can make a positive statement based on the fact that the network is *passive*. This positive statement is that the net energy flow, from generator to network (i.e., from left to right in Fig. 4.02–A), must be positive (or zero) for all values of time greater than zero. This is simply a recognition of the fact that there are no sources of energy within the network. To reduce this to a mathematical statement, we form the net energy flow W by integrating the expression for the power. Since the operations $\operatorname{Re} [\ ]$ and $\int_0^t [\ ] \, dt$ are commutative, we get

$$W = \int_0^t vi \, dt = \tfrac{1}{2} \operatorname{Re} \left[Y_1 \left(\frac{e^{2\alpha t}}{2\alpha} - \frac{e^{2p_1 t}}{2p_1} \right)_0^t \right] + \int_0^t N e^{\alpha t} \sin \beta t \, dt. \qquad (4.03\text{–}1)$$

We can save ourselves unnecessary work if we notice that the result of evaluating the parenthesis at the lower limit will be a constant and that the result of evaluating the integral involving N will be of the order of $e^{\alpha t}$, since N is bounded. In other words, because the natural response N cannot increase in size beyond some definite limit (because the network is passive), the integral in (4.03–1) will not exceed (in magnitude) the product of some constant and $e^{\alpha t}$. So for large enough t, both of these will be negligible in comparison with the terms involving $e^{2\alpha t}$—for α is a positive number. Hence we merely write the symbol B for the sum of the constant and the integral involving N; B, then, is of the order of $e^{\alpha t}$, and

$$W = \frac{e^{2\alpha t}}{4} \text{Re} \left(\frac{Y_1}{\alpha} - \frac{Y_1 e^{j2\beta t}}{\alpha + j\beta} \right) + B. \tag{4.03-2}$$

Now we make the crucial statement. For sufficiently large t, the first of the two terms in (4.03-2) will certainly exceed the second in magnitude (except perhaps for isolated instants in the cycle of the sinusoidal part). This is because B is of the order of $e^{\alpha t}$ whereas the first term is multiplied by $e^{2\alpha t}$—and this first term cannot vanish, for $Y_1 \neq 0$ (as discussed above).

We know that W must remain positive, for all t. Whether this will be so or not is controlled by the factor

$$\text{Re} \left(\frac{Y_1}{\alpha} - \frac{Y_1 e^{j2\beta t}}{\alpha + j\beta} \right) \tag{4.03-3}$$

in (4.03-2). If this factor is ever negative, then surely W goes negative, and this is an impossible situation. Hence it is certainly true (because the network is passive) that

$$\text{Re} \left(\frac{Y_1}{\alpha} - \frac{Y_1 e^{j2\beta t}}{\alpha + j\beta} \right) = \left[\frac{\text{Re } Y_1}{\alpha} - \frac{|Y_1|}{|p_1|} \cos (2\beta t + \phi_1 - \theta_1) \right] \geqq 0. \tag{4.03-4}$$

The second of the two terms in the brackets is a sinusoid, the first is a constant. From (4.03-4), then, we can draw two conclusions:

(a) $$\text{Re } Y_1 = \text{Re } Y(p_1) \geqq 0, \tag{4.03-5}$$

(b) $$\frac{\text{Re } Y_1}{\alpha} \geqq \frac{|Y_1|}{|p_1|}, \quad \text{or} \quad \frac{\text{Re } Y_1}{|Y_1|} \geqq \frac{\alpha}{|p_1|}, \tag{4.03-6}$$

for if $\text{Re } Y_1$ were negative, or not large enough to satisfy (4.03-6), then (4.03-4) would be violated for certain parts of the time cycle of the sinusoid. More than that, the $=$ sign (as opposed to the $>$ sign) of the second part of (4.03-5) can hold only if $Y_1 = 0$, by (4.03-6). But Y_1 cannot vanish at p_1, for it has no zeros in the right half of the plane—refer to the discussion just after (4.02-5). Hence (4.03-5) can be written

(a) $$\text{Re } Y_1 = \text{Re } Y(p_1) > 0. \tag{4.03-7}$$

It seems that relation (b) implies (a) also—and so it does. But we shall find it convenient to have both statements, and so we retain them.

Now let us back off a little and see how general these results are.   In
the first place, there is nothing magic about the value of p_1, except that it
must be finite and its real part must be positive (else the argument above
about relative values of parts of expressions fails).   This means that our
conclusions about the real part of $Y(p)$ apply for *any* finite value of the
argument p, provided that value has a positive real part.   Put in equation
form, with the notation

$$p = \sigma + j\omega = |p|\, e^{j\theta}$$

and
                                                                    (4.03–8)

$$Y(p) = |Y|\, e^{j\phi},$$

what we have found is that the following must be true of the admittance
function of a passive network:

(*a*) When p is in the right half plane, i.e., when $\sigma > 0$, then

$$\textbf{Re } Y(p) > 0,   \tag{4.03–9}$$

i.e., the angle (phase) of $Y(p)$ must satisfy the inequality

$$-\frac{\pi}{2} < \phi < \frac{\pi}{2}.   \tag{4.03–10}$$

(*b*) When p is in the right half plane, i.e., when $\sigma > 0$, then

$$\frac{\textbf{Re } Y(p)}{|Y(p)|} \geqq \frac{\sigma}{|p|} = \frac{\textbf{Re } p}{|p|}.   \tag{4.03–11}$$

Since these ratios are the cosines of the angles of Y and of p, we can also
write this last as

$$\cos \phi \geqq \cos \theta   \tag{4.03–12}$$

or (since these apply only for $\sigma > 0$) as

$$|\phi| \lessgtr |\theta|.   \tag{4.03–13}$$

Figure 4.03–A shows three possible cases, here, in explanation; Fig.
4.03–B is more general.   In the latter, if p lies anywhere on either dashed
line, then $Y(p)$ must lie somewhere in the shaded area (or on its boundary).
If $\theta = 0$, we have the corollary result:

(*c*) When p is in the right half plane, i.e., when $\sigma > 0$, then

$$Y(p) \text{ is real when } p \text{ is real,}   \tag{4.03–14}$$

which follows from the fact that if $\theta = 0$, then only $\phi = 0$ satisfies
(4.03–13).

Condition (c) is closely connected with the condition that $Y(\bar{p})$ be the same as $\overline{Y(p)}$ (see § 3.09).

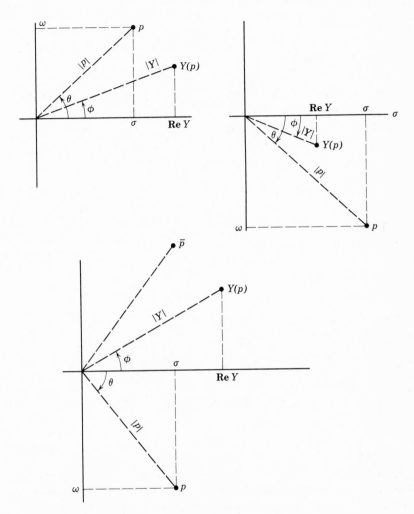

Fig. 4.03–A

This investigation has led us to the conclusion that certain facts must be true of $Y(p)$ when p lies in the right half plane or, more precisely, when p is finite and $\sigma = \mathbf{Re}\, p > 0$. That there should be some distinction between the right and left halves of the plane we should more or less expect (from transient arguments, as in § 4.02, if for no other reason), and this investigation confirms the expectation. It will be convenient to divide the plane up into these two halves—and, further, to define the right half plane and left half plane as the *interiors* of these two halves (as implied in the discussion of this section). This calls for a division of the plane into the following four parts:

the *right half plane* ($\sigma > 0$ but p finite),
the *left half plane* ($\sigma < 0$ but p finite),
the *boundary* ($\sigma = 0$ but p finite),   (4.03–15)
infinity ($|p| \to \infty$, the angle of p being usually unimportant because of the nature of the functions we shall be dealing with).

From here on, we shall utilize this division of the p plane. In all the analysis of this section the expression "right half plane" agrees in meaning with this definition.

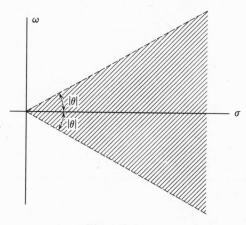

Fig. 4.03–B

4.04 Equivalence between conditions

There seems to be some overlapping among the three conditions (a), (b), (c) which we have just derived. If we consider a function $Y(p)$ (unrelated, for the moment, to physical problems) of which (b) is true, then surely (a) and (c) are also true of it. What is not at all obvious, but equally true (and important), is that if (a) and (c) are true of a function $Y(p)$, then (b) is also; in other words, (b) on the one hand and (a) and (c) together on the other hand, are equivalent statements. This we now digress a little to prove. The proof (GU 3) will require some of the tools of Chapter 3.

Since the conditions are concerned only with values of p in the right half plane, we first map this half of the p plane to a convenient finite region of a new (w) plane by means of the bilinear transformation (3.24–4). For generality, let σ_1 be any real, positive value of p, and define the mapping by

$$F(p) = w = \frac{p - \sigma_1}{p + \sigma_1}, \qquad \sigma_1 > 0. \qquad (4.04\text{–}1)$$

Then

$$p = \sigma_1 \frac{1 + w}{1 - w}. \qquad (4.04\text{–}2)$$

The mapping is conformal for all right-half-plane values of p and all imaginary values of p (the boundary values), and our interest is confined to these. Note that it is not conformal at infinity, and that the point at infinity in the p plane maps into the point $w = 1$. The interior of the right half of the p plane maps into the interior of the unit circle of the w plane, the imaginary axis of the p plane into the unit circle itself, the origin to the point $w = -1$, the point σ_1 to the origin, and infinity to the point $w = +1$. This is summarized in Fig. 4.04–A. (A useful concept

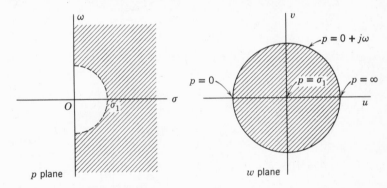

Fig. 4.04–A

is to imagine the mapping constructed by bending the imaginary axis of the p plane around to the right into circular form, at the same time compressing the right half of the plane into the circle's interior, and then translating the circle.)

We want to show that conditions (a) and (c) together imply (b) also. Since (a) makes a statement which has to do with positive values of $\mathbf{Re}\, Y(p)$, it is convenient also to map the right half of the $Y(p)$ plane to the interior of a circle. This proceeds just as above. First let

$Y(\sigma_1) = Y_0$. This particular value of Y is real and positive, by conditions (c) and (a), which we are assuming to hold for the function $Y(p)$. Then let the mapping take this point to the origin of a new (y) plane, so

$$y = \frac{Y(p) - Y_0}{Y(p) + Y_0}. \tag{4.04-3}$$

This transformation maps the interior of the right half of the Y plane to the interior of the unit circle in the y plane, with the same additional properties that the p-to-w transformation above has (cf. Fig. 4.04–B).

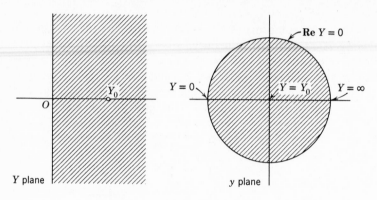

Fig. 4.04–B

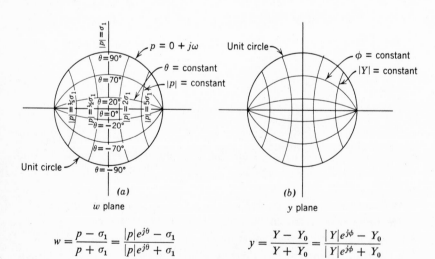

$$w = \frac{p - \sigma_1}{p + \sigma_1} = \frac{|p|e^{j\theta} - \sigma_1}{|p|e^{j\theta} + \sigma_1} \qquad\qquad y = \frac{Y - Y_0}{Y + Y_0} = \frac{|Y|e^{j\phi} - Y_0}{|Y|e^{j\phi} + Y_0}$$

Fig. 4.04–C

Note that y is a function of w, whose specific form would be obtained by substituting the value of p given by (4.04–2) in (4.04–3), and that when $w = 0$ (and $p = \sigma_1$) then $y = 0$ also. We now consider the relations between the w and y planes. These are drawn side by side in Fig. 4.04–C, with loci of points of constant angle and constant magnitude in the parent planes also shown.

We are assuming (a) and (c) to hold, i.e., that when p is in the right half plane, so also is $Y(p)$, and in particular when p is on the positive half of the real axis, $Y(p)$ is real (and of course positive, by the above). In terms of w and y, this means that any point in the interior of one unit circle corresponds to a point in the interior of the other. Suppose now that p traverses the curve C, composed of a vertical line just to the right of the imaginary axis and a large semicircle (Fig. 4.04–D). Since every

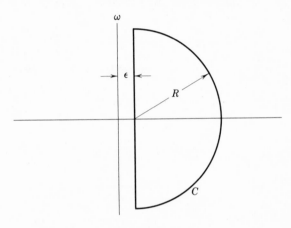

Fig. 4.04–D

point on C has a positive real part, every corresponding value of $Y(p)$ will have a positive real part, and hence the corresponding curve in the y plane will lie entirely within the unit circle. If we imagine R to approach infinity, and ϵ to approach zero, then in the limit C maps to the unit circle in the w plane. The corresponding curve in the y plane will lie on or within the unit circle, since it cannot jump outside. Formally,

$$\text{if} \quad |w| < 1, \quad \text{then} \quad |y| < 1 \qquad (4.04\text{–}4)$$

and

$$\text{if} \quad |w| = 1, \quad \text{then} \quad |y| \leqq 1. \qquad (4.04\text{–}5)$$

We can immediately say also that

$$\text{if} \quad |w| = 1, \quad \text{then} \quad \left| \frac{y(w)}{w} \right| \leqq 1, \qquad (4.04\text{–}6)$$

since we have merely divided (4.04-5) by unity. Now the new function $y(w)/w$ is analytic for all values of w within the unit circle, for y is there analytic—and we have seen that $y(0) = 0$. Hence the Maclaurin series for $y(w)$ is

$$y(w) = 0 + y'(0)w + y''(0)\frac{w^2}{2!} + \cdots \qquad (4.04\text{-}7)$$

and so

$$\frac{y(w)}{w} = y'(0) + y''(0)\frac{w^2}{2!} + \cdots \qquad (4.04\text{-}8)$$

is regular at $w = 0$ and throughout the unit circle. The maximum-modulus theorem (3.25-5) tells us then that this function $y(w)/w$ is limited in magnitude by unity when w is inside the unit circle, for its maximum value on the boundary is unity, by (4.04-6). Formally,

$$\left|\frac{y(w)}{w}\right| \leqq 1 \qquad \text{for } |w| < 1, \qquad (4.04\text{-}9)$$

in which the $=$ sign holds nowhere unless it holds everywhere in this region. Hence

$$|y(w)| \leqq |w| \qquad \text{for } |w| < 1, \qquad (4.04\text{-}10)$$

and at points for which $0 < |w| < 1$ the $=$ sign holds only if it holds at all such points. If $w = 0$, then of course the $=$ sign always holds in (4.04-10), though in (4.04-9) it need not and will not unless it holds everywhere; the difference is occasioned by the multiplication (or division) by w called for in developing one equation from the other—zero cannot be treated in so cavalier a fashion.

Now let p take any value on the semicircle $|p| = \sigma_1$ (Fig. 4.04-A) so that $p = \sigma_1 e^{j\theta}$. Then

$$w = \frac{\sigma_1 e^{j\theta} - \sigma_1}{\sigma_1 e^{j\theta} + \sigma_1} = \frac{e^{j\theta} - 1}{e^{j\theta} + 1} = j \tan\frac{\theta}{2} \qquad (4.04\text{-}11)$$

which corresponds to the part of the imaginary axis within the unit circle in Fig. 4.04-C(a). There

$$|w| = \left|\tan\frac{\theta}{2}\right|. \qquad (4.04\text{-}12)$$

From (4.04-10) we conclude that

$$|y| \leqq \left|\tan\frac{\theta}{2}\right| \qquad (4.04\text{-}13)$$

under these circumstances. But if $|y|$ is so restricted, then the angle of Y is restricted in magnitude to the value $|\theta|$ or less, as an inspection of

Fig. 4.04–C(b) will show. But σ_1 could have been *any* point on the positive real axis, so this covers the entire right half of the p plane. Hence

$$|\phi| \leq |\theta| \qquad (4.04\text{--}14)$$

for values of p in the right half plane, i.e., for $\sigma > 0$. Thus, if conditions (a) and (c) hold, then (b) does also. The $=$ sign again holds for points off the real axis only if it holds at every point in question, i.e., throughout the right half plane.

We can add a little bit to our knowledge of necessary properties of $Y(p)$ gained in § 4.03, then: in condition (b), i.e., in (4.03–11), (4.03–12), (4.03–13) and the accompanying figures, the $=$ sign cannot hold, except on the real axis, unless it holds *everywhere* in the right half plane. (On the real axis, of course, both θ and ϕ are zero.) This we did not know at the time, but it follows from the facts that (a) and (c) must hold for a physical $Y(p)$, and that (a) and (c), by the work of this section, imply the statement above.

This has been quite a long song and dance to prove what here may seem an unimportant point. But we shall find it very convenient to know that this equivalence between conditions holds. The proof here is due, to Guillemin (GU 3); Brune originally proved this by a different method (BR 1).

To recapitulate, what we have shown is that

if conditions (a) and (c) of § 4.03 are true of a function $Y(p)$, then condition (b) is also true. $\qquad (4.04\text{--}15)$

We have already noted that if (b) is true of $Y(p)$, then (a) and (c) are so also, by mere inspection. Hence we have found complete equivalence between (a) and (c) together on the one hand, and (b) on the other. We shall apply this in the next section.

4.05 Discussion

The results of our investigation of the flow of energy into a passive network have led to some remarkable conclusions. In words, they are that the admittance function of a passive network, when the independent variable p has a value in the right half plane, is itself in the right half plane (has a nonzero, positive real part), and further, its angle (phase) is bounded in magnitude by the angle of the variable. Of these two it seems that the second is much the tighter restriction. One might envisage the positions of p and $Y(p)$ in Fig. 4.03–A to be interchanged, e.g., a situation in which (4.03–9) [condition (a)] would be satisfied, but (4.03–13) [condition (b)] would not. We have just shown, however (in § 4.04), that the two are equivalent, provided that condition (c) is joined with condition (a). Hence even without knowledge of condition (b) we see that this interchange is *not* a possible situation if (*a*) and (*b*) hold, even though it does not immediately appear to violate them. This is a consequence of the fact that (*a*) and (*c*) hold *everywhere* in the right half plane; from this we have seen that the angle of the admittance function is further restricted by condition (*b*).

We now know that conditions (*a*), (*b*), and (*c*) must be true of the admittance function of a passive network. We know also that (*b*) alone implies (*a*) and (*c*) also, and that (*a*) and (*c*) together imply (*b*) also, so that there is some redundancy among the three. We have said nothing about sufficiency; we know these things must be true, but we have no inkling as yet as to whether a given function $Y(p)$, of which these things *are* true, can be the admittance function of any network at all. To answer this requires true synthesis, to come in due time.

Another important result which we can obtain with very little effort is that everything we have said about the admittance function is equally true of its reciprocal, the impedance function. To prove this, we might go back to Fig. 4.02–A and replace the voltage source by a current source. We would then calculate the voltage across the input terminals, etc. But we need do none of this work at all, for it would be exactly the same as that we did except for the following changes in notation:

$$v(t) \rightarrow i(t),$$
$$i(t) \rightarrow v(t),$$
$$I(p) \rightarrow V(p), \qquad\qquad (4.05\text{–}1)$$
$$V(p) \rightarrow I(p),$$
$$Y(p) \rightarrow Z(p),$$

in which $Z(p)$ represents the ratio of $V(p)$ to $I(p)$, i.e., the *impedance* function. We would take (4.02–2) as the form of the current source, and go through exactly the same (mathematical) work. Here is the great advantage of knowing about duality, for all we have said is that there is a dual process which leads to the same statements about the dual quantities.

The remarkable results of § 4.03 and § 4.04, then, are equally true of $Z(p)$, the driving-point impedance function of a passive network. (And common sense should have told us, on the basis of things we have encountered in the past, that what is true of one is more than likely true of the other.)

Thus, for p in the right half plane, immittance functions of passive networks (*a*) have positive, nonzero, real parts, (*b*) their angles are bounded, in magnitude, by the angle of p, and (*c*) they are real when p is real.

These are the first in a long series of properties of one-terminal-pair network functions which we shall obtain. We shall see, before long, that everything else of importance is implied by, and can be derived from, these conditions, of which (*b*) is implied by (*a*) and (*c*), and vice versa, and that we really have what we want, right here, in the line of deeper knowledge of network properties. So important are these properties we have derived that a function with them has a special name, due to Brune (BR 1). We say that

a function of *p* is *positive-real* when it satisfies condition (*b*), (4.03–13), *or* when it satisfies conditions (*a*) and (*c*), (4.03–9) and (4.03–14). (4.05–2)

To put this entirely in words,

a *positive-real function*, by definition, is a function with these properties *in the right half plane*: either its angle does not exceed in magnitude the angle of the independent variable, *or* its real part is positive, and it is real when the variable is real. (4.05–3)

We have demonstrated the complete equivalence of the two definitions, so either may be used at will. The difference between them is that definition (*b*) is a polar-coordinate definition, and the definition which uses (*a*) and (*c*) is a rectangular-coordinate definition. Sometimes one is useful, sometimes the other.

This new name, *positive-real*, comes from the fact that the function has a *positive* real part when *p* does, and is *real* when *p* is real—both conditions being required only in the right half plane, of course. Of this, much more will be said later.

4.06 Further discussion

A rather natural question to ask now is, what can be said about the function $Y(p)$, or $Z(p)$, when *p* is *not* in the right half plane? A little reflection would indicate that perhaps "not very much" is the answer—for after all, it is perfectly legitimate for immittances to have poles in the left half plane, and even on the boundary line (the imaginary axis), and poles are singularities, peculiar things which probably induce a much wider range of behavior near them. Nevertheless we can say something about behavior on the boundary line, although our arguments based on energy are of no use in the left half plane proper.

Let us consider the case where $\alpha = 0$ in the reasoning of § 4.02. We have to go back to (4.02–13); everything prior to that is just as valid when $\alpha = 0$ as it was before. Now, for $\alpha = 0$, we find that (4.02–13) becomes

$$vi = \tfrac{1}{2}\,\mathbf{Re}\,[\,Y_1(1 - e^{j2\beta t})\,] + N \sin \beta t. \qquad (4.06–1)$$

Then, much as in § 4.03,

$$W = \int_0^t vi\, dt = \tfrac{1}{2}\, \mathbf{Re}\left[Y_1 \left(t - \frac{e^{j2\beta t}}{j2\beta} \right) \right] + B,$$

in which B is now a bounded quantity, less in magnitude than some constant, for all positive t; hence

$$W = \tfrac{1}{2}(\mathbf{Re}\ Y_1)t + \text{bounded terms.} \qquad (4.06\text{--}2)$$

From this equation in which the first term dominates for sufficiently large t, and from the fact that W cannot go negative, we conclude that

$$\mathbf{Re}\ Y(j\omega) \geqq 0 \qquad \text{for passive networks} \qquad (4.06\text{--}3)$$

and, by dual reasoning, that

$$\mathbf{Re}\ Z(j\omega) \geqq 0 \qquad \text{for passive networks.} \qquad (4.06\text{--}4)$$

(In the above, β is replaced by ω because β is arbitrary, and our symbol for the variable is ω.) Common sense could have told us these things, for they simply say that a passive network, in the sinusoidal a-c steady state, cannot supply energy *on the average* (which it would do if the real part of the immittance, i.e., the resistance or conductance, went negative at any frequency).

In this section we have tacitly assumed that the immittance function has no pole at the point $p = j\omega$ at which we are driving the network. If a pole of the network function coincides with a pole of the driving function, which can certainly happen, the analysis requires investigation of the response with a double pole in the transform. This we could make, but the results come more easily in another way, which we shall develop later. (As mentioned above, all we need to know, really, is the positive-real property; from it follows everything else.)

Both (4.06–3) and (4.06–4) hold for indefinitely large ω, i.e., at infinite frequency also. By a limiting process we can also see that **Re** $Y(\infty)$ and **Re** $Z(\infty)$ are *positive* if p approaches infinity along any curve lying in the right half plane, i.e., any curve on which $|\theta| < \pi/2$. Hence at infinity the real part of an immittance function is at least zero, and if infinity is approached along some curve lying to the right of the imaginary axis, the real part is greater than zero and perhaps infinite.

Note that there is no hope of gaining any result for values of p in the left half plane, for then the N terms in § 4.02 could easily outgrow the forced terms, and we could say nothing about the latter.

We have completed the first of the two developments promised in § 4.01. We shall now go on to the second, a treatment of the power and energy functions of a network in terms of the elements, the energy they store, and related matters.

4.07 Power and energy functions

This second discussion will lead us to the same result, to the notion of *positive reality*, but by a somewhat different route, and with corollary results which will be very useful in proving certain important things later on.

We proceed now to find out what we can say about power and energy *within* networks—and shortly we shall limit ourselves to the two-terminal pair. For the moment, however, let us talk about any network which is passive and composed of a finite number of bilateral elements only, as defined in Chapters 1 and 2. This is a comparatively restricted case, to be sure, and we must expect less general results.

Let us go back to fundamentals and talk about *instantaneous* power, first in each of the three types of network elements individually, and then in the network as a whole, without any restriction as to how the currents and voltages vary with time. In other words, we are going right back to the beginning and starting over again.

The purpose of this discussion is the same as that of the first part of this chapter: to try to shed more light on what the fundamental nature of a one-terminal pair is. The utility of the power and energy functions shortly to appear is that they will lead to an expression for immittance in terms of related functions—and about energy we at least know something very definite (the energy stored in an inductor is positive, for instance). This expression will again shed light on the conditions for physical realizability of immittance functions, and (later) on the properties of one-terminal pairs made up of various combinations of elements, and even on such familiar things as the Q of a circuit.

Consider now the power and energy relations for individual elements, which are comparatively simple (but necessary for understanding the same relations for the whole network). Table 4.07–A lists the appropriate relations, on both bases of analysis. In each case, $p(t)$ represents instantaneous power supplied to the element; for the two elements which can store energy, $W(t)$ represents the instantaneous value of the energy stored in the element.

One of the fundamental things we know, and on which this analysis is based, is that the *power* and *energy functions*

$$Ri^2 = Gv^2, \qquad \tfrac{1}{2}Li^2 = \tfrac{1}{2}\Gamma\psi^2, \qquad \tfrac{1}{2}Sq^2 = \tfrac{1}{2}Cv^2 \qquad (4.07\text{--}1)$$

are all real, *positive* numbers, or zero. From their very physical nature, they cannot be anything else. Mathematically, they are products of real,

Table 4.07-A

$$p(t) = vi$$
$$= Ri^2$$

$$p(t) = iv$$
$$= Gv^2$$

$$RG = 1$$

$p(t)$ = instantaneous power dissipated,
　　　= instantaneous rate of dissipation of energy.

$$p(t) = vi$$

$$= Li\frac{di}{dt}$$

$$= \frac{d}{dt}(\tfrac{1}{2}Li^2)$$

$$= \frac{dW}{dt}$$

$$p(t) = iv = v\Gamma \int v\, dt$$

$$= \Gamma \psi \frac{d\psi}{dt}$$

$$= \frac{d}{dt}(\tfrac{1}{2}\Gamma \psi^2)$$

$$= \frac{dW}{dt}$$

$$L\Gamma = 1$$
$$W(t) = \tfrac{1}{2}Li^2$$
$$= \tfrac{1}{2}\Gamma \psi^2$$

$p(t)$ = instantaneous rate of change of stored energy,
　　　= power flowing in.
$W(t)$ = instantaneous value of stored energy.

$$p(t) = vi = iS\int i\, dt$$

$$= Sq\frac{dq}{dt}$$

$$= \frac{d}{dt}(\tfrac{1}{2}Sq^2)$$

$$= \frac{dW}{dt}$$

$$p(t) = iv$$

$$= Cv\frac{dv}{dt}$$

$$= \frac{d}{dt}(\tfrac{1}{2}Cv^2)$$

$$= \frac{dW}{dt}$$

$$SC = 1$$
$$W(t) = \tfrac{1}{2}Cv^2$$
$$= \tfrac{1}{2}Sq^2$$

$p(t)$ = instantaneous rate of change of stored energy,
　　　= power flowing in.
$W(t)$ = instantaneous value of stored energy.

positive numbers and squares of real numbers, which implies the same conclusion. These functions, then, can have the value zero, but can never be negative. Note that the power functions associated with the inductor and the capacitor are *derivatives* of energy functions, and hence need not always be positive.

Consider now the arbitrary network of passive elements which is our main interest. What we want to do is to develop expressions for stored energy (and rate of dissipation of energy) in the network, in terms of the elements. This we can do most easily by first considering how energy changes with time, i.e., by considering *power*. We consider an arbitrary network (passive, composed of bilateral R, L, S elements, possibly with mutual-inductance coupling). Assume that the loops are defined and numbered in the usual way for loop-basis analysis, and that all elements are on at least one loop (elements with one terminal not connected to anything are of no interest, nor are their duals, short-circuited elements). There can, of course, be no power and no energy in the network without the aid of connected sources.

Suppose, then, that an arbitrary collection of voltage sources is connected into the network by breaking the connections and inserting voltage generators arbitrarily so that each of the net loop-basis driving forces in the formal loop-basis equations of analysis (2.03–1) is determined as an appropriate sum of the voltage generators just introduced. Let us rewrite these equations in the form (4.07–2), in which the terms are grouped according to the nature of the elements: all inductance terms are together, all resistance terms together, and all elastance terms together. In the last group, the integral of the loop current is replaced by its equivalent, the loop charge, for the latter will be more convenient.

$$
\left.
\begin{aligned}
&\left(L_{11}\frac{di_1}{dt} + L_{12}\frac{di_2}{dt} + \cdots + L_{1l}\frac{di_l}{dt}\right) \\
&+ (R_{11}i_1 + R_{12}i_2 + \cdots + R_{1l}i_l) \\
&+ (S_{11}q_1 + S_{12}q_2 + \cdots + S_{1l}q_l)
\end{aligned}
\right\} = v_1,
$$

$$
\left.
\begin{aligned}
&\left(L_{21}\frac{di_1}{dt} + L_{22}\frac{di_2}{dt} + \cdots + L_{2l}\frac{di_l}{dt}\right) \\
&+ (R_{21}i_1 + R_{22}i_2 + \cdots + R_{2l}i_l) \\
&+ (S_{21}q_1 + S_{22}q_2 + \cdots + S_{2l}q_l)
\end{aligned}
\right\} = v_2, \qquad (4.07\text{–}2)
$$

$$
\vdots \qquad\qquad\qquad \vdots
$$

$$
\left.
\begin{aligned}
&\left(L_{l1}\frac{di_1}{dt} + L_{l2}\frac{di_2}{dt} + \cdots + L_{ll}\frac{di_l}{dt}\right) \\
&+ (R_{l1}i_1 + R_{l2}i_2 + \cdots + R_{ll}i_l) \\
&+ (S_{l1}q_1 + S_{l2}q_2 + \cdots + S_{ll}q_l)
\end{aligned}
\right\} = v_l.
$$

Now multiply the first equation through by i_1, the second equation by i_2, the third by i_3, etc. The results are

$$
\left.
\begin{aligned}
&\left(L_{11}i_1\frac{di_1}{dt} + L_{12}i_1\frac{di_2}{dt} + \cdots + L_{1l}i_1\frac{di_l}{dt}\right) \\
&+ (R_{11}i_1^2 + R_{12}i_1i_2 + \cdots + R_{1l}i_1i_l) \\
&+ (S_{11}i_1q_1 + S_{12}i_1q_2 + \cdots + S_{1l}i_1q_l)
\end{aligned}
\right\} = i_1v_1 = p_1,
$$

$$
\left.
\begin{aligned}
&\left(L_{21}i_2\frac{di_1}{dt} + L_{22}i_2\frac{di_2}{dt} + \cdots + L_{2l}i_2\frac{di_l}{dt}\right) \\
&+ (R_{21}i_2i_1 + R_{22}i_2^2 + \cdots + R_{2l}i_2i_l) \\
&+ (S_{21}i_2q_1 + S_{22}i_2q_2 + \cdots + S_{2l}i_2q_l)
\end{aligned}
\right\} = i_2v_2 = p_2, \quad (4.07\text{–}3)
$$

$$
\vdots \qquad\qquad\qquad\qquad \vdots
$$

$$
\left.
\begin{aligned}
&\left(L_{l1}i_l\frac{di_1}{dt} + L_{l2}i_l\frac{di_2}{dt} + \cdots + L_{ll}i_l\frac{di_l}{dt}\right) \\
&+ (R_{l1}i_li_1 + R_{l2}i_li_2 + \cdots + R_{ll}i_l^2) \\
&+ (S_{l1}i_lq_1 + S_{l2}i_lq_2 + \cdots + S_{ll}i_lq_l)
\end{aligned}
\right\} = i_lv_l = p_l,
$$

in which p_1 is the instantaneous power supplied by the (voltage) sources on loop 1 by way of i_1, p_2 is the instantaneous power supplied by the sources on loop 2 by way of i_2, etc. We now add up the l equations in (4.07–3) to get the single equation (4.07–4):

$$
\sum_{r=1}^{r=l}\left(\sum_{s=1}^{l}L_{rs}i_r\frac{di_s}{dt}\right) + \sum_{r=1}^{l}\left(\sum_{s=1}^{l}R_{rs}i_ri_s\right) + \sum_{r=1}^{l}\left(\sum_{s=1}^{l}S_{rs}i_rq_s\right)
$$

$$
= \sum_{r=1}^{l}i_rv_r = \sum_{r=1}^{l}p_r = p. \quad (4.07\text{–}4)
$$

Since the individual p_r represent the instantaneous power supplied by the sources on the various loops, the sum of these p_r is the *total* power supplied to the network, instantaneously, by *all* the sources—this is p above. (The algebra automatically takes care of power supplied by the sources on one loop by way of the loop current of another loop.) This is the total (net) instantaneous rate of energy flow *into* the network of passive elements. Evidently the expression for p in (4.07–4) has three essentially different components, one due to the L's, one to the R's, and one to the S's. Each of these components must be the total instantaneous power supplied to all of the elements of that particular kind.

Before going further, let us write the "dual" of (4.07–4). This would arise from a dual treatment of the original network, to which would now be attached arbitrary current generators. The node-basis equations of analysis (2.04–1) would then be rearranged, multiplied through by the appropriate voltages, and added to give us (4.07–6) below. But there is no real need to do this, because of the exact parallelism of the two methods, provided we simply make these changes:

$$L \to C, \qquad i \to v,$$
$$R \to G, \qquad v \to i, \qquad (4.07–5)$$
$$S \to \Gamma, \qquad q \to \psi.$$

The parallel to (4.07–4) is thus

$$\sum_{r=1}^{n} \left(\sum_{s=1}^{n} C_{rs} v_r \frac{dv_s}{dt} \right) + \sum_{r=1}^{n} \left(\sum_{s=1}^{n} G_{rs} v_r v_s \right) + \sum_{r=1}^{n} \left(\sum_{s=1}^{n} \Gamma_{rs} v_r \psi_s \right)$$
$$= \sum_{r=1}^{n} v_r i_r = \sum_{r=1}^{n} p_r = p. \quad (4.07–6)$$

In (4.07–4) and in (4.07–6) p has the same meaning, the total power supplied instantaneously to the elements of the (passive) network, but will not necessarily be the same numerically, unless the conditions of excitation lead to the same power input to the network in the two cases.

The result (4.07–6) or (4.07–4) shows that it is possible, at least formally, to write the total instantaneous supplied power as a simple sum of three items, each item depending on one kind of element only (though involving a perhaps complicated summation over every element of that kind in the network). We proceed now to investigate each of these three terms by itself and see how it is related to energy. What we are looking for is a set of relations analogous to those in (4.07–1), but applying to the network *as a whole*, i.e., relations describing the stored energy and dissipation of the whole network rather than of isolated elements one by one. This we can easily do by using the results (4.07–4) and (4.07–6).

4.08 Magnetic stored energy

For a solitary inductor of inductance L, the instantaneous stored energy, from Table 4.07–A, is

$$T = \tfrac{1}{2} L i^2 = \tfrac{1}{2} \Gamma \psi^2. \quad (4.08–1)$$

The symbol T is taken from mechanics, because of the analogy with kinetic energy. From (4.07–4) we conclude that the rate at which energy is stored in *all* the inductors of the network is

$$\frac{dT}{dt} = \sum_{r=1}^{l} \sum_{s=1}^{l} L_{rs} i_r \frac{di_s}{dt}. \quad (4.08–2)$$

To obtain T itself, we integrate this expression, as follows.

$$T = \int \sum_r \sum_s L_{rs} i_r \frac{di_s}{dt} \, dt$$

$$= \sum_r \sum_s L_{rs} \int i_r \, di_s, \qquad (4.08\text{-}3)$$

for this is a finite summation in which the order of integration and summation may be changed.   Integration by parts gives

$$\sum_r \sum_s L_{rs} \int i_r \, di_s = \sum_r \sum_s L_{rs} \left(i_r i_s - \int i_s \, di_r \right)$$

$$= \sum_r \sum_s L_{rs} i_r i_s - \sum_r \sum_s L_{rs} \int i_s \, di_r. \qquad (4.08\text{-}4)$$

This manipulation may not seem to have accomplished much, but from the above we have

$$\left(\sum_r \sum_s L_{rs} \int i_r \, di_s \right) + \left(\sum_r \sum_s L_{rs} \int i_s \, di_r \right) = \sum_r \sum_s L_{rs} i_r i_s, \quad (4.08\text{-}5)$$

in which the double summations on the left have the *same* value.   To show this, recall that the notation for indices of summation is of course arbitrary (they do not appear, once the sum is evaluated), so that the second parenthesis could equally well be written

$$\sum_s \sum_r L_{sr} \int i_r \, di_s. \qquad (4.08\text{-}6)$$

Since the network is composed of bilateral elements only, $L_{rs} = L_{sr}$; hence

$$\sum_s \sum_r L_{sr} \int i_r \, di_s = \sum_s \sum_r L_{rs} \int i_r \, di_s. \qquad (4.08\text{-}7)$$

Finally, we can interchange the summation signs (the sum is finite) and find that the second parenthesis in (4.08-5) can be written

$$\sum_r \sum_s L_{rs} \int i_r \, di_s \qquad (4.08\text{-}8)$$

which is the same as the first parenthesis in (4.08-5).   Hence

$$T = \sum_r \sum_s L_{rs} \int i_r \, di_s = \frac{1}{2} \sum_{r=1}^{l} \sum_{s=1}^{l} L_{rs} i_r i_s. \qquad (4.08\text{-}9)$$

The constant of integration, omitted above, is zero, for when all the $i_r = 0$, then surely $T = 0$, as (4.08-9) indicates.   The effects of any mutual inductance present are automatically taken care of in the coefficients L_{rs}.

In (4.08–9) we have an expression for the energy stored in all the inductors of the network, in form analogous to the first part of (4.08–1). It is cumbersome, to be sure, but we shall not need to use it much. To clarify it a little, consider, as an example, a network with but two inductors, and those inductively coupled but not on the same loops. Figure 4.08–A,

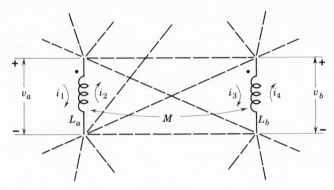

Fig. 4.08–A

in which only the inductive elements of the network are shown, gives the notation, in which the (only) four loops carrying inductance are arbitrarily numbered 1, 2, 3, 4 for convenience.

We have, by inspection,

$$L_{11} = L_a, \qquad L_{12} = -L_a = L_{21}, \qquad L_{13} = M = L_{31},$$

$$L_{14} = -M = L_{41}, \qquad L_{22} = L_a, \qquad L_{23} = -M = L_{32}, \qquad (4.08\text{–}10)$$

$$L_{24} = M = L_{42}, \qquad L_{33} = L_b, \qquad L_{34} = -L_b = L_{43}, \qquad L_{44} = L_b.$$

The magnetic stored energy is, from (4.08–9),

$$
\begin{aligned}
T &= \frac{1}{2} \sum_{r=1}^{4} \left(\sum_{s=1}^{4} L_{rs} i_r i_s \right) \\
&= \tfrac{1}{2}[L_{11} i_1 i_1 + L_{12} i_1 i_2 + L_{13} i_1 i_3 + L_{14} i_1 i_4 + L_{21} i_2 i_1 + L_{22} i_2 i_2 \\
&\quad + L_{23} i_2 i_3 + L_{24} i_2 i_4 + L_{31} i_3 i_1 + L_{32} i_3 i_2 + L_{33} i_3 i_3 + L_{34} i_3 i_4 \\
&\quad + L_{41} i_4 i_1 + L_{42} i_4 i_2 + L_{43} i_4 i_3 + L_{44} i_4 i_4] \\
&= \tfrac{1}{2}[L_a i_1^2 - L_a i_1 i_2 + M i_1 i_3 - M i_1 i_4 - L_a i_2 i_1 + L_a i_2^2 - M i_2 i_3 \\
&\quad + M i_2 i_4 + M i_3 i_1 - M i_3 i_2 + L_b i_3^2 - L_b i_3 i_4 - M i_4 i_1 + M i_4 i_2 \\
&\quad - L_b i_4 i_3 + L_b i_4^2]
\end{aligned}
$$

$$= \tfrac{1}{2}[L_a(i_1{}^2 - 2i_1i_2 + i_2{}^2) + 2M(i_1i_3 - i_1i_4 - i_2i_3 + i_2i_4)$$
$$+ L_b(i_3{}^2 - 2i_3i_4 + i_4{}^2)]$$
$$= \tfrac{1}{2}L_a(i_1 - i_2)^2 + M(i_1 - i_2)(i_3 - i_4) + \tfrac{1}{2}L_b(i_3 - i_4)^2. \tag{4.08-11}$$

If $M = 0$ this is obviously correct, being merely the result of applying (4.08-1) to each inductor and adding the results. If $M \neq 0$, (4.08-1) alone does not give the additional term. We can check (4.08-11) easily, however, as follows. In terms of the voltages across the inductors, the power supplied to the two inductors is

$$\frac{dT}{dt} = v_a(i_1 - i_2) + v_b(i_3 - i_4) \tag{4.08-12}$$

in which T is the magnetic stored energy (a function of time). For the voltages we can write

$$v_a = L_a \frac{d}{dt}(i_1 - i_2) + M \frac{d}{dt}(i_3 - i_4),$$
$$v_b = M \frac{d}{dt}(i_1 - i_2) + L_b \frac{d}{dt}(i_3 - i_4), \tag{4.08-13}$$

and by substituting these in (4.08-12) we obtain

$$T = \int \left[L_a(i_1 - i_2) \frac{d}{dt}(i_1 - i_2) + M(i_1 - i_2)\frac{d}{dt}(i_3 - i_4) \right.$$
$$\left. + M(i_3 - i_4)\frac{d}{dt}(i_1 - i_2) + L_b(i_3 - i_4)\frac{d}{dt}(i_3 - i_4) \right] dt$$
$$= \tfrac{1}{2}L_a(i_1 - i_2)^2 + M(i_1 - i_2)(i_3 - i_4) + \tfrac{1}{2}L_b(i_3 - i_4)^2 + \text{constant.}$$
$$\tag{4.08-14}$$

Since T surely is zero when the currents are zero, the constant of integration is zero, and (4.08-14) agrees with (4.08-11) as it should. This is not at all different from the derivation of the general expression (4.08-9), but because it is specific it may give that expression more meaning.

Before leaving the magnetic stored energy, let us see what the parallel to (4.08-9) on the node-basis analysis is. From (4.07-6) we have

$$\frac{dT}{dt} = \sum_{r=1}^{n} \left(\sum_{s=1}^{n} \Gamma_{rs} v_r \psi_s \right). \tag{4.08-15}$$

This is not quite in the form in which (4.08-2) was; we cannot integrate it as easily. But, since

$$v_r = \frac{d\psi_r}{dt} \tag{4.08-16}$$

(see § 2.04), (4.08–15) can be written

$$\frac{dT}{dt} = \sum_r \left(\sum_s \Gamma_{rs} \psi_s \frac{d\psi_r}{dt} \right). \tag{4.08-17}$$

Integration of this proceeds mathematically almost exactly as did integration of (4.08–2).

$$T = \int \sum_r \sum_s \Gamma_{rs} \psi_s \frac{d\psi_r}{dt} \, dt$$

$$= \sum_r \sum_s \Gamma_{rs} \int \psi_s \, d\psi_r$$

$$= \sum_r \sum_s \Gamma_{rs} \left(\psi_s \psi_r - \int \psi_r \, d\psi_s \right). \tag{4.08-18}$$

$$\sum_r \sum_s \Gamma_{rs} \int \psi_s \, d\psi_r + \sum_r \sum_s \Gamma_{rs} \int \psi_r \, d\psi_s = \sum_r \sum_s \Gamma_{rs} \psi_s \psi_r. \tag{4.08-19}$$

The two sums on the left are equal, by the same reasoning as that leading to equality of the two sums on the left side of (4.08–5). Hence

$$T = \frac{1}{2} \sum_{r=1}^{n} \left(\sum_{s=1}^{n} \Gamma_{rs} \psi_r \psi_s \right) \tag{4.08-20}$$

(for the constant of integration is again zero), which is the parallel to (4.08–9), and is analogous to the second part of (4.08–1). Again it is cumbersome, but that will not bother us.

4.09 Electric stored energy

The corresponding analysis of the energy stored in the capacitors of the network is exactly the same mathematically. We can write the results directly, from (4.08–1), (4.08–20), and (4.08–9), by duality. They are

$$V = \tfrac{1}{2} S q^2 = \tfrac{1}{2} C v^2 \tag{4.09-1}$$

for a single capacitor, in which V represents the electric stored energy (*not* voltage), the symbol again being taken from mechanics (because of the analogy with potential energy), and, for the instantaneous stored energy of *all* the capacitors in the network

$$V = \frac{1}{2} \sum_{r=1}^{l} \left(\sum_{s=1}^{l} S_{rs} q_r q_s \right), \tag{4.09-2}$$

and

$$V = \frac{1}{2} \sum_{r=1}^{n} \left(\sum_{s=1}^{n} C_{rs} v_r v_s \right). \tag{4.09-3}$$

The first form is appropriate for the loop basis, the second for the node basis of analysis.

4.10 Dissipated energy

Of the three terms on the left side of (4.07–4), or of (4.07–6), there remains the term representing the energy fed to the resistors—which is dissipated, of course, and not stored. For that reason we care little about its integrated value, and leave it as it is, an expression for power, or *rate* of dissipation of energy in the resistors. In order to have symmetrical results, we define a dissipation function F with a coefficient of $\frac{1}{2}$, so that it represents only *one half* of the energy dissipation rate. For a single resistor we write

$$F = \tfrac{1}{2}Ri^2 = \tfrac{1}{2}Gv^2 \qquad (4.10\text{–}1)$$

and for the whole network, from (4.07–4), on the loop basis,

$$F = \frac{1}{2} \sum_{r=1}^{l} \left(\sum_{s=1}^{l} R_{rs}i_r i_s \right) \qquad (4.10\text{–}2)$$

and from (4.07–6), on the node basis,

$$F = \frac{1}{2} \sum_{r=1}^{n} \left(\sum_{s=1}^{n} G_{rs}v_r v_s \right). \qquad (4.10\text{–}3)$$

Notice carefully that F is a rate of dissipation of energy, in contrast to T and V which are expressions for energy proper. For that reason, these terms in (4.07–4) and (4.07–6) require no manipulation. In terms of these three functions, the equations of § 4.07 which give the instantaneous power supplied to the network elements, (4.07–4) and (4.07–6), can be written

$$p = \frac{dT}{dt} + 2F + \frac{dV}{dt} = 2F + \frac{d}{dt}(T + V). \qquad (4.10\text{–}4)$$

In words, the total power supplied instantaneously is equal to the sum of the dissipated power and the "stored power," or, more exactly, to the sum of the dissipated power and the rate of change of the stored energy. We now proceed to examine these three functions more closely.

4.11 Quadratic forms

We have set up three functions, F, T, and V, which are physically identified with power and energy, and hence must, by their very nature, be *positive* (or zero). All three are of the same form, a form which mathematicians call a *quadratic form*,

$$\sum_{r,s} a_{rs}x_r x_s. \qquad (4.11\text{–}1)$$

Here all the numbers involved are real, and when the sum is written out, the result is a rational, entire function which is homogeneous and quadratic in the (variables) x's. For our purposes the a's are physical element values (or combinations thereof into the loop- or node-basis coefficients of Chapter 2) and are real numbers, though not necessarily positive (since some of them represent mutual terms). They do, however, have some interrelation, since they come from a physical network. The x's are instantaneous values of currents, voltages, integrated currents (charges), or integrated voltages (flux linkages), and are also real, though not necessarily positive. The x's, in fact, can be made to have any set of values we like by suitably adjusting the various generators in the network.

For example, suppose we are considering T, in which the x's represent loop currents. Given any set of l real numbers, we can make the loop currents have these values by giving suitable values to l voltage generators in the network. In order to do this we specify that the loop currents shall have the prescribed values at time t_1. We then set up some functional form for each loop current, which has the prescribed value at $t = t_1$, and is zero at $t = 0$, when the network excitation begins. [This could be linear, $i_r(t) = Kt$, for example.] From these functions and the loop-basis equations of analysis (2.03–1), we can readily calculate the necessary net loop voltage sources, $v_r(t)$. If such net sources exist on the loops, then the loop currents will have the prescribed variation with time, for the solution of (2.03–1) with these driving forces must lead back to the originally prescribed currents—they satisfy the equations, which can have only one physical solution. In order to cause the net loop driving voltages to have these values, we could insert a voltage generator in each of the b branches of the network and write the relations between these and the net loop driving voltages. There would be b generators but only l equations to determine their values. We can, however, discard $(b - l)$ of these generators as unnecessary, using a little discretion and keeping at least one on each loop; the remaining l generators have values related to the l prescribed net loop driving voltages by l equations in which the coefficients are simply $+1$, 0, or -1. Since the l loops are *independent* loops by hypothesis (Chapter 2), the determinant of these coefficients does not vanish and the equations can be solved for the actual generators needed. When they are connected, currents will flow, and at time t_1 the loop currents will have the prescribed values, as was to be shown. If we are concerned with F, the x's still represent currents and the same procedure will give them arbitrary prescribed values. If it is V that interests us, however, the x's represent charges, the integrals of the loop currents. In the procedure above, the functions chosen for the loop currents must now be such that their integrals, from the moment when the network is at rest and excitation begins, up to time t_1, have the proper values. This condition can easily be met (and simultaneously with conditions on the values of the currents themselves, if desired), and thereafter the procedure is the same. If we prefer the node basis, exactly dual procedures will cause arbitrary voltages or their integrals (flux linkages) to exist. Hence it is easy to make the x's in our quadratic forms have *any* set of (real) values desired, by a physical process.

The important thing which we know, however, is that each of the three (F, T, V) must always be *positive* (or zero), regardless of the signs and values of the x's at the moment (because F, T, V represent either energy stored in elements or the rate at which elements are dissipating energy). This is a rather startling fact, if we view (4.11-1) as a purely mathematical expression. It is not at all clear, just from their form (without the physical reasoning), that F, T, and V can never be negative (though it *is* obvious in the single-element case). But such quadratic forms, which are always positive (or zero), are well known in the literature of mathematics, and show up in other physical problems also. It is possible, by a suitable change of variables (GU 3) to reduce the "mutual" coefficients to zero, and leave only "self" terms, whose coefficients are positive—from which it becomes obvious, even by inspection (since only squares of variable terms appear), that the form is always positive (or zero). The mathematical term for such a form is *positive* (*semi*) *definite* quadratic form.

Each of our three energy functions, F, T, V, then, is a positive definite quadratic form. That is, the set of a's has the remarkable property that the form is positive (or zero) regardless of the values of the x's.

A specific illustration may clarify how it is that these forms are always positive, even though some of the terms in them may be negative. Consider a nondissipative transformer, characterized only by self and mutual inductances. Suppose this is part of a network in which no other

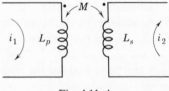

Fig. 4.11–A

inductance appears, and is part of loops 1 and 2, as Fig. 4.11–A shows. Then the energy function for the inductances of the network is

$$T = \frac{1}{2} \sum_{r,s} L_{rs} i_r i_s = \tfrac{1}{2}(L_{11}i_1{}^2 + L_{12}i_1 i_2 + L_{21}i_2 i_1 + L_{22}i_2{}^2). \quad (4.11\text{-}2)$$

To show that this is positive, no matter what i_1 and i_2 are, let us make the change of variables mentioned above. One suitable transformation (there are others) is

$$i_1 = Ki_a + i_b,$$

$$i_2 = i_a, \qquad (4.11-3)$$

in which

$$K = -\frac{L_{12}}{L_{11}}. \qquad (4.11-4)$$

Here i_a and i_b represent linear combinations of the loop currents i_1 and i_2, and are the new variables. By straightforward substitution of (4.11-3) in (4.11-2) we find

$$T = \tfrac{1}{2}(L_{aa}i_a^2 + L_{bb}i_b^2). \qquad (4.11-5)$$

The algebra we omit. It shows that the term in $i_a i_b$ has a zero coefficient and hence does not appear above, and will also show that both L_{aa} and L_{bb} are positive (or at least zero) if L_{11} and L_{22} are positive, and $0 \leqslant k^2 \leqslant 1$. Now in (4.11-2) L_{11} and L_{22} are the primary and secondary inductances and are positive (whereas $L_{12} = L_{21}$ represents the mutual inductance, whose sign depends on the construction of the transformer). Further, $|k|$ represents the coefficient of coupling, and we know this does not exceed unity. Hence T is positive (or zero), by (4.11-5)—and this is true whatever the values of i_1 and i_2.

We know that (4.11-2) and the previous general forms are positive, even without arguments like that above, because of the energy argument we have been following. The mathematicians in their study of quadratic forms have found independently that a quadratic form is definite (positive or negative) when certain relations hold between the coefficients, say the a's of (4.11-1). Let us take their results without discussion and merely state that

a quadratic form is positive definite when the determinant formed by the coefficients, and all the principal minors of this determinant, are positive (or zero). (4.11-6)

This excludes certain singular forms which we do not need. All it means is that a quadratic form is positive definite if the determinant formed by its coefficients, the determinant formed by striking out the last row and column of that determinant, the determinant formed by striking out the last row and column of that new determinant, etc., are all positive (or zero). This condition is both necessary and sufficient, and is mathematically equivalent to saying that (4.11-1) is always positive (or zero), regardless of the values of the variables. In the case of the transformer of Fig. 4.11–A this condition becomes

$$\begin{vmatrix} L_{11} & L_{12} \\ L_{21} & L_{22} \end{vmatrix} \geqq 0 \quad \text{and} \quad |L_{11}| \geqq 0 \qquad (4.11\text{–}7)$$

(in which the bars denote determinants), or

$$(L_{11}L_{22} - L_{12}{}^2) \geqq 0 \quad \text{and} \quad L_{11} \geqq 0, \qquad (4.11\text{–}8)$$

or

$$L_p L_s \geqq M^2 \quad \text{and} \quad L_p \geqq 0,$$
$$\text{and consequently } L_s \geqq 0 \text{ also.} \qquad (4.11\text{–}9)$$

The second and third inequalities of (4.11–9) mean merely that the elements must be positive, as of course they are, and the first inequality can be written as

$$\frac{M^2}{L_p L_s} \leqq 1, \quad \text{or} \quad k^2 \leqq 1, \qquad (4.11\text{–}10)$$

in which $|k|$ is the coefficient of coupling of the transformer.

In this case then, the positive definiteness means that the coupling coefficient cannot exceed unity, which of course is always true of physical transformers. If this is true, and L_p is positive, then no matter what the values of the two currents in Fig. 4.11–A (positive, negative, zero) the energy function T is always positive (or zero). This would certainly not be true for arbitrary values of the L parameters, but so long as they are "consistent" in the sense discussed, i.e., belong to a physical system, then the quadratic form is positive definite.

If there are more than two loops, the situation becomes more complicated, but the basic reasoning and ideas are the same. The coefficients must obey certain interrelations and these are the equivalent, mathematically, of saying that the coefficients must be the loop (node) parameters of a physical network. Then the form is positive definite.

Similarly, it can be shown that the physically obvious fact that the energy functions F, T, and V are always positive, and the positive definiteness of these quadratic forms, are merely restatements of physical facts, such as the requirement that coupling coefficients not exceed unity.

We shall not have occasion to go into the mathematics of any quadratic forms, but we shall have to recognize later that the functions F, T, V, are never negative. Indeed, this fact is our only reason for spending time on the generation of these functions; it will prove to have vital importance.

To recapitulate, we have found three quadratic forms, T, F, V, each of which has the form

$$\sum_{r,s} a_{rs} x_r x_s \qquad (4.11\text{–}11)$$

whether developed on a loop or node basis. Because the set of coefficients a_{rs} came from the elements of a physical network, these quadratic forms are always positive (or zero), regardless of the (real) values of the x's. This follows from our analysis of power and energy, and means incidentally that the network coefficients a_{rs} (which are the L_{rs}, R_{rs}, S_{rs}, or their duals) are mathematically the coefficients of a positive (semi) definite quadratic form.

The mathematics of positive definite quadratic forms, incidentally, with its determinant tests, gives a method of testing whether a given collection of numbers can possibly represent, say, the self and mutual impedance coefficients of a network—the conditions are both necessary and sufficient (GU 2).

4.12 The utility of these functions

In §§ 4.07–4.11 we have been concerned with laying foundations for a structure whose plan is not at all obvious. Now at last we are in a position to complete the structure and obtain useful results.

Suppose we are analyzing a network on the loop basis (from initial conditions of rest), and that the transform equation for loop r is

$$\sum_{s=1}^{l} \left(L_{rs}p + R_{rs} + \frac{S_{rs}}{p}\right) I_s = E_r \qquad (4.12\text{–}1)$$

in which E_r represents the (transform of) the net driving voltage on loop r. Now multiply this equation by $\bar{I}_r$ (I_r being the transform of loop current r).

$$\sum_{s=1}^{l} \left[(L_{rs}\bar{I}_r I_s)p + (R_{rs}\bar{I}_r I_s) + \frac{(S_{rs}\bar{I}_r I_s)}{p}\right] = E_r \bar{I}_r. \qquad (4.12\text{–}2)$$

The equation applies, of course, for each of the l values 1, 2, 3, $\cdots$, l which r can assume. Write the equation for each of these values, and add up the l resulting equations. The result is

$$\sum_{r=1}^{l} E_r \bar{I}_r = \left(\sum_r \sum_s L_{rs}\bar{I}_r I_s\right) p + \left(\sum_r \sum_s R_{rs}\bar{I}_r I_s\right) + \left(\sum_r \sum_s S_{rs}\bar{I}_r I_s\right)\frac{1}{p} \qquad (4.12\text{–}3)$$

$$= T'p + F' + V'/p, \qquad (4.12\text{–}4)$$

in which

$$T' = \sum_{r,s} L_{rs}\bar{I}_r I_s,$$

$$F' = \sum_{r,s} R_{rs}\bar{I}_r I_s, \qquad (4.12\text{–}5)$$

$$V' = \sum_{r,s} S_{rs}\bar{I}_r I_s.$$

We use nearly the same notation as we did for the energy functions, because the forms of these coefficients closely resemble the functions of the preceding sections. These T', F', V', however, have not been shown to have any definite relation to energy—they merely *resemble* the energy functions in form. At this point, in fact, we hardly know just what the primed letters do mean, physically.

Some things we can say about these three new functions, though. They are, each of them, *real* and *positive* (or zero). This is not at all obvious, but with the aid of what we have already found out about energy functions, we can rapidly prove the statement. Let us do just that.

The three functions in (4.12–5) are quadratic forms, even though the variables (the I's) are now complex. To be sure, these quadratic forms *seem* complex, so we first convert each of them into two real quadratic forms. To do this we adopt the notation

$$I_r = a_r + jb_r \tag{4.12–6}$$

in which, of course, everything is a function of p, or better, of σ and ω, but a_r and b_r are at least *real*. Then we have, for example,

$$T' = \sum_{r,s} L_{rs} \bar{I}_r I_s = \sum_{r,s} L_{rs}(a_r - jb_r)(a_s + jb_s)$$

$$= \sum_{r,s} L_{rs}(a_r a_s + b_r b_s) + j\sum_{r,s} L_{rs}(a_r b_s - a_s b_r)$$

$$= \sum_{r,s} L_{rs} a_r a_s + \sum_{r,s} L_{rs} b_r b_s + 0. \tag{4.12–7}$$

The result above has a zero imaginary part for the following reasons. $L_{rs} = L_{sr}$ and hence

$$\sum_{r,s} L_{rs} a_s b_r = \sum_{r,s} L_{sr} a_s b_r. \tag{4.12–8}$$

But the notation for indices is arbitrary, and so is the order in which the summations are made. Hence

$$\sum_{r,s} L_{sr} a_s b_r = \sum_{s,r} L_{rs} a_r b_s = \sum_{r,s} L_{rs} a_r b_s \tag{4.12–9}$$

so that the two components of the imaginary part of T' add up to zero. This proves the first point, that T' is *real*, in spite of the introduction of p and the resulting complex numbers and functions.

By the discussion of § 4.11 we know that the quadratic forms $\sum_{r,s} L_{rs} a_r a_s$ and $\sum_{r,s} L_{rs} b_r b_s$ are always positive (or zero), a fact deduced from their relation to the energy function $T = \frac{1}{2}\sum_{r,s} L_{rs} i_r i_s$ of (4.08–9), which is always positive (or zero) no matter what values the loop currents may have.

But this is just what we need to show that (4.12–7) is always positive (or zero)—for T' is thus the sum of two nonnegative numbers and therefore *positive* (or zero). This proves the second of our two asseverations.

A glance at (4.12–5) shows that the forms of F' and V' are the same as that of T', and with the aid of what we already know about the positiveness of F and V (the energy functions), exactly the same reasoning (§ 4.11) shows that F' and T' are also *real* and *positive* (or zero).

To recapitulate:

the forms T', F', and V' of (4.12–5) are *real* numbers, and they are *positive* (or zero). (4.12–10)

We return to (4.12–4), in which we now know that the coefficients of p^1, p^0, and p^{-1} are real, positive (possibly zero) numbers. Our interest, for the present, is in the one-terminal pair, so we now particularize to that case. That is, we consider the case of one source only, or of a single driving point. The terminals of this source we consider the input terminals of the one-terminal-pair network, and let us say this solitary

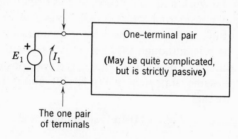

Fig. 4.12–A

source is on loop 1, as in Fig. 4.12–A. The left side of (4.12–4) now has but one term, for $E_2 = E_3 = \cdots = E_l = 0$. Hence (4.12–4) becomes

$$E_1 \bar{I}_1 = T'p + F' + V'/p. \qquad (4.12-11)$$

Divide this through by $I_1 \bar{I}_1 = |I_1|^2$. This action excludes cases where $I_1 = 0$, but this will not trouble us. It gives

$$\frac{E_1}{I_1} = \frac{T'p + F' + V'/p}{|I_1|^2} \qquad (4.12-12)$$

$$= T_0 p + F_0 + \frac{V_0}{p} = Z(p). \qquad (4.12-13)$$

Note that we have redefined the coefficients in order to absorb the denominator of the right side of (4.12–12), i.e., we have let

$$T_0 = \frac{T'}{|I_1|^2}, \qquad F_0 = \frac{F'}{|I_1|^2}, \qquad V_0 = \frac{V'}{|I_1|^2}. \qquad (4.12\text{–}14)$$

Note also the introduction of the symbol $Z(p)$. The ratio of the transforms E_1 and I_1 is of course the *driving-point impedance function* of the network, i.e., the volt-ampere ratio (generalized, if you will, to complex frequencies) at the input or driving-point terminals. Hence Z is appropriate notation. Remember also, as seen in the development of the Laplace-transformation analysis, that $Z(p)$, the input impedance function in terms of p, is exactly the input impedance function (for these terminals) of a-c steady-state analysis, with $j\omega$ replaced by p—though of course, since it is written here in terms of things which resemble energy functions, it does not look like it.

Now this is a linear network, by hypothesis. Hence the *ratio* E_1/I_1 is independent of the particular values which E_1 and I_1 have, and so too are the three functions T_0, F_0, V_0. These three quantities depend only on what is inside the network and could (presumably) be computed from its schematic, without considering whether any source were connected or current flowing. Put another way, these three quantities of (4.12–14) are constant so long as p is, although they certainly vary with p.

Since the only difference between T' and T_0 is a real, positive multiplier, we can make the same statement as (4.12–10) about the three new coefficients, and say that

the forms T_0, F_0, and V_0 of (4.12–14) are *real* numbers, and they are *positive* (or zero). $\qquad (4.12\text{–}15)$

The dual analysis, on the node basis, leads to the dual relation for the ampere-volt ratio (generalized), or *admittance* function

$$Y(p) = V_0 p + F_0 + \frac{T_0}{p}, \qquad (4.12\text{–}16)$$

in which, of course, the symbols are defined differently:

$$V_0 = \frac{\sum\limits_{r,s} C_{rs}\bar{E}_r E_s}{|E_1|^2},$$

$$F_0 = \frac{\sum\limits_{r,s} G_{rs}\bar{E}_r E_s}{|E_1|^2}, \qquad (4.12\text{–}17)$$

$$T_0 = \frac{\sum\limits_{r,s} \Gamma_{rs}\bar{E}_r E_s}{|E_1|^2}.$$

Statement (4.12–15) is equally true of these (different) quantities, which are *not* the same as those in (4.12–14).

4.13 Positive-real functions

In the two equations (4.12–13) and (4.12–16) we have an alternative basis for setting up the positive-real property which we encountered in §§ 4.03–4.05. These particular forms, derived from energy considerations for the different kinds of elements, are particularly useful in developing certain properties later on.

Let us concentrate for the moment on the driving-point impedance function in the form (4.12–13), and let us substitute $(\sigma + j\omega)$ for p in order to separate the real and imaginary parts. We get

$$Z(p) = T_0 p + F_0 + \frac{V_0}{p}$$

$$= F_0 + T_0(\sigma + j\omega) + \frac{V_0}{\sigma + j\omega} \tag{4.13-1}$$

$$= \left(F_0 + T_0\sigma + \frac{V_0\sigma}{\sigma_2 + \omega^2}\right) + j\left(T_0\omega - \frac{V_0\omega}{\sigma^2 + \omega^2}\right).$$

Because F_0, T_0, and V_0 are real, by (4.12–15), the real and imaginary parts of $Z(p)$ have actually been separated in (4.13–1). In fact, for any p,

$$\mathrm{Re}\, Z(p) = F_0 + T_0\sigma + \frac{V_0\sigma}{\sigma^2 + \omega^2}, \tag{4.13-2}$$

$$\mathrm{Im}\, Z(p) = T_0\omega - \frac{V_0\omega}{\sigma^2 + \omega^2}. \tag{4.13-3}$$

Notice now that

(1) when p is real, i.e., when $\omega = 0$, then $Z(p)$ is also real;
(2) when p is in the right half plane, i.e., when $\sigma > 0$, then $Z(p)$ is also in its right half plane. In other words, when the real part of p is positive, the real part of $Z(p)$ is also positive. (4.13–4)

The first statement above follows from inspection of (4.13–3) (with the possible exception of the point $p = 0$, which need not concern us). The second comes from (4.13–2) and the fact that F_0, T_0, and V_0 are not only real, they are *positive* (or zero), by (4.12–15); further, unless Z is identically zero (which is a trivial case) at least one of the terms in (4.13–2) will have a nonzero value. The case $I_1 = 0$, excluded by division by $|I_1|^2$ in § 4.12, would require that Z be infinite. But we already know, from transient arguments (§ 4.02), that Z can have neither zeros nor poles for

$\sigma > 0$, except for the trivial cases of short and open circuits—hence the exclusion does not affect our results here.

These are almost the same conditions as (c) and (a) of § 4.03. There is one difference: here, in (4.13–4), condition (1) applies for all real values of p, in both right and left halves of the plane, whereas in (4.03–14) the condition applies only for real values of p in the right half plane. There is no inconsistency here and we can explain this immediately, for (4.03–14) is general in that the network need not be composed of a finite number of lumped elements to reach that result, as we remarked. In general, the condition of reality when p is real does apply only to the right half of the plane. But if the network is composed of a finite number of lumped elements [and we have made this assumption in all our consideration of energy leading up to (4.13–4)], we know that the input immittance functions must be *rational*. And surely a rational function, if it is real for real values of p in the right half plane, is also real for real values of p in the left half plane, for then its coefficients are real. In fact, we know independently, from the nature of the elements, that these rational functions have real coefficients, and could say therefore without further ado that they must be real when p is, and it matters not whether p be in the left half plane or the right half plane. The difference comes when we extend our vision to include, for example, networks with an infinite number of lumped elements (a concept which will prove useful). Then the reasoning leading up to (4.13–4) would have to be re-examined, and we should find that the more general conclusions of § 4.03 are the ones which hold. Some such functions are briefly discussed in § 4.14.

On the basis of the Brune investigation, §§ 4.02–4.03, then, we still define *positive-real* functions as those which obey part (1) of (4.13–4) in the right half plane, as well as part (2); whether they obey part (1) in the left half plane also (as rational functions do) does not concern us here.

Let us also recall that the conclusions (4.13–4) are only one of two possible, and completely equivalent, methods of definition of positive-real functions. This one amounts to (a) and (c) of § 4.03; the other is (4.03–11) or (b) of § 4.03. In (4.05–2) and (4.05–3) both are given.

We are thus led once more to the fact that it is *necessary* that a driving-point immittance function of a passive network be positive-real. Such a function must be real when the independent variable is real and in the right half plane; its real part must be positive when the independent variable is in the right half plane (i.e., has itself a positive real part). This notion of *positive reality* is of fundamental importance in the discussion of physical realizability of one-terminal pairs. We shall often abbreviate *positive-real* to simply *p-r*, which we shall later see can usually be read to mean, equally well, "*physically-realizable*"!

Evidently any physical two-terminal network that is passive has a driving-point impedance function which is p-r. All the discussion of this chapter culminates in that fact. Hence positive reality is a *necessary* condition that a given function $Z(p)$ represent the driving-point impedance function of a one-terminal, passive pair.

We do not have to repeat the duals of (4.13–1) and their consequences; they lead to exactly the same conclusions about driving-point admittance functions.

Positive reality can also be shown to be *sufficient* for a given rational function to be realizable as either driving-point immittance of a finite one-terminal pair. The proof is lengthy, and we postpone it to a more appropriate time.

Our next task is to investigate in more detail the nature of positive-real functions. They are so intimately related to immittance functions, however, that we might as well perform this investigation in network (i.e., electrical) terms rather than purely as mathematics—and this we do in Chapter 5.

4.14 Positive-real functions, continued

Before beginning our investigation of positive-real functions in network terms, which will necessarily limit us chiefly to rational functions, we stop to discuss briefly an important class of nonrational functions. Their physical meaning will not be discussed until Chapter 14 and later, but we may conveniently discuss them mathematically here—and this may shed some light on the small difference between the results of our two developments, discussed above.

The functions of interest here are those which are the geometric means of pairs of positive-real functions. In symbols, if F_1 and F_2 represent two positive-real functions, then we consider F, defined by

$$F^2 = F_1 F_2. \tag{4.14–1}$$

This function $F(p)$ is multivalued and hence presents some difficulties we have not previously had to face. Because F as defined above has two values in general, it is not analytic, nor can it be positive-real, for if one value has a positive real part at some point in the right half plane, the other must have a negative real part! The natural resolution of this difficulty is to choose *one* of the two values and to define F as a function having that particular value. This is not very difficult to do, and does make F uniform (single-valued) and analytic for most values of p, so that we can then proceed to test it for p-r character. But we must introduce some new ideas in order to clarify and make precise our choice between the two values of F.

Consider first, by way of example, the function F defined by letting $F_1 = 1$ and $F_2 = p$ in (4.14–1). These two functions are incontrovertibly positive-real. Then

$$F^2 = 1 \times p, \quad \text{or} \quad F = \sqrt{p}, \tag{4.14–2}$$

which is two-valued. For any value of p (except zero and infinity) it is no trick at all to calculate the corresponding two values of F, which will be the negatives of each other. Nor is it difficult to select one of the two at any given point, say p_1. It is a little more difficult to give a rule which will determine which of the two values of F we are to take at some other value of p, say p_2, so that it "corresponds" to the choice at p_1, and F is thereby made uniform. In Fig. 4.14–A suppose we settle on a choice at

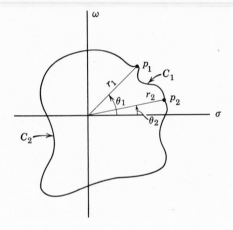

Fig. 4.14–A

p_1—say that value (of the two) which has a positive real part. Now let p move continuously to p_2 along the curve C_1. We have taken

$$F(p_1) = \sqrt{r_1}e^{j\theta_1/2} \tag{4.14–3}$$

(in which $\sqrt{r_1}$ is to be interpreted as a positive number) and as p moves along C_1 this continuously varies to

$$F(p_2) = \sqrt{r_2}e^{j\theta_2/2} \tag{4.14–4}$$

which also has a positive real part. But suppose we move from p_1 to p_2 along the curve C_2. Then the value of F varies continuously to become, at p_2,

$$F(p_2) = \sqrt{r_2}e^{j(\theta_2/2+\pi)} = -\sqrt{r_2}e^{j\theta_2/2} \tag{4.14–5}$$

which is the negative of the value reached at p_2 if p moves along C_1. More generally, we can say that if a closed curve C be drawn through p_1 and p_2 to enclose the origin (i.e., so O lies inside C), this curve provides two alternative paths from p_1 to p_2 (as C_1 and C_2 in Fig. 4.14–A); if p moves from p_1 to p_2 along one path, one of the two values of $F(p_2)$ is reached, and if p moves on the other path, the other value of $F(p_2)$ is reached.   A little consideration will show that the important point here is this:

According as p does or does not "go around" the origin, different values of F at p_2 are reached—or, better, the radius vector $p = re^{j\theta}$ may change in angle by only a small amount (as $\theta_1 - \theta_2$) or it may change by this amount plus (or minus) 360°, as p moves from p_1 to p_2, depending on the path p takes.   The square root makes this 360° difference in angle appear as only 180°, or a change in sign (i.e., the other square root appears).

To insure that as p moves from p_1 to p_2 we introduce no ambiguity as to $F(p_2)$, $F(p_1)$ having been chosen, we must erect some sort of barrier to make p move as we wish, to make p keep to one side or the other of the origin, to restrict the amount of change in the angle θ.   It does not mathematically matter what the shape of the barrier is, except that it *must* go through the origin, the important point, and must extend to infinity.   In Fig. 4.14–B the curve C represents such a barrier, which is

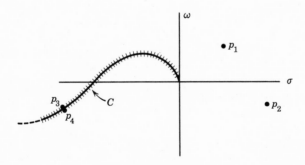

Fig. 4.14–B

to be insurmountable by p.   The independent variable p may now move from p_1 to p_2 along a curve like C_1 of Fig. 4.14–A, but not along a curve such as C_2; hence there is no question as to the value of $F(p_2)$ once the value of $F(p_1)$ has been chosen.   Such a device, the drawing of a curve over which p is forbidden to cross, may seem artificial, but it is the solution of our difficulty.   The curve is to cut the plane from the origin to infinity, may have any shape whatever so long as it runs from the origin to infinity (it might be any of the four semiaxes, for example), and is called a *branch cut*. A definite choice of one of the two values of F at any point like p_1 then determines which of the two *branches*, the two possible uniform functions of definition (4.14–2), is meant by "*F(p)*." Notice that this function is now uniform and analytic *except on the branch cut*. At two points such as p_3 and p_4, which are on opposite sides of the branch cut, but only an infinitesimal distance apart, the uniform function $F(p)$ has different values, one the negative of the other, and is therefore discontinuous and not analytic, at all points on the branch cut. This unpleasant situation will not actually trouble us, for we shall be careful to take full advantage of the arbitrariness of the branch cuts we need by locating them in unimportant regions in which we have little interest. Here, since we are interested in positive-real functions, whose important characteristics are defined in the right half plane, we let the branch cut lie entirely in the left half plane (the abscissae of all points on the branch cut, except the origin, are to be negative), as in Fig. 4.14–B. If we then select that one of the two values of F given by (4.14–2) whose real part is positive at p_1, and designate it by a small $+$ sign in the radical (to avoid ambiguity), we have $F = \sqrt[+]{p}$. In the right half plane ($\sigma > 0$) the function so defined is clearly real for real values of p, and has a real part greater than zero, for

$$\mathbf{Re}\ F = \mathbf{Re}\ r e^{j\theta/2} = r \cos \frac{\theta}{2} > 0 \qquad (4.14\text{–}6)$$

since $|\theta| < \pi/2$. Hence, by the second definition of (4.05–2), F is p-r. Alternatively, the first or polar-coordinate definition is fulfilled, since $\overline{F} = \theta/2$, which is surely less than or equal in magnitude to θ. We have selected, as between the two branches, the *positive-real branch* (the other branch will be "negative-real"). Notice that we have here an example of a function which is not real when p is real and negative—but there is no reason it should be, as discussed in § 4.13, for part (1) of (4.13–4) applies only to rational functions.

The artificial character of the branch cut is logically annoying. This artificiality can easily be removed by introducing a further complication, the concept of the Riemann surface. However elegant and satisfactory this may be, it is not essential for our work, and so we shall not discuss it here. It becomes rather important in some aspects of network theory, particularly in certain approximation problems (Chapter 14).

Consider now another function, defined by

$$F^2 = p(p + a), \qquad (4.14\text{–}7)$$

in which a is real and positive, and each of the two factors is clearly p-r.

Unless more closely defined, F is again two-valued. Let $F(p_1)$ again be taken as that value (of the two) with positive real part, i.e., as

$$F(p_1) = \sqrt{r_1}\sqrt{r_1'} \; e^{j(\theta_1 + \theta_1')/2} \qquad (4.14\text{--}8)$$

(rather than as the negative of this, which is obtained by adding 2π to one

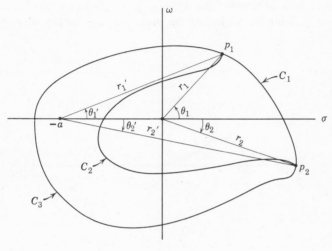

Fig. 4.14–C

of the angles). If p moves from p_1 to p_2 along C_1 (Fig. 4.14–C), we obtain

$$F(p_2) = \sqrt{r_2}\sqrt{r_2'} \; e^{j(\theta_2 + \theta_2')/2}, \qquad (4.14\text{--}9)$$

but if the motion is along C_2, we obtain

$$\begin{aligned} F(p_2) &= \sqrt{r_2}\sqrt{r_2'} \; e^{j(\theta_2 + 2\pi + \theta_2')/2} \\ &= -\sqrt{r_2}\sqrt{r_2'} \; e^{j(\theta_2 + \theta_2')/2}, \end{aligned} \qquad (4.14\text{--}10)$$

whereas if p moves on C_3 we obtain

$$\begin{aligned} F(p_2) &= \sqrt{r_2}\sqrt{r_2'} \; e^{j(\theta_2 + 2\pi + \theta_2' + 2\pi)/2} \\ &= \sqrt{r_2}\sqrt{r_2'} \; e^{j(\theta_2 + \theta_2')/2}. \end{aligned} \qquad (4.14\text{--}11)$$

C_1 and C_3 lead to the same value of $F(p_2)$, but C_2 leads to the other value of the two. Consideration of the angles involved shows clearly that the important thing here, important if $F(p_2)$ is to remain unambiguous, is to avoid crossing the negative-real axis between the origin and $-a$. Alternatively, the important thing is to insure that the complex numbers

$p = re^{j\theta}$ and $(p + a) = r'e^{j\theta'}$ either both change by the smallest amounts or both by these amounts plus (or minus) 360° each; the trouble comes when only *one* of them acquires the 360°, i.e., when p passes between the two critical points, or when only one (rather than both) of these points is "encircled."

This leads us again to the erection of a barrier, which may be the negative-real axis between the origin and $-a$, but need not, and may be *any* curve joining the origin and the point $-a$, as C in Fig. 4.14–D. This

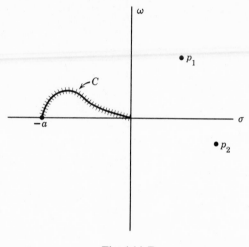

Fig. 4.14–D

is again a *branch cut*, and once it is laid down, and a choice made for the value of F at some particular point, $F(p)$ is uniform and is analytic except on the branch cut. Since we are interested in positive-real functions, we again restrict the branch cut to the left half plane, and choose that branch which has a positive real part at some right-half-plane point such as p_1. Then

$$F(p) = \overset{+}{\sqrt{p(p + a)}} \qquad (4.14\text{--}12)$$

is p-r, as either definition shows on investigation.

We need not continue this detailed discussion further, for the general idea should now be clear. If F is defined by (4.14–1), the ambiguity can be removed and F made uniform by the use of branch cuts. In general, more than one branch cut is necessary. These terminate at those values of p for which $F = 0$ (points at which there is no ambiguity) and sometimes at those values of p for which $F \to \infty$, as in the first example above (which may be considered as a limiting case of the second, when $a \to \infty$)

—their courses in between are generally arbitrary. These termini are called *branch points* of the function and are singularities of a new kind. Figure 4.14–E (pp. 151–2) gives more examples. It shows possible branch

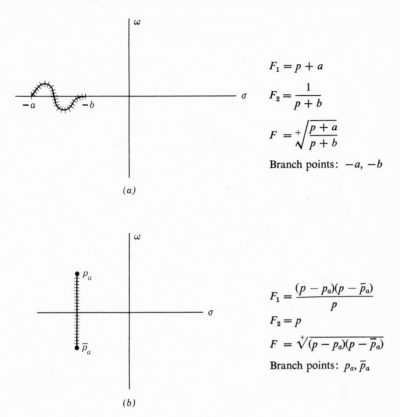

$$F_1 = p + a$$

$$F_2 = \frac{1}{p + b}$$

$$F = \sqrt[+]{\frac{p + a}{p + b}}$$

Branch points: $-a, -b$

(a)

$$F_1 = \frac{(p - p_a)(p - \bar{p}_a)}{p}$$

$$F_2 = p$$

$$F = \sqrt[+]{(p - p_a)(p - \bar{p}_a)}$$

Branch points: $p_a, \bar{p}_a$

(b)

Fig. 4.14–E

cuts which, in each case, make F single-valued. If the proper branch is then chosen, F is p-r. In these examples, no branch points occur in the right half plane. Nor need branch points ever occur in the right half plane when F is defined by $F^2 = F_1 F_2$ and F_1 and F_2 are each p-r. A positive-real function, by definition, has a positive real part for values of p in the right half plane, and hence cannot vanish there (that would require a zero real part); further, the reciprocal of a positive-real function is again p-r (the reciprocation does not change the magnitude of the angle of the function and the polar definition is clearly still met by the reciprocal) and hence cannot vanish in the right half plane—so the original function

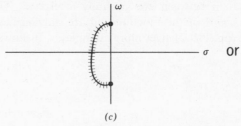

(c)

$$F_1 = ap + \frac{b}{p}$$
$$F_2 = cp$$

a, b, c real and positive

$$F = \sqrt[+]{acp^2 + bc}$$
$$= \sqrt[+]{ac(p^2 + b/a)}$$

Branch points: $\pm j\sqrt{b/a}$

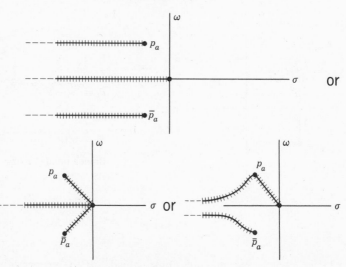

(d)

$$F_1 = \frac{(p - p_a)(p - \bar{p}_a)}{p}$$
$$F_2 = K \text{ (real and positive)}$$
$$F = \sqrt[+]{\frac{(p - p_a)(p - \bar{p}_a)}{p}}$$

Branch points: $p_a, \bar{p}_a, 0, \infty$

Fig. 4.14–E (cont.)

cannot become infinite there. This confines the branch points of this class of function to the imaginary axis and the left half plane. In cases where F_1 and F_2 are other than simple rational functions, the branch-cut picture can become quite complicated, but the above will meet our needs.

To sum up our results, if the function $F(p)$ is defined by

$$F^2 = F_1 F_2 \qquad (4.14\text{-}13)$$

we can generally make F single-valued by introducing suitable branch cuts. If F_1 and F_2 are individually p-r, these branch cuts can always be confined to the left half plane and the boundary, for neither F_1 nor F_2 can vanish or become infinite in the right half plane—and one of the two branches of F is p-r. We have illustrated these points only with rational functions F_1 and F_2, to be sure, but they hold for any p-r functions. We designate the positive-real branch as the function

$$F = \sqrt[+]{F_1 F_2}. \qquad (4.14\text{-}14)$$

4.15 Summary

In this chapter we have gone through two discussions, both concerned with power and energy and based on the primary fact of *passivity* of our networks. The results are the same: the concept of *positive reality* and the fact that driving-point (input) impedances and admittances are necessarily p-r. The derivations have been lengthy, but it will not be necessary to use them; it is the *result*, the notion of positive reality, which is important. Of this property we have two equivalent definitions: one based on rectangular co-ordinates and forms, and one based on polar coordinates and forms.

We can now set this concept into our frame of work, the three-step outline of Chapter 1, at least in part. Step 1 in the synthesis process is really to test the "requirements" (data) for realizability, to answer the question "Can they be met?" We cannot yet do this in full, but if a given $Z(p)$ or $Y(p)$ is not p-r, we can reject it here and now and say it cannot be realized. If it *is* p-r, then we can go on. We shall later find that positive reality is also sufficient for realization, at least in the rational case where our interest lies. Evidently a practical test for positive reality is needed (the definitions themselves are clumsy in application), and such a test will then be all that is needed to answer the question of step 1. If the given function is p-r, at least one realization can be found; if it is not, none can—and we have to take step 2, a matter of *approximation*. But these remarks put us considerably ahead of our present state of knowledge, and any further development ought to wait its turn in the logical scheme of things.

Our next task is to exploit our new-found concept of positive reality, to develop a feeling for and understanding of this quality, its meaning, and its implications. This we shall do in terms of the properties of driving-point immittance functions, which in many ways are synonymous with positive-real functions.

4.16 References

Positive-real functions (introductory): BR 1, CA 2, GU 3.
Energy functions: BO 3, GU 2, CA 2.
Quadratic forms: GU 3, CA 2.
Branch cuts and branch points: GU 3, CH 3, AP 1, MC 1.

PROBLEMS

4-1. In mechanics it is often convenient to use a form of *Lagrange's equations* of motion,

$$\frac{d}{dt}\frac{\partial}{\partial \dot{x}_r}(T - V) - \frac{\partial}{\partial x_r}(T - V) + \frac{\partial F}{\partial \dot{x}_r} = f_r,$$

in which

T = total kinetic energy of the system,

V = total potential energy of the system,

F = one half the total rate of dissipation of energy (in heat),

x_r = coordinates of the system ($r = 1, 2, \cdots, l$),

$$\dot{x}_r = \frac{dx_r}{dt},$$

f_r = externally applied forces.

(a) By analogy, apply these to the analysis of networks, taking electric charge to be analogous to mechanical coordinate, and voltage to force. Carry out the indicated partial differentiations and show that the resulting equation is one of Kirchhoff's laws.

(b) Repeat (a) on the dual basis (voltage analogous to velocity, etc.).

4-2. Verify Fig. 4.04–C by discussing the mapping in detail, explaining all the constructions and drawing your illustrations to scale.

4-3. Show, in § 4.11, that the equations for the generators can actually be solved.

4-4. Explain in detail, with examples, why $L_{rs} = L_{sr}$ and $\Gamma_{rs} = \Gamma_{sr}$ (§ 4.08).

4-5. Carry out the transformation (4.11–3) and show that (4.11–2) becomes (4.11–5), in which neither L_{aa} nor L_{bb} can be negative, so that T is never negative for any values whatever of i_1 and i_2.

4-6. Determine a transformation from the loop currents i_1 and i_2 in the figure to a new pair of coordinates i_a, i_b such that the magnetic stored energy $T = Ai_a{}^2 + Bi_b{}^2$ in which A and B are positive (real) numbers, so that T is obviously not negative.   If familiar with matrix algebra, recast this as a problem in matrix diagonalization and explain the equivalence.

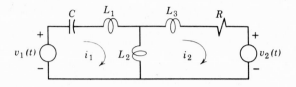

Prob. 4–6

4-7. Determine a transformation from the node voltages v_1 and v_2 in the figure to a new pair of voltage coordinates such that the electric stored energy V becomes obviously nonnegative.

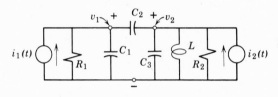

Prob. 4–7

4-8. For each of the networks shown, calculate the driving-point immittances, (1) in the usual rational-function-of-p form, and (2) in the form of (4.12–13) or

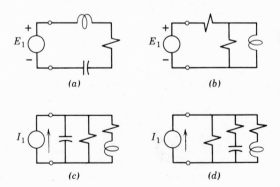

Prob. 4–8

(4.12–16), i.e., evaluate the functions T_0, F_0, etc.   How do these latter depend upon p?

4-9. Write out in full detail the expression for the imaginary part of T' in (4.12–7) for these cases and thus verify that T' is always real. (See the accompanying figure.) Repeat for V'. Repeat on the dual basis, for the dual problems.

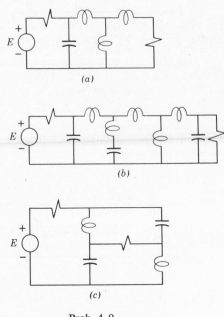

(a)

(b)

(c)

Prob. 4–9

4-10. Demonstrate for rational functions the equivalence of the rectangular and polar forms of the positive-real criterion, (4.04–15), using an evaluation of the angles of the expressions (4.12–13) and (4.12–16) at an arbitrary point in the right half plane.

4-11. From your knowledge of how zeros and poles of a passive network's driving-point impedance function affect the transient response (as to an impulse) at that point, and from this only, explain carefully why neither zeros nor poles of the impedance function can occur in the right half plane. To what extent do the arguments of Chapter 4 rest on this, and to what extent is this fact proved therein from other considerations?

From a transient analysis demonstrate that if either a zero or pole of the network occurs on the imaginary axis, it must be *simple*. Show further that the real part of the residue at such a real-frequency pole must be *positive*, using only arguments similar to those of §§ 4.02–4.03.

4-12. Consider the function $F(p) = \sigma + j\omega^2$. According to the rectangular form of definition, this function is positive-real. According to the polar form of definition, it is not. Verify these statements and resolve the paradox. What condition, over and above those stated in (4.05–2), must therefore be added to the definitions? Is this new, or is it implicit therein?

4-13. For each of the following functions determine the limitations on the literal parameters that will insure that the functions be positive-real,

(a) a polynomial of degree n;
(b) $\ln (p + a)$, a real and positive;
(c) the logarithm of a polynomial of degree n;
(d) $\exp (Kp)$;
(e) $\sinh (Kp)$;
(f) $\tanh (Kp)$.

4-14. If $F_1(p)$ and $F_2(p)$ are each p-r, discuss the following functions as to p-r character. State in particular whether they are definitely p-r, definitely not p-r, or may be p-r under certain conditions. In the last case, what are these conditions?

(a) the sum of F_1 and F_2;
(b) their difference;
(c) their product;
(d) their quotient;
(e) the square root of their product;
(f) the square root of their quotient.

4-15. If $F_1(p)$ and $F_2(p)$ are each p-r, show that $F_1[F_2(p)]$ is p-r.

4-16. Show that $Y(p) = Kp$ and $Y(p) = K/p$ are the only p-r functions for which the $=$ sign holds in (4.03–13), i.e., in the polar form of definition of positive reality, throughout the right half plane. What are the corresponding networks?

4-17. Show, by calculating the immittances, that for the networks shown the immittance functions obey (4.03–13). In which cases does the $=$ sign apply, rather than the $<$ sign?

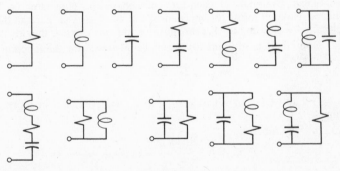

Prob. 4–17

4-18. Classify each of the following functions as p-r or not p-r.

p^n (n a positive integer, zero, or a negative integer),

$$\frac{1}{p + 1} \qquad \tan p \qquad \sqrt{p + 1}$$

$$\frac{p-1}{p+1} \qquad \sin p \qquad \coth p$$

$$\frac{p}{p+1} \qquad \ln p \qquad \frac{p^2 - 2p + 16}{p^2 + 2p + 16}$$

4-19. Which of the following are p-r functions?

$$\sqrt{1 + p^2} \qquad \frac{p^2 + 3p + 10}{2p} \qquad \frac{p^2 + 4}{6p}$$

$$\sqrt{1 + p^3} \qquad \frac{p^2 + 7p + 22}{2p + 6} \qquad \frac{p + 5}{6p + 5}$$

$$\frac{\sqrt{1 + p^2}}{p} \qquad \frac{1}{p - 1}$$

4-20. Show that the coefficients of the powers of p in the numerator and denominator of a rational p-r function must be real. Show further that these coefficients must *all* be positive (or negative), by considering the possible locations of zeros and poles, with the exception of special cases in which all the zeros (or poles, or both) are purely imaginary. Under what conditions may powers of p be missing in numerator or denominator?

4-21. Show that, in general, if $F(p)$ is p-r the locus of points that satisfy $\mathbf{Re}\, F(p) = 0$ must lie entirely in the left half plane except for points of contact with the imaginary axis (including infinity). If this curve touches the imaginary axis, what direction(s) must it have at the point(s) of contact? Show, as by plotting the loci for the immittances of the networks shown in the figure for Prob. 4-17, that there may or may not be such points of contact, and explain the rather special behavior of the locus in some of these cases. (Where different sorts of behavior may exist, depending on the relative values of the elements, choose typical examples of each sort of behavior.) How are the loci for admittance related to those for impedance? Indicate in what parts of the plane, in each case, $\mathbf{Re}\, Z(p)$ and $\mathbf{Re}\, Y(p)$ are positive and in what parts they are negative.

4-22. Draw the loci of points for which $\mathbf{Re}\, F(p) = 0$ for the function

$$F(p) = \frac{4p^2 + p + 2}{p^2 + 2p + 2} + K,$$

for $K = -1, 0, +1$. In which cases is $F(p)$ p-r? Explain in terms of your drawings.

4-23. (*a*) The function

$$F(p) = \frac{2p^2 + 2p + 1}{p + 1} = 2p + \frac{1}{p + 1}$$

is p-r. Demonstrate this both by mathematical consideration of $F(p)$ and by synthesis of networks that realize it (1) as a driving-point impedance and (2) as a driving-point admittance.

(*b*) Consider now the function

$$G(p) = \frac{2p^2 + ap + 1}{p + 1}$$

in which a is real, but otherwise arbitrary. For what values of a will $G(p)$ be p-r? Explain both mathematically and in terms of networks, as in (*a*). Is it apparent, in general, from casual inspection of $G(p)$ that it is or is not p-r?

4-24. Consider a network of a finite number of lumped, linear, constant elements, with two external terminals that constitute a driving point at which impedance $Z(p)$ and admittance $Y(p)$ may be measured or computed. At some internal point a wire that connects one of the elements to ground is broken and a coaxial cable connected to the two ends. The cable runs to a waveguide, at which it is connected to a small antenna within the guide. The guide is closed at both ends. Discuss the nature of $Z(p)$ and $Y(p)$ in the altered situation, including their positive reality.

4-25. The *ladder* network of (*a*) is infinite in extent, with the periodic construction illustrated. Show that

$$Z = \frac{Z_1}{2} + \sqrt[+]{\frac{Z_1}{2}\left(\frac{Z_1}{2} + 2Z_2\right)}.$$

(*Hint:* How does the impedance to the right of the line *A–A* compare with Z?) What network would have an input impedance equal simply to the square-root

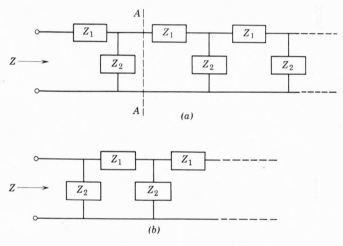

Prob. 4–25

portion of the expression above? What is the input impedance in the network of (*b*)?

Notice that the concept of sinusoidal-steady-state input immittance for an infinite network is nebulous, since it is difficult to actually set up the steady state. Still one can evidently calculate Z and Y at the driving points (and these functions are useful, and will be utilized in Volume II). Discuss the meaning of these steady-state immittances in terms of a limiting process.

Such immittance functions must have branch points. In what parts of the p plane will they lie, and how are they related to the functions $Z_1(p)$ and $Z_2(p)$?

4-26. In the networks of the figure for Prob. 4-25, let $Z_1 = 2Z_a$ and $Z_2 = Z_b/2$. The infinite networks may then have the forms of which a portion is shown here. Show that the input immittances to such an infinite network, measured to the right of any of the dotted lines, are given by

$$Z = \sqrt[+]{Z_a(Z_a + Z_b)} \qquad \text{or} \qquad Y = \sqrt[+]{Y_b(Y_b + Y_a)}.$$

Explain mathematically, in the light of § 4.14, why such immittance functions

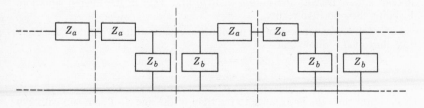

Prob. 4–26

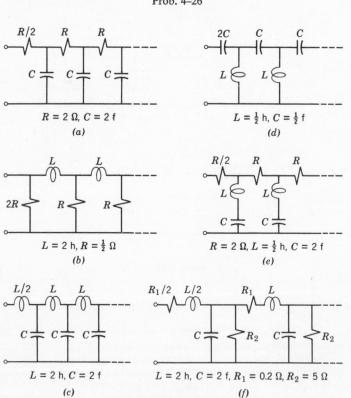

$R = 2\ \Omega,\ C = 2\ \text{f}$

(a)

$L = \tfrac{1}{2}\ \text{h},\ C = \tfrac{1}{2}\ \text{f}$

(d)

$L = 2\ \text{h},\ R = \tfrac{1}{2}\ \Omega$

(b)

$R = 2\ \Omega,\ L = \tfrac{1}{2}\ \text{h},\ C = 2\ \text{f}$

(e)

$L = 2\ \text{h},\ C = 2\ \text{f}$

(c)

$L = 2\ \text{h},\ C = 2\ \text{f},\ R_1 = 0.2\ \Omega,\ R_2 = 5\ \Omega$

(f)

Prob. 4–27

are p-r. For what physical reason are they p-r? What restriction is placed on them?

4-27. Determine the input immittance functions for each of the recurrent (infinite) networks shown, locate the branch points, and sketch suitable branch cuts.

4-28. The impedance function $Z(p)$ is defined in the figure. Find all the singularities of $Z(p)$ and classify them. Are there any in the right half plane? Do this under each of the conditions:

(a) Z_1 is a resistor;
(b) Z_1 is an inductor;
(c) Z_1 is a capacitor;
(d) Z_1 is the series combination of an inductor and a capacitor.

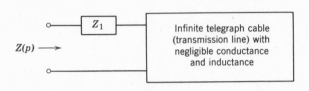

Prob. 4–28

4-29. (a) If the functions $F_1(p)$, $F_2(p)$, $F_3(p)$, $\cdots$ are individually p-r, are the following derived functions also p-r? Explain carefully.

$$\sqrt[3]{F_1 F_2 F_3} \qquad \sqrt[4]{F_1 F_2 F_3 F_4} \qquad \sqrt[5]{F_1 F_2 F_3 F_4 F_5}$$

(b) Is the function $\dfrac{p^2 + 2}{\sqrt[+]{p^2 + 1}\,(p^2 + 3)}$ p-r?

4-30. Let $F_1(p) = (p - p_a)(p - \bar{p}_a)/p$, in which $\mathrm{Re}\, p_a < 0$, $F_2(p) = 1/p$, and $F(p) = \sqrt[+]{F_1 F_2}$. Locate the branch points of $F(p)$ and define suitable branch cuts. In particular, is the origin a branch point? Show that one branch of $F(p)$ is p-r, as implied above.

4-31. With regard to termini (not to intermediate shapes of curves) sketch other possible sets of branch cuts for Fig. 4.14–E(d). What is the total number of possibilities?

Locate branch points and branch cuts (how many possibilities are there?) for the function $F(p)$ defined by

$$\sqrt{\dfrac{p(p^2 + \omega_2{}^2)}{p^2 + \omega_1{}^2}} \qquad \omega_1,\, \omega_2 \text{ real and } 0 < \omega_1 < \omega_2,$$

so that $F(p)$ is p-r.

4-32. The proposition of Prob. 4-15 is the basis of some interesting and useful transformations. The following is a simple illustration of its application.

Plot the magnitude, angle, resistance, and reactance of the input impedance to the network of (a). Suppose now that in the network the inductor L is replaced by a capacitor C', and the capacitor C by an inductor L', such that $LC' = \omega_0{}^{-2}$

and $L'C = \omega_0^{-2}$. What happens to the frequency characteristics that you have plotted? Illustrate with plots for the new network.

The new driving-point impedance function is of course p-r (it represents an actual network). Show how Prob. 4-15 applies mathematically to demonstrate

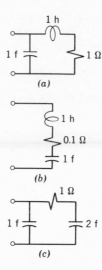

(a)

(b)

(c)

Prob. 4–32

its positive reality. Discuss this transformation as a conformal mapping. What feature of the mapping guarantees that the p-r quality remains under the transformation?

Repeat the discussion for each of the other networks shown.

4-33. Repeat Prob. 4-32 with the change that an inductor is to be replaced by the series combination of an inductor and a capacitor, and a capacitor by the parallel combination of an inductor and a capacitor, in such a fashion that in the new network p is replaced by $K[(p/\omega_0) + (\omega_0/p)]$.

4-34. Repeat Prob. 4-33 with the interchange of the words *series* and *parallel*.

4-35. Repeat Prob. 4-32 with the interchange of the words *inductor* and *capacitor*.

5.

Properties of Driving-Point Immittance Functions—I

Science is the knowledge of Consequences,
and dependance of one fact upon another.
—Thomas Hobbes

We have, contained in the positive-real quality, almost all the important properties of driving-point immittance functions, i.e., of the input immittances of one-terminal pairs. This is not at all obvious, but as we shall see below, these properties are implicit in the p-r property. It is marvellous, indeed, how much is contained in the concept of positive reality.

5.01 A corollary

We have observed that both $Y(p)$ and $Z(p)$, which are reciprocals, must meet the p-r restriction—for the parallel (dual) approach in either method leads to this same result. We here show, analytically and in general, that if a function is p-r, so also is its reciprocal. This fact has been mentioned (in § 4.14) but it deserves emphasis.

When the reciprocal of a complex number is formed, the angle of the new number differs in sign from the angle of the original number, but the *magnitude* of the angle is unchanged. Since one definition of a positive-real function considers only the magnitude of the angle of the function (which cannot exceed the magnitude of the angle of the independent variable when the latter is in the right half plane), it follows immediately that if a function is p-r, so also is its reciprocal. We need no equations to prove this; it is inherent in the polar-form definition, which does not really distinguish between a function and its reciprocal.

The rectangular-form definition yields the same result with but little more work. Let $F(p) = x + jy$ be p-r. Its reciprocal is

$$\frac{1}{F(p)} = \frac{1}{x + jy} = \frac{x - jy}{x^2 + y^2}. \tag{5.01-1}$$

163

When p is in the right half plane and is real, $y = 0$ (for F is p-r); hence $1/F$ is then also real. When p is in the right half plane, x is positive (for F is p-r), and from this fact we see that then

$$\text{Re } \frac{1}{F(p)} = \frac{x}{x^2 + y^2} > 0 \qquad (5.01-2)$$

also. Hence $1/F$, when p is in the right half plane, is real for real p, and has a positive real part, which means that $1/F$ is p-r.

We thus reach the conclusion, via either path, that

the reciprocal of a positive-real function is again a positive-real function.

$$(5.01-3)$$

This fact will be useful for the main business of this chapter, which is to list the properties of driving-point immittance functions, as we know them so far, and as we can further develop them from the p-r property. Incidentally we shall learn more about p-r functions in general.

5.02 First property

Without further ado we can say that

a driving-point immittance function is positive-real. $(5.02-1)$

This must be true, if the function represents an immittance of a physical (existing) network, because of the (somewhat lengthy) arguments of Chapter 4. Positive reality is a *necessary* condition for physical realizability, beyond any doubt, and therefore is characteristic of any physical (passive) driving-point immittance function.

5.03 Second property

For networks of the type we consider (made up of a finite number of elements), the immittance functions are further restricted to a subclass of p-r functions, the *rational* class. In Chapter 3 (§ 3.06) we saw that the usual network functions, of which driving-point impedance and admittance are two, must be rational. Yet a function need not be rational to be p-r; in the definitions of positive-real functions (4.05–3) there is nothing about the *form* of a function (though, to be sure, the second approach of Chapter 4 can by its very nature consider only rational functions). But the immittance functions of networks made up of only a finite number of lumped elements must be *rational* as well as p-r. For emphasis we write again the general form of a rational function of p, from (3.06–2) and (3.06–5). Thus

$$\frac{a_n p^n + a_{n-1} p^{n-1} + \cdots + a_1 p + a_0}{b_m p^m + b_{m-1} p^{m-1} + \cdots + b_1 p + b_0} \qquad (5.03-1)$$

and

$$K \frac{(p - p_1)(p - p_2) \cdot \cdot \cdot (p - p_n)}{(p - p_1')(p - p_2') \cdot \cdot \cdot (p - p_m')} \qquad (5.03\text{-}2)$$

in which the ratio a_n/b_m has been given a single symbol K, and in which the p_i and p_i' are complex numbers in general (and may in some cases coincide), are two useful and general forms of the rational function.

Rational functions may or may not be p-r; p-r functions may or may not be rational; the quality of positive reality is totally distinct from the quality of rationality, and each should be investigated separately. But our driving-point immittance functions must belong to *both* the p-r class and the rational class, if a network with only a finite number of elements is involved. Hence "driving-point-immittance function" and "positive-real function" are not synonymous, but are nevertheless very closely related terms.

To elaborate a little on this, consider Fig. 5.03–A. We may imagine the class of all positive-real functions to be represented by the region A,

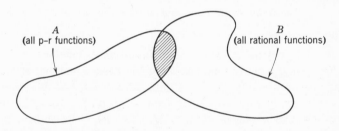

Fig. 5.03–A

or that all p-r functions are rounded up and placed in region A. If we try similarly to collect all rational functions in the region B, we cannot succeed unless we take from region A those p-r functions which are rational —or, better, indicate some overlap between the two, as shown. In the shaded region now lie all functions which are *both* p-r and rational. Our work in Chapter 4 led to the conclusion that the driving-point immittance functions of all passive systems lie in region A (are p-r); if the system is a *network* within our definition (made up a finite number of lumped elements), the immittance functions are also rational, and hence may lie only in the overlap (shaded region). If a function is rational but not p-r, i.e., lies in the part of B outside the overlap, we know definitely that it cannot be realized as such an immittance. If a function lies in the overlap, we cannot yet say definitely that it is therefore realizable in that way—but it is one of the primary objectives of this book to prove that it *is* then realizable, and this objective we shall reach in due time. We know already that at least many of the functions in the overlap *are* so realizable. As to functions which are p-r but not rational, i.e., lie in the part of region A which is outside the overlap, they are in general beyond the scope of this book, though we shall meet some such immittances later; these have to do with "infinite networks" (cf. Prob. 4–25).

For the present our concern is with the properties of network driving-point immittances. Such functions lie in the overlap, but we do not yet know how much of the overlap they fill. Technically, then, we are here discussing properties of *some* of the functions in the overlap—but we anticipate the fact, mentioned above, that *all* of the functions in the overlap are driving-point-immittance functions.

We shall not harp further on this classification until the time (later) when we first encounter "networks" in which some of the network functions are not rational. For the time being, then, let it be understood that we are talking only about networks with a finite number of elements, and hence about rational network functions. The second property is then

a driving-point immittance function is rational.   (5.03–3)

5.04 Third property

If (5.03–1) represents a driving-point immittance function, the coefficients (the a's and b's) are obtained from the basic equations of analysis by manipulation which involves addition, subtraction, multiplication, and division of terms in which the coefficients of p^1, p^0, p^{-1} are real numbers (the network element values, R, L, S, M, G, C, Γ). Hence these a's and b's must be *real numbers*. This is a truism, to be sure, but from it follows an important fact: the values of the function at two conjugate values of p are themselves conjugate. Since each individual term in numerator and denominator takes conjugate values when p does, this is also true of the whole function (but would not be true if the a's and b's were not real). Here we have evidence of the symmetry of the upper and lower half planes mentioned in § 3.05. To approach this from a different point, our (rational) driving-point immittance functions are surely p-r, and are therefore real when p is real and in the right half plane; and since they are rational as well as p-r, they are real for all real values of p. From this fact we can say that $F(\bar{p}) = \overline{F(p)}$ (see § 3.09). This symmetry is evidently related to the p-r property and is not merely an effect due to the rational character of our driving-point immittance functions, but this is a point we need not develop.

The particular property of interest here is a consequence of this symmetry property: no zero can be complex (i.e., have an imaginary part which is not zero) unless its conjugate is also present as a zero, nor can any pole be complex unless its conjugate is also present as a pole. In other words, zeros and poles, when not real, must occur in *conjugate complex pairs*. This follows from the symmetry property immediately, for if p_1 is a zero of say $Z(p)$, i.e., if $Z(p_1) = 0$, then the value of $Z(\bar{p}_1)$ must be the conjugate of zero, which is again zero. Consideration of the reciprocal of $Z(p_1)$, if p_1 is a pole, completes the proof. Hence our third property:

zeros and poles of driving-point immittance functions, if not real, occur in conjugate pairs. (5.04–1)

This is a consequence of the fact that all the coefficients in (5.03–1) are *real* numbers; but evidently it can also be considered to stem from the fact that the p-r quality requires driving-point immittance functions to be real when p is real; hence the function conjugates when p conjugates. This third property might well be stated as (3.09–3). Again it could be written in the equivalent form

the coefficients of the various powers of p in a driving-point immittance function are real numbers. (5.04–2)

5.05 Fourth property

In the previous section we have an inkling of the fact that important properties can be deduced from the p-r property alone. The fourth property we are to state is one we already know, yet it is instructive to derive it again, but from the p-r property.

If a function $F(p)$ is p-r, then for values of p in the right half plane, **Re** $F(p) > 0$. Since the real part of F is not zero, F itself cannot be zero in the right half plane. Nor can F become infinite in the right half plane, for its reciprocal must also be p-r (§ 5.01) and therefore cannot vanish. Hence

no point at which a positive-real function vanishes or becomes infinite can lie in the right half plane. (5.05–1)

Note that this adds somewhat to our knowledge, for although we knew this to be true of driving-point immittances, from physical reasoning, we had as yet no proof that *all* p-r functions are necessarily realizable as driving-point immittances—and so we had no previous knowledge that the zero points, and infinity points, of all p-r functions are excluded from the right half plane. This is an example of conclusions about p-r functions which are not obvious from the definitions but are implicit in the p-r property.

The driving-point immittance functions of interest to us are not only p-r; they are also rational. Hence the points at which they vanish are zeros and the infinity points are poles, and (5.05–1) as applied to them becomes our fourth property:

> no zero or pole of a driving-point immittance function can lie in the right
> half plane.   (5.05–2)

This we know, almost intuitively, by physical reasoning from the passive character of the network (and we used this in § 4.02, in fact), but it is an important property, worth restatement in the equivalent form:

> the zeros and poles of a driving-point immittance function are confined to
> the left half plane and the imaginary axis—none are in the right half
> plane.   (5.05–3)

To be sure, there are the two perfectly realizable cases of the short and open circuit which might be considered violations of (5.05–3); but these we have excluded and agreed to handle, when the need arises, merely by common sense (§ 4.02).

5.06 Fifth property

If a driving-point immittance function is to have any interesting behavior, it must vary with p, and it must therefore have zeros and poles. These we know cannot lie in the right half plane. The next region in the quadripartite division of the p plane in § 4.03 is the boundary line between the right and left halves of the plane, the imaginary axis. An orderly treatment would then pose the question: can a driving-point immittance function have purely imaginary zeros or poles? We know the answer is yes, as evidenced by simple "tuned circuits" consisting of an inductor and capacitor. But such zeros and poles are subject to certain rules, and these constitute our fifth property.

The positive-real property, from which stem this and most of the other important properties of driving-point immittances, says nothing directly about behavior on the imaginary axis; the definition is limited to properties of a function in the right half plane, and it is only by some process of extrapolation or extension that we can find out whether the right-half-plane behavior of a p-r function implies anything about behavior on the imaginary axis. Any point an infinitesimal distance to the right of a point on that axis, however, is in the right half plane, and consequently a p-r function must there have a positive real part. To make use of this fact, let p describe a small circle of radius r, centered on the point $j\omega_0$ (which is on the imaginary axis, but otherwise arbitrary). On this small circle we have (Fig. 5.06–A)

$$p = j\omega_0 + re^{j\theta}, \qquad (5.06-1)$$

and for $-\pi/2 < \theta < \pi/2$, p is definitely in the right half plane, however small r may be, so long as r does not vanish.

Now consider an arbitrary p-r function $F(p)$. Suppose it to vanish at $j\omega_0$ and that in the vicinity of $j\omega_0$

$$F(p) = 0 + A(p - j\omega_0)^s + B(p - j\omega_0)^{s+1} + \cdots \quad (5.06\text{-}2)$$

in which s is real and positive. The real part of $F(p)$ is then given by

$$\mathbf{Re}\, F(p) = \mathbf{Re}\, A(re^{j\theta})^s + \mathbf{Re}\, B(re^{j\theta})^{s+1} + \cdots. \quad (5.06\text{-}3)$$

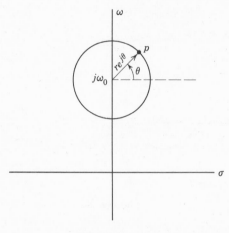

Fig. 5.06–A

To extract the real part more clearly, let the (generally) complex number A be written as $ae^{j\alpha}$ in which a is real and positive. Then

$$\mathbf{Re}\, F(p) = \mathbf{Re}\, ar^s e^{j(\alpha + s\theta)} + \cdots$$
$$= ar^s \cos(\alpha + s\theta) + \cdots \quad (5.06\text{-}4)$$

in which the terms omitted (indicated by the dots) are negligible in comparison with the term shown, for sufficiently small (though not zero) r—except perhaps at certain isolated points where the cosine vanishes, which need not concern us. The term $ar^s \cos(\alpha + s\theta)$ must then be positive for $-\pi/2 < \theta < \pi/2$, since F is p-r.

The last statement leads immediately to the rules we seek. For as θ varies from $-\pi/2$ through zero to $+\pi/2$, the real part of F will describe s half cycles of a cosine wave—and yet this real part of F must remain positive, except at the two end points of the semicircle. This immediately restricts s to a maximum value of unity. Further, if $s = 1$, then necessarily $\alpha = 0$, else the requirement of a positive real part is violated somewhere on the right-half-plane half of the circle. Figure 5.06–B shows the behavior of **Re** $F(p)$ on this semicircle, as well as the semicircle itself. With $s = 1$, any value of α other than zero would shift the wave to the left or right, causing the real part of F to vanish and even go negative at points in the right half plane; with $s < 1$, less than half a period of the cosine wave corresponds to right-half-plane points, and the restriction on α here is relaxed somewhat; such may occur near the branch points discussed in § 4.14, for example, but not with rational functions.

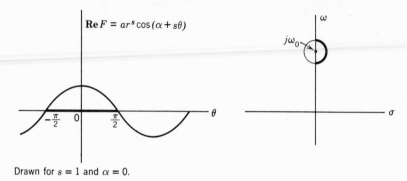

Drawn for $s = 1$ and $\alpha = 0$.

Fig. 5.06–B

Similar conclusions can be drawn immediately about imaginary-axis points where F becomes infinite. Suppose this happens at $j\omega_0$ and that F in the vicinity can be expanded as

$$F = \frac{1}{A(p - j\omega_0)^s} + \frac{1}{B(p - j\omega_0)^{s-1}} + \cdots$$

$$= \frac{1}{A(p - j\omega_0)^s}\left[1 + \frac{A(p - j\omega_0)}{B} + \cdots\right]$$

$$= \frac{1}{A(p - j\omega_0)^s\left[1 - \frac{A}{B}(p - j\omega_0) + \cdots\right]}$$

$$= \frac{1}{A(p - j\omega_0)^s - \dfrac{A^2}{B}(p - j\omega_0)^{s+1} + \cdots} \tag{5.06-5}$$

in which the first terms predominate. Since $1/F$ is also p-r, it follows immediately that again s is limited to a maximum value of unity and α must be zero if $s = 1$. To sum up in words,

if a p-r function vanishes or becomes infinite at a point on the imaginary axis, say $j\omega_0$, in such a fashion that the leading term in its expansion thereabout is $ae^{j\alpha}(p - j\omega_0)^s$, then $-1 \leq s \leq 1$, and if $|s| = 1$, then $\alpha = 0$.

(5.06–6)

In the above we have assumed something about expansion near a "fractional zero or pole" which we have not really investigated, but such expansions can often be made, in particular near simple branch points. Our real interest here, however, is in driving-point immittance functions, which are rational and can therefore admit only integer values of s in any of the above formulas, i.e., only true zeros and poles—and *simple* ones. In the case of a zero, the A above is $F'(j\omega_0)$; in the case of a pole, the A is the reciprocal of the residue of $F(p)$ thereat [cf. (3.21–7)]. Both this derivative and this residue must be real and positive, for $\alpha = 0$ is required. We can thus state the fifth property:

purely imaginary zeros and poles of driving-point immittance functions are simple; at such a zero the derivative of the function is real and positive; at such a pole the residue is real and positive. (5.06–7)

The zeros and poles of driving-point immittance functions, the sources of their interesting behavior, are excluded from the right half plane and are severely restricted in character if they occur on the boundary between the right and left halves of the plane.

We cannot say much about zeros and poles in the left half plane, for there we have no direct information on the consequences of positive reality. Such zeros and poles, we shall find, can be multiple, nor are there any simple restrictions on derivatives or residues. There remains the point at infinity to consider, which we shall do next.

5.07 Sixth property

For large values of $|p|$, our general rational function, (5.03–1) or (5.03–2), can be written

$$K \frac{p^n \left(1 + \dfrac{a_{n-1}}{a_n} \dfrac{1}{p} + \cdots\right)}{p^m \left(1 + \dfrac{b_{m-1}}{b_m} \dfrac{1}{p} + \cdots\right)} = K p^{n-m} \left(1 + A \frac{1}{p} + \cdots\right). \quad (5.07–1)$$

For sufficiently large values of $|p|$, the function is essentially $K p^{n-m}$, which indicates the behavior allowed at infinity. In the first place, if the function is p-r, consideration of large real, positive values of p shows that K must be real and positive, in order that the real part of the function remain positive (which we already knew, since K is essentially a coefficient —cf. § 5.04). Secondly, n and m are rather closely bound together. To show this, we let $p = Re^{j\theta}$, so that

$$Kp^{n-m} = KR^{n-m}e^{j(n-m)\theta}. \tag{5.07-2}$$

For large R, (5.07-2) has essentially the value of the rational p-r function in which we are interested. Its angle is $(n-m)\theta$, whereas the angle of p is simply θ. From the polar definition of positive reality, we know then that in the right half plane

$$|(n-m)\theta| \leqq |\theta|, \tag{5.07-3}$$

hence

$$|n-m| \leqq 1. \tag{5.07-4}$$

Since n and m are positive integers, (5.07-4) implies one of these three relations:

$$n = m + 1,$$
$$n = m, \tag{5.07-5}$$
$$n = m - 1,$$

and these are the only possible relations. The first corresponds to a simple pole at infinity, the second to a regular point (where the function has a nonzero value) at infinity, and the third to a simple zero at infinity. This rounds out our fourth and fifth properties by describing the limitations on zeros and poles at infinity. To sum this up, our sixth property is:

at infinity a driving-point immittance function must have a simple pole, a simple zero, or a regular point at which it does not vanish; in any case the multiplier K must be real and positive.   (5.07-6)

The reasoning above, applied to any function which behaves as Kp^s for large values of p (K and s being real), shows that the general restriction on s imposed by positive reality is $-1 \leqq s \leqq 1$, of which our sixth property is a special case, the rational-function application.

5.08 Seventh property

The seventh property is but a corollary of the sixth, but is worth separate statement:

the degrees of the numerator and denominator of a driving-point immittance function can differ at most by unity.   (5.08-1)

This amounts to a restatement of (5.07-5), since the degrees of the numerator and denominator are n and m respectively. An alternative way of saying this is that the exponents of the highest powers of p in the numerator and in the denominator can differ at most by unity.

5.09 Eighth property

For the sake of symmetry, let us also consider the other ends of the numerator and denominator polynomials, the lower powers of p. For small values of $|p|$ the general rational function (5.03–1), which we take to be a driving-point immittance function and therefore p-r, can be written

$$\frac{a_0 + a_1 p + \cdots}{b_0 + b_1 p + \cdots} \qquad (5.09\text{--}1)$$

in which the terms indicated by dots are negligible in comparison with those given. All the coefficients (the a's and b's) are of course real. We assume that the fraction has been reduced to lowest terms now, so that a_0 and b_0 are not both zero, though either one may be. There are then three possibilities:

$$(1) \; a_0 = 0, \; b_0 \neq 0,$$
$$(2) \; a_0 \neq 0, \; b_0 \neq 0, \qquad (5.09\text{--}2)$$
$$(3) \; a_0 \neq 0, \; b_0 = 0.$$

In the first case, the function behaves, for small $|p|$, as $(a_1/b_0)p + \cdots$. This implies a zero at the origin, which is a point on the imaginary axis. The zero must then be simple, by (5.06–7), and the value of the function's derivative there real and positive. Hence the coefficient a_1 *cannot vanish*, and (a_1/b_0), which we already know to be real, must be *positive*.

In the second case, the behavior of the function near the origin (in particular just to the right of the origin) is given by $(a_0/b_0) + \cdots$ which is consistent with positive reality, provided this (real) ratio is positive.

In the third case, the behavior is as $(a_0/b_1)p^{-1} + \cdots$. This implies a pole at the origin, which must be simple, by (5.06–7), and have a real, positive residue. Hence the coefficient b_1 *cannot vanish* and the real number (a_0/b_1) must be *positive*.

By collecting the results above we see that the lowest powers of p in the numerator and denominator are bound by a tie similar to that which restricts the highest powers. This is the eighth property:

the exponents of the lowest powers of p in the numerator and denominator of a driving-point immittance function can differ at most by unity. (5.09–3)

The positive character of certain coefficient ratios, found above, will be included in a later, more complete statement (5.12–5).

5.10 Even and odd parts

The functions we shall use are sometimes even functions, sometimes odd functions, though quite often neither. Yet the latter can still be split into parts which are purely odd or purely even, a simple yet important fact worth discussion here.

To begin with, we have the definitions

$$(a) \text{ a function } F(p) \text{ is } even \text{ if } F(-p) = F(p), \qquad (5.10\text{–}1)$$

and

$$(b) \text{ a function } F(p) \text{ is } odd \text{ if } F(-p) = -F(p). \qquad (5.10\text{–}2)$$

These are conventional definitions and imply certain symmetries with respect to the origin of the complex plane. In general, of course, a function $F(p)$ is neither odd nor even. But it is always a mixture of the two and can be split into even and odd *parts*, which we define as

$$\text{Ev } F(p) = \tfrac{1}{2}[F(p) + F(-p)] \qquad (5.10\text{–}3)$$

and

$$\text{Od } F(p) = \tfrac{1}{2}[F(p) - F(-p)], \qquad (5.10\text{–}4)$$

respectively. The first of these is an even function, the second an odd function, and their sum is

$$F(p) = \text{Ev } F(p) + \text{Od } F(p). \qquad (5.10\text{–}5)$$

Separation of a function into its even and odd parts is formally a simple matter, then. The operator notation **Ev** and **Od** is somewhat akin to the familiar **Re** and **Im** but the meanings are "even part of" and "odd part of" respectively. The even part is that part whose sign does not change when the sign of p is changed; the odd part is that part whose sign reverses when the sign of p is changed; together they make up the whole function.

Let us apply these operations to a simple example now, to the polynomial $Q(p) = 17p^4 + 16p^3 + 3p^2 + 4$, for illustration. The results are

$$\text{Ev } Q(p) = 17p^4 + 3p^2 + 4,$$
$$\text{Od } Q(p) = 16p^3. \qquad (5.10\text{–}6)$$

The even part of *any* polynomial is evidently the sum of the even-power terms, and the odd part the sum of the odd-power terms; the constant term is to be considered as the zeroth, an even power. This splitting of a polynomial is a frequent operation, for the results of which two notations are in use in network-theory literature, each with its own advantages. The even and odd parts of a polynomial are both polynomials, one even and one odd: the even one contains only even powers of p, the odd one only odd powers. One notation (GU 3) assigns the letter M, say, to represent an even polynomial, and the letter N, say, to represent an odd polynomial. The other notation comes from the school of thought

(DA 1) which says: after all, an odd polynomial is merely an even polynomial multiplied by p, so why not use capital-letter symbols for even polynomials only, and write the product of p and such a symbol for an odd polynomial? The notation here is then A, B, and the like for even polynomials, and pA, pB, and the like for odd ones. In symbols, we can state all said so far about notation, in terms of a typical polynomial, thus:

$$Q(p) = a_n p^n + a_{n-1} p^{n-1} + \cdots + a_1 p + a_0$$
$$= (a_0 + a_2 p^2 + a_4 p^4 + \cdots) + (a_1 p + a_3 p^3 + a_5 p^5 + \cdots)$$
$$= \underbrace{(a_0 + a_2 p^2 + a_4 p^4 + \cdots)}_{\text{even part of } Q(p)} + \underbrace{p(a_1 + a_3 p^2 + a_5 p^4 + \cdots)}_{\text{odd part of } Q(p)}$$

$$= \text{Ev } Q + \text{Od } Q \tag{5.10-7}$$

$$= M + N \tag{5.10-8}$$

$$= A + pB. \tag{5.10-9}$$

The last three lines above are a résumé of notation. In (5.10–7) is the general notation indicating a split into even and odd parts; in (5.10–8) one capital letter represents the even part and another the odd part—and we shall consistently use M for even polynomials and N for odd polynomials when we use this system; in (5.10–9) the letters A and B both stand for even polynomials and the odd polynomial is written pB.

Suppose now that $F(p)$ represents a general rational function; let us write corresponding equations for it. For the numerator and denominator polynomials we here use both the notations developed above, for comparison, with subscripts to distinguish numerator from denominator,

$$F(p) = \frac{(\text{polynomial})_1}{(\text{polynomial})_2} = \frac{M_1 + N_1}{M_2 + N_2} = \frac{A_1 + pB_1}{A_2 + pB_2}. \tag{5.10-10}$$

The parts are

$$\text{Ev } F = \frac{M_1 M_2 - N_1 N_2}{M_2^2 - N_2^2} \tag{5.10-11}$$

$$= \frac{A_1 A_2 - p^2 B_1 B_2}{A_2^2 - p^2 B_2^2}, \tag{5.10-12}$$

and

$$\text{Od } F = \frac{N_1 M_2 - M_1 N_2}{M_2^2 - N_2^2} \tag{5.10-13}$$

$$= p \frac{B_1 A_2 - A_1 B_2}{A_2^2 - p^2 B_2^2}. \tag{5.10-14}$$

These may be derived simply by application of (5.10–3) and (5.10–4), or by first multiplying both numerator and denominator of $F(p)$ by the polynomial $(M_2 - N_2)$ or $(A_2 - pB_2)$. The latter device makes the denominator even and it is then necessary to split only the new numerator; the process is much like rationalization of a complex-number fraction.

The following example illustrates this decomposition.

$$F(p) = \frac{p^2 + 6p + 1}{p^2 + 7p + 2}$$

$$= \frac{(p^2 + 1) + (6p)}{(p^2 + 2) + (7p)} \times \frac{(p^2 + 2) - (7p)}{(p^2 + 2) - (7p)}$$

$$= \frac{[(p^2 + 1)(p^2 + 2) - (6p)(7p)] + [(6p)(p^2 + 2) - (p^2 + 1)(7p)]}{(p^2 + 2)^2 - (7p)^2}$$

$$= \underbrace{\frac{p^4 - 39p^2 + 2}{p^4 - 45p^2 + 4}}_{\text{Ev } F} + \underbrace{\frac{-p^3 + 5p}{p^4 - 45p^2 + 4}}_{\text{Od } F}.$$

The negative signs in the above are characteristic of the operation.

5.11 Ninth property

There is a close connection between the operations **Ev** and **Re** and between **Od** and **Im**. But in neither case are they in general the same thing. We are familiar with the symmetry property of p-r functions which makes $F(\bar{p}) = \overline{F(p)}$, a consequence of the fact that $F(\sigma)$ must be real, at least in the right half plane (cf. § 3.09). This is a property of vertical symmetry about the real axis. Evenness and oddness, however, have to do with symmetry about the origin, a sort of diagonal symmetry. The two kinds have much in common when p is limited to the imaginary axis, for then vertical symmetry is also symmetry about the origin. Then the equation $F(\bar{p}) = \overline{F(p)}$ becomes $F(-j\omega) = \overline{F(j\omega)}$, from which we conclude that

$$\mathbf{Re}\, F(-j\omega) = \mathbf{Re}\, F(j\omega) \tag{5.11-1}$$

and

$$\mathbf{Im}\, F(-j\omega) = -\mathbf{Im}\, F(j\omega), \tag{5.11-2}$$

or that on the imaginary axis the real part is even and the imaginary part odd.

In the case of rational functions with real coefficients, a similar result follows from the discussion of § 5.10. For, since the even part involves only even powers of p and the coefficients are real, the even part is real when p is imaginary; and the odd part, since it involves only odd powers of p with real coefficients and a common even factor, is then purely imaginary. Hence

$$\text{Ev } F(j\omega) = \text{Re } F(j\omega), \qquad\qquad (5.11\text{–}3)$$

$$\text{Od } F(j\omega) = j \text{ Im } F(j\omega). \qquad\qquad (5.11\text{–}4)$$

Evidently these statements are true of any p-r function, for they amount to a restatement of (5.11–1) and (5.11–2). But for general, complex values of p, there is no connection between the two pairs of operations. All we can say in general is that the various parts are related by sums:

$$\begin{aligned} F(p) &= \text{Ev } F + \text{Od } F \\ &= \text{Re } F + j \text{ Im } F. \end{aligned} \qquad\qquad (5.11\text{–}5)$$

The property of interest here, however, is the symmetry property on the imaginary axis. It is the ninth property:

at real frequencies, i.e., for $p = j\omega$, the real part of a driving-point immittance function is an even function of ω and the imaginary part is an odd function of ω. $\qquad\qquad (5.11\text{–}6)$

A similar statement holds for any vertical line in the plane, but it is in the imaginary axis that our chief interest lies. The previous discussion also indicates that the property is not limited to rational functions, but is characteristic of all p-r functions.

For the example of § 5.10, we have

$$\text{Re } F(j\omega) = \text{Ev } F(j\omega) = \frac{\omega^4 + 39\omega^2 + 2}{\omega^4 + 45\omega^2 + 4},$$

$$\text{Im } F(j\omega) = \frac{1}{j} \text{Od } F(j\omega) = \frac{\omega^3 + 5\omega}{\omega^4 + 45\omega^2 + 4},$$

which are of course even and odd respectively.

The equivalent statement in polar form, that

at real frequencies, i.e., for $p = j\omega$, the magnitude of a driving-point immittance function is an even function of ω and the angle is an odd function of ω $\qquad\qquad (5.11\text{–}7)$

follows from (5.11–6) with a small amount of algebra. This, of course, is not limited to rational p-r functions either.

5.12 Hurwitz polynomials

The immittance functions we have to consider are quotients of two polynomials, and the zeros of these polynomials cannot lie in the right half plane. We have seen that they *may* lie on the boundary line under certain conditions, but these (purely imaginary) locations are perhaps somewhat rarer than those with negative real parts. Hence we give a name to a polynomial all of whose zeros have negative (nonzero) real parts: such we call *Hurwitz polynomials* (HU 3). (In the interests of simplicity we do not make a broader definition, which would cover the complete numerators and denominators of driving-point immittance functions and permit the polynomials to have imaginary zeros also; we also assume real coefficients.) These Hurwitz polynomials have many interesting properties, and their study is called for not only here, in the study of (passive) networks, but also in discussing the stability of systems which contain active elements.

The numerators and denominators of driving-point immittance functions must be either Hurwitz polynomials, or polynomials all of whose zeros are simple and lie on the imaginary axis in conjugate pairs, or (generally) products of the two, as

$$\begin{pmatrix} \text{polynomial all of whose zeros} \\ \text{have negative real parts} \end{pmatrix} \times \begin{pmatrix} \text{polynomial all of whose} \\ \text{zeros have zero real parts} \end{pmatrix}.$$

(5.12–1)

The first of these is by definition a Hurwitz polynomial. The second has no particular name, but its factors must be of the form $(p^2 + \omega_0^2)$, ω_0^2 being real and positive; there may also be a factor which is simply p, in the case of a zero at the origin. Consequently this second polynomial is either *odd* or *even*.

There are criteria for determining from the coefficients of a given polynomial whether or not it is Hurwitz, i.e., whether or not all of its zeros have negative real parts, and also (possibly by additional testing) whether or not it contains as a factor a polynomial of the second type above. Routh's rule and Nyquist's criterion amount to such tests (BO 5, GU 3, MA 5). But with these we shall not concern ourselves: another (different) test will be given shortly (§ 5.14). One thing we do say now, considering only polynomials with real coefficients (for physical reasons), that

all of the coefficients of a Hurwitz polynomial, after division by the coefficient in the leading term, must be positive, and not zero.   (5.12–2)

(The converse is by no means necessarily true, as we shall soon see.) Thus, if

$$Q(p) = p^n + a_{n-1}p^{n-1} + \cdots + a_1 p + a_0 \qquad (5.12\text{–}3)$$

is a Hurwitz polynomial (the coefficient of the leading term being unity or having been divided out), then all of the a's are positive (as well as real), and none of them are zero. This may be proved by experimentation with the various possible ways of building up polynomials with left-half-plane zeros. An alternative is to consider the elementary symmetric functions of the (left-half-plane) zeros with their signs changed (so that they then lie in the right half plane); these functions are the coefficients of the polynomial. If the coefficient of the leading term is present (not divided out), then the coefficients may all be negative, but they must in any case have the same sign, and no term in the sequence of powers of p can vanish.

We may formalize these conclusions as an additional property of driving-point immittance functions, whose numerators and denominators must be of the form (5.12–1) in general. Written out with the coefficients expressly stated, let the function be

$$K \frac{p^n + a_{n-1}p^{n-1} + \cdots + a_1 p + a_0}{p^m + b_{m-1}p^{m-1} + \cdots + b_1 p + b_0}. \tag{5.12–4}$$

Then the (real) coefficients (the a's and b's) are in general all positive and not zero; it is possible for a_0 or b_0 to vanish; it is also possible that the numerator or the denominator be a purely even (or purely odd) polynomial (in which alternate a's or b's are zero) but then all the even (or all the odd) powers of p below the leading power are present, so that no even subscript (or no odd subscript) a or b is then zero; it is possible that *both* numerator and denominator fall in the foregoing special category, but then one must be odd and the other even.   (5.12–5)

This we may consider our tenth property. It is easily derived from the preceding conclusions of this section and from previously listed properties. Phrased somewhat differently, the property can be stated, in essence, as follows:

when the (simple) real-frequency-zero factors have been removed, the numerators and denominators of driving-point immittance functions are Hurwitz polynomials.   (5.12–6)

5.13 A test for positive reality

Since our end is network synthesis, we are very much interested in being able to decide whether or not a given function is realizable as a driving-point immittance function. So far we have accumulated some ten properties which we know such functions must have; these are *necessary* properties. All of these (except the first and second) follow from positive reality and are implied thereby. But it is not difficult to show that these eight properties, impressive though the list may be, are not enough to insure that a rational function be p-r. Consider the function

$$F(p) = \frac{2p^2 + p + 2}{p + 1}, \tag{5.13–1}$$

for example. $F(p)$ has all the ten properties developed so far, except the first: it is not positive-real. To demonstrate this, calculate the real part of $F(p)$, which can be obtained by simple algebra; it is

$$\text{Re } F(p) = \frac{(1 + \sigma)(2 + \sigma + 2\sigma^2) - \omega^2(1 - 2\sigma)}{(1 + \sigma)^2 + \omega^2}, \qquad (5.13\text{-}2)$$

which clearly is negative at points in the vertical strip $0 < \sigma < \frac{1}{2}$ when ω is sufficiently large in magnitude. Hence $F(p)$ is not p-r.

Since the function given is not p-r, the list of nine properties is not sufficient to insure positive reality. Even if it were, to test a given function by examining it for these properties could be very tedious. But we know that the first property, positive reality, implies all the others, and that positive reality is *necessary* if a function is to represent a driving-point immittance function of a physical one-terminal pair. If positive reality is also *sufficient* for realizability, and if a test for this property alone can be made easily, then it is reasonable to limit our attention to it. Positive reality is actually sufficient, as well as necessary for realizability; the sufficiency will be demonstrated later by actual synthesis of networks based solely on the positive reality of given functions. Anticipating this fact, we immediately realize that a practical method of testing a given function for p-r character would be extremely useful, if not essential, in the synthesis process. This one test would determine whether or not we can hope to synthesize a network whose driving-point impedance, say, is a given function $Z(p)$—it would answer the first question which prompted the division of the synthesis problem into three parts (§ 1.01): is the datum function realizable as an immittance? The development of the list of properties, which we have just shown to be insufficient for positive reality, is not wasted effort, though, as a knowledge of these basic properties is essential for understanding the manner in which networks act, and for synthesis methods to come.

To test by applying the basic definitions of positive reality is theoretically possible, but practically difficult, for they require investigation of the given function's behavior at every point in the right half plane. Yet it is not difficult to set up an equivalent definition which concerns itself only with the function's behavior on a curve, the boundary of the right half plane. This definition, which is equally a test for positive reality, arises from the Cartesian form of the definition through an application of the theorem of § 3.25. In the development below, it is assumed that a rational function is to be tested, but the test can be readily extended, with the ideas previously developed, to any function.

A positive-real function, to begin with, must in the right half plane be real when p is real.   To test a given $F(p)$ for this is a simple matter of inspecting the coefficients and making sure that all of them are real.

To find the sign of the real part of the function throughout the right half plane is a more difficult matter.   But we know, from § 3.25, that the minimum value of the real part of an analytic function, the minimum value attained as p varies over a region, occurs on the boundary of that region.   Let us take for our region the right half of the p plane, as outlined by a large-radius semicircle and the imaginary axis modified by small semicircles which bend the outline to the right around any poles that may be there, the contour C of Fig. 5.13–A.   Suppose that the radius of the

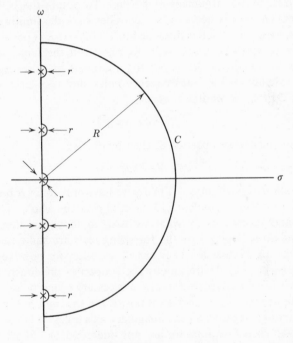

Fig. 5.13–A

large semicircle is very large (eventually to become infinite) and that the radii of the small semicircles are very small (eventually to become infinitesimal).   Then the region inside C is effectively the right half of the p plane, the region in which we have to find out whether **Re** $F(p)$ is positive.

Suppose that we test $F(p)$ for poles in the right half plane, and for poles on the imaginary axis.   (An actual test procedure is to be described later.) If there are poles on the imaginary axis, we test that they are simple and have real, positive residues. If the real-frequency poles do not obey these restrictions, or if there are any poles within the right half plane, then of course we need go no further: $F(p)$ is not p-r. But suppose this preliminary testing done, and that $F(p)$ is analytic within and on C and that the poles on the imaginary axis are simple, with real, positive residues.

The theorem of § 3.25 is now applicable, and states that $\mathbf{Re}\ F(p)$ attains its minimum value (the minimum of all values attained within C) somewhere on C. In order to determine this minimum value, we must calculate $\mathbf{Re}\ F(p)$ for all points on C. This is not quite the job it may seem, however, for the fact that the real-frequency poles are simple, with real and positive residues, insures that $\mathbf{Re}\ F(p)$ is positive on the small semicircles, by the argument of § 5.06. To obtain the behavior on the large semicircle it is necessary to consider only the limiting behavior of $F(p)$ for large $|p|$, which is discussed in § 5.07. If K is positive, and n and m differ at most by unity, then $\mathbf{Re}\ F > 0$ on the large semicircle. It remains to investigate $\mathbf{Re}\ F(j\omega)$ for all values of ω (except in the immediate vicinity of the real-frequency poles, and very large values, which are outside C). If we find that

$$\mathbf{Re}\ F(j\omega) \geqq 0 \qquad\qquad (5.13\text{--}3)$$

on the imaginary-axis part of C, then by (3.25–9)

$$\mathbf{Re}\ F(p) > 0 \qquad\qquad (5.13\text{--}4)$$

for all values of p within C. Finally we have only to let R become infinite and r infinitesimal to make (5.13–4) valid over the whole of the right half plane—and this is exactly what we wish to show, for then $F(p)$ is p-r. The conditions imposed by the foregoing tests are sufficient for positive reality, as just discussed. They are all necessary for positive reality, also, for all except (5.13–3) are among the properties previously listed in this chapter. Condition (5.13–3) is also a necessary property for p-r functions, for if the real part of a function is positive in the right half plane, the real part cannot be negative on the imaginary axis unless it has a discontinuity there—and such functions we are not interested in. If we were to add (5.13–3) to our list as the eleventh property, then the new list of ten properties (the first one excluded) would evidently be sufficient for positive reality, as well as necessary. Function (5.13–1) does in fact violate (5.13–3), even though it has the other nine properties.

The discussion above comes down to this test for positive reality: given a (rational) function of p, $F(p)$,

1. examine the coefficients in $F(p)$—they must be real;
2(a). examine the behavior of $F(p)$ at infinity—it must be as Kp, K, or K/p, K being positive;

2(b). determine whether $F(p)$ has any poles in the right half plane—$F(p)$ must be analytic there;

2(c). determine whether $F(p)$ has any poles on the imaginary axis—these poles must be simple and the residues thereat real and positive;

3. examine **Re** $F(j\omega)$—it must not be negative for any value of ω.   (5.13–5)

If at any step in the above process $F(p)$ fails to meet the requirement, $F(p)$ is not positive-real. If $F(p)$ passes all these tests, it is p-r. We have not, to be sure, considered the amount of work required in this, nor the mechanics of performing the individual tests, but we have formally set up a test which will solve the problem: given a rational function $F(p)$, determine whether it is p-r. (The test is easily modified to cover non-rational functions.) And this, of course, is what we set out to do in this section.

Basically, the test amounts to checks on these things: that the function being tested is analytic in the right half plane, that any real-frequency poles it may have are of the restricted kind allowed, and that its real part is not negative at any real frequency. The additional items, 1 and 2(a), are required, but are matters of simple inspection. The test is sufficient, and covers all necessary properties; such non-p-r properties as right-half-plane zeros, or multiple zeros on the imaginary axis, for example, will not be directly exposed, but the function will fail to pass one or more of the five tests in (5.13–5) as a consequence of these non-p-r properties.

The test is a fine example of the utility of the theory of functions of a complex variable, which here essentially converts the tedious task of examining a function over the whole of the right half plane into the equivalent, but comparatively easy, task of examining it only on a *line*, the axis of real frequencies.

Steps 1 and 2(a) require little effort; the remaining steps do require work, and we next discuss the mechanics of these individual tests.

5.14 A test for pole location

The next step, 2(b), amounts to determining where the zeros of the denominator of the given function $F(p)$ are. An exception arises if the function $F(p)$ is not in lowest terms, for then a right-half-plane zero in the denominator may be cancelled by a right-half-plane zero of the numerator. Hence a function is not to be rejected immediately if its denominator has right-half-plane zeros—one must make sure that they are not cancelled by right-half-plane zeros of the numerator; i.e., the highest common factor of the numerator and denominator must be determined, or some similar step taken to investigate this possibility. For the present, we assume $F(p)$ to be in lowest terms.

If F is written in the form (5.10–10), then the immediate task is to locate the zeros of $A_2 + pB_2 = M_2 + N_2$. If this polynomial does not fall in category (5.12–1), then $F(p)$ has right-half-plane pole(s) and is not p-r. The simplest procedure here is one which does not *locate* the zeros (their actual numerical values are not of much interest here anyway) but does determine essentially whether any are located in the right half of the plane, i.e., have positive real parts, and indicates whether there are any at real frequencies.

Development of this test requires further investigation of the properties of Hurwitz polynomials and of polynomials of the form (5.12–1). Suppose, to begin with, that

$$Q(p) = a_n p^n + a_{n-1} p^{n-1} + \cdots + a_1 p + a_0$$
$$= a_n(p - p_1)(p - p_2) \cdots (p - p_n) = A + pB = M + N \qquad (5.14\text{–}1)$$

is a Hurwitz polynomial with real coefficients. Then $p_1, p_2, \cdots, p_n$ all lie to the left of the imaginary axis, in the left half plane. From this stems an important fact: when p is in the left half plane, $Q(p)$ is in magnitude less than $Q(-p)$—or the value of the polynomial at some point p_0 in the left half plane is less in magnitude than its value at $-p_0$, the image (in the origin) of p_0. One might expect this merely because $\bar{p}_0$ is "nearer" the zeros than is $-p_0$, but a rigorous demonstration is necessary, and quite simple.

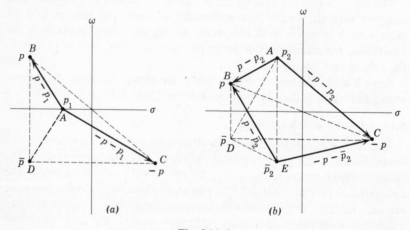

Fig. 5.14–A

In Fig. 5.14–A are shown the geometrical lines involved in the contribution of (a) the factor corresponding to a real zero of $Q(p)$, and (b) the factors corresponding to a pair of complex zeros, p_2 and $\bar{p}_2$. In (a) the factor under consideration is $(p - p_1)$; the magnitude of this factor for p in the left half plane as shown is the length of the line AB, whereas if p is reflected in the origin to $-p$, the magnitude becomes AC. From inspection of the figure, $AC > AD = AB$, or

$$|p - p_1| < |-p - p_1|, \qquad \mathbf{Re}\, p < 0, \qquad (5.14\text{--}2)$$

and this is evidently true for *any* left-half-plane position of p. In (*b*) the product of the two factors involved, $(p - p_2)(p - \bar{p}_2)$, is in magnitude equal to the product of line lengths, $AB \times EB$, for p in the left half plane as shown. When p is reflected in the origin to $-p$, the magnitude becomes $AC \times EC$. But $AC > AD = EB$, and $EC > ED = AB$, so that $(AC \times EC) > (EB \times AB)$, or

$$|(p - p_2)(p - \bar{p}_2)| < |(-p - p_2)(-p - \bar{p}_2)|, \qquad \mathbf{Re}\, p < 0. \qquad (5.14\text{--}3)$$

Since Q can have factors of these types only (for its coefficients are real, and complex zeros occur in conjugate pairs) the conclusions above apply to Q itself,

$$|Q(p)| < |Q(-p)|, \qquad \mathbf{Re}\, p < 0. \qquad (5.14\text{--}4)$$

This could equally well be written to express the fact that in the right half plane the magnitude is greater than at the image points,

$$|Q(p)| > |Q(-p)|, \qquad \mathbf{Re}\, p > 0. \qquad (5.14\text{--}5)$$

To complete the picture, on the boundary line $Q(p)$ and $Q(-p)$ are of course conjugates, so

$$|Q(p)| = |Q(-p)|, \qquad \mathbf{Re}\, p = 0. \qquad (5.14\text{--}6)$$

An alternative expression of these results is

$$\text{if} \quad \sigma < 0, \quad \text{then} \quad \left| \frac{Q(p)}{Q(-p)} \right| < 1,$$

$$\text{if} \quad \sigma = 0, \quad \text{then} \quad \left| \frac{Q(p)}{Q(-p)} \right| = 1, \qquad (5.14\text{--}7)$$

$$\text{if} \quad \sigma > 0, \quad \text{then} \quad \left| \frac{Q(p)}{Q(-p)} \right| > 1,$$

in which σ denotes the real part of p, as usual.

The set (5.14–7) is based on the assumption that all the zeros of $Q(p)$ have negative real parts; these conditions are necessarily met if Q is Hurwitz. And it is of considerable interest to know whether they are also *sufficient* to insure that Q be Hurwitz. Suppose $Q(p)$ has a zero in the right half plane, say at p_a (Fig. 5.14–B); then of course Q is infinitesimal as p approaches p_a, and generally $Q(p_a)/Q(-p_a)$ will also vanish, and contradict the third condition in (5.14–7)—which would indicate that if Q satisfies the three conditions, then Q has no right-half-plane zeros. But an anomalous behavior is perfectly possible: that Q have another zero at the point $-p_a$, in which case $Q(p_a)/Q(-p_a)$, evaluated as a limit, may well satisfy the conditions. The presence in $Q(p)$ of a right-half-plane

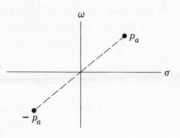

Fig. 5.14–B

zero p_a, if accompanied also by a zero at the negative (image in the origin) point $-p_a$, will give to Q a factor $(p^2 - p_a{}^2)$ which has the same value at any two points which are the negatives of each other. Such a factor in Q (or the product of any factors even in p) clearly does not enter into the calculation of the three magnitudes in (5.14–7), and so these conditions, regarded as a test, will not reveal its presence. Evidently the same holds if there is in Q an imaginary zero, accompanied by its conjugate (the factor then is $p^2 + \omega_a{}^2$) or a zero at the origin. But if there is a zero at the origin, it is a simple matter to factor out a power of p from Q and to remove it, and hereafter we assume this done. (This is not essential, but it simplifies the discussion.)

Although the set of conditions (5.14–7) does not provide a test for Hurwitz character, yet if these conditions are met by a given polynomial $Q(p)$, that polynomial must in form be a product,

$$\text{(Hurwitz polynomial)} \times \text{(even polynomial)}, \qquad (5.14\text{–}8)$$

for it is only if right-half-plane (or imaginary) zeros are accompanied by their negatives that the conditions can be met by a non-Hurwitz polynomial, and such pairs of zeros, one the negative of the other, give rise to even polynomials. The zeros of an even polynomial with real coefficients must be in pairs or groups of four, as shown in Fig. 5.14–C, or at the origin (which has been excluded here). This is a property which follows from the evenness, or from the fact that the equation formed by setting such a polynomial equal to zero can first be solved for its roots in terms of p^2 (which may be real and positive, zero, real and negative, or complex) from each of which result two roots, one the negative of the other, which must lie as in Fig. 5.14–C. Because the coefficients of the polynomial are real, the zeros of the even polynomials we meet are symmetrically located about the real axis, and because the polynomial is even, they are symmetrically located with respect to the origin. It follows that they also have symmetry with respect to the imaginary axis, and all of these symmetries are conveniently expressed by the term *quadrantal symmetry*.

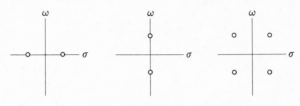

Fig. 5.14–C

Such zeros may be at the origin, real (in pairs), imaginary (in pairs), or complex (in tetrads) (cf. Fig. 5.14–C), but can occur only in these combinations or in combinations of these combinations. These properties of even polynomials are important and will be very valuable later. The presence of any even (or odd) polynomial as a factor of Q clearly has no effect on the magnitude of the ratio $Q(p)/Q(-p)$, regardless of the value of p.

Although conditions (5.14–7), regarded as a test, do not tell us, then, whether a given polynomial $Q(p)$ is Hurwitz, they do, if met, restrict $Q(p)$ to the class defined by (5.14–8)—and this will turn out to be almost as useful. The test in this form is not, however, any more practical than would be straightforward calculation of the zeros of $Q(p)$, for it requires investigation for all values of p in a half plane. A more practical test results from a consideration of the function

$$W(p) = \frac{[Q(p)/Q(-p)] + 1}{[Q(p)/Q(-p)] - 1} = \frac{Q(p) + Q(-p)}{Q(p) - Q(-p)} = \frac{\text{Ev } Q(p)}{\text{Od } Q(p)} = \frac{A}{pB} = \frac{M}{N}.$$

$$(5.14\text{–}9)$$

This function is merely the quotient of the even and odd parts of $Q(p)$. It also suggests, in the first form given, the bilinear transformation or mapping of § 3.24 (though it differs slightly in notation and signs). It relates the planes of W and of $\Phi = Q(p)/Q(-p)$; the latter in turn represents a mapping of the p plane on the Φ plane, so that we have a succession of transformations which map the p plane on the W plane— or, simply, $W(p)$ is a transformation from the p plane to a new W plane. The relations between these two last are both simple and important, and are easily obtained by combining the foregoing results. The imaginary axis of the p plane maps into the unit circle of the Φ plane, with the left half of the p plane mapped inside the circle, by (5.14–7). Then, since

$$W = \frac{\Phi + 1}{\Phi - 1},\qquad (5.14\text{–}10)$$

it follows that

$$\Phi = \frac{W + 1}{W - 1},\qquad (5.14\text{–}11)$$

and from this inversion the mapping of the W plane on the Φ plane is outlined by the following particular relations:

$$\begin{aligned}
&\text{if} \quad \mathbf{Re}\ W < 0, \quad &&\text{then} \quad &&|\Phi| < 1;\\
&\text{if} \quad \mathbf{Re}\ W = 0, \quad &&\text{then} \quad &&|\Phi| = 1; \quad\quad (5.14\text{–}12)\\
&\text{if} \quad \mathbf{Re}\ W > 0, \quad &&\text{then} \quad &&|\Phi| > 1.
\end{aligned}$$

Alternatively, viewing this as a transformation from the Φ plane to the W plane, we see that

$$\begin{aligned}
&\text{if} \quad |\Phi| < 1, \quad &&\text{then} \quad &&\mathbf{Re}\ W < 0;\\
&\text{if} \quad |\Phi| = 1, \quad &&\text{then} \quad &&\mathbf{Re}\ W = 0; \quad\quad (5.14\text{–}13)\\
&\text{if} \quad |\Phi| > 1, \quad &&\text{then} \quad &&\mathbf{Re}\ W > 0.
\end{aligned}$$

Combining (5.14–7) and (5.14–13) shows us that

$$\begin{aligned}
&\text{if} \quad \sigma < 0, \quad &&\text{then} \quad &&\mathbf{Re}\ W < 0;\\
&\text{if} \quad \sigma = 0, \quad &&\text{then} \quad &&\mathbf{Re}\ W = 0; \quad\quad (5.14\text{–}14)\\
&\text{if} \quad \sigma > 0, \quad &&\text{then} \quad &&\mathbf{Re}\ W > 0;
\end{aligned}$$

which express the fact that the function $W(p)$ maps the p plane on the W plane left half to left half, imaginary axis to imaginary axis, and right half to right half. The three planes are shown in Fig. 5.14–D, the successive mappings of the right half of the p plane being shaded. The transformation relating p and W is not an identity—far from it—but it does maintain the half-plane relationships in the manner shown. Any p-r function of p will map the right half of the p plane into the right half of a new plane, but in general it will also (unlike this transformation) map parts, at least, of the p-plane imaginary axis and of the left half of the p

plane into the right half of the new plane. Since $W(p)$ is real when p is real, and has a positive real part when $\sigma > 0$, by (5.14–14), $W(p)$ is surely p-r. Its special distinction among p-r functions in general is that it is also *odd*. [Any odd p-r function has the properties of (5.14–14) in fact.] From these two properties stem the test which we are here developing; and the transformations above had for their sole purpose the creation of this function $W(p)$, which we have seen is both p-r and odd. Properties

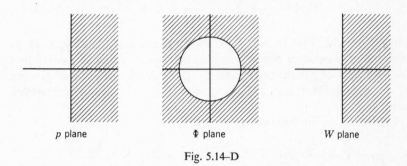

p plane Φ plane W plane

Fig. 5.14–D

of such functions beyond those immediately necessary, and their physical interpretation as driving-point immittance functions, will be developed in Chapter 6.

Since $W(p)$ is rational, p-r, and is also odd, it must at infinity have either a simple pole or simple zero, by the arguments of § 5.07, for the third type of behavior at infinity is not possible for odd functions. Hence either $W = A/pB$, or $(W)^{-1} = pB/A$ has a simple pole at infinity, and both of these functions are p-r. Let Ψ denote that one of the two which has a pole at infinity, so that

$$\Psi = \frac{a_n p^n + a_{n-2} p^{n-2} + \cdots}{a_{n-1} p^{n-1} + a_{n-3} p^{n-3} + \cdots} \tag{5.14–15}$$

in which the numerator is even and the denominator odd, or vice versa, and Ψ is of course p-r. Further, it has no poles in the left half plane, for such would have to be accompanied by their negatives (in the right half plane), because of the purely odd (or even) character of the denominator. All its poles are imaginary and therefore simple, with real and positive residues. The partial-fraction expansion of Ψ will accordingly be of the form

$$\Psi = \frac{b_0}{p} + \sum_k \frac{b_k}{p - j\omega_k} + C + \frac{a_n}{a_{n-1}} p \tag{5.14–16}$$

in which the b_k are real and positive, C is a constant, and every pole is accompanied by its conjugate (except the pole at the origin, if it is present). Further, the residues b_k are identical at two conjugate poles—for in finding the two we evaluate $(p - p_k)\Psi'(p)$ at two conjugate points, and because of the real-coefficient property the results, b_k, must be conjugate; since they are also real, the two b_k must be identical. Hence by combining in pairs the terms due to conjugate poles we can write

$$\Psi'(p) = \frac{b_0}{p} + \sum_k \frac{2b_k p}{p^2 + \omega_k^2} + C + \frac{a_n}{a_{n-1}} p. \qquad (5.14\text{-}17)$$

Since Ψ' is odd, $\Psi'(p) = -\Psi'(-p)$, which immediately requires C to be zero, the only constant which is an odd function. Notice in passing that the coefficient of p in the expansion, a_n/a_{n-1}, is simply the result of division of the denominator into the numerator in (5.14-15), and is real and positive.

Consider now the function

$$\frac{1}{\Psi_1} = \Psi' - \frac{a_n}{a_{n-1}} p = \frac{a_{n-2}' p^{n-2} + \cdots}{a_{n-1} p^{n-1} + \cdots} = \frac{b_0}{p} + \sum_k \frac{b_k}{p - j\omega_k}$$

$$= \frac{b_0}{p} + \sum_k \frac{2b_k p}{p^2 + \omega_k^2}. \qquad (5.14\text{-}18)$$

It also is odd, and it also is p-r, for the reciprocal of each term in the last expression is in form $(ap + b/p)$ in which a and b are real and positive, which is clearly p-r. At infinity, however, $1/\Psi_1$ has a zero rather than a pole. Its reciprocal, Ψ_1, has the same general properties that Ψ' has, including a pole at infinity, but its order is less than the order of Ψ' by one. We have

$$\Psi_1 = \frac{a_{n-1} p^{n-1} + a_{n-3} p^{n-3} + \cdots}{a_{n-2}' p^{n-2} + a_{n-4}' p^{n-4} + \cdots} = \frac{b_0'}{p} + \sum_k \frac{b_k'}{p - j\omega_k'} + \frac{a_{n-1}}{a_{n-2}'} p$$

$$(5.14\text{-}19)$$

in which the primes indicate coefficients different from the previous ones. Again a_{n-1}/a_{n-2}', the coefficient of p in (5.14-19), is the result of the division indicated above, and is real and positive.

In similar fashion, the function

$$\frac{1}{\Psi_2} = \Psi_1 - \frac{a_{n-1}}{a_{n-2}'} p = \frac{a_{n-3}'' p^{n-3} + \cdots}{a_{n-2}' p^{n-2} + \cdots} = \frac{b_0'}{p} + \sum_k \frac{b_k'}{p - j\omega_k'} \qquad (5.14\text{-}20)$$

is both p-r and odd, and its reciprocal, Ψ_2, has a pole at infinity. The continuing process of thus generating new Ψ's eventually terminates, for the order is reduced by one at each step. A summary of what we have been doing is

$$\Psi = \frac{a_n}{a_{n-1}} p + \frac{1}{\Psi_1} = \frac{a_n}{a_{n-1}} p + \cfrac{1}{\cfrac{a_{n-1}}{a_{n-2}} p + \cfrac{1}{\Psi_2}}$$

$$= c_1 p + \cfrac{1}{c_2 p + \cfrac{1}{c_3 p + \cfrac{1}{\Psi_3}}}$$

$$= c_1 p + \cfrac{1}{c_2 p + \cfrac{1}{c_3 p + \cfrac{1}{c_4 p + \cfrac{1}{\ddots}}}}$$

$$\cdots + \frac{1}{c_n p}$$

(5.14–21)

in which the (real, positive) coefficients $c_1, c_2, \cdots, c_n$ replace the ratios of a's. This is called a *continued-fraction expansion* of the function Ψ. [There is a well-developed theory of continued-fraction expansions (FR 2, PE 1, WA 2), but it need not distract us.] To show that this particular continued-fraction expansion terminates, consider the orders of the successive Ψ's, or, better, the degrees of their numerators and denominators, tabulated in Table 5.14–A. From this it is clear that there are in general only n "terms" in the continued-fraction expansion, as shown in (5.14–21). (An exceptional case will be discussed shortly.)

Table 5.14–A

Function	Degree of Numerator	Degree of Denominator
Ψ	n	$n - 1$
Ψ_1	$n - 1$	$n - 2$
Ψ_2	$n - 2$	$n - 3$
Ψ_3	$n - 3$	$n - 4$
$\cdots$	$\cdots$	$\cdots$
Ψ_{n-2}	2	1
Ψ_{n-1}	1	0

To recapitulate: if a given polynomial $Q(p)$ is the product of a Hurwitz polynomial with real coefficients and an even polynomial, then Ψ, the quotient of its even and odd parts or of its odd and even parts (whichever has a pole at infinity), has the continued-fraction expansion of (5.14–21) in which c_1, c_2, c_3, $\cdots$, c_n are real and positive. Conversely, if this quotient Ψ' has such a continued-fraction expansion, then Ψ' is odd (by inspection) and is also p-r (for $c_n p$ is p-r, $1/c_n p$ is p-r, $c_{n-1}p + 1/c_n p$ is p-r, etc., by direct application of the rectangular definition of positive reality). Hence

$$\text{if} \quad \sigma > 0, \qquad \mathbf{Re}\,\Psi' > 0;$$
$$\text{if} \quad \sigma = 0, \qquad \mathbf{Re}\,\Psi' = 0; \qquad\qquad (5.14\text{–}22)$$
$$\text{if} \quad \sigma < 0, \qquad \mathbf{Re}\,\Psi' < 0.$$

Then

$$\Phi = \frac{\Psi' + 1}{\Psi' - 1} = \pm\,\frac{\mathbf{Ev}\,Q + \mathbf{Od}\,Q}{\mathbf{Ev}\,Q - \mathbf{Od}\,Q} = \pm\,\frac{Q(p)}{Q(-p)} \qquad (5.14\text{–}23)$$

(the sign depending on which quotient was selected above) has the property

$$\text{if} \quad \sigma > 0, \qquad |\Phi| = \left|\frac{Q(p)}{Q(-p)}\right| > 1;$$

$$\text{if} \quad \sigma = 0, \qquad |\Phi| = \left|\frac{Q(p)}{Q(-p)}\right| = 1; \qquad (5.14\text{–}24)$$

$$\text{if} \quad \sigma < 0, \qquad |\Phi| = \left|\frac{Q(p)}{Q(-p)}\right| < 1.$$

Hence, by the discussion of (5.14–7), $Q(p)$ is the product of a Hurwitz polynomial and an even polynomial.

The continued-fraction expansion given above is quite easy to obtain, given the polynomial Q, for determination of c_1 amounts merely to performing an ordinary long division. The remainder fraction is then inverted, and another long division is performed. The new remainder fraction is inverted, and the process repeated until it terminates. The coefficients of p in the quotients are c_1, c_2, $\cdots$, c_n. If these are all positive, then Q is of the form (5.14–8); if any c is negative, then Q is not such, but contains additional factor(s) representing one or more zeros in the right half plane. Further, the presence of the even polynomial is clearly indicated in the process—and more than that, it is specifically evaluated. Suppose Q has the expression

$$Q(p) = (M_1 + N_1)(b_0 + b_2 p^2 + \cdots + b_{2m} p^{2m})$$
$$= (M_1 + N_1)E(p) = M_1 E + N_1 E = M + N, \quad (5.14\text{–}25)$$

in which $(M_1 + N_1)$ is a Hurwitz polynomial and $E(p)$ an even polynomial. Note that $E(p)$ must be a factor of *both* the even part of Q and the odd part of Q. Then the test developed above proceeds, on the assumption that the even part of Q is of higher degree than the odd part, as follows. (It would make no difference if the situation were the reverse.)

$$W = \frac{M}{N} = \frac{M_1 E}{N_1 E} = \Psi = c_1 p + \frac{1}{\Psi_1}. \qquad (5.14\text{--}26)$$

The E's (common factors) will not automatically be cancelled in setting up W, for the numerator and denominator are not given in factored form. Then

$$\frac{1}{\Psi_1} = \frac{M_1 E}{N_1 E} - c_1 p = \frac{M_1 E - c_1 N_1 E p}{N_1 E} = \frac{(M_1 - c_1 N_1 p)E}{N_1 E} = \frac{M_2 E}{N_1 E};$$

$$\Psi_1 = \frac{N_1 E}{M_2 E} = c_2 p + \frac{1}{\Psi_2};$$

$$\Psi_2 = \frac{M_2 E}{(N_1 E - c_2 M_2 p)E} = \frac{M_2 E}{N_2 E} = c_3 p + \frac{1}{\Psi_3}; \qquad (5.14\text{--}27)$$

$$\cdots \cdots \cdots \cdots \cdots$$

$$\Psi_{n-2} = \frac{(ap^2 + b)E}{cpE} = \frac{a}{c} p + \frac{bE}{cpE};$$

$$\Psi_{n-1} = \frac{cpE}{bE} = c_n p.$$

Here a, b, and c are the real, positive constants appearing at this last stage. When the final division is made, the work of dividing bE into cpE will be

$$bb_{2m}p^{2m} + bb_{2m-2}p^{2m-2} + \cdots \overline{)cb_{2m}p^{2m+1} + cb_{2m-2}p^{2m-1} + \cdots} \left(\frac{c}{b} p = c_n p\right.$$

$$\frac{cb_{2m}p^{2m+1} + cb_{2m-2}p^{2m-1} + \cdots}{0 \qquad\qquad 0 \qquad\qquad \cdots}.$$

$$(5.14\text{--}28)$$

Previous to this stage there will have been no indication of E's existence; the c's will appear just as though E were not in Q. But in this last step the remainder will consist of the sequence of zeros shown above (rather than of a single zero if E is absent or, better, if E is merely a constant). This indicates the presence of E, and of course the subtrahend immediately above the zeros is the factor E, except for a constant multiplier, and perhaps for a factor p (to be discarded, if present). Notice also that the c_1, c_2, $\cdots$, c_n obtained with E present are exactly the same as would be obtained if E were absent and only $(M_1 + N_1)$ were being tested. Hence this test provides a means of separating out any even polynomial which may be a factor of a given polynomial, and simultaneously testing the noneven factor for Hurwitz character. (Zeros at the origin are first to be removed, as mentioned above.)

Although the test does not directly answer the immediate question— Does the given $F(p)$, which is being tested for positive reality, have any poles in the right half plane?—it does remove the product of any even factors which the denominator of $F(p)$ may have, and does state whether the remaining part of the denominator is Hurwitz or has one or more right-half-plane zeros.

If the test indicates an even factor $E(p)$, then $E(p)$ must be tested by itself for right-half-plane zeros. This may be done by factoring in simple cases, by plotting, or by use of Sturm's theorem (discussed in § 5.15). If the number of zeros appearing at positive values of ω^2 (i.e., at real frequencies) is not equal to the total number of zeros of E, then some are in the right half plane (corresponding to nonreal values of ω). If F has real-frequency poles (except at the origin, which are obvious poles), the denominator will have such a factor E, and this test will reveal such poles, which can then be tested for simple character, and the residues can be examined for real, positive character.

The application of this test in the process of testing a given $F(p)$ is

1. to remove from the denominator of $F(p)$ the factor causing a zero thereof at the origin, if any;
2. to perform the sequence of division, inversion, division, inversion, · · · on the even and odd parts of the reduced denominator;
3. to examine the coefficients of p in the resulting quotients—they must all be positive if the denominator is to have all of its zeros in the left half plane;
4. if the last step in the sequence above shows the denominator of F to have an even-polynomial factor, or if the (reduced) denominator is such begin with, this polynomial (determined in the process) is to be investigated at real frequencies—if not all of its zeros are there, the denominator of F has right-half-plane zero(s); if all of the zeros are at real frequencies, these are real-frequency poles of F and their orders and residues must be checked.   (5.14–29)

If right-half-plane zeros are indicated in step 3 or in step 4, the numerator of $F(p)$ must also be examined to make sure that these zeros do not also occur there, for if they do, F may not have right-half-plane poles. The same test can be applied to the numerator polynomial. If the result is that right-half-plane zeros are present, then they must be determined, for both numerator and denominator, for comparison. Fortunately F is likely to be in lowest terms, so that this work is not necessary. It is occasionally very useful, however, deliberately to insert right-half-plane zeros in both numerator and denominator of a p-r function, as an aid in synthesis (cf. Chapter 10).

If multiple imaginary zeros are indicated in step 4, the numerator of $F(p)$ must also be examined at these points, for similar reasons, before rejecting $F(p)$. This includes the zero at the origin, if present, but that should have been taken care of in the beginning.

The description of the mechanics of a method of carrying out steps 2(b) and 2(c) of the positive-reality test (5.13–5) is thus nearly complete. It remains only to illustrate the process with numerical examples, to clarify the technique. In the following, the given polynomial $Q(p)$ represents the denominator of $F(p)$, which is assumed to be in lowest terms.

Example 1. $Q(p) = p^5 + 16p^4 + 2p^2 + 3p + 6$. Since there is a zero coefficient (the third power of p is missing) and this polynomial is not in the special category of purely odd and purely even polynomials, there is at least one zero of $Q(p)$ in the right half plane, and no further testing is necessary.

Example 2. $Q(p) = p^4 + 7p^3 - 3p^2 + 4p + 10$. Since one coefficient is negative (and not all of the coefficients are negative), this need not be tested—Q has a right-half-plane zero.

Example 3. $Q(p) = 192p^4 + 48p^3 + 76p^2 + 15p + 3$. There are no apparent flaws, so we proceed to the test developed in this section. The successive divisions can be arranged under each other in the following manner, to save some unnecessary rewriting.   Here

$$\Psi = \frac{192p^4 + 76p^2 + 3}{48p^3 + 15p}$$

and the test is

$$48p^3 + 15p)\overline{192p^4 + 76p^2 + 3}(4p \leftarrow \text{first division}$$
$$\underline{192p^4 + 60p^2}$$
$$16p^2 + 3)\overline{48p^3 + 15p}(3p \leftarrow \text{second division}$$
$$\underline{48p^3 + 9p}$$
$$6p)\overline{16p^2 + 3}(2.667p \leftarrow \text{third division}$$
$$\underline{16p^2}$$
$$3)\overline{6p}(2p \leftarrow \text{fourth division}$$
$$\underline{6p}$$
$$0 \ .$$

The divisions can be performed with detached coefficients, with a corresponding saving in writing, as

```
48   15)192  76   3(4
         192  60
          ─────────
          16   3)48   15(3
                  48    9
                  ──────────
                   6)16   3(2.667
                      16
                      ─────────
                       3)6(2
                         6
                         ─
                         0
```

Hence

$$\Psi = 4p + \cfrac{1}{3p + \cfrac{1}{2.667p + \cfrac{1}{2p}}}$$

The numbers c_1, c_2, c_3, c_4 are all (real and) positive, there is no even factor; therefore all the zeros of $Q(p)$ are in the left half plane, and F is satisfactory for positive reality as far as this part of the test goes.

Example 4. $Q(p) = 4.2p^6 + 2.1p^5 + 17.6p^4 + 7.3p^3 + 15p^2 + 3p$. There is a simple zero at the origin; after its removal we have the polynomial $(4.2p^5 + 2.1p^4 + 17.6p^3 + 7.3p^2 + 15p + 3)$. Its test is

```
2.1  7.3  3)4.2  17.6  15(2
              4.2  14.6   6
             ─────────────
              3.0   9)2.1  7.3  3(0.7
                       2.1  6.3
                      ─────────
                       1.0  3)3.0  9(3
                            3.0  9
                           ───────
                            0    0  .
```

$Q(p)$ is therefore the product of $(3p^2 + 9)$ and a Hurwitz polynomial (for c_1, c_2, c_3 are positive and two c's are missing). $F(p)$ has simple poles at $p = \pm j\sqrt{3}$, as well as at the origin (and the residues at these poles require investigation), but no right-half-plane poles and no other imaginary poles.

Example 5. $Q(p) = 2p^6 + 26p^4 + 94p^2 + 70$. There are missing powers here, but this is a purely even polynomial, which may be satisfactory. To find out, we examine

$$Q(j\omega) = -2\omega^6 + 26\omega^4 - 94\omega^2 + 70.$$

Application of Sturm's theorem (Example 10 of § 5.15) shows this, regarded as a polynomial in ω^2, to have three simple zeros at real positive values of ω^2; i.e., the zeros of $Q(p)$ are all imaginary and simple. It is still necessary to determine the residues at the corresponding poles of $F(p)$—and if these are real and positive, then $F(p)$ passes this part of the test for positive reality.

Example 6. $Q(p) = p^4 + 3p^3 + 2p^2 + p + 1$. The test is

```
3  1)1  2        1(0.333
     1  0.333
    ──────────
     1.667  1)3  1  (1.8
              3  1.8
             ────────
            -0.8)1.667  1(-2.08  .
```

Since c_3 is negative, it is unnecessary to carry the test further; $Q(p)$ has at least one zero in the right half plane. (One might equally well have stopped when the remainder -0.8 appeared.)

Example 7. $Q(p) = 2p^7 + 8p^6 + 16p^5 + 22p^4 + 28p^3 + 28p^2 + 24p + 12$. The test is

```
8   22   28   12)2   16    28   24(0.25
              2    5.5    7    3
              10.5   21   21)8    22    28    12(0.761
                          8     16    16
                          6     12    12)10.5   21   21(1.75
                                       10.5   21   21
                                        0     0    0 .
```

$Q(p)$ is therefore the product of a Hurwitz polynomial and $(p^4 + 2p^2 + 2)$. Since the latter has two zeros in the right half plane, so also does $Q(p)$.

Example 8. $Q(p) = p^7 + 8p^5 + 17.5p^3 + 12.5p$. This is purely odd, and may be admissible. On removal of the zero at the origin, we have left $Q_1 = p^6 + 8p^4 + 17.5p^2 + 12.5$. Investigation through the use of Sturm's theorem (Example 11, § 5.15) discloses that there is but one real positive value of ω^2 for which $Q_1 = 0$. Since Q_1 has three zeros (in terms of ω^2), either there is a multiple zero at that real positive value of ω^2, or Q_1 has zeros at values of ω^2 which are not real and positive. In either case, the requirements for positive reality are not met, and $F(p)$ is not p-r.

The convenient numbers in these examples illustrate the principle perfectly well, but would usually be replaced in practical work, of course, by nonintegral numbers (though the general order of magnitude, with proper normalization, need not often be much different).

Steps $2(b)$ and part of step $2(c)$ of the test for positive reality (5.13–5) can be taken, then, by the method above; to check the residues at real-frequency simple poles which appear requires only application of the methods of § 3.21 to their calculation. There still remains step 3 to discuss.

5.15 Tests for sign of Re $F(j\omega)$

Step 3 requires that the real part of $F(p)$, or, alternatively, the angle of $F(p)$ be examined at all points on the imaginary axis, to determine whether it goes negative at any such point. This is apt to be the most laborious step, but if the given $F(p)$ passes the earlier tests, this one must then be taken.

If

$$F(p) = \frac{M_1 + N_1}{M_2 + N_2}, \qquad (5.15\text{–}1)$$

then

$$\mathrm{Re}\ F(j\omega) = [\mathrm{Ev}\ F(p)]_{p=j\omega} = \left(\frac{M_1 M_2 - N_1 N_2}{M_2^2 - N_2^2} \right)_{p=j\omega} \qquad (5.15\text{–}2)$$

as discussed in § 5.11 and § 5.10. The denominator in this expression is the square of the magnitude of the complex number $(M_2 + N_2)$, for at real frequencies M_2 is real and N_2 is imaginary. Hence $(M_2^2 - N_2^2)$ must be positive for all ω, and need not be considered here. Should $F(p)$

have real-frequency poles, then it might seem that $\mathbf{Re}\,F(j\omega)$ would there become infinite. Such poles cannot occur if the function $F(p)$ has passed test 2(c), but we need not demonstrate this here, for even if $(M_2{}^2 - N_2{}^2)$ did vanish at some frequency, it would not affect the *sign* of $\mathbf{Re}\,F(j\omega)$, because $(M_2{}^2 - N_2{}^2)$ is certainly not negative for any value of ω. It is necessary, however, to evaluate the numerator, $(M_1 M_2 - N_1 N_2)$, which will be a polynomial in ω^2. If this polynomial is positive at some one (real) frequency, and has no odd-order zeros at real values of ω, then it will be positive (or zero) at all real frequencies, and this of course is what is required of positive-real functions.

In some cases, mere inspection of the polynomial $(M_1 M_2 - N_1 N_2)$ will be enough (as when all the coefficients of powers of ω^2 have the same sign, when the polynomial definitely remains positive—or when the coefficient of the leading power is negative and the polynomial definitely goes negative). In many cases a rough plot, with perhaps more detailed sketching in regions where doubt arises, provides a fairly rapid, practical method of testing $\mathbf{Re}\,F(j\omega)$. Additional mathematical apparatus is available for this test, however (US 1, e.g.), in *Sturm's theorem* which is a part of the theory of equations. If the order of $F(p)$ is high, this may be a useful tool; hence it is worth description.

Suppose the polynomial $(M_1 M_2 - N_1 N_2)$ computed, $j\omega$ substituted for p, and then the substitution $\omega^2 = x$ made. Since the polynomial is even in ω, the result will be a polynomial in x (with real coefficients) in whose values at real, positive values of x we are interested,

$$f(x) = a_n x^n + a_{n-1} x^{n-1} + \cdots + a_1 x + a_0. \qquad (5.15\text{--}3)$$

To apply Sturm's theorem it is necessary to compute a sequence of related polynomials. Of these the first is simply the derivative of the given polynomial,

$$f_1 = f'(x) = n a_n x^{n-1} + (n-1) a_{n-1} x^{n-1} + \cdots + a_1. \qquad (5.15\text{--}4)$$

The second is found by carrying out the division f/f_1, and writing, as f_2, the remainder with altered sign; i.e., f_2 is defined by

$$f = q_1 f_1 - f_2 \qquad (5.15\text{--}5)$$

in which q_1 (a polynomial) represents the quotient of f/f_1, and $(-f_2)$ the remainder. The third and higher polynomials, f_3, f_4, $\cdots$, are defined similarly:

$$f_1 = q_2 f_2 - f_3,$$
$$f_2 = q_3 f_3 - f_4,$$
$$\cdots \cdots \cdots \qquad (5.15\text{--}6)$$
$$f_{m-2} = q_{m-1} f_{m-1} - f_m.$$

The nature of the Sturm functions $f_1, f_2, f_3, \cdots$ depends on the multiplicity of the zeros of $f(x)$. Suppose first that $f(x)$ has no multiple zeros, that all of its zeros are simple. Then f_1 and f have no common factor, for when $f = 0$ the derivative, f', cannot be zero. Then, from (5.15–5), f_2 and f_1 have no common factor (for if they had, it would also be a factor of f). The polynomial f_2, incidentally, is of degree less than the degree of f_1. Similarly, f_3 and f_2 have no common factor, and f_3 is a polynomial of degree less than the degree of f_2. Continuing in this fashion, we conclude that no two consecutive f's can have any common factors, and that some f, say f_m ($m \leq n$), is a polynomial of degree zero, i.e., a constant, and it is not zero (else the two previous f's would have common factors). Then $f_{m+1} = 0$, and we consider the sequence only through f_m.

The utility of these Sturm functions $f_1, f_2, f_3, \cdots, f_m$ stems from the fact that, once they are computed, it is a simple matter to determine by inspection how many of the zeros of $f(x)$ (still assumed all to be simple) lie at real, positive values of x—and this is our concern. This fact depends on the behavior of the *signs* of these f's as x varies. The sign of f_i can change only at a value of x such that $f_i = 0$, i.e., at a zero of f_i, say x_0. From the preceding discussion of common factors we know that neither $f_{i-1}(x_0)$ nor $f_{i+1}(x_0)$ is zero. For this reason we can mark off a range of variation of x, from $(x_0 - k)$ through x_0 to $(x_0 + k)$ (k being real and positive, though small), in which neither f_{i-1} nor f_{i+1} vanishes, and neither changes sign. Further, the two numbers $f_{i-1}(x_0)$ and $f_{i+1}(x_0)$ are opposite in sign, from the appropriate equation in (5.15–6) or (5.15–5), since $f_i(x_0) = 0$. The signs of $f_i(x_0 - k)$ and $f_i(x_0 + k)$ may or may not differ, and it is not necessary to know. The various possibilities as to signs of these three f's at these three points are summed up in Table

Table 5.15–A

$x:$ $f:$	$(x_0 - k)$	x_0	$(x_0 + k)$	$(x_0 - k)$	x_0	$(x_0 + k)$
f_{i-1}	$+$	$+$	$+$	$-$	$-$	$-$
f_i	$\pm$	0	$\pm$	$\pm$	0	$\pm$
f_{i+1}	$-$	$-$	$-$	$+$	$+$	$+$

5.15–A in which $\pm$ indicates an undetermined sign, and the two possibilities as to sign of $f_{i-1}(x_0)$ are considered separately.

What is of importance here is the number of changes in sign in the sequence of f's at $x = x_0 - k$ in comparison with the number of changes of sign in the sequence of f's at $x = x_0 + k$. In each of the eight possible cases there is *one* change of sign in the sequence (f_{i-1}, f_i, f_{i+1}) at $x = x_0 - k$, and *one* change of sign in the sequence at $x = x_0 + k$; the number of changes of sign in the sequence *does not change* as x passes through x_0, a zero of $f_i(x)$. The number of changes of sign in the sequence does not change as x passes through any value of x not a zero of one of the f's, for all signs remain the same. The argument above applies at any zero of the functions $f_1, f_2, f_3, \cdots, f_{m-1}$. It does not, however, apply at a zero of $f(x)$, which has no "preceding" function. At such a value of x, say x_0, $f(x)$ must change sign, whereas $f'(x) = f_1$ cannot change sign because of our assumption of simple zeros only in $f(x)$. The summary of sign changes for this case is that of Table 5.15–B, and there are but two possibilities. In each case the number of changes of sign in the sequence (f, f_1) is *one* just before the zero, and is *zero* just after: the number of changes of sign *decreases by one* as x (increasing) goes through a zero of $f(x)$.

The number of changes of sign in the entire sequence $(f, f_1, f_2, \cdots, f_m)$, as x increases, thus decreases by one when x goes through a zero of $f(x)$, and does not change at any other value of x, if $f(x)$ has only simple zeros.

Table 5.15–B

x: f:	$(x_0 - k)$	x_0	$(x_0 + k)$	$(x_0 - k)$	x_0	$(x_0 + k)$
$f(x)$	+	0	−	−	0	+
f_1	−	−	−	+	+	+

Hence if we compute this number of changes of sign at $x = 0$, and again for very large positive values of x,

the decrease in the number of changes of sign is equal to the number of zeros of $f(x)$ (assumed simple) occurring for real, positive values of x. (5.15–7)

Should any f have the value zero, and hence no sign, it is simply to be ignored; consideration of the tables above shows the argument still valid. This is a very simple method of determining the number of real, positive roots of $f(x) = 0$ (or, for that matter, the number of roots lying between any two real values of x).

To make the test generally applicable, we must further consider what happens if $f(x)$ has multiple zeros. When $f(x)$ has multiple zeros, the nature of the sequence $(f, f_1, f_2, \cdot \cdot \cdot)$ is somewhat different. Suppose $f(x)$ split into two factors, one of which, $g(x)$, has all the zeros of $f(x)$, but only as simple, first-order zeros; the other factor, $h(x)$, has the remaining factors of $f(x)$:

$$f(x) = a_n x^n + a_{n-1} x^{n-1} + \cdot \cdot \cdot + a_1 x + a_0$$
$$= \underbrace{[a_n(\ )(\ )(\ ) \cdot \cdot \cdot]}_{g(x)} \underbrace{[(\ )(\ )(\ ) \cdot \cdot \cdot]}_{h(x)} \qquad (5.15\text{--}8)$$

Here $(\ )$ indicates a factor like $(x - x_1)$, possibly raised to some higher power if in $h(x)$. We now define a *distinct zero* of $f(x)$ as a distinct value of x for which $f(x) = 0$, regardless of the order of the zero at that point. Then $f(x)$ may have as many as n distinct zeros or as few as one distinct zero, depending on the orders of its zeros; $g(x)$ has a simple zero at each of the distinct zeros of $f(x)$, and the excess (duplicate) factors in $f(x)$ go to form $h(x)$. The zeros of $h(x)$ are located at the multiple zeros of $f(x)$, and in $h(x)$ the multiplicities of the zeros are each one less than the multiplicities of the corresponding zeros in $f(x)$. Then

$$f_1(x) = f'(x) = na_n x^{n-1} + (n-1)a_{n-1} x^{n-2} + \cdot \cdot \cdot + a_1$$
$$= \underbrace{[na_n(\ )(\ )(\ ) \cdot \cdot \cdot]}_{g_1(x)} h(x). \qquad (5.15\text{--}9)$$

The function $h(x)$ appears here again *in toto*, for each multiple zero of $f(x)$ appears in $f'(x)$ with its multiplicity reduced by one, and this is exactly how $h(x)$ was defined. Further, the multiple zeros of $f(x)$ appear in $f_1(x)$ *only* in $h(x)$. The simple zeros of $f(x)$ cannot be zeros of $f'(x)$, i.e., of $f_1(x)$, for at a simple zero $f'(x) \neq 0$. Hence the factors in the bracket, $g_1(x)$, are new factors and do not vanish at any zero of $f(x)$. The highest common factor of f and f_1 (except possibly for a constant multiplier) is $h(x)$, and the appearance of this common factor $h(x)$ is the chief change in the nature of the Sturm functions. A strong resemblance between the work of applying Sturm's theorem and that of finding the highest common factor of two polynomials becomes apparent here.

By comparing (5.15–8) and (5.15–9) we see that

$$f(x) = \frac{g(x)}{g_1(x)} f_1(x), \qquad (5.15\text{--}10)$$

and from this it is easy to discover the general nature of the next function in the sequence, f_2, which is defined by (5.15–5), just as in the previous case. Since $g(x)$ and $g_1(x)$ have no common factors, and g is of degree one more than the degree of g_1, we have

$$f(x) = \left[\frac{1}{n} x + A + \frac{-g_2(x)}{g_1(x)} \right] f_1 = q_1 f_1 - f_2 \qquad (5.15\text{-}11)$$

in which A is a constant, and $g_2(x)$ is a polynomial (of degree less than that of g_1), the negative of the remainder in the division of f_1 into f.

$$q_1 = \frac{1}{n} x + A,$$

$$f_2 = \frac{g_2(x)}{g_1(x)} f_1 = g_2(x) h(x). \qquad (5.15\text{-}12)$$

The common factor $h(x)$ in f_1 and f_2 is the highest common factor, for f and f_1 have no common factor except h, i.e., $g_2(x)$ and $g_1(x)$ have no common factor (except perhaps a constant).

In similar fashion,

$$f_1 = \frac{g_1(x)}{g_2(x)} f_2(x) = q_2 f_2 - f_3 \qquad (5.15\text{-}13)$$

$$= \left[\text{polynomial} + \frac{-g_3(x)}{g_2(x)} \right] f_2$$

$$= (\text{polynomial}) f_2 - g_3(x) h(x).$$

Hence

$$f_3(x) = g_3(x) h(x) \qquad (5.15\text{-}14)$$

and much as before, g_2 and g_3 have no common zeros, or $h(x)$ is the highest common factor of f_2 and f_3. The degree of g_3 is less than the degree of g_2. This process will continue, each f_i being the product of $h(x)$ and a polynomial $g_i(x)$, the degree of g_i decreasing at each step, until a stage, say the $(m + 1)$st, is reached at which $g_{m+1} = 0$ and hence f_{m+1} is identically zero. This must occur, for the degree of g_i decreases at each step and eventually reaches zero, and the remainder in the next division will be zero. Since $f_{m+1} = 0$,

$$f_{m-1} = g_{m-1} h = q_m f_m + 0 = q_m (g_m h) + 0 \qquad (5.15\text{-}15)$$

and g_m is therefore a nonzero constant. [If it were not, then g_m and g_{m-1} would have a common factor, by (5.15-15).] Our interest, as in the first (simple-zero) case, is in the sequence of Sturm functions $(f_1, f_2, \cdots, f_m)$, f_m being the last function which is not identically zero.

In $g(x)$ we have a polynomial to which (5.15-7) can be applied.

Although the sequence $(g_1, g_2, g_3, \cdots)$ is not the set of Sturm functions for the polynomial $g(x)$, still these g_i can be used as would the Sturm functions, to determine the number of zeros of $g(x)$ in an interval of x. As x passes through a value x_0 which causes $g_i(x)$ to vanish, g_i may or may not change sign; g_{i-1} and g_{i+1} do *not* change sign, for consecutive members of the sequence have no common factors. Hence Table 5.15–A, with f everywhere replaced by g, applies here, and the number of changes of sign in the sequence (g_{i-1}, g_i, g_{i+1}) does not change as x passes through a zero of $g_i(x)$. Just as before, however, there is a decrease of one in the number of changes of sign in the complete sequence $(g, g_1, g_2, \cdots, g_m)$ as x passes through a zero of $g(x)$. Hence (5.15–7) can be applied, f being everywhere replaced by g. As far as changes of sign go, however, the sequence of Sturm functions in this the general case where $f(x)$ may have multiple zeros is equally useful, and the g's need not be separated out (which would require extra work). For we have, in résumé,

$$f(x) = g(x)h(x),$$
$$f_1 = g_1 h,$$
$$f_2 = g_2 h,$$
$$f_3 = g_3 h,$$
$$\cdots \cdots$$
$$f_m = g_m h,$$

(5.15–16)

and at any value of x which is not a zero of $h(x)$ the sign of each f_i will either be the same as that of g (if $h > 0$) or the opposite (if $h < 0$). The number of changes of sign in the sequence $(f, f_1, f_2, \cdots, f_m)$ is accordingly the same as that in the sequence $(g, g_1, g_2, \cdots, g_m)$. [At a value of x for which $h(x) = 0$, all the members of the f sequence vanish, and there are no signs to consider; as x goes through such a value the signs of all the g's are affected in the same manner, to become the signs of the f's.] Hence the decrease in the number of changes of sign in the f sequence, when it is computed first at $x = 0$, and then for very large values of x, gives the number of zeros of $g(x)$ which occur at real, positive values of x. But $f(x)$ has no distinct zeros apart from the zeros of g; the only difference between f and g in regard to zeros is that f has perhaps multiple zeros in place of the simple zeros of g, but they do not occur at any points which are not zeros of g. Hence the test of the f's will determine the number of distinct real, positive zeros of $f(x)$. This is Sturm's theorem:

the number of distinct, real roots of $f(x) = 0$ between $x = x_1$ and $x = x_2$ is equal to $|\Delta(x_1) - \Delta(x_2)|$, in which $\Delta(x)$ is the number of changes of sign in the sequence $(f, f_1, f_2, \cdots, f_m)$ when the independent variable has the value x.

(5.15–17)

The Sturm functions $f, f_1, f_2, \cdots$ are to be computed according to the previous rules, regardless of the multiplicities of the zeros of $f(x)$, which are, of course, unknown. Should x_1 or x_2 happen to be a zero of $f(x)$, this will become evident immediately, for $f(x_1)$ or $f(x_2)$ will vanish. Thus one zero has been located, and the factor $(x - x_1)$ or $(x - x_2)$ may be divided out of $f(x)$, and tests made on the reduced polynomial; or the original polynomial may be tested, the zero being ignored in computing the changes in sign (consideration of Table 5.15–B will justify this); or the evaluations may be made at a value of x an infinitesimal distance away. In the application of Sturm's theorem here, we take $x_1 = 0$, and x_2 to be some very large (real) positive value of x such that there can be no zeros beyond it. The sign of any Sturm function at $x = 0$ is of course the sign of the constant term in that function; the sign for very large values of x is the sign of the coefficient of the highest power of x in that f. Determination of the signs in this application is easy—the labor involved in applying Sturm's theorem is primarily in the calculation of the sequence of Sturm functions.

In general, the calculation of the Sturm functions gives a sequence of polynomials $f, f_1, f_2, \cdots, f_m$ in which f_m is the last function that is not identically zero. Now

$$f_m = g_m h \qquad (5.15\text{–}18)$$

in which $h(x)$ has zeros at every point where f has a multiple zero, and g_m is a constant. If $f(x)$ has simple zeros only, then h is a constant and f_m is a constant; if $f(x)$ has any multiple zeros, then h is a polynomial with these zeros (the multiplicities each reduced by one). Hence we can by inspection of f_m determine whether $f(x)$ has multiple zeros:

if f_m is a constant, $f(x)$ has no multiple zeros; if f_m is a polynomial, then $f(x)$ has multiple zeros and the zeros of f_m are these multiple zeros of $f(x)$, the multiplicities each being reduced by one. $\qquad (5.15\text{–}19)$

The polynomial $h(x)$ is f_m as determined above, except for a constant multiplier, which of course does not affect the zeros. This may be divided into f, if desired, to obtain $g(x)$. We then have separated f into the polynomials $g(x)$ and $h(x)$:

$$f(x) = g(x)h(x) \qquad (5.15\text{–}20)$$

in which g contains all the zeros of f, but only as simple zeros, and h contains the excess factors due to multiple zeros. Application of the entire process to the polynomial h will similarly split it into two polynomials,

$$h(x) = g_a(x)h_a(x) \qquad (5.15\text{–}21)$$

in which g_a contains all the second- and higher-order zeros of $f(x)$, but only as simple zeros, and h_a contains the excess factors due to zeros of multiplicity greater than two. A third application, this time to h_a, gives

$$h_a(x) = g_b(x)h_b(x) \qquad (5.15\text{–}22)$$

in which g_b contains all the third- and higher-order zeros of $f(x)$ but only as simple zeros, and h_b contains the excess factors due to zeros of multiplicity greater than three. Repeated applications lead eventually to

$$h_i(x) = g_i(x) \times \text{constant} \qquad (5.15\text{–}23)$$

in which all the zeros of $f(x)$ of highest multiplicity appear as simple zeros, and i indicates this highest multiplicity. The original polynomial $f(x)$ has then been factored;

$$f = g \times g_a \times g_b \cdots g_i \times \text{constant} \qquad (5.15\text{–}24)$$

where

g contains all the zeros of $f(x)$, as first-order zeros;
g_a contains all the second- and higher-order zeros of $f(x)$ as first-order zeros;
g_b contains all the third- and higher-order zeros of $f(x)$ as first-order zeros;

.

.

.

g_i contains all the highest-order zeros of $f(x)$ as first-order zeros. (5.15–25)

This procedure may assist in factoring polynomials, but generally it will not be necessary. Our aim here is merely to determine whether $f(x)$ has any real, positive, odd-order zeros. To determine this, much of the above procedure is usually unnecessary. What is necessary is outlined below.

Given a function to be examined, first remove the zero at $x = 0$, if present, by dividing out a power of x. (This step is optional.) Then with the reduced function, $f(x)$, compute the sequence of Sturm functions, $(f_1, f_2, f_3, \cdots, f_m)$, f_m being the last function which is not identically zero. Now tabulate the signs of the members of the sequence $(f, f_1, f_2, f_3, \cdots, f_m)$ at $x = 0$—which calls merely for observing the sign of the constant term in each—and determine the number of changes of sign in the sequence. (If any f is zero, that member has no sign and is to be ignored; Table 5.15–A shows that this has no effect on the validity of the process.) Repeat this tabulation for very large, positive values of x, i.e., observe the signs of the coefficients of the highest powers of x in each member, and determine the number of changes of sign in the sequence. The difference between the two numbers of sign changes is the number of (real) positive values of x for which $f(x) = 0$; call this difference N: If $N = 0$, then $f(x)$ does not vanish for positive x, i.e., for real frequencies, and if $f(x)$ is positive for some positive x, then $\mathbf{Re}\, F(j\omega) > 0$.   If $N \neq 0$, then examine $f_m(x)$.   If f_m is a constant, then all the zeros of $f(x)$ are simple, and since some occur at real frequencies, $F(p)$ is not p-r.   But if $f_m(x)$ is a polynomial, rather than a mere constant, then some of the zeros of $f(x)$ are multiple, and further investigation is required.

The information available at this point is:

N: the number of distinct real, positive zeros of $f(x)$, multiplicities not being considered, and

r: the degree of $f_m(x)$, which is the degree of $h(x)$.

If $f(x)$ is not to be negative, then r must be at least equal to N, if it is to be possible that all the real, positive zeros of $f(x)$ be of even order.   Hence if $r < N$, we need go no further: $F(p)$ is not p-r.   If $r \geq N$, then we may examine f_m more closely.   If $f_m(x)$ is of low enough degree to be easily factored, and the factorization is made, then the locations and multiplicities of these multiple zeros of $f(x)$ are apparent; one can immediately determine, from them and N, whether $F(j\omega)$ is negative at any real frequencies.   If f_m is not readily factored, then still further investigation is required.   A repetition of the entire process, this time applied to f_m, i.e. to h, will yield a number N_a which is the number of distinct (real) positive zeros of $h(x)$.   This cannot exceed N, of course.   If $N_a < N$, then $f(x)$ has at least one (real) positive simple zero and $F(p)$ is not p-r. If $N_a = N$, then it is possible that all the real positive zeros of $f(x)$ are of even order, but it is necessary to look still further.   We shall not continue the discussion, but in a given numerical case, further repetition of the process will give additional information, which usually will settle the matter.   It may finally be necessary to factor, or to plot a function (or functions), but in any event this process based on Sturm's theorem is of great help in determining whether $\mathbf{Re}\, F(j\omega)$ is ever negative.   The following examples illustrate the process; in each of them $G(\omega^2)$ represents the result of evaluating the numerator of

$$\mathbf{Ev}\, F(p) = \frac{M_1 M_2 - N_1 N_2}{M_2^{\,2} - N_2^{\,2}}$$

for $p = j\omega$, a polynomial even in ω.

Example 1.   Here are four cases, typical of those in which mere inspection suffices.   In the first two G is positive (or at least zero) at all real frequencies and this particular requirement for positive reality is met; in the last two G is negative for sufficiently small or large frequencies, respectively, so that $F(p)$ is not p-r.

$$G = \omega^8, \qquad\qquad\qquad G = 2\omega^6 - 9\omega^4 + 13\omega^2 - 5,$$
$$G = 10\omega^6 + 3\omega^4 + 13\omega^2 + 5, \qquad G = -0.1\omega^{12} + 17\omega^{10} + 3\omega^8 + 5.$$

Example 2. $G(\omega^2) = 3\omega^6 - 3\omega^4 + 35$. Here it is not immediately apparent whether G goes negative at real frequencies, so we apply the test based on Sturm's theorem. With $x = \omega^2$, G becomes

$$f(x) = 3x^3 - 3x^2 + 35,$$

so that

$$f_1(x) = f'(x) = 9x^2 - 6x.$$

To obtain $f_2(x)$, we divide f_1 into f, thus:

$$9x^2 - 6x)3x^3 - 3x^2 + 0 \qquad + 35(0.333x - 0.111$$
$$\underline{3x^3 - 2x^2}$$
$$- x^2 + 0 \qquad + 35$$
$$\underline{- x^2 + 0.667x}$$
$$- 0.667x + 35 \quad .$$

Hence

$$f_2(x) = 0.667x - 35,$$

which is the remainder, with the sign changed. The division may conveniently be carried out with detached coefficients (and the work can be even further compressed, as suggested in Prob. 5-49); it resembles the Hurwitz-test process of § 5.14, but careful attention must here be paid to the signs required in the f's, and the divisions may require several steps. In this example, the work of finding f_2 would be written

$$9 \quad -6)3 \quad -3 \quad 0 \qquad 35(0.333 \quad -0.111$$
$$\underline{3 \quad -2}$$
$$-1 \quad 0 \qquad 35$$
$$\underline{-1 \quad 0.667}$$
$$-0.667 \quad 35 \rightarrow f_2(x) = 0.667x - 35.$$

The quotients need not actually be written down, and will henceforth be omitted. The next step is to find f_3:

$$0.667 \quad -35)9 \quad - \quad 6 \ (13.5$$
$$\underline{9 \quad -472.5}$$
$$466.5 \rightarrow f_3(x) = -466.5.$$

Since f_3 is a constant, f_4 will be zero, and we need go no further. The table of signs is

x	f	f_1	f_2	f_3	Δ
0	+	0	−	−	1
∞	+	+	+	−	1
					$N = 0$

The difference in the number of sign changes in the sequence N is zero; hence $f(x)$ has no zeros for real, positive values of x, i.e. for real frequencies. Since

$G(0)$ is positive, the real part of the function $F(p)$ from which came G is therefore never negative on the imaginary axis, and $F(p)$ is p-r, at least as far as this part of the over-all test is concerned.

Example 3. $G(\omega^2) = 10\omega^{10} - 20\omega^8 + 16\omega^6 - 6.4\omega^4 + 1.28\omega^2 + 17$. Again it is not immediately apparent whether G goes negative at real frequencies, so we apply the test. The work is

$$f(x) = 10x^5 - 20x^4 + 16x^3 - 6.4x^2 + 1.28x + 17,$$
$$f_1(x) = 50x^4 - 80x^3 + 48x^2 - 12.8x + 1.28;$$

```
50 −80 48 −12.8 1.28)10 −20   16   −6.4   1.28   17
                      10 −16  9.6  −2.56  0.256
                      ─────────────────────────────
                       − 4  6.4 −3.84  1.024  17
                       − 4  6.4 −3.84  1.024 −0.10
                      ─────────────────────────────
                         0    0     0   17.10 → f₂(x) = −17.10.
```

In this case the sequence stops with $f_2(x)$.
The table of signs is

x	f	f_1	f_2	Δ
0	+	+	−	1
∞	+	+	−	1
				$N = 0$

and since N, the change in Δ, is zero, and G is positive at zero, G is positive for all real frequencies.

Example 4. $G(\omega^2) = 2\omega^{10} + 6\omega^8 - 4\omega^6 - 6\omega^4 + 4\omega^2 + 12$. Again it is necessary to apply the test. The work is

$$f(x) = 2x^5 + 6x^4 - 4x^3 - 6x^2 + 4x + 12,$$
$$f_1(x) = 10x^4 + 24x^3 - 12x^2 - 12x + 4;$$

```
10  24  −12  −12  4)2  6     −4     −6     4    12  (
                    2  4.8   −2.4   −2.4   0.8
                    ──────────────────────────────
                     1.2  −1.6  −3.6   3.2   12
                     1.2   2.88 −1.44 −1.44  0.48
                    ──────────────────────────────
                        −4.48 −2.16  4.64  11.52
```

Thus $f_2(x) = 4.48x^3 + 2.16x^2 - 4.64x - 11.52$.

```
4.48  2.16  −4.64  −11.52)10  24    −12    −12     4  (
                           10  4.82  −10.36 −25.7
                           ────────────────────────────
                              19.18  − 1.64  13.7
                              19.18    9.25 −19.9  −49.3
                           ────────────────────────────
                                    −10.89  33.6   53.3
```

and $f_3(x) = 10.89x^2 - 33.6x - 53.3$.

$$10.89 \quad -33.6 \quad -53.3)4.48 \quad\quad 2.16 \quad\quad 4.64 \quad -11.52($$
$$4.48 \quad -13.82 \quad -21.93$$
$$\overline{15.98 \quad\quad 17.29}$$
$$15.98 \quad -49.3 \quad -78.2$$
$$\overline{66.6 \quad\quad 66.7}$$

and $f_4(x) = -66.6x - 66.7$.

$$-66.6 \quad -66.7)10.89 \quad -33.6 \quad -53.3($$
$$10.89 \quad\quad 10.9$$
$$\overline{-44.5}$$
$$-44.5 \quad -44.6$$
$$\overline{- 8.7} \to f_5(x) = 8.7.$$

The sign table is

x	f	f_1	f_2	f_3	f_4	f_5	Δ
0	$+$	$+$	$-$	$-$	$-$	$+$	2
∞	$+$	$+$	$+$	$+$	$-$	$+$	2

	$N = 0$

Again $G(\omega^2)$ is positive at zero frequency and remains so for all real frequencies.

Example 5. $G(\omega^2) = \omega^8 - 2\omega^6 + 1$. The test must be applied.

$$f(x) = x^4 - 2x^3 + 1,$$
$$f_1(x) = 4x^3 - 6x^2;$$

$$4 \quad -6 \quad 0 \quad 0)1 \quad -2 \quad\quad 0 \quad\quad 0 \quad 1($$
$$1 \quad -1.5$$
$$\overline{-0.5}$$
$$-0.5 \quad\quad 0.75$$
$$\overline{-0.75 \quad 0 \quad 1} \to f_2(x) = 0.75x^2 - 1.$$

$$0.75 \quad 0 \quad -1)4 \quad -6 \quad -0 \quad\quad\quad 0($$
$$4 \quad\quad 0 \quad -5.33$$
$$\overline{-6 \quad\quad 5.33}$$
$$-6 \quad\quad 0 \quad\quad 8$$
$$\overline{5.33 \quad -8} \to f_3(x) = -5.33x + 8.$$

$$-5.33 \quad 8)0.75 \quad\quad 0 \quad\quad -1 \quad ($$
$$0.75 \quad -1.125$$
$$\overline{1.125 \quad -1}$$
$$1.125 \quad -1.69$$
$$\overline{0.69} \to f_4(x) = -0.69.$$

x	f	f_1	f_2	f_3	f_4	Δ
0	$+$	0	$-$	$+$	$-$	3
∞	$+$	$+$	$+$	$-$	$-$	1

$$N = 2$$

There are two distinct zeros of $f(x)$ at real positive values of x, since the number of sign changes decreases by two. And since f_4 is a constant, $f(x)$ has no multiple zeros. Hence these zeros at real frequencies are simple zeros, the real part of $F(p)$ changes sign there, and accordingly $F(p)$ is not p-r.

Example 6. $G(\omega^2) = 3\omega^{12} - 6\omega^{10} + 6\omega^8 - 48\omega^6 + 72\omega^4$. Here there is a zero at zero frequency, but it is of even order and cannot cause a sign change in G. On dividing out $3\omega^4$ and proceeding as before, we get:

$$f(x) = x^4 - 2x^3 + 2x^2 - 16x + 24,$$
$$f_1(x) = 4x^3 - 6x^2 + 4x - 16;$$

$$
\begin{array}{l}
4 \quad -6 \quad 4 \quad -16)1 \quad -2 \quad 2 \quad -16 \quad 24(\\
1 \quad -1.5 \quad 1 \quad -4 \\
\hline
-0.5 \quad 1 \quad -12 \\
-0.5 \quad 0.75 \quad -0.5 \quad 2 \\
\hline
0.25 \quad -11.5 \quad 22 \to f_2(x) = -0.25x^2 + 11.5x - 22.
\end{array}
$$

$$
\begin{array}{l}
-0.25 \quad 11.5 \quad -22)4 \quad -6 \quad 4 \quad -16(\\
4 \quad -184 \quad 352 \\
\hline
178 \quad -348 \\
178 \quad -8188 \quad 15,664 \\
\hline
7840 \quad -15,680 \to f_3(x) = -7840x + 15,680.
\end{array}
$$

$$
\begin{array}{l}
-7840 \quad 15,680)-0.25 \quad 11.5 \quad -22(\\
-0.25 \quad 0.5 \\
\hline
11.0 \\
11.0 \quad -22 \\
\hline
0 \to f_4(x) = 0.
\end{array}
$$

x	f	f_1	f_2	f_3	Δ
0	$+$	$-$	$-$	$+$	2
∞	$+$	$+$	$-$	$-$	1

$$N = 1$$

There is one distinct zero of $f(x)$ on the positive (real) x-axis. But $f(0)$ and $f(\infty)$ are both positive, so this zero must be of even multiplicity and does not cause $f(x)$ to change sign. Alternatively, since f_3 is not a constant, while $f_4 = 0$, we know there is a multiple zero in $f(x)$, and further (from f_3) that this zero is of order two, and located at $x = 2$. The original $G(\omega^2)$ accordingly vanishes both at the origin and at another real frequency, but is never negative for real frequencies. This meets the p-r requirement.

Example 7. $G(\omega^2) = \omega^8 - 10\omega^6 + 37\omega^4 - 60\omega^2 + 36$. The calculations of the test are:

$$f(x) = x^4 - 10x^3 + 37x^2 - 60x + 36,$$
$$f_1(x) = 4x^3 - 30x^2 + 74x - 60;$$

```
4 −30 74 −60)1 −10    37    −60     36 (
             1 − 7.5  18.5  −15
               − 2.5  18.5  −45
               − 2.5  18.75 −46.25  37.5
                      −0.25   1.25  −1.5 → f₂(x) = 0.25x² − 1.25x + 1.5.

          0.25  −1.25  1.5)4  −30  74  −60(
                         4  −20  24
                           −10  50
                           −10  50  −60
                             0       0 → f₃(x) = 0.
```

x	f	f_1	f_2	Δ
0	+	−	+	2
∞	+	+	+	0
				$N = 2$

There are two distinct, real, positive zeros of $f(x)$. But in this case there are multiple zeros, for f_2 is not a constant. Although f_2 here can be factored by inspection, it is instructive to carry the test on:

$$h(x) = x^2 - 5x + 6 \quad \text{(from } f_2, \text{ to which } h \text{ is proportional).}$$

The test, applied to $h(x)$, gives

$$h_1(x) = h'(x) = 2x - 5;$$

```
2 −5)1  −5     6 (
     1 −2.5
       −2.5
       −2.5   6.25
         −0.25 → h₂(x) = 0.25.
```

x	h	h_1	h_2	Δ
0	+	−	+	2
∞	+	+	+	0

$$N = 2$$

Hence $h(x)$ has two distinct real, positive zeros; and these are simple zeros, and all of h's zeros. This means that the two distinct zeros of $f(x)$ are *double* zeros; hence G does not change sign—and, by inspection, of $G(0)$ is always positive, as required if $F(p)$ is to be p-r.

Example 8. $G(\omega^2) = 2.2\omega^8 - 9.9\omega^6 + 15.4\omega^4 - 9.9\omega^2 + 2.2$. It is convenient to divide through by the coefficient of the leading term, which will not affect the sign of the polynomial. We get

$$f(x) = x^4 - 4.5x^3 + 7x^2 - 4.5x + 1,$$
$$f_1(x) = 4x^3 - 13.5x^2 + 14x - 4.5;$$

```
4  −13.5  14  −4.5)1   −4.5      7         −4.5        1   (
                  1    −3.375    3.5       −1.125
                 ────────────────────────────────
                      −1.125     3.5       −3.375
                      −1.125     3.7969    −3.9375     1.2656
                 ────────────────────────────────────────────
                                −0.2969    0.5625     −0.2656
```
$$\to f_2(x) = 0.2969x^2 - 0.5625x + 0.2656.$$

```
0.2969  −0.5625  0.2656)4  −13.5      14       −4.5
                         4  − 7.579    3.579
                        ──────────────────────
                            − 5.921   10.421
                            − 5.921   11.219    −5.298
                        ───────────────────────────────
                                     −0.798     0.798
```
$$\to f_3(x) = 0.798x - 0.798.$$

```
0.798  −0.798)0.2969   −0.5625    0.2656(
               0.2969   −0.2969
              ───────────────────
                        −0.2656
                        −0.2656    0.2656
              ─────────────────────────────
                           0          0
```
$$\to f_4(x) = 0.$$

x	f	f_1	f_2	f_3	Δ
0	+	−	+	−	3
∞	+	+	+	+	0

$$N = 3$$

There are three distinct zeros of $f(x)$ at real, positive values of x to consider. Since f_3 is not a constant, but in fact $h(x) = (x - 1)$, we know that there is a double zero at one of these points ($x = 1$), but no other multiple zeros. Hence the other two must be simple zeros, $f(x)$ must change sign, and $F(p)$ is not p-r.

The numbers used in these examples are forced, of course, to illustrate points, but it is well to notice that occasionally, as here, rather good accuracy may be necessary in the calculations. This implies that the coefficients of the original polynomial G must be equally accurately known; slight changes in them, in critical cases like this one, may change the character of the polynomial completely, as by splitting up multiple zeros.

Example 9. $G(\omega^2) = \omega^{12} - \omega^{10} - 7\omega^8 + 9\omega^6 + 10\omega^4 - 20\omega^2 + 8$. Here we get

$$f(x) = x^6 - x^5 - 7x^4 + 9x^3 + 10x^2 - 20x + 8,$$
$$f_1(x) = 6x^5 - 5x^4 - 28x^3 + 27x^2 + 20x - 20;$$

$$
\begin{array}{l}
6 \quad -5 \quad -28 \\
27 \quad 20 \quad -20
\end{array}\Big)
$$
1	−1	−7	9	10	−20	8
1	−0.8333	−4.6667	4.5	3.333	− 3.333	
	−0.1667	−2.3333	4.5	6.667	−16.667	8
	−0.1667	0.1389	0.778	−0.75	− 0.556	0.556
		−2.4722	3.722	7.417	−16.111	7.444

$$\rightarrow f_2(x) = 2.472x^4 - 3.722x^3 - 7.417x^2 + 16.111x - 7.444.$$

$$
\begin{array}{l}
2.4722 \quad -3.722 \quad -7.417 \\
\quad\; 16.111 \quad -7.444
\end{array}\Big)
$$
6	−5	−28	27	20	−20
6	−9.034	−18.000	39.10	−18.07	
	4.034	−10.000	−12.10	38.07	−20
	4.034	− 6.073	−12.10	26.29	12.15
		− 3.927	0.00	11.78	− 7.85

$$\rightarrow f_3(x) = 3.927x^3 - 11.78x + 7.85.$$

$$3.927 \quad 0 \quad -11.78 \quad 7.85\,)$$
2.472	−3.722	−7.417	16.111	−7.444(
2.472	0	−7.417	4.944	
	−3.722	0	11.167	−7.444
	−3.722	0	11.167	−7.444
		0	0.000	0.000

$$\rightarrow f_4(x) = 0.$$

The sign table is

x	f	f_1	f_2	f_3	Δ
0	+	−	−	+	2
∞	+	+	+	+	0
					$N = 2$

Here the number of distinct real, positive zeros of $f(x)$ is two; and $r = 3$, i.e., $h(x)$ has three zeros, which are distributed on top of those of $g(x)$ to make the multiple zeros of $f(x)$. Of these three "excess" zeros it may well be that one lies at each of the real, positive zeros of $f(x)$, making them double zeros, and the other elsewhere—this would be an acceptable situation. To determine this we proceed to test the polynomial $h(x)$, proportional to $f_3(x)$.

$$h(x) = x^3 - 3x + 2,$$
$$h_1(x) = 3x^2 - 3;$$

$$
\begin{array}{r}
3 \quad 0 \quad -3)1 \quad 0 \quad -3 \quad 2(\\
\underline{1 \quad 0 \quad -1} \\
0 \quad -2 \quad 2 \rightarrow h_2(x) = 2x - 2.
\end{array}
$$

$$
\begin{array}{r}
2 \quad -2)3 \quad 0 \quad -3(\\
\underline{3 \quad -3} \\
3 \\
\underline{3 \quad -3} \\
0 \rightarrow h_3(x) = 0.
\end{array}
$$

x	h	h_1	h_2	Δ
0	+	−	−	1
∞	+	+	+	0

$$N = 1$$

Since $N = 1$, there is but one real, distinct positive zero of $h(x)$. It is impossible then for the two zeros of $f(x)$ both to be double—one must be simple—hence $f(x)$ must change sign at one of them. [This might have been concluded, even without the last sign table, for one of the three zeros of $h(x)$ is superimposed on another, h_3 being zero and h_2 being $2(x - 1)$.]

In the discussion of § 5.14 it was found possible for the denominator of $F(p)$ to have a factor $E(p)$, an even polynomial, and the test there actually disclosed $E(p)$. Again, the denominator may itself be an even or odd polynomial. There arises then the problem of testing an even polynomial for right-half-plane zeros, a test which Sturm's theorem makes easy. The polynomial $E(p)$, disclosed by the Hurwitz test, is even, and therefore on substituting $-x$ for p^2 we obtain a polynomial

$$f(x) = a_n x^n + a_{n-1} x^{n-1} + \ldots$$

which represents $E(j\omega)$. $E(p)$ must have all its zeros on the imaginary axis if $F(p)$ is to be p-r [otherwise there is at least one zero in the right half plane, because of the even character of $E(p)$], and they must in addition be simple, or else $F(p)$ is not p-r. This requires that $f(x)$ have all its zeros at real, positive values of x, and that they all be simple. If Sturm's theorem is applied to $f(x)$, and N, the number of real, positive, distinct zeros is obtained, then we need only compare N and n. If $N = n$, then all the zeros of $E(p)$ are imaginary and simple—for there are only n zeros of $f(x)$ altogether, and there are n distinct zeros on the real positive axis, which implies that they are all simple. In terms of p, this means that the $2n$ zeros of $E(p)$ are imaginary (in conjugate pairs) and simple. If $N < n$, then either some of the zeros of $E(p)$ are in the right half plane or some of the imaginary zeros are of multiplicity greater than one, because the $(n - N)$ "excess" zeros of $f(x)$ must either coincide with some of the first N real, positive (distinct) zeros, or else lie at real negative, or at complex values of x. In either case $F(p)$ is not p-r, for some of its poles are in the right half plane or some of its imaginary poles are not simple. The following examples from § 5.14 illustrate this application of Sturm's theorem.

Example 10 (from Example 5 of § 5.14). In this case the denominator of $F(p)$ is the polynomial $2p^6 + 26p^4 + 94p^2 + 70$ which becomes, with the substitution $p^2 = -x$,

$$f(x) = -2x^3 + 26x^2 - 94x + 70.$$

Then

$$f_1(x) = -6x^2 + 52x - 94.$$

```
-6   52  -94)-2   26      -94      70(
            -2   17.33  -31.33
            ─────────────────────
                  8.67  -62.67
                  8.67  -75.1    136
                  ─────────────────────
                        12.4    -66 → f₂(x) = -12.4x + 66.
```

$$f_2(x) = -12.4x + 66.$$

```
-12.4  66)-6   52      -94(
          -6   31.9
          ─────────────
               20.1
               20.1    -107
               ─────────────
                     13 → f₃(x) = -13.
```

$$f_3(x) = -13.$$

x	f	f_1	f_2	f_3	Δ
0	$+$	$-$	$+$	$-$	3
∞	$-$	$-$	$-$	$-$	0
					$N = 3$

Since the degree of $f(x)$ is also three, all of its zeros are real, positive, and simple. The denominator of $F(p)$ is acceptable, accordingly, but the residues of $F(p)$ at these poles must also be checked.

Example 11 (from Example 8 of § 5.14). On removal of the (simple) zero at the origin, the denominator of $F(p)$ becomes, in this case, $p^6 + 8p^4 + 17.5p^2 + 12.5$, which yields, with the usual substitution,

$$f(x) = -x^3 + 8x^2 - 17.5x + 12.5,$$

and

$$f_1(x) = -3x^2 + 16x - 17.5;$$

$$-3 \quad 16 \quad -17.5)-1 \quad 8 \qquad -17.5 \qquad 12.5($$

$$\underline{-1 \quad 5.33 \quad -5.833}$$

$$\underline{2.67 \quad -11.67}$$

$$\underline{2.67 \quad -14.24 \quad 15.58}$$

$$2.57 \quad -3.08 \rightarrow f_2(x) = -2.57x + 3.08.$$

$$-2.57 \quad 3.08)-3 \quad 16 \qquad -17.5($$

$$\underline{-3 \quad 3.60}$$

$$12.40$$

$$\underline{12.40 \quad -14.9}$$

$$- 2.6 \rightarrow f_3(x) = 2.6.$$

x	f	f_1	f_2	f_3	Δ
0	$+$	$-$	$+$	$+$	2
∞	$-$	$-$	$-$	$+$	1

$$N = 1$$

Since $N = 1$ while the degree of $f(x)$ is three, we can say that $f(x)$ has multiple zeros at real positive values of x, has zero(s) elsewhere, or possibly both. Accordingly, $F(p)$ has multiple poles at real frequencies, or has at least one right-half-plane pole, and is not p-r. In addition we can see, since f_3 is a constant, that there are no multiple poles and hence that $F(p)$ definitely has at least one right-half-plane pole.

Any even polynomial $E(p)$ which appears in the application of the test of § 5.14 can be handled similarly. This completes our discussion of the mechanics of the test for positive reality.

5.16 Discussion

In (5.13–5) we have a test which may be applied to any given rational function $F(p)$ to determine whether or not it is p-r. Steps 1 and 2(a) are taken simply by inspection; the remaining three steps may require an appreciable amount of work: the mechanics of these have been discussed in § 5.14 and § 5.15. On reflection, one may wonder whether all five of these steps are necessary. That they are is of course demonstrated in the development of the test, but it is informative to consider some examples, in each of which all but one of the steps lead to satisfactory conclusions.

Example 1. $F(p) = \dfrac{2p^3 + j6p^2 + 8p + j18}{p^2 + 3}$. This function does not pass the first test, nor does it have the third property (equivalent to the requirements of the first test), for not all of its coefficients are real; hence $F(p)$ is not p-r. But it does pass the other four. Before applying these other tests, to demonstrate this, notice that F has imaginary poles whose residues will be required in step 2(c); calculation of these residues amounts to partial-fraction expansion, which it is convenient to make immediately:

$$F(p) = \frac{1}{p - j\sqrt{3}} + \frac{1}{p + j\sqrt{3}} + j6 + 2p.$$

The remaining tests are now easily made:

2(a). at infinity F behaves as $2p$—which is satisfactory;

2(b). there are no right-half-plane poles—which is satisfactory;

2(c). there are two imaginary poles, but they are simple, and the residues are real and positive—which is satisfactory;

3. **Re** $F(j\omega) = 0$—which is satisfactory.

Hence a function may violate the first requirement without violating any of the other four, as we should expect (for this amounts to but one part of the definition of positive reality).

Example 2. $F(p) = 4\dfrac{p^4 + 3p^3 + 3p^2 + 10p + 2}{p + 3}$.   The testing is:

1. the coefficients in F are real—which is satisfactory;

2(a). at infinity F behaves as $4p^3$—which is *not* satisfactory, so that $F(p)$ is not p-r—but we continue the testing;

2(b). there are no right-half-plane poles—which is satisfactory;

2(c). there are no imaginary poles—which is satisfactory;

3. **Re** $F(j\omega) = 4 \left[\dfrac{3p^4 + 9p^2 + 6 - 3p^4 - 10p^2}{9 - p^2} \right]_{p = j\omega}$

$\qquad = 4\dfrac{\omega^2 + 6}{9 + \omega^2}$—which is always positive, and therefore satisfactory.

This shows that a function may violate the second requirement but none of the others. In this case $F(p)$, by inspection, does not have the required sixth and seventh properties, but these are equivalent to test 2(a). The test, however, should stand on its own feet, and not require a knowledge of the properties listed before.

Example 3. $F(p) = \dfrac{5p^3 + 2p + 4}{p^4 + 3}$.   The testing is:

1. the coefficients in F are real—which is satisfactory;

2(a). at infinity $F(p)$ behaves as $5/p$—which is satisfactory;

2(b). the roots of $p^4 + 3 = 0$ are given by $p^4 = -3$ or by $p = \sqrt[4]{3}\, e^{j\theta}$, in which θ can have the four values $\pm\pi/4$, $\pm 3\pi/4$; of these two are in the right half plane, and are not zeros of the numerator also (as shown by substitution therein, for the imaginary part of the numerator is certainly not zero for any of the four)—which is *not* satisfactory, so that $F(p)$ is not p-r;

2(c). there are no imaginary poles—which is satisfactory;

3. $\operatorname{Re} F(j\omega) = \left[\dfrac{4(p^4 + 3) - 0}{(p^4 + 3)^2 - 0}\right]_{p=j\omega} = \dfrac{4(\omega^4 + 3)}{(\omega^4 + 3)^2} = \dfrac{4}{\omega^4 + 3}$ —which is never

negative and therefore is satisfactory.

With a knowledge of the properties we should be tempted to reject $F(p)$ on inspection, for there are too many missing powers of p in both numerator and denominator. To be certain, however, we would have to make sure that the right-half-plane zeros and right-half-plane poles are not common to numerator and denominator (do not cancel each other out), as done above; inspection is not enough. This example shows also that a function may violate the third requirement, but none of the others.

Example 4. $F(p) = \dfrac{1.2p^2 + 6}{p^3 + 4p}$. Here the work is:

1. the coefficients in $F(p)$ are real—which is satisfactory;
2(a). at infinity F behaves as $1.2/p$—which is satisfactory;
2(b). there are no right-half-plane poles—which is satisfactory;
2(c). there are imaginary poles, but they are simple (as they must be for positive reality); the residues are given in the partial-fraction expansion:

$$F(p) = \frac{1.5}{p} + \frac{-0.15}{p - j2} + \frac{-0.15}{p + j2}$$ —since they are negative, $F(p)$ is not p-r;

3. $\operatorname{Re} F(j\omega) = 0$—which is satisfactory.

The function $F(p)$ cannot here be rejected on mere casual inspection; it illustrates that the fourth requirement alone may be violated by a function.

Example 5. $F(p) = \dfrac{2p^2 + p + 2}{p + 1}$. This function was shown in § 5.13 not to be p-r by a different method. The application of test (5.13–5), with which we are here concerned, follows:

1. the coefficients in $F(p)$ are real—which is satisfactory;
2(a). at infinity F behaves as $2p$—which is satisfactory;
2(b). there are no right-half-plane poles—which is satisfactory;
2(c). there are no imaginary poles—which is satisfactory;

3. $\operatorname{Re} F(j\omega) = \left[\dfrac{(2p^2 + 2)(1) - (p)(p)}{(1)^2 - (p)^2}\right]_{p=j\omega} = \dfrac{-\omega^2 + 2}{1 + \omega^2}$ —which is negative

for large values of ω, so that F is not p-r.

It is only the fifth requirement, however, that $F(p)$ fails to meet.

The purpose of these five examples is to emphasize the fact that *all five steps* of the test are necessary; each example is an instance of a function which satisfies all but one of the requirements, yet is not p-r. To recapitulate the general reasons for each of the five steps, their genesis is summed up below.

Step 1 is required by the first part of the fundamental definition of positive reality, which requires that $F(p)$ be real when the independent variable is real (at least in the right half plane). Steps 2 and 3 are a substitute for (equivalent to) testing specifically for the requirements of the second part of the definition, that **Re** $F(p)$ be positive when **Re** p is positive—in that the boundary of the right half plane replaces the right half plane itself in the investigation, through the use of theorem (3.25–6). Step 2(b) is required for the theorem to be applicable [and $F(p)$ would not be p-r if it did not meet this requirement, assuming of course that $F(p)$ is in lowest terms]. The remaining steps are to investigate **Re** $F(p)$ on the boundary: 2(a) covers the infinite-radius semicircle, 2(c) the infinitesimal-radius semicircles on the imaginary axis made necessary by the poles there, and step 3 the imaginary axis itself. Since the theorem requires investigation of **Re** $F(p)$ on the *whole* boundary, none of these can be omitted. Step 3, for example, does not cover the small semicircles, infinitesimal though the latter are; the five examples above further emphasize the need for all five tests. The five tests as a group are sufficient, as shown in the derivation, so that in test (5.13–5) we have enough of a test to be sure that a function passing all parts of it is positive-real, and yet not any more than is necessary to be certain. The test is conclusive, and stands on its own feet: a knowledge of the list of properties previously developed is not necessary to apply the test, though it may be useful in detecting and immediately eliminating obviously non-p-r functions before going to the work of applying (5.13–5). Such knowledge is not enough, however (§ 5.13), and we should not rely on it.

There are some useful devices which occasionally can shorten the work of testing a function for positive reality. As in some of the examples above, a preliminary partial-fraction expansion of $F(p)$ may be helpful; to separate out the real-frequency-pole terms at least is usually worthwhile, if this does not in itself involve much work—but this is required by step 2(c) in any event if the work progresses that far. Again, it may be easier to test the *reciprocal* of $F(p)$ rather than $F(p)$ itself, particularly if the numerator of F is simpler, so that it is more readily checked for right-half-plane zeros. Note incidentally that it is unnecessary to check the locations of the zeros of the numerator of the function under test (if the denominator is Hurwitz), and that it proves nothing to do so and find no right-half-plane zeros: the function may still not be p-r. If there is a right-half-plane zero in such a case, then **Re** $F(p)$ will be negative somewhere in the immediate vicinity thereof, and hence step 3 of the test will disclose that **Re** $F(j\omega)$ is negative at some frequencies.

In general, the quality of positive reality cannot be determined by casual inspection; that a function is p-r is not obvious (unless it is known to be a driving-point immittance of a physical network). Test (5.13–5) whose details we have been discussing at some length, or some equivalent, must be applied.

5.17 Conclusion

In this chapter we have developed a list of properties which driving-point immittance functions must have. The most important of these is that they be positive-real, and from this stem most of the other properties. Since the list of these derived properties is not long enough in that they alone are not sufficient to insure positive reality, we have developed a test which can be applied, without knowledge of the listed properties, to any given rational function, to determine whether it is p-r. The list of properties is valuable knowledge, however, and we shall later develop even more properties of driving-point immittance functions—but we are not quite ready for them yet.

The long discussion of the consequences of positive reality, and of means for detecting it, is justified solely by the fact that positive reality is not only necessary for physical existence of corresponding networks, it is also *sufficient* for synthesis to be possible. This will be demonstrated later by actual synthesis of one or more networks which realize any given p-r driving-point immittance function. Before this general demonstration, however, other properties of these functions must be considered. And these properties will be more readily understood if we first demonstrate that positive reality is sufficient for synthesis in certain special, simple cases. For these we shall develop complete synthesis procedures as well as additional properties of such special driving-point immittance functions. Then we shall find that the further discussion of general driving-point immittance function properties is easier to understand, and that the synthesis procedures in the general case (the proof of the sufficiency of positive reality) develop quite naturally.

5.18 References

Properties of driving-point immittance functions: BR 1, CA 2.
Properties of positive-real functions (in addition to the references above): GU 3, RI 2, RI 3.
Hurwitz polynomials and testing: FR 3, GU 3, HU 3, WA 1.
Sturm's theorem: FI 1, TU 1, US 1, WE 1, WI 3 (and similar works on algebra, theory of equations, numerical analysis).

PROBLEMS

5-1. Lacunae exist in the text in that the following relations are at most only partially derived. Derive them, or complete their derivations.

(a) (5.07–1); calculate K and A in terms of the a's and b's of (5.03–1);

(b) (5.10–11) through (5.10–14), inclusive;

(c) (5.11–7);

(*d*) (5.12–2), (5.12–3) (do by *two* methods, as suggested in § 5.12);

(*e*) (5.12–5);

(*f*) (5.13–2).

5-2. Derive the property of a positive-real function that no zeros or poles lie in the right half plane by the method used in § 5.06. Contrast this with the method used in § 5.05.

5-3. Demonstrate (5.06–6) by using the polar form of the definition of positive reality. (The Taylor-series expansion of a p-r function in the vicinity of an imaginary zero may be helpful.)

5-4. To what extent can the fifth property (§ 5.06) be derived merely from considerations of network analysis, using only the passivity of the network and considering its behavior in the transient state? (Cf. Prob. 4-11.)

5-5. Expand each of the following functions near each of its imaginary zeros in the form (5.06–2) and find the values of s, a, α. Do these meet the requirements of positive reality? Make similar calculations for the reciprocals of these functions in the vicinity of their imaginary poles, following (5.06–5).

$$(a)\ \sqrt[+]{p(p+1)} \qquad (b)\ \sqrt[+]{p^2+1} \qquad (c)\ \sqrt[+]{1+p^{-2}}$$

5-6. Suppose the function $F(p)$ to have a simple pole, at which the residue is real and positive, at $p = j\omega_0$. Prove that $\mathbf{Re}\ F(j\omega)$ is then bounded (does not become infinite) at that point. (The Laurent series may be useful.)

5-7. The left-half-plane zeroes and poles of p-r functions are not in general restricted as to multiplicity, nor are their derivatives and residues restricted as in § 5.06. Illustrate this by examining the behavior of the following functions (which are to be shown to be p-r), and their reciprocals, at the left-half-plane zeros and poles.

$$(a)\ \frac{p+0.2}{(p+1)^2} \qquad (b)\ \frac{p}{p+1} \qquad (c)\ \frac{p}{p^2+2p+2}$$

5-8. Derive the eighth property from the seventh by making a change of variable from p to p^{-1} and using the result of Prob. 4-15.

5-9. Derive the eighth property by considering the behavior of the function on a small semicircle centered on the origin and using the polar-coordinate form of the definition of positive reality.

5-10. Show that on any vertical line of the p plane the real part of a rational function with real coefficients is an even function of ω and the imaginary part an odd function of ω. Can a similar statement be made with regard to a horizontal line?

5-11. Find the even, odd, real, and imaginary parts of the following functions:

(*a*) $F(p) = p + 1$;

(*b*) $F(p) = (p + 1)^{-1}$;

(*c*) $F(p) = \dfrac{p^2 + 2p + 6}{4p}$;

(*d*) $F(p) = \dfrac{p}{p^2 + 3}$;

(*e*) $F(p) =$ driving-point admittance function of the network shown (p. 222).

Show that in general the even and real parts are not equal, nor are the odd and imaginary parts (taking the factor j into account), except on the imaginary axis. What are the real and imaginary parts of **Ev** $F(p)$ and of **Od** $F(p)$ in each case?

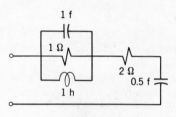

Prob. 5–11

5-12. Find the even and odd parts of the immittance functions of these networks. Plot the zeros and poles of each part and observe the symmetry. (Where normalization is not enough to enable a numerical plot to be made,

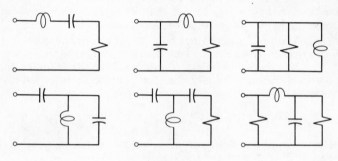

Prob. 5–12

choose cases representative of the various possible behaviors.) Sketch the behavior of each part at real frequencies, and relate these curves to those of driving-point resistance, reactance, conductance, and susceptance.

5-13. Find the even and odd parts of the functions below, and plot their real-frequency behavior as functions of ω:

$$(a) \ \sqrt[+]{p} \qquad (b) \ \sqrt[+]{1+p} \qquad (c) \ \sqrt[+]{1+p^2}$$

5-14. Find the even and odd parts of $\ln F(p)$ in terms of $F(p)$ and $F(-p)$. How are these related to the magnitude and to the angle of $F(p)$, (a) at real frequencies? (b) in general?

5-15. How are the poles of **Ev** $F(p$ related to those of $F(p)$ itself? What relation is there between the zeros of the two functions? Repeat for **Od** $F(p)$. Illustrate with sketches of the pole and zero locations for the functions of Probs. 5-7 and 5-11.

5-16. Of each of the following functions, find the even and odd parts; locate the zeros, poles, and other singularities of these parts; and give the order (or other description) of each one. Plot carefully the real, imaginary, even, and odd parts as functions of ω for $p = j\omega$.

(a) $p + \sqrt[+]{p^2 + 1}$;

(b) $\dfrac{\sqrt[+]{p^2 + 1} + mp}{\sqrt[+]{p^2 + 1} - mp}$, m real and $0 < m < 1$;

(c) the same function, but with $1 < m$;

(d) $\dfrac{\sqrt[+]{p^2 + 1} + \bar{m}p}{\sqrt[+]{p^2 + 1} - mp}$, m complex;

(e) $\dfrac{\sqrt[+]{p^2 + 1} + \bar{m}p}{\sqrt[+]{p^2 + 1} - mp} \dfrac{\sqrt[+]{p^2 + 1} + mp}{\sqrt[+]{p^2 + 1} - \bar{m}p}$.

5-17. Show that a driving-point immittance function cannot be of the form of the quotient of two even (or odd) polynomials, except in one very special case. What is that?

5-18. Show that a driving-point immittance function of the form of the quotient of an even polynomial and an odd polynomial can have only imaginary poles and zeros. What is the nature of the residues and the derivatives thereat?

5-19. (a) Consider an even polynomial, all of whose coefficients are real. Determine what restrictions these two assumptions place on the locations of its zeros, and thereby show that such a polynomial cannot be Hurwitz. Under what additional conditions might such a polynomial be the numerator or denominator of a driving-point immittance function?

(b) Repeat (a) for an *odd* polynomial with real coefficients.

(c) Show that a polynomial of the second of the two kinds in (5.12-1) is a Hurwitz polynomial in the variable p^2, and that a Hurwitz polynomial in p^2 is not necessarily admissible as a possible numerator or denominator of a driving-point immittance function.

5-20. Show that if $Q(p) = A + pB$ is either a Hurwitz polynomial or the product of a Hurwitz polynomial and an even polynomial, then in form

$$A = (p^2 + \omega_1^2)(p^2 + \omega_2^2) \cdot \cdot \cdot ,$$
$$pB = p(p^2 + \omega_a^2)(p^2 + \omega_b^2) \cdot \cdot \cdot ,$$

i.e., the zeros and poles of $R = A/pB$ are confined to the imaginary axis and are simple. Show also that the residues of R and of $1/R$ at the poles are real and positive. Show also that the zeros and poles of R and of $1/R$ alternate along the imaginary axis, and that the slope of $\mathbf{Im}\,R$ and of $\mathbf{Im}\,1/R$ is positive there, as a function of ω.

5-21. If a polynomial has only positive (real) coefficients, and has a right-half-plane zero(s), the number of such zeros must be *even*. Demonstrate and explain this statement.

5-22. Let $F(p)$ be a p-r (rational) function with a zero at $p = +j\omega_0$, so that $(p^2 + \omega_0^2)$ is a factor of its numerator. Show that the function remaining after removal of these real-frequency zeros, $F_1(p) = F(p)/(p^2 + \omega_0^2)$, is not p-r.

5-23. A network design problem calls for the function $F(p) = E_2/E_1$ to be a prescribed rational function of p. In order to be able to achieve a realizable design for the impedances Z_1 and Z_2 (see figure), is it necessary that $F(p)$ be

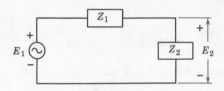

Prob. 5–23

positive-real? For the same end, is it necessary that the function $(F^{-1} - 1)$ be p-r? What necessary restrictions on the locations and orders of the zeros and poles of $(F^{-1} - 1)$ can be laid down on the basis of realizability of Z_1 and Z_2? What necessary restriction on the real-frequency angle of $(F^{-1} - 1)$?

5-24. Delineate the portion of the right half plane in which the function (5.13–1) has a negative real part, by giving the equation of the bounding curve and illustrating with a sketch. How does this demonstrate that the function is not p-r?

5-25. Develop a test for positive reality that is the test (5.13–5) so modified that it can be applied to *any* function (not necessarily rational). (Positive reality may be assumed to require analytic character in the right half plane; cf. Prob. 4-12.) Illustrate by application to the functions:

$$(a)\ \sqrt{p + 1} \qquad (b)\ \sqrt{p - 1} \qquad (c)\ \sqrt{p} \qquad (d)\ \sqrt[3]{p} \qquad (e)\ e^p$$

$$(f)\ \frac{p^2 + 1}{\sqrt{p}(p^2 + 2)} \qquad (g)\ \frac{\sqrt{p + 1}(p + 3)}{p^2 + 2p + 4} \qquad (h)\ \sqrt{p^2 + 1} \qquad (i)\ \ln{(p + 1)}$$

$$(j)\ \sqrt{(R + Lp)(G + Cp)}, \ \sqrt{(R + Lp)/(G + Cp)}, \ \tanh{[\sqrt{(R + Lp)(G + Cp)}]}$$

in which the literal parameters are real and positive.

5-26. Consider each of the six properties in §§ 5.04–5.09 in turn, and show how a violation of it will appear in applying the test (5.13–5) to a rational function of p.

5-27. Show that any rational function that meets the following requirements can be written as the difference of two p-r functions, and that if it does not have all these properties it cannot be so written. The function must (1) have real coefficients, (2) be analytic in the right half plane, (3) have at most simple poles on the imaginary axis, at which the residues are real, and (4) at infinity have at most a simple pole (it may approach a finite, nonzero value, or have a zero of any order there).

5-28. Demonstrate the truth of the following statement from one of the parts of the test (5.13–5). "At real frequencies the real part of a positive-real function never becomes infinite." What is the physical interpretation to be given this with regard to driving-point immittances? Can the point be made merely on the basis of physical reasoning? (Cf. Prob. 5-6.)

5-29. Explain fully how an even polynomial $E(p)$ can be tested for right-half-plane zeros by making a plot of $E(j\omega)$ and examining it. Illustrate with the following polynomials:

    (*a*) $1 + p^{2n}$ (*n* an integer)   (*b*) $1 + p^2 + p^4$ (*c*) $1 + 2p^2 + p^4$

5-30. Discuss the validity of this statement: If a function that is being tested for p-r character is found in 2(*c*) of (5.13–5) to have imaginary poles, it may be simpler to stop the test there and begin the test again on the reciprocal function.

5-31. Demonstrate that in § 5.14 the transformation (mapping) from p to Φ is unique, but that from Φ to p is not, and that the transformation from p to W is unique, but that W to p is not. Determine into how many points in the p plane a given point of the W plane maps. How many branches does the multivalued function that expresses p in terms of W have? Where are its branch points? Demonstrate that this multivalued property in no way affects the validity of the arguments of § 5.14.

5-32. Given a polynomial $Q(p) = A + pB$, form $R(p) = A/pB$. Show that if the partial-fraction expansion of $R(p)$ is

$$R(p) = \sum_k \frac{b_k}{p - j\omega_k} + b_\infty p$$

in which all the b's are real and positive, then $Q(p)$ is either a Hurwitz polynomial or the product of a Hurwitz polynomial and an even (or odd) polynomial. (This is another test, different from that based on the continued-fraction expansion of R or R^{-1}, for such character, though not as practical.) Show also that if $Q(p)$ has such character, its partial-fraction expansion must have the form above.

5-33. Let $Q(p) = A + pB$ be a Hurwitz polynomial, for which $Q(0)$ is a positive number. Show that the zeros of A and of pB are imaginary and mutually separate each other, i.e., form an interlacing pattern on the imaginary axis. What is the nature of the locus of $Q(j\omega)$ as ω varies from zero to infinity?

5-34. Show that the process of dividing up a polynomial into its even and odd parts, followed by continued-fraction expansion of the ratio, will remove from the polynomial any purely even or purely odd factors, regardless of whether the polynomial has right-half-plane zeros or not.

5-33. By using the transformation (3.24–5), devise a procedure for determining whether a given polynomial has all of its zeros within the unit circle centered on the origin. Modify this to a circle of arbitrary radius. (Cf. WA 2, p. 190.)

5-36. Show how a test for right-half-plane zeros of a given polynomial may be based on the theorem of § 3.22, using the imaginary axis and a large semicircle to form the closed contour. Illustrate by drawing the necessary diagrams for the polynomials $(p^2 + ap + b)$ and $(p^3 + ap^2 + bp + c)$ in which the coefficients are real but may be zero or have either sign (consider all the possibilities). Is this method comparable in efficiency with that of § 5.14? What particular difficulty arises if the given polynomial happens to have imaginary zeros, and how may it be overcome?

5-37. The test of § 5.14 has been developed and expressed in various (equivalent) ways. One of these, due to Hurwitz (HU 3), involves certain determinants formed from the coefficients of the given polynomial. Derive this form of the test (cf. GU 3). Another form is that known as *Routh's rule* (GA 1, GU 3, RO 2, WA 2). State and derive this form of the test. Illustrate, by examples chosen from the polynomials of later problems, the application of these two forms as well as that of § 5.14. How do the three compare in efficiency, and which do you prefer?

5-38. Show, by the test of § 5.14, that a polynomial of degree two is a Hurwitz polynomial if and only if all of its (real) coefficients have the same sign, none being zero. Show that this same-sign condition is not sufficient for a third-degree polynomial, but must be augmented by an additional condition; what is the latter? Is it feasible to carry this further and tabulate conditions for a fourth-degree polynomial? For higher degree polynomials?

5-39. Determine, by the test of § 5.14, for what range of values of the (real) parameter a the polynomial $(p^3 + ap^2 + 3p + 1)$ is Hurwitz. When a has a critical (borderline) value, where are the zeros of the polynomial? Where are the zeros when a is just below this value? Just above? Describe what happens to the zeros as a is varied continuously through all real values.

5-40. In general, as the coefficients of a polynomial are varied, the zeros move accordingly. They may enter and leave one half of the plane or the other, by crossing the imaginary axis (cf. Prob. 5-39). Are the crossings necessarily confined to any part of the imaginary axis? What must happen to one or more of the coefficients c in the test of § 5.14 as a zero crosses? Illustrate by forming the polynomial $(p + 2)(p^2 + ap + 1)$ and observing both the loci of the zeros and the behavior of the c's as a is varied from large positive values through zero to large negative values. Repeat with the polynomial $(3 + a)p^3 + (3 + a)p^2 + 2p + 1$. What, in general, seems to be the behavior of the c's when a certain number of right-half-plane zeros are present in the polynomial? (Cf. Prob. 5-41.)

5-41. When a polynomial $Q(p)$ is tested according to § 5.14, some of the c's are found to be negative, indicating the existence of right-half-plane zeros of $(M_1 + N_1)$ in (5.14-23). Show that the number of such negative c's is equal to the number of right-half-plane zeros of $(M_1 + N_1)$. (Cf. WA 2.)

5-42. When certain special relations exist among the coefficients of a polynomial, the "test fraction" Ψ of § 5.14 may not exist, as will be evidenced by some of the c's becoming indeterminate. Determine, by means of the examples below, how this occurs. Then discuss the use of each of the three devices given as a means of circumventing this difficulty. Can a polynomial in which this anomaly occurs ever be Hurwitz? For the designer of one-terminal pairs, are these devices of importance? If one is interested in the number of right-half-plane zeros of the polynomial, are they important (cf. Prob. 5-41)?

(a) $4p^4 + 3p^3 + 1$.

(b) $p^4 + 3p^3 + 2p^2 + 6p + 2$.

(c) $p^5 + 2p^4 + 2p^3 + 4p^2 + 8p + 6$.

(d) $p^7 + p^6 + 2p^5 + 2p^4 + 6p^3 + 3p^2 + 8p + 4$.

(1) Alter one or more of the coefficients by the addition of a small quantity, ϵ. Then, when the c's have been found in terms of ϵ, determine their signs by giving ϵ a small value. Does it matter which sign ϵ has? What principle, with regard to relation between location of zeros and small changes in coefficients, is involved here?

(2) Multiply the polynomial by, for example, $(p + a)$, a being some real number, and then test the modified polynomial.

(3) Transform the variable by the substitution, for example, of $s = p^{-1}$. (WA 2, p. 191.)

5-43. When Sturm's theorem is applied to a certain polynomial of degree n, f_m comes out to be a polynomial of degree r. Show that the number of distinct zeros of the polynomial (over the whole plane) is then $s = n - r$. Determine the number of points in the p plane at which the polynomial $(p^8 + 8p^7 + 31p^6 + 74p^5 + 118p^4 + 128p^3 + 92p^2 + 40p + 8)$ vanishes. How many simple zeros does it have? How many double ones? How many triple ones?

5-44. Show that, in applying Sturm's theorem, if a function f_r is encountered which remains positive (or remains negative) for x between x_1 and x_2, then the members of the sequence beyond f_r may be ignored.

5-45. Show that, in applying Sturm's theorem, any Sturm function can be multiplied by a positive constant (to avoid fractions, for example, or to make the magnitudes more convenient), or by any polynomial in x that is positive for $x_1 < x < x_2$, and that this modified Sturm function can be used in computing all further Sturm functions.

5-46. Apply Sturm's theorem to the bounding of the zeros of $f(x)$, as between integers (i.e., to the determination of the integer part of its zeros). Illustrate with $f(x) = x^3 - 4x^2 - 8.6x + 8.4$. Determine its zeros to four significant figures by applying Sturm's theorem.

5-47. Determine, by Sturm's theorem, the number of positive real zeros, the number of negative real zeros, the number of nonreal zeros (counting multiple zeros as the appropriate number of zeros), of $(p^8 + 2p^7 - 6p^6 + 2p^5 + 2p^4 + 2p^3 - 6p^2 + 2p + 1)$.

5-48. If, in applying Sturm's theorem, a stage is reached where in $f_k = ax^n + \cdots$ all coefficients have the same sign, show that it is not necessary to go further to determine the number of distinct real zeros of $f(x)$, but that it *is* necessary to proceed if their multiplicities are to be found. Illustrate with $f(x) = x^5 - ax + b$, in which a and b are real and positive.

5-49. Show how it is possible to arrange the work of applying Sturm's theorem in a compact arrangement of two parallel vertical columns between which the work shifts, taking advantage of the fact that some quotients need not then be rewritten. Illustrate by writing the most compact arrangement of the work in the case $f(x) = x^4 - 2x^3 + 1$. (Cf. TU 1, WE 1.)

5-50. Which of the following polynomials are Hurwitz polynomials?

(a) $p^4 + 10p^3 + 35p^2 + 50p + 24$.

(b) $p^5 + p^4 + p^3 + p^2 + p + 1$.

(c) $p^5 + 2p^4 + 22p^3 + 12p^2 + 56p + 16$.

(d) $p^7 + 4p^6 + 25p^5 + 54p^4 + 102p^3 + 144p^2 + 90p + 16$.

(e) $p^5 + 6p^4 + 3p^3 + 2p^2 + p + 1$.

(f) $p^5 + 4p^3 + 3p^2 + 2p + 6$.

(g) $p^5 + 6p^4 + 13p^3 + 15p^2 + 10p + 3$.

(h) $p^5 + p^4 + 3p^3 + 9p^2 + 16p + 10$.

(i) $p^7 + 14p^6 + 89p^5 + 330p^4 + 752p^3 + 1024p^2 + 740p + 200$.

(j) $p^5 + 6p^4 + 2p^3 - p^2 + 1$.

5-51. Test the following polynomials and determine whether they have any right-half-plane zeros. If not, are they Hurwitz polynomials?

(a) $p^7 + 3p^6 + 8p^5 + 6p^4 + p^3 + 3p^2 + 8p + 6$.

(b) $p^7 + 2p^6 + 7p^5 + 5p^4 + 2p^2 + 6p + 4$.

(c) $p^3 + 3p^2 - 2p + 8$.

(d) $p^3 + 6p^2 + 1$.

(e) $p^6 + 3p^5 + 4p^4 + 6p^3 + 5p^2 + 3p + 2$.

(f) $p^5 + 4p^4 + 11p^3 + 16p^2 + 10p + 12$.

(g) $2p^4 + 3p^3 + 6p^2 + 7p + 2$.

(h) $p^4 + p^3 + 14p^2 + 254p + 240$.

(i) $p^7 + 5p^6 + 11p^5 + 10p^4 + p^3 + 5p^2 + 11p + 10$.

(j) $p^7 + 4p^6 + 15p^5 + 40p^4 + 72p^3 + 108p^2 + 108p + 72$.

(k) $p^4 + 2.1p^3 + 1.91p^2 + 1.701p + 0.891$.

5-52. Which of the following polynomials could be denominators of p-r functions (with suitable numerators)?

(a) $p^5 + 6p^4 + 11p^3 + 14p^2 + 10p + 8$.

(b) $p^5 + 4p^4 + 2p^3 + 8p^2 + p + 4$.

(c) $p^7 + p^6 + 3p^5 + 3p^4 + 3p^3 + 3p^2 + p + 1$.

(d) $p^5 + 8p^4 + 27p^3 + 50p^2 + 52p + 24$.

(e) $p^6 + 6p^4 + 11p^2 + 6$.

(f) $p^3 + 0.2p^2 + 5.2p + 6$.

(g) $p^5 + 3p^3 + 2p$.

5-53. Determine how many zeros each of the polynomials below has in the right half plane, in the left half plane, and on the imaginary axis. (Cf. Probs. 5-41 and 5-42.)

(a) $3p^5 + 9p^4 + 4p^3 + 18p^2 + 6p + 30$.

(b) $p^4 + 2p^3 + 3p^2 + 1$.

(c) $p^4 + p^3 + p^2 + p + 1$.

(d) $p^3 + 3p^2 + p$.

(e) $p^4 + 1$.

Continue for the polynomials of Probs. 5-42, 5-43, 5-47, 5-50, 5-51, and 5-52.

5-54. Classify each of the following functions as p-r or not.

(1) $\dfrac{2p^4 + 15p^3 + 34p^2 + 27p + 8}{p^4 + 4p^3 + 4p^2 + 4p + 3}$

(2) $\dfrac{3p^4 + 3p^3 + 7p^2 + 5p + 4}{p^3 + p^2 + 2p + 2}$

(3) $\dfrac{17p^5 + 4p^4 + j2p^3 + 4p^2 + 3p + 6}{p^4 + 6p^3 + 9p^2 + 17p + 8}$

(4) $\dfrac{p^7 + 6p^6 + 5p^5 + 4p^4 + 3p^3 + 2p^2 + p}{p^5 + 8p^4 + 3p^3 + 6p^2 + 7p + 4}$

(5) $\dfrac{p^4 + 3p^3 + 2p^2 + 6p + 2}{p^5 + p^4 + p^3 + p^2 + p + 1}$

(6) $\dfrac{p^2}{6p^3 + 2p^2 + 3p + 7}$

(7) $\dfrac{p^8 + 9p^7 + 8p^6 + 5p^5 + 3p^4 + 7p^3 + 4p^2 + p + 1}{18p^7 + 6p^6 + 12p^5 + 4p^4 + 6p^3 + 2p^2 + 3p + 1}$

(8) $\dfrac{p^4 + 4p^2 + 4}{p^3 + 5p}$

(9) $\dfrac{p^3 + 3p^2 + 2p + 8}{p^3 + 3p^2 - 2p + 8}$ (10) $\dfrac{p^5 + 6p^4 + 3p^3 + 2p^2 + 8p + 10}{p^4 + 1}$

(11) $\dfrac{p^5 + 18p^3 + 72p}{p^4 + 12p^2 + 27}$ (12) $\dfrac{p^2 + 4p + 3}{p^3 + 6p^2 + 8p}$

(13) $\dfrac{7p^3 + 6p^2 + 5p + 4}{23.6p + 1}$ (14) $\dfrac{p^3 + 8p^2 - 4p + 7}{p^2 + 2p + 2}$

(15) $\dfrac{p^3 + 4p^2 + 7p + 3}{p^3 + 3p^2 + 4p + 2}$ (16) $\dfrac{2p^6 + 5p^5 + 10p^4 + 22p^3 + 15p^2 + 12p + 12}{p^5 + 3p^4 + 5p^3 + 9p^2 + 6p}$

(17) $\dfrac{p^6 + 12p^4 + 44p^2 + 48}{p^7 + 9p^5 + 23p^3 + 15}$ (18) $\dfrac{p^6 + 12p^4 + 44p^2 + 48}{p^6 + 9p^4 + 23p^2 + 15}$

(19) $\dfrac{p^3 + 3p + 1}{p^2 + 2p + 1}$ (20) $\dfrac{p^2 + 2p + 1}{p^2 - 2p + 1}$

(21) $\dfrac{p^2 + 3p + 1}{p^3 + 3p^2 + 4p + 2}$ (22) $\dfrac{p^2 + 4p + 1}{p^3 + 3p^2 + 4p + 2}$

(23) $\dfrac{p^2 + 2p + 2}{p^3 + 3p^2 + 4p + 2}$ (24) $\dfrac{p^5 + 17p^4 + 10p^3 + p^2 + 8p + 1}{p^4 + 9p^3 + 2p^2 + p + 1}$

(25) $\dfrac{p^3 + 6p^2 + 13p + 10}{p^3 + 3p^2 + 4p + 2}$ (26) $\dfrac{p^4 + 4p^3 + 3p^2 + 4p + 1}{3p^4 + 4p^3 + 7p^2 + 4p + 3}$

(27) $\dfrac{p^3 + 3p^2 + 2p + 1}{p + 10}$ (28) $\dfrac{p^2 - 2p + 1}{p + 6}$

(29) $\dfrac{p^2 + 1}{p}$ (30) $\dfrac{p^3 + 1}{p^2 + 10p + 6}$

(31) $\dfrac{p^4 + 16p^2 + 64}{p^3 + 10p}$ (32) $\dfrac{p^2 + 16p + 64}{p}$

(33) p^2 (34) $\dfrac{p^2 + 3p + 1}{p^2 + p + 1}$

(35) $\dfrac{p^2 + 0.67p + 3}{p^2 + p + 0.67}$ (36) $\dfrac{p^3 + 6p^2 + 7p + 3}{p^2 + 2p + 1}$

(37) $\dfrac{75p^5 + 74p^4 + 73p^3 + 72p^2 + 71p + 70}{p^4 + 10p^3 + 5p^2 + 3p + 1}$ (38) $\dfrac{7p^3 + 6p^2 + 10p + 1}{p + 6}$

(39) $\dfrac{p^7 + 3p^6 + 2p^5 + 3p^3 + 4p^2 + p + 6}{p^6 + 6p^5 + 10p^4 + 3p^3 + 2p^2 + p + 1}$ (40) $\dfrac{p^3 + 4p^2 + 8p + 3}{p^3 + 3p^2 + 4p + 2}$

5-55. The following functions are obviously not p-r. Why is this so? In what steps of the test (5.13–5) will the non-p-r character become evident?

(a) $\dfrac{(p^2 + 4)^2}{p(p^2 + 2)}$ (b) $\dfrac{(p^2 + 5)^2}{(p + 1)^3}$

Of the functions in Prob. 5-54, some are obviously not p-r. In each case, what part of the test (5.13–5) confirms this?

5-56. The function $(p^3 + 4p)/(p^2 + ap + 1)$ is not p-r, regardless of the value of a (which is real). Demonstrate this. If this function represents a driving-point impedance, of which only the reactance is of interest, how might the function be made p-r without affecting the reactance?

5-57. A network is desired to have the driving-point reactance function

$$X(\omega) = (1 + \epsilon \sin \omega^2/\omega_0{}^2);$$

the resistance part of the impedance is of no concern in this problem. Explain why it is impossible to design such a network.

5-58. Show that if a function $F(p)$ is p-r, and its behavior at infinity is given by the series $(Lp + K_0 + K_1/p + \cdots)$ in which L, K_0, and K_1 are real and positive, then the function $[F(p) - Lp]$ is still p-r.

5-59. Modify the test of § 5.13 so that, as far as possible, the *angle* of the function is examined rather than its real part or other parts. Illustrate by testing the function $F(p)$ for positive reality, given that $F(\sigma)$ is real for $\sigma > 0$, $F(p)$ is analytic in the right half plane, and $F(j\omega) = |F|e^{j\beta}$, $\beta = \tan^{-1}(\omega/\omega_0)^n$, n a positive integer.

5-60. Given the following data on a function $F(p)$, show that $F(p)$ has a right-half-plane zero(s).

(a) $\mathrm{Re}\, F(j\omega) \geq 0$;

(b) $\mathrm{Re}\, F(\infty) \geq 0$;

(c) imaginary poles of $F(p)$ are simple, with residues that are real and positive;

(d) at one or more right-half-plane points, $F(p)$ is not analytic.

5-61. If a function $F(p)$ that is to be tested for positive reality has imaginary poles but no imaginary zeros, compare the work of testing $F(p)$ with that of testing $1/F(p)$.

5-62. In the test for positive reality of a function $F(p)$, (5.13–5),

(a) show that the work of step 3 is identical, whether it be $F(p)$ or $1/F(p)$ that is tested;

(b) show that step 2 could equally well be that stated with *pole* replaced by *zero* and *residue* replaced by *derivative*;

(c) show that if the numerator of $F(p)$ has no imaginary or right-half-plane zeros, then steps 2(b) and 2(c) of the test may be omitted.

5-63. To emphasize the independence of the properties of *positive reality* and *rationality*, give examples of each of the following kinds of functions: (a) rational, but not p-r; (b) p-r but not rational; (c) both; (d) neither.

6.

The Nondissipative *(L-C)*
One-Terminal Pair

Our topic in Volume I is the synthesis of one-terminal pairs. Toward that end we have been investigating in detail the properties that such pairs must have; we have been performing *analysis*. Our aim has been to acquire a knowledge of the fundamental properties of driving-point immittance functions in order to be able eventually to decide whether or not a given (desired) function is realizable; that is step 1 in the synthesis problem's solution. In Chapter 5 we developed a list of properties that a physically realizable driving-point immittance function must have. We specifically listed some ten such properties, and then went on to methods of testing for positive reality. Before we go on to further properties and actual synthesis in the general case, it seems reasonable that we should consider any simpler special cases that may exist, both because they ought to be easier to handle, and because they may make the general problem clearer and simpler. In this chapter we consider such a special case, and before its end we shall be able to carry out some simple syntheses.

The general one-terminal pair (Fig. 1.03–C) has in it, of course, all three kinds of elements. The simplest special case is that in which the box has but one kind of element in it; this is trivial, for synthesis amounts merely to calculating the value of an equivalent single element. The next simplest case is that in which the box has in it *two* kinds of elements only, and here there are three possibilities: the *L-C*, *R-C*, and *R-L* cases, as they are usually called (cf. § 2.01). We shall consider each of these three special cases in turn. In each we shall (1) endeavor to carry *analysis* even further, to obtain additional properties peculiar to each case, and (2) seek to *synthesize* as we can within the limits of the case.

231

6.01 The L-C case

We start now to discuss the case in which the one-terminal pair has in it *no resistance* at all, i.e., it is *nondissipative*. (The term "lossless" is sometimes used, but this term is apt to cause confusion in Volume II, when we shall be talking about "loss" in a sense quite different; hence we shall not employ it here.) In the box there may be inductors and capacitors, arbitrary in number, arrangement, and values, and mutual inductance is also allowed, but there are *no* resistors, and all the F functions of Chapter 4 are *zero*.

Of the three special cases listed above, this (the L-C) case is the most important, and the time spent on it is easily justified. We shall find, for example, in our study of two-terminal pairs in Volume II, that we shall need to draw heavily on the stock of knowledge we are about to build up here. In addition, synthesis of one-terminal L-C pairs is important in its own right, and we shall have practical examples of this fact fairly soon.

Since there is no resistance in the network, the driving-point impedance, at real frequencies, will be purely reactive, and will have a zero real part (for finite networks, at least). Hence the term *reactive* network can be applied as well as the term L-C; we shall use both terms, as well as the term *nondissipative*. From the dual point of view, the driving-point admittance will be purely susceptive, but the term *susceptive* is not in much use. We shall first analyze such a network in general terms to see if we can extend our list of properties to additional ones which are more special and hold only in the absence of dissipation. It turns out that there are several such restricted properties, and some of them are rather important.

The driving-point impedance function $Z(p)$, in the L-C case, must of course be p-r and rational; the coefficients must be real numbers; and the zeros and poles (if complex) must occur in conjugate pairs. No zeros can lie in the right half plane, nor can any poles; poles on the imaginary axis must be simple, with real, positive residues, and zeros there are correspondingly restricted. The highest and lowest powers of p in numerator and denominator can differ in degree by unity at most, and at real frequencies the real part of $Z(p)$ is even and the imaginary part is odd. Every statement holds also for $Y = 1/Z$, i.e., for the admittance function also. These are general properties that hold for *any* driving-point immittance function, not just for those in the L-C category.

6.02 Zeros and poles

Consider again the fourth property, that which eliminates zeros and poles from the right half plane. It still leaves, however, the whole left half plane and the imaginary axis as permitted regions. Is there any further restriction in the L-C case?

Here we have $F_0 = 0$, hence (4.12–13) becomes

$$Z(p) = T_0 p + \frac{V_0}{p}, \tag{6.02–1}$$

and similarly (4.12–16) becomes

$$Y(p) = V_0 p + \frac{T_0}{p}, \tag{6.02–2}$$

both based, of course, on the absence of resistance in the network (Fig. 6.02–A). Notice (extraordinary fact) that when $p = j\omega$, i.e., for real

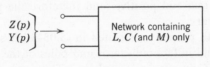

$$\left.\begin{array}{c} Z(p) \\ Y(p) \end{array}\right\} \longrightarrow \boxed{\begin{array}{c} \text{Network containing} \\ L,\, C \text{ (and } M\text{) only} \end{array}}$$

Fig. 6.02–A

frequencies, $Z(j\omega)$ is purely imaginary, i.e., the resistance part of the impedance is zero. This is, of course, as it should be, and leads us to call a function of this type a *reactance function*. (It might equally well be called a "susceptance" function, but reactance is the word commonly used to characterize absence of dissipation.) Such a function is by definition a positive-real function that, on the imaginary axis (i.e., for $p = j\omega$), has a zero real part. The value of the function is then (for $p = j\omega$) purely imaginary, and the imaginary part represents the driving-point reactance of an L-C network if the function is actually a driving-point impedance function. Note that the values of the reactance and of the reactance function differ by a factor j—which is unfortunate, but need cause no difficulty. The driving-point immittance functions of L-C networks (both Z and Y) must necessarily be reactance functions. Conversely, any such function represents a driving-point immittance of a physically realizable network, a point which will be proved shortly by actual synthesis.

When p has such a value that $Z(p)$ vanishes, i.e., at a zero of Z, we have

$$T_0 p + \frac{V_0}{p} = 0, \tag{6.02–3}$$

or

$$p^2 = -\frac{V_0}{T_0}, \tag{6.02–4}$$

or

$$p = \pm j \sqrt{\frac{V_0}{T_0}}. \qquad (6.02\text{-}5)$$

Since V_0 and T_0 are real and positive numbers (even though functions of p), by (4.12-15), these values of p which make $Z(p)$ vanish, the zeros of $Z(p)$, are purely imaginary, or occur only at real frequencies.

When p has such a value that $Z(p)$ becomes infinite, i.e., at a zero of $Y(p)$, we have, from (6.02-2), in a similar fashion,

$$p = \pm j \sqrt{\frac{T_0}{V_0}}. \qquad (6.02\text{-}6)$$

These numbers T_0 and V_0 are of course defined differently [cf. (4.12-17)] but they are still real and positive, and therefore the poles of $Z(p)$ are also purely imaginary.

Hence the fourth property, as stated in (5.05-3), is severely restricted in the L-C case, and in fact only zeros and poles of the type discussed in § 5.06 occur in L-C immittance functions. This is more or less obvious physically, from the familiar resonant and antiresonant properties of nondissipative circuits, but to avoid any lingering doubt we need the argument above.

We could reach this conclusion in a simpler fashion if we observed that the constituent elements have impedances Lp and $1/Cp$ only, that these are *odd* functions, and hence that the whole immittance must be an odd function of p (by the rules for combining series and parallel impedances). Thus if $Z(p)$ is zero, then

$$Z(-p) = -Z(p) = 0 \qquad (6.02\text{-}7)$$

also. But if p is in the left half plane, then $-p$ is in the right half plane, where $Z = 0$ is not allowed. The only possibility, then, is that the zeros (and poles) be purely imaginary. This point of view leads to an alternative definition of a reactance function, as simply a p-r function which is also *odd*. Evidently any driving-point immittance function of a non-dissipative network is both p-r and odd, hence the name is appropriate. We have already discussed such functions in some detail (§ 5.14), and the information gathered there will shortly be of value in proving that any such function actually represents a driving-point immittance function. (The two definitions of "reactance function" given here are completely equivalent.)

In the light of the discussion above, and of the third and fifth properties, (5.04-1) and (5.06-7), we can sum up by saying that

in the L-C case $Z(p)$ and $Y(p)$ are odd, all the zeros and all the poles of

$Z(p)$ and of $Y(p)$ occur on the imaginary axis (and are therefore simple), each zero and each pole is accompanied by its negative (i.e., its conjugate), the residue at each pole is real and positive, and the derivative at each zero is also real and positive.   (6.02–8)

These statements are true of any positive-real function which is also odd, i.e., of any reactance function, but we have yet to demonstrate that an arbitrary reactance function is actually a physically realizable driving-point immittance function (of an *L-C* network).

Incidentally, the reciprocal of a reactance function is also a reactance function, from the definition above.

6.03 Reactance (susceptance) slope and the separation property

Consider now an arbitrary reactance function, i.e., any p-r function which is also odd. (All driving-point immittance functions of *L-C* networks fall in this category.) Since such functions are so intimately connected with *L-C* networks, we designate this function $Z(p)$ [although $Y(p)$ would be an equally apt designation, since impedances and admittances have the same properties]. At real frequencies, Z is purely imaginary and we write, using the usual symbol for reactance,

$$Z(j\omega) = 0 + jX(\omega). \qquad (6.03–1)$$

At the zeros of $Z(p)$ (which are on the imaginary axis) $Z'(p)$ is real and positive, by (6.02–8). Hence

$$\frac{dX}{d\omega} = \frac{1}{j}\frac{dZ(j\omega)}{d\omega} = Z'(j\omega) \qquad (6.03–2)$$

is also real and positive. A zero, negative, or nonreal value of this derivative is ruled out by the assumption of positive reality (as discussed in § 5.06). Thus the slope of the driving-point reactance of an *L-C* network is positive when the reactance is zero. More than that, it is positive at *all* frequencies. To demonstrate this, consider the artificial function

$$Z_1(p) = Z(p) + jK \qquad (6.03–3)$$

in which K is a real constant. $Z_1(p)$ is not p-r, but it is a "positive" function in that $\mathbf{Re}\, Z_1(p) > 0$ when $\sigma > 0$, for $\mathbf{Re}\, Z_1(p) = \mathbf{Re}\, Z(p)$ and Z is p-r. The arguments of § 5.06 are based only on the property of a positive real part in the right half plane, and therefore we can say that the zeros of $Z_1(p)$ are also imaginary and simple, and that at such points $Z_1'(p)$ is real and positive. Consider now some arbitrary frequency ω_0, and let $K = -X(\omega_0)$. Then $Z_1(j\omega_0) = 0$ and therefore $Z_1'(j\omega_0)$ is real and positive. But

$$\frac{dX}{d\omega} = \frac{1}{j}\frac{d}{d\omega}[Z_1(j\omega) - jK] = Z_1'(j\omega), \qquad (6.03–4)$$

for K is a constant. Hence the slope of the reactance $X(\omega)$ is positive at the frequency ω_0—and because ω_0 is arbitrary, this holds at all frequencies. Our conclusion is an important property of purely reactive impedances, that

the slope of the driving-point reactance of an L-C network, plotted against frequency, is always positive.   (6.03–5)

All that we have said is equally valid if we interpret $Z(p)$ as an L-C driving-point admittance function, or write $Y(p)$ and B in place of $Z(p)$ and X above.   To emphasize this, we write the dual statement,

the slope of the driving-point susceptance of an L-C network, plotted against frequency, is always positive.   (6.03–6)

From this slope property follows another important fact about the zeros and the poles: they separate each other.   We could not have two zeros in succession, with no poles between them, without having negative

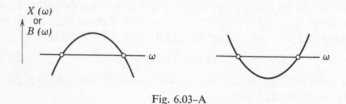

Fig. 6.03–A

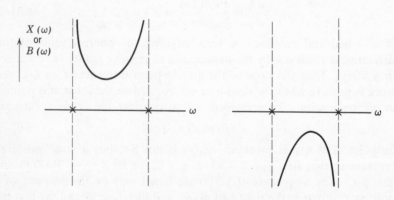

Fig. 6.03–B

slope (Fig. 6.03–A), nor could we have two poles with no intervening zeros (Fig. 6.03–B).   Hence

the zeros and the poles of a reactance function are interlaced in the pattern
· · · zero–pole–zero–pole · · ·   (6.03–7)

and the general behavior of $X(\omega)$ or $B(\omega)$ is that shown in Fig. 6.03–C.

The general appearance of the plot of reactance or susceptance versus frequency resembles that of a section of a tangent-function plot. The

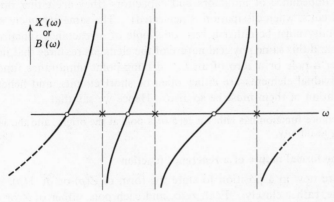

Fig. 6.03–C

spacings of consecutive zeros and poles are not necessarily equal, but at the same time the shape of the curve between zeros and poles is not entirely arbitrary, as will be shown later.

On a sketch of the p plane, the layout of zeros and poles will be of one of the two types shown in Fig. 6.03–D. Notice that the origin (frequently

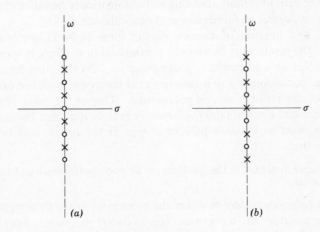

Fig. 6.03–D

referred to as "d-c" because it corresponds to zero frequency or direct current as opposed to alternating current, in the steady state) must be either a pole or a zero of a reactance function. This follows from the separation property and the requirement that $X(\omega)$ be odd. It is also obvious, for L-C driving-point immittances, from the physical nature of the d-c impedance of inductors and capacitors (they are either open or short circuits, when dissipation is neglected). The same argument shows that infinity must be either a zero or a pole of a reactance function (cf. § 5.14), and this same physical nature of the elements requires that infinity be either a pole or a zero of an L-C driving-point immittance function: the individual elements are either open or short circuits, and hence any combination of them must be so also. Hence we say that

a reactance function has either a zero or a pole at the origin, and the same is true at infinity.   (6.03–8)

6.04 The formal nature of a reactance function

We are now in a position to state the form of $Z(p)$ or of $Y(p)$, in the L-C case, rather closely. Each zero, and each pole, either of Z or of Y, must be caused by a factor of the form $(p - j\omega_0)$. Since every zero, and every pole, the origin and infinity excepted, is accompanied by its negative, (its conjugate) we can combine the two related factors and get

$$(p - j\omega_0)(p + j\omega_0) = (p^2 + \omega_0^2) \qquad (6.04–1)$$

as a typical factor of numerator and denominator. The factor corresponding to a pole or zero at the origin is simply p, which is *not* mated with another factor, because the zero must be simple. There remains only the pole or zero at infinity, but this will automatically be taken care of by the relative degrees of numerator and denominator.

When any number of factors of the form (6.04–1) are multiplied together, the result must be an even polynomial in p; there is no possible way in which an odd power of p can creep in. On the other hand, when the factor corresponding to a zero (pole) at the origin is tacked onto such a product, the result is an *odd* polynomial. One or the other of the two (numerator and denominator) will remain even as the other becomes odd, for there must be either a pole or a zero at the origin, and hence we conclude that

a reactance·function is the quotient of an even polynomial and an odd polynomial.   (6.04–2)

The odd polynomial may be either the numerator or the denominator but the denominator or numerator (respectively) is even. Formally, a reactance function, which includes all L-C driving-point impedance and admittance functions, must be pB/A or A/pB. Here A and B are even polynomials, as usual, and hence pB is an odd polynomial. In the alternative notation in which M is an even polynomial and N an odd one, the form would be M/N or N/M. Since a reactance function is by definition an odd p-r function, and we are considering only rational functions here, we might well have stated the results above as following immediately from this definition.

The mixed polynomials formed by adding together numerator and denominator of a reactance function have no zeros on the imaginary axis or in the right half plane, i.e., they are Hurwitz polynomials. This has, in effect, been demonstrated in § 5.14, where it was shown that if the numerator and denominator of an odd, rational p-r function in lowest terms are taken as the even and odd parts of a polynomial, that polynomial is a Hurwitz polynomial. Hence

the sum of numerator and denominator of any *L-C* immittance function is a Hurwitz polynomial.   (6.04–3)

A converse statement can be shown to hold also.

Since of the two (numerator and denominator) one is even and one is odd, they must differ in degree by unity. Not by any other odd integer (§ 5.08), but by unity. Notice how the *L-C* case suffers the restriction that the degrees of numerator and denominator cannot be equal, as they may be in the general p-r case. From this difference in degree of unity it is apparent that at infinity the function must have either a pole or a zero, which of course we already knew.

We can now say that in (factored) form a reactance function is either

$$\frac{pB}{A} = Hp\frac{(p^2 + \omega_2{}^2)(p^2 + \omega_4{}^2)\cdots}{(p^2 + \omega_1{}^2)(p^2 + \omega_3{}^2)\cdots} \tag{6.04–4}$$

in which

$$0 < \omega_1 < \omega_2 < \omega_3 < \omega_4 \cdots \tag{6.04–5}$$

and $(A + pB)$ is a Hurwitz polynomial, or

$$\frac{A}{pB} = \frac{H(p^2 + \omega_1{}^2)(p^2 + \omega_3{}^2)\cdots}{p(p^2 + \omega_2{}^2)(p^2 + \omega_4{}^2)\cdots} \tag{6.04–6}$$

in which

$$0 < \omega_1 < \omega_2 < \omega_3 < \omega_4 \cdots \tag{6.04–7}$$

and $(A + pB)$ is a Hurwitz polynomial.

All driving-point admittance and impedance functions of *L-C* networks have one of these forms. Notice that the second form is essentially the reciprocal of the first—nothing more—so that really there is only one form. The constant H is merely a multiplier (scale factor) which must be real and positive, but is otherwise unrestricted.

Equations (6.04–4) and (6.04–6) show the two possible behaviors at the origin (d-c). At infinity we have again the possibility of either a pole or a zero. In the former case the degree of the numerator will be one more than the degree of the denominator; in the latter case the reverse is true. In (6.04–4) we can have then either (a) the same number of $(p^2 + \omega_i^2)$ factors in numerator and in denominator, in which case infinity is a pole, or (b) one less such factor in the numerator than in the denominator, in which case infinity is a zero. In (6.04–6) we can have either (a) one more such factor in numerator than in denominator, in which case infinity is a pole, or (b) the same number of such factors in numerator and denominator, in which case infinity is a zero. There are thus four possible cases in all, if we ignore the number of zeros between zero and infinity, and classify on the basis of zero- and infinite-frequency behavior. This classification in detail is not at all necessary, for there is really only one possible kind of functional behavior, that shown (for $p = j\omega$) in Fig. 6.03–C. The detailed classification has some advantage in its specificity, however, and permits one to draw the curves of Table 6.04–A and tabulate the formulas given there. These show possible behaviors of reactance (susceptance) as frequency varies, with appropriate formulas.

Notice that Cases A and B are reciprocals, and so are Cases C and D, and that the only difference between A and C is in the number of factors (behavior at infinity), so that this division into four cases is somewhat forced. Again, there is really only one general type of function, but the classification may clarify things for those who like to categorize. In every case, of course, the zeros and poles mutually separate each other, i.e.

$$0 < \omega_1 < \omega_2 < \omega_3 < \cdots < \omega_{n-1} < \omega_n. \qquad (6.04\text{–}8)$$

6.05 Partial fractions and synthesis

In the class of functions we have defined as reactance functions are certainly included all driving-point immittance functions of L-C networks. We are not yet entirely certain, however, that all reactance functions are realizable as such driving-point immittance functions. Our next task is to demonstrate that they actually are so realizable, and in so doing we shall develop our first actual synthesis procedures.

Consider first the reactance function of Case D in Table 6.04–A. We designate it $F(p)$ and make its partial-fraction expansion,

$$F(p) = \frac{H(p^2 + \omega_1^2)(p^2 + \omega_3^2) \cdots (p^2 + \omega_n^2)}{p(p^2 + \omega_2^2)(p^2 + \omega_4^2) \cdots (p^2 + \omega_{n-1}^2)}$$

$$= \frac{K_0}{p} + \frac{K_2}{p - j\omega_2} + \frac{K_2}{p + j\omega_2} + \cdots + \frac{K_{n-1}}{p + j\omega_{n-1}} + 0 + Hp.$$

$$(6.05\text{–}1)$$

Table 6.04-A

Case	Origin Is	Infinity Is	Formula for $Z(p)$ or $Y(p)$	n	$X(\omega)$ or $B(\omega)$ versus ω
A	Zero	Pole	$Hp\dfrac{(p^2+\omega_2^2)(p^2+\omega_4^2)\cdots(p^2+\omega_n^2)}{(p^2+\omega_1^2)(p^2+\omega_3^2)\cdots(p^2+\omega_{n-1}^2)}$	Even	
B	Pole	Zero	$\dfrac{H}{p}\dfrac{(p^2+\omega_1^2)(p^2+\omega_3^2)\cdots(p^2+\omega_{n-1}^2)}{(p^2+\omega_2^2)(p^2+\omega_4^2)\cdots(p^2+\omega_n^2)}$	Even	
C	Zero	Zero	$Hp\dfrac{(p^2+\omega_2^2)(p^2+\omega_4^2)\cdots(p^2+\omega_{n-1}^2)}{(p^2+\omega_1^2)(p^2+\omega_3^2)\cdots(p^2+\omega_n^2)}$	Odd	
D	Pole	Pole	$\dfrac{H}{p}\dfrac{(p^2+\omega_1^2)(p^2+\omega_3^2)\cdots(p^2+\omega_n^2)}{(p^2+\omega_2^2)(p^2+\omega_4^2)\cdots(p^2+\omega_{n-1}^2)}$	Odd	

Since $F(p)$ is both p-r and odd, all of its poles are simple, occur at purely imaginary values of p (in conjugate pairs, except for that at the origin), and have residues which are real and positive.   The residues at conjugate poles are themselves conjugate, hence are identical (a real number is its own conjugate).   The constant term in the expansion must be zero, for no other constant is an odd function.   Since the function has a pole at infinity, the term Hp of course appears.   All of these facts were discussed and used in the corresponding expansions (5.14–16) and (5.14–17), and follow immediately from the combination of properties: $F(p)$ is both p-r and odd.

Our next step is to combine the terms corresponding to conjugate poles. This will remove imaginary coefficients from the expression, which is certainly an important step, as network-function coefficients must be real numbers.   We thus obtain

$$F(p) = \frac{K_0}{p} + \frac{2K_2 p}{p^2 + \omega_2{}^2} + \frac{2K_4 p}{p^2 + \omega_4{}^2} + \cdots + \frac{2K_{n-1} p}{p^2 + \omega_{n-1}{}^2} + Hp.$$

$$(6.05\text{–}2)$$

The poles are governed by the inequalities of (6.03–7) and n here is an *odd* number (in order that infinity be a pole).   The p-plane plot of the zeros and poles of $F(p)$ is shown in Fig. 6.03–D(b).   In (6.05–2) we have, not the partial fraction of $F(p)$, but an expansion so frequently to be used and one so very closely related that we may well refer to it as the partial-fraction expansion of $F(p)$, though it differs from the actual partial-fraction expansion in that imaginary coefficients have been eliminated by combining in pairs the terms representing conjugate poles.   Although (6.05–2) was developed for Case D, the other three cases are in reality merely special cases of this one, as we can easily see by going through the same process for each of them.   The results we can write by inspection,
in Case A (n is even):

$$F(p) = \frac{2K_1 p}{p^2 + \omega_1{}^2} + \frac{2K_3 p}{p^2 + \omega_3{}^2} + \cdots + \frac{2K_{n-1} p}{p^2 + \omega_{n-1}{}^2} + Hp, \quad (6.05\text{–}3)$$

in Case B (n is even):

$$F(p) = \frac{K_0}{p} + \frac{2K_2 p}{p^2 + \omega_2{}^2} + \frac{2K_4 p}{p^2 + \omega_4{}^2} + \cdots + \frac{2K_n p}{p^2 + \omega_n{}^2}, \quad (6.05\text{–}4)$$

in Case C (n is odd):

$$F(p) = \frac{2K_1 p}{p^2 + \omega_1{}^2} + \frac{2K_3 p}{p^2 + \omega_3{}^2} + \cdots + \frac{2K_n p}{p^2 + \omega_n{}^2}. \quad (6.05\text{–}5)$$

Except for the trivial matter of how the poles are numbered, we see that
(6.05–2) is the general case. The other three are merely variations in
which (*A*) the pole at the origin is missing, (*B*) the pole at infinity is
missing, (*C*) both the pole at the origin and the pole at infinity are missing.
Hence we concentrate on (6.05–2).

Everything said above applies equally well whether the function be
regarded as potentially an admittance function or an impedance function.
The same general forms and expansions hold in both cases.

Let us now consider how this general form of a reactance function,
(6.05–2), might be realized. We are here, for the first time, attempting a
true *synthesis* (simple and special though the case may be). In the
language of § 1.01, we have passed stage 1, ignored stage 2 for the time
being because we deal here with a function that *is* realizable, and are now
at stage 3. We are talking only about one-terminal pairs that are nondissipative, to be sure, but this is no trivial case, as we shall later see.

In (6.05–2) we have a series of terms which are to add up to $Z(p)$, an
impedance function, *or* (dually) a series of terms which are to add up to
$Y(p)$, an admittance function: that is mathematics. To an engineer, this
is a series of terms which are to represent little two-terminal networks
connected in *series* (because the impedances are added), *or* (dually) a
series of terms which represent little two-terminal networks connected in
parallel (because the admittances add). If we can identify the individual
terms in (6.05–2) with definite small networks, then we can connect these
together and complete our synthesis.

A typical term of (6.05–2) is

$$\frac{2K_m p}{p^2 + \omega_m^2} = \frac{1}{\left(\dfrac{1}{2K_m}\right)p + \left(\dfrac{\omega_m^2}{2K_m}\right)\dfrac{1}{p}}. \qquad (6.05\text{–}6)$$

If (6.05–6) represents an *impedance*, then this term is clearly the impedance
of the little network of Fig. 6.05–A and (6.05–7) applies. The *element
values* (numerical values of L and C) are real and positive (physical)

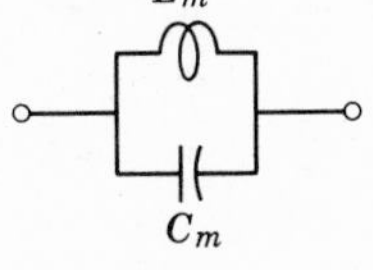

$$C_m = \frac{1}{2K_m}, \quad \text{or} \quad S_m = 2K_m,$$

$$L_m = \frac{2K_m}{\omega_m^2} = \frac{1}{C_m \omega_m^2} = \frac{S_m}{\omega_m^2}, \qquad (6.05\text{–}7)$$

Fig. 6.05–A

because the residues are real and positive. If (6.05–6) represents an *admittance*, then this term is clearly the admittance of the small network of Fig. 6.05–B and (6.05–8) applies.

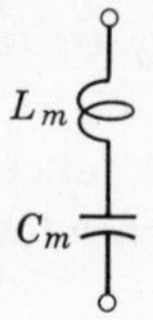

$$L_m = \frac{1}{2K_m}, \quad \text{or} \quad \Gamma_m = 2K_m.$$

$$C_m = \frac{2K_m}{\omega_m^2} = \frac{1}{L_m \omega_m^2} = \frac{\Gamma_m}{\omega_m^2}. \tag{6.05–8}$$

Fig. 6.05–B

The two special kinds of terms which occur at each end of (6.05–2) are realized by simpler networks. The term K_0/p, if it represents an impedance, is realized in Fig. 6.05–C, to which (6.05–9) applies.

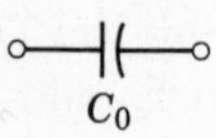

$$C_0 = \frac{1}{S_0} = \frac{1}{K_0}. \tag{6.05–9}$$

Fig. 6.05–C

If K_0/p represents an admittance, it is realized in Fig. 6.05–D, to which (6.05–10) applies.

$$L_0 = \frac{1}{\Gamma_0} = \frac{1}{K_0}. \tag{6.05–10}$$

Fig. 6.05–D

The realization of the term Hp is similarly described in Fig. 6.05–E and (6.05–11) if it is an impedance, and in Fig. 6.05–F and (6.05–12) if it represents an admittance.

$$L_n = \frac{1}{\Gamma_n} = H. \tag{6.05–11}$$

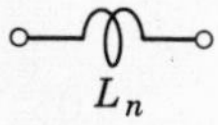

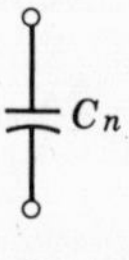

$$C_n = \frac{1}{S_n} = H. \tag{6.05–12}$$

Fig. 6.05–E   Fig. 6.05–F

An alternative point of view is to consider that we have only parallel-tuned networks, as in Fig. 6.05–A (impedance case), or series-tuned networks as in Fig. 6.05–B (admittance case), and that the end terms represent special cases in which the lowest resonant frequency goes to zero, or the highest resonant frequency goes to infinity, so that one element attains a vanishing value. These are degenerate cases then, in which a pair of conjugate poles is reduced to a single pole. This point of view makes the differences in the four cases of Table 6.04–A merely a matter of what the extreme resonances are, and not a question of presence or absence of terms (or corresponding elements).

Without further ado, then, we can write down the realization of (6.05–2), in the general case, as an impedance in the form shown in Fig. 6.05–G, or as an admittance in the form shown in Fig. 6.05–H. Designations of element values and even symbols for the elements are purposely omitted in these two schematics, to avoid confusion between the several cases of Table 6.04–A. The only differences between these cases are in the presence or absence of the lone capacitor and the lone inductor in each case: there are then four possibilities, and these correspond to the four cases. The number of "tuned-circuit" *L-C* combinations is the same as the number of ($p^2 + \omega_i^2$) factors in the denominator of Z or Y.

If there is a pole at the origin, the lone capacitor in Fig. 6.05–G or the lone inductor in Fig. 6.05–H is present; if there is no pole at the origin,

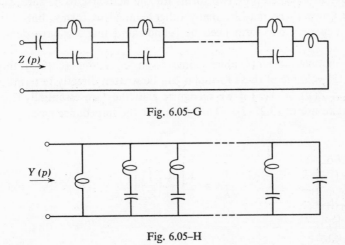

$Z(p)$

Fig. 6.05–G

$Y(p)$

Fig. 6.05–H

it is absent. If there is a pole at infinity, the lone inductor of Fig. 6.05–G is present, or the lone capacitor of Fig. 6.05–H is present; if there is no pole at infinity, these elements are absent. Hence the four cases boil down to the two simple schematic forms shown, with the minor differences between them.

There is an important philosophical point to be made here. We have hinted that positive reality of a rational function may be *sufficient* for the physical realization of that function as a one-terminal-pair driving-point immittance. The necessity of positive reality was well established in Chapter 4; to establish the *sufficiency* of positive reality in the general case requires apparatus we do not yet have, and must be postponed. But in the L-C case we have in effect demonstrated this sufficiency. For we have taken the most general form of (rational) odd p-r function, i.e., of reactance function, and demonstrated that it can be realized as either the driving-point impedance or driving-point admittance of an L-C network (Figs. 6.05–G and 6.05–H). This removes the distinction between "reactance function" and "driving-point immittance function of an L-C network": we now know that the two are synonymous and equivalent. We have taken the most general possible positive-real function within the nondissipative class, and have obtained a realization—in fact, we have obtained *two* realizations, for the given function may be realized in one of the two forms in Figs. 6.05–G and 6.05–H (whichever is appropriate to its dimensions), or inverted and realized in the other form. Hence we have established, for the nondissipative (odd-function) case, that positive reality is *sufficient* for physical realizability, as well, of course, as necessary. We have established only two forms for the network, to be sure, and for all we know there may be many other equivalent forms, but to prove sufficiency only *one* form need be found—and that we have done, and more.

The actual element values come from equations (6.05–7) through (6.05–12). Some of these formulas can be written directly in terms of the function $Z(p)$ or $Y(p)$ if we recognize that they are essentially residues, and make use of (3.21–7). This gives, for the impedance case,

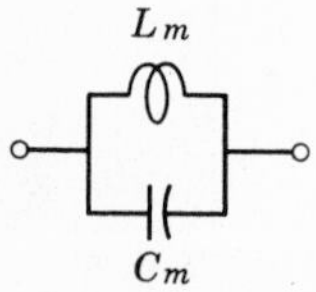

$$C_m = \frac{1}{2K_m} = \frac{1}{2}\left[\frac{d}{dp}\left(\frac{1}{Z}\right)\right]_{p=j\omega_m} \quad (m \neq 0), \quad (6.05\text{–}13)$$

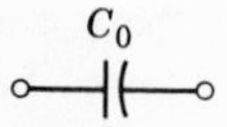

Fig. 6.05–I

$$C_0 = \frac{1}{K_0} = \left[\frac{d}{dp}\left(\frac{1}{Z}\right)\right]_{p=0}, \quad (6.05\text{–}14)$$

Fig. 6.05–J

and for the admittance case,

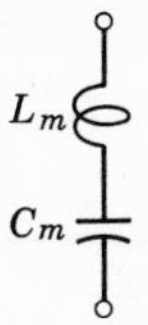

$$L_m = \frac{1}{2K_m} = \frac{1}{2}\left[\frac{d}{dp}\left(\frac{1}{Y}\right)\right]_{p=j\omega_m} \quad (m \neq 0), \quad (6.05\text{--}15)$$

Fig. 6.05–K

$$L_0 = \frac{1}{K_0} = \left[\frac{d}{dp}\left(\frac{1}{Y}\right)\right]_{p=0}. \quad (6.05\text{--}16)$$

Fig. 6.05–L

In each case the other element has such a value that it will resonate with the element given, at the correct frequency. These formulas can further be modified by recognizing that the functions $Z(p)$ and $Y(p)$ are purely imaginary (purely reactive or purely susceptive) at these imaginary values of p. Then we get

$$Z(j\omega) = 0 + jX(\omega) = \frac{1}{0 + jB(\omega)} = \frac{1}{Y(j\omega)}, \quad (6.05\text{--}17)$$

$$X(\omega) = \frac{-1}{B(\omega)}. \quad (6.05\text{--}18)$$

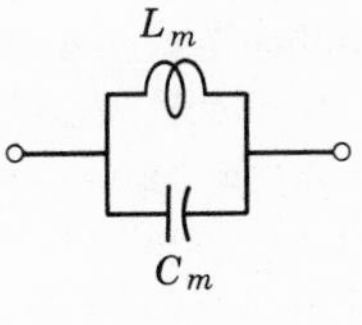

$$C_m = \frac{1}{2}\left[\frac{d}{j\,d\omega}\left(\frac{1}{jX}\right)\right]_{p=j\omega_m}$$
$$= \frac{1}{2}\left(\frac{dB}{d\omega}\right)_{\omega=\omega_m} \quad (m \neq 0), \quad (6.05\text{--}19)$$

Fig. 6.05–M

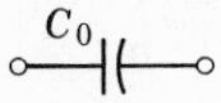

$$C_0 = \left(\frac{dB}{d\omega}\right)_{\omega=0}, \quad (6.05\text{--}20)$$

Fig. 6.05–N

$$L_m = \frac{1}{2}\left[\frac{d}{j\,d\omega}\left(\frac{1}{jB}\right)\right]_{p=j\omega_m}$$
$$= \frac{1}{2}\left(\frac{dX}{d\omega}\right)_{\omega=\omega_m} \quad (m \neq 0), \quad (6.05\text{--}21)$$

Fig. 6.05–O

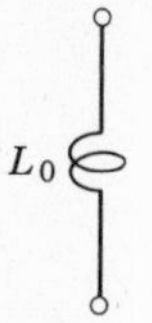

$$L_0 = \left(\frac{dX}{d\omega}\right)_{\omega=0}. \qquad (6.05\text{-}22)$$

L_0

Fig. 6.05–P

The equations in this form show that the *slope* of the *susceptance* curve (with, of course, the frequency of resonance) determines the elements in the impedance case, and that the slope of the *reactance* curve (with, of course, the frequency of resonance) determines them in the admittance case.

In practice, the collection of formulas for element values given here is entirely unnecessary. Once the partial-fraction expansion is obtained and the residues and resonant frequencies are known, the element values can be written down by inspection: one need only compare the very-low-frequency behavior of the term in the partial-fraction expansion with that of the corresponding tuned circuit, and repeat the comparison at very high frequencies; none of the mathematical formulas above need be remembered. To illustrate this, suppose $11p/(p^2 + 3)$ represents a term in the partial-fraction expansion of a given reactance function. If the function is an impedance function, measured in ohms, then Fig. 6.05–A is the realization. At very low frequencies, the impedance of the tuned circuit is $L_m p$, the value of the term above is $11p/3$, and accordingly $L_m = 11/3$ h. At very high frequencies, the circuit impedance approaches $1/C_m p$ and the term above $11/p$; accordingly, $C_m = 1/11$ f. As a check, $L_m C_m = 11/3 \times 1/11 = 1/3$ so that the resonant frequency is given by $\omega_m^2 = 3$, which corresponds to the poles of the term given. If the function is an admittance, measured in mhos, then Fig. 6.05–B applies. As $p \to 0$, the circuit admittance approaches $C_m p$, which is to be compared to $11p/3$; hence $C_m = 11/3$ f. As $p \to \infty$, the circuit admittance approaches $1/L_m p$, which is to be compared to $11/p$; hence $L_m = 1/11$ h. Again the product LC checks the pole positions.

The end terms of the expansion, corresponding to single elements, are even easier to evaluate.

All that need be done to effect a synthesis in this form, then, is to obtain the partial-fraction expansion of the given reactance function (or of its reciprocal, depending on the form desired). In order to do this, the denominator (at least) must be in factored form; since the zeros of this polynomial are all real in the variable p^2, this is easily done, and very likely has already been done, either in testing the function for positive reality or in setting up the function originally (as a part of the solution of an approximation problem). From the number of terms present in this expansion, the appropriate schematic diagram (Fig. 6.05–G or 6.05–H) can be drawn, with the requisite number of elements, and the element values can be read from the partial-fraction expansion, as illustrated above.

Several numerical examples of the synthesis procedure will be given in § 6.14. They are postponed until then in order that various methods (there are others to come) may be illustrated simultaneously. However, one simple example is given here as an aid in crystallizing the ideas. Suppose the reactance function

$$Z(p) = \frac{6(p^2 + 2)(p^2 + 4)}{p(p^2 + 3)} \quad \text{ohms} \tag{6.05–23}$$

is to be realized. Its partial-fraction expansion (with conjugate-pole terms combined) is

$$Z(p) = \frac{16}{p} + \frac{2K_2 p}{p^2 + 3} + 6p \tag{6.05–24}$$

in which the coefficients in the first and third terms have been written by inspection of the behavior of $Z(p)$ near the origin and at infinity. For the unknown coefficient we find

$$2K_2 = \left[\frac{(p^2 + 3)Z(p)}{p}\right]_{p^2 = 3} = \frac{6(-3 + 2)(-3 + 4)}{(-3)} = 2. \tag{6.05–25}$$

It remains only to rewrite the expansion of $Z(p)$ and to associate with each term the corresponding realization, with element values determined

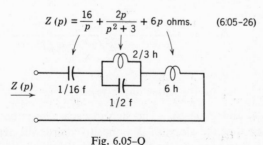

$$Z(p) = \frac{16}{p} + \frac{2p}{p^2 + 3} + 6p \text{ ohms.} \tag{6.05–26}$$

Fig. 6.05–Q

by inspection. These component networks, connected in series, form the realization shown in Fig. 6.05–Q.

Had the given reactance function (6.05–23) represented an *admittance*, we would have performed the same arithmetic and obtained the realization shown in Fig. 6.05–R.

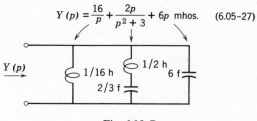

$$Y(p) = \frac{16}{p} + \frac{2p}{p^2 + 3} + 6p \text{ mhos.} \qquad (6.05\text{--}27)$$

Fig. 6.05–R

The networks of Figs. 6.05–Q and 6.05–R are totally different and have totally different impedance functions (one is the reciprocal of the other) as is evident by the fact that one approaches a short circuit at low frequencies, the other an open circuit. They are related in that they are dual networks, which subject is discussed further in § 6.09.

6.06 The reactance proper

Since the impedance at real frequencies is purely imaginary, for any one of these functions, we might well discard the j multiplier and summarize what we have in terms of reactance. For general forms, we have

$$X(\omega) = \pm H\omega \frac{(\omega^2 - \omega_2^2)(\omega^2 - \omega_4^2) \cdots}{(\omega^2 - \omega_1^2)(\omega^2 - \omega_3^2) \cdots}, \qquad (6.06\text{--}1)$$

in which

$$0 < \omega_1 < \omega_2 < \omega_3 < \cdots, \qquad (6.06\text{--}2)$$

and

$$X(\omega) = \pm \frac{H(\omega^2 - \omega_1^2)(\omega^2 - \omega_3^2) \cdots}{\omega(\omega^2 - \omega_2^2)(\omega^2 - \omega_4^2) \cdots}, \qquad (6.06\text{--}3)$$

in which

$$0 < \omega_1 < \omega_2 < \omega_3 < \cdots, \qquad (6.06\text{--}4)$$

from (6.04–4) and (6.04–6). The sign in each case is not arbitrary but must be such that the slope of X is positive, and will depend upon the number of factors, i.e., on the behavior at infinity. In Cases A and B it is positive, in Cases C and D it is negative (cf. Table 6.04–A). Everything said here is of course equally valid if the function $X(\omega)$ is interpreted as susceptance.

We could write out $X(\omega)$ or $B(\omega)$ for these four cases specifically, from Table 6.04–A, but it is not really necessary to do so. All four behave much the same; the only difference is in the behavior at the ends of the frequency spectrum (d-c or zero, and infinity), and all can be realized by the networks of Figs. 6.05–G and 6.05–H, allowing special cases in which the end elements disappear from the picture. Graphically, we can plot one characteristic, that of Fig. 6.06–A, to cover all the cases (cf. Fig.

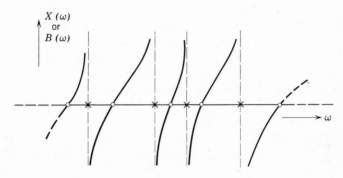

Fig. 6.06–A

6.03–C). To make this general curve fit any given function, we need merely lop it off so that we have enough poles and zeros, and not too many, align it with the frequency scale so that the origin is zero or pole as the case may be, and there it is. The four cases have the curves given in Table 6.04–A which are, in effect, obtained this way.

We can now make the following general observation. Evidently

a driving-point reactive immittance function is uniquely determined by specifying the locations of its (real-frequency) zeros and poles (origin and infinity excepted) *and* one additional piece of information.   (6.06–5)

A glance at the general forms (§ 6.04) shows that the nonzero, finite pole and zero locations and the multiplier H are all that the functions contain in the way of information (for we know that the zeros and poles must alternate, and hence when all the nonzero, finite poles and zeros have been specified, the behavior at "d-c" and infinity is automatically determined, and would be superfluous information if given). The "one additional piece of information" may be H itself, or it may be the value of the reactance at some frequency, or the slope thereof at some point, or any equivalent data. It serves only to fix the vertical scale in Fig. 6.06–A and is necessary only for that purpose.

Although the literature of network theory in journal papers is enormous, and few can even sample it adequately, there are some papers whose historical importance, clarity, and accessibility make their reading essential; one such is Foster's classic paper *A Reactance Theorem* (FO 1), which appeared in 1924. In it almost all the general forms we have given and the properties we have listed are described. But many of these things were known long before, in their analog forms in the theory of dynamics (RO 2).

6.07 The frequency pattern

Although Fig. 6.06–A (appropriately truncated) clearly expresses all that there is to be said about a given reactance function, once the scales have been applied, there is an even simpler, shorthand method of giving the data. Since the general nature of the reactance curve between zeros and poles is always the same, we can omit the curve entirely, and merely draw an abbreviated version of the real-frequency axis, marking thereon each zero with O and each pole with ✕. This sketch, called a *frequency pattern*, then has on it all essential information about the reactance function; only the scale factor H is missing, if the zero and pole frequencies are stated. For convenience, we include infinity as a finite point at the right end of the scale, and we show the positive half of the axis only; the negative half has symmetry and would add nothing. Frequency patterns for the four cases are given in Fig. 6.07–A. In any specific case,

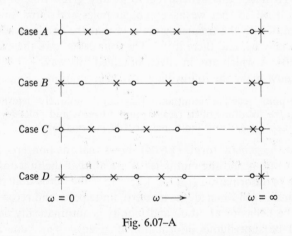

Fig. 6.07–A

the diagram should be marked as an *impedance* (reactance) frequency pattern, say by Z, or as an *admittance* (susceptance) frequency pattern, say by Y, to avoid confusion; the two are not the same (but are "inverted") for any given network.

We shall call zeros and poles at the origin and at infinity *external*, and nonzero, finite, positive zeros and poles *internal*, in the spirit of these patterns, bounded by zero and infinity. And by *critical frequencies* we shall mean those frequencies at which a zero or pole occurs.

We note now that the number of pieces of information needed completely to specify a reactance function is *one more* than the number of internal critical frequencies. Within broad limits, these frequencies and the multiplier are arbitrary. The only requirements are that the multiplier be positive, and that the zeros and poles alternate (starting from a zero or pole at the origin and occurring in conjugate pairs). Consequently the *shape* of the reactance curve is controllable to a large extent, but only within the category of shapes resulting when zeros and poles alternate as required. From this we conclude that at the very least,

the minimum number of elements required for a realization of a reactance function is one more than the number of internal critical frequencies. (6.07–1)

That this number is sufficient and that no larger number of elements is necessary can be demonstrated by considering the forms in Figs. 6.05–G and 6.05–H and their derivations. An alternative statement is

the minimum number of elements required for a realization of a reactance function is equal to the total number of poles of that function, or to the total number of zeros of that function, i.e., to the order of the function. (6.07–2)

It is always possible to find a realization which uses *more* than this minimum number required, if only by the device of splitting an element(s) in two. We shall later find that it is occasionally advantageous to introduce additional surplus elements (surplus in that the number of elements then exceeds the minimum needed), not in any such trivial fashion, but to the end of obtaining a network better in configuration, element values, impedance level, or other characteristics.

6.08 Element values

We are now in a position to *synthesize* certain kinds of networks. In particular, if we have given a function of p which is a reactance function (that is, p-r and odd, or p-r and in addition purely imaginary at real frequencies), the discussion of § 6.05 has already indicated how to do this job. (We assume here that the original data are in the form of a reactance function, hence that we need not solve an approximation problem; in general, of course, it would be necessary first to find a reactance function which approximates the data sufficiently closely.) All the necessary information is really contained in § 6.05. What we shall do here is merely to make the procedure a little more concrete.

The basic procedure, given the reactance function, is merely to make the partial-fraction expansion, i.e., to find the residues (the K's), and then to obtain the actual element values from these K's by the formulas of § 6.05. But, as mentioned there, it is not necessary to remember these formulas; if one puts the basic two-element circuit alongside the corresponding term in the expansion, and observes the behavior of the two at low, and again at high, frequencies, the element values become apparent.

Since any physical impedance function can be inverted to obtain a physical admittance function, we immediately have two choices open to us: to work with the given function itself or with its reciprocal. The results will be in the forms of Figs. 6.05–G and 6.05–H. These will then be two *equivalent* networks, networks which have the same driving-point immittances. One form stresses the poles of the impedance function (the zeros of the admittance function), the other stresses the poles of the admittance function (the zeros of the impedance function) by expressing them as resonant frequencies which are apparent by inspection of the network schematic diagram.

Consider the most general form, (6.05–1), which we take first to represent an *impedance*. It is rewritten in (6.08–1), first in factored form, and then as its partial-fraction expansion, which is repeated in terms of the element values of the corresponding network in Fig. 6.08–A.

$$Z(p) = \frac{H(p^2 + \omega_1^2)(p^2 + \omega_3^2) \cdots (p^2 + \omega_n^2)}{p(p^2 + \omega_2^2)(p^2 + \omega_4^2) \cdots (p^2 + \omega_{n-1}^2)}$$

$$= \frac{K_0}{p} + \frac{2K_2 p}{p^2 + \omega_2^2} + \cdots + \frac{2K_{n-1} p}{p^2 + \omega_{n-1}^2} + Hp \qquad (6.08\text{--}1)$$

$$= \frac{S_0}{p} + \frac{S_2 p}{p^2 + \omega_2^2} + \cdots + \frac{S_{n-1} p}{p^2 + \omega_{n-1}^2} + L_n p.$$

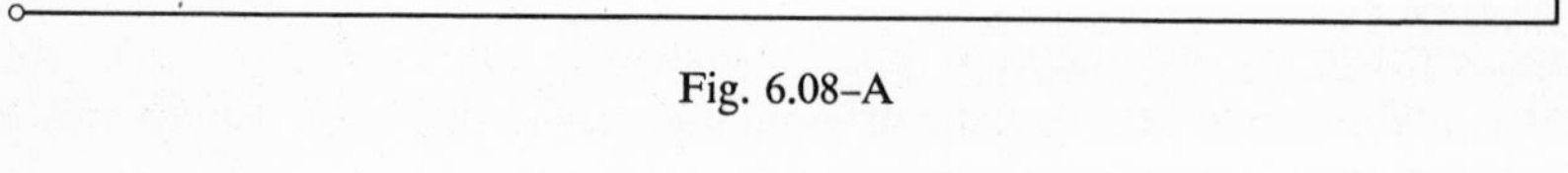

Fig. 6.08–A

$$L_2 = \frac{S_2}{\omega_2^2}, \cdots, \quad L_{n-1} = \frac{S_{n-1}}{\omega_{n-1}^2}. \qquad (6.08\text{--}2)$$

The synthesis of § 6.05 has all been summarized in (6.08–1), (6.08–2), and Fig. 6.08–A: first the partial-fraction expansion of the data, then the same with the residues replaced by element-value symbols, and finally the schematic diagram of the corresponding network, with the additional formulas necessary. Elastance values are used because mathematically they fit in neatly; in practice capacitance would be used instead, for capacitor (condenser) values are always specified as capacitances.

Secondly, if the original function represents an *admittance*, we take exactly the same steps, but use different symbols (a matter strictly of convention), as shown in (6.08-3) and Fig. 6.08-B. Again reciprocal inductance symbols are used merely for neatness; in practice inductance values would be used.

$$Y(p) = \frac{H(p^2 + \omega_1{}^2)(p^2 + \omega_3{}^2)\cdots(p^2 + \omega_n{}^2)}{p(p^2 + \omega_2{}^2)(p^2 + \omega_4{}^2)\cdots(p^2 + \omega_{n-1}{}^2)}$$

$$= \frac{K_0}{p} + \frac{2K_2 p}{p^2 + \omega_2{}^2} + \cdots + \frac{2K_{n-1}p}{p^2 + \omega_{n-1}{}^2} + Hp \qquad (6.08\text{-}3)$$

$$= \frac{\Gamma_0}{p} \quad + \quad \frac{\Gamma_2 p}{p^2 + \omega_2{}^2} + \cdots + \frac{\Gamma_{n-1}p}{p^2 + \omega_{n-1}{}^2} \quad + \quad C_n p.$$

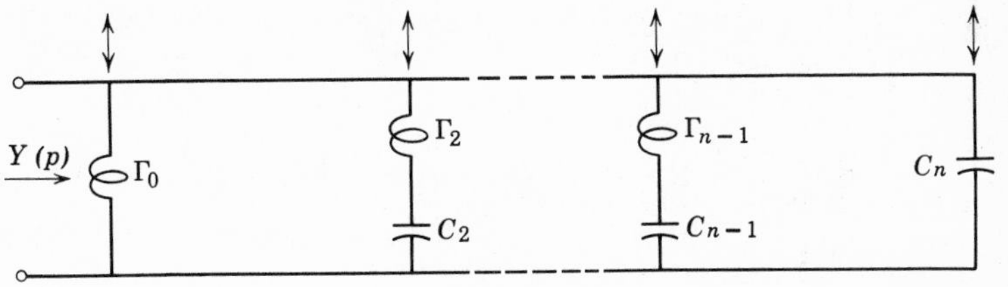

Fig. 6.08–B

$$C_2 = \frac{\Gamma_2}{\omega_2{}^2} \cdots, \quad C_{n-1} = \frac{\Gamma_{n-1}}{\omega_{n-1}{}^2}. \qquad (6.08\text{-}4)$$

In each case, the lone inductor, or the lone capacitor, or both, may be missing. In practice we go through exactly these procedures in synthesizing a reactive network from the impedance function, or from the admittance function, if a network in one of these forms is desired (there are other forms).

It remains to indicate specifically how the residues (or better, the element values) are computed. Here again one can write down formulas and substitute in them, but it is far simpler to remember merely the *principle* involved and to work from that in each case. In § 3.19 were given procedures for making partial-fraction expansions. All the ideas necessary here were given there, but there we have a possibility of simplification: not only have we *simple* poles but also the poles are in conjugate (purely imaginary) pairs, which we wish to handle in pairs rather than separately. We take the fraction form, (6.08–1), as the data, and the expanded form there (with the S's) as the result desired. To obtain each S, we merely multiply through by the corresponding denominator, $(p^2 + \omega_i^2)$, divide through by p, and then let p have the proper value. The external poles, those at the origin and at infinity, require slightly different, but simpler treatment, as indicated below. Thus in

$$Z(p) = \frac{H(p^2 + \omega_1^2)(p^2 + \omega_3^2) \cdots (p^2 + \omega_n^2)}{p(p^2 + \omega_2^2)(p^2 + \omega_4^2) \cdots (p^2 + \omega_{n-1}^2)}$$

$$= \frac{S_0}{p} + \frac{S_2 p}{p^2 + \omega_2^2} + \cdots + \frac{S_{n-1} p}{p^2 + \omega_{n-1}^2} + L_n p, \quad (6.08–5)$$

we multiply through in turn by each denominator on the right, divide through by p (except for the first and last terms), and then let p have the appropriate value (which will make all other terms on the right vanish). We obtain:

$$S_0 = (pZ)_{p=0} = H \frac{\omega_1^2 \omega_2^2 \cdots \omega_n^2}{\omega_2^2 \omega_4^2 \cdots \omega_{n-1}^2} = (-\omega X)_{\omega=0} = \frac{1}{C_0}. \quad (6.08–6)$$

$$S_2 = \left[\frac{(p^2 + \omega_2^2)}{p} Z \right]_{p^2 = -\omega_2^2}$$

$$= \left[\frac{H(p^2 + \omega_1^2)(p^2 + \omega_3^2) \cdots (p^2 + \omega_n^2)}{p^2(p^2 + \omega_4^2)(p^2 + \omega_6^2) \cdots (p^2 + \omega_{n-1}^2)} \right]_{p^2 = -\omega_2}$$

$$= \left[\frac{(\omega_2^2 - \omega^2)}{\omega} X \right]_{\omega = \omega_2} = \frac{1}{C_2}. \quad (6.08–7)$$

$$L_2 = \frac{S_2}{\omega_2^2} = \frac{1}{C_2 \omega_2^2}. \quad (6.08–8)$$

$$\cdot \quad \cdot \quad \cdot \quad \cdot \quad \cdot \quad \cdot \quad \cdot \quad \cdot \quad \cdot \quad \cdot \quad \cdot \quad \cdot \quad \cdot \quad \cdot$$

$$S_{n-1} = \left[\frac{(p^2 + \omega_{n-1}^2)}{p} Z \right]_{p^2 = -\omega_{n-1}^2}$$

$$= \left[\frac{H(p^2 + \omega_1^2)(p^2 + \omega_3^2) \cdots (p^2 + \omega_n^2)}{p^2(p^2 + \omega_2^2)(p^2 + \omega_4^2) \cdots (p^2 + \omega_{n-3}^2)} \right]_{p^2 = -\omega_{n-1}^2}$$

$$= \left[\frac{(\omega_{n-1}^2 - \omega^2)}{\omega} X \right]_{\omega = \omega_{n-1}} = \frac{1}{C_{n-1}}. \quad (6.08–9)$$

$$L_{n-1} = \frac{S_{n-1}}{\omega_{n-1}^2} = \frac{1}{C_{n-1} \omega_{n-1}^2}. \quad (6.08–10)$$

$$L_n = \left[\frac{Z(p)}{p} \right]_{p \to \infty} = H = \left(\frac{X}{\omega} \right)_{\omega \to \infty}. \quad (6.08–11)$$

Notice that no complex numbers, not even any imaginary numbers, enter into these computations. Only real numbers are involved, and the work consists merely of a number of subtractions, multiplications, and divisions (on the assumption that the numerator of the given function, as well as the denominator, is given in factored form—if it is not, there is no essential change in the process, as examination shows). Note that the denominators of the expressions for the *S*'s are in general the same as the denominator of the given $Z(p)$, except for the omission of the corresponding pole term and for multiplication by an extra p; the numerator is unchanged. In practice the capacitance values are either calculated directly (the formulas reciprocated), or the elastance values reciprocated to give them. The inductance values are then such that the inductors resonate with or "tune" the capacitors at the proper frequencies.

A variant of these formulas is to write them purely in terms of reactance, $X(\omega)$, rather than in terms of p. Although this replaces the complex variable p by the real variable ω, drops the j, and makes the function real, the advantages are small. This procedure leads to the same results, of course, but the formulas are cluttered up with a number of minus signs. Not that one does not have to deal with these subtractions, for of course one does, but there seems to be no need to put them in the general formulas. In each of the formulas above, however, the equivalent in terms of reactance has also been given, for reference.

The artifice used, that of multiplying through by $(p^2 + \omega_k{}^2)/p$ for each term, and then letting p have the appropriate value, effectively removes all other terms on the right side (they are then multiplied by zero), leaving only the S sought at the moment, while on the other side an apparently indeterminate form appears. The indeterminacy is easily removed, because a cancellation always occurs, and the expressions given above result. To evaluate these and get the actual element values is merely a matter of arithmetic. Note again that there is no need to remember any of these details—all that is necessary is the *principle*, and with that the answer comes just as quickly as when the formulas are used, perhaps more so, and possibly with less likelihood of error.

Should either or both of the end elements be missing, i.e., should either or both the origin and infinity be zeros rather than poles, the procedure is in principle exactly the same. The only difference is that p will appear in the numerator rather than in the denominator, or the number of factors in the numerator will be reduced. It is possible to derive any number of formulas for special cases, but it is better to remember only the principle involved.

If the original function is an *admittance*, the arithmetic work is identical, but the interpretation of the final numbers is as the *duals* of the symbols above. The numbers obtained and the appropriate schematic diagram (Fig. 6.08–A or 6.08–B), constitute the end result of the synthesis.

To recapitulate, the synthesis procedure given here is to

1. factor the denominator of the given reactance function if this has not already been done;
2. examine the function and write the appropriate combined-pair partial-fraction expansion with literal coefficients; this contains the proper number of terms of the form $S_r p/(p^2 + \omega_r^2)$, as well as S_0/p and $L_n p$ if the latter are appropriate—or the dual forms;
3. consider each term in turn, multiply through by its denominator and divide through by p (except for the "d-c" and infinity pole terms, if present), let p have the value corresponding to this pole, i.e., let $p^2 = -\omega_r^2$, and thus determine the coefficient of that term (determine the coefficients of the d-c and infinity pole terms by inspection);
4. draw a schematic diagram corresponding to the expansion (interpreted as admittance or impedance as the case may be);
5. determine the values of the elements in the schematic diagram by comparison of the component tuned circuits and the corresponding terms in the expansion at very low and at very high frequencies; and
6. check the results by calculating the impedance (admittance) function from the final schematic diagram (at least at a few well-chosen frequencies) and comparing it with the datum function from which the synthesis started.   (6.08–12)

The sixth step, the check, is not in theory necessary. As a practical matter it should always be taken; it is far too easy to make errors in arithmetic, and if the synthesis is to be useful, it must be correct.

There is little more to be said about realization in the two forms we have been discussing; those of Figs. 6.08–A and 6.08–B. In § 6.14 illustrative examples are given (they are placed there for ready comparison with examples of other synthesis methods)—and there is no substitute whatever for actual practice, actual performance of the synthesis. This, one must do oneself to gain a real understanding of the process. But no more explanation is necessary. Mastery requires practice in carrying the procedure through—but no more explanation.

6.09 Biformity

In the preceding discussion we found a direct method of realization of a certain special kind of positive-real function, the reactance function. But we have advanced further than that—for, as indicated in § 6.05 and § 6.08, we have found not one realization (synthesis) method, but two. If the given reactance function represents an impedance $Z(p)$, it can be developed straightforwardly into a network with the configuration of Fig. 6.05–G. But the function can also be inverted to form another reactance function which represents the admittance $Y = 1/Z$, and this function can be developed into a network with the configuration of Fig. 6.05–H. We have this choice between the two forms in every *L-C* one-terminal-pair synthesis problem: to develop the impedance function in partial fractions, or to develop the admittance function in partial fractions. The two procedures lead to two different networks (except in the two simplest cases, where the order of the reactance function is one or two— then the networks contain but one or two elements and are the same), and these networks must have the *same* driving-point impedance and the *same* driving-point admittance, and hence must in this sense be *equivalent*. This is an instance of the multiple-valued nature of the solution to synthesis problems in general. There is usually not one answer, but several, perhaps a very large number. The engineer must consider them all, for it may well be that though all are mathematically equivalent and in that sense equally good solutions, physically and economically one or two may be much better solutions than the others (e.g., the element values are more realistic, or the configurations are better adapted to practical construction which must deal with parasitic effects). Hence the concept of *equivalent networks* is one to be kept continually in mind.

Related to the ideas above is that of designing two networks which are not equivalent, but rather are *reciprocal* with respect to driving-point impedance (driving-point admittance). Given a reactance function $F(p)$ which represents, say, an impedance $Z_1(p)$, we may proceed to expand it in partial fractions and obtain a realization in the form of Fig. 6.05–G. There is nothing to prevent us from using our imagination to rename the same function $Y_2(p)$, to consider it now an admittance function, and to use the same partial-fraction expansion to obtain a realization in the form of Fig. 6.05–H. We then have two networks (those in Fig. 6.09–A, to

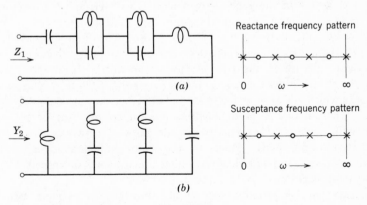

Reactance frequency pattern

Susceptance frequency pattern

(a)

(b)

Fig. 6.09–A

give a concrete example) for which $Z_1(p)$ and $Y_2(p)$ are mathematically the same function.

Physically the functions Z_1 and Y_2 are of different dimensions, however, so we must write

$$Z_1(p) = R_0{}^2 Y_2(p) \tag{6.09-1}$$

in which the constant R_0 has the dimensions of resistance, and is numerically equal to one ohm. Alternatively, using $Z_2 = 1/Y_2$,

$$\frac{Z_1(p)}{R_0} = R_0 Y_2(p) = \frac{R_0}{Z_2(p)}. \tag{6.09-2}$$

With R_0 chosen as a reference level, and impedance normalized to this level, then we can write

$$Z_1 = Y_2 = \frac{1}{Z_2} \quad or \quad Z_1 Z_2 = 1, \tag{6.09-3}$$

in which the symbols refer to normalized immittances and are dimensionless. The two networks obtained in this manner from a single function are called *reciprocal* networks because in normalized form (or in actual form with $R_0 = 1$ ohm) the two driving-point impedance functions (or the two driving-point admittance functions) are reciprocals. If R_0 has some other value, there is no essential change in the ideas, but then the networks are better called *inverse*, with respect to R_0. Reciprocal and inverse networks are very useful, as we shall see later. When developed in the fashion indicated above, they are dual networks, as the example of Fig. 6.09-A clearly shows. But the original function $F(p)$ may be inverted, and then developed in partial fractions, yielding a realization of $Y_1 = 1/Z_1 = 1/F$ in the general form of Fig. 6.05-H, and a realization of $Z_2 = 1/Y_2 = 1/F$ in the general form of Fig. 6.05-G. For the example which yielded the networks of Fig. 6.09-A, Fig. 6.09-B shows these two new networks. These two networks are dual to each other, and are equivalent pairwise to the two previously obtained. If we now take network (a) of Fig. 6.09-A and network (b) of Fig. 6.09-B, we have two networks which are inverse, for (6.09-2) holds, but they are definitely not duals. There may well be many other equivalents to either or both of these, with accompanying possibilities of pairs of networks which are inverse but are not duals. Hence the important characteristic here is the *inverse* property, and not duality, which applies only in special cases. (These matters are discussed further in § 10.07.)

The two synthesis procedures developed thus far in this chapter permit us then to find a one-terminal pair equivalent to any given L-C network, a different network (except in the very simplest cases) yet one with the same driving-point immittances. The procedures also permit us to find two one-terminal pairs which are inverse to any given network with respect to an arbitrary resistance R_0. And they show that a given

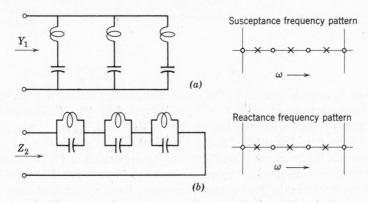

Susceptance frequency pattern

Reactance frequency pattern

Fig. 6.09–B

synthesis problem in this (*L-C*) class has in general at least *two* solutions; in other words the synthesis problem does not have a unique solution. Nor is there any reason to believe that there are not many other methods of synthesis, leading to still other realizations, yet to be found.

6.10 The nonuniqueness of synthesis

Both of the realizations found so far have been based on partial-fraction expansion of the given immittance or of its reciprocal. Two basic schematic forms resulted, those of Figs. 6.05–G and 6.05–H. But these are not all: there are other forms of expansion, equally valid and useful, which give rise to different networks.

Suppose the given reactance function represents an impedance $Z(p)$, and is written, not in factored form, but as the quotient of two polynomials,

$$Z(p) = \frac{a_n p^n + a_{n-2} p^{n-2} + \cdots}{a_m p^m + a_{m-2} p^{m-2} + \cdots}. \tag{6.10-1}$$

Of the two polynomials involved, one of course is even and the other is odd, by (6.04–2). There is either a pole or a zero at infinity, and the degree of one polynomial exceeds that of the other by unity. Let us assume for the moment that infinity is a *pole*, that $m = n - 1$. We need not at present concern ourselves with the d-c (zero-frequency) behavior.

We now form the continued-fraction expansion (discussed in § 5.14) of $Z(p)$. This is

$$Z(p) = b_1 p + \cfrac{1}{b_2 p + \cfrac{1}{b_3 p + \cfrac{1}{\ddots}}}$$

$$\cdots + \cfrac{1}{b_n p} \qquad (6.10\text{–}2)$$

in which $b_1 = a_n/a_{n-1}$ and the other b's are obtained by successive processes of division, inversion, division, $\cdots$, as discussed in § 5.14. There will be n terms in the expansion, and all of the coefficients $b_1, b_2, b_3, \cdots, b_n$ will be positive—for we are starting with a reactance function, i.e., a positive-real function that is also odd, and the arguments of § 5.14 showed that then the coefficients in the quotients are positive. The $\Psi(p)$ of that treatment becomes the $Z(p)$ of this discussion; there is then no difference in ideas whatever.

The numerical work involved, when performed with detached coefficients with the successive operations arranged under each other, is not particularly laborious, as illustrated by the example below (cf. also the examples in § 5.14). Let

$$Z(p) = \frac{180p^4 + 45p^2 + 1}{30p^3 + 5p} \quad \text{ohms} \qquad (6.10\text{–}3)$$

which is a reactance function (as is easily demonstrated by testing the odd function $Z(p)$ for positive reality), with the frequency pattern shown in Fig. 6.10–A.

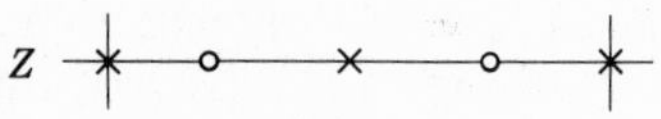

Fig. 6.10–A

The work of expansion is

```
30  5)180  45  1(6
      180  30
      ────
       15  1)30  5(2
           30  2
           ──
            3)15  1(5
              15
              ──
               1)3(3
                 3
                 ─
                 0          (6.10–4)
```

so that

$$Z(p) = 6p + \cfrac{1}{2p + \cfrac{1}{5p + \cfrac{1}{3p}}}$$

(6.10–5)

For simplicity, the example is one with round numbers; in practice the numbers would not be integral, but the principle would be unchanged. It is important to remember that the powers of p (omitted in the skeletal divisions above) are not consecutive, but change by two from one term of a polynomial to the next, because only odd or even polynomials are involved. (This will not be true of similar processes to be met later.)

It remains now to show why this continued-fraction expansion is of interest in realization. Consider the impedance function of the network in Fig. 6.10–B, $Z(p)$. It is given in (6.10–6).

$$Z(p) = L_1p + \cfrac{1}{C_2p + \cfrac{1}{L_3p + \cfrac{1}{C_4p + \cfrac{1}{L_5p + \cfrac{1}{\ddots}}}}}$$

(6.10–6)

The network is an example of a *ladder* structure, whose impedance function is formed by adding in contributions alternately as impedance and admittance in the fractional form of (6.10–6). The structure evidently has an impedance function which appears naturally in continued-fraction form. We need merely compare (6.10–2) and (6.10–6) to see that the coefficients in the continued-fraction expansion are directly the inductance

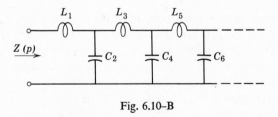

Fig. 6.10–B

and capacitance values in the network of Fig. 6.10–B. For the numerical example (6.10–5), the result will be the network of Fig. 6.10–C.

The foregoing discussion contains all the essentials of this new method of finding a network.   It amounts to making a continued-fraction expansion of the given impedance function and then reading off the element values.   We have only to discuss the different cases which may arise.

If the given impedance function $Z(p)$ has a pole at infinity, the network of Fig. 6.10–B results, in which the inductor L_1 clearly gives rise to a pole of impedance at infinity.

If the given impedance function $Z(p)$ has a zero at infinity (the only other possibility), then it will be necessary to invert $Z(p)$ before making the expansion.   That means we start with an admittance function $Y(p) = 1/Z(p)$ (which has a pole at infinity), make the same sort of continued-fraction expansion, and get a function which looks like (6.10–2) —from which we can immediately read off element values for the network

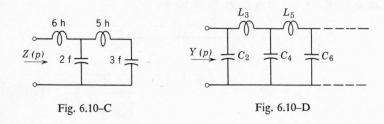

Fig. 6.10–C   Fig. 6.10–D

of Fig. 6.10–D.   The only difference is the absence of L_1.   In fact, an alternative point of view would be to proceed as in the first case, merely saying that the first coefficient is zero, and hence the value of L_1 is zero. The zero of impedance at infinity is evident in C_2.

If the given function represents an *admittance* $Y(p)$ which has a pole at infinity, we have already treated the case in Fig. 6.10–D and the discussion above.

If the given function represents an admittance $Y(p)$ which has a zero at infinity, we have already covered this in Fig. 6.10–B and its accompanying text.

Hence we now have a *third* type of network which we can readily obtain from any given *L-C* immittance function.   It consists of a ladder of series inductors and shunt capacitors, and may start either with an inductor or with a capacitor, depending upon the nature of the immittance (specifically, on its behavior at infinity).

We have so far ignored the *d-c* behavior of the function, which has not yet influenced our arguments.   The behavior of the function at the origin will determine how the network *terminates*.   If the impedance function has a zero (the admittance function has a pole) at the origin, the ending is like that in Fig. 6.10–E; if the impedance function has a pole (the admittance function has a zero) at the origin, the ending is like that in Fig. 6.10–F. It is merely a matter of common-sense observation to determine which happens in any given case.

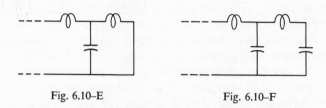

Fig. 6.10–E   Fig. 6.10–F

To recapitulate, the synthesis procedure given here is to

1. write the given reactance function as the quotient of two polynomials with terms arranged in descending order of powers of p;
2. obtain a continued-fraction expansion of the reactance function or of its reciprocal (whichever has a pole at infinity) by the divide-invert-divide $\cdots$ process;
3. draw a schematic diagram corresponding to the expansion, the element values of which are the coefficients obtained in step 2;
4. check the result by calculating the impedance (admittance) function from the final schematic diagram (at least at a few well-chosen points).

(6.10–7)

In the existence of this third form, we see further evidence of the non-uniqueness of the solution to the synthesis problem. For any given immittance function we can now design *three* network realizations, all of which (the simplest cases excepted) are different, yet all of which are equivalent at their driving points. Furthermore, we can equally well design three networks whose immittance functions are inverse to the given function at the driving points.

6.11 Another point of view

One might expect that there should be a fourth type of realization, related symmetrically to the third type, just because the first two types are symmetrically related. The relation between the first two is in duality: one is a series combination of antiresonant networks, the other is a parallel combination of resonant networks, and the impedance function of one can be made the admittance function of the other. But the dual of the third type is essentially nothing new: if in Fig. 6.10–B series inductors are replaced by shunt capacitors and shunt capacitors are replaced by series inductors, the same form of network results. This particular network form is basically its own dual, and duality here gives us nothing new.

There is a fourth type, however, and it is again obtained by continued-fraction expansion, but with the point of view somewhat altered. The realization of § 6.10 was in effect obtained by concentrating on the behavior at infinity, removing poles at infinity, alternately in impedance and admittance, so that corresponding elements appeared in a ladder form. Now we concentrate on the behavior at the origin, i.e., on the d-c behavior, and attempt to make the corresponding expansion and realization.

To do this, we first rewrite the given reactance function with the polynomials turned end-for-end, in other words, with the powers of p arranged in ascending order rather than in descending order. Suppose, to be specific, the given reactance function represents an impedance $Z(p)$ that has a pole at the origin; then the rewritten form is

$$Z(p) = \frac{a_0 + a_2 p^2 + \cdots}{a_1 p + a_3 p^3 + \cdots}. \tag{6.11-1}$$

We now proceed much as in § 5.14 (q.v.), but with our attention focused on poles at the origin rather than at infinity. The partial-fraction expansion of $Z(p)$ is

$$Z(p) = \frac{K_0}{p} + \sum_r \frac{2K_r p}{p^2 + \omega_r^2} + Hp, \tag{6.11-2}$$

as in (6.05-2). The residue K_0 is the result of division of the denominator into the numerator in (6.11-1), a_0/a_1, and is real and positive. For generality, a pole at infinity is indicated in (6.11-2), but infinity may be a zero, in which case the last term is absent; this need not concern us here.

Consider now the function

$$Z_1(p) = Z(p) - \frac{K_0}{p} = \sum_r \frac{2K_r p}{p^2 + \omega_r^2} + Hp$$

$$= \frac{a_1' p + a_3' p + \cdots}{a_1 + a_3 p^2 + \cdots} \tag{6.11-3}$$

which is p-r (each term is p-r) and odd, i.e., also a reactance function. At the origin it has a zero, not a pole; hence we turn our attention to its reciprocal, $Y_1(p) = 1/Z_1(p)$, which there has a pole. Since Z_1 has one less pole than has Z, the order of Z_1 is one less than the order of Z (cf. § 3.11). But the order of Y_1 is the same as the order of Z_1 and hence is less than the order of $Z(p)$ by one.

Now $Y_1(p)$ is a reactance function with a pole at the origin,

$$Y_1(p) = \frac{a_1 + a_3 p^2 + \cdots}{a_1' p + a_3' p^3 + \cdots}, \tag{6.11-4}$$

and its partial-fraction expansion is

$$Y_1(p) = \frac{K_0'}{p} + \sum_r \frac{2K_r'p}{p^2 + \omega_r^2} + H'p. \qquad (6.11\text{--}5)$$

Again, the residue K_0' is the result of the division indicated in (6.11–4) and is real and positive.

In similar fashion the function

$$Y_2 = Y_1 - \frac{K_0'}{p} = \frac{a_1''p + a_3''p^3 + \cdots}{a_1' + a_3'p^2 + \cdots} \qquad (6.11\text{--}6)$$

is again a reactance function, has a zero at the origin, and its order is one less than the order of Y_1. Its reciprocal,

$$Z_2 = \frac{1}{Y_2} = \frac{a_1' + a_3'p^2 + \cdots}{a_1''p + a_3''p^3 + \cdots}, \qquad (6.11\text{--}7)$$

has a pole at the origin, and on removing this another reactance function is obtained, of order one less than that of Z_2. The continuing process eventually terminates (as in § 5.14). What we have done is to obtain a continued-fraction expansion of $Z(p)$, not that of § 6.10 but rather one in the variable $1/p$, for we have

$$Z(p) = \frac{K_0}{p} + Z_1(p) = \frac{K_0}{p} + \frac{1}{Y_1(p)}$$

$$= \frac{K_0}{p} + \cfrac{1}{\cfrac{K_0'}{p} + Y_2}$$

$$= \frac{K_0}{p} + \cfrac{1}{\cfrac{K_0'}{p} + \cfrac{1}{\cfrac{K_0''}{p} + \cfrac{1}{\cdot}}} \qquad (6.11\text{--}8)$$

$$\cdot + \frac{K_a}{p}$$

in which K_a represents the residue at the pole at the origin of the last (unit-order) function. The number of terms in the expansion is equal to the order of $Z(p)$. We need little imagination to interpret the impedance function, in the form (6.11–8), as that of the network of Fig. 6.11–A. This network has the impedance function

$$Z(p) = \frac{1}{C_1 p} + \cfrac{1}{\cfrac{1}{L_2 p} + \cfrac{1}{\cfrac{1}{C_3 p} + \cfrac{1}{\cfrac{1}{L_4 p} + \cfrac{1}{.}}}} \qquad (6.11\text{–}9)$$

which, on comparison with (6.11–8), indicates that the residues obtained in the continued-fraction expansion represent elastance and reciprocal-inductance values in the network. One must be careful in interpreting

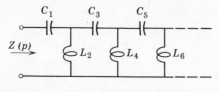

Fig. 6.11–A

the numbers as element values, for capacitance and inductance are the values usually used, and in this fourth method of realization the numbers obtained must accordingly be inverted. In the network realization we use capacitors where before we used inductors, and inductors where before we used capacitors, in keeping with our shift of attention from poles at infinity to poles at the origin.

Except for the first step of reversing the sequence of terms in the numerator and denominator of the given reactance function, the numerical work involved here is identical with that in § 6.10. If the continued-fraction expansion is performed with detached coefficients, the powers of

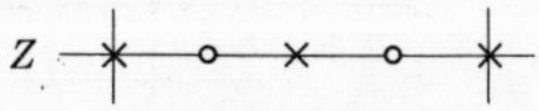

$$Z \;\; \xrightarrow{\;\;\times\;\;\circ\;\;\times\;\;\circ\;\;\times\;\;}$$

Fig. 6.11–B

the variable are not written down, so that the appearance of $1/p$ instead of p is not apparent. To illustrate, suppose the reactance function

$$Z(p) = \frac{p^4 + 35p^2 + 120}{9p^3 + 40p} \quad \text{ohms} \qquad (6.11\text{–}10)$$

with the frequency pattern of Fig. 6.11–B is to be realized in this third form. We first write

$$Z(p) = \frac{120 + 35p^2 + p^4}{40p + 9p^3} \tag{6.11–11}$$

and then perform the arithmetic of expansion in the usual manner,

$$
\begin{array}{ll}
40 \quad 9)\overline{120 \quad 35} \quad 1(3 \\
\quad \quad \underline{120 \quad 27} \\
\quad \quad \quad \quad \; 8 \quad 1)\overline{40 \quad 9}(5 \\
\quad \quad \quad \quad \quad \quad \underline{40 \quad 5} \\
\quad \quad \quad \quad \quad \quad \quad 4)\overline{8} \quad 1(2 \\
\quad \quad \quad \quad \quad \quad \quad \; \underline{8} \\
\quad \quad \quad \quad \quad \quad \quad \quad 1)\overline{4}(4 \\
\quad \quad \quad \quad \quad \quad \quad \quad \; \underline{4}
\end{array}
\tag{6.11–12}
$$

Hence

$$Z(p) = \frac{3}{p} + \cfrac{1}{\cfrac{5}{p} + \cfrac{1}{\cfrac{2}{p} + \cfrac{1}{\cfrac{4}{p}}}} \tag{6.11–13}$$

The round numbers are used here for simplicity; in practice they would not be integers, of course, but the principle would be the same. The network realization is shown in Fig. 6.11–C.

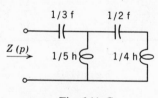

Fig. 6.11–C

We have now a fourth form in which any reactance function can be realized, that of Fig. 6.11–A in general. It is obtained by continued-fraction expansion also, but with emphasis on the d-c behavior of the function rather than on the behavior at infinity. Just as with the third method, there are two different possibilities at each end of the network, which, in the light of our experience with the third method, require only brief discussion.

If the given function represents an impedance with a pole at the origin, or an admittance with a zero at the origin, the network of Fig. 6.11–A results from this continued-fraction expansion of the *impedance* function. If the given function represents an impedance with a zero at the origin, or an admittance with a pole at the origin, then the first element is a shunt inductor, but thereafter the network is like that of Fig. 6.11–A. (Alternatively, we might say that C_1 becomes infinite, and this element is merely a short circuit.)   The network results from a continued-fraction expansion of the *admittance* function in the variable $(1/p)$.

The high-frequency behavior of the function, hitherto ignored, determines the manner in which the network terminates, in exact parallel with the third type.   If at infinity the impedance function has a pole (the admittance function has a zero), the last element is an inductor; if at infinity the impedance function has a zero (the admittance function has a pole), the last element is a capacitor.   It is not necessary to remember these cases, for in any given case the continued-fraction expansion indicates, term by term, what elements the network should have.   For

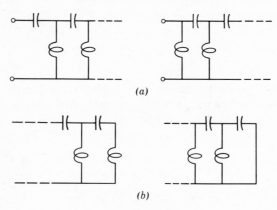

(a)

(b)

Fig. 6.11–D

completeness, the four possibilities are shown in Fig. 6.11–D which illustrates (a) the two methods of starting and (b) the two methods of ending the network.   The four possible methods of combining these give rise to the four cases of Table 6.04–A.

The process of finding element values is exactly that of the third method, except that the polynomials are arranged in *ascending* powers of p, rather than in descending powers, before starting the divisions.   Whether the given function represents impedance or admittance makes little difference; we take as the function to expand either the given function or its reciprocal, whichever has the even polynomial in the numerator. If this is then an impedance, the network starts with a series capacitor; if it is an admittance, the network starts with a shunt inductor. The coefficients obtained are values of elastance and reciprocal inductance, rather than of capacitance and inductance.

To recapitulate, the synthesis procedure given here is to

1. write the given reactance function as the quotient of two polynomials with terms arranged in ascending order of powers of p;
2. obtain a continued-fraction expansion of the reactance function or of its reciprocal (whichever has a pole at the origin) by the divide-invert-divide $\cdots$ process;
3. draw a schematic diagram corresponding to the expansion, the element values of which are the reciprocals of the coefficients obtained in step 2; and
4. check the result by calculating the impedance (admittance) function from the final schematic diagram. (6.11–14)

Here then is the fourth form, and further evidence as to the multiplicity of solutions to the synthesis problem in general. For any given reactance function we can now design four network realizations (all different, except in the simplest cases), and four networks with driving-point immittance functions inverse to the datum functions.

6.12 Canonic forms

We have found four different ways of synthesizing a network that has any given reactance function as one of its immittance functions. The four are fundamental methods, lead to simple and significant forms of network, and in each case use only the minimum number of elements. The four realizations are customarily called *canonic forms* for these reasons. The first two (Fig. 6.12–A) are called *Foster's* forms (FO 1) and the second two (Fig. 6.12–B) are called *Cauer's* forms (CA 1). Each of the four uses only the minimum number of elements, and in each the behavior at zero frequency and at infinite frequency determines a salient characteristic of the network (whether the lone elements are present or not in the Foster forms, and how the ladder starts and ends in the Cauer forms). Any given immittance function can be realized in each of the four forms (though in the simplest cases they are not all different), and so can its inverse function.

Yet these four methods of realization are not really distinct. Two depend on partial-fraction expansion of an immittance function, and two on continued-fraction expansion thereof. But our development of the continued-fraction expansion depends in turn on partial-fraction expansion, so that we may well say that all four depend on partial-fraction expansion. The differences arise in the manner of treating the partial-fraction expansion, once it is made. If it is left untouched, and network elements put down for each term, the two Foster forms result. But if only *part* of the expansion is thus realized, specifically that term corresponding to a pole at infinity or at the origin, the remaining part is still positive-real and odd, and hence a reactance function, and so is its reciprocal. The reciprocal may be expanded, but again realized only to

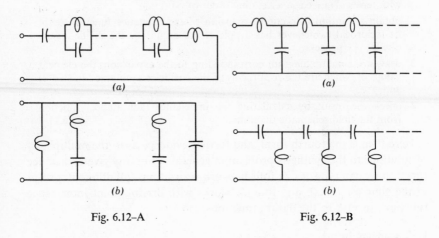

(a)

(a)

(b)

(b)

Fig. 6.12–A   Fig. 6.12–B

the extent of one term. If this process is continued until it terminates, the Cauer forms result. Hence the only real difference is in the number of terms of a partial-fraction expansion realized before inverting and shifting attention to the other (impedance or admittance) point of view: if *all* terms are realized, the Foster networks are created; if only *one* term is realized, the Cauer networks are created. The Foster networks are ladder networks with but one arm (albeit a complicated arm); the Cauer networks are ladder networks with many arms (each of which consists of but one element). We may well consider the two pairs as merely extreme examples of a general *L-C* synthesis process which can be called either a partial-fraction process (with inversions and shifts of impedance to admittance and back again, etc.) or a continued-fraction process (with varying sorts of terms). Between the two lie many other possibilities in which varying ladder arms are extracted before the change of approach from impedance to admittance or vice versa. All will be essentially the same: they will all reduce the order of the reactance function by removing poles, but they will differ in how many poles (how much reactance) are removed at each step, i.e., in when the attack is changed. The Foster forms exhibit the resonances directly (poles of impedance or zeros of admittance in the first Foster form, zeros of impedance or poles of admittance in the second Foster form), as a consequence of their extreme position in this spectrum of possible methods, whereas in the Cauer forms no resonant frequencies are apparent (except zero and infinity). These four forms, lying in pairs at the extremes of the general process, are very important and deserve their name of canonic forms.

6.13 Alternative forms

In § 6.12 we have dimly seen the possibility of other forms of realization of reactance functions, forms which belong to the same family, of which Foster's forms are one extreme and Cauer's the other. We shall discuss these only briefly, as their number clearly increases rapidly with the order of the reactance function, and the principle of their generation should be clear.

The process of partial-fraction expansion sets out the (pairs of) poles of the reactance function. One method of realization immediately associates with each pair a two-element resonant network; another does so only for one pole, and then proceeds to recombine the remainder into a rational function which is inverted—then the process is repeated. Physically we have *removed* all the poles *or* just one pole as a subnetwork, to be connected in series or in parallel at the input terminals. In one case the process is complete; in the other it has just begun. But we have in general numerous choices as to how many of the poles we remove in this manner. We may choose to remove two pairs, or the pole at infinity (if present) and one pair of finite poles, or some other combination. Then, when the remainder is inverted and the new partial-fraction expansion made, we have again a choice, an independent one. For networks of great complexity, a large number of equivalent, different realizations can thus be built up, all with only the minimum number of elements. (In practice, however, the order of the reactance functions to be realized does not often become very large.) We can best illustrate this multiplicity of

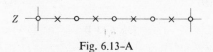

Fig. 6.13–A

networks with a specific example, say a reactance function which represents an impedance and has the frequency pattern of Fig. 6.13–A. (It is not necessary to give its formula or to consider numerical values here.)

Various realizations of this are given in Fig. 6.13–B. There (*a*) is the first Foster realization, obtained by removing *all* of the poles, i.e., the whole function, as a series impedance. In (*b*) is a form which results when one pair of finite poles is removed, the remainder inverted to become an admittance from which the d-c pole and a pair of finite poles are

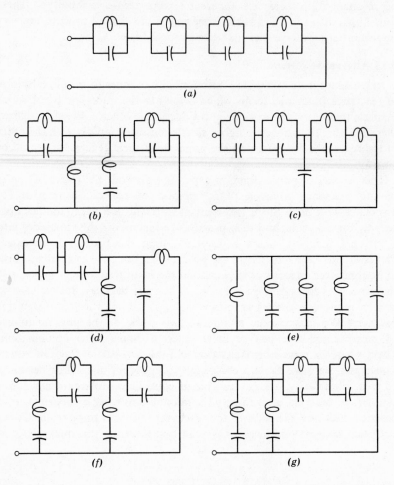

Fig. 6.13–B

removed, and finally the new remainder inverted to become an impedance again, from which all poles are removed. If two pairs of finite poles are first removed from the impedance function, then one or two poles in the reduced admittance, then finally the poles of the further-reduced impedance realized, the networks of (*c*) and (*d*) result. Further equivalent networks may be generated by starting with the admittance that is the reciprocal of the given impedance function; the networks of (e) (the second Foster realization), (f), and (g) illustrate the possibilities. In all but the Foster forms there are still further possibilities according to which poles are first removed, and it is not easy to state the total number of minimum-number-of-element realizations possible. There are other possibilities for this function, including, of course, the two Cauer realizations.

A slightly different point of view may help in clarifying this multiple nature of synthesis and in re-emphasizing the importance of the four fundamental forms. For we can obtain these various realizations merely by combining and mixing the four methods. We may start with the first Foster realization, for example, of which we retain only a few of the parallel-resonant combinations; the balance we recombine into a new, simpler reactance function which we might proceed to realize by one of the other three methods. We might halt part way in this realization, and treat what is left by the first method again, or by one of the other two. The four methods can be intermingled at will, we can switch from one to another as we wish, and since the fundamental principle (6.07–1) holds for each reduced reactance function, the total number of elements need never exceed the minimum determined by the order of the original reactance function. All of the network realizations of Fig. 6.13–B can equally well be interpreted as results of successive applications of the four methods in various appropriate sequences. The higher the degrees of the polynomials, the more possibilities there are, though the total number of them is, of course, finite. Nevertheless, there may be many different solutions, all of the same problem. The best one to use will depend on practical matters, which we discuss later.

If one admits the (sometimes useful) device of removing only "part of a pole," i.e., of splitting an element or combination of elements into two parts, one of which is retained, the other combined with the remaining reactance, the number of possibilities increases much more. Then the number of elements is no longer minimum, of course, but there are instances (§ 14.16 and Volume II) in which this is useful.

By a mixture of the four basic (canonic) techniques we can now realize a given reactance function in many forms. All stem from the same principle: removal of poles of impedance as series L-C networks (Fig. 6.13–C), followed by removal of poles of admittance as shunt L-C networks, with alternate repetitions of these until the realization is complete. Each component network may be realized in any of the four canonic forms or in more, depending on its complexity. The principle is aptly called *reactance (susceptance) removal*, for by removing series reactance (shunt susceptance) the order of the reactance function is reduced until only an open circuit or a short circuit is left. From this point of view the process is fundamental, and the various forms result only from variations in the amount of reactance (susceptance) removed at the various stages.   The process will prove to be very useful in the general (*R-L-C*) case as well. Networks of the form shown in Fig. 6.13–C result, the number of ladder arms (boxes) depending on the detailed method of realization (on the amounts of reactance and susceptance removed).   The two Foster

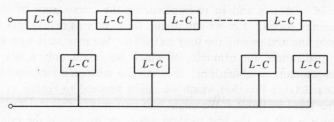

Fig. 6.13–C

methods each yield one box alone (containing a number of elements equal to the order of the reactance function); the two Cauer methods yield a number of boxes, each containing one element, equal to the order of the reactance function.   Generally, there are many intermediate possibilities; in these each box represents a network which may well have various different (equivalent) realizations of its own, a fact which even further increases the number of possible realizations.   There remains the possibility of still other realizations that are not of the ladder form, which we do not discuss.

6.14 Examples

As with any process, numerical examples help greatly in understanding. Only a few have been given above, but more are given here, where all the canonic forms can be developed simultaneously for the same reactance function.   The examples are largely confined to the four canonic forms, but the foregoing discussion should make realization in certain other possible forms a simple matter.

Example 1.   An *L-C* network is to have a driving-point impedance function with the frequency pattern shown in Fig. 6.14–A and the multiplier *H* equal to 0.150 h.   The corresponding function is

$$Z(p) = \frac{0.150[p^2 + (2\pi \times 2200)^2][p^2 + (2\pi \times 6100)^2]}{p[p^2 + (2\pi \times 4000)^2]} \quad \text{ohms.}$$

The (actual) numbers are unwieldy and the work can be greatly simplified by normalization (§ 2.09).   A convenient choice of reference frequency here is

$f_0 = 4000$ cps, or $\omega_0 = 2\pi \times 4000$ radians per sec. With p normalized to this reference, the function is

$$Z(p) = H_0 \frac{[p^2 + (0.55)^2][p^2 + (1.525)^2]}{p[p^2 + 1]} \quad \text{ohms}$$

$$= H_0 \frac{(p^2 + 0.3025)(p^2 + 2.326)}{p(p^2 + 1)},$$

in which $H_0 = 0.150 \times 2\pi \times 4000 = 1200\pi$ ohms, and p represents, not the actual complex variable, but the same divided by ω_0. (Use of a different symbol

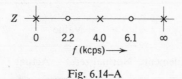

$$
\begin{array}{ccccc}
0 & 2.2 & 4.0 & 6.1 & \infty \\
\end{array}
$$
f (kcps) $\longrightarrow$

Fig. 6.14–A

is usually unnecessary, provided one is careful to remember whether it is normalized or actual frequency that is in use at any given point.) The precision with which the computations must be made depends, of course, on that desired in the final network; in these examples the arithmetic has been done accurately and results arbitrarily rounded off to four significant figures. Since the multiplier H_0 is merely an impedance scale factor, it can be temporarily ignored, and restored in the final design (this amounts to choosing H_0 as the reference value for impedance R_0).

The first Foster realization process is

$$\frac{(p^2 + 0.3025)(p^2 + 2.326)}{p(p^2 + 1)} = \frac{0.7035}{p} + \frac{Ap}{p^2 + 1} + p,$$

where

$$A = \left[\frac{(p^2 + 0.3025)(p^2 + 2.326)}{p(p^2 + 1)} \times \frac{(p^2 + 1)}{p} \right]_{p^2 = -1}$$

$$= \frac{(-0.6975)(1.326)}{(-1)} = 0.9246.$$

The network, drawn directly from the expression above, is shown in Fig. 6.14–B, together with the element values. Although element values in normalized schematic diagrams technically have no dimensions, they are given here in "normalized" henrys and farads (and later in ohms where resistance appears) for convenience in recording the fact that the values represent L, C, and R respectively, and not their reciprocals. The normalized element values are obtained directly from the partial-fraction expansion; the actual element values are obtained from the normalized values by (2.09–7) with $\omega_0 = 8000\pi$ radians per sec and $R_0 = H_0 = 1200\pi$ ohms. Thus

$$L_{\text{actual}} = \frac{R_0}{\omega_0} L_{\text{normalized}} = 0.15 \times L_{\text{normalized}}$$

and

$$C_{\text{actual}} = \frac{C_{\text{normalized}}}{R_0 \omega_0} = 0.01055 \times 10^{-6} \times C_{\text{normalized}}.$$

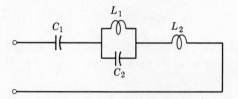

Value

Element	Normalized	Actual
L_1	0.9246 h	138.7 mh
L_2	1.0 h	150.0 mh
C_1	1.421 f	0.01500 μf
C_2	1.082 f	0.01141 μf

Fig. 6.14–B

The second Foster realization process is

$$\frac{p(p^2 + 1)}{(p^2 + 0.3025)(p^2 + 2.326)} = \frac{Ap}{p^2 + 0.3025} + \frac{Bp}{p^2 + 2.326}$$

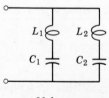

Value

Element	Normalized	Actual
L_1	2.901 h	435.1 mh
L_2	1.526 h	228.9 mh
C_1	1.140 f	0.01203 μf
C_2	0.2817 f	0.002974 μf

Fig. 6.14–C

in which

$$A = \frac{0.6975}{2.023} = 0.3448, \qquad B = \frac{-1.326}{-2.023} = 0.6552.$$

The network and element values, obtained by comparison with the partial-fraction expansion and by restoration of scales, are given in Fig. 6.14–C. For the first Cauer realization process we write $Z(p)$ as

$$Z(p) = H_0 \frac{p^4 + 2.628p^2 + 0.7035}{p^3 + p}.$$

The realization process is

```
1   1)1   2.628   0.7035(1
    1   1
        1.628   0.7035)1   1      (0.6142
                        1   0.4321
                            0.5679)1.628   0.7035(2.867
                                   1.628
                                       0.7035)0.5679(0.8073
                                              0.5679
```

Therefore

$$Z(p) = H_0 \left(p + \cfrac{1}{0.6142p + \cfrac{1}{2.867p + \cfrac{1}{0.807p}}} \right).$$

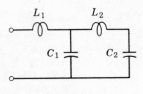

Value

Element	Normalized	Actual
L_1	1.0 h	150.0 mh
L_2	2.867 h	430.0 mh
C_1	0.6142 f	0.006483 μf
C_2	0.8073 f	0.008520 μf

Fig. 6.14–D

The corresponding network and element values are given in Fig. 6.14–D.

The second Cauer realization process is

```
1    1)0.7035  2.628    1(0.7035
     0.7035    0.7035
     ─────────
             1.925   1)1   1      (0.5196
                      1   0.5196
                      ──────────
                        0.4804)1.925   1(4.006
                               1.925
                               ───────
                                    1)0.4804(0.4804
                                      0.4804
                                      ──────
```

Hence

$$Z(p) = H_0 \left\{ \frac{0.7035}{p} + \cfrac{1}{\cfrac{0.5196}{p} + \cfrac{1}{\cfrac{4.006}{p} + \cfrac{1}{0.4804/p}}} \right\}.$$

The network is given in Fig 6.14–E.

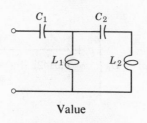

Value

Element	Normalized	Actual
L_1	1.925 h	288.7 mh
L_2	2.082 h	312.2 mh
C_1	1.421 f	0.01500 μf
C_2	0.2496 f	0.002635 μf

Fig. 6.14–E

In this example, where the immittance functions are of fourth order, our synthesis process can give no other realizations with only four elements. Notice that the two Cauer forms could be obtained from the first Foster form by retaining one element and converting the remaining three to their equivalent network (cf. § 6.13). Notice also the range of element values in the different realizations.

Example 2.   On a normalized basis, a nondissipative admittance function is to have poles at unit frequency, zeros at 0.8 and 1.2, a susceptance of -2 (normalized) mhos at 0.5, and the minimum possible number of elements. The references are 3 mcps and 75 ohms.

The frequency pattern must be that shown in Fig. 6.14–F if the number of elements is kept to a minimum: The admittance function is then

$$Y(p) = H_0 \frac{(p^2 + 0.64)(p^2 + 1.44)}{p(p^2 + 1)},$$

in which H_0 is determined by the requirement

$$Y(j0.5) = -j2 = H_0 \frac{(0.39)(1.19)}{j0.5(0.75)} = -j1.238H_0,$$

whence $H_0 = 1.616$. We can conveniently ignore H_0 (i.e., use a unit multiplier)

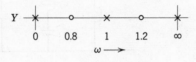

Fig. 6.14–F

until the final calculation of actual element values, and insert it at that point. The conversion factors to be used will then be

for inductance: $\dfrac{75}{2\pi(3 \times 10^6)} \times \dfrac{1}{1.616} = 2.462 \times 10^{-6}$,

for capacitance: $\dfrac{1.616}{75 \times 2\pi(3 \times 10^6)} = 1143 \times 10^{-12}$.

The first Foster realization process is (Fig. 6.14–G)

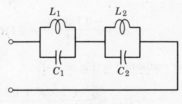

	Value	
Element	Normalized	Actual
L_1	0.7031 h	1.731 μh
L_2	0.3819 h	0.940 μh
C_1	2.222 f	2540 $\mu\mu$f
C_2	1.818 f	2078 $\mu\mu$f

Fig. 6.14–G

$$Z(p) = \frac{p(p^2 + 1)}{(p^2 + 0.64)(p^2 + 1.44)} = \frac{Ap}{p^2 + 0.64} + \frac{Bp}{p^2 + 1.44},$$

$$A = \frac{0.36}{0.80} = 0.45, \qquad B = \frac{-0.44}{-0.80} = 0.55.$$

The second Foster realization process is (Fig. 6.14–H)

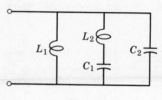

Value

Element	Normalized	Actual
L_1	1.085 h	2.672 μh
L_2	6.313 h	15.54 μh
C_1	0.1584 f	181.1 $\mu\mu$f
C_2	1 f	1143 $\mu\mu$f

Fig. 6.14–H

$$Y(p) = \frac{(p^2 + 0.64)(p^2 + 1.44)}{p(p^2 + 1)} = \frac{0.9216}{p} + \frac{Ap}{p^2 + 1} + p,$$

$$A = \frac{-0.36(0.44)}{-1} = 0.1584.$$

The first Cauer realization is (Fig. 6.14–I)

$$Y(p) = \frac{p^4 + 2.08p^2 + 0.9216}{p^3 + p}.$$

```
1   1)1   2.08   0.9216(1
      1   1
      ─────────────
      1.08   0.9216)1   1        (0.9259
             1   0.8533
             ──────────────
             0.1467)1.08   0.9216(7.364
                    1.08
                    ───────────────
                    0.9216)0.1467(0.1591
                           0.1467
```

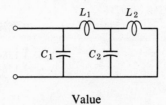

	Value	
Element	Normalized	Actual
L_1	0.9259 h	2.280 μh
L_2	0.1591 h	0.3918 μh
C_1	1 f	1143 $\mu\mu$f
C_2	7.364 f	8417 $\mu\mu$f

Fig. 6.14–I

The second Cauer realization is (Fig. 6.14–J)

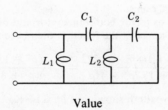

	Value	
Element	Normalized	Actual
L_1	1.085 h	2.672 μh
L_2	0.1180 h	0.2906 μh
C_1	1.158 f	1324 $\mu\mu$f
C_2	7.313 f	8360 $\mu\mu$f

Fig. 6.14–J

$$Y(p) = \frac{0.9216 + 2.08p^2 + p^4}{p + p^3}.$$

```
1   1)0.9216   2.08      1(0.9216
       0.9216   0.9216
       ─────────────────
       1.1584   1)1   1       (0.8633
                1   0.8633
                ─────────────
                0.1367)1.1584   1(8.472
                       1.1584
                       ─────────────
                       1)0.1367(0.1367
                         0.1367
```

As in the first example, our process can give no other realizations that use only the minimum number of elements. The two Cauer forms could be obtained from the second Foster form, in this case, by retaining one element and replacing the remaining three by equivalent networks. Again the range of element values required differs from one realization to another: the second Cauer realization requires a rather small inductance value, and the second Foster realization a comparatively small capacitance value, for example.

Example 3. The result of a solution of an approximation problem is the function

$$\frac{2.7p^4 + 22p^2 + 19.5}{p^5 + 15.7p^3 + 41p}$$

which is p-r and is to be realized as a driving-point impedance. The references are 30 kcps and 600 ohms.

The first task is to factor both numerator and denominator (for both Foster forms are to be obtained); the function then becomes

$$2.7\frac{p^4 + 8.148p^2 + 7.222}{p^5 + 15.7p^3 + 41p} = 2.7\frac{(p^2 + 1.012)(p^2 + 7.136)}{p(p^2 + 3.309)(p^2 + 12.39)},$$

with the frequency pattern shown in Fig. 6.14–K. Incorporating the multiplier

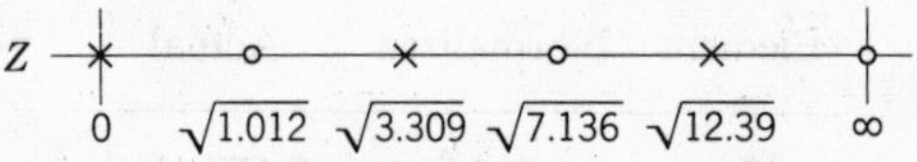

Fig. 6.14–K

2.7, the conversion factors to be applied to the results of realizations that ignore the multiplier are

for inductance: $\dfrac{600}{2\pi(30,000)}\,2.7 = 8.594 \times 10^{-3}$,

for capacitance: $\dfrac{1}{600 \times 2\pi(30,000) \times 2.7} = 0.003275 \times 10^{-6}$.

The first Foster realization process is (Fig. 6.14–L)

$$Z(p) = \frac{(p^2 + 1.012)(p^2 + 7.136)}{p(p^2 + 3.309)(p^2 + 12.39)} = \frac{0.1762}{p} + \frac{Ap}{p^2 + 3.309} + \frac{Bp}{p^2 + 12.39},$$

$$A = \frac{(-2.297)(3.827)}{(-3.309)(9.082)} = 0.2925, \qquad B = \frac{(-11.38)(-5.255)}{(-12.39)(-9.082)} = 0.5313.$$

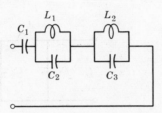

Value

Element	Normalized	Actual
L_1	0.08840 h	759.8 μh
L_2	0.04288 h	368.5 μh
C_1	5.677 f	0.01859 μf
C_2	3.419 f	0.01120 μf
C_3	1.882 f	0.00616 μf

Fig. 6.14–L

The second Foster realization process is (Fig. 6.14–M)

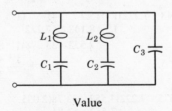

Value

Element	Normalized	Actual
L_1	0.2343 h	2.014 mh
L_2	0.3045 h	2.617 mh
C_1	4.217 f	0.01381 μf
C_2	0.4602 f	0.001507 μf
C_3	1 f	0.003275 μf

Fig. 6.14–M

$$Y(p) = \frac{p(p^2 + 3.309)(p^2 + 12.39)}{(p^2 + 1.012)(p^2 + 7.136)} = \frac{Ap}{p^2 + 1.012} + \frac{Bp}{p^2 + 7.136} + p,$$

$$A = \frac{2.297 \times 11.38}{6.124} = 4.268, \qquad B = \frac{-3.827 \times 5.255}{-6.124} = 3.284.$$

The first Cauer realization process is (Fig. 6.14–N)

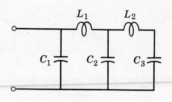

Value

Element	Normalized	Actual
L_1	0.1324 h	1.138 mh
L_2	0.1941 h	1.668 mh
C_1	1 f	0.003275 μf
C_2	2.055 f	0.006729 μf
C_3	2.622 f	0.008587 μf

Fig. 6.14–N

$$Y(p) = \frac{p^5 + 15.7p^3 + 41p}{p^4 + 8.148p^2 + 7.222}.$$

```
1   8.148   7.222)1   15.7     41    (1
              1     8.148    7.222
              ─────────────────────
                   7.552   33.778)1    8.148    7.222(0.1324
                               1     4.473
                               ─────────────────
                                    3.675    7.222

      3.675   7.222)7.552   33.78(2.055
              7.552   14.84
              ──────────────
                    18.94)3.675    7.222(0.1941
                          3.675
                          ──────────────
                               7.222)18.94(2.622
                                     18.94
```

The second Cauer realization process is (Fig. 6.14–O)

$$Z(p) = \frac{7.222 + 8.148p^2 + p^4}{41p + 15.7p^3 + p^5}.$$

41   15.7   1)7.222   8.148   1   (0.1762
            7.222   2.766   0.1762
            ───────────────────
                    5.382   0.8238)41   15.7   1(7.617
                                    41   6.275
                                    ───────────
                                        9.425   1

      9.425   1)5.383   0.8238(0.5711
              5.383   0.5711
              ─────────────────
                      0.2527)9.425   1(37.29
                             9.425
                             ────────────
                                  1)0.2527(0.2527
                                    0.2527

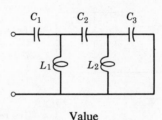

Value

Element	Normalized	Actual
L_1	0.1313 h	1.128 mh
L_2	0.02682 h	0.2305 mh
C_1	5.677 f	0.01859 μf
C_2	1.751 f	0.005734 μf
C_3	3.957 f	0.01296 μf

Fig. 6.14–O

The impedance function of this example is sufficiently complicated to have a number of additional (different, but equivalent) realizations; it can also be realized in the forms shown in Fig. 6.14–P, which develop when the canonic methods are mixed.

In the various realizations, of which we have pointed out twelve, the range of element values will of course be a point to consider in determining which to use.

6.15 Summary

In this chapter we have developed certain properties which are possessed by the driving-point immittance functions of nondissipative networks, in addition to those possessed by all p-r functions.   The L-C functions are odd as well as p-r, are called reactance functions, have zeros and poles only on the imaginary axis and only in interlaced patterns, and the reactance and susceptance always increase with frequency. Of any given reactance function four canonic realizations can be obtained, and generally a number of other realizations, all using the minimum number of elements possible (which number is equal to the order of the reactance function).

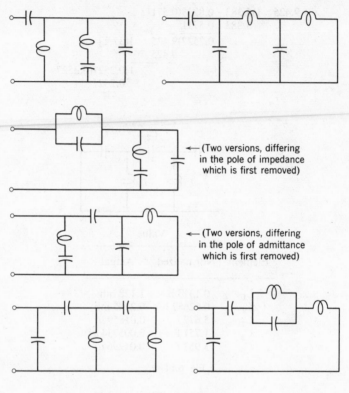

Fig. 6.14–P

We have thus a variety of methods for solving this, the first synthesis problem we have directly attacked. And discussion of the first of the three possible two-kinds-of-element cases listed at the beginning of this chapter has been completed. Any given reactance function can be realized, and usually in more than one form. And in demonstrating this fact we have accomplished even more; for we have made a start on demonstrating the *sufficiency* of positive reality for realization. We know that all network driving-point immittance functions are both rational and p-r, i.e., lie in the overlap region in Fig. 5.03–A. It is a primary objective of Volume I to demonstrate that all p-r functions which are rational, i.e., *all* functions in the overlap, are realizable by networks with those functions as driving-point immittance functions, and that there is no gap, no portion of the rational, p-r functions which are not physically realizable network functions. For the *L-C* case we have shown that nondissipative-network driving-point immittance functions are confined to that part of the overlap which contains odd functions, and every odd function in the overlap (every reactance function) has a realization. Hence if a function is odd, positive reality is both necessary and sufficient for physical realizability; "p-r" can be interpreted in either sense.

As to functions which are both p-r and even, there are none except constants—and they are realizable by resistors. Hence our next attack must be on p-r functions which are mixed, neither odd nor even, and this we discuss in Chapter 7.

6.16 References

BA 3 (Chap. 13), BO 3, CA 1, CA 2, FO 1, FR 2, GU 2, GU 3, and SH 1.

PROBLEMS

6-1. In § 6.02 are given two definitions of a reactance function: (*a*) a p-r function that is imaginary for $p = j\omega$; (*b*) a p-r function that is also odd. Show that these two definitions are completely equivalent.

6-2. (*a*) Show that the real part of a reactance function is negative everywhere in the left half plane. (*b*) Show that at least one of the natural modes of the

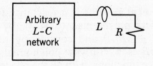

Prob. 6–2

network shown corresponds to a value of *p* whose real part lies between zero and $-R/L$ (i.e., a loop impedance vanishes at such a point).

6-3. The following functions are, from the context of their discussion in the text, obviously reactance functions. Show that they are so merely from mathematical examination of the functions: (6.05–23), (6.10–3), (6.11–9), the functions in § 6.14.

6-4. Show that any rational p-r function that is *even* must be a constant, so that the parallel (to *L-C*) synthesis for *even* p-r functions is extremely simple. What is it? In broad physical terms, why is it that even functions are so restricted in ability to do interesting things as functions of frequency, in such contrast to the odd functions? Extend the first statement to even p-r functions that may be irrational.

6-5. Demonstrate (6.03–5) and (6.03–6) by each of the following methods.

(a) Making use of the fact that $Z(p)$, or $Y(p)$, is p-r and odd, and using the Cauchy-Riemann equations, evaluate the real part R for $\sigma = 0$ and for $\sigma > 0$, calculate $\partial R/\partial \sigma$ on the imaginary axis and hence $\partial X/\partial \omega$.

(b) Make the partial-fraction expansion of the function in question and examine the expression it yields for the imaginary part, for $p = j\omega$.

(c) Expand the function in a Taylor series about a point on the imaginary axis and examine the leading terms in the real part at points on and near the imaginary axis.

(d) From (4.13–2) evaluate the partial derivative of the real part with respect to σ; consider its sign on the imaginary axis and use the Cauchy-Riemann equations.

(e) Show that $dX/d\omega \geqq |X|/\omega$ (BO 3, p. 181).

(f) Starting from the expression for $Z(p)$ in (4.12–13), with $p = j\omega$, evaluate $dX/d\omega$ in terms of T_0 and V_0. Show that I_r may equally well be considered the complex-number representation in the sinusoidal steady state of the sinusoidal current $i_r(t)$ in T_0 and V_0. Make use of the fact that then all currents are in phase (or $180°$ apart in phase), so that all I_r may be considered real. From this show

$$\frac{dT_0}{d\omega} = 2 \sum_{r,s} L_{rs} I_s' \frac{dI_r'}{d\omega}, \quad \text{in which } I_r' = \frac{I_r}{|I_1|}.$$

From this, and a similar expression for $dV_0/d\omega$ show that

$$\omega \frac{dT_0}{d\omega} - \frac{1}{\omega} \frac{dV_0}{d\omega} = 0, \quad \text{hence that } \frac{dX}{d\omega} = T_0 + \frac{V_0}{\omega^2}.$$

Show in addition that $dX/d\omega$ is greater than the slope of the straight line to the origin from the point in question, X/ω.

Discuss the interrelation of these demonstrations, and of that in the text.

6-6. (a) Show that if $F(p) = pB/A$ is a reactance function (is p-r and odd), then $A + pB$ is a Hurwitz polynomial, (6.04–3), by realizing the impedance (admittance) function $(1 + pB/A)$ and considering the locations of its zeros.

(b) Show that if $A + pB$ is a Hurwitz polynomial, then $F(p) = pB/A$ and $G(p) = A/pB$ are reactance functions, with all the properties of such, by factoring the polynomial and considering the behavior, at real frequencies, of the angle of the polynomial as ω varies from $-\infty$ to $+\infty$. (Cf. TE 2.)

6-7. A p-r function $F(p)$ has only imaginary zeros, though its poles are not restricted. Show that it can be realized as a driving-point impedance by an L-C network in combination with one resistor. In what similar way can it be realized as a driving-point admittance? What can be said about a p-r function with only imaginary poles, of a similar nature?

6-8. Show that if the partial-fraction expansion of a reactance function is made, and any number of its terms removed (conjugate-pole terms being taken in pairs), the remaining part is still a reactance function. Discuss and illustrate the application of this principle to realization of L-C networks in forms which combine the various canonic forms in various ways.

6-9. Show that if a function is odd, has only simple zeros and poles that are all on the imaginary axis and alternate, has real coefficients and a multiplier of appropriate sign, the function is p-r. How is it realizable? If the slope property is added to the list, what property or properties may be deleted?

6-10. Show that the reciprocal of a reactance function is also a reactance function.

6-11. Check the validity of (6.07–1) for each of the four possible cases in Table 6.04–A and thus show that this number of elements is always enough for realization. Then prove (6.07–2). Why is the minimum number of elements necessary for the realization of an L-C immittance function equal to the *order* of the function? What relation does this minimum number bear to the degree of the highest power of p in numerator and denominator of the function? To the number of constants (coefficients) in the function?

6-12. Show that the number of inductors used in the realization of a reactance function is the same for all the canonic realizations; repeat for the number of capacitors. Show also that the number of inductors is equal to the number of poles in the impedance function at positive frequencies greater than zero (including infinity). Show that the number of capacitors is equal to the number of zeros in the impedance function at such frequencies. Phrase these statements also in admittance terms.

6-13. If $F(p) = (M_1 + N_1)/(M_2 + N_2)$ is p-r (and not purely odd or even), show that *all* the ratios formed by taking one even polynomial M and one odd polynomial N therefrom are reactance functions. (Cf. GU 3.)

6-14. Explain to what extent the shape of the curve of reactance (susceptance) versus frequency of an L-C one-terminal pair is determined, once the critical frequencies are fixed. Illustrate.

6-15. Develop the canonic form of § 6.11 in the following manner. Rewrite the given reactance function as a function of p^{-1}, obtained by dividing numerator and denominator by the highest power of p appearing. Show that the theory of § 5.14 is applicable to the new function of p^{-1} and hence this function can be developed in continued fractions, a typical term being $c_1 p^{-1}$. Discuss the interpretation of this method as an application of frequency transformation (Prob. 4-32) and explain the mapping involved.

6-16. Construct a chart tabulating the following properties of the simpler L-C canonic networks, for all L-C impedance functions of orders one, two, three, four, five, six. Give the frequency patterns, the schematics of the four canonic realizations and of all other realizations that can be obtained by using combinations of the canonic procedures, list the number of such realizations possible, the number of inductors used, the number of capacitors used. Consider, in each case, all possibilities as to poles and zeros, and sketch the reactance-frequency and susceptance-frequency curves.

6-17. Repeat Prob. 6-16 for L-C admittance functions.

6-18. The two terminals of a network that contains two capacitors, three inductors, and no resistors are available for measurement, but the only additional information available as to the network configuration is that the same impedance could not be obtained with a smaller number of elements. What impedance would be measured at zero frequency? At very high frequency? Explain your reasoning and give the frequency pattern and sketch the reactance-frequency curve. Give the schematic realizations of the impedance in the four canonic forms. *Must* the network be in one of these forms? Explain your answer.

6-19. Draw the schematic of a ladder-form one-terminal pair in which a capacitor appears across the input terminals as one rung, then an inductor forms a leg, then a capacitor another rung, etc., until you have seven elements in all. Now give the frequency pattern of the input impedance and sketch the driving-point reactance as a function of frequency. Give the schematic diagrams of the four canonic realizations of this impedance and of other realizations that use no more than the minimum number of elements necessary.

6-20. An L-C network contains three pure capacitors and four pure inductors. There are no other elements, the inductors are shielded from each other, and the seven elements are connected together in a reasonable manner (not in any trivial fashion, i.e., the same driving-point impedance could not be obtained with fewer elements). Give the frequency pattern of the driving point admittance $Y(p)$, sketch the susceptance against frequency, and give the schematic diagrams of the canonic realizations. Can you find other realizations that use no more than seven elements?

— 6-21. Given that the impedance function $Z(p)$ is p-r, odd, has a pole at the origin, and is of order six, what is the minimum number of elements necessary for its realization? How many realizations that use only this number of elements can you find? Give the schematic diagrams of all of them. What additional information do you need in order to find actual element values?

6-22. Draw the schematic diagrams of all four canonic realizations of the L-C impedance functions with the following properties: (a) pole at the origin and seven internal critical frequencies; (b) zero at the origin and seven internal critical frequencies.

— 6-23. Find the four canonic realizations, with element values, of the admittance function

$$Y(p) = \frac{p(p^2 + 4)}{(p^2 + 1)(p^2 + 9)} \quad \text{mhos (normalized).}$$

Can you find any additional realizations that use no additional elements? Find actual element values in all your realizations, if the normalizing factors used were $72\,\Omega$ and 3 mcps.

6-24. The internal structure of a one-terminal pair is known to consist of the parallel connection of (a) an L-C network and (b) an R-L-C network. The R-L-C network is known to have no imaginary zeros in its impedance function. Show that each zero of the L-C network contributes a double zero to the even part of the input impedance $Z(p)$ of the one-terminal pair. Illustrate this with a simple specific example and explain its physical meaning in terms of resonance phenomena. If the R-L-C network is simply a resistor, where are the poles and the zeros of $Z(p)$, as closely as can be stated?

6-25. An L-C driving-point admittance is to have infinite susceptance at 1 mcps and at 4 mcps, and $+0.1$ mho susceptance at 3 mcps. How many zeros of admittance will it have, if the minimum possible number of elements is used? To what extent are their locations arbitrary? Where they are arbitrary, locate them at the arithmetical mid-points of the allowed ranges and find the canonic realizations, with element values.

6-26. A generator is connected directly to a resistance load; its internal impedance is also purely resistive. For purposes of harmonic separation it is desired to design an L-C network to be inserted between the generator and its load, either in series or in shunt (consider both cases) with the object of preventing transmission to the load at some frequencies, and not interfering with transmission at others. Give several schematic diagrams of possible realizations of the *L-C* network in each case, using the minimum possible number of elements. Find the actual element values, making reasonable assumptions where necessary. Which network seems preferable?

Frequencies of no transmission: 2, 4, 6 kcps; frequencies of perfect transmission: 1, 3, 5 kcps.

6-27. For the function

$$F(p) = \frac{H(p^2 + 1)(p^2 + 3)(p^2 + 5)}{p(p^2 + 2)(p^2 + 4)}$$

which is both p-r and odd, give the schematic diagrams of networks that realize it in the following ways, each in the four canonic forms. Describe the relations between the four sets of networks by pointing out which are equivalent, which are inverse, and which are dual. All immittances are normalized.

    (a) $Z_1(p) = F(p)$ (c) $Z_3(p) = 1/F(p)$

    (b) $Y_2(p) = 1/F(p)$ (d) $Y_4(p) = F(p)$

6-28. Give the schematic diagrams of realizations of each of the following *L-C* impedance functions according tö the principle of removing both the pole at the origin and that at infinity in impedance (admittance), then removing both the pole at the origin and that at infinity in admittance (impedance), then repeating the first step, then the second, etc., each step to be taken as far as the nature of the function will permit. What is the general nature of such a "canonic" realization? Does it use more than the minimum number of elements? The functions to be considered are each of order eight and distinguished by

    (a) poles at both the origin and infinity;

    (b) pole at the origin, zero at infinity;

    (c) zero at the origin, pole at infinity;

    (d) zeros at both the origin and infinity.

6-29. Show that for *L-C* immittance functions of order three, the four canonic forms are not all different. In each of the possible cases (as to zero-pole distribution) give the schematic diagrams of the canonic forms that are different, with literal element values, and find the relations between the element values of each realization and those of the others.

6-30. An *L-C* network is to have a driving-point impedance that meets the following requirements: very low impedance at low frequencies; substantially infinite impedance at the frequencies 900, 1125, 1350, 1575 kcps; no more elements than necessary; an impedance of $+j75\,\Omega$ at the frequency 1000 kcps.

Design such a network in four different forms and discuss their relative merits from the point of view of the practical man.

6-31. "Mutual inductance may exist, within limits, between pairs of inductance element coils in reactance arms, without altering fundamentally the nature of the arms. That is, such structures are potentially equivalent to similar structures without the mutual inductances but with, in general, different values of inductances and capacitances" (SH 1, p. 155, quoted by permission). *Arm* in the above means *one-terminal pair*. Verify Shea's statements for all canonic *L-C* networks in which only two inductors appear, first modifying them by adding electromagnetic coupling between inductors. In each case find the inductance element values of the "similar structure without mutual inductance" in terms of those of the structure that has mutual inductance. Are the capacitor element values different? If the coupling is perfect (100%) what forms do these formulas take? Why is the phrase "within limits" included?

6-32. Find additional network realizations to augment those of Fig. 6.13–B by replacing one-terminal pairs that appear therein as "subnetworks" (i.e., as one-terminal pairs that form only part of the whole network) by equivalent but different networks.

6-33. Draw the schematic diagram of an L-C network in the third (first Cauer) canonic form, using three inductors and three capacitors. Find the schematic diagram of a network inverse as to driving-point impedance, in the same canonic form. Are the two networks dual? Are there any simple relations between the element values of one and those of the other?

6-34. Let a reactance function $Z_1(p)$ be realized in the first Foster form. Now let the inverse function $Y_2(p) = Z_1(p)/R_0^2$ be realized in the second Foster form. Explain why the two networks are duals. Show that when appropriate pairings are made between the elements of one and those of the other, the relation $L/C = R_0^2$ holds throughout the networks, L and C having their customary meanings as element values.

6-35. An L-C impedance function is to have low reactance at very low and at very high frequencies, very high reactance at 440 cps, and an impedance of $+j1000\,\Omega$ at 500 cps. Find the simplest impedance function and realize it in the canonic forms.

6-36. An L-C impedance function of order three has a pole at the origin. Give the frequency pattern and sketch the reactance versus frequency. Show that the function must have the form

$$Z(p) = H \frac{(p^2 + \omega_1^2)}{p(p^2 + \omega_2^2)} = \frac{a_0 + a_2 p^2}{p + a_3 p^3}.$$

The parameters are to be determined by specifying the reactance at three points in the interval $\omega_1 < \omega < \omega_2$. Write the simultaneous equations that must be solved, both in terms of the a's and in terms of the other parameters, as unknowns. Which seems preferable to use?

Discuss the limitations imposed by physical realizability on the values of reactance that may be specified. Is it possible, for example, to specify three equal values of reactance? Is it sufficient that the three specified values of reactance be successively greater when arranged in order of frequency?

6-37. The frequency pattern of an L-C impedance is that shown in the figure. Find the element values of its realization in all the canonic forms, in terms of

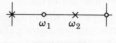

Prob. 6–37

ω_1 and ω_2. What happens to the numerical values of the elements as these two critical frequencies approach each other? What practical difficulties then arise?

When the two frequencies are very close, though not equal, which form is preferable, if the network *has* to be built? What happens in the limit as they coalesce?

6-38. An *L-C* admittance function has a zero at the origin, two internal poles, and a pole at infinity. An important specification in its application is the value of the susceptance at a certain frequency lying between the internal poles. What limitations as to value are imposed on this specification?

6-39. An *L-C* network is required to have a driving-point impedance of 600 Ω in *magnitude* at 25 kcps and 35 kcps, and zero impedance at 30 kcps. What is the minimum possible number of elements for the realization? Sketch it in schematic form, for the canonic realizations.

Suppose now that the sign to be attached to the 600 Ω reactance is also specified at each frequency (there are four possibilities). Answer the same questions.

6-40. Realize the functions below both as impedance and as admittance in all canonic forms.

$$(a) \ \frac{300p^4 + 86p^2 + 1}{150p^3 + 3p} \qquad (b) \ \frac{10p + 24p^3}{(1 + 2p^2)(1 + 3p^2)}$$

6-41. A one-terminal pair is to meet the following specifications with the minimum possible number of elements. Design the network in each of the canonic forms. Specifications: zero impedance at 10 kcps; infinite impedance at 20 kcps; behavior that of a 0.01-μf capacitor at high frequencies.

6-42. Find, among the four canonic realizations, what you consider to be the most practical realization of the driving-point reactance

$$X(\omega) = \frac{\omega(5 - 12\omega^2)}{(3 - 10\omega^2)(1 - 0.8\omega^2)} \quad \text{normalized ohms.}$$

The reference frequency is 2500 cps, the impedance scale factor is 750 Ω.

6-43. An *L-C* network has five elements, none of which are redundant. Sketch the general shape of the reactance-frequency curves that are possible. Give the schematic diagrams of the four canonic forms for each possibility.

In Table 1 are given four sets of design (impedance) data purporting to apply to such a network. In each case determine whether the data are so realizable, and (*a*) if not, state why not; (*b*) if realizable, give the element values of the canonic realizations. The units of the zero and pole locations are megacycles per second of real frequency.

Table 1

Set Number	Zeros	Poles	Additional Data
1	0, 2, 4	1, 3, 5	None
2	0, 3	1, 2, 4	None
3	0, 2, 4	1, 3, ∞	$\frac{dX}{d\omega} \to 2$ henrys as $\omega \to \infty$
4	0, 2, ∞	1, 3	None

6-44. A box contains two capacitors and three inductors. There are no other elements, the inductors are shielded, and the five elements are connected together in a reasonable manner, not in any trivial fashion—the same impedance $Z(p)$ cannot be obtained with fewer elements. How does $Z(p)$ behave at very low frequencies? At very high frequencies? How many internal critical frequencies of each kind are there in $Z(p)$? Give the schematic diagrams of the canonic realizations and of any additional five-element realizations of $Z(p)$ that you can find. Repeat for the case of three capacitors and three inductors.

6-45. The impedance function

$$Z(p) = 12p \frac{60p^4 + 20p^2 + 1}{360p^4 + 60p^2 + 1} \quad \text{ohms (normalized)}$$

can be realized in one or more of the forms shown in the figure. For each of

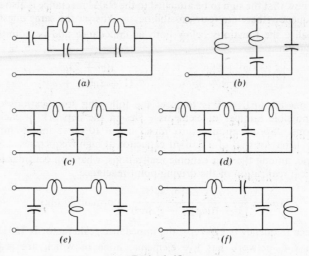

(a)   (b)

(c)   (d)

(e)   (f)

Prob. 6–45

the six diagrams give the element values or good reasons why they cannot be found.

6-46. In the network shown, $L_1 = 10\,\text{mh}$, $L_2 = 5\,\text{mh}$, $C_1 = 0.02\,\mu\text{f}$, $C_2 = 0.01\,\mu\text{f}$. Normalize to convenient frequency and impedance scales and

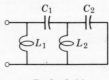

C_1 C_2

L_1 L_2

Prob. 6–46

then sketch accurately the reactance-frequency and the susceptance-frequency characteristics of the network. What are the numerical values of all the critical frequencies? Design three *L-C* networks equivalent to this one in driving-point immittances. Compare the element values in the four realizations and discuss their relative practicality. Can you find additional four-element realizations?

6-47. Find network realizations in each of the canonic forms of the impedance function

$$Z(p) = \frac{p^3 + 4p}{p^4 + 10p^2 + 20} \quad \text{normalized ohms.}$$

The scale factors to be used are $72\,\Omega$ and 3 mcps. Which realization is the most practical?

6-48. An *L-C* driving-point impedance is to have zero value at zero frequency, zero value at 4000 cps, a reactance which is $800\,\Omega$ in magnitude at 2000 cps and $100\,\Omega$ in magnitude at 3000 cps. The network realization is to have three elements only. Find two different realizations. Are there any other three-element realizations that meet these same requirements?

6-49. A purely reactive driving-point impedance is to have the following zeros and poles, and its reactance is to have a slope of $60\,\Omega$ per kcps at the lower zero. Give schematic (with element values) of all four-element realizations of this driving-point impedance. Zeros: 20 kcps, 50 kcps; pole: 30 kcps.

6-50. You are asked to design an *L-C* network whose driving-point admittance is to be infinite at 1 mcps and at 4 mcps, and to take the value $+1000$ mhos at 3 mcps. Carry through the canonic designs, using the minimum possible number of elements and making reasonable decisions where there is arbitrariness. In what way, and for what reason, is the construction of the network not practical? On the assumption that there was a typographical error in the specification of the value of susceptance at 3 mcps, what is a reasonable value, and what values do the elements then take?

6-51. Given two inductors and two capacitors, enumerate and draw all the possible nontrivial networks that can be made from them. How many forms different from the four canonic forms are included? For each network give the frequency pattern of the various possible driving-point impedances. How many duplications occur? Discuss very briefly the possibilities of network realizations of *L-C* impedance functions of order five or greater in forms that are not among the four canonic forms nor are simple combinations of them. It is not intended that any consideration be given in this problem to relative numerical values of the elements.)

6-52. The frequency pattern of an *L-C* driving-point immittance is that shown in the illustration. What is the minimum number of elements required for its

Prob. 6–52

realization? Give the schematic diagrams of four different realizations, each using only the minimum number of elements, and each having a capacitor across the terminals. Find the element values if the critical frequencies are

90, 100, 110, and 120 kcps, the high-frequency behavior being taken as that of a 1-f capacitor for impedance normalization. As the impedance scale is varied, within what limits, roughly, are the element values capable of practical realization?

6-53. An L-C network is to meet the following specifications: very high impedance at 0, 30, 60 kcps; reactance of $+600\,\Omega$ at 20, 50, 80 kcps; reactance of $-600\,\Omega$ at 40 kcps.

Give schematic diagrams, with element values, of such a network in each of the four canonic forms. Which design appears the most practical? Why?

6-54. Among the four canonic realizations of a given reactance function, which is easier to adjust (to compensate for minor deviations of element values) in laboratory use or in production-line testing, (a) as to zeros, (b) as to poles?

6-55. The normalized values of the elements of this network are

$$L_1 = \tfrac{1}{2} \quad L_2 = \tfrac{1}{4} \quad L_3 = \tfrac{1}{8} \quad C_1 = \tfrac{1}{2} \quad C_2 = \tfrac{1}{4}$$

Determine the critical frequencies and sketch the reactance-frequency curve.

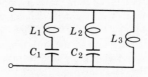

Prob. 6-55

Due to faulty shielding, a network constructed according to this schematic embodies electromagnetic coupling between L_1 and L_3 of 20% of the maximum possible coupling. How do the critical frequencies and reactance curve change because of the mutual inductance?

6-56. A "canonic" realization procedure for L-C networks might be based on a succession of stages, each consisting of the removal of one internal pole (by a network of one inductor and one capacitor), alternately of impedance and of admittance, with perhaps a single element in the last stage. Correlate this procedure with Probs. 6-8 and 6-28, and give the general form of the schematic diagram and its specific form for the four possible cases of immittance functions of order 12. Give the immittance frequency patterns at each stage and explain how this procedure is only a variant of the four canonic forms of the text. Show that, in mathematical terms, this amounts to a continued-fraction expansion of the immittance function and explain how this expansion differs from those of the two Cauer canonic forms.

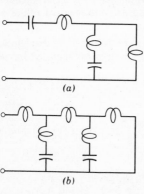

(a)

(b)

Prob. 6-57

6-57. For each of the networks shown give the frequency pattern at the input, sketches of reactance and susceptance versus frequency, and the four canonic realizations. Does the given form appear among the canonic forms? Explain.

What is the minimum number of elements required to realize the given network's driving-point impedance? Explain the discrepancy with the number of elements in the given network.

6-58. Starting from the driving-point reactance-frequency curve for each of the networks of Prob. 6-57, show by purely graphical means (a succession of reactance-frequency and susceptance-frequency curves) how these realizations, which do not use the minimum number of elements, may be obtained. Upon what principle, mentioned in the text (§ 6.13), does this method of realization depend? In addition to the numerical data in the driving-point impedance function, what data are required actually to carry out a numerical design leading to the forms given in the figure for Prob. 6-57? To what extent is it arbitrary? (Realizations such as these, with "excess" elements, are of value in two-terminal-pair synthesis, as Volume II will point out.)

6-59. Problems 6-57 and 6-58 are to be replaced throughout by their duals, with the same discussion.

6-60. In Prob. 6-37 let $\omega_2 = 1.01\omega_1$. Discuss and illustrate the possibility of improving the element values by the use of an excess element, i.e., by removing only part of the pole at the origin in the impedance, or part of the pole at infinity in the admittance. Explain the process by graphical reactance and susceptance treatment at the different stages of reduction. Give the element values of your four-element realizations and compare with those of the three-element realizations. In what way is this problem related to Probs. 6-57, 6-58, 6-59?

6-61. Explain when a realization of an *L-C* immittance function could be effected in each of the forms shown. Are excess elements required? In

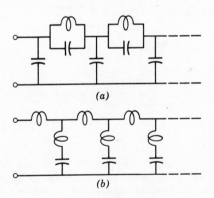

(a)

(b)

Prob. 6–61

addition to the driving-point immittance function, what data are necessary for such a realization? Your explanation is to include reactance-frequency and susceptance-frequency curves for each stage of the realization. What sort of continued-fraction expansion is involved? Illustrate with a specific example of an *L-C* immittance function of order five. How many excess elements are required?

6-62. An *L-C* impedance function has a zero at infinity and four internal critical frequencies (at normalized values 4, 5, 6, 7). Half the pole of admittance at infinity is first removed. Show graphically (by a susceptance-frequency curve) how this changes the zeros and poles. Complete the realization by using the first canonic procedure. Compare the element values with those of a realization of the whole impedance in the first canonic form.

6-63. Consider for each of the networks illustrated the possibility that redundant (excess) elements have been used, i.e., that the same driving-point immittances could be realized with a smaller number of elements. In each case state the minimum number of elements required and give schematic diagrams of realizations using only that number of elements but equivalent to the networks shown. How many redundant elements do the latter use? Where the answer depends on numerical element values, consider and point out all the possibilities.

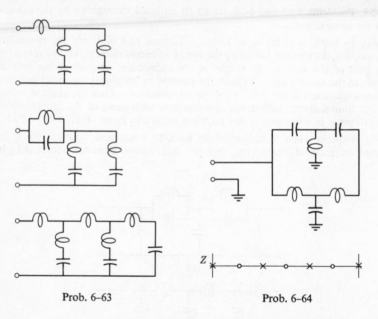

Prob. 6-63   Prob. 6-64

6-64. Show that this "twin-T" or "parallel-T" network is a realization of the reactance function whose frequency pattern is that shown, with no more than the minimum number of elements required, under certain circumstances. What are these circumstances?

6-65. Draw the schematic diagrams of the canonic realizations of each of the two possible types of reactance function of order three. Within each set derive formulas that express the element values of one canonic realization in terms of those of the other canonic realizations. Express your results as a (complete) table. In what points of the development is it possible to assist algebraic manipulation by such physical devices as examination of the behavior of the two networks under consideration at very low or at very high frequencies? Which of the formulas can be thus written by inspection?

6-66. Repeat Prob. 6-65 for reactance functions of order four.

6-67. In the proposition of Prob. 4-15, with regard to frequency transformations, let $F_2(p)$ be a reactance function. What is this reactance function in Probs. 4-32, 4-33, 4-34, 4-35? How are realizations as *L-C* networks of the reactance function related there to the transformation?

Explain the effect of making such a transformation in general by plotting the reactance-frequency characteristics of a typical inductor and of the reactance function and showing what happens to the former under the transformation. What happens in the physical network as to changes in elements? What is the corresponding discussion for the capacitors? What is the conformal-mapping interpretation of the transformations? Illustrate specifically for all reactance functions of orders one, two, and three.

6-68. The function $F(p) = \tanh p$ represents the (normalized) driving-point impedance of a length of short-circuited nondissipative transmission line. The function, though not rational, is p-r. On the assumption that the *tanh* function is capable of "infinite partial-fraction" expansion, find the terms of this expansion and an infinite realization, in the first canonic form, of the transmission line's impedance. Similarly, find a realization, infinite in extent, in the second canonic form.

Repeat for the driving-point impedance of an open-circuited nondissipative transmission line.

6-69. The following functions, though not rational, are p-r. By expanding them according to the suggestions given, find infinite-network realizations (*a*) as driving-point impedance, (*b*) as driving-point admittance.

Function	*Suggestions*
(1) $\sqrt[+]{p^2 + 1}$	Remove poles at infinity, noting that $(\sqrt[+]{p^2 + 1} - p)^{-1} = (\sqrt[+]{p^2 + 1} + p)$.
(2) $\sqrt[+]{1 + p^{-2}}$	Remove poles at the origin.
(3) $\dfrac{1}{2} \dfrac{\sqrt[+]{3p^2 + 1}}{(p^2 + 1)}$	Remove finite poles.

6-70. Let $Z_n(p)$ represent the driving-point impedance of the network shown, truncated so that only the first *n* elements remain. Compute and plot in the

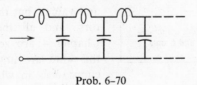

Prob. 6-70

p plane the zeros and poles of $Z_n(p)$ for $n = 1, 2, 3, 4, 5$. Discuss the trend toward a limit of their positions and compare with the singularities of the driving-point impedance when *n* becomes infinite. (Cf. WA 2.)

7.

The R-C and R-L
One-Terminal Pairs

*Nature is an endless combination
and repetition of a very few laws.*
—Emerson

In Chapter 6 we discussed in some detail the realization of those
(rational) p-r functions that are odd—such are the driving-point immittance functions that characterize L-C networks. The next type of network
we consider (of those which contain two kinds of elements only) is the
R-C type. The immittance functions here are mixed (neither odd nor
even). They are restricted to a special class, however, and we shall
investigate their properties, and methods for their realization, in a fashion
closely paralleling the treatment in Chapter 6. We do this not merely for
convenience but because there is a very close relation between the two,
and we shall be able to make good use here, in the R-C case, of the
properties of L-C networks.

7.01 The R-C case

We start now to discuss the case in which the one-terminal pair contains
no inductance (Fig. 7.01–A). In it there may be resistors and capacitors
in arbitrary number, arrangement,
and values, but there are no inductors, and all the T functions of
Chapter 4 are zero. Networks of
this kind are important under circumstances in which inductors are
difficult to build and are, if possible,
to be avoided; such is often true at

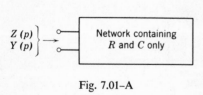

$$Z\,(p)\,\Big]$$
$$Y\,(p)\,\Big]$$

Network containing
R and C only

Fig. 7.01–A

low frequencies, when the inductance values needed become large. True,
the capacitances needed also become large, but large capacitors are often
easier to build than are large inductors.

302

Let us first analyze such a network in general terms, going through our list of general properties of one-terminal pairs, to see how they can be further specialized for this case. We shall follow the treatment of the *L-C* case in as nearly parallel a manner as possible. The driving-point immittance functions, $Z(p)$ and $Y(p)$, in the *R-C* case must be positive-real and rational; the coefficients must be real numbers; the zeros and poles (if complex) must occur in conjugate pairs, and none can lie in the right half plane. If a pole occurs on the imaginary axis, it must be simple, with a residue which is real and positive; a zero on the imaginary axis must also be simple and the derivative of the function there must be real and positive. The highest and the lowest powers of p in numerator and denominator can differ in degree by unity at most, and at real frequencies the real parts are even, the imaginary parts odd. These are general properties which hold for *any* driving-point immittance function, not just for those in the *R-C* case.

7.02 Zeros and poles

Consider once more the properties which restrict the zeros and poles to the left half plane and the imaginary axis. Does the absence of inductance further restrict their locations? Without inductors to resonate with, capacitors cannot produce zeros or poles at real frequencies (zero and infinity excepted). Hence we expect to find zeros and poles of *R-C* immittance functions only in the left half plane (and possibly at the origin and infinity), probably also only in some *part* of that half plane, too, for the networks are weaker in that they have less to work with: the capacitors behave as before, but the inductors whose impedances vary with p are replaced by resistors whose impedances are *constant*. Hence we cannot expect *R-C* networks to be able to do what *L-C* networks can do, at least not without a much larger number of elements, and then only approximately.

In the absence of all inductance, (4.12–13) becomes

$$Z(p) = F_0 + \frac{V_0}{p}, \tag{7.02–1}$$

and (4.12–16) becomes

$$Y(p) = F_0 + V_0 p. \tag{7.02–2}$$

The symbols F_0 and T_0 stand for different things in the two equations, but that is not important; what is important is that F_0 and T_0 are always *real* and *positive*, by (4.12–15).

At real frequencies Z and Y each have real and imaginary parts which are not zero, the impedance is a mixture of resistance and reactance, and the admittance is a mixture of conductance and susceptance. We do not expect to find zeros and poles on the imaginary axis. When p has such a value that $Z(p)$ vanishes, in fact, we have

$$F_0 + \frac{V_0}{p} = 0, \qquad (7.02\text{--}3)$$

so that the zeros of $Z(p)$ are given by

$$p = \frac{-V_0}{F_0}. \qquad (7.02\text{--}4)$$

Since F_0 and V_0 are real, positive numbers (regardless of the value of p), these values of p which make Z vanish, the zeros of $Z(p)$, are purely *real*, and they are negative.

When p has such a value that $Z(p)$ becomes infinite, i.e., at a zero of $Y(p)$, we have, from (7.02–2),

$$p = -\frac{F_0}{V_0}. \qquad (7.02\text{--}5)$$

These numbers F_0 and V_0 are of course defined differently but they are still real and positive, and therefore the poles of $Z(p)$ are also purely real and negative.

Hence the fourth property is again severely restricted, even more so than in the L-C case, for here we have only half an axis to work with, there we had the whole of the imaginary axis. To sum up,

in the R-C case, all the zeros and all the poles of $Z(p)$ and of $Y(p)$ occur on the negative real axis.   (7.02–6)

The zeros and poles are confined to a single line in the plane, as in the L-C case, but this time to a semi-infinite line rather than to a line extending to infinity in both directions. The line of interest has in a sense been rotated through $90°$, half in one direction, half in the other, so that the two halves are made to coincide and the infinite line is compressed to a semi-infinite line. This is in keeping with our expectation that R-C networks are roughly only half as powerful as L-C networks.

7.03 The slope and separation properties

We now seek for the R-C case the analogs of the slope and separation properties of the L-C case. By (4.13–1) we have

$$Z(p) = F_0 + \frac{V_0}{p} = F_0 + \frac{V_0}{\sigma + j\omega}$$

$$= \left(F_0 + \frac{\sigma V_0}{\sigma^2 + \omega^2} \right) + j \left(\frac{-V_0 \omega}{\sigma^2 + \omega^2} \right)$$

$$= R(\sigma, \omega) + jX(\sigma, \omega) \qquad (7.03\text{--}1)$$

in which R and X represent the real and imaginary parts of $Z(p)$ respectively, and F_0 and T_0 are real and positive (though not constant). The properties we seek come readily from the above by an application of the Cauchy–Riemann equations. We have

$$\frac{\partial X}{\partial \omega} = \frac{\partial}{\partial \omega} \left(\frac{-V_0 \omega}{\sigma^2 + \omega^2} \right) = -\omega \frac{\partial}{\partial \omega} \left(\frac{V_0}{\sigma^2 + \omega^2} \right) - \frac{V_0}{\sigma^2 + \omega^2}, \quad (7.03\text{–}2)$$

and when $\omega = 0$,

$$\frac{\partial X}{\partial \omega} = -\frac{V_0}{\sigma^2} < 0 \quad (7.03\text{–}3)$$

since V_0 is real and positive. The derivative above cannot be zero, except at infinity, for V_0 does not vanish. (This excludes networks in which there is no capacitance, but these are networks with *one* kind of element only.) But

$$\frac{\partial R}{\partial \sigma} = \frac{\partial X}{\partial \omega} \quad (7.03\text{–}4)$$

by (3.10–6), and therefore

$$\frac{\partial R}{\partial \sigma} < 0. \quad (7.03\text{–}5)$$

Hence for (finite) real values of p, when $\omega = 0$, $X = 0$, and $Z(p) = R + j0$, the derivative of $Z(p)$ (which is $\partial R / \partial \sigma$, since the derivative is independent of the direction of computation), is *negative*.

In dual fashion

$$Y(p) = F_0 + V_0 p = (F_0 + V_0 \sigma) + j(V_0 \omega)$$

$$= G(\sigma, \omega) + jB(\sigma, \omega), \quad (7.03\text{–}6)$$

$$\frac{\partial B}{\partial \omega} = \frac{\partial}{\partial \omega} (V_0 \omega) = \omega \frac{\partial V_0}{\partial \omega} + V_0, \quad (7.03\text{–}7)$$

and when $\omega = 0$,

$$\frac{\partial \omega}{\partial B} = V_0 > 0. \quad (7.03\text{–}8)$$

But by (3.10–6)

$$\frac{\partial G}{\partial \sigma} = \frac{\partial B}{\partial \omega} \quad (7.03\text{–}9)$$

and therefore

$$\frac{\partial G}{\partial \sigma} > 0. \quad (7.03\text{–}10)$$

Hence for finite real values of p, when $\omega = 0$, $B = 0$, and $Y(p) = G + j0$, the derivative of $Y(p)$ (which is $\partial G/\partial \sigma$, since the derivative is independent of the direction of computation), is *positive*.

Since Z and Y are both real under these special conditions of real p, (7.03–10) could be written directly from (7.03–5), for if a (real) function is decreasing, its reciprocal is increasing. Our conclusion is that R-C networks possess a slope property similar to that of L-C networks, but applicable to the real axis rather than the imaginary axis. In contrast to L-C networks, the property is different for impedance and admittance. The property is

the slope of the driving-point impedance function of an R-C network, plotted against real values of p, is always negative, except possibly at infinity. (7.03–11)

and

the slope of the driving-point admittance function of an R-C network, plotted against real values of p, is always positive, except possibly at infinity. (7.03–12)

From this property follows a separation property much like that of L-C networks. We have found that all the zeros and all the poles of $Z(p)$ occur on the negative real axis. We know further that on this negative real axis $Z(p)$ is real and also that its derivative is negative and not zero (except possibly at infinity). From these facts we conclude that the zeros and poles separate each other; if they did not, the slope of the curve of $Z(p)$ versus real p would necessarily be positive at some intermediate points, much as in Fig. 6.03–A or 6.03–B. Just as in the L-C case, zeros and poles alternate, but in this case along the negative real axis. At a zero, moreover, the requirement of negative slope means that the impedance, plotted against σ, goes through zero with a finite, nonzero slope, and hence that the zero is *simple*; by considering zeros of $Y(p)$ we see that the poles are simple also. To sum up these facts,

the zeros and poles of R-C network driving-point immittance functions are all on the negative real axis, are simple, and are interlaced in the pattern $\cdots$ zero-pole-zero-pole $\cdots$. (7.03–13)

We can now draw sketches showing the general behavior (on the real axis) of R-C driving-point impedance functions (Fig. 7.03–A) and of R-C driving-point admittance functions (Fig. 7.03–B). Again there is a general resemblance to the plot of a tangent or cotangent function (with appropriate change of signs).

We have not yet investigated what sort of behavior is required of R-C immittance functions at the extreme points of the line on which the zeros and poles must lie, at the origin and at infinity. Nor is it quite as simple a matter as in the L-C case to state these requirements.

At *infinity* a p-r function can have a simple zero, a simple pole, or approach some positive, nonzero constant value, by (5.07–6). Since the impedance functions of the individual elements here are in form constants, or $1/Cp$ which approaches zero at infinity, only the simple zero and constant possibilities exist for *R-C* network impedance functions. If infinity is not a zero, then the value at infinity is positive, and the impedance function of Fig. 7.03–A goes through a zero before reaching a pole,

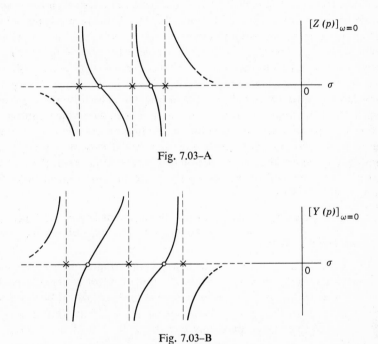

Fig. 7.03–A

Fig. 7.03–B

as p comes in from infinity. Alternatively, it is physically obvious that at very high (real) frequencies an *R-C* network can present a very low impedance (approaching zero at infinity) because the capacitors approach short circuits, or it may present an impedance which approaches a finite, nonzero, positive (resistive) value, depending on the manner in which the resistors and capacitors are connected, but it cannot present an infinite impedance. Since for rational functions the limit approached as p goes to infinity is the same regardless of the direction of approach, these conclusions apply equally well to the limit approached as p recedes to infinity along the negative real axis, confirming the remarks first made. Generalizing the terms found useful in the *L-C* case, we call the zeros and poles *critical frequencies* (they are imaginary frequencies of course) and refer to them as high and low, according to their *magnitude*. Then we can say that

the highest critical frequency of an R-C driving-point impedance function is a zero, which may occur at infinity; if it does not, $Z(\infty)$ is a positive, finite (real) number.   (7.03–14)

At the origin, positive reality again restricts the behavior of the function to the same three possibilities, but this time the possibility of a zero is excluded (the individual element impedances do not approach zero except in the trivial, excluded case of a short circuit). If the origin is not a pole, then the value at the origin is positive (not zero) and the impedance function of Fig. 7.03–A goes through a pole before reaching a zero as p recedes to the left from the origin. Alternatively, it is physically obvious that at very low (real) frequencies an R-C network can present a very high impedance (approaching infinity at zero frequency) because the capacitors approach open circuits, or it may present an impedance which approaches a nonzero, positive (resistive) value, depending on the manner in which the resistors and capacitors are connected, but it cannot present a zero impedance. Since the limit approached is the same regardless of the direction of approach to the origin, these conclusions confirm those first made. We can now say that

the lowest critical frequency of an R-C driving-point impedance function is a pole, which may occur at the origin; if it does not, $Z(0)$ is a positive, nonzero (real) number.   (7.03–15)

The general shape of things, then, will be a string of alternating zeros and poles along the negative real axis. None can, of course, be on the positive half of the axis. There *may* be one of these critical points at the origin (but it must be a pole); there *may* be one at infinity (but it must be a zero). The lowest one may, however, be to the left of the origin, and the highest one may be "to the right of infinity." These statements refer to impedance functions; since they distinguish different rules for zeros and for poles, they do not apply to the driving-point admittance functions of R-C networks. But if the words *zero* and *pole* are interchanged everywhere in the above and in (7.03–14) and (7.03–15), and the word *admittance* substituted for the word *impedance*, the corresponding properties of R-C network admittance functions are obtained.

Figure 7.03–C shows the pole-zero layout on the p plane in a particular case (six critical frequencies, none at the origin or infinity). These are poles and zeros of impedance, and would have to be interchanged to show the diagram for the corresponding admittance—which makes it important that such diagrams be marked Z or Y. In any case the smallest critical frequency of impedance is a pole, the largest a zero.

Figure 7.03–D shows the *frequency pattern*, to carry over more of our *L-C* case terminology. This is drawn for a different case from that of Fig. 7.03–C, and is one in which both infinity and the origin are critical

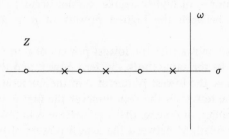

Fig. 7.03–C

points. Note again, though, that we start with a zero, reading from left to right, and end up with a pole. This diagram should also be marked *Z* or *Y* to avoid confusion.

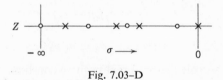

Fig. 7.03–D

To sum up the important properties discovered in this section,

in the *R-C* case, the origin may be a pole of impedance, or a noncritical point [in which case $Z(0)$ is a positive, nonzero number]; infinity may be a zero of impedance, or a noncritical point [in which case $Z(\infty)$ is a positive, finite number]; all the zeros and poles are simple and lie on the negative real axis in an interlaced pattern of alternating zeros and poles.   (7.03–16)

The summary above holds equally well if the words *zero* and *pole* are interchanged, and the word *admittance* substituted for the word *impedance*.

7.04 The formal nature of an *R-C* impedance function

We are now in a position to state the form of $Z(p)$ in the *R-C* case. Each zero, and each pole, must be caused by a factor of the form $(p - \sigma_0)$, in which σ_0 is a *negative* real number; this is a typical factor of numerator and denominator. It follows that the numerator and denominator polynomials are mixed (neither odd nor even), for both even and odd powers of p appear in the expanded products. From our analysis we see that these polynomials may be of the same degree (infinity a regular point and not a zero) *or* the degree of the denominator may be one more than the degree of the numerator (infinity a zero). (The reverse situation, in which the numerator is of higher degree, cannot occur.) This states the allowed relations between the highest powers of p in numerator and denominator.

Our analysis also shows that the lowest powers of p in numerator and denominator may be the same (both the zero power, and the origin not a critical frequency) *or* the lowest power of p in the numerator may be the zero power and the lowest in the denominator the first power (the origin a pole). This assumes, of course, that the fraction is in lowest terms, and states the allowed relations between the lowest powers of p in numerator and denominator. With the usual interchange of *zero* and *pole*, substitution of *admittance* for *impedance*, and the additional interchange of *numerator* and *denominator*, all of the remarks above apply also to R-C admittance functions.

We can now say that in factored form an R-C driving-point impedance function is

$$Z(p) = H \frac{(p - \sigma^2)(p - \sigma_4) \cdots}{(p - \sigma_1)(p - \sigma_3) \cdots} \qquad (7.04\text{--}1)$$

in which

$$\cdots \sigma_4 < \sigma_3 < \sigma_2 < \sigma_1 \leqq 0. \qquad (7.04\text{--}2)$$

H is again merely a scale factor, a real positive constant. The σ_i are real *negative* numbers obeying the inequality (7.04–2). The "lowest" of these, the first critical frequency met in starting out from the origin, may be zero, in which case the origin is a pole; it need not be zero, however, and if it is not, $Z(p)$ has a nonzero positive value at the origin. The behavior at infinity is governed by the number of factors in numerator and denominator: if the numbers are the same, $Z(\infty)$ is a real, positive, nonzero number, whereas if the number of factors in the denominator is one greater than the number in the numerator, then infinity is a zero (there are no other possibilities).

We can now say that

a driving-point R-C immittance function is uniquely determined by specifying the locations of its (imaginary-frequency) zeros and poles *and* one additional piece of information. (7.04–3)

This follows from the general form (7.04–1). The additional piece of information may be H itself or some other data from which H can be computed. The given zeros and poles must be mutually consistent, of course, for R-C behavior.

We can draw *frequency patterns* for *R-C* driving-point immittance functions, as already indicated in Fig. 7.03–D, but the frequencies are purely imaginary. There need be no *external* (zero or infinite) critical frequencies in the *R-C* case, for all may well be *internal* (then neither the origin nor infinity is pole or zero).

We evidently have again four possible cases, in a categorization according to the d-c and high-frequency behaviors. These are summed up in Table 7.04–A. Here the term *R point* means a point at which *Z* has a finite, real, positive, nonzero (resistive) value. This classification in detail is not at all necessary, for there is really only one possible kind of functional behavior, that shown (for $p = \sigma$) in Fig. 7.03–A. The detailed classification has some advantage in its specificity, however, and permits one to draw the curves of Table 7.04–A and tabulate the formulas given there.

It is worthwhile to compare Table 7.04–A with Table 6.04–A. The two have much in common—as well as differences, which can be considered to result from the restriction to half an axis (instead of a whole axis) in the *R-C* case. Again there is really only one general type of function; the classification merely shows the possible locations of the origin and of infinity in the general sketch of Fig. 7.03–A. Notice that $R(\infty) < R(0)$ in Case *A*, because at the origin each factor in the numerator is divided by one of smaller magnitude, a fact which is apparent from the sketch of $Z(\sigma)$, however, and could be written $Z(0) > Z(\infty)$. Notice also that the behavior for $\sigma > 0$ is quite simple: it is merely a consistent monotonic continuation toward the same asymptotic value at $+\infty$ as at $-\infty$. There are of course no poles or zeros on the positive real axis.

The *R-C* admittance function does *not* have exactly the same properties as the *R-C* impedance function, in contrast with the *L-C* case. The zeros and poles are still real, negative, simple, and mutually separate each other, but the slope is *positive* (rather than negative) for real p; the value at infinity is either real, positive, nonzero, and finite *or* infinity is a pole; the value at the origin is either real, positive, and finite *or* the origin is a zero. The lowest critical frequency is a zero, the highest a pole. The degree of the denominator is equal to or one less than the degree of the numerator. All of these follow immediately from the properties of $Z(p)$ because $Y(p)$ is the reciprocal of $Z(p)$. In the *L-C* case, because we deal with two kinds of elements which are dual, the reciprocation process makes no difference in the properties; here in the *R-C* case it makes a great deal of difference.

7.05 The partial-fraction expansion

In the class of rational functions that have only simple zeros and poles —all of which are on the negative real axis (zeros and poles alternating),

Table 7.04-A

Case	Origin Is	Infinity Is	Formula for $Z(p)$	n	$Z(\sigma)$ versus σ
A	R point	R point	$H\dfrac{(p-\sigma_2)(p-\sigma_4)\cdots(p-\sigma_n)}{(p-\sigma_1)(p-\sigma_3)\cdots(p-\sigma_{n-1})}$	Even	
B	Pole	Zero	$H\dfrac{(p-\sigma_2)(p-\sigma_4)\cdots(p-\sigma_{n-1})}{p(p-\sigma_3)\cdots(p-\sigma_n)}$	Odd	
C	R point	Zero	$H\dfrac{(p-\sigma_2)(p-\sigma_4)\cdots(p-\sigma_n)}{(p-\sigma_1)(p-\sigma_3)\cdots(p-\sigma_n)}$	Odd	
D	Pole	R point	$H\dfrac{(p-\sigma_2)(p-\sigma_4)\cdots(p-\sigma_n)}{p(p-\sigma_3)\cdots(p-\sigma_{n-1})}$	Even	

have negative slope when plotted against σ, have a pole closer to the origin than any zero (which pole may actually be at the origin) and either a zero or a finite value at infinity—are certainly included all driving-point impedance functions of *R-C* networks. We are not yet certain, however, that all such functions are realizable as *R-C* driving-point impedance functions. Our next task is to demonstrate that they are actually so realizable, and in so doing we shall develop actual synthesis procedures.

Consider first such a function, one that has finite nonzero values at the origin and infinity (Case *A* of Table 7.04–A). Designate it $Z(p)$ and make its partial-fraction expansion

$$Z(p) = H \frac{(p - \sigma_2)(p - \sigma_4) \cdots (p - \sigma_n)}{(p - \sigma_1)(p - \sigma_3) \cdots (p - \sigma_{n-1})} \qquad (7.05\text{–}1)$$

$$= \frac{K_1}{p - \sigma_1} + \frac{K_3}{p - \sigma_3} + \cdots + \frac{K_{n-1}}{p - \sigma_{n-1}} + H. \qquad (7.05\text{–}2)$$

Here

$$\cdots \sigma_{n-1} < \sigma_{n-3} < \cdots < \sigma_3 < \sigma_1 < 0 \qquad (7.05\text{–}3)$$

and the residues, the K's, are real numbers. They have the values

$$K_i = [(p - \sigma_i)Z(p)]_{p=\sigma_i} \qquad (7.05\text{–}4)$$

which are *positive*. This follows from (7.05–1) and (7.05–3) on consideration of the signs of the factors involved. More clearly, it follows from the fact that the residue of $Z(p)$ at a pole is the reciprocal of $Y'(p) = d/dp(1/Z)$ evaluated at that point, by (3.21–7). This derivative is positive because of the assumption of negative slope of the curve of $Z(\sigma)$, which proves the point. The actual calculation of K_i calls merely for erasing the pole-causing term in $Z(p)$ and evaluating what remains at the pole, the usual procedure for simple poles.

In (7.05–2) we have the partial-fraction expansion of such a function for the case assumed. Functions of this kind may also be of the other three types classified in Table 7.04–A, but they will then differ slightly, thus:

in Case *B*, $\sigma_1 = 0$ and the constant term is missing;

in Case *C*, the constant term is missing;

in Case *D*, $\sigma_1 = 0$.

Evidently Case *A*, or (7.05–2), can be considered the general case.

Notice in passing that this same process, applied to the reciprocal of $Z(p)$, will work mathematically with equal ease, but the K's this time will be *negative*. As above, these K's are residues, and they are here equal to the reciprocal of $Z'(p)$ evaluated at the zeros of Z, and this derivative we have assumed to be negative. This may be expected to cause difficulty in physical realization by little networks corresponding to each admittance term, and requires further thought—but more of that later.

Let us now consider how to realize this general form (7.05–2). A typical term is

$$\frac{K_i}{p - \sigma_i} = \frac{K_i}{p + |\sigma_i|} = \frac{1}{\left(\dfrac{1}{K_i}\right)p + \dfrac{|\sigma_i|}{K_i}} \qquad (7.05\text{–}5)$$

which is clearly the impedance of the little network of Fig. 7.05–A, to which formulas (7.05–6) apply.

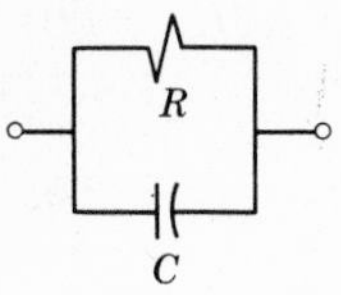

$$C = \frac{1}{K_i} = \frac{1}{S},$$

$$R = \frac{K_i}{|\sigma_i|} = \frac{1}{C|\sigma_i|} = \frac{1}{G}. \qquad (7.05\text{–}6)$$

Fig. 7.05–A   The element values are positive, and the network is realizable. Notice the relation between the corresponding pole of $Z(p)$, $\sigma_i = -|\sigma_i|$, and the "time constant" of this little network,

$$|\sigma_i| = \frac{1}{RC} = \frac{1}{\text{time constant}}, \qquad (7.05\text{–}7)$$

which is to be expected from transient-analysis considerations. Notice also that the impedance of this small network becomes infinite at $p = \sigma_i = -1/RC$. This is exactly parallel to the resonance of the network of Fig. 6.05–A at $p = \pm j\omega_m$. In the R-C case, however, the resonance occurs at an imaginary frequency $(\omega_i = p_i/j = -j\sigma_i = j1/RC)$ and only at one frequency, for there is no conjugate pole. The network of Fig. 7.05–A can be considered a "tuned circuit" just as can the parallel combination of inductor and capacitor, but the tuning point (resonance) occurs at a real value of p or at an imaginary frequency. The frequency is imaginary in a physical sense (as well as a mathematical sense) for the word *frequency* implies steady-state oscillation, which is not the natural behavior of such circuits. (By interpreting imaginary frequency properly such frequencies can be considered to exist, however, but they are related to decaying exponential transients rather than to steady-state sinusoidal oscillations.)

The constant term in (7.05–2) is of course realized by a mere resistor.

Hence we have our first form of *R-C* driving-point impedance realization, Fig. 7.05–B.

When $\sigma_1 = 0$, we have merely a special case in which the appropriate resistance becomes infinite and the first capacitor stands alone.   The

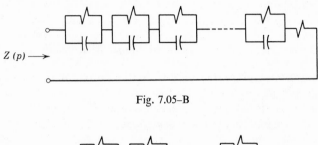

$Z(p) \longrightarrow$

Fig. 7.05–B

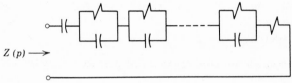

$Z(p) \longrightarrow$

Fig. 7.05–C

realization of Fig. 7.05–C then results.   This form is exactly that of the first canonic realization in the *L-C* case, with inductors everywhere replaced by resistors (cf. Fig. 6.05–G).   We can consider it to apply generally, and that in Case *A* the lone capacitor is absent, in Case *B* the lone resistor is absent, in Case *C* the lone capacitor and the lone resistor are both absent, and in Case *D* the network is as shown in Fig. 7.05–C. This we call then the first canonic realization of *R-C* driving-point impedance functions.   It uses the minimum possible number of elements and can always be made (these properties are discussed below).   The extension of the work of Chapter 6 to the *R-C* case was first made by Cauer (CA 1), and his paper is another of the important original sources which should be read.

The designations of the elements and formulas for their values are purposely omitted to avoid confusion.   To determine the element values it is necessary merely to remember the principle of partial-fraction expansion, and to compare the component networks with the component terms of the expansion for p large and p small, much as in the corresponding *L-C* process.

There is again an important philosophical point to be made here. The assumptions we have made about the given function $Z(p)$, guided by our knowledge of necessary properties of R-C network driving-point impedance functions, are that

1. $Z(p)$ has only simple zeros and poles, all of which are on the negative-real axis, where zeros and poles alternate;
2. the slope of $Z(\sigma)$ plotted versus σ is negative [the multiplier H in (7.05–1) is positive];
3. the lowest critical point (zero or pole) of $Z(p)$ is a pole, which may be at the origin;
4. the highest critical point is a zero, which may be at infinity.   (7.05–8)

These are necessary properties of R-C driving-point impedance functions, and any such function is p-r.   Further, these properties are sufficient for realization as the driving-point impedance of an R-C network, as we have just shown.   We have here further evidence as to the sufficiency of positive reality for realization: those p-r functions which fall in this category are always realizable.   Such functions we call R-C (*impedance*) *realizable*. The synthesis procedure is to

1. factor the denominator of the given R-C impedance-realizable function if this has not already been done;
2. examine the function and write the ordinary partial-fraction expansion with literal coefficients;
3. determine the coefficient (residue) for each term in the expansion;
4. draw a schematic diagram corresponding to the expansion, like Fig. 7.05–C;
5. determine the element values by comparison of the behavior of the component networks and the corresponding terms in the expansion, at very low and very high frequencies;
6. check the results by calculating the impedance function from the final schematic diagram.   (7.05–9)

The number of "tuned circuits" is equal to the number of poles of $Z(p)$ (one of which may be at the origin), and hence to the order of $Z(p)$, and each resonates at one of these poles.   The element values are more conveniently determined by inspection of the behavior of a component network (pair of elements) and of the corresponding term in the partial-fraction expansion at very low and at very high frequencies than by use of formulas for element values.   [A check can be obtained by determining the "resonant frequency," which should agree with the corresponding pole of $Z(p)$.]   The residue is actually the elastance; the resistance has that value which "tunes" the capacitor at the (purely imaginary) frequency of resonance.

It is again appropriate to postpone most of the illustrative examples to a point where all methods which we may develop can be illustrated simultaneously.   One simple example follows here, however, as an aid in crystallizing the ideas.   Consider the function

$$Z(p) = \frac{6(p + 2)(p + 4)}{p(p + 3)} \quad \text{ohms} \qquad (7.05\text{-}10)$$

which is in the *R-C* impedance-realizable class.   Its partial-fraction expansion is

$$Z(p) = \frac{16}{p} + \frac{K_3}{p + 3} + 6 \qquad (7.05\text{-}11)$$

in which

$$K_3 = [(p + 3)Z(p)]_{p=-3} = \frac{6(-3 + 2)(-3 + 4)}{(-3)} = 2. \quad (7.05\text{-}12)$$

The partial-fraction expansion with numerical values, and the corresponding realization with element values determined by inspection, are given in (7.05–13) and Fig. 7.05–D.

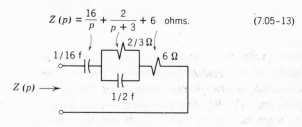

$$Z(p) = \frac{16}{p} + \frac{2}{p + 3} + 6 \quad \text{ohms.} \qquad (7.05\text{-}13)$$

Fig. 7.05–D

7.06 Elements

We have paid little attention to the number of elements required in the realization of § 7.05, but it is rather important to know whether it uses any more than are absolutely necessary.   To discover this, suppose that the *R-C* impedance function has no critical frequency at the origin or at infinity.   Then the frequency pattern and the realization are those shown in Fig. 7.06–A.   The number of constants contained in the specification of the impedance function is one more than the number of critical frequencies, from (7.04–1).   In this case the number of elements used is also one more than the number of critical frequencies, and therefore only the minimum possible number of elements has been used.

If now the left-hand zero recedes to infinity and becomes an external critical frequency, then the number of elements used drops by one (the lone resistor disappears).   Similarly, if the right-hand pole moves to the origin and becomes external, the number of elements drops by one (a resistor disappears from one of the parallel combinations). If both recessions occur, the number of elements used drops by two. Hence the number of elements used is one more than the number of *internal* critical frequencies in any case.

In each of the three cases the number of constants contained in the specification similarly drops by one (or two), for one (or two) of the

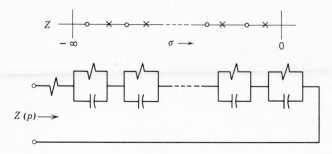

Fig. 7.06–A

constants takes an extreme value and disappears, as do the corresponding elements in the realization. Hence the number of constants in the specification is always one more than the number of internal critical frequencies. (If the lowest internal critical frequency is a zero, then the origin must be a pole, and it is not necessary to specify this fact; if the highest is a pole, then infinity must be a zero and this need not be specified.) In none of the four cases are any more elements used than the minimum required by the amount of data in the specified impedance function. Therefore the actual number used is in all cases related simply to the number of internal critical frequencies:

the minimum number of elements required for realization of an *R-C* driving-point impedance function is one more than the number of internal critical frequencies.   (7.06–1)

This number is sufficient, as demonstrated above, and represents the minimum number always required. Hence it is appropriate to call the realization method of § 7.05 a canonic method and the resulting network a canonic form.

For realization of an *R-C* driving-point impedance function by the method of § 7.05 note also that

the minimum number of capacitors required (the minimum number of reactive elements required) is equal to the total number of poles of the

function, or to the total number of zeros of the function, i.e., to the order
of the function. (7.06–2)

The minimum number of resistors required here differs at most by one
from the minimum number of capacitors required.

7.07 Corollaries

In § 7.05 we have found that the set of conditions (7.05–8) which must
hold for any *R-C* driving-point impedance function is also sufficient for
its realization in the form of Fig. 7.05–C. These characteristics define a
class of functions which plays the role in the theory of *R-C* networks that
reactance functions play in the theory of *L-C* networks—for any *R-C*
driving-point impedance function is in this class and any function in this
class is *R-C* realizable. The important properties of these functions are
displayed on the negative real axis of the *p* plane, in marked contrast to
the properties of reactance functions which are displayed on the imaginary
or real-frequency axis. This is unfortunate in a way, for our interest, in
this book, is confined to the sinusoidal steady state, i.e., to behavior on
the imaginary axis. Hence we ought now to discuss the real-frequency
properties of *R-C* driving-point immittance functions. Since the network
of Fig. 7.05–C is canonic and *any R-C* driving-point impedance function
can be realized in that form, it is convenient to use it as a basis for
discussion.

At real frequencies we cannot lay down the properties of *R-C* functions
as concisely as in the *L-C* case. But something can be said about the
behavior of *R-C* driving-point impedance functions. We are surely going
to find both resistance and reactance at real frequencies. Any one of the
two-element component networks in Fig. 7.05–C, such as that of Fig.
7.07–A, has the resistance and reactance behavior developed below.

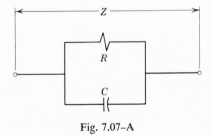

Fig. 7.07–A

For $p = j\omega$,

$$Z = \frac{1}{1/R + jC\omega} = \frac{R}{1 + jRC\omega} = \frac{R(1 - jRC\omega)}{1 + R^2C^2\omega^2}. \qquad (7.07\text{–}1)$$

Therefore

$$\operatorname{Re} Z(j\omega) = \frac{R}{1 + R^2C^2\omega^2},$$

$$\operatorname{Im} Z(j\omega) = \frac{-R^2C\omega}{1 + R^2C^2\omega^2}.$$

(7.07–2)

The resistance-versus-frequency characteristic of this elementary network is thus of the form shown in Fig. 7.07–B; the reactance-versus-frequency

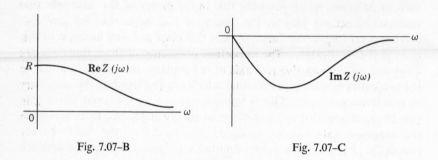

Fig. 7.07–B   Fig. 7.07–C

characteristic is of the form shown in Fig. 7.07–C. The fact that the resistance decreases continually with frequency is physically apparent from the network and the behavior of capacitors, as well as from the formulas. The general shape of the reactance curve is similarly apparent from physical considerations.

In addition we may have the lone capacitor and the lone resistor whose behaviors are shown in Figs. 7.07–D and 7.07–E respectively.

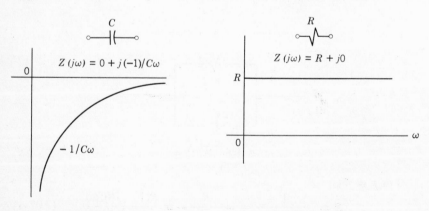

Fig. 7.07–D   Fig. 7.07–E

Any *R-C* driving-point impedance function, regardless of the actual configuration of the network or of the approximation process from which it may have come, can be realized as a series connection of a number of these two-element networks and possibly a capacitor or resistor or both. At real frequencies the resistance characteristic of such a function must then be the sum of a number of curves like that of Fig. 7.07–B (and possibly a constant). The reactance characteristic of such a function must be the sum of a number of curves like that of Fig. 7.07–C (and possibly one like that of Fig. 7.07–D). Hence we can say the following about the real-frequency behavior of *R-C* driving-point impedance functions:

1. the maximum value of the resistance occurs at zero frequency;
2. the minimum value of the resistance occurs at infinite frequency;
3. the resistance decreases steadily with frequency;
4. the reactance is never positive;
5. the d-c reactance is either zero or (negatively) infinite;
6. the infinite-frequency reactance is zero. (7.07–3)

If the function is very simple and realizable by a resistor and capacitor in series, then the resistance is constant—but in general (7.07–3) sums up what we can say about the behavior of *R-C* impedance functions at real frequencies. The resistance curve may wriggle, but it must always have a negative slope (the simple case mentioned above excepted); the reactance curve must lie below the axis, and may bob up and down, but little more can be said about it. We can draw no general characteristic curves analogous to those in Fig. 6.06–A, but we can say that, no matter what form an *R-C* network may actually take, it has an equivalent in the form of Fig. 7.05–C and its impedance can be thought of as a superposition of a number of functions like those characterized by the illustrations above.

7.08 A second canonic realization

It is too much to expect, after finding an *R-C* canonic realization so closely parallel to the first *L-C* canonic realization, that there are not also three other (parallel) *R-C* canonic realizations. The second of these should come from a partial-fraction development of the *R-C* admittance function. But we found in § 7.05 that this expansion led to terms with negative coefficients, which therefore cannot individually be p-r. And since *R-C* admittance functions have properties different from those of *R-C* impedance functions, it is entirely reasonable to expect that somewhat different treatment is required of the admittance.

The first of the four *L-C* canonic forms has its exact parallel in the realization of Fig. 7.05–C. The schematic diagrams are the same, except that inductors have given way to resistors; the principles by which they were obtained are the same, concentration on the poles of the given impedance function and making the partial-fraction expansion. And we expect for the second canonic R-C form to get the sort of network shown in Fig. 7.08–A.

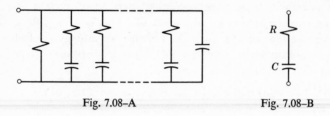

Fig. 7.08–A   Fig. 7.08–B

Let us take a typical branch out of this, that of Fig. 7.08–B, and compute its admittance. It is

$$Y(p) = \frac{1}{R + 1/Cp} = \frac{(1/R)p}{p + 1/RC}. \qquad (7.08-1)$$

Were we to apply the technique of expanding $Y(p)$ (all of whose poles must be simple, real, and negative) in partial fractions, we should obtain terms like

$$\frac{K_n}{p - \sigma_n}, \qquad (7.08-2)$$

rather than terms like (7.08–1). More than that—the K_n would be negative. Here then is our trouble: we do not find the right sort of terms in the partial-fraction expansion of $Y(p)$. But we can get what we want, terms like (7.08–1), by a slight modification. The function $Y(p)/p$ will have a partial-fraction expansion with terms similar to (7.08–2)—and since the poles are at (real) negative values of p, the residues will now be *positive* rather than negative, because of the extra p. Finally, on multiplying through by p, we shall have exactly the sort of expansion we need.

Suppose we consider a function in the R-C impedance-realizable category of Case C of Table 7.04–A. (We shall see in a moment that this can well be considered a general case from the admittance point of view.) Let us invert this function $Z(p)$ (it has the properties of R-C impedance functions as it stands and therefore if inverted will have the properties of R-C admittance functions) to form the function $Y(p)$, and then expand $Y(p)/p$.

$$\frac{Y(p)}{p} = \frac{H}{p} \times \frac{(p - \sigma_1)(p - \sigma_3) \cdots (p - \sigma_n)}{(p - \sigma_2)(p - \sigma_4) \cdots (p - \sigma_{n-1})} \tag{7.08-3}$$

$$= \frac{K_0}{p} + \frac{K_2}{p - \sigma_2} + \frac{K_4}{p - \sigma_4} + \cdots + \frac{K_{n-1}}{p - \sigma_{n-1}} + H. \tag{7.08-4}$$

The multiplier H is not the same as that in Table 7.04–A (but rather its reciprocal) but the inequalities of (7.04–2) apply.   Now the residues, the K's, are *positive*.   This can be established by independent consideration of (7.08–3), or from the simple consideration that there is now an additional minus sign in the expression for the residues, due to the additional p.   Alternatively, these K's are the reciprocals of $(d/dp)(pZ)$, evaluated at the poles of Y (the zeros of Z).   This is easily shown to be positive, for dZ/dp is negative, and so is p.   Formally, the K's are computed from

$$K_0 = \left(p \times \frac{Y}{p}\right)_{p=0} = Y(0),$$

$$K_2 = \left[(p - \sigma_2) \times \frac{Y(p)}{p}\right]_{p=\sigma_2},$$

$$\cdots \cdots \cdots \cdots \cdots \tag{7.08-5}$$

$$K_{n-1} = \left[(p - \sigma_{n-1}) \times \frac{Y(p)}{p}\right]_{p=\sigma_{n-1}}.$$

This procedure amounts to removing the factor of the denominator that causes the pole in question, dividing by p, and evaluating the result at the pole.

If now we multiply through by p, we get

$$Y(p) = K_0 + \frac{K_2 p}{p - \sigma_2} + \frac{K_4 p}{p - \sigma_4} + \cdots + \frac{K_{n-1} p}{p - \sigma_{n-1}} + Hp, \tag{7.08-6}$$

which is exactly the expansion we need.   The corresponding network is shown in Fig. 7.08–C, in which the element values are easily obtained by

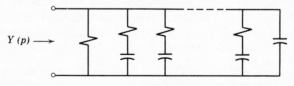

$Y(p) \longrightarrow$

Fig. 7.08–C

inspection, on comparison of the behaviors of component branches of the network and of corresponding terms in the expansion (7.08–6).   Or

(7.08–1) may be referred to. The element values will all be positive and the network is physically realizable. K_0 and H represent the conductance and the capacitance of the lone elements; the intermediate K's represent the conductances of the resistors in the corresponding R-C branches. The capacitor in each case "tunes" the resistor in series resonance at the corresponding (imaginary) resonant frequency; these frequencies are the poles of Y (zeros of Z), and related as in (7.05–7) to the transient-behavior time constants of the branches.

If we are given a function of one of the other three types classified in Fig. 7.04–A, only slight differences will arise. They are:

in Case A, infinity is a zero of Y/p, the term H is missing in (7.08–4), and the lone capacitor does not appear in the network;

in Case B, the origin is a zero of Y, Y/p has no d-c pole, the term with K_0 is missing, and the lone resistor does not appear in the network;

in Case D, the origin is a zero of Y and infinity is a zero of Y/p so that both changes occur and neither lone element appears in the network.

Hence we can consider this our second realization to be perfectly general. The four cases are generated by the two lone elements, each of which may be present or absent. The low-frequency and high-frequency behavior of the network, and the corresponding mathematical behavior of $Z(p)$ or $Y(p)$ immediately point out what is appropriate; no rules or formulas are required at all.

The realization we have obtained, that of Fig. 7.08–C, corresponds exactly to the second L-C canonic form with inductors everywhere replaced by resistors. It is perfectly general and can always be obtained from any R-C realizable function, for we have just shown that any R-C realizable impedance function, when inverted, leads to a physical realization of the above form, and every R-C realizable admittance function must be the reciprocal of an R-C realizable impedance function. This we designate our second canonic form for the R-C case.

Although it is not really necessary, it may be helpful to state explicitly the assumptions made about the function $Y(p)$, which insure that the above realization lead to a network with positive element values. They are merely those of (7.05–8) inverted to apply to admittance rather than impedance.

1. $Y(p)$ has only simple zeros and poles, all of which are on the negative-real axis, where zeros and poles alternate;
2. the slope of $Y(\sigma)$ plotted versus σ is positive (the multiplier H is positive);
3. the lowest critical point (zero or pole) of $Y(p)$ is a zero, which may be at the origin;
4. the highest critical point is a pole, which may be at infinity. (7.08–7)

These are necessary properties of *R-C* driving-point admittance functions, and any such function is p-r. Further, these properties are sufficient for realization as the driving-point admittance of an *R-C* network, as just shown. Functions with these properties are *R-C* admittance realizable, and the synthesis procedure just developed is to

1. factor the denominator of the given *R-C* admittance-realizable function if this has not already been done;
2. divide the function by *p* and write the ordinary partial-fraction expansion of this new function with literal coefficients;
3. determine the coefficient (residue) for each term in the expansion;
4. draw a schematic diagram corresponding to the expansion, like Fig. 7.08–C;
5. determine the element values by comparison of the behavior of the component networks and the corresponding terms in the expansion, at very low and very high frequencies;
6. check the results by calculating the admittance function from the final schematic diagram.   (7.08–8)

The number of "tuned circuits" required is equal to the number of poles in $Y(p)$. A discussion similar to that of § 7.06 leads to an alternative derivation of (7.06–1), based on this second method of realization. Since this second method can always be successfully used, and since it requires only the minimum number of elements, it too is a canonic method and the result, Fig. 7.08–C, is a canonic form of *R-C* network. The minimum number of capacitors required is again determined by (7.06–2) and the minimum number of resistors differs from this by one at the most.

It is important to observe now that any function in the class of *R-C* realizable functions [i.e., any impedance function $Z(p)$ with the properties (7.05–8) or any admittance function $Y(p)$ with the properties (7.08–7)] can be realized by *either* of the two canonic methods. One method is applicable to the function as given, the other to its reciprocal. There are always these two realizations—and perhaps more.

It is again appropriate to postpone most of the illustrative examples to a point where all methods we may develop can be illustrated simultaneously. To crystalize the ideas of the second method here, however, suppose the function of (7.05–10) is to be realized by the second canonic method. The given function, as an admittance function, is

$$Y(p) = \frac{p(p + 3)}{6(p + 2)(p + 4)} \quad \text{ohms.} \qquad (7.08\text{–}9)$$

The partial-fraction expansion of Y/p is

$$\frac{Y(p)}{p} = \frac{(p + 3)}{6(p + 2)(p + 4)} = \frac{1/12}{p + 2} + \frac{1/12}{p + 4}, \qquad (7.08\text{–}10)$$

from which the admittance itself and the realization can be written immediately, as in (7.08–11) and Fig. 7.08–D.

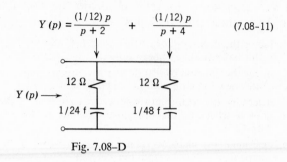

$$Y(p) = \frac{(1/12)\,p}{p+2} \;+\; \frac{(1/12)\,p}{p+4} \qquad (7.08\text{-}11)$$

Fig. 7.08–D

7.09 Discussion

In close parallel to the *L-C* case, the *R-C* case has canonic forms of synthesis, of which we have developed two. Any function suitable for *R-C* realization can be developed into a network by either method (partial-fraction expansion of the impedance function, or of the admittance function after division by p) and the resulting networks are identical in form with the *L-C* canonic forms except for the substitution of resistors for inductors. The two possibilities emphasize that synthesis is not unique, and they afford equivalent networks, as in the *L-C* case. There is an important difference, however, in that they do *not* help us to design reciprocal *R-C* networks: two *R-C* networks cannot be reciprocal, in fact, for the admittance and impedance functions have different properties and cannot be mathematically the same. This does not mean that networks reciprocal to given *R-C* networks do not exist; it only means that we have not yet the apparatus necessary for their design.

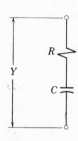

Fig. 7.09–A

Just as the first canonic form, a series connection of simple networks, led to some general properties of *R-C* driving-point impedance functions (§ 7.07), so does the second form, a parallel connection of simple networks like that of Fig. 7.09–A, lead to properties of *R-C* driving-point admittance functions. Any one of the two-element component networks in Fig. 7.08–C has the conductance and susceptance behavior developed below.

For $p = j\omega$,

$$Y = \frac{1}{R + 1/(jC\omega)} = \frac{jC\omega}{1 + jRC\omega} = \frac{jC\omega(1 - jRC\omega)}{1 + R^2C^2\omega^2}. \qquad (7.09\text{-}1)$$

Therefore

$$\textbf{Re } Y(j\omega) = \frac{RC^2\omega^2}{1 + R^2C^2\omega^2},$$

$$\textbf{Im } Y(j\omega) = \frac{C}{1 + R^2C^2\omega^2}. \tag{7.09-2}$$

The conductance-versus-frequency characteristic of this elementary net-work is thus of the form shown in Fig. 7.09–B; the susceptance-versus-frequency characteristic is of the form shown in Fig. 7.09–C. The fact

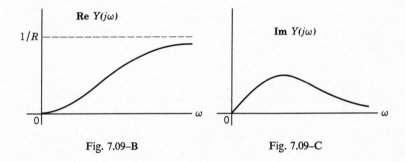

Fig. 7.09–B   Fig. 7.09–C

that the conductance increases continually with frequency is physically apparent from the network diagram and the behavior of capacitors, as well as from the formulas. The general shape of the susceptance curve is similarly apparent from physical considerations.

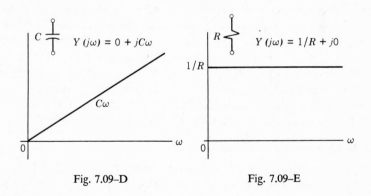

Fig. 7.09–D   Fig. 7.09–E

In addition we may have the lone capacitor and the lone resistor, whose behaviors are illustrated in Figs. 7.09–D and 7.09–E respectively.

Any *R-C* driving-point admittance function, regardless of the actual configuration of the network or of the approximation process from which it may have come, can be realized as a parallel connection of a number of these two-element networks and possibly a capacitor or resistor or both. At real frequencies the conductance characteristic of such a function must then be the sum of a number of curves like that of Fig. 7.09–B (and possibly a constant). The susceptance characteristic of such a function must be the sum of a number of curves like that of Fig. 7.09–C (and possibly one like that of Fig. 7.09–D). Hence we can say the following about the real-frequency behavior of *R-C* driving-point admittance functions:

1. the minimum value of the conductance occurs at zero frequency;
2. the maximum value of the conductance occurs at infinite frequency;
3. the conductance increases steadily with frequency;
4. the susceptance is never negative;
5. the d-c susceptance is zero;
6. the infinite-frequency susceptance is either zero or (positively) infinite.

$$(7.09\text{–}3)$$

If the function is very simple and realizable by a resistor and capacitor in parallel, then the conductance is constant—but in general (7.09–3) sums up what we can say about the behavior of *R-C* admittance functions at real frequencies. The conductance curve may wriggle, but it must always have a positive slope (the simple case mentioned above excepted); the susceptance curve must lie above the axis, and may bob up and down, but little more can be said about it. We can draw no general characteristic curves like those of the *L-C* case, but we can say that, no matter what form an *R-C* network may actually take, it has an equivalent in the form of Fig. 7.08–C and its admittance can be thought of as a superposition of a number of functions like those characterized by the illustrations above.

The two canonic forms we have so far developed provide us with some information on real-frequency properties of *R-C* impedance functions and admittance functions as well as two different methods of synthesis. Both of these resemble the *L-C* case closely, and we expect then that there are other *R-C* canonic forms. To these we next turn our attention.

7.10 Another canonic *R-C* network

We now have two canonic forms, one based on the poles of the impedance function, and one based on the poles of the admittance function. Both were obtained by partial-fraction expansion, and both parallel the reactive-case canonic forms (with inductors replaced by resistors). Now we seek the parallels to the third and fourth (Cauer) *L-C* canonic forms.

These two additional forms, in the *L-C* case, were obtained by continued-fraction expansion and resulted in ladder networks. It requires little imagination to decide what we should do in this, the *R-C*, case—but there are some differences which require attention.

Suppose the given function $Z(p)$, which is *R-C* realizable, is written as the quotient of two polynomials,

$$Z(p) = \frac{a_n p^n + a_{n-1} p^{n-1} + \cdots}{b_m p^m + b_{m-1} p^{m-1} + \cdots}. \tag{7.10-1}$$

The two polynomials are mixed (neither odd nor even) and either $m = n$ (*R* point at infinity) or $m = n + 1$ (zero at infinity). Assume for the moment that $m = n$. We expect that appropriate continued-fraction development of $Z(p)$ will result in a ladder network in which the series arms are resistors and the shunt arms capacitors, by analogy with the third *L-C* canonic form. We must prove this to be true, and determine an appropriate method of expansion.

The partial-fraction expansion of $Z(p)$, to begin with, is

$$Z(p) = \frac{a_n}{b_n} + \sum_i \frac{K_i}{p - \sigma_i} \tag{7.10-2}$$

in which the σ_i are negative and the K_i are positive, by the arguments of § 7.05. Each term in the expansion above is p-r (the terms may be tested or compared with the realization in § 7.05), and the first term represents the quotient in the division indicated by (7.10-1). This is also the first term of the continued-fraction expansion that concentrates on behavior at infinity. At infinity $Z(p)$ has a nonzero (resistive) value which we remove as the first term. The remainder,

$$Z_1 = \sum_i \frac{K_i'}{p - \sigma_i} = \frac{a_{n-1}' p^{n-1} + a_{n-2}' p^{n-2} + \cdots}{b_n p^n + b_{n-1} p^{n-1} + \cdots} \tag{7.10-3}$$

is not only p-r but is still *R-C* realizable (if only in the first two canonic forms). Its order is unchanged; it has, however, a zero at infinity, so we invert it to obtain the improper fraction

$$Y_1 = \frac{1}{Z_1} = \frac{b_n p^n + b_{n-1} p^{n-1} + \cdots}{a_{n-1}' p^{n-1} + a_{n-2}' p^{n-2} + \cdots} \tag{7.10-4}$$

which has more interesting behavior (a pole) at infinity. Since it is *R-C* realizable, we may expand according to the process for obtaining the second canonic form (§ 7.08),

$$\frac{Y_1}{p} = \frac{b_n}{a_{n-1}'} + \sum_k \frac{K_k}{p - \sigma_k'} \tag{7.10-5}$$

and

$$Y_1 = \frac{b_n}{a_{n-1}'}p + \sum_k \frac{K_k p}{p - \sigma_k'}, \tag{7.10-6}$$

with assurance that the σ_k' are negative and the K_k positive. Each term in (7.10–6) is p-r and R-C realizable, and the first term represents the first term of the quotient in the division indicated by (7.10–4). On removing this first term we have left

$$Y_2 = \sum_k \frac{K_k p}{p - \sigma_k'} = \frac{b_n' p^{n-1} + \cdots}{a_{n-1}' p^{n-1} + \cdots} \tag{7.10-7}$$

which is p-r, R-C realizable, and of order one less than Y_1 (or Z_1, or Z), for a pole has been removed. Its reciprocal,

$$Z_2 = \frac{a_{n-1}' p^{n-1} + \cdots}{b_n' p^{n-1} + \cdots} \tag{7.10-8}$$

is p-r and R-C realizable, and its order is one less than that of $Z(p)$, from which we started. We have completed one cycle of the continued-fraction expansion process and obtained

$$Z(p) = \frac{a_n}{b_n} + Z_1 = \frac{a_n}{b_n} + \cfrac{1}{\cfrac{b_n}{a_{n-1}'}p + \cfrac{1}{Z_2}}. \tag{7.10-9}$$

The two terms specifically evaluated result simply from division (but only the first term of the quotient is retained where the quotient has two terms). Since Z has been reduced in order by one, we need merely repeat the same cycle until the reduction is complete, and we have

$$Z = c_1 + \cfrac{1}{c_2 p + \cfrac{1}{c_3 + \cfrac{1}{c_4 p + \cdots}}} \tag{7.10-10}$$

in which all the c's are obtained by ordinary division (with inversion after each division) and are positive. The last term may be of either type (cp or constant) but the expansion will definitely terminate; it will contain either $2n$ or $(2n + 1)$ terms. The corresponding network realization is a ladder network drawn from (7.10–10), which is exactly the form expected, that of the third L-C canonic form with inductors replaced by resistors; see Fig. 7.10–A. The resistance values are the odd c's in (7.10–10); the

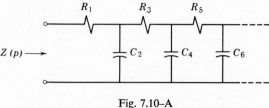

Fig. 7.10–A

capacitance values are the even c's. Before discussing some details not covered above, let us work a simple example. The impedance function

$$Z(p) = \frac{180p^2 + 45p + 1}{30p^2 + 5p} \quad \text{ohms} \tag{7.10–11}$$

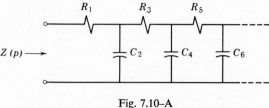

Fig. 7.10–B

with the frequency pattern shown in Fig. 7.10–B is both p-r and R-C realizable. The continued-fraction expansion just developed is obtained by the division-inversion-division $\cdots$ process:

$$
\begin{array}{r}
30p^2 + 5p \overline{)180p^2 + 45p + 1}(6 \\
\underline{180p^2 + 30p} \\
15p + 1 \overline{)30p^2 + 5p}(2p \\
\underline{30p^2 + 2p} \\
3p \overline{)15p + 1}(5 \\
\underline{15p} \\
1 \overline{)3p}(3p \\
\underline{3p}
\end{array}
\tag{7.10–12}
$$

so that

$$Z(p) = 6 + \cfrac{1}{2p + \cfrac{1}{5 + \cfrac{1}{3p}}} \tag{7.10–13}$$

which yields the network of Fig. 7.10–C.

Notice that the second division leaves a remainder which is not a proper fraction, but that the division is not completed; rather we invert and proceed. This difference from the behavior in the corresponding L-C

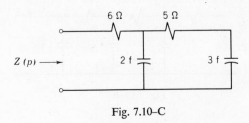

Fig. 7.10–C

expansion arises because we have mixed polynomials for numerators and denominators, and they do not necessarily differ in degree by one; the reduction in order occurs at alternate steps, not at every step. In practice we should of course perform the division with detached coefficients, thus:

$$
\begin{array}{llll}
30\ \ 5)180 & 45 & 1(6 & \\
\quad\ \ \underline{180} & 30 & & \\
\quad\quad 15 & 1)30 & 5(2 & \\
\quad\quad & \underline{30} & 2 & \quad\quad\quad (7.10\text{–}14)\\
\quad\quad & & 3)15 & 1(5 \\
\quad\quad & & \underline{15} & \\
\quad\quad & & & 1)3(3 \\
\quad\quad & & & \underline{3}
\end{array}
$$

When the powers of p are not written, one must be careful in interpreting the quotients, for some are constants and some are cp in form. The forms alternate, however, and with the assumption that $Z(\infty)$ is not zero, the first is a constant.

The general idea is essentially that of the third L-C canonic expansion, with the minor differences due to replacement of L by R: the polynomials are mixed, the terms alternate between first and zero powers of p, and the ladder network has series arms that are resistors. The arithmetic of obtaining an expansion is identical with that of obtaining the L-C expansion (compare the numerical example above with that of § 6.10).

It remains only to discuss the special cases that may arise (of which we expect four). If the given R-C impedance function $Z(p)$ has a nonzero value at infinity, the process is that above and the network of Fig. 7.10–A results. The value of R_1 is $Z(\infty)$, as the diagram indicates (for large p the capacitor C_2 approaches a short circuit). If the given function $Z(p)$

has a zero at infinity [the only other possibility, in which $m = n + 1$ in (7.10–1)], then it is necessary to invert the function before beginning the expansion. Or we might consider R_1 to be zero and the first step to be unnecessary. The resulting network is that in Fig. 7.10–D whose input

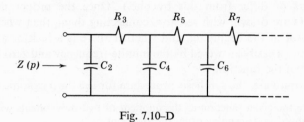

Fig. 7.10–D

impedance is clearly zero at infinity. If the function is given as an admittance rather than as an impedance, the methods above are still applicable, but to the *reciprocal* of the given function. This third form then can be obtained for any *R-C* realizable function. It uses only the minimum number of elements, as do the first two (in fact, exactly the same number of elements of each kind) and is also a canonic form.

To complete the discussion we have only to consider how the network terminates. Here there are two possibilities; since the behavior at infinity determines how the network begins, we expect the manner of ending to be determined by the d-c behavior. If the impedance function has a finite (resistive) value at the origin, then the network ends as in Fig. 7.10–E and the last term in the continued-fraction expansion is a constant. If the impedance function has a pole at the origin, then the network ends as in Fig. 7.10–F and the last term is cp in form.

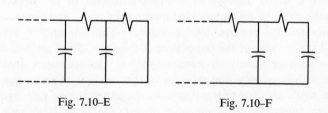

Fig. 7.10–E   Fig. 7.10–F

It is now merely a matter of common-sense observation of the given function to determine the schematic form of this third canonic realization. It is a ladder of series resistors and shunt capacitors; the first element is a resistor when $Z(\infty)$ is not zero [$Y(\infty)$ is finite], and is a capacitor when

$Z(\infty)$ is zero (Y has a pole at infinity); the last element is a resistor when $Z(0)$ is finite [$Y(0)$ is not zero], and is a capacitor when Z has a pole at the origin [$Y(0)$ is zero]. The number of capacitors is equal to the order of the function, i.e., to the number of zeros or the number of poles of the function. (The number of resistors may be the same as the number of capacitors or differ from this by one.) Once the proper number of capacitors are drawn, with resistors connecting them, then whether there is a resistor at the beginning, and whether there is a resistor at the end, are questions easily answered by the infinite-frequency and zero-frequency behavior of the function.

To recapitulate, the synthesis procedure for the third canonic form is to

1. write the given function as the quotient of two polynomials with terms arranged in descending order of powers of p;
2. obtain a continued-fraction expansion of the impedance function if $Z(\infty)$ is not zero, or of the admittance function if $Z(\infty)$ is zero, by the divide-invert-divide · · · process;
3. draw a schematic diagram corresponding to the expansion, the element values of which are the coefficients obtained in step 2;
4. check the result by calculating the impedance (admittance) function from the final schematic diagram.   (7.10–15)

The synthesis problem has many solutions, and any R-C realizable function can be developed in this third form, as well as in the others.

In developing this third process we have paid too little attention to the physical meaning of the continued-fraction expansion, and it is profitable to look at this now. The third L-C canonic realization was obtained by a process of reactance and susceptance removal, one pole (at infinity) being removed at each step and appearing as an (one-element) arm of the ladder network. In the R-C case, the shunt arms are generated in exactly the same manner: each by removal of a single pole of admittance (at infinity), which appears as a shunt capacitor in the network and reduces the order of the immittance function by one. But the series arms are generated by removal of *resistance*. The amount of resistance removed is the value of the impedance at infinity. Since all R-C driving-point impedance functions have resistance characteristics that never increase with frequency, the removal of this amount of resistance can at no time make the remaining resistance negative at any real frequency. Hence an important characteristic of p-r functions (real part never negative for $p = j\omega$) is preserved, and indeed all the requirements of test (5.13–5) are still met by the reduced impedance function. Note that the function is not reduced in order by removal of resistance, but that a zero of impedance is thereby introduced at infinity—and on this zero depends the success of the following step. Removal of resistance, as well as reactance and susceptance, will be important in general synthesis processes of the *R-L-C* case, but requires no further discussion here.

7.11 The fourth canonic *R-C* network

Common sense says there must be a fourth canonic form and that it is to be obtained by a continued-fraction expansion that concentrates on d-c behavior rather than behavior at infinity. Suppose the given *R-C* realizable impedance function has a pole at the origin. With the polynomials written in ascending order of powers of p rather than descending order, we have

$$Z(p) = \frac{a_0 + a_1 p + \cdots}{b_1 p + \cdots}. \tag{7.11-1}$$

Proceeding much as in § 6.11, we remove the pole at the origin and write

$$Z(p) = \frac{a_0}{b_1 p} + \sum_i \frac{K_i}{p - \sigma_i} + H \tag{7.11-2}$$

in which, by the arguments of §7.05, we know that all the K_i are positive; the constants a_0/b_1 (the result of division) and H are also positive; and the σ_i are negative. The reduced impedance function

$$Z_1 = \sum_i \frac{K_i}{p - \sigma_i} + H = \frac{a_0' + a_1' p + \cdots}{b_1 + b_2 p + \cdots} \tag{7.11-3}$$

is p-r, *R-C* realizable, and its order is one less than that of *Z*. At the origin Z_1 has a finite value. We invert the function and expand according to the usual process for *R-C* admittance functions (§ 7.08):

$$Y_1 = \frac{1}{Z_1} = \frac{b_1 + b_2 p + \cdots}{a_0' + a_1' p + \cdots}, \tag{7.11-4}$$

$$\frac{Y_1}{p} = \frac{b_1}{a_0' p} + \sum_k \frac{K_k}{p - \sigma_k'} + H', \tag{7.11-5}$$

$$Y_1 = \frac{b_1}{a_0'} + \sum_k \frac{K_k p}{p - \sigma_k'} + H'p. \tag{7.11-6}$$

The first term is as usual the result of the division indicated by (7.11-4); in it the K_k and H' are positive and the σ_k' are negative. The next reduction (removal of the positive constant b_1/a_0') gives us

$$Y_2 = \sum_k \frac{K_k p}{p - \sigma_k'} + H'p = \frac{b_1' p + b_2' p^2 + \cdots}{a_0' + a_1' p + \cdots} \tag{7.11-7}$$

which is p-r, R-C realizable, and of the same order as Y_1. The same properties hold for its reciprocal,

$$Z_2 = \frac{1}{Y_2} = \frac{a_0' + a_1'p + \cdots}{b_1'p + b_2'p^2 + \cdots} \tag{7.11-8}$$

which has a pole at the origin. This completes a cycle of the process, which has reduced the order of the impedance function by one and given us

$$Z(p) = \frac{a_0}{b_1 p} + \cfrac{1}{\cfrac{b_1}{a_0'} + \cfrac{1}{Z_2}}. \tag{7.11-9}$$

The two positive constants a_0/b_1 and b_1/a_0' result from ordinary divisions, with inversion after the first division. Evidently the cycle need merely be repeated, giving

$$Z(p) = \frac{c_1}{p} + \cfrac{1}{c_2 + \cfrac{1}{\cfrac{c_3}{p} + \cfrac{1}{c_4 + \cdot}}} \tag{7.11-10}$$

in which all the c's are obtained by ordinary division (with inversion after each division) and are positive. The expansion will terminate and will contain either $2n$ or $(2n - 1)$ terms. The corresponding network realization, illustrated in Fig. 7.11–A, is, as expected, in exact parallel to the

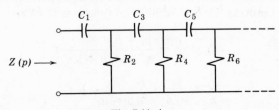

Fig. 7.11–A

fourth L-C canonic form. The capacitance values are the *reciprocals* of the odd c's in (7.11-10); the resistance values are the *reciprocals* of the even c's in (7.11-10).

To illustrate the process, consider the R-C realizable impedance function

$$Z(p) = \frac{p^2 + 35p + 120}{9p^2 + 40p} \quad \text{ohms} \tag{7.11-11}$$

with the frequency pattern of Fig. 7.11–B. The realization process calls
for writing $Z(p)$ as

$$Z(p) = \frac{120 + 35p + p^2}{40p + 9p^2} \qquad (7.11\text{–}12)$$

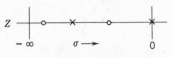

Fig. 7.11–B

and the development

$$
\begin{array}{l}
40p + 9p^2)\overline{120 + 35p + p^2}(3/p \\
\quad \underline{120 + 27p} \\
\qquad 8p + p^2)\overline{40p + 9p^2}(5 \\
\qquad \quad \underline{40p + 5p^2} \\
\qquad \qquad 4p^2)\overline{8p + p^2}(2/p \\
\qquad \qquad \quad \underline{8p} \\
\qquad \qquad \qquad p^2)\overline{4p^2}(4 \\
\qquad \qquad \qquad \quad \underline{4p^2}
\end{array}
\qquad (7.11\text{–}13)
$$

which states that

$$Z(p) = \frac{3}{p} + \cfrac{1}{5 + \cfrac{1}{\dfrac{2}{p} + \dfrac{1}{4}}} \qquad (7.11\text{–}14)$$

yielding the network of Fig. 7.11–C. The arithmetic is identical with that

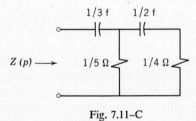

Fig. 7.11–C

of the corresponding *L-C* expansion, when the work is done with detached
coefficients as below (cf. the example of § 6.11).

$$
\begin{array}{l}
40 \quad 9)120 \quad 35 \quad 1(3 \\
\underline{120 \quad 27} \\
8 \quad 1)40 \quad 9(5 \\
\underline{40 \quad 5} \\
4)8 \quad 1(2 \\
\underline{8} \\
1)4(4 \\
\underline{4}
\end{array}
\qquad (7.11\text{-}15)
$$

The powers of p omitted are alternately p^{-1} and p^0, and one must be careful to associate with each coefficient the correct power of p and corresponding type of network element. An additional nuisance is that the coefficients must be *inverted* to obtain capacitance and resistance values—but this is to be expected.

There are again four possible cases. If the given R-C impedance function $Z(p)$ has a pole at the origin, the network starts with a series capacitor as in Fig. 7.11–A. If $Z(p)$ does not have a pole at the origin, then the capacitor C_1 is omitted (Fig. 7.11–D) and the expansion begins

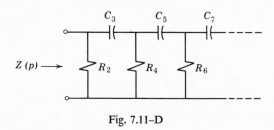

Fig. 7.11–D

with $1/Z$. Alternatively, the first coefficient in the expansion (7.11–10) can be considered zero and the first capacitance infinite. If the function is given as an admittance, it need merely be inverted before expansion to obtain the network for Fig. 7.11–A if that is appropriate; if the admittance is not zero at the origin, then it can be expanded immediately to give the network of Fig. 7.11–D.

This fourth form can be obtained for any R-C realizable function. It uses only the minimum number of elements (the same number of each kind as do the first three forms) and is also a canonic form. To complete its discussion we have only to observe that the network can end in a resistor (the impedance is not zero at infinity and the last term of the continued-fraction expansion is a constant) as in Fig. 7.11–E, or in a capacitor (the impedance is zero at infinity, and the last term of the continued-fraction expansion is in p^{-1}) as in Fig. 7.11–F.

To draw the schematic diagram of this fourth canonic realization of an R-C realizable immittance function of order n, we need merely put down n capacitors with $n - 1$ intermediate resistors, and then determine whether

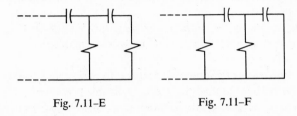

Fig. 7.11–E   Fig. 7.11–F

additional resistors appear at the beginning and the end by common-sense consideration of the d-c and infinite-frequency behaviors. To recapitulate, the synthesis procedure is to

1. write the given function as the quotient of two polynomials with the terms arranged in ascending order of powers of p;
2. obtain a continued-fraction expansion of the impedance function if $Z(0)$ is not finite, or of the admittance function if $Z(0)$ is finite, by the divide-invert-divide $\cdots$ process;
3. draw a schematic diagram corresponding to the expansion, the element values of which are the reciprocals of the coefficients obtained in step 2;
4. check the result by calculating the impedance (admittance) function from the final schematic diagram. (7.11–16)

This process provides a fourth solution to the R-C synthesis problem, always obtainable and different from the other three except in the simplest cases.

A physical view of the process shows it to consist of (a) removal of series reactance (one pole, that at infinity, for each series arm) which reduces the order by one, and (b) removal of shunt *conductance*. The conductance removed is the value at the origin, and since all R-C driving-point admittance functions have conductance characteristics that never decrease with frequency, the removal of this amount of conductance cannot ever make the remaining conductance negative at any real frequency. Its removal does not reduce the order of the immittance functions, but it does create a zero in the admittance function at the origin, which provides the basis for the next step (removal of the corresponding pole of impedance). The end result is similar to the fourth L-C canonic form, but with inductors replaced by resistors.

7.12 R-C realization

Inductance-free networks have driving-point impedance functions which fall into a well-defined class. They have certain properties, and when a suitable list of these is made, as in (7.05–8), this class of functions is thereby defined. The driving-point admittance functions of such networks have somewhat different properties, as those in the list mentioned above do not remain the same when the function is inverted; the corresponding definition of R-C admittance functions is (7.08–7). Immittance functions in these classes are to R-C networks what reactance functions are to L-C networks.

We have found four canonic realizations, four different ways of synthesizing a network that has any given R-C realizable function (i.e., a function from one of the classes mentioned above) as one of its immittance functions (Fig. 7.12–A). (Networks inverse to these do not belong to the R-C class.) The four are fundamental methods, lead to simple and significant forms of network, and in each case use only the minimum number of elements. They are all logical extensions of the four canonic L-C realizations (in which L gives way to R); the extensions were made by Cauer (CA 1).

Yet these four methods of realization, just as in the L-C case, really represent applications of but one technique—and they do not exhaust that technique (not to mention other methods of realization). The technique is to remove part of the network as a series arm of a ladder, then part of the remainder as a shunt arm, then part of what is left as another series arm, etc. Figure 7.12–B illustrates the resulting network, which may begin with either a series box or a shunt box. The first canonic method removes the entire impedance, in the first box, as a series connection of small networks which exhibit the poles of $Z(p)$ [zeros of $Y(p)$]. The second canonic method also removes the entire immittance, but rather in a shunt box which by its configuration exhibits the zeros of $Z(p)$ [poles of $Y(p)$]. At the other extreme in amount of immittance removed lie the third and fourth canonic methods which remove but one element at a time, so that in the network of Fig. 7.12–B each box contains only a resistor or a capacitor. Between these two extremes lie many other possibilities (except for immittance functions of low order) in which varying amounts of immittance are removed in each box. Any such development can be considered to come from alternate application of the first two canonic methods; only part of the realization is retained at any stage, the remainder being recombined and inverted for development by the other method, but again only a part of the resulting network is retained; etc. At each step some of the poles of an immittance function are removed, or some of the resistance (conductance) corresponding to the value of the impedance at infinity (admittance at the origin), or both. An R-C realizable impedance function with the frequency pattern of

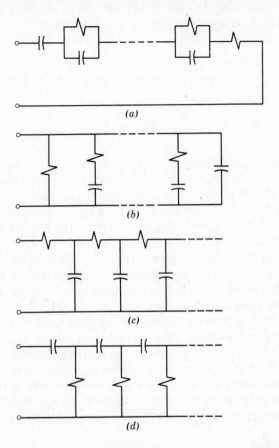

Fig. 7.12–A

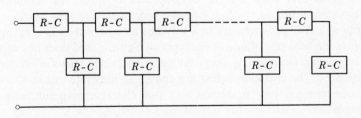

Fig. 7.12–B

Fig. 7.12–C has, for example, realizations which are those of Fig. 6.13–B with inductors replaced by resistors, and many more.

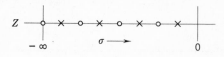

Fig. 7.12–C

With the notable change that poles of impedance at infinity (poles of admittance at the origin) are replaced by values of resistance at infinity (of conductance at the origin), the various processes are identical with those possible for L-C networks (§ 6.12, § 6.13). Poles (on the negative-real axis) can be removed without disturbing the p-r and R-C character of the remaining immittance; also, resistance (conductance) can be removed up to a certain point. Thus in addition to reactance and susceptance removal, we have found it useful to remove resistance and conductance in the synthesis process. This new device will also be useful later, in the general (R-L-C) case.

The number of possible realizations increases rapidly with the order of the immittance functions. Further solutions of the synthesis problem arise when equivalent networks for the individual ladder arms are considered. Then there is also the possibility of realization in other than this ladder form, which we do not discuss. (The possibility of removing only "part of a pole" or of a resistance extends the number of solutions to infinity, though with more than the minimum number of elements.)

7.13 Examples

Numerical examples are essential in explaining any synthesis process. Those given here illustrate the development of given R-C immittance functions according to the four canonic processes developed above.

Although R-C networks are in a way not as powerful as L-C networks (because the behavior of one of the types of element used does not depend on frequency), nevertheless they can do some things that L-C networks cannot do. The examples below are chosen to illustrate this fact.

A one-terminal pair possesses only one characterizing function, the driving-point impedance (or admittance) function. In the steady state ($p = j\omega$) this is

$$Z(j\omega) = R(\omega) + jX(\omega) = |Z|\, e^{j\beta} \tag{7.13–1}$$

or

$$Y(j\omega) = G(\omega) + jB(\omega) = |Y|\, e^{-j\beta}. \tag{7.13–2}$$

Sometimes one is interested in the behavior of the magnitude function ($|Z|$ or $|Y|$), sometimes of the angle or phase β, sometimes of the real part (resistance or conductance), and sometimes of the imaginary part (reactance or susceptance). In the *L-C* case the possible kinds of behavior are severely limited. Both X and B must fit the standard reactance-function pattern of alternating zeros and poles, and the magnitude function must be the magnitude of such a function. The functions R and G must be zero, and β is always $\pm\pi/2$ radians (90°). There are engineering problems in which it is useful to have a network whose driving-point impedance (admittance) function closely approximates a prescribed constant value (over a band of frequencies) in magnitude, angle, real part, or imaginary part. No *L-C* network can do this, but here *R-C* networks are rather powerful. To determine a suitable function of p calls for the solution of an approximation problem (cf. Chapters 13, 14) and then for the realization of the resulting function. We shall not discuss approximation until we complete our study of the properties of one-terminal pairs, but we may well take the results of such approximations to illustrate *R-C* network realization.

Example 1. An *R-C* impedance function, Fig. 7.13–A, which has the property that is reactance is substantially constant over a frequency band is, in normalized form,

$$Z(p) = 46.41 \frac{(p + 0.2011)(p + 5.399)}{p(p + 3.268)(p + 26.11)}$$

$$= 46.41 \frac{p^2 + 5.600p + 1.086}{p^3 + 29.37p^2 + 85.31p} \quad \text{ohms.}$$

Realizations in which 200 cps corresponds to unit normalized frequency, and the impedance level is raised by a factor of 700 ohms, are desired.

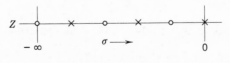

Fig. 7.13–A

For convenience we ignore the given multiplier until the final step of correctly scaling the element values. The factors to be used there are

for resistance: $700 \times 46.41 = 32.49 \times 10^3$ (ohms),

for capacitance: $\dfrac{1}{700 \times 46.41(2\pi \times 200)} = 0.02449 \times 10^{-6}$ (f).

The process of realization in the first canonic form is

$$\frac{(p + 0.2011)(p + 5.399)}{p(p + 3.268)(p + 26.11)} = \frac{0.01273}{p} + \frac{A}{p + 3.268} + \frac{B}{p + 26.11}$$

in which

$$A = \frac{(-3.067)(2.131)}{(-3.268)(22.84)} = 0.08756,$$

$$B = \frac{(-25.91)(-20.71)}{(-26.11)(-22.84)} = 0.8997.$$

The network, drawn directly from the above, is shown in Fig. 7.13–B. The normalized element values come immediately from the partial-fraction expansion,

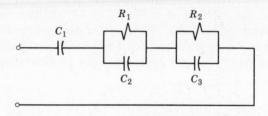

Element	Value	
	Normalized	Actual
R_1	$0.02680\,\Omega$	$870.6\,\Omega$
R_2	$0.03446\,\Omega$	$1120\,\Omega$
C_1	78.56 f	$1.924\,\mu$f
C_2	11.42 f	$0.2797\,\mu$f
C_3	1.111 f	$0.02722\,\mu$f

Fig. 7.13–B

the actual values from these by multiplication by the conversion factors calculated above.

The second canonic realization process is

$$\frac{1}{p} \times \frac{p(p + 3.268)(p + 26.11)}{(p + 0.2011)(p + 5.399)} = \frac{A}{p + 0.2011} + \frac{B}{p + 5.399} + 1,$$

in which

$$A = \frac{(3.067)(25.91)}{(5.198)} = 15.28,$$

$$B = \frac{(-2.131)(20.71)}{(-5.198)} = 8.489,$$

so that the normalized admittance function is

$$\frac{15.28p}{p + 0.2011} + \frac{8.489p}{p + 5.399} + p,$$

and the realization is shown in Fig. 7.13–C.

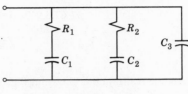

Value

Element	Normalized	Actual
R_1	$0.06543\,\Omega$	$2126\,\Omega$
R_2	$0.1178\,\Omega$	$3827\,\Omega$
C_1	75.99 f	$1.861\,\mu f$
C_2	1.572 f	$0.03851\,\mu f$
C_3	1 f	$0.02449\,\mu f$

Fig. 7.13–C

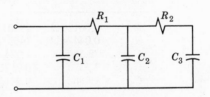

Value

Element	Normalized	Actual
R_1	$0.04206\,\Omega$	$1367\,\Omega$
R_2	$0.02870\,\Omega$	$932.5\,\Omega$
C_1	1 f	$0.02449\,\mu f$
C_2	11.56 f	$0.2831\,\mu f$
C_3	66.00 f	$1.617\,\mu f$

Fig. 7.13–D

In the third canonic realization process, Fig. 7.13–D, since the impedance is zero at infinity, the admittance is developed:

```
1   5.600   1.086)1   29.37   85.31(1
                  1    5.60    1.08
                      23.77   84.22)1   5.600   1.086(0.04206
                                   1    3.543
                                       2.057   1.086

   2.057   1.086)23.77   84.22(11.56
                 23.77   12.55
                        71.67)2.057   1.086(0.02870
                              2.057
                                  1.086)71.67(66.00
                                        71.67
```

The fourth canonic realization is shown in Fig. 7.13–E.

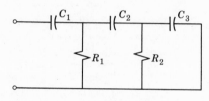

Value

Element	Normalized	Actual
R_1	0.06126 Ω	1990 Ω
R_2	0.04474 Ω	1453 Ω
C_1	78.56 f	1.924 μf
C_2	2.537 f	0.06213 μf
C_3	1.686 f	0.04130 μf

Fig. 7.13–E

```
85.31   29.37   1)1.086   5.600   1       (0.01273
                   1.086   0.374   0.0127
                          5.226   0.9873)85.31   29.37   1)16.32
                                         85.31   16.11
                                                13.26   1

        13.26   1)5.226   0.9873(0.3942
                  5.226   0.3942
                         0.5931)13.26   1(22.35
                               13.26
                                   1)0.5931(0.5931
                                     0.5931
```

There are additional realizations, but these are enough to illustrate the techniques. Note the capacitance values required in the realizations; some are inconveniently large (though not equally so in all the realizations), because of the characteristics of the particular function chosen.

Example 2. An *R-C* admittance function, Fig. 7.13–F, which has the property

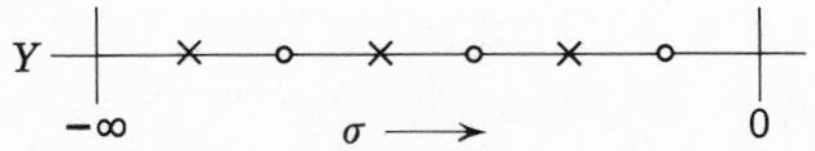

Fig. 7.13–F

that its angle is substantially constant over a frequency band is, in normalized form,

$$Y(p) = \frac{(p + 0.3694)(p + 2.983)(p + 14.57)}{(p + 1.311)(p + 6.406)(p + 51.70)}$$

$$= \frac{p^3 + 17.92p^2 + 49.94p + 16.05}{p^3 + 59.42p^2 + 407.4p + 434.2} \quad \text{mhos.}$$

The impedance level is to be raised by a factor of 12 (ohms), and unit normalized frequency is to correspond to 2 mcps. The scale factors for conversion to actual values are accordingly

for resistance: 12 (ohms)

for capacitance: $\dfrac{1}{12(2\pi \times 2 \times 10^6)} = 6631 \times 10^{-12}$ (f).

The first canonic realization process follows.

$$Z = \frac{(p + 1.311)(p + 6.406)(p + 51.70)}{(p + 0.3694)(p + 2.983)(p + 14.57)}$$

$$= \frac{A}{p + 0.3694} + \frac{B}{p + 2.983} + \frac{C}{p + 14.57} + 1,$$

in which

$$A = \frac{(0.9414)(6.036)(51.33)}{(2.613)(14.20)} = 7.862,$$

$$B = \frac{(-1.672)(3.423)(48.72)}{(-2.613)(11.59)} = 9.209,$$

$$C = \frac{(-13.26)(-8.163)(37.14)}{(-14.20)(-11.59)} = 24.43.$$

The realization is shown in Fig. 7.13–G.

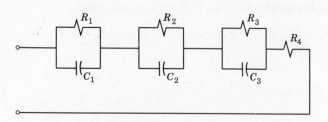

Value

Element	Normalized	Actual
R_1	21.28 Ω	255.4 Ω
R_2	3.087 Ω	37.05 Ω
R_3	1.677 Ω	20.12 Ω
R_4	1 Ω	12.00 Ω
C_1	0.1272 f	843.5 μμf
C_2	0.1086 f	720.1 μμf
C_3	0.04093 f	271.5 μμf

Fig. 7.13–G

The second canonic realization process is

$$\frac{Y}{p} = \frac{(p + 0.3694)(p + 2.983)(p + 14.57)}{(p + 1.311)(p + 6.406)(p + 51.70)p}$$

$$= \frac{A}{p} + \frac{B}{p + 1.311} + \frac{C}{p + 6.406} + \frac{D}{p + 51.70}$$

in which

$$A = \frac{(0.3694)(2.983)(14.57)}{(1.311)(6.406)(51.70)} = 0.03698,$$

$$B = \frac{(-0.9414)(1.672)(13.26)}{(-1.311)(5.095)(50.39)} = 0.06200,$$

$$C = \frac{(-6.036)(-3.423)(8.163)}{(-6.406)(-5.095)(45.30)} = 0.1141,$$

$$D = \frac{(-51.33)(-48.72)(-37.14)}{(-51.70)(-50.42)(-45.30)} = 0.7865.$$

The normalized admittance function can thus be written

$$Y = 0.03698 + \frac{0.06200p}{p + 1.311} + \frac{0.1141p}{p + 6.406} + \frac{0.7865p}{p + 51.70},$$

and the realization is illustrated in Fig. 7.13–H.

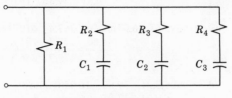

Value

Element	Normalized	Actual
R_1	27.04 Ω	324.5 Ω
R_2	16.13 Ω	193.5 Ω
R_3	8.766 Ω	105.2 Ω
R_4	1.271 Ω	15.26 Ω
C_1	0.04730 f	313.7 $\mu\mu$f
C_2	0.01781 f	118.1 $\mu\mu$f
C_3	0.01521 f	100.9 $\mu\mu$f

Fig. 7.13–H

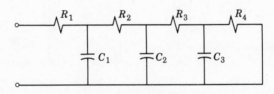

Value

Element	Normalized	Actual
R_1	1 Ω	12.00 Ω
R_2	4.459 Ω	53.50 Ω
R_3	8.200 Ω	98.40 Ω
R_4	13.39 Ω	160.6 Ω
C_1	0.02410 f	159.8 $\mu\mu$f
C_2	0.05180 f	343.5 $\mu\mu$f
C_3	0.1020 f	676.3 $\mu\mu$f

Fig. 7.13–I

The third canonic realization process, Fig. 7.13–I, is

$$1 \quad 17.92 \quad 49.94 \quad 16.05)1 \quad 59.42 \quad 407.3 \quad 434.2(1$$
$$1 \quad 17.92 \quad 49.9 \quad 16.1$$
$$\overline{\quad\quad\quad 41.50 \quad 357.4 \quad 418.1}$$

41.50   357.4   418.1)1   17.92   49.94   16.05(0.02410

                 1   8.61   10.07

                      9.31   39.86   16.05

9.31   39.86   16.05)41.50   357.4   418.1(4.459

                41.50   177.7   71.6

                      179.7   346.5

179.7   346.5)9.31   39.86   16.05(0.05180

              9.31   17.95

                 21.91   16.05)179.7   346.5(8.200

                            179.7   131.6

                                 214.9

214.9)21.91   16.05(0.1020

        21.91

               16.05)214.9(13.39

                    214.9

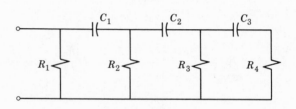

Value

Element	Normalized	Actual
R_1	27.05 Ω	324.5 Ω
R_2	6.068 Ω	72.82 Ω
R_3	3.297 Ω	39.56 Ω
R_4	2.021 Ω	24.25 Ω
C_1	0.08033 f	532.7 $\mu\mu$f
C_2	0.03736 f	247.8 $\mu\mu$f
C_3	0.01899 f	125.9 $\mu\mu$f

Fig. 7.13–J

The fourth canonic realization process, Fig. 7.13–J. is

434.2   407.4   59.42   1)16.05   49.94   17.92   1   (0.03698

                       16.05   15.06   2.20   0.0370

                            34.88   15.72   0.9630

34.88   15.72   0.9630)434.2   407.3   59.42   1(12.45
$$\underline{434.2\ \ \ \ \ 195.7\ \ \ \ 11.99}$$
$$211.6\ \ \ \ \ 47.43\ \ \ 1$$

211.6   47.43   1)34.88   15.72   0.9630(0.1648
$$\underline{34.88\ \ \ \ \ 7.81\ \ \ \ 0.1648}$$
$$7.91\ \ \ \ 0.7982)211.6\ \ \ \ 47.43\ \ \ 1(26.76$$
$$\underline{211.6\ \ \ \ 21.36}$$
$$26.07\ \ \ 1$$

26.07   1)7.91   0.7982(0.3033
$$\underline{7.91\ \ \ \ 0.3033}$$
$$0.4949)26.07\ \ \ 1(52.67$$
$$\underline{26.07}$$
$$1)0.4949(0.4949$$
$$\underline{0.4949}$$

There are many alternative (equivalent) realizations, but those above suffice as illustrations. Notice again the differences in element values between the realizations, and the ranges of element values required (determined, of course, by the function prescribed, not just by the realization process).

7.14 *R-L* networks

We found it possible to discuss the *R-C* case more easily by using our *L-C* results than by starting afresh; the results of the *L-C* discussion shortened the work there. Now here in the *R-L* case we should be even better off with a knowledge of both *L-C* and *R-C* networks, and this is true. In fact, we can dispose of the *R-L* case in short order. It is not especially important, for there are no circumstances, analogous to those mentioned in § 7.01, in which *R-L* networks are particularly desirable.

The basis of the short cut is the duality of the *R-C* and *R-L* cases. The basic elements and their laws, in the two cases, are given in Table 7.14–A.

Table 7.14–A

R-C Case	*R-L* Case
$—\!\!\wedge\!\!\!\vee\!\!—\ v = Ri$	$—\!\!\wedge\!\!\!\vee\!\!—\ i = Gv$
$—\!\!\mid\!\mid\!\!—\ i = C\dfrac{dv}{dt}$	$—\!\!\Omega\!\!—\ v = L\dfrac{di}{dt}$

We used only the left column in discussing *R-C* networks, and derived all their properties on the basis of those laws. Here, in the *R-L* case, we use only the right column, which is dual to the left column. We need only *consistently* replace quantities by their duals, as in Table 7.14–B,

Table 7.14–B

R-C Case		R-L Case
v	$\longrightarrow$	i
R	$\longrightarrow$	G
i	$\longrightarrow$	v
C	$\longrightarrow$	L

throughout the analysis and the results of the discussion of the *R-C* case. Evidently this means we also replace *impedance* by *admittance*, *series* by *parallel* (or *shunt*), and vice versa. Without further ado, then, we can write the results of a similar treatment of the *R-L* case. The following statements are dual to statements made earlier in this chapter.

In the *R-L* case, all the zeros and all the poles of $Y(p)$ and of $Z(p)$ occur on the negative real axis.   (7.14–1)

A driving-point *R-L* immittance function is uniquely determined by specifying the locations of its (imaginary-frequency) zeros and poles *and* one additional piece of information.   (7.14–2)

The slope of the driving-point admittance function of an *R-L* network, plotted against real values of p, is always negative, except possibly at infinity.   (7.14–3)

The slope of the driving-point impedance function of an *R-L* network, plotted against real values of p, is always positive, except possibly at infinity.   (7.14–4)

The zeros and poles of *R-L* network driving-point immittance functions are all on the negative-real axis, are simple, and are interlaced in the pattern $\cdots$ zero-pole-zero-pole $\cdots$.   (7.14–5)

The highest critical frequency of an *R-L* driving-point admittance function is a zero, which may occur at infinity; if it does not, $Y(\infty)$ is a positive, finite (real) number.   (7.14–6)

The lowest critical frequency of an *R-L* driving-point admittance function is a pole, which may occur at the origin; if it does not, $Y(0)$ is a positive, nonzero (real) number.   (7.14–7)

The statements, formulas, and curves of § 7.04, with *impedance* and *admittance* everywhere interchanged, apply to *R-L* networks.   (7.14–8)

The following properties are necessary and sufficient for a function $Z(p)$ to be realizable as the driving-point impedance function of an *R-L* network.

　1. $Z(p)$ has only simple zeros and poles, all of which are on the negative real axis, where zeros and poles alternate;

2. the slope of $Z(\sigma)$ plotted against σ is positive (the multiplier H in the usual factored form is positive);

3. the lowest critical point (zero or pole) of $Z(p)$ is a zero, which may be at the origin;

4. the highest critical point is a pole, which may be at infinity.   (7.14–9)

Corresponding requirements are imposed on *R-L* admittance functions.

There are four canonic *R-L* forms, obtained exactly as were the *R-C* forms, except for the changes imposed by duality. Thus the first canonic form is obtained by making the partial-fraction expansion of the given admittance function, which yields Fig. 7.14–A, exactly the dual of the

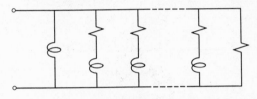

Fig. 7.14–A

network in Fig. 7.05–C. Expansion, not of the *R-L* impedance function, but rather of $Z(p)/p$ (for we must follow the procedure of § 7.08), leads to the network of Fig. 7.14–B. If we make a continued-fraction expansion,

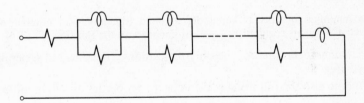

Fig. 7.14–B

concentrating on removal of poles of impedance at infinity and of conductance representing infinite-frequency behavior, we get the network of Fig. 7.14–C. If we make a continued-fraction expansion that concentrates on removal of resistance representing d-c behavior and of poles of admittance at the origin, we get the network of Fig. 7.14–D. These are the four canonic *L-C* forms, with the substitution of resistors for capacitors, as we should expect.

The numerical work in any specific design will be exactly as it was in the *R-C* case.   The procedures given in (7.05–9), (7.08–8), (7.10–15), and (7.11–16) can be followed exactly, except for the changes in wording

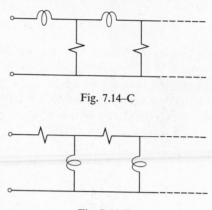

Fig. 7.14–C

Fig. 7.14–D

required by duality (chiefly the interchange of *impedance* and *admittance*). As in the *L-C* and *R-C* cases,

> the minimum number of elements required for realization of an *R-L* driving-point immittance function is one more than the number of internal critical frequencies. (7.14–10)

In addition,

> the minimum number of inductors required (the minimum number of reactive elements required) is equal to the order of the function. (7.14–11)

The canonic forms are not the only realizations; there will in general be others, too.

We note also the following real-frequency properties of *R-L* immittance functions.

1. the maximum value of the conductance and the minimum value of the reactance occur at zero frequency;
2. the minimum value of the conductance and the maximum value of the resistance occur at infinite frequency;
3. the conductance decreases steadily with frequency, the resistance increases steadily with frequency;
4. the susceptance is never positive, the reactance never negative;
5. the d-c susceptance is either zero or (negatively) infinite, the d-c reactance is zero;
6. the infinite-frequency susceptance is zero, the infinite-frequency reactance is either zero or (positively) infinite. (7.14–12)

7.15 Summary

In this chapter we have developed certain properties which networks containing resistors and only one kind of reactive element must have, in addition to the p-r property. The corresponding immittance functions cannot be described by as simple a statement as can the immittance functions of *L-C* networks. But

> if the zeros and poles of a rational function of p are *simple* and *real* (infinity is a permitted location), if they alternate in kind and none occur in the right half plane, if the smallest and largest (in magnitude) are of opposite kind (one a zero, one a pole), and if the multiplier is real and positive,   (7.15-1)

then this function is realizable either as

(*a*) the driving-point impedance of an *R-C* network and the driving-point admittance of an *R-L* network, or as

(*b*) the driving-point admittance of an *R-C* network and the driving-point impedance of an *R-L* network.

No further test is necessary, if a function has the properties listed in (7.15-1), for then the partial-fraction expansion of the function (or of the function divided by p) will be of the correct form, with positive coefficients, and networks with physical (positive) elements will result.

Notice again that the four canonic realization procedures in each of the three cases (*L-C*, *R-C*, *R-L*) can be regarded as techniques of removing a pole or a constant, followed by removal of a pole or a constant from the reciprocal of the reduced function, with repetitions until the process terminates. Physically, this is removal of a small network, followed by removal of a small network in shunt, etc., until the realization, as a ladder network, is complete. The processes always produce physical (positive-element) ladder networks if the immittance function from which we start is not only p-r but also in the appropriate (*L-C*, *R-C*, or *R-L*) class. Unless the immittance function is of very low order, we have a number of options as to the amount of impedance (admittance) removed at each step, so that the four canonic forms are not the only ladder-network realizations obtainable by this process. Generally there are still other realizations, not in ladder form, but the aims of this book are attained in the ladder-network realizations. The canonic forms are more than sufficient to demonstrate the realizability of such functions; they are usually adequate in practice; and the technique used is basic not only to the two-kinds-of-element cases but also in the general *R-L-C* case.

Networks with driving-point immittance functions *inverse* to given *L-C* driving-point immittance functions are found in the same (*L-C*) class, including dual and reciprocal networks. But this is not true of *R-C* networks.   Networks inverse in driving-point impedance (admittance) to any given *R-C* network cannot be *R-C* networks, but must be *R-L* networks (or possibly *R-L-C* networks, which we have not yet investigated). Networks inverse in driving-point admittance (impedance) to any given *R-L* network cannot be *R-L* networks, but must be *R-C* networks (or possibly *R-L-C* networks).   These statements follow immediately from the results of this chapter, and the design of a number of networks inverse to given *R-C* or *R-L* networks requires merely the application of appropriate procedures from those given above; a given *R-C* driving-point impedance function, for example, can be considered (on division by the constant $R_0{}^2$) to be an *R-L* driving-point admittance function, from which inverse networks can be designed.   Networks *equivalent* in driving-point immittance to given *L-C* networks are again *L-C* networks.   Networks so equivalent to a given *R-C* network cannot be *R-L* networks, but can be found in the various other realizations of the given *R-C* immittance function (and possibly in *R-L-C* networks).   Similarly, networks equivalent to given *R-L* networks are also *R-L* (possibly *R-L-C*) networks.

In Fig. 5.03–A the region of overlap includes all functions that are both rational and p-r.   We had shown (Chapter 6) that all odd functions in this region are realizable, and have now shown also that all functions in the category (7.15–1), which represents another portion of the overlap, are realizable.   Diagrammatically, Fig. 7.15–A shows how far we have

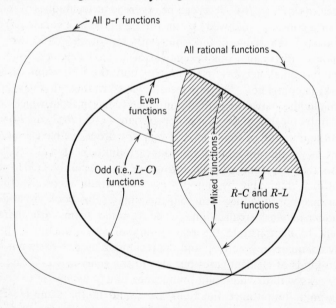

Fig. 7.15–A

progressed in proving that all functions that are both rational and p-r are realizable. Of the functions in the overlap, the purely odd functions, the purely even functions (which must be constants, realizable by resistors), and the functions realizable by *R-C* or *R-L* networks represent a large and useful part, but not all. There remain some mixed (neither odd nor even) functions, the functions in the shaded region, of whose realizability we have as yet no proof. These require all three kinds of elements and, we shall see, can all be realized as driving-point immittances of *R-L-C* networks.

From a somewhat different point of view, we conclude from our results in the *L-C*, *R-C*, and *R-L* cases that if a network immittance function is to have any zeros or poles that are not on one or the other of the axes of the *p* plane, the network must contain *all three* kinds of elements. But it does not follow that a network containing all three kinds of elements must have all or even *any* of its zeros and poles off the axes. In fact, *R-L-C* networks need not have any poles or zeros at all (which means that such networks are equivalent to simple resistors—§ 10.08)!

We are not yet ready to investigate the general (*R-L-C*) case, however. There are additional important properties of driving-point immittance and of p-r functions which we have not yet discussed. Some of these are important in *R-L-C* realizations, so that our next task is to pick up the threads of Chapter 5 again, and describe further properties of driving-point immittance functions. We shall find our knowledge of *L-C*, *R-C*, and *R-L* networks useful here.

7.16 References

BA 3, BO 3, CA 1, CA 2, FR 2, GU 2.

PROBLEMS

7-1. Show that the number of elements used in the realization of Fig. 7.06–A is equal to the number of critical frequencies, plus one. As the zero largest in magnitude approaches infinity, show that the isolated resistor disappears. As the zero smallest in magnitude approaches the origin, what element vanishes?

7-2. Prove (7.06–2), (7.06–1), and then verify the sentence after (7.06–2). Now show that these three statements apply also to the second, third, and fourth canonic *R-C* realization methods, and that all four canonic methods use the same number of capacitors and the same number of resistors in any given application.

Make and demonstrate corresponding statements for *R-L* networks.

7-3. Prove that the expansion (7.10–10) terminates and contains the number of terms stated.

7-4. Show that the function (7.10–11) is p-r and realizable without the use of inductors.

7-5. Prove that the third canonic R-C form uses only the minimum number of elements, and that the number of capacitors used is the same in *all* the canonic forms. Repeat for the resistors.

7-6. Show that when resistance is removed from a (p-r) driving-point R-C impedance function $Z(p)$, in amount $Z(\infty)$, the remainder is still p-r and R-C realizable.

7-7. Show that the expansion (7.11–10) terminates, with the number of terms there stated.

7-8. Show independently of the actual realizations that the function (7.11–11) is p-r and R-C realizable.

7-9. A function $F(p)$ meets the requirements of (7.15–1).

(*a*) Prove that $F(p)$ is p-r, following the standard test, (5.13–5).

(*b*) Prove that $F(p)$ is p-r by the following procedure. Consider an arbitrary right-half-plane value of p, draw the complex numbers (vectors) that represent each factor of numerator and denominator, mark the angle of each, and thus show that the angle condition (4.03–13) is satisfied.

(*c*) Either of the above shows that the R-C or R-L conditions, (7.15–1), are sufficient for positive reality. Are they also necessary therefor?

7-10. Show that if any pole of an R-C impedance function is removed, the remaining impedance function is still p-r and R-C realizable. What do the frequency patterns of the original impedance and of the reduced impedance have in common? How do they differ?

Show that resistance can be removed similarly up to a certain amount. What is this limitation?

Can similar statements be made about an R-C admittance function? Formulate the corresponding statements for R-L immittance functions.

— 7-11. Fill in Table 1 and show that the entries are the same for all four canonic R-C forms. The immittance function in question is of order n, and the entries to be made are the numbers of elements used in the realizations.

Table 1

Case (Table 7.04–A)	Number of Capacitors	Number of Resistors
A		
B		
C		
D		

7-12. Draw up à table similar to Table 1, but for R-L networks.

7-13. Obtain the fourth canonic R-C realization procedure from the third by dividing numerator and denominator of the immittance function by the highest power of p present in both, taking p^{-1} as a new frequency variable, and making a continued-fraction expansion that concentrates on the behavior at infinity.

7-14. Construct a chart tabulating the following properties of the simpler *R-C* canonic networks, for all *R-C* impedance functions of orders one, two, three, four, five, six. Give the frequency patterns, the schematics of the four canonic realizations and of all other realizations that can be obtained by using combinations of the canonic procedures; list the number of such procedures possible, the number of capacitors used, the number of resistors used. Consider, in each case, all possibilities among the four cases (Table 7.04–A).

7-15. Repeat Prob. 7-14 for *R-C* admittance functions. Construct similar charts for *R-L* immittance functions.

7-16. The two terminals of a network that contains five capacitors, four resistors, and no inductors are available for measurement, but the only additional information available as to the network configuration is that the same impedance could not be obtained with a smaller number of elements. What impedance would be measured at zero frequency? At very high frequency? Explain your reasoning and give the frequency pattern and sketch (as closely as can be done) the resistance-frequency and reactance-frequency curves. Give the schematic realizations of the impedance in the four canonic forms. *Must* the network be in one of these forms? Explain your answer.

7-17. An *R-C* impedance function of order four does not have critical frequencies at either infinity or the origin. Give the schematic diagrams of all four canonic realizations and show what happens in each one as (*a*) the lowest critical frequency approaches zero, (*b*) the highest becomes infinite, (*c*) both changes occur. Verify your results by evaluating in literal terms the element values that change most radically and finding their limits. In all four cases compare the number of elements with the number of internal critical frequencies, and the number of capacitors with the order of the impedance function. Repeat the problem for an *R-L* impedance function.

7-18. Show that the second *R-C* canonic form can be obtained from the first by (*a*) taking the dual function and (*b*) replacing p therein by p^{-1}. Contrast this with the relation between the first and second canonic forms in the *L-C* case; does this procedure give the correct result there? Does any simpler procedure?

7-19. Draw the schematic of a ladder-form one-terminal pair in which a capacitor appears across the input terminals as one rung, then a resistor forms a leg, then a capacitor another rung, etc., until you have seven elements in all. Now give the frequency pattern of the input impedance and sketch, as closely as can be done, the driving-point reactance and resistance against frequency. Give the schematic diagrams of the four canonic realizations of this impedance and of other realizations that use no more than the minimum number of elements necessary.

7-20. Given that an impedance function $Z(p)$ is p-r, has a pole at the origin, a zero at infinity, is of order six, and has zeros and poles only on the real axis of the p plane, where they interlace, what is the minimum number of elements necessary for its realization? How many realizations that use only this number of elements can you find? Draw the schematic diagrams of all of them. What additional information do you need in order to find actual element values?

7-21. Criticize carefully the following statement; in particular draw up a modified statement that is correct in all details.

"If in any reactance (odd, p-r) function, (*a*) the factor p that creates the zero or pole at the origin is either removed or squared, and (*b*) p^2 is then everywhere replaced by p, the resulting function is realizable as an *R-C* or *R-L* immittance."

Illustrate the principle involved by converting the immittance functions of § 6.14 to *R-C* functions where possible and obtaining the canonic realizations. Use the arithmetical work given in § 6.14 as far as possible.

7-22. In realizing the network of Example 1, § 7.13, the maximum capacitance that can be obtained in a particular application is $0.02\,\mu\mathrm{f}$. What impedance level (scale) is made necessary by this?

7-23. Find more realizations of the impedance functions of Examples 1 and 2, § 7.13.

7-24. Upon what principles would a canonic realization in the form shown be based? Which elements might disappear? Will more than the minimum

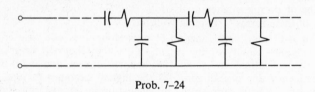

Prob. 7–24

number of elements be used? Realize the functions of Examples 1 and 2, § 7.13, in this form.

7-25. Give the four canonic realizations of a driving-point impedance that has simple poles at -1 and at -3, has simple zeros at -2 and at -4, and has the value $+16\,\Omega$ at zero frequency.

7-26. Give the four canonic realizations of the following driving-point impedance function, and two additional realizations that still use only the minimum number of elements and have each a capacitor directly across the input terminals.

$$Z(p) = K\frac{(p + a)(p + c)}{p(p + b)(p + d)}, \qquad a, b, c, d, K \text{ all real and positive, and} \\ a < b < c < d.$$

7-27. The poles and zeros (all simple) of an impedance function are

Poles	*Zeros*
origin	$-\tan 18°$
$-\tan 36°$	$-\tan 54°$
$-\tan 72°$	infinity

Obtain realizations of this function. (The peculiar numerical values stem from a certain approximation procedure, cf. Prob. 14-192; what it accomplishes can be seen by carefully plotting the magnitude of the impedance against frequency and comparing it with $\omega^{-1/2}$.)

7-28. Find network realizations of the following admittance function, in such form that a capacitor appears across the driving-point terminals.

$$Y(p) = \frac{p^2 + 9p + 8}{18p + 32}.$$

The normalization factors are 10 cps and 1000 Ω.

7-29. Find network realizations of

$$Z(p) = \frac{p^2 + 5p + 5}{p^2 + 2.5p},$$

the normalization factors being 1000 cps and 1000 Ω.

7-30. Construct an *R-C* driving-point impedance function with zeros at −1, −3, and poles at the origin, −2, −4, that behaves as $2/p$ at infinity. Find the element values of the four canonic realizations, taking 10 kcps and 600 Ω as scale factors. Which realization would be the easiest to construct?

7-31. An *R-C* impedance function is to have a pole at the origin, a zero at infinity, and six internal critical frequencies equally spaced in the region $-3 > \sigma > -6$ (on a scale on which unit value corresponds to an actual frequency of 6 cps), and a reactance of $-600\,\Omega$ at 10 cps. Find realizations.

7-32. Draw the four canonic realizations of all *R-C* impedance and admittance functions of orders one, two, three, four. Find the relations between the element values in all equivalent realizations.

7-33. Repeat Prob. 7-32 for *R-L* immittance functions.

7-34. Show that the function

$$F(p) = \frac{(p + 1)(p + 3)(p + 5)}{p(p + 2)(p + 4)}$$

is p-r. Find realizations of it in each of the following ways, utilizing all the canonic forms in each case. Describe the relations between the four sets of networks by pointing out which are equivalent, which are inverse, and which are dual. All immittances are normalized.

(*a*) $Z_1(p) = F(p)$ (*c*) $Z_3(p) = 1/F(p)$
(*b*) $Y_2(p) = 1/F(p)$ (*d*) $Y_4(p) = F(p)$

7-35. Tabulate the canonic *R-L* networks for immittance functions of orders one, two, three. In each case some electromagnetic coupling is now introduced between two inductors. Show that the modified networks have equivalents in *R-L* form without mutual inductance, and find the formulas relating the element values of the realizations with and without mutual inductance.

7-36. A driving-point impedance function has a multiple zero. Which of the three kinds of elements (*R*, *L*, *C*) are necessarily in it? Explain. Must such a network in general have multiple zeros or poles?

7-37. Show that for both *R-C* and *R-L* driving-point impedance functions the odd part has zeros and poles that are all simple and alternate on the real axis of the p plane. How do the zeros and poles of the even part lie? Are they all simple? [*Suggestion:* Sketch $Z(p)$ and $Z(-p)$ for real p.] (Cf. Prob. 8-127.)

7-38. Calculate and plot carefully the resistance, reactance, magnitude, and angle of the function of Example 1, § 7.13, versus frequency. What characteristic of interest do you find? (This is due to the approximation procedure used in forming the function, a matter for later discussion.)

7-39. For each of the networks shown give the frequency pattern at the input, and the four canonic realizations, on the assumption that no particular relations exist among the element values. Does the given form appear among the canonic forms? Explain. What is the minimum number of elements

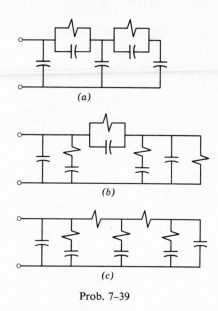

(a)

(b)

(c)

Prob. 7–39

required to realize the given network's driving-point impedance? Explain the discrepancy with the number of elements in the given network. In what way(s) will your answers be changed if special relations among element values happen to exist? Describe these relations and what effect they have.

7-40. Repeat Prob. 7-39 in dual form.

7-41. Starting from the frequency pattern at the input for each of the networks in Prob. 7-39, show by purely graphical means (a succession of impedance and admittance curves plotted against $p = \sigma + j0$) how these realizations, which do not use the minimum number of elements, may be obtained. Upon what principle, not used in canonic realization, does this method of realization depend? In addition to the numerical data in the driving-point immittance function, what data are required actually to carry out a numerical design leading to the forms given in the figure for Prob. 7-39? To what extent is it arbitrary? (Cf. Prob. 6-58.)

7-42. Realize the impedance function

$$Z(p) = \frac{10(p + 4)(p + 6)}{p(p + 5)(p + 7)}$$

in the form shown.   Find also the canonic realizations and compare them with your first result.

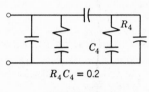

$$R_4 C_4 = 0.2$$

Prob. 7–42

7-43. Rephrase Prob. 6-60 in *R-C* network terms and then solve it.   (The frequency pattern may be taken as that of the *R-C* admittance on the proper axis.)

7-44. An *R-C* impedance function has a zero at infinity, a pole at the origin, and four internal critical frequencies (at normalized values -2, -4, -6, -8). One third of the pole at infinity in the admittance is first removed.   Show graphically (by curves against σ) how the frequency pattern is altered by this step. What is the minimum number of elements required for the realization of the remaining immittance?   Of the original immittance?   Complete the realization in each of the canonic forms.   Realize the original function in each of the canonic forms.   Compare the element values among the realizations you now have.

7-45. As an example of the realization of an *R-C* impedance in a form not among the canonic ones or simple combinations thereof, consider the "parallel-T" or "twin-T" network shown.   Show that, barring a special relation among the

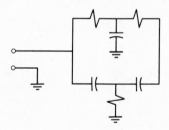

Prob. 7–45

values of the elements, it uses only the minimum number of elements required. Give the frequency pattern and the canonic realizations.

If the special relation implied above does hold, how are the answers to the above questions changed?

7-46. In deriving (7.03–3) from (7.03–2) it was assumed that $\dfrac{\partial}{\partial\omega}\left(\dfrac{V_0}{\sigma^2+\omega^2}\right)$ was finite (for $\omega=0$; infinity is included). If a network contains both resistance and capacitance, prove that this expression is not infinite, as required. Prove also that V_0 does not vanish (hence is real and positive).

7-47. Investigate the slopes of driving-point immittance functions of L-C networks, plotted against real values of p. Are they necessarily positive, negative, or may they vary from one to the other as σ varies? Give examples to illustrate your conclusions. Compare the behavior of L-C networks in this respect with that of R-C and that of R-L networks.

7-48. In the first and second canonic R-C forms derive expressions for the element values in terms of the derivatives of $Z(p)$ or of $Y(p)$ at the poles. These should be compared with (6.05–13) et seq.

7-49. Show that the residues (7.05–4) are positive, by following the method there suggested. Prove that a function that obeys (7.05–8) is p-r, and show that the function (7.05–10) is in the class (7.05–8).

7-50. Show that the residues in (7.08–4) are positive, (a) by considering the signs of the factors in the rational expressions for the K's, (b) by determining the sign of $d(pZ)/dp$.

7-51. For the network shown, draw the schematic diagrams, with element values, of (a) the dual network, (b) a network reciprocal as to driving-point impedance, according to $Z_1 Z_2 = R_0{}^2$, (c) an equivalent (as to driving-point

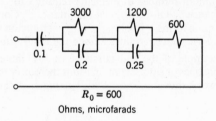

$R_0 = 600$

Ohms, microfarads

Prob. 7–51

impedance). In each case how many different answers can you give? Between which of the networks obtained does the relation $L/C = R_0{}^2$ obtain, L being an inductor element value of one network and C a capacitor value of another? For each of the networks you have, give an equivalent, single-element network that represents (1) the high-frequency behavior, (2) the low-frequency behavior, this element to be obtained by inspection.

7-52. Show that the numerator and denominator of R-C driving-point immittance functions are Hurwitz polynomials (except for the possibility of a zero at the origin). Show that the polynomial formed by adding numerator and denominator is again a Hurwitz polynomial, all of whose zeros are simple and lie on the negative real axis. (Suggestion: Plot the polynomials versus σ.)

Show, conversely, that a given Hurwitz polynomial, all of whose zeros are simple and lie on the negative real axis (the origin excluded), can be split into two polynomials such that their ratio is an R-C driving-point immittance function. What are the requirements on the zeros of these two polynomials with respect to those of the given Hurwitz polynomial?

Rephrase the statements above to apply to *R-L* networks.

7-53. Show that the following function is p-r.

$$Z(p) = \frac{48p^5 + 438p^4 + 1186p^3 + 807p^2 + 344p + 68}{36p^5 + 366p^4 + 990p^3 + 565p^2 + 164p + 84}.$$

Make its partial-fraction expansion and test the individual terms for positive reality. Realize (as impedance) each term except those which are not p-r, and the constant term. Combine the constant term and the non-p-r terms, show that the sum is p-r, and realize (as impedance). Combine your results to give a realization of the whole function as an impedance.

7-54. Show that the positive reality of functions in the class (7.15–1) may quickly be established by drawing lines from *p* (an arbitrary right-half-plane point) to the zeros and poles, and examining angles on the figure so created. Show that for *R-C* and *R-L* immittance functions the polar-coordinate expression for the definition of p-r functions, (4.03–13), holds in the left half plane as well as the right half plane. (It is helpful to take the negative real axis as a branch cut, in order to precisely define the angles involved.) Does the rectangular-coordinate expression also hold in the left half plane for these functions? (Contributed by B. J. Dasher.)

7-55. The figure shows the behavior of two functions for real values of *p*. Consider each in turn and state whether the function is definitely realizable as an

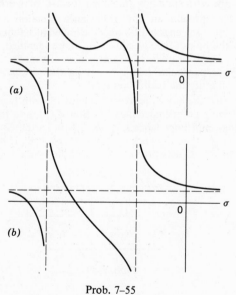

Prob. 7–55

R-C or *R-L* immittance, is definitely not so realizable, or it is not possible to say without further information. Explain your answers carefully.

7-56. An impedance function, normalized on the bases of 12 kcps and 750 Ω, is

$$Z(p) = \frac{0.3(p + 0.8)(p + 2)(p + 3.5)}{(p + 1)(p + 3)}.$$

Find as many realizations as you can that use no more than three inductors and three resistors. Can you find any that use fewer elements? How do your realizations compare among themselves as to element sizes?

7-57. Show that the driving-point impedance of the accompanying network takes the form of an R-C impedance for certain values of R. What are these values, and how does the critical-frequency pattern of the impedance change

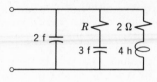

Prob. 7–57

as R varies? Find an equivalent R-C network both for the borderline case and for one removed from this. In the light of this problem, does it seem that a given impedance function that satisfies (7.15–1) must be realized in R-C or R-L form? What is the corresponding statement for L-C networks?

7-58. Let $Z_1(p)$ represent an R-C impedance function and $Z_2(p)$ an R-L impedance function. In general, how may the impedance function $Z_3 = Z_1 + Z_2$ be realized? If the poles of $Z_1(p)$ and of $Z_2(p)$ are identical, in what way may the realization of Z_3 be simplified? (*Suggestion:* Examine the partial-fraction expansions.) What particular relations among the residues of Z_1 and of Z_2 will particularly simplify the realization of Z_3?

7-59. Suppose that the box Z_1 represents a network with two kinds of elements only, with the driving-point impedance function $Z_1(p)$, and that the box Z_2 has an inverse driving-point impedance function $Z_2(p)$, so that $Z_1 Z_2 = R_0^2$. Show that if $R_1 = R_2 = R_0$, then $Z(p)$ is a constant, R_0, independent of p. Show that this network is an R-L-C network, and one with no zeros or poles.

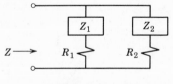

Prob. 7–59

Let Z_1 be a 3-f capacitor, take $R_0 = 1\,\Omega$ and $R_2 = R_0$. Plot the loci of the zeros and poles of $Z(p)$ as R_1 varies. What happens to these zeros and poles as R_1 approaches R_0?

As an alternative to the statement made above that $Z(p)$ has no zeros or poles under certain conditions, what statement can you make consistent therewith and also with the statement that $Z(p)$ is a function whose order is equal to the number of reactive elements in the network?

7-60. The following functions, though not rational, are p-r. By expanding them according to the general principles of the third and fourth *R-C* and *R-L* canonic forms, find infinite-network realizations of them, as both kinds of immittance.

$$(a) \ +\sqrt{\frac{p+1}{p}} \qquad (b) \ \frac{\sqrt[+]{p+2}}{p} \qquad (c) \ \sqrt[+]{p(p+1)} \qquad (d) \ \sqrt[+]{p+2}$$

7-61. Choose one of the realizations made in Prob. 7-60. Let $Z_n(p)$ represent the driving-point impedance of the network truncated so that it contains only n elements. Compute and plot in the p plane the zeros and poles of $Z_n(p)$ for $n = 1, 2, 3, 4, 5$. Discuss the trend toward a limit of their positions and compare with the singularities of the driving-point impedance when n becomes infinite. (Cf. Prob. 6-70.)

8.

Properties of
Driving-Point
Immittance Functions—II

· · · a bundle of relations, a knot of roots · · · .
—Emerson

In our search for synthesis methods for the one-terminal pair we have made a good deal of progress—really more than has been pointed out. Positive reality is necessary if a function is to be realized as a network driving-point immittance function. Positive reality is also sufficient for those functions which have the restricted properties characteristic of networks which contain but one or two kinds of elements. Such networks we can now synthesize in a variety of forms. But there is still that large group of functions that are p-r and not realizable by L-C, R-C, or R-L networks. We have yet to show that these remaining p-r functions are realizable (by R-L-C networks), hence that positive reality is sufficient as well as necessary, and to develop actual synthesis methods. Before doing this we must examine the nature of p-r and driving-point immittance functions more closely. They have additional properties worth studying —and these properties will assist us in treating the general synthesis problem (for which we shall find some of the techniques of Chapters 6 and 7 useful, too).

8.01 The concept of minimum reactance and minimum susceptance

In the synthesis of L-C networks it was convenient to "remove" a certain amount of the reactance in the form of an L-C network connected in series with the remainder (which was of reduced order). This appeared as the first box in Fig. 6.13–C, and could contain one, two, three, or any number of elements up to the order of the immittance function. In R-C synthesis the same could be done to a certain extent, for the "series" capacitors of the first and fourth canonic forms were effectively obtained by this process—and the same is true in the third R-L form. Since a reduction in the order of the immittance function is made by this process of reactance removal, it represents progress in the realization, reduction to a simpler immittance function (and presumably to a simpler realization problem). It is natural then to attempt to apply the same technique in the general case, even though the function in hand does not have L-C, R-C, or R-L properties (but is p-r), to see if it will assist us in the general synthesis problem.

Suppose the function $Z(p)$ is p-r (but not in any particular subclass of p-r functions) and is intended to represent a driving-point impedance function. Assume that some network N exists and has this driving-point impedance function. The process of reduction by removal of reactance amounts, in physical terms, to extracting from the box N an L-C one-terminal pair of driving-point impedance Z_1 (Fig. 8.01–A). If this can

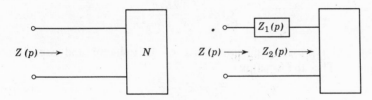

$$Z(p) \longrightarrow N$$

$$Z(p) \longrightarrow Z_2(p) \longrightarrow$$ with $Z_1(p)$

Fig. 8.01–A

be done without making the remainder Z_2 non-positive-real, then the order of Z is reduced by the order of Z_1 (i.e., the order of Z_2 is less than the order of Z by the order of Z_1), and definite progress in the realization of Z has probably been made. We must determine carefully under what conditions this can be done. When it can be done, then $Z(p)$ is in some sense reducible; when it cannot be done, then $Z(p)$ is a *minimum-reactance* function (to be precisely defined later).

If the removal can be made, then Z_1 is a reactance function, and Z_2 is p-r and of reduced order. The poles of Z_1 are imaginary, simple, and have real and positive residues; any poles that Z_2 may have on the imaginary axis are also simple, with real positive residues. From the fact that

$$Z = Z_1 + Z_2 \tag{8.01–1}$$

it follows then that the poles of Z_1, the extracted poles, must be present originally in Z. (They cannot possibly be cancelled out by Z_2 because of the requirement of positive residues in both Z_1 and Z_2.) Hence if the reduction is to be possible, $Z(p)$ must have imaginary (real-frequency) poles. This is the important necessary condition—and it is also sufficient; i.e., all such poles can be removed without destroying the positive reality of Z_2. For if $Z(p)$ is p-r, and has a (conjugate) pair of real-frequency poles, say at $\pm j\omega_0$, then $(p^2 + \omega_0^2)$ is a factor of the denominator and [from the partial-fraction expansion of $Z(p)$]

$$Z(p) = \frac{K_1}{p - j\omega_0} + \frac{K_2}{p + j\omega_0} + Z_2(p) \qquad (8.01\text{-}2)$$

in which K_1 and K_2 are real and positive, and Z_2 represents the remainder of the expansion. By the same reasoning as used in deriving (5.14–17) from (5.14–16), $K_2 = K_1$ and so

$$Z(p) = \frac{2K_1 p}{p^2 + \omega_0^2} + Z_2(p). \qquad (8.01\text{-}3)$$

The function

$$Z_1(p) = \frac{2K_1 p}{p^2 + \omega_0^2} \qquad (8.01\text{-}4)$$

is p-r and represents the impedance of an inductor and capacitor in parallel. That the function

$$Z_2 = Z - Z_1 \qquad (8.01\text{-}5)$$

is p-r is easily shown by applying test (5.13–5); in particular $\mathbf{Re}\, Z_1(j\omega) = 0$ and so $\mathbf{Re}\, Z_2(j\omega) = \mathbf{Re}\, Z(j\omega) \geqq 0$. The function Z_2 is of order two less than the order of Z (for two poles have been removed). In this manner all the real-frequency poles of $Z(p)$ can be removed (including those at infinity and the origin, if present) and incorporated in Z_1. $Z_1(p)$ is then a reactance function, and the corresponding network may be realized in any of the forms discussed in Chapter 6. The remaining function, $Z_2(p)$, will be p-r and reduced in order by the number of (real-frequency) poles in $Z(p)$. This reduction can be performed if and only if $Z(p)$ possesses real-frequency poles to begin with.

The dual result, arrived at by exactly the same mathematical argument in terms of dual quantities, is that a given p-r admittance function $Y(p)$ can be reduced by the removal of its real-frequency poles in the form of a parallel-connected L-C network (Fig. 8.01–B). The admittance function Y_2 is then still p-r and is reduced in order, in comparison with $Y(p)$, by the number of real-frequency poles of $Y(p)$.

The process need not remove all of the real-frequency poles in either case, of course, but there is a definite upper limit to the number that can be removed: the number present in the original $Z(p)$ or $Y(p)$. When an immittance function has no real-frequency poles it cannot be reduced in this manner, i.e., no series- or shunt-connected reactance can be removed,

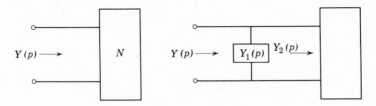

Fig. 8.01–B

for the remainder will not be p-r. On the basis of this demonstration we can now define the term *minimum reactance* precisely, as well as its dual.

A *minimum-reactance* driving-point immittance function is a driving-point impedance function with no poles on the imaginary axis, or a driving-point admittance function with no zeros on the imaginary axis. (8.01–6)

A *minimum-susceptance* driving-point immittance function is a driving-point admittance function with no poles on the imaginary axis, or a driving-point impedance function with no zeros on the imaginary axis. (8.01–7)

When such imaginary poles are present, a reactive network can be removed, at least without destroying the p-r character of the (reduced) remaining immittance function. This process, in one or the other form, or in a combination of alternate applications in the two forms, is in fact exactly the process used in Chapter 6 to demonstrate the realizability of reactance functions as *L-C* networks, and to obtain the various forms discussed there. *Minimum* functions in this sense cannot be reduced by the removal of reactance, but nonminimum functions can, and this will be a very useful technique in handling the general (*R-L-C*) synthesis problem. (But such removal of the imaginary poles is not required; synthesis, being nonunique, may well proceed in other ways.)

If a driving-point admittance function is to be minimum-reactance, it must have no real-frequency *zeros*, and if a driving-point impedance function is to be minimum-susceptance, it must have no zeros at real frequencies. It is perfectly possible for an immittance function to be minimum-reactance and not minimum-susceptance, minimum-susceptance and not minimum-reactance, both minimum-reactance and minimum-susceptance, or neither.

These two new terms describe properties of certain kinds of immittance (or of p-r) functions, properties which are both interesting and important. They permit immittance functions to be classified (mathematically)

Network Synthesis

according to their real-frequency zeros and poles, or (physically) according to the possibility of a reduction by removal of series or shunt reactance without destroying positive reality. When an immittance function is not minimum in both senses, it contains something which is easily removed, with an accompanying reduction in complexity and assistance in the realization process.

To illustrate this, consider the p-r impedance function

$$Z(p) = \frac{p^5 + 12p^4 + 35p^3 + 43p^2 + 42p + 30}{p^5 + 3p^4 + 5p^3 + 6p^2 + 6p} \quad \text{ohms.} \quad (8.01\text{--}8)$$

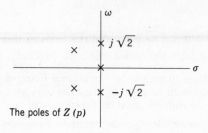

The poles of $Z(p)$

Fig. 8.01–C

There are imaginary poles at $p = 0$, $\pm j\sqrt{2}$ (as can be determined by the method of § 5.14), and the function is not minimum-reactance; see Fig. 8.01–C. A compressed partial-fraction expansion is

$$Z = \frac{5}{p} + \frac{4p}{p^2 + 2} + \frac{p^2 + 3p + 6}{p^2 + 3p + 3}. \quad (8.01\text{--}9)$$

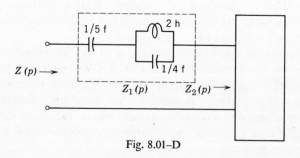

Fig. 8.01–D

In the above the conjugate imaginary-pole terms are combined and so are the terms corresponding to nonimaginary poles—this is an appropriate form, the coefficients in which can be found directly without determining the complete partial-fraction expansion.   Schematically, the reduction is shown in Fig. 8.01–D.

The function

$$Z_2 = \frac{p^2 + 3p + 6}{p^2 + 3p + 3}$$

(8.01–10)

is p-r and reduced in order by three.   It has no real-frequency poles (or zeros) and cannot be reduced further by removal of reactance or suscept-ance.   (Other methods, yet to come, are necessary.)   Nevertheless this step has accomplished a good part of the realization.

Had the original function been an admittance function, then we should have

$$Y(p) = \frac{p^5 + 12p^4 + 35p^3 + 43p^2 + 42p + 30}{p^5 + 3p^4 + 5p^3 + 6p^2 + 6p} \quad \text{mhos} \quad (8.01\text{–}11)$$

$$= \frac{5}{p} + \frac{4p}{p^2 + 2} + \frac{p^2 + 3p + 6}{p^2 + 3p + 3}$$

and the reduction shown in Fig. 8.01–E.

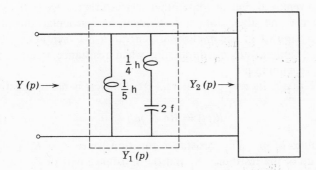

Fig. 8.01–E

8.02 The concept of minimum resistance and minimum conductance

We should expect the possibility of removing reactance (susceptance) up to a certain point to be accompanied by a corresponding property having to do with the other part, the resistance (conductance) of im-mittance functions.   In the synthesis of R-C (and R-L) networks the third and fourth canonic forms in fact utilize resistance or conductance removal. And it is generally possible to remove resistance (conductance), but the process is somewhat different from the removal of reactance (susceptance).

For one thing, the removal cannot reduce the order of an immittance function, for only a constant (no pole) is removed; for another, the extracted network is only a single resistor (or its equivalent). The process is useful, however, so we proceed to discuss it.

Suppose again that the function $Z(p)$ is p-r (but otherwise unrestricted) and is intended to represent a driving-point impedance function. The process of reduction by removal of resistance amounts, in physical terms, to extracting from the box N, which is assumed to be a network of driving-point impedance $Z(p)$, a resistor R_1 (Fig. 8.02–A). If this can be done

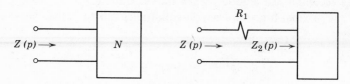

Fig. 8.02–A

without making the remainder Z_2 non-p-r, then Z_2 is presumably in some fashion "reduced" in comparison with Z. Not in *order*, for no poles have been removed, but in some other characteristic; we shall postpone to Chapter 9 the discussion of this point, in particular the utility of resistance removal in accomplishing general *R-L-C* synthesis. For the present we concentrate on discussing when resistance removal can be made, Z_2 remaining p-r.

Since Z is p-r, its real part, at real frequencies, is never negative. In symbols,

$$R(\omega) = \mathbf{Re}\, Z(j\omega) \geqq 0 \qquad (8.02\text{–}1)$$

for all values of ω. This resistance function, since $Z = R_1 + Z_2$, must be made up of the resistance R_1 and the resistance part of Z_2, i.e.

$$R(\omega) = R_1 + R_2(\omega) \qquad (8.02\text{–}2)$$

in which $R_2(\omega) = \mathbf{Re}\, Z_2(j\omega)$. We are interested only in situations where R_1 represents a physically realizable resistor and Z_2 is p-r. It is surely necessary then, for the removal to be made, that $R(\omega)$ never drop to zero, i.e., that

$$R(\omega) = \mathbf{Re}\, Z(j\omega) > 0 \qquad (8.02\text{–}3)$$

for all values of ω. If there were a frequency ω_0 such that $R(\omega_0) = 0$, then either R_1 would necessarily equal zero or R_2 would be negative, and neither case interests us. In (8.02–3) we have a necessary condition for resistance removal, and it is also sufficient. To show this, we test the remainder, $Z_2(p)$, for positive reality by (5.13–5). Since

$$Z_2(p) = Z(p) - R_1 \qquad (8.02\text{--}4)$$

and R_1 is a real positive constant, the fact that $Z(p)$ is p-r will enable $Z_2(p)$ to pass parts 1, 2(b), and 2(c) of the test by inspection. The crucial test is part 3, which requires that

$$\mathbf{Re}\, Z_2(j\omega) = R_2(\omega) = R(\omega) - R_1 \qquad (8.02\text{--}5)$$

not be negative for any value of ω. If we include extremely large values of ω (infinity), as we must, then 2(a) is also covered (essentially) by this test. Hence all that is required for $Z_2(p)$ to be p-r is that

$$R(\omega) \geqq R_1 \qquad (8.02\text{--}6)$$

or, in words, that the amount of resistance removed not exceed the minimum value of the resistance part of $Z(j\omega)$, the entire range of ω being considered in determining the minimum. If $R_{\min}$ denotes this minimum value of $R(\omega)$, then the maximum amount of resistance that can be removed is exactly $R_{\min}$. Removal of resistance up to and including $R_{\min}$ leaves Z_2 still p-r; any further removal of resistance makes Z_2 non-p-r.

In the terms of the test for positive reality, (5.13–5), the only thing it is necessary to consider is the resistance (at real frequencies), and so a plot of the resistance part of $Z(j\omega)$ provides a graphic statement of the limit

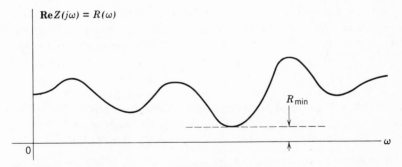

Fig. 8.02–B

on resistance removal. In Fig. 8.02–B, $R_{\min}$ again represents the minimum value of $\mathbf{Re}\, Z(j\omega)$. (Since this is an even function, it is not necessary to consider negative values of ω.) When a resistance R_1 is removed, a plot of the resistance remaining, i.e., of $R_2(\omega) = R(\omega) - R_1$, is obtained by merely dropping the curve a vertical distance R_1. If R_1 exceeds R_{min}, then clearly $R_2(\omega)$ goes negative and Z_2 is not p-r. But if $R_1 \leqq R_{min}$, then $R_2(\omega)$ does not go negative and Z_2 remains p-r. If the minimum value R_{min} is zero, then no resistance can be removed at all; if R_{min} is greater than zero, then any amount of resistance up to and including (but not exceeding) R_{min} can be removed without destroying the p-r character of Z_2.

The dual result, arrived at by exactly the same mathematical argument in terms of dual quantities, is that from a given p-r admittance function $Y(p)$, conductance, in the form of a parallel-connected resistor, can be removed (Fig. 8.02–C). The admittance function $Y_2(p)$ is still p-r pro-

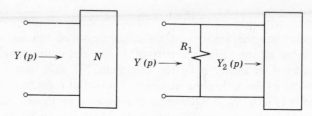

Fig. 8.02–C

vided only that the amount of conductance removed, $G_1 = 1/R_1$, does not exceed the minimum value of $\text{Re } Y(j\omega) = G(\omega)$. If Fig. 8.02–B is interpreted as a plot of the conductance function $G(\omega)$, then $G_1 \leqq G_{min}$ is required.

We thus see under what conditions removal of resistance (conductance) can be accomplished without making the remainder non-p-r. The test is to compute $\text{Re } Z(j\omega)$, or $\text{Re } Y(j\omega)$, and determine its minimum value R_{min} (or G_{min}) by plotting or by the calculus. (For complicated functions this may require considerable work, of course.) The minimum value may well be zero, and resistance (conductance) removal impossible; but if R_{min} (G_{min}) is not zero, then resistance (conductance) can be removed in an amount not exceeding R_{min} (G_{min}). On the basis of this discussion, we make two definitions corresponding to (8.01–6) and (8.01–7):

A *minimum-resistance* driving-point immittance function is a driving-point impedance function whose real part vanishes at some real frequency (which may be zero or infinity), or a driving-point admittance function of whose reciprocal this is true.   (8.02–7)

A *minimum-conductance* driving-point immittance function is a driving-point admittance function whose real part vanishes at some real frequency (which may be zero or infinity), or a driving-point impedance function of whose reciprocal this is true.   (8.02–8)

From such minimum functions resistance (conductance) cannot be removed. Functions nonminimum in this sense are susceptible to the removal process, and this is exactly how the resistors in the third and fourth R-C (and R-L) canonic forms are obtained. The technique will be found useful in the R-L-C case also.

In minimum-resistance and minimum-conductance immittance functions the order of the zero of the real part, at a frequency where the real part vanishes, is immaterial; the necessary property is merely that the real part vanish—and it may do so at other frequencies as well. (The meaning and utility of these zeros will be discussed later.)

It is perfectly possible for an immittance function to be minimum-resistance only, minimum-conductance only, both, or neither. One may be tempted to say that "if the resistance part of an impedance function vanishes at some real frequency ω_0, then the impedance function has an angle of $\pm 90°$, so also does its reciprocal (the admittance function), and hence 'minimum-resistance' implies 'minimum-conductance' also." This need not be true, however. For if

$$Z(j\omega) = R(\omega) + jX(\omega), \qquad (8.02\text{-}9)$$

then

$$Y(j\omega) = \frac{1}{Z(j\omega)} = \frac{1}{R + jX} = \frac{R - jX}{R^2 + X^2} = G + jB \qquad (8.02\text{-}10)$$

and

$$G = \frac{R}{R^2 + X^2}. \qquad (8.02\text{-}11)$$

If $R(\omega_0) = 0$, then $G(\omega_0) = 0$ *unless* $X(\omega_0)$ also vanishes. If $X(\omega_0) = 0$, then (8.02-11) is an indeterminate form; in fact, $Z(p)$ has a zero at $j\omega_0$, $Y(p)$ has a pole at that point, and $G(\omega_0)$ may have a nonzero value.

The networks in Fig. 8.02–D illustrate this. In (a) $Z(j\omega_0) = 0$, $R(\omega_0) = \mathbf{Re}\, Z(j\omega_0) = 0$, and therefore Z is minimum-resistance. But

$$G(\omega_0) = \mathbf{Re} \left[\frac{1}{Z(j\omega_0)} \right] = G_0 + \mathbf{Re}\, Y_a(j\omega_0) \qquad (8.02\text{-}12)$$

which is certainly not zero, so that the immittance function is *not* minimum-conductance. In (b) $Y(j\omega_0) = 0$, $G(\omega_0) = \mathbf{Re}\, Y(j\omega_0) = 0$, and therefore Y is minimum-conductance. But again

$$R(\omega_0) = \mathbf{Re} \left[\frac{1}{Y(j\omega_0)} \right] = R_0 + \mathbf{Re}\, Z_b(j\omega_0) \qquad (8.02\text{-}13)$$

which is not zero, so that the immittance function is *not* minimum-resistance. Hence the minimum-resistance and minimum-conductance properties are really independent, and an immittance function may have one and not the other. But one does imply the other unless the point where the appropriate real part vanishes is also a zero of the whole function; then (8.02–11) or its dual becomes an indeterminate form and the real part of the reciprocal function need not also vanish, though it may.

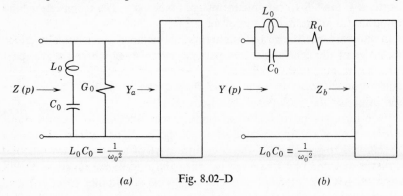

(a)　　　　　　　Fig. 8.02–D　　　　　　　(b)

These two new terms describe properties important in the general (R-L-C) synthesis problem. They are not immediately apparent on inspection of the pole-zero plot of an immittance function (as are the minimum-reactance and minimum-susceptance properties), but are related rather to the locations of the zeros of the real (better the *even*) part—of which more will be said later. When an immittance function is not both minimum-resistance and minimum-conductance, it contains something which is removable without destroying the p-r character of the remainder. There is no accompanying reduction in immittance function order, but the removal of resistance or conductance does assist in the realization (as already seen in the R-C and R-L cases, and to be seen in the R-L-C case).

To illustrate the process, consider the p-r impedance function

$$Z(p) = \frac{p^2 + 1.25p + 2.5}{p^2 + 2p + 1} \quad \text{ohms.} \tag{8.02–14}$$

This function is both minimum-reactance and minimum-susceptance, and is not capable of reduction by the removal of reactance or susceptance. To determine whether it is minimum-resistance, we first compute the resistance function. It is

$$R(\omega) = \text{Re } Z(j\omega) = \text{Ev } Z(j\omega)$$

$$= \left[\frac{(p^2 + 2.5)(p^2 + 1) - (1.25p)(2p)}{(p^2 + 1)^2 - (2p)^2}\right]_{p=j\omega}$$

$$= \left(\frac{p^4 + p^2 + 2.5}{p^4 - 2p^2 + 1}\right)_{p=j\omega} = \frac{\omega^4 - \omega^2 + 2.5}{\omega^4 + 2\omega^2 + 1}. \tag{8.02–15}$$

The resistance does not vanish at any ω (the zeros of the function are complex) so that $Z(p)$ is neither minimum-resistance nor minimum-conductance. There is evidently a minimum of resistance at some frequency above zero (for the denominator increases while the numerator decreases, in the vicinity of the origin). To determine $R_{\min}$ we first set $R'(\omega)$ equal to zero. It is convenient to replace ω^2 by x and differentiate with respect to x; this will give the locations of the maxima and minima (except that at the origin) equally well. We obtain

$$(x^2 + 2x + 1)(2x - 1) = (x^2 - x + 2.5)(2x + 2),$$
$$x^2 - x - 2 = 0,$$
$$x = 2, -1. \tag{8.02–16}$$

Hence $\omega = \sqrt{2}$ is the frequency of minimum resistance. (There is only one; the root $x = -1$ is extraneous.) There

$$R(\sqrt{2}) = R_{\min} = \frac{4 - 2 + 2.5}{4 + 4 + 1} = 0.5 \quad \text{ohm.} \tag{8.02–17}$$

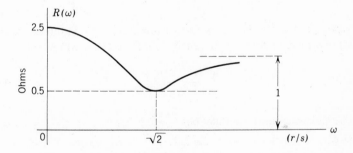

Fig. 8.02–E

The general character of $R(\omega)$ is shown in Fig. 8.02–E. We may remove as much as 0.5 ohm from $Z(p)$ without destroying its p-r character. The maximum resistance reduction possible is illustrated in Fig. 8.02–F, in which

$$Z_2 = Z - 0.5 = \frac{0.5p^2 + 0.25p + 2}{p^2 + 2p + 1} \quad \text{ohms.} \tag{8.02–18}$$

The same function, (8.02–14), is not minimum-conductance, and conductance could be removed in the manner of Fig. 8.02–C. (The frequency of minimum conductance is quite different, and $G_{\min}$ is not simply related to $R_{\min}$ above.)

Had the original function been an admittance function, then we should have had exactly the same arithmetic (Y replacing Z and G replacing R)

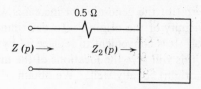

Fig. 8.02–F

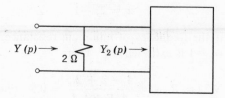

Fig. 8.02–G

in investigating its conductance function, and the maximum conductance reduction would be that illustrated in Fig. 8.02–G, in which

$$Y_2 = \frac{0.5p^2 + 0.25p + 2}{p^2 + 2p + 1} \quad \text{mhos.} \qquad (8.02\text{–}19)$$

8.03 Minimum immittance functions

The four definitions we have made are each concerned with one step in a realization process. Each of the four "removes" from a given immittance function a reactive network (in series or shunt) or a resistor (in series or shunt). The remaining immittance function is still p-r, and may have been reduced in order. It may be possible, after the removal of reactance or resistance or both, to remove susceptance or conductance, even if this could not be done with the original immittance function. By alternate application of the removal processes we may even be able to complete the realization in many R-L-C problems, though not necessarily in all. A stage may be reached at which the immittance function has no zeros or poles on the imaginary axis, and its real part vanishes at one or more points thereon. Such a function is minimum-reactance, minimum-susceptance, minimum-resistance, and minimum-conductance, and may well be called simply a *minimum* immittance function. Its realization requires additional techniques.

Before discussing these, however (this will be done in Chapter 9), it is appropriate to consider exactly what relations between resistance and reactance (conductance and susceptance) exist. Evidently the two are not tied too closely together, for if as in Fig. 8.01–A it is possible to remove an L-C network, then both $Z(p)$ and $Z_2(p)$ have the same (real-frequency) resistance function, though not the same reactance function. Again, in Fig. 8.02–A, $Z(p)$ and $Z_2(p)$ have the same reactance function, but not the same resistance function.   Yet in Chapter 3 (§ 3.23) we found certain mathematical relations between the real and imaginary parts of a function of a complex variable.   We must reconcile these two points of view, and in so doing we shall also find additional important properties of driving-point immittance functions.   The four "minimum" concepts will be important in the discussion.

8.04 The relation between resistance and reactance (conductance and susceptance)

The implications of the results of § 3.23 are considerable.   There we found certain integral relations, which indicate some interrelation between the real and imaginary parts of a function of a complex variable, on the imaginary axis: these parts are not in general independent.   Yet in the developments immediately above we have found, for example, that the resistance parts of two different impedance functions can be the same, though their reactance parts are not.   In order to explain the paradox we must consider the results of § 3.23 as applied to driving-point immittance functions in more detail.

It is possible to obtain much more general relations that indicate how under certain circumstances either the real or the imaginary part of a function of a complex variable determines the other part over most of the p plane (GU 3).   But we shall confine our attention to the imaginary axis, the axis of real frequencies, where real and imaginary parts are resistance and reactance (conductance and susceptance), of great engineering importance.   Suppose the function of p in question to be a driving-point impedance function, $Z(p)$.   In order to apply the results of § 3.23, $Z(p)$ must be analytic in the right half plane (as it is, for it is p-r), and have no poles on the imaginary axis (infinity included).   Such an impedance function is a minimum-reactance function—which we assume $Z(p)$ to be. The relations (3.23–11) then indicate a specific relation between R and X, the real and imaginary parts of $Z(j\omega)$.   This is a startling fact to the engineer not acquainted with the mathematics we are using—for ordinary circuit analysis, limited to "$j\omega$", reveals no such relation.   Yet it is not unreasonable, nor is it new.   In electrical engineering literature it goes back at least to 1926 (MU 1, KU 1, LE 1), although not of all of its engineering implications were then recognized; in physics it goes back at least to 1925 (MU 1); and in mathematics the relations are much older. The detailed network-theory applications that we shall discuss were first given by Bayard (BA 1) and Bode (BO 1, 2, 3), but they stem from much older mathematics.

Positive reality is neither necessary nor sufficient for the legitimate application of (3.23–11) to a given function of p. If a driving-point impedance function $Z(p)$, to take a specific example, is minimum-reactance, however, then these integral relations can be applied to it, as previously stated. Let us rewrite the relations in the notation of resistance and reactance. We have

$$Z(j\omega) = R(\omega) + jX(\omega) \tag{8.04-1}$$

and thus, from (3.23–11),

$$R(\omega_1) = -\frac{1}{\pi} \int_{-\infty}^{\infty} \frac{X(\omega)}{\omega - \omega_1}\, d\omega + R(\infty), \tag{8.04-2}$$

and

$$X(\omega_1) = \frac{1}{\pi} \int_{-\infty}^{\infty} \frac{R(\omega)}{\omega - \omega_1}\, d\omega. \tag{8.04-3}$$

In the second relation, $X(\infty)$ has been taken as zero; $X(\omega)$ is an odd function, is continuous, and therefore must have either a zero or a pole at infinity—and the latter possibility is ruled out by our assumption of minimum reactance. These are improper integrals and must always be interpreted as limits, in the manner discussed in § 3.23. The equations state that

with a knowledge of the reactance at all frequencies we can determine the resistance, within a constant, at the arbitrary frequency ω_1, and hence at all frequencies, (8.04–4)

and

with a knowledge of the resistance at all frequencies we can completely determine the reactance as a function of frequency. (8.04–5)

These in no way contradict the previous developments in this chapter. For while $Z(p)$ and $Z_2(p)$ in Fig. 8.01–A have the same resistance but different reactance, one of them, at least, is not minimum-reactance, so that (8.04–3) could not be applied to both. Similarly, in Fig. 8.02–A while $Z(p)$ and $Z_2(p)$ have the same reactance but different resistance, these resistance functions differ only by an additive constant, so (8.04–2) is not violated.

The relation between resistance and reactance is not something definite and precise—this we can say for purely physical reasons. We can alter the resistance of a one-terminal pair, without changing the reactance at all, by connecting an arbitrary resistor in series at the input, i.e., by adding an arbitrary real positive constant to the driving-point impedance function; we can also alter the resistance without changing the reactance by extracting a resistance, as R_1 in Fig. 8.02–A (provided R_1 does not exceed R_{min}), and the remaining impedance function will at least still be p-r. If an impedance function is minimum-resistance, the resistance cannot be reduced, but it can always be increased—and the reactance will be unaffected. Furthermore, we can alter the reactance of a one-terminal pair without changing the resistance at all, by connecting an arbitrary L-C network in series at the input; we can also alter the reactance without changing the resistance by extracting a reactance function (an L-C network, as Z_1 in Fig. 8.01–A), provided the original impedance function is not minimum-reactance, and the remaining impedance function will at least still be p-r. There are limitations on the amount of reactance that can be removed, but none on how much we can add—all without affecting the resistance. Hence in general there is no definite relation between the resistance and the reactance of a one-terminal pair.

But if the driving-point impedance function is minimum-reactance, then the integral relations may be applied, and by (8.04–3) the resistance function uniquely determines the reactance function. The reactance function also determines the resistance function, by (8.04–2), but only if $R(\infty)$ is known does it do so uniquely. Yet we can determine the minimum value of the function $[R(\omega_1) - R(\infty)]$ as ω_1 varies through all real values, and from this determine the minimum value that $R(\infty)$ must necessarily have if $R(\omega_1)$ is never to go negative. With this particular value of $R(\infty)$, $R(\omega_1)$ becomes the *minimum* resistance function associated with the given reactance—and this can be determined uniquely. Hence if the driving-point impedance function is both minimum-resistance and minimum-reactance, then the reactance and the resistance are definitely related: either determines the other. A given reactance (as a function of ω) determines uniquely the associated minimum resistance function, and a given resistance function determines uniquely the associated minimum reactance at all frequencies. To the reactance determined in this way from a given resistance function can be added the reactance of any L-C network, and to the resistance function determined in this way from a given reactance can be added any positive constant, without destroying positive reality.

If a given reactance function is not minimum, then of course (8.04–2) should not be used until the real-frequency poles have been removed, for the derivation of the integral relations required that there be no poles on the imaginary axis. If a given resistance function is not minimum, however, it can still be inserted in (8.04–3) and the corresponding minimum reactance will still be correctly determined. To show this we have only to demonstrate that

$$\int_{-\infty}^{\infty} \frac{R_0}{\omega - \omega_1} \, d\omega = 0, \qquad (8.04\text{–}6)$$

in which R_0 is a constant. Then any constant can be added to or subtracted from a given resistance function without altering the associated minimum reactance, which is exactly as it should be. In mathematics, it is only the *variation* of resistance with frequency that counts; whether the resistance goes negative is immaterial to this point—but we usually have no interest in subtracting such a constant for then the resistance function becomes negative at some frequencies. The proof of (8.04–6) follows. Bearing in mind the particular manner in which the integral must be evaluated (§ 3.23), and omitting the constant, we write

$$\int_{-\infty}^{\infty} \frac{d\omega}{\omega - \omega_1} = \lim_{\substack{r \to 0 \\ R \to \infty}} \left(\int_{-R}^{\omega_1 - r} \frac{d\omega}{\omega - \omega_1} + \int_{\omega_1 + r}^{R} \frac{d\omega}{\omega - \omega_1} \right)$$

$$= \lim \left(\ln \frac{-r}{-R - \omega_1} + \ln \frac{R - \omega_1}{r} \right)$$

$$= \lim \left(\ln \frac{r}{R + \omega_1} \times \frac{R - \omega_1}{r} \right)$$

$$= 0, \qquad (8.04\text{–}7)$$

from which (8.04–6) follows immediately, for R_0 is a constant. Hence a given resistance function need not be examined for minimum character but can be inserted immediately into (8.04–3) to determine the associated minimum reactance function. A given reactance, however, must be reduced to minimum before the associated resistance is calculated from (8.04–2). [But it can be shown that even if the reactance is not reduced to minimum, the resistance calculated from (8.04–2) is the same, provided the integration through the poles of $X(\omega)$ is performed in the same limiting fashion as through the pole at $\omega = \omega_1$.] The resistance obtained is known only within a constant, but the appropriate value of this constant, for the resistance function to be minimum, can be calculated; it is that which reduces the resistance function to zero at some frequency (frequencies) but does not allow it ever to go negative.

To recapitulate, we have formulas which uniquely relate the resistance and reactance of a driving-point impedance function, provided the function is minimum-reactance and minimum-resistance. From these formulas either function can be computed with a knowledge of the other alone. To emphasize the fact that ω_1 is arbitrary, we make the same change of variable as in (3.23–12); the formulas then are

$$R(\omega) = -\frac{1}{\pi} \int_{-\infty}^{\infty} \frac{X(\lambda)}{\lambda - \omega} \, d\lambda + R(\infty), \qquad (8.04\text{–}8)$$

$$X(\omega) = \frac{1}{\pi} \int_{-\infty}^{\infty} \frac{R(\lambda)}{\lambda - \omega} \, d\lambda. \qquad (8.04\text{–}9)$$

In (8.04–8) $R(\infty)$ can be considered an arbitrary constant; it must, however, have a certain minimum value if $R(\omega)$ is never to go negative, and that particular value gives the minimum $R(\omega)$ associated with $X(\omega)$. Any greater value is physically acceptable also, in keeping with the arbitrariness in $R(\omega)$ discussed above. Consistent with this, any constant can be added to $R(\omega)$ in (8.04–9) without affecting $X(\omega)$, by (8.04–6). The $X(\omega)$ determined by (8.04–9) is the minimum reactance associated with the given $R(\omega)$. If it is $X(\omega)$ that is given, it should be reduced to minimum before being used in (8.04–8).

All of the work above applies to *any* function $Z(p)$ that has no singularities in the right half plane or on the imaginary axis (including infinity). If the function is rational and p-r it represents a driving-point impedance function of a one-terminal pair (we shall prove this in Chapter 9), and hence these results apply to all one-terminal-pair driving-point impedance functions. By duality they apply also to all one-terminal-pair driving-point admittance functions. For admittance functions, the conductance function uniquely determines the associated minimum susceptance function, and the susceptance function uniquely determines the associated minimum conductance function. The explicit formulas are

$$G(\omega) = -\frac{1}{\pi} \int_{-\infty}^{\infty} \frac{B(\lambda)}{\lambda - \omega} \, d\lambda + G(\infty) \qquad (8.04\text{–}10)$$

and

$$B(\omega) = \frac{1}{\pi} \int_{-\infty}^{\infty} \frac{G(\lambda)}{\lambda - \omega} \, d\lambda. \qquad (8.04\text{–}11)$$

The constant $G(\infty)$ is to be determined after the integration, so that $G(\omega)$ vanishes at some point(s), but is never negative, if $G(\omega)$ is to be minimum-conductance.

To illustrate the operation of these relations, consider the driving-point impedance function of the network of Fig. 8.04–A, which is p-r and minimum-reactance. At real frequencies the impedance function is

$$Z(j\omega) = \frac{1}{G + jC\omega} = \frac{G - jC\omega}{G^2 + C^2\omega^2} \quad \text{ohms.} \qquad (8.04\text{–}12)$$

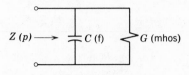

$$Z(p) \longrightarrow \quad \rightleftharpoons C \text{ (f)} \quad \gtrless G \text{ (mhos)}$$

Fig. 8.04–A

The resistance function is

$$R(\omega) = \frac{G}{G^2 + C^2\omega^2}. \qquad (8.04\text{–}13)$$

The reactance, as determined from $R(\omega)$ by (8.04–9), is then

$$
\begin{aligned}
X(\omega) &= \frac{1}{\pi} \int_{-\infty}^{\infty} \frac{G}{G^2 + C^2\lambda^2} \times \frac{1}{\lambda - \omega} \, d\lambda \\
&= \frac{G}{\pi C^2} \int_{-\infty}^{\infty} \frac{d\lambda}{(\lambda^2 + \gamma^2)(\lambda - \omega)}, \qquad \gamma = G/C.
\end{aligned}
\qquad (8.04\text{–}14)
$$

The integral may be evaluated by expansion in partial fractions (or by contour integration). We have

$$\frac{1}{(\lambda^2 + \gamma^2)(\lambda - \omega)} = \frac{K_0}{\lambda - \omega} + \frac{K_1}{\lambda - j\gamma} + \frac{\bar{K}_1}{\lambda + j\gamma}. \qquad (8.04\text{–}15)$$

We need not evaluate K_0, for the contribution of the first term to the integral is zero, by (8.04–6). The other constant is

$$K_1 = \frac{1}{(j\gamma + j\gamma)(j\gamma - \omega)} = \frac{1}{-2\gamma(\gamma + j\omega)} = \frac{\gamma - j\omega}{-2\gamma(\gamma^2 + \omega^2)}. \qquad (8.04\text{–}16)$$

The individual terms in (8.04–15) integrate readily as simple logarithms; but since they are complex, the interpretation of the difference of the values at the limits requires careful attention. This can be avoided by combining the conjugate terms to get

$$\frac{1}{(\lambda^2 + \gamma^2)(\lambda - \omega)} = \frac{K_0}{\lambda - \omega} + \frac{-\lambda - \omega}{(\lambda^2 + \gamma^2)(\gamma^2 + \omega^2)}. \qquad (8.04\text{–}17)$$

Thus, finally,

$$X(\omega) = \frac{-G}{\pi C^2(\gamma^2 + \omega^2)} \int_{-\infty}^{\infty} \frac{\lambda + \omega}{\lambda^2 + \gamma^2} \, d\lambda$$

$$= \frac{-G}{\pi(G^2 + C^2\omega^2)} \int_{-\infty}^{\infty} \left(\frac{\lambda}{\lambda^2 + \gamma^2} + \frac{\omega}{\lambda^2 + \gamma^2} \right) d\lambda$$

$$= \frac{-G}{\pi(G^2 + C^2\omega^2)} \left(0 + \frac{\omega}{\gamma} \pi \right) = \frac{-C\omega}{G^2 + C^2\omega^2}, \qquad (8.04\text{-}18)$$

in agreement with (8.04–12). From $X(\omega)$, $R(\omega)$ can be determined in corresponding fashion. The integral relations are seldom used for calculations like this (where rational functions are involved), for they become rather involved even in simple cases. Alternative methods, to be discussed later, are usually to be preferred.

8.05 Additional forms of the relations

The integral relations between resistance and reactance (conductance and susceptance) are of philosophical importance in that they indicate the extent to which resistance and reactance are interdependent. Should we have an impedance function $Z(p)$, it is of no particular interest to calculate $R(\omega)$ from $X(\omega)$ or the reverse, for we already have both. It may happen, however, that we have only one of the two parts (e.g., as the solution of an approximation problem in a case where that part is the important characteristic of the network), and wish to determine the other, and hence the whole function. This we can do, using the integral relations, subject of course to the restriction that only the minimum associated resistance (reactance) is thereby obtained. Since this is an important process, we proceed now to derive some other forms in which these relations can be stated.

The integrals as written, for example in (8.04–8) and (8.04–9), seem improper because of the singularity of the integrand at $\lambda = \omega$. But they are not really so, because they are to be interpreted not as continuous integrals but as made up of two parts whose ends come together as r approaches zero (§ 3.23). (This amounts to evaluation by approaching the singular point symmetrically from both sides, keeping a sort of balance about this point as we evaluate the integrals.) It is not difficult to remove the impropriety and write the relations as single proper integrals, however, and this we do next. By virtue of (8.04–7), which could be written

$$\int_{-\infty}^{\infty} \frac{d\lambda}{\lambda - \omega} = 0 \qquad (8.05\text{-}1)$$

we may add any constant we choose to $X(\lambda)$ or to $R(\lambda)$ in the integrands. If we add the constant $-X(\omega)$ in (8.04–8) and the constant $-R(\omega)$ in (8.04–9), we obtain

$$R(\omega) = -\frac{1}{\pi} \int_{-\infty}^{\infty} \frac{X(\lambda) - X(\omega)}{\lambda - \omega} \, d\lambda + R(\infty) \qquad (8.05\text{–}2)$$

and

$$X(\omega) = \frac{1}{\pi} \int_{-\infty}^{\infty} \frac{R(\lambda) - R(\omega)}{\lambda - \omega} \, d\lambda. \qquad (8.05\text{–}3)$$

Since the numerator of the integrand now vanishes at $\lambda = \omega$ in each case, the integrands have no singularities and are perfectly proper.

All the functions of interest to us are p-r, and at real frequencies their real and imaginary parts are respectively even and odd functions of ω. This enables us to develop alternative forms of the relations, in which the integration runs over only half the axis.   From (8.04–8) we have

$$R(\omega) = -\frac{1}{\pi} \int_{-\infty}^{0} \frac{X(\lambda)}{\lambda - \omega} \, d\lambda - \frac{1}{\pi} \int_{0}^{\infty} \frac{X(\lambda)}{\lambda - \omega} \, d\lambda + R(\infty). \qquad (8.05\text{–}4)$$

The first of the two integrals can be written

$$\frac{1}{\pi} \int_{0}^{-\infty} \frac{X(\lambda)}{\lambda - \omega} \, d\lambda = -\frac{1}{\pi} \int_{0}^{\infty} \frac{X(-\lambda)}{-\lambda - \omega} \, d\lambda = \frac{1}{\pi} \int_{0}^{\infty} \frac{X(\lambda)}{-(\lambda + \omega)} \, d\lambda \qquad (8.05\text{–}5)$$

by appropriate interchange of limits, change of sign of variable, and use of the odd-function property of $X(\lambda)$.   Then

$$R(\omega) = -\frac{1}{\pi} \int_{0}^{\infty} \left(\frac{1}{\lambda - \omega} + \frac{1}{\lambda + \omega} \right) X(\lambda) \, d\lambda + R(\infty)$$

$$= -\frac{2}{\pi} \int_{0}^{\infty} \frac{\lambda X(\lambda)}{\lambda^2 - \omega^2} \, d\lambda + R(\infty). \qquad (8.05\text{–}6)$$

Similarly, from (8.04–9), using this time the fact that $R(\lambda)$ is an even function, we obtain

$$X(\omega) = \frac{2\omega}{\pi} \int_{0}^{\infty} \frac{R(\lambda)}{\lambda^2 - \omega^2} \, d\lambda. \qquad (8.05\text{–}7)$$

Notice how the form of (8.05–7) differs from that of (8.05–6), and how each exhibits clearly the fact that the function provided on integration is an even or odd function of ω.

In these forms the limiting process is to be understood in evaluating the integrals through the point $\lambda = \omega$.   Just as for the doubly infinite integrations we can obtain forms for the singly infinite integrations that have no singularity in the integrand.   We first convert (8.05–2) to a singly infinite integral as follows.   Since

$$\int_{-\infty}^{\infty} \frac{d\lambda}{\lambda - \omega} = \int_{-\infty}^{0} \frac{d\lambda}{\lambda - \omega} + \int_{0}^{\infty} \frac{d\lambda}{\lambda - \omega}$$

$$= \int_{0}^{\infty} \left(\frac{-1}{\lambda + \omega} + \frac{1}{\lambda - \omega} \right) d\lambda = \int_{0}^{\infty} \frac{2\omega}{\lambda^2 - \omega^2} d\lambda, \quad (8.05\text{–}8)$$

we find by using (8.04–7) (for ω is constant in this integration) that

$$\int_{0}^{\infty} \frac{d\lambda}{\lambda^2 - \omega^2} = 0. \qquad (8.05\text{–}9)$$

Hence we may add constants to the numerators of the integrands in (8.05–6) and (8.05–7) without affecting the validity of the equations.   If these constants are chosen to remove the singularities of the integrands, we obtain the proper-integral forms

$$R(\omega) = -\frac{2}{\pi} \int_{0}^{\infty} \frac{\lambda X(\lambda) - \omega X(\omega)}{\lambda^2 - \omega^2} \, d\lambda + R(\infty) \qquad (8.05\text{–}10)$$

and

$$X(\omega) = \frac{2\omega}{\pi} \int_{0}^{\infty} \frac{R(\lambda) - R(\omega)}{\lambda^2 - \omega^2} \, d\lambda. \qquad (8.05\text{–}11)$$

In some applications, notably that discussed in § 8.09, it is more convenient to have the *derivative* of the given function in the integrand than the function itself.   Such forms are easily obtained through integration by parts.   Since logarithms appear in the results, it is appropriate to use the singly infinite forms of the relations and avoid negative frequencies. From (8.05–10) we obtain, in convenient form for integration,

$$R(\omega) = -\frac{1}{\pi\omega} \int_{0}^{\infty} [\lambda X(\lambda) - \omega X(\omega)] \left(\frac{1}{\lambda - \omega} - \frac{1}{\lambda + \omega} \right) d\lambda + R(\infty).$$

$$(8.05\text{–}12)$$

It is also convenient to divide the integration into two sections, one covering values of λ from 0 to ω, the other from ω to ∞, and to integrate the two separately, in order to avoid logarithms of negative numbers. For the first we have, on integrating by parts,

$$\int_{0}^{\omega} [\lambda X(\lambda) - \omega X(\omega)] \left(\frac{-1}{\omega - \lambda} - \frac{1}{\omega + \lambda} \right) d\lambda$$

$$= \left\{ [\lambda X(\lambda) - \omega X(\omega)] \ln \left(\frac{\omega - \lambda}{\omega + \lambda} \right) - \int \frac{d(\lambda X)}{d\lambda} \ln \left(\frac{\omega - \lambda}{\omega + \lambda} \right) d\lambda \right\}_{0}^{\omega}.$$

$$(8.05\text{–}13)$$

At the upper limit the first term behaves as $(\omega - \lambda) \ln (\omega - \lambda)$ which vanishes in the limit; at the lower limit the logarithm is zero, so that again the first term vanishes and there remains only

$$- \int_0^\omega \frac{d(\lambda X)}{d\lambda} \ln \left(\frac{\omega - \lambda}{\omega + \lambda} \right) d\lambda. \qquad (8.05\text{--}14)$$

For the integration over values of λ greater than ω, we have

$$\int_\omega^\infty [\lambda X(\lambda) - \omega X(\omega)] \left(\frac{1}{\lambda - \omega} - \frac{1}{\lambda + \omega} \right) d\lambda$$

$$= \left\{ [\lambda X(\lambda) - \omega X(\omega)] \ln \left(\frac{\lambda - \omega}{\lambda + \omega} \right) - \int \frac{d(\lambda X)}{d\lambda} \ln \left(\frac{\lambda - \omega}{\lambda + \omega} \right) d\lambda \right\}_\omega^\infty.$$

$$(8.05\text{--}15)$$

At the lower limit the first term vanishes, as before; at the upper limit this term vanishes again, for X approaches zero and the whole term behaves as X. There remains only

$$- \int_\omega^\infty \frac{d(\lambda X)}{d\lambda} \ln \left(\frac{\lambda - \omega}{\lambda + \omega} \right) d\lambda. \qquad (8.05\text{--}16)$$

Hence this integration of (8.05–12) by parts gives

$$R(\omega) = \frac{1}{\pi \omega} \int_0^\infty \frac{d(\lambda X)}{d\lambda} \ln \left| \frac{\lambda - \omega}{\lambda + \omega} \right| d\lambda + R(\infty) \qquad (8.05\text{--}17)$$

in which the argument of the logarithm is never negative. The corresponding integration of (8.05–11) proceeds in similar fashion; again the first terms contribute nothing, and the result is

$$X(\omega) = - \frac{1}{\pi} \int_0^\infty \frac{dR}{d\lambda} \ln \left| \frac{\lambda - \omega}{\lambda + \omega} \right| d\lambda. \qquad (8.05\text{--}18)$$

In (8.05–17) and (8.05–18) we have a form of the relations in which only the derivative of the given function (or of the same multiplied by frequency) appears. Their utility lies principally in applications where the given function is essentially linear, the derivative constant, and the integrals are simplified thereby.

An even more useful form is one in which not frequency itself, but rather the logarithm of frequency is the variable. If we let

$$u = \ln \frac{\lambda}{\omega}, \qquad (8.05\text{--}19)$$

then $\lambda = \omega e^u$ and the last two relations become

$$R(\omega) = \frac{1}{\pi\omega} \int_{-\infty}^{\infty} \frac{d(\lambda X)}{du} \ln \left| \frac{e^u - 1}{e^u + 1} \right| du + R(\infty)$$

$$= \frac{1}{\pi\omega} \int_{-\infty}^{\infty} \frac{d(\lambda X)}{du} \ln \tanh \left| \frac{u}{2} \right| du + R(\infty) \qquad (8.05\text{-}20)$$

and

$$X(\omega) = -\frac{1}{\pi} \int_{-\infty}^{\infty} \frac{dR}{du} \ln \tanh \left| \frac{u}{2} \right| du. \qquad (8.05\text{-}21)$$

An application of this last pair of relations will be given in § 8.09.

In each of these relations the *slope* of the curve of R (or of λX) plotted on a linear or logarithmic frequency scale is the important characteristic. Its effect is weighted by a logarithmic function which makes its behavior in the vicinity of the frequency at which X or R is being evaluated of prime importance. The previous forms of the relations have not pointed this out.

To obtain corresponding formulas for admittance functions, we need only replace R by G and X by B, according to the principle of duality.

Other forms of these relations exist, and by changing the integrand in the fundamental contour integral of § 3.23 from which these came, many other relations between resistance and reactance (conductance and susceptance) can be obtained (BO 3, GU 3). Some of these are given in the problems at the end of this chapter. But those above are the most important.

8.06 The reactance and resistance integral theorems

Two useful theorems are immediate consequences of the relations we have been discussing. From either (8.05–6) or (8.05–10) we find, on setting $\omega = 0$, that

$$R(\infty) - R(0) = \frac{2}{\pi} \int_0^{\infty} \frac{X(\lambda)}{\lambda} \, d\lambda = \frac{2}{\pi} \int_0^{\infty} \frac{X(\omega)}{\omega} \, d\omega. \qquad (8.06\text{-}1)$$

The expression in terms of ω (which can cause no confusion here) emphasizes the meaning of (8.06–1), that the area under the curve of reactance divided by frequency, when plotted against frequency, depends only on the net change in resistance between zero and infinite frequency, not on the intermediate behavior of the resistance. A neater form of this uses the logarithm of frequency as the variable. With $u = \ln \omega$ (8.06–1) becomes

$$\int_{-\infty}^{\infty} X \, du = \frac{\pi}{2} [R(\infty) - R(0)]. \qquad (8.06\text{-}2)$$

If the reactance is plotted on a logarithmic frequency scale, the area under the curve depends only on the difference between the infinite-frequency and the d-c values of the resistance. Whether the impedance function is minimum-resistance or not does not matter, for any additive (resistive) constant cancels out in (8.06–2). This *reactance integral theorem* has important applications in amplifier design (BO 3).

To obtain the corresponding theorem concerning the integral of resistance, multiply (8.05–11) by ω, obtaining

$$\omega X(\omega) = \frac{2\omega^2}{\pi} \int_0^\infty \frac{R(\lambda) - R(\omega)}{\lambda^2 - \omega^2}\, d\lambda, \qquad (8.06\text{–}3)$$

and then let ω become indefinitely large. The result is

$$\lim_{\omega \to \infty} [\omega X(\omega)] = -\frac{2}{\pi} \int_0^\infty [R(\lambda) - R(\infty)]\, d\lambda \qquad (8.06\text{–}4)$$

or

$$\int_0^\infty [R(\omega) - R(\infty)]\, d\omega = -\frac{\pi}{2} \lim_{\omega \to \infty} [\omega X(\omega)]. \qquad (8.06\text{–}5)$$

This *resistance integral theorem* states that the area under the curve of resistance versus frequency (shifted vertically so that the curve approaches zero at infinity) is determined only by the high-frequency behavior of the reactance. Again, any excess resistance cancels out in the formula, which applies only to the difference between the resistance at various frequencies and the resistance at infinity.

The resistance integral theorem also has important applications in amplifier theory. To illustrate this, suppose the (minimum-reactance) impedance function $Z(p)$ vanishes at infinity, in particular that the network whose driving-point impedance it represents has a capacitor connected

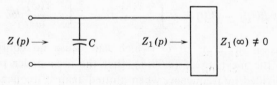

Fig. 8.06–A

across the input terminals (Fig. 8.06–A), while the impedance to the right of the capacitor does not vanish at high frequencies (i.e., C represents the total capacitance across the terminals). Then we have $Z(\infty) = 0$, $R(\infty) = 0$, and

$$\lim_{\omega \to \infty} [\omega X(\omega)] = \lim_{\omega \to \infty} \left[\omega \left(\frac{-1}{C\omega} \right) \right] = -\frac{1}{C} \qquad (8.06\text{--}6)$$

and from (8.06–5),

$$\int_0^\infty R(\omega)\, d\omega = \frac{\pi}{2C}. \qquad (8.06\text{--}7)$$

The capacitance C completely determines the area under the resistance-versus-frequency curve. From this derives the well-known limitation on the product of gain and bandwidth of certain amplifier configurations (BO 3); cf. Problem 14-141.

It can also be shown that if an impedance $Z(p)$ is not minimum-reactance, but still behaves as $1/Cp$ for large values of p, i.e., $R(\infty) = 0$ and $\lim_{\omega \to \infty} \omega X(\omega) = -1/C$ still, then the resistance integral (8.06–7) is less than $\pi/2C$. In general, whether $Z(p)$ is minimum-reactance or not, so long as Z behaves as $1/Cp$ as p approaches infinity,

$$\int_0^\infty R(\omega)\, d\omega \leqq \frac{\pi}{2C}. \qquad (8.06\text{--}8)$$

The dual theorems, of less practical importance, follow from the above with the usual substitutions.

8.07 The relation between magnitude and angle

In the integral relations so far developed we have, under certain circumstances, explicit relations between the real and imaginary parts of immittance functions. In practice, not only the resistance and reactance (conductance and susceptance) components of immittances are important; the *magnitude* and *angle* (phase) may be equally so. In other words, the polar-coordinate point of view may be as useful as the rectangular-coordinate one. We consider now the relations, at real frequencies, between magnitude and angle of immittance functions.

The previous relations came from contour integration of an analytic function whose real and imaginary parts, on the imaginary axis, became resistance and reactance (conductance and susceptance). An analytic function whose real and imaginary parts are essentially the magnitude and angle of an immittance function is the *logarithm* of the immittance function. To determine whether such a function can be treated in similar fashion, we must re-examine the development in § 3.23. Let $F(p)$ now be the natural logarithm of a (normalized) p-r function $Z(p)$,

$$\begin{aligned} F(p) &= \ln Z(p), \\ Z(p) &= e^{F(p)}. \end{aligned} \qquad (8.07\text{--}1)$$

Since $Z(p)$ is p-r, it cannot vanish or become infinite in the right half plane, by (5.05–1). But the logarithm function has singularities only where its argument vanishes or becomes infinite, and therefore $F(p)$ is analytic in the right half plane, provided we remove the ambiguity of the multiple values of the logarithm function. This we do by selecting that branch which has a zero imaginary part when p is on the positive real axis. On the imaginary axis $Z(p)$ may well vanish and become infinite, though only in the fashion described in (5.06–6), and at such points $F(p)$ is not analytic. For the moment we restrict the behavior of $Z(p)$ at infinity and require $Z(\infty)$ to be finite and not zero, so that $F(\infty)$ is a meaningful finite, nonzero constant. Then, proceeding as in § 3.23, we integrate

$$G(p) = \frac{F(p)}{p - j\omega_1} = \frac{\ln Z(p)}{p - j\omega_1} \qquad (8.07\text{–}2)$$

around the contour C of Fig. 8.07–A. This is carefully indented to the right, not only around the point $j\omega_1$ but also around the real-frequency

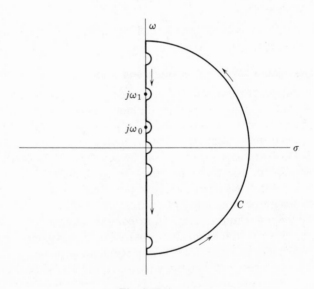

Fig. 8.07–A

singularities of $F(p)$; the semicircles will disappear in the limit in the usual manner. The contour integral has the value zero, by Cauchy's theorem. The contributions from the infinite semicircle, the infinitesimal semicircle around $j\omega_1$, and the imaginary axis can be taken immediately from § 3.23.

But the contributions from the infinitesimal semicircles introduced to avoid the singularities of the logarithm function are novel, and must be calculated. Near such a point, say $j\omega_0$, we write as usual

$$p = j\omega_0 + re^{j\theta} \qquad (8.07\text{-}3)$$

and have

$$\ln Z(p) = \ln\{A(p - j\omega_0)^s[1 + A_1(p - j\omega_0) + \cdots]\}, \qquad (8.07\text{-}4)$$

in which A and A_1 are constants—as is s. Over the corresponding small semicircles

$$\int G(p)\, dp = \int \frac{\ln A + s \ln (re^{j\theta}) + \ln (1 + A_1 re^{j\theta} + \cdots)}{j(\omega_0 - \omega_1) + re^{j\theta}}\, re^{j\theta} j\, d\theta.$$

$$(8.07\text{-}5)$$

When the integral is expanded into three terms, corresponding to the three terms of the numerator of the integrand, and r is allowed to approach zero, both the first and third terms vanish (provided $\omega_1 \neq \omega_0$). The second term gives

$$r(\ln r + j\theta) \int \frac{jse^{j\theta}\, d\theta}{j(\omega_0 - \omega_1) + re^{j\theta}}. \qquad (8.07\text{-}6)$$

This yields two terms of which the second approaches zero; and since

$$\lim_{r \to 0} (r \ln r) = 0, \qquad (8.07\text{-}7)$$

the first term also vanishes. Hence the singularities of $F(p)$ contribute nothing to the contour integral, because they are *logarithmic* singularities, too weak to affect the value of the integral. We must remember, however, when questions of the change of angle of the integrand as p goes through them arise, that the path of integration skirts them by detours in the right half plane, in order to remain on the branch of the logarithm function that we originally selected.

The results of § 3.23 can therefore be used with $F(p) = \ln Z(p)$, if $Z(p)$ is p-r and has a finite, nonzero value at infinity—and even if the restriction on the behavior at infinity is removed (this is discussed below). For magnitude and angle we use the notation

$$Z(j\omega) = |Z(j\omega)|e^{j\beta(\omega)},$$

$$\ln Z(j\omega) = \ln |Z(j\omega)| + j\beta(\omega), \qquad (8.07\text{-}8)$$

in which $\beta(0)$ is either zero, or $\pi/2$ (if approached from above) and $-\pi/2$

(if approached from below), in accord with our choice of the value of the logarithm function.   Then (3.23–12) gives

$$\ln |Z(j\omega)| = \ln |Z(\infty)| - \frac{1}{\pi} \int_{-\infty}^{\infty} \frac{\beta(\lambda)}{\lambda - \omega} \, d\lambda \qquad (8.07\text{–}9)$$

and

$$\beta(\omega) = \frac{1}{\pi} \int_{-\infty}^{\infty} \frac{\ln |Z(j\lambda)|}{\lambda - \omega} \, d\lambda. \qquad (8.07\text{–}10)$$

Here $\beta(\infty)$ has been taken as zero, as it must with our choice of branch of the logarithm function.

The equations do not apply for those values of ω at which $Z(p)$ has poles (i.e., when $\omega_1 = \omega_0$ in the previous discussion).   At such points the functions are singular (the magnitude function becomes infinite and the angle function is discontinuous) in fashions which can be investigated by a limiting process, but will be evident from the data.   Equations corresponding to the other forms in which the real-imaginary part relations appear in § 8.05 can be written merely by substituting $\ln |Z(j\omega)|$ for $R(\omega)$, and $\beta(\omega)$ for $X(\omega)$.

The extent to which the corresponding angle function may be determined from a given magnitude function, and the reverse, is apparent from the integral formulas.   Any constant added to $\ln |Z(j\omega)|$ will not affect $\beta(\omega)$ as determined from (8.07–10), for (8.05–1) states that the contribution of the constant is zero.   Similarly, any constant added to $\beta(\omega)$ will not affect the function $\ln |Z(j\omega)|$ calculated from (8.07–9).   This is in agreement with the common-sense observation that multiplication of $Z(p)$ by any real positive constant will not affect its angle, and that multiplication of $Z(p)$ by the constant $e^{j\gamma}$ (in which γ is real) will not affect its magnitude.   In other words, a knowledge of the angle function at real frequencies determines the magnitude function only within a multiplicative constant.   This property corresponds to the ambiguity in the resistance (conductance) function as determined from a given reactance (susceptance), except that here there is no prescribed minimum value.   Whether the p-r requirement is met is determined essentially by the angle, and in the calculation of the angle function from a given magnitude function no ambiguity exists; the function $\beta(\omega)$ must be odd and cannot exceed $\pi/2$ radians (90°) in magnitude—these requirements rule out the addition of any constant to the value determined by (8.07–10).   Nor are the concepts of minimum reactance and minimum resistance relevant here.   We can, for example, add reactance without affecting the corresponding resistance, but not without affecting the magnitude and angle of the impedance function.

The restriction on the behavior at infinity is not necessary, and $\ln Z(\infty)$ need not be finite. If $Z(p)$ vanishes or becomes infinite at infinity, the singularity there is only logarithmic, but still the argument above does not immediately apply. Instead we may reason as follows. (This argument lacks rigor but may clarify the point.) Let Fig. 8.07–B represent

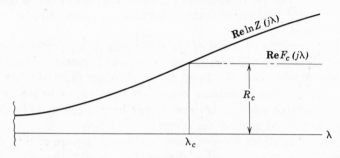

Fig. 8.07–B

the behavior of **Re** $\ln Z(j\lambda)$ for large values of λ. Consider now the function $F_c(j\lambda)$ whose real part is the same as that of $\ln Z(j\lambda)$ for $|\lambda| < \lambda_c$, but is constant at the value $R_c = $ **Re** $\ln Z(j\lambda_c)$ for $|\lambda| > \lambda_c$. This may be placed in the appropriate integral relation, as (8.04–9) or (8.07–10), to yield the corresponding imaginary part of F_c. From the nature of the integral, this imaginary part will vanish at infinity, so that $F_c(\infty) = R_c + j0$ and $F_c(p)$ is actually a function to which the integral relations may be applied. This is true no matter how large λ_c may be. We need only make λ_c large enough that the difference between the two curves in Fig. 8.07–B for $\lambda > \lambda_c$ will have no appreciable effect at the lower frequencies where we are working, and if the integrals converge we may even take the limit as $\lambda_c \to \infty$. If $Z(p)$ vanishes or becomes infinite at infinity, then the calculation of $\beta(\omega)$ by (8.07–10) requires only that the integral therein should converge. The integrand itself need not vanish at infinity for this to happen. From the form (8.05–7), for example, we observe that if $R(\lambda)$ behaves as λ^r for large λ, then the integral is essentially λ^{r-1} and converges for $r < 1$, i.e., if $R(\lambda)/\lambda$ vanishes at infinity. In our particular case we have a logarithmic function; when divided by λ it vanishes at infinity, so that the integral in (8.07–10) is meaningful. (The divergence in the doubly infinite or $\int_{-\infty}^{\infty}$ forms is not an obstacle, for the symmetry properties remove it, as the singly infinite or $\int_0^{\infty}$ forms, which are based on these symmetries, show.) Such a singularity in the real part is usually accompanied by a discontinuity in the imaginary part, which approaches a final value β_c for large positive values of λ, and the final value $-\beta_c$ for large negative values of λ, and we may consider $\beta(\infty)$ itself to be zero. A similar discussion shows how the integral in (8.07–9) can be interpreted with meaning. We conclude that the relations (8.07–9) and (8.07–10) apply to all p-r functions $Z(p)$, even if the logarithm is singular at infinity. (Their application is not restricted to p-r functions, but our interest in them is.)

Since the logarithms of Z and of $1/Z$ differ only in sign, there is even less difference in the application of these results to admittance functions than duality usually provides. Formulas (8.07–9) and (8.07–10) may be applied to the inverted admittance magnitude function, or to the angle function with altered sign; or $|Z|$ may simply be replaced by $|Y|$—then β is to be taken as the angle of the admittance function.

These integral relations between magnitude and angle are of little use for calculating one, given the other, for specific networks, because of the complexity of the integrals. They are of great value in demonstrating that any device found useful in calculating, say, reactance from given resistance, by means which avoid the integrals as given, is equally applicable to the calculation of angle from given magnitude. Such a device is discussed in § 8.09.

8.08 Summary

The various forms in which we have cast the fundamental relations (3.23–12) are here tabulated for convenient reference. Since they may be used for impedance and admittance functions, and for their logarithms (and for other functions to be discussed in Volume II), the general notation

$$H(j\omega) = H_1(\omega) + jH_2(\omega) \tag{8.08–1}$$

is used. Then H can represent Z, Y, $\ln Z$ or $\ln Y$. (The relations can be applied more generally, but our interest is confined to these functions.) The forms are tabulated in Table 8.08–A; in them $H(j\omega)$ may have any of the interpretations (with the restrictions) given in Table 8.08–B. Neither the table of relations nor the table of interpretations of H is exhaustive. More relations can be found in the problems and in the literature (BO 3, GU 3), and further applications will be discussed in Volume II.

8.09 An application of the integral relations

There are practical situations in which it is at least helpful, if not essential, to be able to calculate, say, $X(\omega)$ when only $R(\omega)$ is known. If

Table 8.08–A

$$H(j\omega) = H_1(\omega) + jH_2(\omega)$$

$$H_1(\omega) = -\frac{1}{\pi}\int_{-\infty}^{\infty}\frac{H_2(\lambda)}{\lambda-\omega}\,d\lambda + H_1(\infty)$$
$$H_2(\omega) = \frac{1}{\pi}\int_{-\infty}^{\infty}\frac{H_1(\lambda)}{\lambda-\omega}\,d\lambda$$

$$H_1(\omega) = -\frac{1}{\pi}\int_{-\infty}^{\infty}\frac{H_2(\lambda)-H_2(\omega)}{\lambda-\omega}\,d\lambda + H_1(\infty)$$
$$H_2(\omega) = \frac{1}{\pi}\int_{-\infty}^{\infty}\frac{H_1(\lambda)-H_2(\omega)}{\lambda-\omega}\,d\lambda$$

$$H_1(\omega) = -\frac{2}{\pi}\int_{0}^{\infty}\frac{\lambda H_2(\lambda)}{\lambda^2-\omega^2}\,d\lambda + H_1(\infty)$$
$$H_2(\omega) = \frac{2\omega}{\pi}\int_{0}^{\infty}\frac{H_1(\lambda)}{\lambda^2-\omega^2}\,d\lambda$$

$$H_1(\omega) = -\frac{2}{\pi}\int_{0}^{\infty}\frac{\lambda H_2(\lambda)-\omega H_2(\omega)}{\lambda^2-\omega^2}\,d\lambda + H_1(\infty)$$
$$H_2(\omega) = \frac{2\omega}{\pi}\int_{0}^{\infty}\frac{H_1(\lambda)-H_1(\omega)}{\lambda^2-\omega^2}\,d\lambda$$

$$H_1(\omega) = \frac{1}{\pi\omega}\int_{0}^{\infty}\frac{d(\lambda H_2)}{d\lambda}\ln\left|\frac{\lambda-\omega}{\lambda+\omega}\right|\,d\lambda + H_1(\infty)$$
$$H_2(\omega) = -\frac{1}{\pi}\int_{0}^{\infty}\frac{dH_1}{d\lambda}\ln\left|\frac{\lambda-\omega}{\lambda+\omega}\right|\,d\lambda$$

$$H_1(\omega) = -\frac{1}{\pi\omega}\int_{-\infty}^{\infty}\frac{d(\lambda H_2)}{du}\ln\coth\left|\frac{u}{2}\right|\,du + H_1(\infty)$$
$$H_2(\omega) = \frac{1}{\pi}\int_{-\infty}^{\infty}\frac{dH_1}{du}\ln\coth\left|\frac{u}{2}\right|\,du$$

Table 8.08–B

$H(j\omega)$	$H_1(\omega)$	$H_2(\omega)$	Restrictions
Impedance $Z(j\omega)$	Resistance $R(\omega)$	Reactance $X(\omega)$	$Z(p)$ is p-r and minimum-reactance
Admittance $Y(j\omega)$	Conductance $G(\omega)$	Susceptance $B(\omega)$	$Y(p)$ is p-r and minimum-susceptance
Logarithm of impedance $\ln Z(j\omega)$	Logarithm of $|Z|$	Angle of impedance	$Z(p)$ is p-r
Logarithm of admittance $\ln Y(j\omega)$	Logarithm of $|Y|$	Angle of admittance	$Y(p)$ is p-r

the actual function $X(\omega)$ or the complete function $Z(j\omega)$ or $Z(p)$ is needed, if the actual function is absolutely necessary, then the integral relations provide a formal solution to the problem of finding it. But for even the extremely simple network discussed in § 8.04 their application is cumbersome. (Simpler methods, applicable to rational functions, will be discussed later.) When it is necessary merely to find an *approximate* form of $X(\omega)$, for which a set of numerical values or a curve will suffice, the integral relations can be used in a much simpler fashion.

The basic idea is to use the integral relations to solve some typical problems, to take some particular $R(\omega)$, for example, and plot the $X(\omega)$ that goes with it, finding what this is by one of the integral formulas. This is to be repeated for other typical $R(\omega)$. In this way we might build up a collection of curves, and should we encounter the $R(\omega)$ for which one of the curves is drawn, then we could immediately read the corresponding $X(\omega)$ from the curve. A sufficiently large collection of these curves might be a valuable tool. The difficulty, of course, is in the tremendous size of a set of curves that would be varied enough to be useful. Hence we drop this idea in favor of a more practical one. We can reduce the problem to one which is limited enough to handle, by saying that we will be willing to *approximate* the given $R(\omega)$ curve by a series of straight-line segments. This can evidently be done, no matter how complicated the nature of the given $R(\omega)$, provided enough straight lines are used. We need now to tabulate or plot the $X(\omega)$ associated with a segment-of-a-straight-line $R(\omega)$ in some general, normalized form, such that it can be employed successively for each of the lines used in the approximation to $R(\omega)$. If it is possible to do this, then we can develop a rapid practical method for determining numerically the reactance associated with any given resistance function, at least to a good approximation—and the same for the various other problems.

The integral relations useful for this purpose are those in which the *derivative* of the known function appears rather than the function itself, for this derivative is a constant when the function is linear. In (8.05–17), (8.05–18), (8.05–20), and (8.05–21) we have such useful forms. Approximate methods can be based on either pair. One will require that the given function be plotted against frequency on a logarithmic scale, the other that it be against frequency on a linear scale. We shall develop the logarithmic-scale method (though the linear scale method is also useful), because certain functions to be discussed in Volume II behave, at high and low frequencies, as the logarithm of some power of ω, say the nth. A plot of the logarithm of ω^n on semilogarithmic coordinate paper is a straight line, so that one straight line will closely match the low- and high-frequency asymptotic behavior of these functions. (On a linear scale the logarithm of ω^n does not plot linearly and might inconveniently require several line segments, rather than one, to represent the behavior at the ends of the frequency scale.) In driving-point immittance functions we can encounter only the values -1, 0, or 1 for n, but for the functions we shall meet in Volume II, n need not be so restricted.

Suppose first that the resistance function $R(\omega)$ is known at all frequencies and $X(\omega)$ is wanted. (This problem typifies the various possible ones.) Let $R(\omega)$ be plotted on a logarithmic frequency scale, as in the example of Fig. 8.09–A (adapted from BO 3 by permission). (This represents the normalized resistance of the parallel R-C network of Fig. 8.04–A with an added series resistor.) An approximation to this curve, made up of one finite line segment and two of infinite extent, is shown in Fig. 8.09–B; in

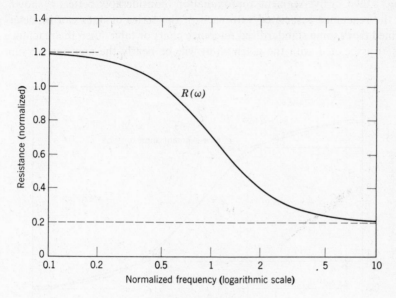

Fig. 8.09-A

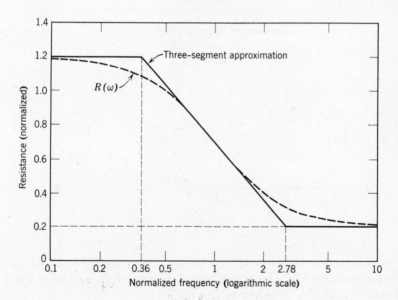

Fig. 8.09-B

Fig. 8.09–C a five-segment approximation (considerably better) is shown. If the reactance associated with each of the series of lines can be determined from some standardized reference chart or table, then the reactance $X(\omega)$ associated with the given $R(\omega)$ will be nearly the appropriate sum

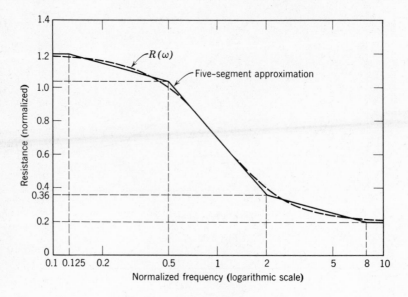

Fig. 8.09–C

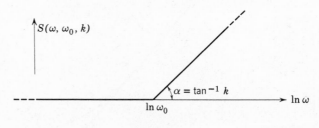

Fig. 8.09–D

of reactances, for the composition is linear. Presumably the approximation furnished by Fig. 8.09–C will be better (but will require more work to obtain) than that furnished by Fig. 8.09–B.

Any approximation to a curve by line segments in the manner above can be thought of as the sum of a number of functions each of the form illustrated in Fig. 8.09–D.

Expressed formally,

$$S(\omega, \omega_0, k) = 0, \qquad \omega \lessgtr \omega_0$$
$$= k \ln \frac{\omega}{\omega_0}, \qquad \omega \gtreqless \omega_0. \tag{8.09-1}$$

The "break" points ω_0 will occur where the line segments in the approximation join, and the slopes $k = \tan \alpha$ will be such that the algebraic sum of the S functions gives the lines in the approximation. The resolution of the approximation in Fig. 8.09–B is given in Fig. 8.09–E, to which

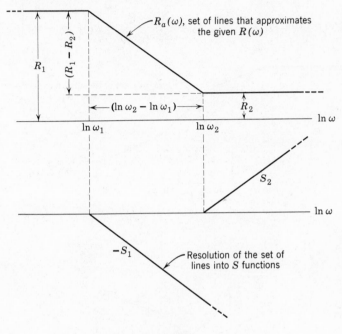

Fig. 8.09–E

equations (8.09–2) apply; similar treatment of the approximation of Fig. 8.09–C is given in Fig. 8.09–F and (8.09–3). In these, and in all discussions of this method, we consider the S functions to have positive slope, all k to be positive, and explicitly write negative signs as necessary.

$$\left.\begin{aligned}
R_a(\omega) &= R_1 - S_1(\omega) + S_2(\omega), \\
S_1(\omega) &= S(\omega, \omega_1, K), \\
S_2(\omega) &= S(\omega, \omega_2, K), \\
K &= \frac{R_1 - R_2}{\ln \omega_2 - \ln \omega_1} = \frac{R_1 - R_2}{\ln (\omega_2/\omega_1)}.
\end{aligned}\right\} \tag{8.09-2}$$

$$R_a = R_1 - S_1(\omega) - S_2(\omega) + S_3(\omega) + S_4(\omega),$$

$$S_1(\omega) = S(\omega, \omega_1, k_1), \qquad k_1 = \frac{R_1 - R_2}{\ln(\omega_2/\omega_1)},$$

$$S_2(\omega) = S(\omega, \omega_2, k_2), \qquad k_2 = \frac{R_2 - R_3}{\ln(\omega_3/\omega_2)} - k_1,$$

$$S_3(\omega) = S(\omega, \omega_3, k_3), \qquad k_3 = -\frac{R_3 - R_4}{\ln(\omega_4/\omega_3)} + k_1 + k_2,$$

$$S_4(\omega) = S(\omega, \omega_4, k_4), \qquad k_4 = \frac{R_3 - R_4}{\ln(\omega_4/\omega_3)} = k_1 + k_2 - k_3$$

$$(8.09-3)$$

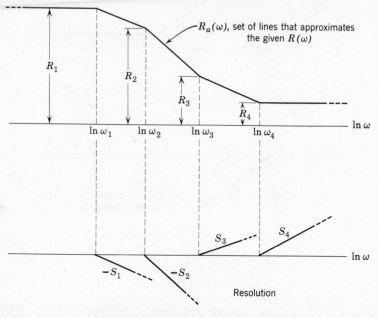

Fig. 8.09–F

The general method should now be apparent. The given function, plotted on a logarithmic frequency scale, is approximated by a series of line segments; this polygonal approximation can be resolved into a sum of S functions (cf. Fig. 8.09–D). If the reactance corresponding to this prototype function $S(\omega)$ can be tabulated once for all, in such fashion that it can easily be read, as a function of frequency, for various ω_0 and k, then the approximate calculation of $X(\omega)$, given $R(\omega)$, will be easy.

Constant terms in the approximation can be ignored, for they contribute no reactance.

The appropriate formula for calculating the reactance associated with S (interpreted as a resistance function) is (8.05–21), which can now be written

$$X(\omega) = \frac{1}{\pi} \int_{-\infty}^{\infty} \frac{dS}{du} \ln \coth \left| \frac{u}{2} \right| du \tag{8.09–4}$$

$$= \frac{k}{\pi} \int_{u_0}^{\infty} \ln \coth \left| \frac{u}{2} \right| du \tag{8.09–5}$$

in which $u = \ln (\lambda/\omega)$ as before, and $u_0 = \ln (\omega_0/\omega)$. For computational purposes it will be convenient to write this in terms of the variable $x = \omega/\lambda$. With $x_0 = \omega/\omega_0$ the formula becomes

$$X(\omega) = -\frac{k}{\pi} \int_{x_0}^{0} \ln \left| \frac{(1/x) + 1}{(1/x) - 1} \right| \frac{dx}{x}$$

$$= \frac{k}{\pi} \int_{0}^{x_0} \ln \left| \frac{1 + x}{1 - x} \right| \frac{dx}{x}. \tag{8.09–6}$$

Because we have chosen straight lines as approximating functions, the derivative form of the relation between reactance and resistance becomes simply

$$X(\omega) = kF_0 \left(\frac{\omega}{\omega_0} \right) \tag{8.09–7}$$

in which

$$F_0 \left(\frac{\omega}{\omega_0} \right) = \frac{1}{\pi} \int_{u_0}^{\infty} \ln \coth \left| \frac{u}{2} \right| du = \frac{1}{\pi} \int_{0}^{x_0} \ln \left| \frac{1 + x}{1 - x} \right| \frac{dx}{x}. \tag{8.09–8}$$

Hence we need only compute and tabulate $F_0(\omega/\omega_0)$, which represents the minimum reactance associated with a unit-slope semi-infinite resistance line, to be able to determine conveniently the minimum reactance associated with *any* given resistance function. Fortunately F_0 is a function only of the ratio of frequency to the break frequency ω_0, but since differences are involved, and nearly equal numbers may have to be subtracted, the computation should be sufficiently detailed to given accurate results when subtraction occurs.

Before considering the computation of this function, we must consider the legitimacy of applying one of our integral relations to the function S, which is certainly not finite at infinity. True, we expect to use only groups of functions S that in combination have finite values at zero and infinity (only resistance functions that are there finite are of interest). But if the method is to be generally useful, it must be possible to find the reactance associated with the unit-slope function S alone. The integral expression itself *is* meaningful, for it has a definite value in spite of the extreme nature of one of the limits (∞ or 0), and of the singularity at $x = 1$ (which we have previously discussed). And the discussion in § 8.07 indicates that the integral relation may be used, for the integral converges.

A method of computing values of the function $F_0(\omega/\omega_0)$ is suggested in Problem 8-66, and in Appendix B; more details may be found in the literature (BO 3, TH 1, CO 2). Tables for use in practical applications are also given in Appendix B, together with a plot of the function that may be a convenient substitute for the table when great accuracy is not required. The general nature of the function is shown in Fig. 8.09–G.

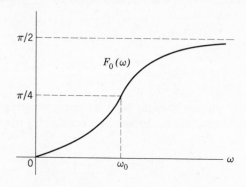

Fig. 8.09–G

In practice the data will be plotted on semilogarithmic graph paper and the approximating lines superimposed thereon. The locations of the break points are then obvious. Some thought must be given, however, to the units of the slope factor k. From such a plot the increment in a line between frequencies ω_1 and ω_2, say $(R_1 - R_2)$, is to be determined; then

$$k = \left| \frac{R_1 - R_2}{\ln (\omega_1/\omega_2)} \right| = \left| \frac{R_1 - R_2}{2.3026 \log (\omega_1/\omega_2)} \right|. \qquad (8.09\text{–}9)$$

Whether normalized or actual values of ω are used is immaterial; any units of frequency may be used, because only ratios of frequencies are involved. Values read from the table or plots of $F_0(\omega/\omega_0)$ must be multiplied by this k. If the two frequencies are one decade apart (correspond to a tenfold change in frequency), then

$$k = 0.4343 \left| R_1 - R_2 \right|. \qquad (8.09\text{–}10)$$

The preceding discussion has assumed that the reactance $X(\omega)$ is to be calculated from a given resistance function $R(\omega)$. The dual calculation of B from G requires only the usual change of symbols.

The determination of resistance from reactance (or of conductance from susceptance) requires additional comment. Formula (8.05–20) differs from (8.05–21) primarily in that not X alone but the product (λX) is in the integrand. (The quotient X/λ may also be used; cf. Problems 8-46, 8-71, and the example at the end of Appendix B.) We have to convert

$$R(\omega) = -\frac{1}{\pi\omega} \int_{-\infty}^{\infty} \frac{d(\lambda X)}{du} \ln \coth \left| \frac{u}{2} \right| du + R(\infty) \qquad (8.09\text{--}11)$$

into a form suitable for use with the apparatus already developed. We must plot now the product of the given reactance and frequency, rather than reactance alone, if we use this formula (there are others). Then we approximate to this by segments of lines. For a semi-infinite line of slope k, as in Fig. 8.09–D,

$$R(\omega) = -\frac{k}{\omega} \left(\frac{1}{\pi} \int_{u_0}^{\infty} \ln \coth \left| \frac{u}{2} \right| du \right) + R(\infty)$$

$$= -\frac{k}{\omega} F_0 \left(\frac{\omega}{\omega_0} \right) + R(\infty). \qquad (8.09\text{--}12)$$

The procedure is then essentially as before. The important difference is that the reactance data must be multiplied by frequency before plotting, and the result must be divided by frequency (and changed in sign) to obtain $R(\omega)$. The units in which the initial multiplication by frequency and the final division by frequency are performed do not matter so long as they are the same. The reactance may be in any units, and the resistance will appear in the same units. The resistance is determined only within an additive constant, as is to be expected; the function is automatically so adjusted that the value of R found at infinity is zero—to this is to be added a constant, $R(\infty)$, at least large enough to prevent the resistance from going negative at any value of frequency. Calculation of conductance from susceptance proceeds in the same manner.

The problem of calculating the angle of an immittance function, given only the magnitude as a function of frequency, can also be solved by this method. The appropriate formula is

$$\beta(\omega) = \frac{1}{\pi} \int_{-\infty}^{\infty} \frac{d \ln |Z(j\omega)|}{du} \ln \coth \left| \frac{u}{2} \right| du. \qquad (8.09\text{--}13)$$

We need only plot $\ln |Z|$ on a logarithmic frequency scale, approximate thereto with straight lines, and observe that for the semi-infinite line of Fig. 8.09–D the corresponding angle is given by

$$\beta(\omega) = kF_0(\omega/\omega_0). \qquad (8.09\text{–}14)$$

If log-log graph paper is used, $|Z|$ itself may be plotted. The slopes k are to be determined from

$$k = \frac{\Delta \ln |Z|}{\Delta \ln \omega} = \frac{\Delta \log |Z|}{\Delta \log \omega} = \left| \frac{\log |Z_1/Z_2|}{\log |\omega_1/\omega_2|} \right|, \qquad (8.09\text{–}15)$$

in which Δf denotes the magnitude of an increment in f. By the nature of this expression it is necessary to use the same base in measuring both the increment of the logarithm of $|Z|$ and the logarithm of frequency, but any base may be used. To convert the resulting angle to degrees [more frequently used than the radians in which (8.09–14) gives β], one need only multiply by the conversion factor $180/\pi = 57.296$ deg/radian. This last change is sufficiently common that the function $F_0(\omega/\omega_0)$ is tabulated in Appendix B both in radians and in degrees. In the above Z may of course be replaced by Y; then β becomes the angle of Y.

To calculate $\ln |Z|$ given $\beta(\omega)$, we have

$$\ln |Z(j\omega)| = -\frac{1}{\pi\omega} \int_{-\infty}^{\infty} \frac{d(\lambda\beta)}{du} \ln \coth \left| \frac{u}{2} \right| du + \ln |Z(\infty)|. \quad (8.09\text{–}16)$$

The required plot is one of the product of the given $\beta(\omega)$ and frequency. (Here too the quotient β/λ may be used.) A semi-infinite line of slope k on such a plot (Fig. 8.09–D) gives the corresponding magnitude function

$$\ln |Z(j\omega)| = -\frac{k}{\omega} F_0(\omega) + \ln |Z(\infty)|. \qquad (8.09\text{–}17)$$

The units used for multiplication of β by frequency and division of the values from the table by frequency may be any units, but must be the same in both cases. If β is measured in radians, then natural logarithms result; to use degrees, or to obtain common logarithms, one must apply a scale factor.

The fundamental function $F_0(\omega/\omega_0)$ is tabulated and plotted in Appendix B. With it we can rapidly calculate the minimum reactance associated with a given resistance function, or the resistance associated with a given reactance, or perform any of the other possible calculations. Instructions for the use of the tables and charts are given in summary form along with them, as well as illustrative examples; their genesis has been given above.

To illustrate how well the process works, Fig. 8.09–H gives scale plots of the reactance associated with the resistance shown in Fig. 8.09–A, as determined by this method, using the approximations of Figs. 8.09–B and 8.09–C, and also the exact reactance. (The details of the calculations are given in Appendix B.)

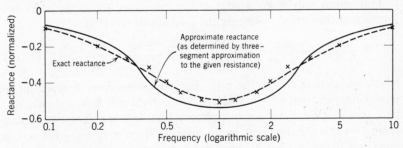

× Indicates values of reactance determined by the five-segment approximation

Fig. 8.09–H

8.10 Interlude

In this chapter we have established the concepts of minimum reactance (susceptance) and minimum resistance (conductance). Associated with any resistance function is a definite minimum reactance; associated with any reactance is a definite minimum resistance. These facts (and their duals) are eloquently expressed by integral relations between the parts, some of which we have developed in detail. For actual computation of one part, given the other, these integral relations may be awkward. They have their place in network theory, an important one, yet in actual computation of network functions they may become unnecessarily complicated (but see Problem 8-77). Based on them is the approximate method discussed in § 8.09, whose value is not to be underestimated—but when we must obtain one part of a rational immittance function from another in exact functional form (as is often necessary), then we use other (algebraic) methods at which we have so far only hinted. These do not require an a priori knowledge of the fact that resistance and reactance (conductance and susceptance) are related; these are methods not only of performing the calculations but of showing the existence of the relations. There are two of them, both requiring work, but neither using integration. One is due to Brune and Gewertz (BR 3, GE 1), the other to Bode (BO 3); both obtain the complete function from the given part, rather than the other part alone. But this is equivalent, and sometimes more directly useful. Other methods also exist (e.g., see Problems 8-79, 10-79), as do many interesting extensions (see the problems).

8.11 The Brune-Gewertz method: from resistance (conductance) to immittance function

Any given resistance (reactance, conductance, susceptance, magnitude, angle) function that relates to a network must have come from a rational function of p, an immittance function. It is this function we seek now to find, given only a knowledge of the resistance (or other part) as a function of frequency. Suppose the (unknown) function is

$$Z(p) = \frac{a_n p^n + a_{n-1} p^{n-1} + \cdots + a_0}{b_m p^m + b_{m-1} p^{m-1} + \cdots + b_0} = \frac{M_1 + N_1}{M_2 + N_2} \quad (8.11-1)$$

which we assume only to be p-r. For concreteness let it represent an impedance function, with (at real frequencies) real part $R(\omega)$ and imaginary part $X(\omega)$. (We have not yet shown that *any* p-r function actually represents the driving-point immittance of some network—that will be done in Chapter 9—but we need use here only the p-r property.) And for the present suppose that $R(\omega)$ is known; $Z(p)$, and hence $X(\omega)$, are to be found, insofar as this is possible.

The function we know, $R(\omega)$, must be generated from $Z(p)$ in the following manner (§ 5.11).

$$R(\omega) = [\text{Ev } Z(p)]_{p=j\omega} = \tfrac{1}{2}[Z(j\omega) + Z(-j\omega)]$$

$$= \left(\frac{M_1 M_2 - N_1 N_2}{M_2{}^2 - N_2{}^2} \right)_{p=j\omega}$$

$$= \frac{c_0 + c_2 \omega^2 + \cdots + c_{2m} \omega^{2m}}{d_0 + d_2 \omega^2 + \cdots + d_{2m} \omega^{2m}} = \frac{N(\omega^2)}{D(\omega^2)}. \quad (8.11-2)$$

Now $\text{Ev } Z(p)$ must be an even function of p with real coefficients. Accordingly, its zeros and poles must occur in the p plane in pairs (one member the negative of the other), as discussed in § 5.14. None of the poles can be imaginary, however. For the partial-fraction expansion of $Z(p)$ includes, as the terms producing such a pole and its mate,

$$\frac{k_0}{p - j\omega_0} + \frac{k_0}{p + j\omega_0} = \frac{2k_0 p}{p^2 + \omega_0{}^2}. \quad (8.11-3)$$

Since this is purely odd, it cannot appear in $\text{Ev } Z(p)$ and hence not in $R(\omega)$. (Such a pole represents excess reactance which could be removed without affecting the resistance, anyway.) Alternatively, if $Z(p)$ has a pole at $j\omega_0$, then $(p^2 + \omega_0{}^2)$ is a factor of both M_2 and N_2; this factor can be shown to disappear from (8.11-2) when $R(\omega)$ is expressed in lowest terms, as we now assume it is. Hence

a resistance function $R(\omega)$ obtained from a p-r function $Z(p)$ can have no real-frequency poles. $(8.11-4)$

The poles of **Ev** $Z(p)$ may lie anywhere in the complex plane, except on the imaginary axis and at infinity, provided they lie in symmetrical pairs if real, or in symmetrical tetrads if complex; they may be of any order. For this reason the highest power of ω in the numerator in (8.11–2) is the $2m$th; it cannot be higher, but may be lower. As to the zeros of **Ev** $Z(p)$, we can make no restrictive statement. They may be anywhere, provided only that they have the required quadrantal symmetry: that they lie in pairs if real or imaginary, or in tetrads if neither. If imaginary, they must be of even order so that $R(\omega)$ does not change sign; their orders are otherwise unrestricted. A real-frequency zero at $j\omega_0$ implies that $R(\omega_0) = 0$, but this is perfectly possible, as, for example, in the network of Fig. 8.02–D(a). These zeros of **Ev** $Z(p)$ will be extremely important in the developments of Chapter 9.

Our datum $R(\omega)$ should accordingly be in the form (8.11–2) in which the c's and d's are real, but generally unrestricted as to sign. Neither d_0 nor d_{2m} can vanish, but any of the other d's and any of the c's may be zero. The constant d_0 must be positive; neither c_0 nor the ratio c_{2m}/d_{2m} can be negative. Otherwise the coefficients are unrestricted—except as the conditions that $R(\omega)$ never go negative and that there be no poles at real values of ω imply restrictions. More succinctly, so long as $R(\omega)$ is rational, even, and is finite, real, and not negative for all values of ω (including infinity), then $R(\omega)$ meets all the requirements we can at present lay down for resistance functions.

Given such a function $R(\omega)$, we can proceed as follows to determine the $Z(p)$ from which it came. Since any real-frequency poles in the original $Z(p)$ function have no effect on the resistance function $R(\omega)$, we can assume that the form (8.11–1) which we seek is *minimum-reactance*; to the function $Z(p)$ which we obtain can be added any odd p-r function, and the result will be an equally good answer to the problem of finding the $Z(p)$ from which came the datum $R(\omega)$. We know all the c's and d's in (8.11–2); we know none of the a's and b's in (8.11–1)—but we can assume $n = m$, for if $n = m + 1$, then $Z(p)$ is not minimum-reactance. (The possibility that $n = m - 1$ is provided for by the possibility that $a_m = 0$.) From $R(\omega)$ we can immediately find **Ev** $Z(p)$. This calls only for replacing ω by p/j [the reverse of the process by which the even part of $Z(p)$ yields the resistance function]:

$$\mathbf{Ev}\, Z(p) = R(p/j). \qquad (8.11\text{–}5)$$

This means of removing the restraint to the imaginary axis will be of use again and again in later work; it is technically a form of analytic continuation, but actually amounts to nothing more than a change of symbols. We now know the polynomials $(M_2{}^2 - N_2{}^2)$ and $(M_1 M_2 - N_1 N_2)$. The next task is to separate out the individual polynomials $(M_1 + N_1)$ and $(M_2 + N_2)$ from these conglomerate forms.

Consider first the denominator, $(M_2{}^2 - N_2{}^2)$, which must have been formed from the product

$$(M_2 + N_2)(M_2 - N_2). \tag{8.11-6}$$

Now $(M_2 + N_2)$ is a Hurwitz polynomial, for if $R(\omega)$ is in lowest terms, it has no real-frequency poles. All the zeros of $(M_2 + N_2)$ lie in the left half plane. All the zeros of $(M_2 - N_2)$ lie in the *right* half plane, for if p_0 is a zero of $(M_2 + N_2)$, then

$$M_2(p_0) + N_2(p_0) = 0. \tag{8.11-7}$$

But the even polynomial M_2 is unaffected by a mere change in sign of the variable, whereas N_2 changes sign, and so

$$M_2(-p_0) - N_2(-p_0) = 0, \tag{8.11-8}$$

which states that $(-p_0)$ is a zero of $(M_2 - N_2)$. Such a zero lies in the right half plane, because p_0 itself lies in the left half plane. The zeros of $(M_2 - N_2)$ are the negatives of the zeros of $(M_2 + N_2)$ and lie in the right half plane. The polynomial $(M_2 - N_2)$ is sometimes called the *Hurwitz conjugate* of $(M_2 + N_2)$ for this reason. The term *anti-Hurwitz* is also occasionally used to describe polynomials, all of whose zeros are in the right half plane.

This fact makes it easy (in theory) to determine the denominator of $Z(p)$, given only the denominator of $R(\omega)$. We need only factor $D(-p^2)$, i.e., find its $2m$ zeros. These zeros will lie in pairs, one member in each half plane (if D has multiple zeros, some pairs will coincide). The member in the left half plane, in each pair, is a zero of the denominator of $Z(p)$; the other is to be rejected. From these left half plane zeros, multiplying together the corresponding factors $(p - p_1)$, $(p - p_2)$, $\cdots$, $(p - p_m)$, we obtain $(M_2 + N_2)$ except for a constant multiplier; this multiplier is evidently $\sqrt{|d_{2m}|}$, so that the determination of the denominator of $Z(p)$ is complete. And so this half of the job of determining $Z(p)$ can be done. Not without work, for the factoring of a polynomial requires labor; but there are devices for shortening this work (Appendix A). We now know the b's in (8.11-1). It remains to find the a's.

To determine the numerator of $Z(p)$ we cannot give similar treatment to the (known) numerator of $\mathrm{Ev}\, Z(p)$, for this is not the product of a Hurwitz polynomial and its Hurwitz conjugate. But we *can* form the even part of $Z(p)$ from this $R(\omega)$, and compare the latter with the datum $R(\omega)$. Only the a's are unknown, and from the comparison results a set of simultaneous equations, just enough to determine the a's. The calculation is

$$R(\omega) = \left[\frac{\begin{array}{c}(a_0 + a_2p^2 + a_4p^4 + \cdots)(b_0 + b_2p^2 + b_4p^4 + \cdots) \\ - (a_1p + a_3p^3 + \cdots)(b_1p + b_3p^3 + \cdots)\end{array}}{(b_0 + b_2p^2 + \cdots)^2 - (b_1p + b_3p^3 + \cdots)^2} \right]_{p=j\omega}$$

$$= \left[\frac{\begin{array}{c}(a_0b_0) + (a_0b_2 - a_1b_1 + a_2b_0)p^2 + (a_0b_4 - a_1b_3 \\ + a_2b_2 - a_3b_1 + a_4b_0)p^4 + \cdots\end{array}}{(b_0 + b_2p^2 + \cdots)^2 - (b_1p + b_3p^3 + \cdots)^2} \right]_{p=j\omega}$$

$$= \frac{c_0 + c_2\omega^2 + \cdots + c_{2m}\omega^{2m}}{d_0 + d_2\omega^2 + \cdots + d_{2m}\omega^{2m}}. \tag{8.11-9}$$

The denominator need not actually be calculated, but does serve as a useful check on the previous work. Since the numerators in the last two expressions must be identical, coefficients of corresponding powers of ω^2 must be equal, and we obtain the set of simultaneous equations

$$b_0a_0 \qquad\qquad\qquad\qquad\qquad\qquad = c_0$$

$$b_2a_0 - b_1a_1 + b_0a_2 \qquad\qquad\qquad\qquad = -c_2$$

$$b_4a_0 - b_3a_1 + b_2a_2 - b_1a_3 + b_0a_4 \qquad\qquad = c_4$$

$$b_6a_0 - b_5a_1 + b_4a_2 - b_3a_3 + b_2a_4 - b_1a_5 + b_0a_6 = -c_6 \qquad (8.11-10)$$

$$\cdots\cdots\cdots\cdots\cdots\cdots\cdots\cdots\cdots$$

$$\pm b_ma_{m-2} \mp b_{m-1}a_{m-1} \pm b_{m-2}a_m = \mp c_{2m-2}$$

$$\pm b_ma_m = \pm c_{2m}$$

In the last equations the upper signs apply if m is even, the lower if m is odd.

The rule of formation of these equations is simple and evident:

$$\sum_{r=0}^{2s} (-1)^r b_{2s-r}a_r = (-1)^s c_{2s}, \qquad s = 0, 1, 2, \cdots, m. \tag{8.11-11}$$

In this, a's and b's with subscripts greater than m are to be taken as zero. On the left side appears the sum, with alternating signs, of all possible products of a's and b's such that in each product the subscripts add up to the subscript of the c on the right; the sign attached to the c alternates from one equation to the next [this alternation of sign could be removed by defining c_{2s} as the coefficient of $(-\omega^2)^s$ if desired].

Equations (8.11-10) show how the coefficients of the unknown a's are made up of the even-subscript b's, and the odd-subscript b's with signs reversed. The vertical columns of coefficients are made up of one group or the other, with vertical shifts from one column to the next; the horizontal rows display the coefficients as in the denominator of Z, except for the sign changes. The detached-coefficient form of equations (8.11–12) (in which $m = 6$ for illustration) shows this even more clearly.

a_0	a_1	a_2	a_3	a_4	a_5	a_6		c
b_0	0	0	0	0	0	0	$=$	c_0
b_2	$-b_1$	b_0	0	0	0	0	$=$	$-c_2$
b_4	$-b_3$	b_2	$-b_1$	b_0	0	0	$=$	c_4
b_6	$-b_5$	b_4	$-b_3$	b_2	$-b_1$	b_0	$=$	$-c_6$
0	0	b_6	$-b_5$	b_4	$-b_3$	b_2	$=$	c_8
0	0	0	0	b_6	$-b_5$	b_4	$=$	$-c_{10}$
0	0	0	0	0	0	b_6	$=$	c_{12}

$$(8.11\text{-}12)$$

In any particular problem these equations can rapidly be written down, either from (8.11–10) or (8.11–11), from (8.11–12) which is convenient for methods of solution that operate on the detached coefficients, or by actually formulating them from $Z(p)$ and $R(\omega)$. It is important, to avoid possible sign errors, to remember that the a's and b's are coefficients of polynomials in p, whereas the c's are coefficients of a polynomial in ω.

In equations (8.11–10) both the b's and c's are known. They form then a set of $m + 1$ simultaneous linear equations in the $m + 1$ variables $a_0, a_1, a_2, \cdot \cdot \cdot, a_m$. Their solution is straightforward and can always be accomplished. Since there are a number of zero coefficients in the early and late equations, the solution is fairly easy to obtain for low-order functions. With the solution we know $Z(p)$ completely. Moreover, this $Z(p)$ is positive-real. For, by the nature of this Brune–Gewertz process, the coefficients in Z will be real, and Z will have no poles in the right half plane, on the imaginary axis or at infinity. Finally, **Re** $Z(j\omega)$ will be the function $R(\omega)$ from which we started; presumably this will not be negative at any value of ω, else we should have recognized its nonphysical character immediately.

We have succeeded in determining the whole impedance function starting from a knowledge of only the real part at real frequencies, of the resistance-versus-frequency characteristic. From this $Z(p)$ the associated reactance can easily be extracted if desired. The function $Z(p)$ thus found can be augmented by any reactance function (any odd p-r function) for this will not affect the corresponding $R(\omega)$. This merely shows, as we should expect, that only the *minimum* associated reactance $X(\omega)$ is determined by $R(\omega)$.

If $\mathrm{Re}\,Z(j\omega)$ is calculated from $Z(p)$ to establish the simultaneous equations, then it does not matter how the factors of the denominator of $Z(p)$ are written, as $(p - p_i)$ or $(p_i - p)$ or a mixture, for the unknown coefficients written in the numerator will automatically take correct values to go with the denominator as written. But if (8.11–10) or (8.11–11) or (8.11–12) is used to set up the simultaneous equations, then the multiplier and proper form of the denominator of $Z(p)$ are required, for the derivation assumed that the denominators of $\mathrm{Re}\,Z(j\omega)$ and of $R(\omega)$ were identical. A convenient method of avoiding this nuisance is initially to divide the numerator and denominator of the datum resistance function through by the coefficient of the highest power of ω in the denominator; then in the denominator of $Z(p)$ the coefficient of the highest power of p is unity. Then the two denominators will be identical (it makes no difference whether m is odd or even) and (8.11–10), (8.11–11), or (8.11–12) may safely be used.

To recapitulate the process we have developed above for calculating the impedance function from the resistance function:

1. if the coefficient of the highest power of ω in the denominator of the given resistance function is not unity, divide numerator and denominator by this coefficient, to set up $R(\omega)$ in the form (8.11–2) with $d_{2m} = 1$;
2. replace ω^2 in the denominator of $R(\omega)$ by $-p^2$;
3. factor this denominator, reject those poles that are in the right half plane, and form the denominator of $Z(p)$ from those that have negative-real parts, with unity as the coefficient of the highest power of p;
4. write for the numerator of $Z(p)$ a polynomial in p, of the same degree as the denominator found in step 3, with literal coefficients;
5. obtain simultaneous equations for the unknown coefficients from (8.11–10), (8.11–11), or (8.11–12) *or* by evaluating $\mathrm{Re}\,Z(j\omega)$ and equating this function to $R(\omega)$;
6. solve these equations for the unknown coefficients.   (8.11–13)

Simplifications are possible, notably in step 3; there the actual poles need not always be found, for it is only the product of factors forming the denominator of Z that is needed (see Appendix A). If the given resistance function is not minimum, it may first be reduced to minimum if the work is thereby simplified, though it need not be so reduced; the resistance subtracted here must of course be added back in the final impedance function. The end coefficients a_m and a_0 can be written by inspection. The final result should, of course, be checked by calculating its resistance function.

The p-r function $Z(p)$ so determined is minimum-reactance and has the resistance function from which we started; it is the associated minimum-reactance impedance function. From it the corresponding reactance can be calculated. Although the formulas given may be useful, the basic idea is easy to remember and is all that is really necessary to solve such problems. We shall next solve some, for illustration.

Example 1. Suppose the normalized datum resistance function is

$$R(\omega) = \frac{1}{1 + \omega^4} \quad \text{ohms.}$$

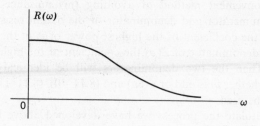

Fig. 8.11–A

(See Fig. 8.11–A.) Then

$$\text{Ev } Z(p) = \frac{1}{1 + p^4} = \frac{1}{(p - p_1)(p - \bar{p}_1)(p - p_2)(p - \bar{p}_2)}$$

in which

$$p_1 = 1\underline{/45°} = \frac{1 + j1}{\sqrt{2}},$$

$$p_2 = 1\underline{/135°} = \frac{-1 + j1}{\sqrt{2}},$$

are the roots of

$$p^4 + 1 = 0.$$

These are the four fourth roots of (-1) and lie on the unit circle, as shown in Fig. 8.11–B.

For the denominator of $Z(p)$ we take only p_2 and $\bar{p}_2$, and write

$$Z(p) = \frac{a_2 p^2 + a_1 p + a_0}{p^2 + \sqrt{2}p + 1}.$$

The corresponding resistance function is

$$\text{Re } Z(j\omega) = \left[\frac{(a_2 p^2 + a_0)(p^2 + 1) - (a_1 p)(\sqrt{2}p)}{(p^2 + 1)^2 - (\sqrt{2}p)^2} \right]_{p = j\omega}$$

$$= \frac{a_2 \omega^4 - (a_0 + a_2 - \sqrt{2}a_1)\omega^2 + a_0}{\omega^4 + 1}.$$

On comparison with the datum function we see that

$$a_2 = 0,$$

$$a_0 + a_2 - \sqrt{2}a_1 = 0,$$

$$a_0 = 1.$$

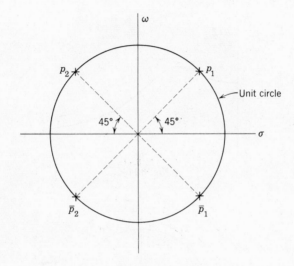

Fig. 8.11–B

These equations might equally well have been written by using (8.11–11), without forming **Re** $Z(j\omega)$.   From them we obtain

$$a_0 = 1,$$

$$a_1 = 1/\sqrt{2},$$

$$a_2 = 0.$$

Hence

$$Z(p) = \frac{(1/\sqrt{2})p + 1}{p^2 + \sqrt{2}p + 1} \quad \text{ohms}$$

is the minimum-reactance impedance function associated with the given $R(\omega)$.

Example 2. $R(\omega) = \dfrac{\omega^2 + 4}{\omega^4 - 4\omega^2 + 16}$ ohms.   (See Fig. 8.11–C.)   Proceeding as before, we obtain

$$\mathbf{Ev}\, Z(p) = \frac{-p^2 + 4}{p^4 + 4p^2 + 16}.$$

The poles are at

$$p^2 = -2 \pm \sqrt{4 - 16} = -2 \pm j2\sqrt{3} = 4\underline{/\pm 120°},$$

i.e., at

$$p_1 = 2\underline{/60°}, \bar{p}_1 = 2\underline{/60°},$$
$$p_2 = 2\underline{/120°} = -1 + j\sqrt{3}, \bar{p}_2 = 2\underline{/120°} = -1 - j\sqrt{3}.$$

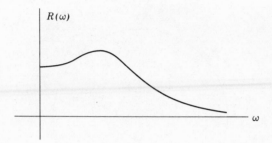

Fig. 8.11–C

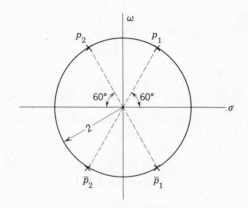

Fig. 8.11–D

(See Fig. 8.11–D.)   Then

$$Z(p) = \frac{a_2 p^2 + a_1 p + a_0}{p^2 + 2p + 4}.$$

Instead of calculating **Re** $Z(j\omega)$, let us write the equations for determining the a's from (8.11–11) or (8.11–10).   We have $d_{2m} = d_4 = 1$, as required, and

$$
\begin{array}{ll}
b_0 = 4 & c_0 = 4 \\
b_1 = 2 & c_2 = 1 \\
b_2 = 1 & c_4 = 0
\end{array}
$$

and the equations are

$$4a_0 \qquad\qquad = 4,$$
$$a_0 - 2a_1 + 4a_2 = -1,$$
$$a_2 = 0.$$

Hence

$$a_0 = 1,$$
$$a_1 = 1,$$
$$a_2 = 0,$$

and finally

$$Z(p) = \frac{p+1}{p^2 + 2p + 4} \quad \text{ohms.}$$

To this could be added the impedance of any L-C network, without disturbing the resistance function, but no reactance can be extracted from it.

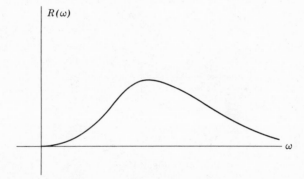

Fig. 8.11–E

Example 3. $R(\omega) = \dfrac{\omega^4}{\omega^6 + 3\omega^4 + 3\omega^2 + 1}$ ohms.   (See Fig. 8.11–E.)

$$\text{Ev } Z(p) = \frac{p^4}{-p^6 + 3p^4 - 3p^2 + 1}.$$

The denominator is simply $-(p^2 - 1)^3$ and hence the three poles of $Z(p)$ are all at $p = -1$; see Fig. 8.11–F.   If

$$Z(p) = \frac{a_3 p^3 + a_2 p^2 + a_1 p + a_0}{(p+1)^3} = \frac{a_3 p^3 + a_2 p^2 + a_1 p + a_0}{p^3 + 3p^2 + 3p + 1},$$

then

$$b_0 = 1 \qquad c_0 = 0$$
$$b_1 = 3 \qquad c_2 = 0$$
$$b_2 = 3 \qquad c_4 = 1$$
$$b_3 = 1 \qquad c_6 = 0.$$

Since $d_{2m} = d_6 = 1$, by (8.11–10) the equations are

$$a_0 \qquad\qquad\qquad = 0,$$
$$3a_0 - 3a_1 + \ a_2 = 0,$$
$$-a_1 + 3a_2 - 3a_3 = 1,$$
$$-a_3 = 0,$$

from which

$$a_0 = 0,$$
$$a_1 = \tfrac{1}{8},$$
$$a_2 = \tfrac{3}{8},$$
$$a_3 = 0.$$

Hence

$$Z(p) = \frac{0.375p^2 + 0.125p}{p^3 + 3p^2 + 3p + 1} \quad \text{ohms.}$$

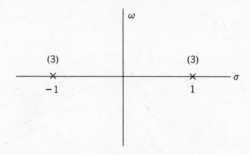

Fig. 8.11–F

Example 4.   Let the given resistance function be

$$R_0(\omega) = \frac{6(\omega^2 - 3)^4}{4\omega^8 - 7\omega^6 + 2\omega^4 + 40\omega^2 + 100} \quad \text{ohms,}$$

as shown in Fig. 8.11–G. Since the leading coefficient in the denominator is not unity, we divide numerator and denominator by it. It is convenient also to normalize, by division by 1.5. Then

$$R(\omega) = \frac{\omega^8 - 12\omega^6 + 54\omega^4 - 108\omega^2 + 81}{\omega^8 - 1.75\omega^6 + 0.5\omega^4 + 10\omega^2 + 25}.$$

To avoid the labor of factoring the denominator of Ev $Z(p)$, which is

$$p^8 + 1.75p^6 + 0.5p^4 - 10p^2 + 25,$$

we use the polynomial-splitting method of Appendix A (§ A.9). The result is the denominator of $Z(p)$ as written below.

$$Z(p) = \frac{a_4p^4 + a_3p^3 + a_2p^2 + a_1p + a_0}{p^4 + 3.700p^3 + 7.721p^2 + 9.338p + 5}.$$

The equations determining the a's are, in detached-coefficient form,

a_0	a_1	a_2	a_3	a_4	c	
5	0	0	0	0	=	81
7.721	−9.338	5	0	0	=	108
1	−3.700	7.721	−9.338	5	=	54
0	0	1	−3.700	7.721	=	12
0	0	0	0	1	=	1

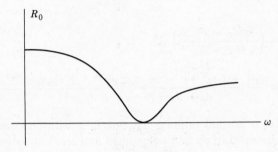

Fig. 8.11–G

The values of the a's (obtained by straightforward solution of the simultaneous equations) are

$$a_0 = 16.20,$$
$$a_1 = 6.618,$$
$$a_2 = 8.945,$$
$$a_3 = 1.261,$$
$$a_4 = 1,$$

so that

$$Z(p) = \frac{p^4 + 1.261p^3 + 8.945p^2 + 6.618p + 16.20}{p^4 + 3.700p^3 + 7.721p^2 + 9.338p + 5}.$$

To obtain the impedance function associated with the original resistance function we must multiply by 1.5 to restore the scale. The final result is

$$Z_0(p) = \frac{1.5p^4 + 1.891p^3 + 13.42p^2 + 9.927p + 24.30}{p^4 + 3.700p^3 + 7.721p^2 + 9.338p + 5} \quad \text{ohms.}$$

The simple arithmetic of most of these examples will not ordinarily be met in practice but the method is adequately illustrated.

The dual problem of calculating $Y(p)$ from $G(\omega)$ requires no discussion, for G simply replaces R and Y replaces X in the above, without further change.

8.12 The Brune-Gewertz method: from reactance (susceptance) to immittance function

The same method may also be used for the computation of $Z(p)$ when it is the reactance $X(\omega)$ that is given, and for the dual computation of $Y(p)$ from $B(\omega)$. There are some differences, but the principle is the same. If the (unknown) p-r function is $Z(p)$ as written in (8.11–1), then the known function $X(\omega)$ must be generated from $Z(p)$ in the following manner (§ 5.11).

$$X(\omega) = \frac{1}{j} [\mathbf{Od}\, Z(p)]_{p=j\omega} = \frac{1}{2j} [Z(j\omega) - Z(-j\omega)]$$

$$= \left(\frac{N_1 M_2 - M_1 N_2}{M_2{}^2 - N_2{}^2} \right)_{p=j\omega}$$

$$= \frac{c_1\omega + c_3\omega^3 + \cdots + c_{2m-1}\omega^{2m-1} + c_{2m+1}\omega^{2m+1}}{d_0 + d_2\omega^2 + \cdots + d_{2m}\omega^{2m}}. \qquad (8.12\text{--}1)$$

Since $\mathbf{Od}\, Z(p)$ is an odd rational function of p with real coefficients, it must be the quotient of an odd polynomial and an even polynomial, i.e., the product of a power of p and the quotient of two even polynomials. Accordingly, its zeros and poles must occur in pairs (one member the negative of the other), except that there must be a zero or pole at the origin and one at infinity. If there is a pole at the origin it must be simple, for $Z(p)$ is p-r and it is $X(\omega)$, not $R(\omega)$, that provides this pole, by (8.11–4); the same is true of a pole at infinity. (If there is a zero at the origin, or at infinity, however, there is no such restriction, so far as we yet know, except that the order must be odd.) Simple poles may occur at any real frequency, but if they do they represent reactance which can immediately be extracted and for which the corresponding impedance function (a pure reactance function) can immediately be written; this must of course have real, positive residues, considered as a function of p. These poles may be considered to correspond to a series L-C network, or to the fact that $Z(p)$, and hence $X(\omega)$, are not minimum-reactance.

We can simplify our work here if we assume that any such excess reactance has been removed from the datum reactance, so that the function from which we start has no real-frequency (or infinite) poles; we further assume that it is in lowest terms. Hence in (8.12–1) we have $c_{2m+1} = 0$; neither d_0 nor d_{2m} is zero, but any of the other d's and any of the c's may be zero. [The denominator is the same as the denominator of the corresponding $R(\omega)$ if $Z(p)$ is minimum-reactance.] The poles of $\mathbf{Od}\, Z(p)$ may now lie anywhere in the complex plane except on the imaginary axis and at infinity, provided they lie in symmetrical pairs if real, or in symmetrical tetrads if complex; they may be of any order. There must be a zero of odd order at the origin, and another at infinity; the other zeros of **Od** $Z(p)$ must also possess quadrantal symmetry, but we make no further restrictive statement about them. So far as we know, any odd rational function of ω that has no poles for real values of ω (including infinity) is suitable for a minimum-reactance $X(\omega)$.

Given such a minimum function $X(\omega)$, we proceed much as before to obtain the $Z(p)$ from which it came. We know all the c's and d's in (8.12–1), but none of the a's and b's in (8.11–1). From $X(\omega)$ we can immediately find **Od** $Z(p)$ by replacing ω by p/j and multiplying by j. Then the denominator of $Z(p)$ can be obtained from the denominator of **Od** $Z(p)$, exactly as before. To determine the numerator of $Z(p)$ we find the odd part of $Z(p)$, and from this $X(\omega)$ and equate it to the datum $X(\omega)$. The calculation is

$$X(\omega) = -\frac{1}{j}\left[\frac{\begin{array}{c}(a_1 p + a_3 p^3 + a_5 p^5 + \cdots)(b_0 + b_2 p^2 + b_4 p^4 + \cdots) \\ -(a_0 + a_2 p^2 + a_4 p^4 + \cdots)(b_1 p + b_3 p^3 + b_5 p^5 + \cdots)\end{array}}{(b_0 + b_2 p^2 + \cdots)^2 - (b_1 p + b_3 p^3 + \cdots)^2}\right]_{p=j\omega}$$

$$= j\left[\frac{\begin{array}{c}(a_0 b_1 - a_1 b_0)p + (a_0 b_3 - a_1 b_2 + a_2 b_1 - a_3 b_0)p^3 + \\ (a_0 b_5 - a_1 b_4 + a_2 b_3 - a_3 b_2 + a_4 b_1 - a_5 b_0)p^5 + \cdots\end{array}}{(b_0 + b_2 p^2 + \cdots)^2 - (b_1 p + b_3 p^3 + \cdots)^2}\right]_{p=j\omega}$$

$$= \frac{c_1\omega + c_3\omega^3 + c_5\omega^5 + \cdots + c_{2m-1}\omega^{2m-1}}{d_0 + d_2\omega^2 + \cdots + d_{2m}\omega^{2m}}. \qquad (8.12\text{–}2)$$

The denominator calculation, if made, serves merely as a check on the previous work. By equating coefficients of corresponding powers of ω in the two numerators, which must be identical, we obtain the following set of simultaneous equations, in which only the a's are unknown.

$$b_1 a_0 - b_0 a_1 \qquad\qquad\qquad\qquad\qquad = -c_1$$
$$b_3 a_0 - b_2 a_1 + b_1 a_2 - b_0 a_3 \qquad\qquad\qquad = c_3$$
$$b_5 a_0 - b_4 a_1 + b_3 a_2 - b_2 a_3 + b_1 a_4 - b_0 a_5 \qquad = -c_5$$
$$b_7 a_0 - b_6 a_1 + b_5 a_2 - b_4 a_3 + b_3 a_4 - b_2 a_5 + b_1 a_6 - b_0 a_7 = c_7 \qquad (8.12\text{–}3)$$
$$\cdot\ \cdot\ \cdot\ \cdot\ \cdot\ \cdot\ \cdot\ \cdot\ \cdot\ \cdot\ \cdot\ \cdot\ \cdot\ \cdot\ \cdot\ \cdot\ \cdot\ \cdot\ \cdot$$
$$\mp b_m a_{m-3} \pm b_{m-1} a_{m-2} \mp b_{m-2} a_{m-1} \pm b_{m-3} a_m = \mp c_{2m-3}$$
$$\mp b_m a_{m-1} \pm b_{m-1} a_m = \pm c_{2m-1}$$

In the last equations the upper signs apply if m is even, the lower if m is odd. The rule of formation is like that in the previous case, except for signs and interchange of the roles of odd- and even-subscript coefficients. Compactly, the equations are

$$\sum_{r=0}^{2s-1} (-1)^r b_{2s-1-r} a_r = (-1)^s c_{2s-1}, \qquad s = 1, 2, \cdots, m, \quad (8.12\text{--}4)$$

in which a's and b's with subscripts greater than m are to be taken as zero. Their formulation is somewhat more lucidly expressed by the detached-coefficient form of (8.12–5), given for $m = 6$.

a_0	a_1	a_2	a_3	a_4	a_5	a_6		c
b_1	$-b_0$	0	0	0	0	0	$=$	$-c_1$
b_3	$-b_2$	b_1	$-b_0$	0	0	0	$=$	c_3
b_5	$-b_4$	b_3	$-b_2$	b_1	$-b_0$	0	$=$	$-c_5$
0	$-b_6$	b_5	$-b_4$	b_3	$-b_2$	b_1	$=$	c_7
0	0	0	$-b_6$	b_5	$-b_4$	b_3	$=$	$-c_9$
0	0	0	0	0	$-b_6$	b_5	$=$	c_{11}

$$(8.12\text{--}5)$$

There is one striking difference between these equations and the set obtained for the calculation of $Z(p)$ from a known $R(\omega)$: here the number of equations is one less than the number of unknowns, for there are $m + 1$ unknown a's, but only m equations to determine them. Yet this is exactly as it should be. For to any $Z(p)$ we may be able to determine from the given $X(\omega)$ we can surely add any real constant we choose, without affecting the imaginary part of $Z(j\omega)$. This will change the a's, but not the b's, and implies that one of the a's is arbitrary, insofar as agreement between $\operatorname{Im} Z(j\omega)$ and the given $X(\omega)$ is concerned. For simplicity we now assume $a_m = 0$, and call the impedance function in which $a_m = 0$, $Z_0(p)$. Then $Z_0(\infty) = 0$ and hence $R_0(\infty) = 0$. To the resulting $Z_0(p)$ we may add any real constant we choose, as far as the mathematics is concerned; physics dictates, however, that the constant added must be at least large enough to insure that the resistance function is not negative at any frequency. The explanation of the arbitrariness is simply that the given reactance does not determine the impedance function uniquely, but only the minimum-resistance associated impedance function; to this we are at liberty to add any (constant) resistance we choose.

With the arbitrary choice $a_m = 0$, the mth column on the left of the simultaneous-equation set drops out, and we have m equations and m unknowns. For example, with $m = 6$, we have not (8.12–5) but (8.12–6).

a_0	a_1	a_2	a_3	a_4	a_5	c
b_1	$-b_0$	0	0	0	0	$= -c_1$
b_3	$-b_2$	b_1	$-b_0$	0	0	$= c_3$
b_5	$-b_4$	b_3	$-b_2$	b_1	$-b_0$	$= -c_5$
0	$-b_6$	b_5	$-b_4$	b_3	$-b_2$	$= c_7$
0	0	0	$-b_6$	b_5	$-b_4$	$= -c_9$
0	0	0	0	0	$-b_6$	$= c_{11}$

$$(8.12\text{-}6)$$

The equations can always be solved for the a's, thus determining an impedance function in which $a_m = 0$, which we have called $Z_0(p)$. Because of the manner of the creation of $Z_0(p)$, $\text{Im } Z_0(j\omega)$ is identical with the datum $X(\omega)$. Two corrections must be made to $Z_0(p)$. The first is to restore any excess reactance that may have been subtracted initially (as an odd p-r function of p). The second is to add to $Z_0(p)$ a real positive constant, at least large enough to insure that the resulting resistance does not become negative at any value of ω. Since $Z_0(\infty) = 0$, the final result may be written

$$Z(p) = Z_0(p) + Z_r(p) + R(\infty) \qquad (8.12\text{-}7)$$

in which the pure reactance function $Z_r(p)$ represents the excess reactance, and $R(\infty)$, the value of $\text{Re } Z(j\infty)$, is the added constant. The minimum value required for this constant must be determined by inspecting $R_0(\omega) = \text{Re } Z_0(j\omega)$; if the minimum value of $R_0(\omega)$ is $R_{\min}$ (a number no greater than zero), then $R(\infty)$ must be at least large enough to satisfy

$$R_{\min} + R(\infty) = 0. \qquad (8.12\text{-}8)$$

It may take any larger value, but the value given by (8.12–8) gives the minimum-resistance result. Then $Z(p)$ is p-r, much as in § 8.11, and has exactly the given reactance.

We have succeeded in determining the whole impedance function, starting from a knowledge of only the imaginary part at real frequencies, of only the reactance-versus-frequency characteristic. From this $Z(p)$ the associated resistance function can be extracted, and indeed must already have been found in order to determine the required additive constant. As expected, only the *minimum* associated resistance function is determined by the reactance.

It is convenient, as before, if d_{2m} is not unity in the given reactance expression, to make it so by·dividing numerator and denominator by the coefficient of the highest power of ω in the denominator. Then b_m is also unity, the denominators of $\text{Od } Z(j\omega)$ and $jX(\omega)$ are identical, and the simultaneous equations may be safely used. The process of calculating the impedance function from the reactance is as follows:

1. remove any real-frequency poles (including a pole at infinity) present in the given reactance;
2. if the coefficient of the highest power of ω in the denominator of the reduced reactance expression is not unity, make it so by dividing numerator and denominator by this coefficient, thus setting up the function $X_0(\omega)$;
3. replace ω^2 in the denominator of $X_0(\omega)$ by $-p^2$;
4. factor this denominator, reject those poles that are in the right half plane, and form the denominator of $Z_0(p)$ from those that have negative real parts, with unity as the coefficient of the highest power of p;
5. write for the numerator of $Z_0(p)$ a polynomial in p of degree one less than the degree of the denominator found in step 4, with literal coefficients;
6. obtain simultaneous equations for the unknown coefficients from (8.12–3) or (8.12–4) with $a_m = 0$, or from (8.12–6), or by evaluating $\mathbf{Im}\, Z_0(j\omega)$ and equating this function to $X_0(\omega)$;
7. solve these equations for the unknown coefficients;
8. determine the minimum value of $\mathbf{Re}\, Z_0(j\omega)$, $R_{\min}$;
9. to $Z_0(p)$ add the impedance function corresponding to the excess reactance removed in step 1, and a real constant equal to $-R_{\min}$.　　　(8.12–9)

The result is the minimum-resistance impedance function associated with the given reactance. As in the first problem, the actual poles need not always be found in step 4 (see Appendix A). The final result should of course be checked by calculating its reactance. For illustration, two examples are given below.

Example 1.　Suppose a network is to have the reactance given by

$$X_1(\omega) = \frac{-3}{\omega^3 + 4\omega} = \frac{-0.75}{\omega} + \frac{0.75\omega}{\omega^2 + 4} \quad \text{ohms.}$$

(See Fig. 8.12–A.) This function meets the known requirements (note that the residue at the origin in the corresponding impedance function is positive). Since it is not minimum, we remove the pole at the origin and set up

$$X_0(\omega) = \frac{\omega}{\omega^2 + 4}$$

as a normalized reactance expression to work with. Then

$$\mathbf{Od}\, Z_0(p) = \frac{p}{4 - p^2},$$

and

$$Z_0(p) = \frac{a_0}{2 + p}.$$

From this

$$X_0(\omega) = \frac{1}{j} \, \text{Od} \, Z_0(j\omega) = \frac{1}{j} \left(\frac{-a_0 p}{4 - p^2} \right)_{p=j\omega}$$

$$= \frac{-a_0 \omega}{4 + \omega^2} = \frac{\omega}{\omega^2 + 4}$$

so that $a_0 = -1$ and

$$Z_0(p) = \frac{-1}{p + 2}.$$

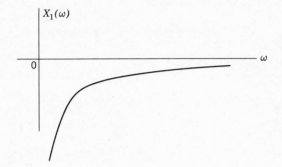

Fig. 8.12–A

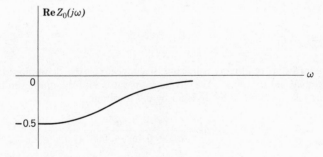

Fig. 8.12–B

The negative coefficient need not disturb us, for $Z_0(p)$ is not generally expected to be p-r, but to require the addition of a constant to make it so. To determine the minimum constant necessary, we calculate

$$\text{Re} \, Z_0(j\omega) = \frac{(-1)(2) - 0}{4 + \omega^2} = \frac{-2}{4 + \omega^2}.$$

Its behavior is shown in Fig. 8.12–B.

Evidently $R_{\min} = -0.5$ so that least 0.5 units of normalized resistance must be added. The final minimum-resistance result is

$$Z(p) = 0.75 \left(\frac{-1}{p+2} + \frac{1}{2} \right) + \frac{0.75}{p}$$

$$= 0.375 \frac{p^2 + 2p + 4}{p^2 + 2p} \quad \text{ohms}$$

which is p-r.

Example 2. Suppose we wish to find the minimum-resistance impedance function associated with the reactance

$$X(\omega) = \frac{2\omega^5 - 3\omega^3}{5\omega^8 - 2\omega^2 + 4} \quad \text{ohms}$$

whose behavior is shown in Fig. 8.12–C.

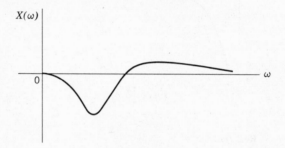

Fig. 8.12–C

This expression is already minimum-reactance, for the denominator has no zeros for real values of ω. We divide numerator and denominator by 5 and simultaneously normalize by division by 0.4 to obtain

$$X_0(\omega) = \frac{\omega^5 - 1.5\omega^3}{\omega^8 - 0.4\omega^2 + 0.8},$$

whose denominator, in terms of p, is

$$p^8 + 0.4p^2 + 0.8.$$

To avoid factoring this we use the polynomial-splitting method of Appendix A (§ A.9) to obtain the denominator of $Z_0(p)$. Then

$$Z_0(p) = \frac{a_3 p^3 + a_2 p^2 + a_1 p + a_0}{p^4 + 2.473p^3 + 3.057p^2 + 2.251p + 0.8944}.$$

From (8.12–6) we obtain the detached-coefficient form of the simultaneous equations (taking a_4, a_5, b_5, b_6 as zero),

a_0	a_1	a_2	a_3	c
2.251	-0.8944	0	0	$= 0$
2.473	-3.057	2.251	-0.8944	$= -1.5$
0	-1	2.473	-3.057	$= -1$
0	0	0	-1	$= 0$

whose solution gives

$$a_0 = 0.2012,$$
$$a_1 = 0.5065,$$
$$a_2 = -0.1996,$$
$$a_3 = 0.$$

Hence

$$Z_0(p) = \frac{-0.1996p^2 + 0.5065p + 0.2012}{p^4 + 2.473p^3 + 3.057p^2 + 2.251p + 0.8944}.$$

Again this is not p-r, but is not expected necessarily to be so.
We next calculate $\mathbf{Re}\, Z_0(j\omega)$ and find its minimum value.

$$\mathbf{Re}\, Z_0(j\omega) = \frac{0.1996\omega^6 - 1.661\omega^4 + 0.7036\omega^2 + 0.1800}{\omega^8 - 0.4\omega^2 + 0.8}.$$

The important features of the behavior of this function (obtained by straight-forward, though lengthy, calculation which we omit) are shown in Fig. 8.12–D.

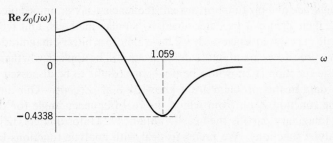

Fig. 8.12–D

Evidently we need to add the constant 0.4338 to Z_0 to obtain a p-r impedance function. At the same time we restore the scale by multiplying by 0.4; the result is

$$Z(p) = 0.1735\, \frac{p^4 + 2.473p^3 + 2.597p^2 + 3.419p + 1.358}{p^4 + 2.473p^3 + 3.057p^2 + 2.251p + 0.8944}\quad \text{ohms.}$$

The functions $Z(p)$ determined in these examples are the minimum-resistance impedance functions associated with the given reactance expressions. The dual process of calculating admittance functions (and hence conductance functions) from given susceptance expressions is mathematically and computationally identical.

The Brune-Gewertz method is a convenient one for calculating rational immittance functions when only the real-frequency resistance (conductance) or reactance (susceptance) is known. The first application is perhaps the more important, and will be found quite useful in certain two-terminal-pair problems (to be discussed in Volume II) as well as in one-terminal-pair problems. Notice how the method points out that there is a relation between resistance and reactance (conductance and susceptance), independently of the integral relations, by actually computing one from the other. It also shows the ambiguities of the results, and gives an alternative approach to the concepts of minimum reactance (susceptance) and resistance (conductance). Still another approach to these concepts and to the actual calculations, one which perhaps shows the relations even more clearly, will be found in Bode's method, to be discussed in § 8.17 and § 8.18.

The extension of the method to the calculation of angle from given magnitude, and the reverse—i.e., the corresponding problems in polar-coordinate form—is our next topic.

8.13 From magnitude to immittance function

With the background of the two previous sections, the corresponding polar-coordinate problems are easily treated. If we have a knowledge of the *magnitude* of a p-r function at real frequencies, say an impedance function Z, then $Z(p)$ can be determined by similar methods, and from this the angle at real frequencies. If we have a more arbitrary magnitude function, the process we are about to develop can still be applied, whether or not the basic function is known to be p-r—with results to be discussed below.

Our data in this problem are a knowledge of $|Z(j\omega)|$. Our aim is to find the function $Z(p)$, from which the real-frequency angle (or the real or the imaginary part) is then easily obtained. Unfortunately, $|Z|$ is not an analytic function. We prefer to deal with analytic functions because of the power of the theory of functions of a complex variable over analytic functions. But in § 8.11 a similar problem arose unnoticed and was solved immediately and unconsciously: there the nonanalytic function was $R(\omega)$, and the key to the problem's solution was to make use of the associated analytic function $\mathrm{Ev}\, Z(p)$. Here the associated analytic function suggests itself as soon as we recall the usual manner of forming the magnitude of a complex number, to multiply by its conjugate. To avoid radicals we use the square of the magnitude rather than the magnitude itself; this is

$$|Z(j\omega)|^2 = Z(j\omega)\overline{Z(j\omega)} = Z(j\omega)Z(-j\omega), \qquad (8.13\text{--}1)$$

for we are interested only in rational functions, with real coefficients. The generalization of this to an analytic function now suggests itself; it is the function

$$Z(p)Z(-p) \tag{8.13-2}$$

which, on the imaginary axis, is essentially the magnitude function we know, our starting point (cf. Problem 5-14). From these data, (8.13-1), we are to extract the function $Z(p)$, on the assumption that $Z(p)$ is p-r— or at least we shall try to make $Z(p)$ p-r by making the appropriate choice whenever a decision is to be made.

Now if $Z(p)$ were known, as

$$Z(p) = \frac{M_1 + N_1}{M_2 + N_2}, \tag{8.13-3}$$

we should obtain from it the real-frequency magnitude (squared) by evaluating

$$[Z(p)Z(-p)]_{p=j\omega} = \left(\frac{M_1 + N_1}{M_2 + N_2} \times \frac{M_1 - N_1}{M_2 - N_2}\right)_{p=j\omega} = \left(\frac{M_1^2 - N_1^2}{M_2^2 - N_2^2}\right)_{p=j\omega} \tag{8.13-4}$$

The function so obtained must, if $Z(p)$ is rational and p-r, be an even rational function of ω with real coefficients (every zero and every pole is accompanied by its negative and, if complex, by its conjugate); it cannot be negative for any value of ω; any zero or pole occurring at a real value of ω must be double; the degrees of numerator and denominator (in ω) must be the same, or differ by two. These properties are necessary if $Z(p)$, when extracted, is to be p-r—but they are not sufficient to insure that the $Z(p)$ extracted from such a magnitude function will be p-r, as we shall see. To perform this extraction we try simply to reverse the process in (8.13-4). To do this we have only to replace ω by p/j in $|Z|^2$ to obtain $Z(p)Z(-p)$, and then to apply the polynomial-decomposition process of § 8.11, but this time to both numerator and denominator. We proceed then to factor numerator and denominator. All zeros (of both polynomials) will occur in pairs, one member the negative of the other, as in § 8.11. These may be complex (lying in the usual tetrad formation) or real (in pairs) of any order. But they may also be imaginary provided that they are *double*, because the requirements of conjugate occurrence and of negative occurrence here coincide, and we have no interest in functions $Z(p)$ with other than simple imaginary zeros and poles. It is convenient to think of the four zeros that must occur if one imaginary zero occurs as a degenerate case of the general tetrad of Fig. 5.14–C in which the two upper-half-plane zeros come together, and so do the two lower-half-plane zeros. A zero at the origin must be double; here only two zeros occur, a degenerate case of the pair of zeros in Fig. 5.14–C. The novelty, in comparison with § 8.11, is not consequential. We have still to consider each pair (one member the negative of the other) in turn, to retain one member and to discard the other. For those pairs whose members lie off the imaginary axis, the procedure is exactly as in § 8.11: to retain the left-half-plane member, for we aim to make $Z(p)$ p-r. From those pairs whose members lie on the axis and not in either half plane, a zero (either one) is to be retained from one pair of the tetrad and its conjugate from the other pair.

Figure 8.13–A illustrates the selection process, which is not in essence changed by the presence of the imaginary zeros (or poles); in the real pair p_a (be it zero or pole) is to be retained, $-p_a$ is to be rejected, whereas in

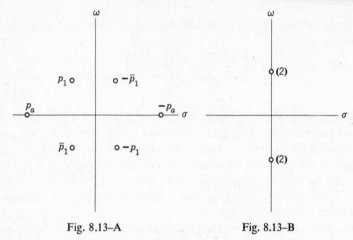

Fig. 8.13–A   Fig. 8.13–B

the complex tetrad p_1 and $\bar{p}_1$ are to be retained, $-p_1$ and $-\bar{p}_1$ are to be rejected—choices surely inevitable if $Z(p)$ is to be p-r, though they do not insure that it will be. If imaginary zeros (poles) appear, they must do so in degenerate tetrads as in Fig. 8.13–B; again the appropriate member of each of the two pairs must be selected, but because of the coincidence, it is not necessary to say more than that one zero (pole) and its conjugate must be taken. A zero at the origin will be double (p_a and $-p_a$ of Fig. 8.13–A coalesce); one is to be retained, the other rejected.

The zeros and poles of $Z(p)$ are thus determined, very easily, from the given magnitude function, by a process that is not really new. There remains only the multiplier; it clearly must be the square root of the multiplier of the datum function (8.13–1), when the latter is written with an external multiplier and the leading coefficients in both numerator and denominator equal to unity. This multiplier must be real and positive, both in $Z(p)$ and in $|Z(j\omega)|^2$, else $Z(p)$ is surely not p-r, and in such situations we have no interest. There is evidently no ambiguity then in the determination of $Z(p)$ from a knowledge only of its magnitude on the imaginary axis, and this is in agreement with § 8.07; the determination is unique. The process, in retrospect, is to:

1. write the datum magnitude function, if not already so, in the form

$$|Z|^2 = K \frac{\omega^{2n} + c_{2n-2}\omega^{2n-2} + \cdots + c_0}{\omega^{2m} + d_{2m-2}\omega^{2m-2} + \cdots + d_0}$$

in which K is of necessity real and positive;

2. replace ω^2 by $-p^2$, and thus obtain the function

$$Z(p)Z(-p) = \pm K \frac{p^{2n} - c_{2n-2}p^{2n-2} + c_{2n-4}p^{2n-4} - \cdots}{p^{2m} - d_{2m-2}p^{2m-2} + d_{2m-4}p^{2m-4} - \cdots};$$

3. factor numerator and denominator, reject right-half-plane zeros and poles and half of any imaginary zeros and poles (but in conjugate pairs);

4. form $Z(p)$ from the remaining zeros and poles as

$$Z(p) = \sqrt{K} \frac{(p - p_1)(p - p_2) \cdots}{(p - p_1')(p - p_2') \cdots} = \frac{M_1 + N_1}{M_2 + N_2}.$$

Whether n and m are odd or even determines the sign effective in step 2, but this is of no consequence and may be ignored, as indicated [the negative sign, if present, belongs to $Z(-p)$ and not to $Z(p)$]. The work of factoring may again be reduced by the method described in Appendix A. The resulting $Z(p)$, obtained in step 4, should of course be checked by evaluating its real-frequency magnitude.

The function $Z(p)$ thus obtained is unique, for the process can give but one result. The function $Z(p)$ will have the correct magnitude on the imaginary axis, but whether it is p-r or not cannot be determined by casual examination of the datum function of ω. Although it is a simple matter to determine whether a given resistance (conductance) function will yield a p-r immittance function (§ 8.11), or whether a given reactance (susceptance) will do so (§ 8.12), there appears to be no equally simple test to determine whether a given magnitude function will do so. The function $Z(p)$ must be tested for positive reality, with results that are completely determined by the magnitude function, but not in explicit form; the test must be performed to extract them. Some parts of the test have been applied already, but some testing remains to be done, either directly or as by the method of Problems 8-73, 8-74—unless it is somehow known that the datum function was originally obtained from a p-r function. This problem of determining the whole function (and hence the angle) from the magnitude alone does not necessarily have a p-r answer because the magnitude function meets some simple requirements.

The dual problem of determining the admittance function $Y(p)$, and hence the angle of $Y(j\omega)$, can be handled by replacing Z by Y in the above, or simply by inverting the data.

Example 1. Suppose, in illustration, that the datum function is the squared magnitude function

$$|Z|^2 = 9\frac{\omega^4 - 4\omega^2 + 4}{\omega^2 + 16} \quad \text{ohms}^2$$

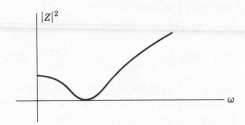

Fig. 8.13–C

(see Fig. 8.13–C) which is even, does not become negative, has only second-order zeros and poles for real values of ω, and thus meets the necessary conditions laid down above for Z to be p-r. The determination of $Z(p)$ is carried out below.

From the datum function,

$$Z(p)Z(-p) = -9\frac{p^4 + 4p^2 + 4}{p^2 - 16} = -9\frac{(p^2 + 2)^2}{p^2 - 16}.$$

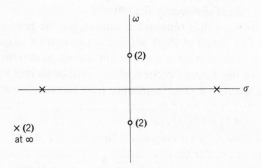

Fig. 8.13–D

(See Fig. 8.13–D.)   Then

$$Z(p) = 3\frac{p^2 + 2}{p + 4}.$$

Tests 1 and 2 of (5.13–5) are evidently passed. For test 3 we find

$$\mathbf{Re}\, Z(j\omega) = 3\left[\frac{(p^2 + 2)(4) - 0}{16 - p^2}\right]_{p=j\omega}$$

$$= 3\frac{8 - 4\omega^2}{16 + \omega^2}$$

which is clearly negative for large ω. Hence the function $Z(p)$ associated with the given magnitude function is not p-r—and this in spite of the fact that the data are superficially satisfactory.

Example 2. Suppose the data are changed now to

$$|Z|^2 = 9\frac{\omega^4 - 4\omega^2 + 4}{\omega^2 + 16} + 36 \quad \text{ohms}^2$$

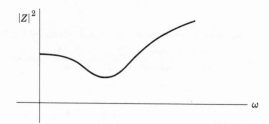

$$|Z|^2$$

$$\omega$$

Fig. 8.13–E

(see Fig. 8.13–E) which alters the function of Example 1 only by the addition of a constant (an upward displacement of the curve). Now the calculation runs

$$|Z|^2 = 9\frac{\omega^4 + 68}{\omega^2 + 16},$$

$$Z(p)Z(-p) = -9\frac{p^4 + 68}{p^2 - 16}$$

(see Fig. 8.13–F),

$$Z(p) = 3\frac{p^2 + 4.061p + 8.246}{p + 4}.$$

The numerator above can be obtained either by straightforward factoring and discarding of right-half-plane zeros, or by the polynomial-splitting method of Appendix A. This function passes tests 1 and 2 for positive reality; for test 3 we have

$$\mathbf{Re}\, Z(j\omega) = 3\left[\frac{(p^2 + 8.246)(4) - (4.061p)(p)}{(4)^2 - (p)^2}\right]_{p=j\omega}$$

$$= 3\frac{32.98 + 0.06108\omega^2}{16 + \omega^2}.$$

Evidently $Z(p)$, this time, is p-r. (Some further discussion of the effect of adding a constant to a magnitude function will be found in Chapter 14.)

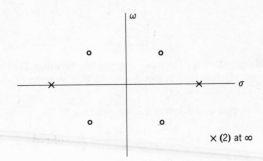

Fig. 8.13–F

Example 3.   A somewhat different illustration is given by the function

$$|Z|^2 = \frac{\omega^2(\omega^6 + 36\omega^4 - 732\omega^2 + 3364)}{6(\omega^2 - 9)^2(\omega^4 + 2.25\omega^2 + 4)} \quad \text{ohms}^2$$

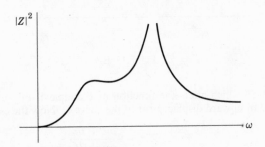

Fig. 8.13–G

(see Fig. 8.13–G).   From this we obtain

$$Z(p)Z(-p) = \frac{-p^2(-p^6 + 36p^4 + 732p^2 + 3364)}{6(p^2 + 9)^2(p^4 - 2.25p^2 + 4)}$$

(see Fig. 8.13–H).   The polynomial-splitting process (Appendix A) extracts the left-half-plane zeros and poles; with these and the natural splitting of the real-frequency critical points, we get

$$Z(p) = \frac{p(p^3 + 8p^2 + 14p + 58)}{\sqrt{6}(p^2 + 9)(p^2 + 2.5p + 2)}.$$

Extraction of the real-frequency poles gives

$$Z(p) = \frac{1}{\sqrt{6}}\left(\frac{2p}{p^2 + 9} + \frac{p^2 + 6p}{p^2 + 2.5p + 2}\right).$$

Of the test to determine whether $Z(p)$ as given above is p-r, the only part not passed by inspection is step 3. We form

$$\text{Re } Z(j\omega) = \frac{1}{\sqrt{6}} \left[\frac{p^2(p^2 + 2) - 15p^2}{(p^2 + 2)^2 - (2.5p)^2} \right]_{p=j\omega}$$

$$= \frac{1}{\sqrt{6}} \frac{\omega^4 + 13\omega^2}{\omega^4 + \cdots}$$

which is not negative for real ω. Hence the $Z(p)$ obtained from the datum magnitude function is in this case p-r.

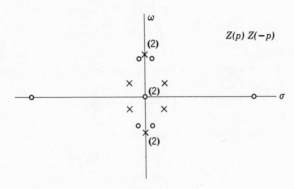

Fig. 8.13–H

8.14 From angle to immittance function

To calculate, say, $Z(p)$, given only a knowledge of the angle of $Z(j\omega)$, is a complementary problem, equally easy to solve. And it is more satisfying in that it is easy to predict whether the resulting $Z(p)$ will be p-r or not.

The data is now $\overline{Z(j\omega)}$, and our problem is to determine $Z(p)$, and hence $|Z(j\omega)|$ (or the real or the imaginary part). Again we have a non-analytic function and should prefer to deal instead with some related but analytic function. Such a function is not the product of $Z(p)$ and $Z(-p)$, used in § 8.13, but rather their quotient,

$$\frac{Z(p)}{Z(-p)}, \tag{8.14–1}$$

which on the imaginary axis is essentially the angle function we know (cf. Problem 5-14). For if

$$Z(j\omega) = |Z|e^{j\beta}, \tag{8.14–2}$$

then

$$\frac{Z(j\omega)}{Z(-j\omega)} = e^{j2\beta}. \tag{8.14-3}$$

It is the function $\beta(\omega)$ from which we start and from which we are to obtain the function $Z(p)$. The relation between Z and its angle is a transcendental one, as evidenced by (8.14-3) or by (8.14-4), which exhibits the method of calculating β when Z is known.

$$\beta(\omega) = \tan^{-1}\left[\frac{\operatorname{Im} Z(j\omega)}{\operatorname{Re} Z(j\omega)}\right]$$

$$= \tan^{-1}\left[\frac{N_1 M_2 - N_2 M_1}{j(M_1 M_2 - N_1 N_2)}\right]_{p=j\omega}. \tag{8.14-4}$$

A rational function, easier to deal with, is obtained simply by considering the tangent of the angle rather than the angle itself, by discussing

$$\tan \beta = \frac{1}{j}\left(\frac{N_1 M_2 - N_2 M_1}{M_1 M_2 - N_1 N_2}\right)_{p=j\omega} \tag{8.14-5}$$

or better yet (to remove the awkward j)

$$\tanh(j\beta) = \left(\frac{N_1 M_2 - N_2 M_1}{M_1 M_2 - N_1 N_2}\right)_{p=j\omega}. \tag{8.14-6}$$

The generalization of this function to arbitrary values of p is clearly

$$T(p) = \tanh(j\beta) = \frac{\operatorname{Od} Z(p)}{\operatorname{Ev} Z(p)} = \frac{Z(p) - Z(-p)}{Z(p) + Z(-p)} \tag{8.14-7}$$

in which β is no longer generally real, but is surely so when $p = j\omega$; our task is simply to obtain $Z(p)$ from (8.14-4), probably by using (8.14-7). Since

$$Z(p) = \operatorname{Ev} Z + \operatorname{Od} Z \tag{8.14-8}$$

and since β and hence the rational function $\tanh(j\beta)$ are known, it seems that simple addition of numerator and denominator of (8.14-7) should give $Z(p)$. This idea is essentially correct, but requires careful attention to detail and alas! some work. For in $\tanh(j\beta)$ we have no explicit statement of the odd and even parts of $Z(p)$, but only of their ratio. Yet this is enough to determine $Z(p)$, though only within a constant multiplier (as we should expect, since a real multiplier has no effect on the angle, and from the discussion of § 8.07). The detailed argument follows.

Let the datum angle be given by the rational function which is its tangent. Such a function must meet certain requirements if $Z(p)$ is to be p-r—not any rational function will do—and we must determine these requirements. If $Z(p)$, assumed to be p-r, is written as in (8.11–1), then its angle is obtained by writing out (8.14–4); this gives

$$\tan \beta = \frac{1}{j}\left[\frac{(a_0b_1 - a_1b_0)p + (a_0b_3 - a_1b_2 + a_2b_1 - a_3b_0)p^3 + \cdots}{(a_0b_0) + (a_0b_2 - a_1b_1 + a_2b_0)p^2 + \cdots}\right]_{p=j\omega}$$

$$(8.14\text{–}9)$$

much like (8.11–9) and (8.12–2), and finally

$$\tan \beta = \frac{(a_0b_1 - a_1b_0)\omega - (a_0b_3 - a_1b_2 + a_2b_1 - a_3b_0)\omega^3 + \cdots}{(a_0b_0) - (a_0b_2 - a_1b_1 + a_2b_0)\omega^2 + \cdots}$$

$$= \frac{c_1\omega + c_3\omega^3 + c_5\omega^5 + \cdots}{d_0 + d_2\omega^2 + d_4\omega^4 + \cdots}. \qquad (8.14\text{–}10)$$

The function $\tan \beta$ must be odd, but the only other requirement we can lay down is that $|\beta|$ must not exceed $90°$ (for we are interested only in p-r functions, whose angle is so restricted at real frequencies). This implies no restrictions on the zeros or poles of (8.14–10); but if β is to be extracted therefrom, careful selection from the multiple values of the $\tan^{-1}$ function is required. Presumably corresponding care is required in extracting $Z(p)$; we shall find, however, that any odd rational function of ω with real coefficients is the tangent of the angle of a p-r function, and we shall determine that function. This means that in this problem, in contrast to that of § 8.13, we know whether the result will be p-r before doing any work.

Suppose then that we are given a rational function of ω, arbitrary except that it is odd and the coefficients, the c's and d's in the form (8.14–10), are real (some may be zero); we assume also that this function is in lowest terms and, merely to be specific, that the numerator is odd, the denominator even. (The other case is treated later.) We shall find a p-r function, the tangent of whose angle β at real frequencies is this datum function. To do this we reverse the process of finding $\tan \beta$ from $Z(p)$, described above, and introduce whatever supplementary processes are necessary. The first step, as usual, is to replace ω in the datum function (8.14–11) by p/j to obtain the generalized function (8.14–12).

$$\tan \beta = \frac{c_1\omega + c_3\omega^3 + c_5\omega^5 + \cdots}{d_0 + d_2\omega^2 + d_4\omega^4 + \cdots} \qquad (8.14\text{–}11)$$

$$\tanh (j\beta) = \frac{c_1p - c_3p^3 + c_5p^5 - \cdots}{d_0 - d_2p^2 + d_4p^4 - \cdots}$$

$$= \frac{pB}{A} = \frac{\text{Od } Z(p)}{\text{Ev } Z(p)}. \qquad (8.14\text{–}12)$$

In (8.14–12) A and B represent (known) even polynomials in p and $Z(p)$ is the function we seek; by (8.14–7), if Z exists, it is thus related to β. Now to add numerator and denominator is an obvious step. But the result,

$$Q(p) = A + pB \qquad (8.14\text{--}13)$$

is a polynomial, certainly not p-r in general and not the $Z(p)$ we seek. Yet its angle has the correct tangent, even though the angle may exceed $\pi/2$ radians at real frequencies when ω is large enough. The inverse tangent function is multivalued, however, and (8.14–13) is not the only rational function whose angle has the given function for its tangent.

Nor is (8.14–13) the only rational function with its real-frequency angle. To understand this we need only observe (Fig. 8.14–A) that when $p = j\omega$,

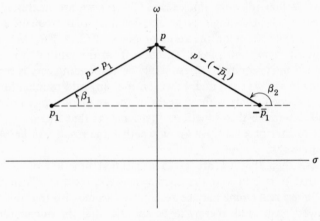

Fig. 8.14–A

the contributions to the angle made by a zero at some left-half-plane point p_1 and by one at the symmetrical right-half-plane point $-\bar{p}_1$ are very closely related. Specifically, the contribution in radians due to a factor $(p - p_1)$ in the numerator is β_1; that due to a factor $(p + \bar{p}_1)$ is β_2, and

$$\beta_2 = \pi - \beta_1 \qquad (8.14\text{--}14)$$

from symmetry, for $-\bar{p}_1$ is the reflection of p_1 in the imaginary axis. Except for a constant, the contributions differ only in sign. If either factor is in the denominator (rather than the numerator), only the sign of its angle contribution is changed thereby. Hence if any zero (pole) of a rational function is reflected in the imaginary axis and changed to a pole (zero), the only effect on the real-frequency angle of that function is the addition or subtraction of the constant π (we shall use radian measure), which amounts only to a change of sign of the function, and can be corrected simply by changing the sign of the multiplier. This process will have considerable effect on the real-frequency magnitude, of course, but it shows how a number of different rational functions can have the same real-frequency angle function.

Since no right-half-plane zeros are allowed in p-r functions, our next step, accordingly, is to reflect all right-half-plane zeros of $Q(p)$ in the imaginary axis and to make them poles. This requires that $Q(p)$ be factored, at least into two parts, representing a certain amount of unavoidable work. There will be no imaginary zeros, incidentally, because of our assumption that (8.14–12) is in lowest terms. We write

$$Q(p) = (\text{constant}) \times \underbrace{[(p - p_1)(p - p_2) \cdot \cdot \cdot]}_{\text{left-half-plane zero factors}} \times \underbrace{[(p - p_a)(p - p_b) \cdot \cdot \cdot]}_{\text{right-half-plane zero factors}}$$

(8.14–15)

and then form

$$Z_1(p) = \frac{(p - p_1)(p - p_2) \cdot \cdot \cdot}{(p + \bar{p}_a)(p + \bar{p}_b) \cdot \cdot \cdot} = \frac{(p - p_1)(p - p_2) \cdot \cdot \cdot}{(p + p_a)(p + p_b) \cdot \cdot \cdot}$$

(8.14–16)

which is not necessarily the final result, though its zeros and poles are all in the left half plane (or at infinity). We need not concern ourselves with the constant (a multiple of π) introduced into the angle by this operation; $Z_1(0)$ will automatically be real and positive when $Z_1(p)$ is written as in (8.14–16), so that the sign of the multiplier (here assumed to be unity) is correct for positive reality—and since the tangent function has a period of π, $\tan \beta$ will still be correct.

In $Z_1(p)$ we have a function whose numerator and denominator are Hurwitz polynomials, and whose real-frequency angle has the required tangent. But Z_1 is not necessarily p-r (though it may be) and our task is not necessarily completed. [The polynomial $Q(p)$ might, for example, be a Hurwitz polynomial, so that Z_1 will not differ from Q.] To obtain $Z(p)$ from $Z_1(p)$ we have to examine the multiple values of the inverse tangent function more closely, for (as previously mentioned) there are other rational functions with different real-frequency angles but the same tangent function. The function Z_1 is not necessarily the correct choice among these. To determine whether it is, and if not, what changes must be made, we have to examine the behavior of (8.14–11) more closely. As ω increases from zero, where the tangent is zero, $\tan \beta$ varies as does any rational function; in particular it may have zeros and poles. The zeros are not important here, but the poles are, for it is at these points that the ambiguity in the value of β becomes important. For a p-r function (in the case under consideration), $\beta(0)$ must be zero (not any other multiple of π), and β will reach one of the values $\pm\pi/2$ at the first pole of $\tan\beta$. We must insure that beyond this pole β does not exceed the limits $\pm\pi/2$ and Z does not enter the second or third quadrant, and that similar behavior occurs at all values of ω where (8.14–11) becomes infinite. Now

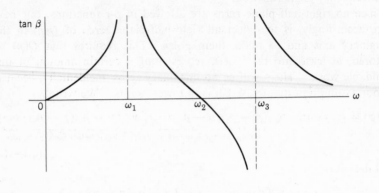

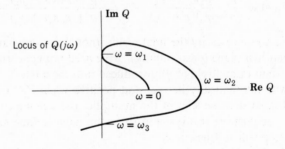

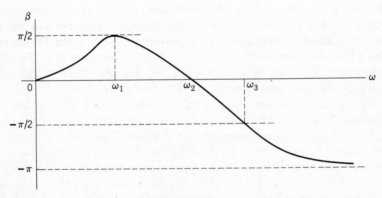

Fig. 8.14–B

the real-frequency angle of Z_1 is the same as that of Q, except possibly for a constant difference (a multiple of π) which we now drop—so that $Q(0)$ is real and positive.   Since Q is a polynomial, the behavior of its angle is easily investigated.   At a finite pole of $\tan \beta$, $A = 0$ while $B \neq 0$.   There $Q(j\omega)$ lies on the imaginary axis.   If the pole is of even order, the zero of A is of even order and A has the same sign on both sides of the pole.   Hence, as ω increases Q returns to the same (first or fourth) quadrant and β behaves as we wish it to.   But if the pole is of odd order, the sign of A changes, Q enters the left half plane, $|\beta|$ becomes greater than $\pi/2$—and this situation must be remedied.

Figure 8.14–B illustrates each of these types of behavior.   We can confine the variation of β very easily by taking advantage of the multiple-valued nature of the $\tan^{-1}$ function: a change in β of π does not affect $\tan \beta$; hence we can confine the variation of β if it is possible to introduce a sudden change, like that illustrated in Fig. 8.14–C.   The dashed curve

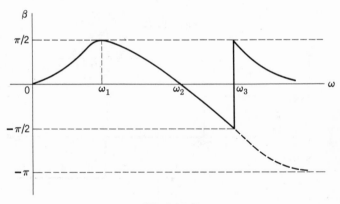

Fig. 8.14–C

shows β as it was; with the sharp change of π introduced at ω_3, β varies as the solid curve, and remains within the desired limits.   (For $\omega > \omega_3$ the original curve is merely displaced upward by the constant π.)   And such a discontinuity in β is not only possible, it is rather natural.   We have as yet no real-frequency zeros or poles in Z_1.   Such zeros and poles are perfectly admissible in p-r functions, provided they are simple and the derivative or residue of the function thereat is real and positive.   And their contributions to the real-frequency angle of the function are exactly the "step" functions we desire.   A simple zero at a point $j\omega_0$ (accompanied of course by its conjugate) contributes the factor $(p^2 + \omega_0^2)$, with the angle function shown in Fig. 8.14–D; for an imaginary pole at $j\omega_0$, Fig. 8.14–E applies. The angle functions are properly drawn exactly as shown, because these imaginary zeros and poles are limiting cases of left-half-plane zeros and poles; the path taken by p in their vicinity should be indented to the *right* half plane, as by a small semicircle around the

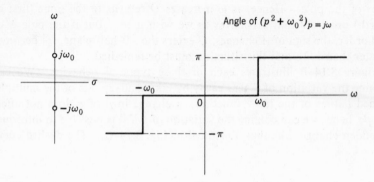

Fig. 8.14–D

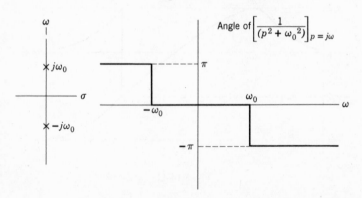

Fig. 8.14–E

critical point, in the right half plane. [Presumably these are connected, in the network realization, with L and C elements, and any slight amount of dissipation (resistance) would move them to the left of the axis.]

In our example, then, we need to introduce a simple zero at $j\omega_3$ (and of course its mate at $-j\omega_3$, where β will behave properly because its components are odd functions). This gives us the function

$$Z_2(p) = Z_1(p) \times (p^2 + \omega_3^2) \tag{8.14–17}$$

whose angle behaves exactly as the solid curve in Fig. 8.14–C.   Although
the angle is affected by the new factor, the tangent is not, because of the
periodicity of the tangent (or because the factor will appear in both odd
and even parts, and cancel out in their ratio).   Notice also that the
derivative $Z_2{}'(j\omega_3)$ is automatically real and positive, as it must be if Z_2
is to be p-r; for, near $j\omega_3$,

$$Z_2 = Z_1(j\omega_3) \times (p + j\omega_3)(p - j\omega_3) \qquad (8.14\text{–}18)$$

and

$$Z_2{}'(j\omega_3) = j2\omega_3 Z_1(j\omega_3). \qquad (8.14\text{–}19)$$

But $Z_1(j\omega_3)$ is clearly $0 - jX_1$, in which X_1 is real and positive, by the
behavior of its angle there.   Accordingly

$$Z_2{}'(j\omega_3) = (j2\omega_3)(-jX_1) = 2\omega_3 X_1 \qquad (8.14\text{–}20)$$

which is real and positive.

The discussion above has all the essentials of a complete treatment.
Wherever the angle of Z_1 crosses $-\pi/2$ (decreasing), a pair of imaginary
zeros will confine it as required.   Wherever the angle of Z_1 crosses $\pi/2$
(increasing), a pair of imaginary poles will confine the variation.   The
number of imaginary zeros and poles required will depend upon the
original excursions of the angle and upon the excursions still made as
zeros (poles) are added.   But in this way all the odd-order poles of the
tangent function can be taken care of (by introducing enough imaginary
zeros and poles at appropriate points), and the even-order poles, as we
have seen, need no attention.   The datum function $\tan \beta$ may have zeros
and poles distributed at random, provided only that it is odd, and the
coefficients are real; the locus of $Q(j\omega)$ may have all sorts of wiggles,
crossings, and excursions into all quadrants—proper introduction of
imaginary zeros and poles will always convert Z_1 into a function $Z(p)$
whose real-frequency angle does not exceed $\pi/2$ in magnitude.

Let us call the function obtained when $Z_1(p)$ has been thus modified,
and a real positive (but otherwise arbitrary) multiplier prefixed, $Z(p)$.
Then $Z(p)$ is p-r and the tangent of its real-frequency angle is the datum
function.   For Z passes the complete test for positive reality because of
its construction: its coefficients are real, it is analytic in the right half
plane, its behavior at infinity and at real-frequency poles is proper, and
its real part does not go negative for any imaginary value of p—and the
tangent of the angle of $Z(j\omega)$ is certainly the datum function, which we
have carefully preserved.

Before summing up the procedure we must consider the case in which
the datum function is reciprocal in form to (8.14–11), i.e., the denominator

is odd and the numerator even.   If the datum function (in lowest terms) is

$$\tan \beta = \frac{d_0 + d_2\omega^2 + d_4\omega^4 + \cdots}{c_1\omega + c_3\omega^3 + c_5\omega^5 + \cdots} \tag{8.14-21}$$

so that

$$\tanh (j\beta) = -\frac{d_0 - d_2 p^2 + d_4 p^4 - \cdots}{c_1 p - c_3 p^3 + c_5 p^5 + \cdots}$$

$$= \frac{A}{pB} = \frac{\text{Od } Z(p)}{\text{Ev } Z(p)}, \tag{8.14-22}$$

then some modification in the procedure must be made.   The tangent function has a pole at the origin (which pole must be of odd order, for the function is necessarily odd);   hence the angle β must there be $\pi/2$ in magnitude.   But the polynomial $Q(p) = A + pB$ will there have a *real* value.   Evidently we need to do more than merely add numerator and denominator;   we must also invert the tangent of the angle of $Q(j\omega)$ and change its sign, which amounts to displacing the angle by $\pi/2$.   And this is easily done, for it calls only for multiplication or division of $Q(p)$ by p. Then it is either

$$Q_1 = p(A + pB) \tag{8.14-23}$$

or

$$Q_2 = \frac{A + pB}{p} \tag{8.14-24}$$

with which we must deal;   both have the required real-frequency tangent function.   Which is appropriate is easily determined by examining the behavior of the angle of $Q(j\omega)$.   Call this angle β_1.   Then

$$\tan \beta_1 = \frac{1}{j}\left(\frac{pB}{A}\right)_{p=j\omega} = -\frac{c_1\omega + c_3\omega^3 + c_5\omega^5 + \cdots}{d_0 + d_2\omega^2 + d_4\omega^4 + \cdots}. \tag{8.14-25}$$

Here d_0 is not zero (for the fraction is in lowest terms);   otherwise the coefficients can have any real values, including zero.   For small values of ω,

$$\beta_1 = \beta_1(0) + \beta_1'(0)\omega + \beta_1''(0)\frac{\omega^2}{2!} + \cdots$$

$$= -\frac{c_r}{d_0}\omega^r + \cdots \tag{8.14-26}$$

in which c_r is the first nonzero coefficient in the numerator of (8.14-25). If c_r/d_0 is negative, then β_1 increases from zero;   if c_r/d_0 is positive, then β_1 decreases.   We are either to add or to subtract $\pi/2$ to convert β_1 into β, the real-frequency angle of a p-r function.   Then in the second case

(c_r/d_0 positive) we must use Q_1, and in the first case (c_r/d_0 negative) we must use Q_2, in order to prevent excursions into the second or third quadrant. From this point on the procedure is exactly as in the original case, except that we use either Q_1 or Q_2 rather than the polynomial Q: right-half-plane zeros are to be reflected in the imaginary axis to become left-half-plane poles, additional imaginary zeros and poles are to be added as necessary to confine the variation of β (taking account of the $\pi/2$ angle contributed by the factor p or $1/p$ which remains unchanged). The resulting $Z(p)$ will be a p-r function with the datum $\tan \beta$. It is in this way that a zero or pole at the origin appears—the first case could produce no such zero or pole.

We have found that any odd rational function of ω with real coefficients can be considered to be the tangent of the real-frequency angle of a p-r function $Z(p)$, and have discussed how to find $Z(p)$. Any odd function $\beta(\omega)$ such that $\tan \beta$ meets these requirements and $|\beta|$ does not exceed $\pi/2$ can accordingly be taken as the angle of a p-r function, and that function can be found. There is ambiguity in the result only in the (real, positive) multiplier, which does not affect the angle. The procedure for determining $Z(p)$ is given below in résumé.

Let the data (obtained from the given angle function, if not already in tangent form) be

$$\tan \beta = \frac{c_1\omega + c_3\omega^3 + \cdots}{d_0 + d_2\omega^2 + \cdots} \qquad \text{(Case 1: } \tan \beta \text{ has a zero at the origin)}$$

or

$$\tan \beta = \frac{d_0 + d_2\omega^2 + \cdots}{c_1\omega + c_3\omega^3 + \cdots} \qquad \text{(Case 2: } \tan \beta \text{ has a pole at the origin)}$$

in which $d_0 \neq 0$; otherwise the coefficients are not restricted, except to real values. Let c_r designate the first nonzero coefficient in the odd polynomial.

  1. Substitute p/j for ω, to obtain

$$\tanh(j\beta) = \frac{c_1 p - c_3 p^3 + \cdots}{d_0 - d_2 p^2 + \cdots} = \frac{pB}{A} \qquad \text{(Case 1)}$$

or

$$\tanh(j\beta) = -\frac{d_0 - d_2 p^2 + \cdots}{c_1 p - c_3 p^3 + \cdots} = \frac{A}{pB} \qquad \text{(Case 2)}$$

in which A and B are even polynomials in p.

  2. Factor the polynomial $(A + pB)$, i.e., determine its zeros. Designate the left-half-plane zeros p_1, p_2, $\cdots$, and the right-half-plane zeros p_a, p_b, $\cdots$.

3. Form the function

$$Z_1(p) = \frac{(p - p_1)(p - p_2) \cdots}{(p + p_a)(p + p_b) \cdots} \qquad \text{(Case 1)}$$

or

$$Z_1(p) = \frac{p(p - p_1)(p - p_2) \cdots}{(p + p_a)(p + p_b) \cdots} \qquad \left(\text{Case 2, } \frac{c_r}{d_0} > 0\right)$$

or

$$Z_1(p) = \frac{(p - p_1)(p - p_2) \cdots}{p(p + p_a)(p + p_b) \cdots} \qquad \left(\text{Case 2, } \frac{c_r}{d_0} < 0\right)$$

4. Find the finite, positive, nonzero, real-frequency poles of the tangent function and determine their orders.

5. For every *odd*-order pole ω_0 modify $Z_1(p)$ as follows.

If $\tan \beta$ is positive for ω slightly less than ω_0 and negative for ω slightly greater than ω_0, divide Z_1 by $(p^2 + \omega_0^2)$;
if $\tan \beta$ is negative for ω slightly less than ω_0 and positive for ω slightly greater than ω_0, multiply Z_1 by $(p^2 + \omega_0^2)$.   (8.14–27)

6. The function

$$Z(p) = KZ_1(p) \times \frac{(\quad)(\quad) \cdots}{(\quad)(\quad) \cdots}$$

in which the parentheses represent the modifications made in step 5, and K is real and positive but otherwise arbitrary, is p-r and at real frequencies has the datum angle or tangent function.   It should be checked, of course, to eliminate numerical errors.

It is not necessary, in step 2, to determine the zeros themselves if the polynomial can be factored in two parts, each containing the zeros in one half of the plane; one may choose to determine the number of zeros in each half plane by the methods of Chapter 5 and to extract the simpler factor by some polynomial-splitting method.   Throughout the work only positive values of ω need be considered, because of the inherent symmetry of all we work with.

In all of the discussion above, and in the examples below, the symbol Z has been used arbitrarily; it may represent either impedance or admittance.   If it is interpreted as impedance, then admittance problems may be handled by first changing the sign of the given angle or tangent function to obtain that of the corresponding impedance function.

Example 1.   Suppose a p-r function is to be found, such that its real-frequency angle is

$$\beta = \tan^{-1}[4\omega(\omega^2 - 1)^2].$$

The calculation, according to the method developed above (Case 1), proceeds as follows.

$$\tan \beta = 4\omega - 8\omega^3 + 4\omega^5,$$

$$\tanh (j\beta) = 4p + 8p^3 + 4p^5.$$

In this case $\tan \beta$ is simply a polynomial, so that $A = 1$. Thus

$$Q = A + pB = 4p^5 + 8p^3 + 4p + 1 = 4(p^5 + 2p^3 + p + 0.25).$$

The work of factoring $Q(p)$ is tedious but straightforward (Appendix A). Its zeros lie as in Fig. 8.14–F(a), and the required factored form of $Q(p)$ is given below.

$$Q(p) = (p^3 + 0.4897p^2 + 1.438p + 0.3120)(p^2 - 0.4897p + 0.8014).$$

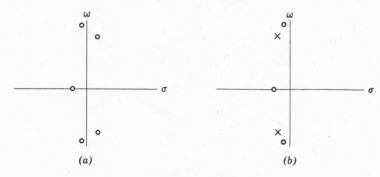

(a)   (b)

Fig. 8.14–F

The function $Z_1(p)$, obtained by reflecting the two right-half-plane zeros and making them poles as in Fig. 8.14–F(b), is

$$Z_1(p) = \frac{p^3 + 0.4897p^2 + 1.438p + 0.3120}{p^2 + 0.4897p + 0.8014}.$$

The tangent function behaves as in Fig. 8.14–G(a) and the angle β as in Fig. 8.14–G(b); since there are no internal poles in the tangent function, no modification of Z_1 is required, and the final result is the p-r function

$$Z(p) = K\frac{p^3 + 0.4897p^2 + 1.438p + 0.3120}{p^2 + 0.4897p + 0.8014}$$

in which K is real and positive, but otherwise arbitrary.

Example 2. Let the real-frequency angle of the (unknown) function $Z(p)$ be given by

$$\tan \beta = \frac{1}{\omega^3},$$

in which the frequency scale has been conveniently normalized. This is an example of Case 2, in which the tangent function has a pole at the origin; in addition $d_0 = 1$, $c_r = c_3 = 1$, and $c_r/d_0 > 0$. This determination of $Z(p)$ follows.

$$\tanh (j\beta) = -\frac{1}{-p^3} = \frac{A}{pB}.$$

$$Q = A + pB = -(p^3 + 1).$$

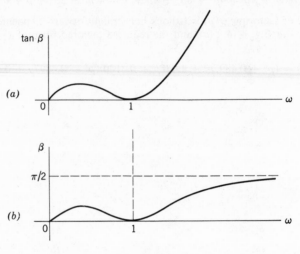

(a)

(b)

Fig. 8.14–G

The zeros of $Q(p)$ are evident by inspection here; they are

$$p = \sqrt[3]{-1} = -1, \quad \tfrac{1}{2}(1 \pm j\sqrt{3}),$$

as in Fig. 8.14–H(a), and

$$Q(p) = -(p + 1)(p^2 - p + 1).$$

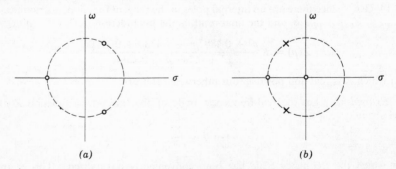

(a)   (b)

Fig. 8.14–H

The function $Z_1(p)$, appropriate for this case, is accordingly

$$Z_1(p) = \frac{p(p + 1)}{p^2 + p + 1}$$

with zeros and poles as shown in Fig. 8.14–H(b). The tangent function behaves as in Fig. 8.14–I(a), the angle as in Fig. 8.14–I(b); since the tangent function has no internal poles, no modification is required. The result is

$$Z(p) = K \frac{p(p + 1)}{p^2 + p + 1}$$

with the usual arbitrariness in the multiplier K.

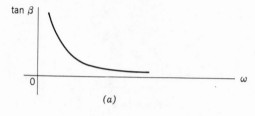

(a)

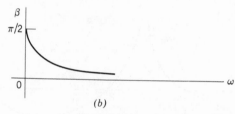

(b)

Fig. 8.14–I

Example 3. A more complicated datum tangent function is

$$\tan \beta = \frac{-1.2 + 1.5\omega^2 - 0.3\omega^4}{4\omega - 4\omega^3 + \omega^5} = -0.3 \frac{(\omega^2 - 1)(\omega^2 - 4)}{\omega(\omega^2 - 2)^2}.$$

This is again an example of Case 2, but here $c_r/d_0 = 4/(-1.2) < 0$. The work of finding the corresponding $Z(p)$ is outlined below.

$$\tanh (j\beta) = \frac{0.3p^4 + 1.5p^2 + 1.2}{p^5 + 4p^3 + 4p} = \frac{A}{pB},$$
$$Q(p) = p^5 + 0.3p^4 + 4p^3 + 1.5p^2 + 4p + 1.2.$$

The work of factoring $Q(p)$, omitted here (cf. Appendix A), leads to

$$Q(p) = (p^3 + 0.5886p^2 + 1.626p + 0.4717)(p^2 - 0.2886p + 2.544).$$

The zeros of $Q(p)$ are shown in Fig. 8.14–J(a).

The appropriate function $Z_1(p)$ is then [cf. Fig. 8.14–J(b)]

$$Z_1 = \frac{p^3 + 0.5886p^2 + 1.626p + 0.4717}{p(p^2 + 0.2886p + 2.544)}.$$

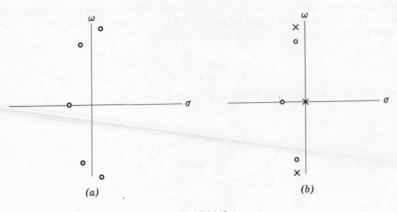

(a)   *(b)*

Fig. 8.14–J

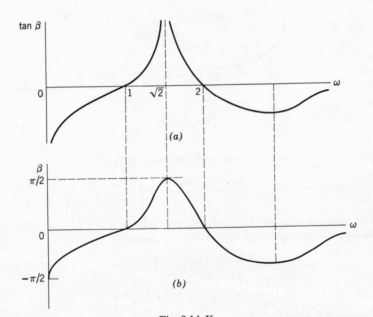

(a)

(b)

Fig. 8.14–K

The tangent function has an internal pole at $\omega = \sqrt{2}$, Fig. 8.14–K(a), but this is of order two; since the order is even, no modification is required; cf. Fig.

8.14–K(b) in which the behavior of β is shown. The end result is the function

$$Z(p) = K\frac{p^3 + 0.5886p^2 + 1.626p + 0.4717}{p^3 + 0.2886p^2 + 2.544p}.$$

Example 4.   In the datum tangent function

$$\tan\beta = \frac{11\omega - \omega^3}{6 - 5\omega^2 + \omega^4} = \frac{\omega(11 - \omega^2)}{(3 - \omega^2)(2 - \omega^2)}$$

we have another instance of Case 1.   Here

$$\tanh(j\beta) = \frac{11p + p^3}{6 + 5p^2 + p^4} = \frac{pB}{A}$$

and

$$Q(p) = p^4 + p^3 + 5p^2 + 11p + 6$$
$$= (p^2 + 2p + 1)(p^2 - p + 6)$$

by factoring, the work of which is omitted. The zeros of $Q(p)$, shown in Fig. 8.14–L(a), include a multiple zero, but this has no effect on the process.

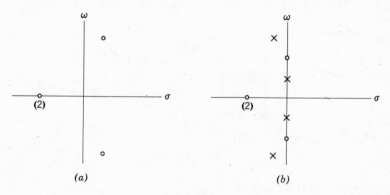

Fig. 8.14–L

The appropriate Z_1 function has the left-half-plane zeros and poles of Fig. 8.14–L(b), and is

$$Z_1 = \frac{p^2 + 2p + 1}{p^2 + p + 6}.$$

The tangent function has two internal simple poles, Fig. 8.14–M(a), which require that Z_1 be modified, for $Z_1(j\omega)$ enters the second quadrant, when ω is between $\sqrt{2}$ and $\sqrt{3}$, as Fig. 8.14–M(b) shows [the dotted line represents the angle of $Z_1(j\omega)$]. At the first pole the tangent changes from positive to negative and accordingly Z_1 must be divided by $(p^2 + 2)$. This introduces the first step in the angle characteristic, Fig. 8.14–M(b), and confines β to the first and fourth quadrants for $\omega < \sqrt{3}$. At the second pole the modified angle will drop below $-\pi/2$ [and $Z(j\omega)$ will enter the third quadrant] unless a second modification is made. At this pole the tangent changes from negative to positive, so that Z_1

must be multiplied by $(p^2 + 3)$. The angle of the function, with these two modifications, is the solid curve of Fig. 8.14–M(b), and the final result is

$$Z(p) = K\frac{(p^2 + 2p + 1)(p^2 + 3)}{(p^2 + p + 6)(p^2 + 2)},$$

with all the zeros and poles of Fig. 8.14–L(b).

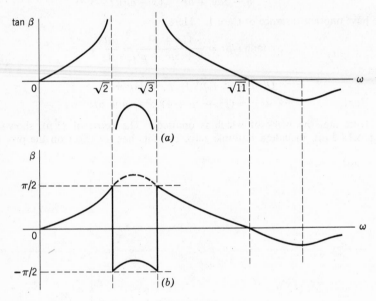

Fig. 8.14–M

Example 5.   Let the data be

$$\tan \beta = \frac{2\omega^3}{\omega^6 - 3\omega^4 + 3\omega^2 - 1} = \frac{2\omega^3}{(\omega^2 - 1)^3},$$

another example of Case 1.   Here

$$\tanh (j\beta) = \frac{-2p^3}{-p^6 - 3p^4 - 3p^2 - 1} = \frac{pB}{A}$$

and

$$Q(p) = -(p^6 + 3p^4 + 2p^3 + 3p^2 + 1).$$

This polynomial has two zeros in the left half plane and can be factored (cf. Appendix A) as

$$Q(p) = (p^2 + 1.260p + 1)(p^4 - 1.260p^3 + 3.587p^2 - 1.260p + 1)$$

[see Fig. 8.14–N(a)].   Hence

$$Z_1 = \frac{p^2 + 1.260p + 1}{p^4 + 1.260p^3 + 3.587p^2 + 1}.$$

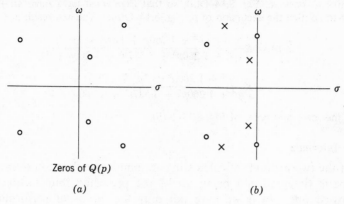

Zeros of $Q(p)$

(a)

(b)

Fig. 8.14–N

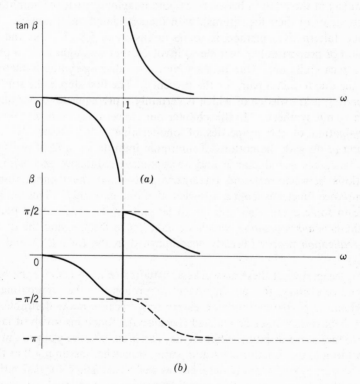

(a)

(b)

Fig. 8.14–O

The tangent function has a third-order internal pole at which it changes from negative to positive, Fig. 8.14–O(a), so that $Z(p)$ must have zeros at $\pm j1$, in order to confine the excursion of β, Fig. 8.14–O(b). The end result is

$$Z(p) = K \frac{(p^2 + 1.260p + 1)(p^2 + 1)}{(p^4 + 1.260p^3 + 3.587p^2 + 1.260p + 1)}$$

$$= K \frac{p^4 + 1.260p^3 + 2p^2 + 1.260p + 1}{p^4 + 1.260p^3 + 3.587p^2 + 1.260p + 1},$$

with the zeros and poles of Fig. 8.14–N(b).

8.15 Interlude

Of the two methods of calculating an immittance function from one of its parts (integrals not being used), the preceding four sections have discussed one. In it we have not only the means of performing the calculation but also concrete evidence (independent of the integral formulas) of the relation between real and imaginary parts (of immittance functions or of their logarithms), with the associated uncertainties. The second (alternative) method is to be discussed in § 8.17. But the discussion of properties has become so involved that we ought now to pause for a recapitulation. Our primary aim is to discuss synthesis methods (for the one-terminal pair, for the present). The first step is the study of *properties*, a knowledge of which is certainly a prerequisite to our ability to carry out synthesis. In this chapter our concern has been with further investigation of the properties of one-terminal pairs, especially those having to do with the notions of minimum immittance, and of resistance and reactance (conductance and susceptance) reduction, and with the relations between real and imaginary parts—and the computation of immittance functions from a knowledge of one part only. This we have done in some detail, and more is to be said on it. The second part of synthesis is *approximation*, which we have yet to discuss, and the third is the *realization* proper (already accomplished in the L-C, R-C, and R-L cases).

The properties of these networks are studied so as to acquire the background necessary for an intelligent approach to the approximation problem. Approximation is necessary only because many desirable network behaviors cannot be realized (because the functions involved fail to be rational or p-r or both)—though they can often be closely approximated with rational p-r functions. Anticipating somewhat (assuming that these two properties are generally sufficient, as well as necessary, for realization), we see that the approximation problem is to set up a rational p-r function having the desired behavior, within reasonable limits. In the one-terminal-pair problem it is often not the complete immittance function whose behavior is important, but rather one of its parts: the resistance, reactance, conductance, susceptance, magnitude, or angle, whose inter-relations we have been discussing in this chapter. It is accordingly important that the designer know what kinds of functions, representing one of these parts, are realizable, i.e., what functions will lead to p-r complete immittance functions. A resistance function, for example, is usually not p-r; but if it meets certain requirements it will lead to a p-r impedance function which has this resistance function at real frequencies. The restrictions imposed on the approximator who is setting up a function of ω to be one of these parts we already know by implication, for we have discussed how to find the complete function from any one of its parts, and by a careful review of the processes we can state some necessary and sufficient conditions for success, some conditions on that part which insure that the whole function will be p-r. It is appropriate to list them here.

8.16 Necessary and sufficient properties of parts of immittance functions

Since the network designer is often interested in realizing a prescribed real-frequency behavior of resistance, or of angle, or of some other part of the immittance, it is important to know what sorts of functions of ω can be used for these parts and when the corresponding immittance function will be p-r. In §§ 8.11–8.14 we have this knowledge, at least by implication, and all we need do here is restate it clearly in appropriate form.

A *resistance* function (associated with a p-r impedance function) is necessarily an even function of ω with real coefficients, and it can have no poles for real values of ω (including infinity). Nor can it go negative for any such value of ω. But these four conditions are also sufficient for the function $Z(p)$ computed from this resistance function to be p-r (as discussed in § 8.11). For conductance functions the same conditions apply, of course, and no more need be said about the real-part functions.

The function describing the *reactance* of a p-r impedance function must be odd, with real coefficients. It may have real-frequency poles if they are simple, and the residues are real and negative (the reactance being considered as a function of ω). But these conditions are also sufficient for the function $Z(p)$ determined from it to be p-r (cf. § 8.12). To susceptance functions the same conditions apply.

As § 8.13 has pointed out, a function representing the (square of the) real-frequency *magnitude* of a p-r immittance function must be even, with real coefficients, not negative for any real value of ω, and any zero or pole occurring at a real value of ω (including infinity) must be of order two.

These conditions are necessary, but generally not sufficient. Given such a function, one must evidently determine the associated immittance function and test it for positive reality.

The function describing the real-frequency *angle* of a p-r immittance function must be such that the tangent of the angle is an odd function of ω with real coefficients. This suffices to insure that the associated immittance function be p-r (see § 8.14).

With the above information, functions of ω can be devised with the primary aim of approximating reasonably closely to desired behavior, yet without wasting time on functions that will turn out not to give p-r results when the complete immittance is calculated. (An exception exists in the case of the magnitude function.) We have yet to actually demonstrate completely that positive reality and realizability are synonymous, but this will be done in Chapter 9. Then we shall be able to set up functions of ω, intended to be the driving-point resistance functions of networks, for example, with assurance that the networks can actually be designed. Before entering on this discussion, however, we shall discuss the second, non-integral, method of calculating complete immittance functions from one of the parts, that due to Bode.

8.17 Bode's method: from resistance (conductance) to immittance function

In the second method of calculating, say, the impedance function $Z(p)$ from a knowledge of only the resistance function $R(\omega)$, Bode presents a different approach, and in some ways a much more illuminating one. Computationally the Brune-Gewertz method may be preferable, but the Bode method (BO 3) shows more clearly just how the part and the whole are related.

To begin with, the resistance function (which we assume to meet the necessary and sufficient conditions of § 8.16) is related to the impedance function thus:

$$R(\omega) = [\text{Ev } Z(p)]_{p=j\omega} \qquad (8.17\text{-}1)$$

so that it is a simple matter to get out into the p plane and to obtain from the given $R(\omega)$ the even part of $Z(p)$, by the substitution of p/j for ω:

$$\text{Ev } Z(p) = R(p/j). \qquad (8.17\text{-}2)$$

In contrast to the first method, the Bode procedure now calls for making the partial-fraction expansion of this (even, real-coefficient) function. Its poles will have quadrantal symmetry (§§ 8.11, 5.14) and none will be imaginary; there will be none at infinity. In the partial-fraction expansion there will be a corresponding symmetry in the terms, which fall naturally into groups. We write

$$\text{Ev } Z(p) = \frac{a_{2n}p^{2n} + a_{2n-2}p^{2n-2} + \cdots + a_0}{p^{2m} + b_{2m-2}p^{2m-2} + \cdots + b_0} \qquad (n \leqq m)$$

$$= \frac{A(p)}{B(p)} \tag{8.17-3}$$

$$= \frac{a_{2n}p^{2n} + a_{2n-2}p^{2n-2} + \cdots + a_0}{[(p - p_1)(p - \bar{p}_1)(p - p_2) \cdots][(p + p_1)(p + \bar{p}_1)(p + p_2) \cdots]}$$

in which A and B are even polynomials, p_1 and $\bar{p}_1$ represent a pair of conjugate complex left-half-plane simple poles (accompanied by their negatives $-p_1$ and $-\bar{p}_1$), and p_2 a real left-half-plane simple pole. We restrict ourselves to simple poles for the moment, so that these are typical of all the poles. See Fig. 8.17–A.

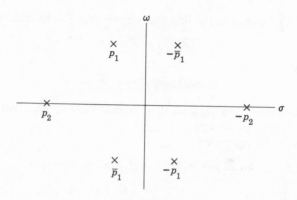

Fig. 8.17–A

Because of the symmetry of the situation of the poles we expect some corresponding symmetry in the terms of the partial-fraction expansion. The residues at the poles p_1 and $-p_1$, for example, ought to be very simply related. At p_1 the residue, by (3.21–8), is

$$K_1 = \frac{A(p_1)}{B'(p_1)} \tag{8.17-4}$$

and at $-p_1$ the residue is

$$\frac{A(-p_1)}{B'(-p_1)} = -K_1, \tag{8.17-5}$$

for the derivative of an even polynomial is an odd polynomial. These residues then differ only in sign—and the same is true of any pair of poles one of which is the negative of the other. The residue at $\bar{p}_1$ is of course $\bar{K}_1$, and at $-\bar{p}_1$ the residue is $-\bar{K}_1$.

The partial-fraction expansion falls naturally into two parts, one with the left-half-plane pole terms, the other with the right-half-plane pole terms and residues simply related to those in the first part. The constant term R_∞ is not peculiar to either part, so we divide it equally between them, an equitable procedure. Thus we obtain

$$\textbf{Ev}\, Z(p) = \left(\frac{K_1}{p - p_1} + \frac{\bar{K}_1}{p - \bar{p}_1} + \frac{K_2}{p - p_2} + \cdots + \frac{R_\infty}{2} \right)$$

$$+ \left(\frac{-K_1}{p + p_1} + \frac{-\bar{K}_1}{p + \bar{p}_1} + \frac{-K_2}{p + p_2} + \cdots + \frac{R_\infty}{2} \right)$$

$$= Z_L(p) + Z_R(p) \qquad\qquad (8.17\text{--}6)$$

in which Z_L designates the first parenthesis and Z_R the second. Now

$$Z_R(p) = Z_L(-p) \qquad\qquad (8.17\text{--}7)$$

by inspection, so that

$$\textbf{Ev}\, Z(p) = Z_L(p) + Z_L(-p). \qquad\qquad (8.17\text{--}8)$$

The function $Z_L(p)$ suggests itself immediately as the answer, or very close to the answer we seek.

Now at real frequencies

$$\textbf{Ev}\, Z(j\omega) = R(\omega) = Z_L(j\omega) + Z_L(-j\omega)$$

$$= 2\,\textbf{Re}\, Z_L(j\omega), \qquad\qquad (8.17\text{--}9)$$

since $Z_L(j\omega)$ and $Z_L(-j\omega)$ must be conjugate. Evidently $2Z_L(p)$ is the function we seek, for its real part has the correct value at all real frequencies, and it passes the complete test for positive reality. That is,

$$Z(p) = 2Z_L(p) = 2\left(\frac{K_1}{p - p_1} + \frac{\bar{K}_1}{p - \bar{p}_1} + \frac{K_2}{p - p_2} + \cdots + \frac{R_\infty}{2} \right)$$

$$(8.17\text{--}10)$$

is the minimum-reactance p-r impedance function with the datum resistance function. To it can, of course, be added any reactance function (any odd p-r function) without disturbing its resistance.

The Bode method thus produces $Z(p)$ from $R(\omega)$ in a very illuminating manner. In effect it utilizes the basic relation

$$\textbf{Ev}\, Z(p) = \tfrac{1}{2}[Z(p) + Z(-p)] \qquad\qquad (8.17\text{--}11)$$

by expanding the datum even part (obtained from the resistance function) into left-half-plane and right-half-plane parts, i.e., into $Z(p)$ and $Z(-p)$, of which the right-half-plane part is simply abandoned. It is possible to split a given even function into two parts, one the Hurwitz conjugate of the other, in a number of ways, but if one part is to be p-r there is only one way, and Bode's method uses this. In calculating the resistance function of a given impedance function something is added to $Z(p)$; the Bode method simply extracts this from the resistance function (to reverse the process) and discards it—a very straightforward method. The end result is of course arbitrary within an additive reactance function.

Purely for simplicity, the discussion above assumed the datum function to have only simple poles. The poles of $\mathrm{Ev}\, Z(p)$ need not be simple, of course, and the Bode procedure is equally valid if they are not. If $\mathrm{Ev}\, Z(p)$ has a left-half-plane pole of order r at p_0 (and consequently a right-half-plane pole, also of order r, at $-p_0$), then $B(p)$ has the factor $(p - p_0)^r(p + p_0)^r$ and we may write

$$\mathrm{Ev}\, Z(p) = \frac{A}{B} = \frac{A}{(p^2 - p_0^2)^r B_1} \tag{8.17–12}$$

in which B_1 is even and is not zero at p_0 or at $-p_0$. To the partial-fraction expansion the pole at p_0 gives the terms

$$\frac{K_{0r}}{(p - p_0)^r} + \frac{K_{0,\,r-1}}{(p - p_0)^{r-1}} + \cdots + \frac{K_{01}}{(p - p_0)} \tag{8.17–13}$$

in which (cf. § 3.19)

$$K_{0r} = \left[\frac{A}{(p + p_0)^r B_1} \right]_{p=p_0},$$

$$K_{0,\,r-1} = \left\{ \frac{d}{dp} \left[\frac{A}{(p + p_0)^r B_1} \right] \right\}_{p=p_0},$$

$$K_{0,\,r-2} = \frac{1}{2!} \left\{ \frac{d^2}{dp^2} \left[\frac{A}{(p + p_0)^r B_1} \right] \right\}_{p=p_0}, \tag{8.17–14}$$

$$\cdots \cdots \cdots \cdots \cdots \cdots \cdots \cdots$$

$$K_{01} = \frac{1}{(r - 1)!} \left\{ \frac{d^{(r-1)}}{dp^{(r-1)}} \left[\frac{A}{(p + p_0)^r B_1} \right] \right\}_{p=p_0}.$$

The pole at $-p_0$ contributes a similar set of terms,

$$\frac{K_{0r}'}{(p + p_0)^r} + \frac{K_{0,\,r-1}'}{(p + p_0)^{r-1}} + \cdots + \frac{K_{01}'}{p + p_0} \tag{8.17–15}$$

in which

$$K_{0r}' = \left[\frac{A}{(p - p_0)^r B_1}\right]_{p = -p_0},$$

$$K_{0, r-1}' = \left\{\frac{d}{dp}\left[\frac{A}{(p - p_0)^r B_1}\right]\right\}_{p = -p_0}, \qquad (8.17\text{--}16)$$

. . . .

$$K_{01}' = \frac{1}{(r - 1)!}\left\{\frac{d^{(r-1)}}{dp^{(r-1)}}\left[\frac{A}{(p - p_0)^r B_1}\right]\right\}_{p = -p_0}.$$

The two sets of K's are very simply related, because A/B_1 is even and the essential difference between the two is a change of sign of p_0. The relations are

$$K_{0r}' \qquad\qquad = (-1)^r K_{0r},$$
$$K_{0, r-1}' \qquad\qquad = (-1)^{r+1} K_{0, r-1},$$
$$K_{0, r-2}' = (-1)^{r+2} K_{0, r-2} = (-1)^r K_{0, r-2}, \qquad (8.17\text{--}17)$$

. . . .

$$K_{01}' \qquad = (-1)^{2r-1} K_{01} \qquad = -K_{01}.$$

In other words, the pairs of K's have alternately the same and opposite signs. If we combine (8.17–13) and (8.17–15) we find that the contribution of the two symmetrical poles to the partial-fraction expansion of **Ev** $Z(p)$ is

$$\left[\frac{K_{01}}{p - p_0} + \frac{K_{02}}{(p - p_0)^2} + \frac{K_{03}}{(p - p_0)^3} + \cdots + \frac{K_{0r}}{(p - p_0)^r}\right]$$
$$+ \left[\frac{-K_{01}}{p + p_0} + \frac{K_{02}}{(p + p_0)^2} + \frac{-K_{03}}{(p + p_0)^3} + \cdots + \frac{(-1)^r K_{0r}}{(p + p_0)^r}\right]. \qquad (8.17\text{--}18)$$

Just as before, reversing the sign of p in the second bracket gives the first one. And every complex pole is accompanied by its conjugate, so that the previous argument still holds. In other words, in the partial-fraction expansion of **Ev** Z those terms due to left-half-plane poles (doubled) and the constant term exactly make up $Z(p)$ in every case.

The Bode procedure again points out (independently) that to a given resistance function there corresponds a definite minimum reactance, and it offers an alternative method of calculating the associated minimum-reactance impedance function. The process is summed up below, in terms of calculating impedance from resistance; only the usual replacement of words by their duals is necessary to convert this into a set of instructions for calculating admittance from conductance.

A suitable resistance function $R(\omega)$ being given, the Bode procedure is to

1. obtain Ev $Z(p)$ by substituting $-p^2$ for ω^2 in $R(\omega)$;
2. factor the denominator of Ev $Z(p)$, i.e., find the poles;
3. calculate the coefficients of the terms in the partial-fraction expansion of Ev $Z(p)$ that correspond to left-half-plane poles, and the constant term;
4. the sum of these terms with the coefficients doubled (but the constant term untouched) is the desired $Z(p)$.   (8.17–19)

In step 2 it may be simpler first to factor the denominator into two polynomials, one of which contains all the left-half-plane zeros and only those (Appendix A). In fact it is not actually necessary to find the poles, or to use complex numbers, if suitable modifications are made in the procedure (Problem 8-82). These modifications lead one eventually back to the Brune–Gewertz method, which may be computationally preferable.

The following examples have the same data as those of § 8.11, but are worked by the Bode method.

Example 1. The normalized datum resistance function is

$$R(\omega) = \frac{1}{1 + \omega^4} \quad \text{ohms}$$

(cf. Fig. 8.11–A) and

$$\text{Ev } Z(p) = \frac{1}{1 + p^4}.$$

The denominator has four simple zeros (the fourth roots of -1) of which two lie in the left half plane and are $p_1 = 1\underline{/135°} = (1/\sqrt{2})(-1 + j1)$ and its conjugate (cf. Fig. 8.11–B). Accordingly,

$$\text{Ev } Z(p) = \frac{K_1}{p - p_1} + \frac{\bar{K}_1}{p - \bar{p}_1} + \frac{-K_1}{p + p_1} + \frac{-\bar{K}_1}{p + \bar{p}_1}.$$

The constant term is zero, for $R(\infty) = 0$; K_1 is calculated below, with the aid of (3.21–8).

$$K_1 = \frac{1}{4p_1{}^3} = \frac{1}{4\underline{/45°}} = \frac{1 - j1}{4\sqrt{2}}.$$

Then

$$Z(p) = \frac{2K_1}{p - p_1} + \frac{2\bar{K}_1}{p - \bar{p}_1} = \frac{2}{4\sqrt{2}} \left(\frac{1 - j1}{p - p_1} + \frac{1 + j1}{p - \bar{p}_1} \right)$$

$$= \frac{1}{2\sqrt{2}} \frac{(2p + \sqrt{2}) - j(j\sqrt{2})}{p^2 + \sqrt{2}p + 1} = \frac{(1/\sqrt{2})p + 1}{p^2 + \sqrt{2}p + 1} \quad \text{ohms}$$

is the minimum-reactance impedance function associated with the datum $R(\omega)$.

Example 2.

$$R(\omega) = \frac{\omega^2 + 4}{\omega^4 - 4\omega^2 + 16} \quad \text{ohms}$$

whose behavior is shown in Fig. 8.11–C. From this we obtain

$$\text{Ev } Z(p) = \frac{-p^2 + 4}{p^4 + 4p^2 + 16}$$

with the four poles given by $p^2 = -2 \pm j2\sqrt{3} = 4\underline{/\pm 120°}$, and left-half-plane poles at $p = 2\underline{/\pm 120°} = -1 + j\sqrt{3}$ (cf. Fig. 8.11–D). The constant term is zero and the residue at the pole in the second quadrant is

$$\left(\frac{-p^2 + 4}{4p^3 + 8p}\right)_{p = -1 + j\sqrt{3}} = \frac{j2\sqrt{3}}{4(-1 + j\sqrt{3})(-j2\sqrt{3})} = \frac{1}{4}.$$

Hence

$$Z(p) = \frac{1}{2}\left(\frac{1}{p + 1 - j\sqrt{3}} + \frac{1}{p + 1 + j\sqrt{3}}\right) = \frac{p + 1}{p^2 + 2p + 4} \quad \text{ohms}$$

is the minimum-reactance result.

Example 3. With

$$R(\omega) = \frac{\omega^4}{\omega^6 + 3\omega^4 + 3\omega^2 + 1} \quad \text{ohms}$$

(cf. Fig. 8.11–E) we find

$$\text{Ev } Z(p) = \frac{p^4}{-p^6 + 3p^4 - 3p^2 + 1} = \frac{p^4}{-(p^2 - 1)^3}$$

whose poles are shown in Fig. 8.11–F. In the partial-fraction expansion of Ev $Z(p)$,

$$\text{Ev } Z(p) = \frac{K_3}{(p + 1)^3} + \frac{K_2}{(p + 1)^2} + \frac{K_1}{(p + 1)} + \text{(right-half-plane pole terms)},$$

we have

$$K_3 = \left[\frac{-p^4}{(p - 1)^3}\right]_{p = -1} = \frac{1}{8},$$

$$K_2 = \left[\frac{-p^4 + 4p^3}{(p - 1)^4}\right]_{p = -1} = -\frac{5}{16},$$

$$K_1 = \frac{1}{2!}\left[\frac{-12p^2}{(p - 1)^5}\right]_{p = -1} = \frac{3}{16}.$$

Hence

$$Z(p) = 2\left[\frac{\frac{1}{8}}{(p + 1)^3} + \frac{-\frac{5}{16}}{(p + 1)^2} + \frac{\frac{3}{16}}{(p + 1)}\right]$$

$$= \frac{3p^2 + p}{8(p + 1)^3} \quad \text{ohms}$$

to which an arbitrary reactance function could be added.

Example 4.

$$R_0(\omega) = \frac{6(\omega^2 - 3)^4}{4\omega^8 - 7\omega^6 + 2\omega^4 + 40\omega^2 + 100} \quad \text{ohms,}$$

whose behavior is shown in Fig. 8.11–G. With the usual substitution we obtain

$$\text{Ev } Z_0(p) = 1.5 \frac{p^8 + 12p^6 + 54p^4 + 108p^2 + 81}{p^8 + 1.75p^6 + 0.5p^4 - 10p^2 + 25}.$$

The left-half-plane zeros of the denominator are

$$p_1 = -0.6300 + j1.599,$$
$$p_2 = -1.220 + j0.453,$$

and their conjugates; the corresponding coefficients in the partial-fraction expansion are

$$K_1 = 0.1461 + j0.02798,$$
$$K_2 = -1.060 - j5.948,$$

and the constant term is 1.5. Hence the minimum-reactance associated impedance function is

$$Z_0(p) = \frac{2K_1}{p - p_1} + \frac{2\bar{K}_1}{p - \bar{p}_1} + \frac{2K_2}{p - p_2} + \frac{2\bar{K}_2}{p - \bar{p}_2} + 1.5$$

$$= \frac{1.5p^4 + 1.894p^3 + 13.45p^2 + 9.989p + 24.34}{p^4 + 3.700p^3 + 7.721p^2 + 9.338p + 5.000} \quad \text{ohms.}$$

The amount of numerical work required here (most of it omitted above) is much greater than that required in reaching the same result by the Brune-Gewertz method (§ 8.11, Example 4). Furthermore, to get accurate results a much larger number of significant figures must be carried; although six such were used in the above, the discrepancies with the other method's result point this out. For numerical work the first method is usually preferable.

8.18 Bode's method: from reactance (susceptance) to immittance function

It is equally simple and lucid to use Bode's method for the calculation of impedance functions from given reactances. The beginning point is the relation

$$X(\omega) = \frac{1}{j} [\text{Od } Z(p)]_{p=j\omega} \tag{8.18-1}$$

which makes it easy to obtain

$$\text{Od } Z(p) = jX(p/j) \tag{8.18-2}$$

from the given reactance X (assumed to meet the necessary and sufficient conditions of § 8.16). This will be an odd rational function, with real coefficients, in form

$$\mathbf{Od}\, Z(p) = \frac{A}{pB} \quad \text{or} \quad \frac{pB}{A}. \tag{8.18-3}$$

The poles of $\mathbf{Od}\, Z(p)$ will have quadrantal symmetry (§§ 8.11, 5.14) and may be imaginary (if simple, with real, positive residues); there may be a simple pole at infinity. In the partial-fraction expansion the imaginary-pole terms (and the term Kp) if any are present are already p-r functions (reactance functions in fact) and need no further attention. The terms corresponding to poles not on the imaginary axis fall naturally into two symmetrical groups, as in § 8.17. Again there are simple relations between the coefficients of corresponding terms in the expansion, and the left-half-plane part is essentially the desired function.

Suppose first that all of the poles are simple. Then the residue of $\mathbf{Od}\, Z(p)$ at a pole p_1 will be, by (3.21–8),

$$K_1 = \frac{A(p_1)}{p_1 B'(p_1)} \quad \text{or} \quad \frac{p_1 B(p_1)}{A'(p_1)}. \tag{8.18-4}$$

At the pole $-p_1$ the residue will be the *same* in value, for both A/pB' and pB/A' are *even*. The residues at conjugate poles are conjugate, of course, and there will be no constant term. Accordingly, the partial-fraction expansion will be

$$
\begin{aligned}
\mathbf{Od}\, Z(p) = &\left[\left(\frac{K_1}{p - p_1} + \frac{\bar{K}_1}{p - \bar{p}_1} + \frac{K_2}{p - p_2} + \cdots\right)\right.\\
&\left. + \frac{1}{2}\left(\frac{K_a}{p - j\omega_a} + \frac{K_a}{p + j\omega_a} + \cdots\right)\right]\\
&+ \left[\left(\frac{K_1}{p + p_1} + \frac{\bar{K}_1}{p + \bar{p}_1} + \frac{K_2}{p + p_2} + \cdots\right)\right.\\
&\left. + \frac{1}{2}\left(\frac{K_a}{p - j\omega_a} + \frac{K_a}{p + j\omega_a} + \cdots\right)\right]\\
= &\; Z_L(p) + Z_R(p)
\end{aligned}
\tag{8.18-5}
$$

in which, for illustration, p_1 is a complex left-half-plane pole, p_2 a real left-half-plane pole, $j\omega_a$ an imaginary pole, and $Z_L(p)$ denotes the first bracket, Z_R the second. The imaginary-pole terms are divided equally between the two since they belong to neither half plane, and the term Kp, if present, is to be similarly treated. By inspection of (8.18–5) we see that

$$Z_R(p) = -Z_L(-p) \tag{8.18-6}$$

so that

$$\text{Od } Z(p) = Z_L(p) - Z_L(-p). \tag{8.18-7}$$

At real frequencies

$$\text{Od } Z(j\omega) = jX(\omega) = Z_L(j\omega) - Z_L(-j\omega)$$

$$= j2 \text{ Im } Z_L(j\omega), \tag{8.18-8}$$

for $Z_L(j\omega)$ and $Z_L(-j\omega)$ must be conjugate. Consequently

$$Z(p) = 2Z_L(p) \tag{8.18-9}$$

is almost the function we seek; its imaginary part has at real frequencies the value $X(\omega)$, and it passes the test for positive reality except possibly for the sign of its real part at real frequencies. The addition of a constant will take care of this last difficulty if it arises. Hence

$$Z(p) = 2 \left(\frac{K_1}{p - p_1} + \frac{\bar{K}_1}{p - \bar{p}_1} + \frac{K_2}{p - p_2} + \cdots \right)$$

$$+ \left(\frac{K_a}{p - j\omega_a} + \frac{K_a}{p + j\omega_a} + \cdots \right) + R(\infty) \quad (8.18\text{-}10)$$

is the minimum-resistance p-r impedance function with the datum reactance. Here $R(\infty)$ is the added constant, large enough to insure that **Re** $Z(j\omega)$ is never negative. To it can be added any real positive constant (resistance), of course.

The Bode procedure thus produces $Z(p)$ from $X(\omega)$ in the same illuminating fashion in which it operated in § 8.17, in effect by expanding the datum reactance as

$$\text{Od } Z(p) = \tfrac{1}{2}[Z(p) - Z(-p)] \tag{8.18-11}$$

and discarding $Z(-p)$. When multiple poles are present the procedure is equally valid, and the arguments of § 8.17 apply with very little change. If to A or B_1 we add the additional factor p, then (8.17-12) represents **Od** $Z(p)$; (8.17-14) and (8.17-16) require only the same addition: and (8.17-13) and (8.17-15) hold as they are. The relations between the K's are merely reversed in sign this time, i.e.,

$$K_{01}' = K_{01},$$

$$K_{02}' = -K_{02},$$

$$K_{03}' = K_{03}, \tag{8.18-12}$$

$$\cdot \ \cdot \ \cdot \ \cdot \ \cdot \ \cdot$$

$$K_{0r}' = (-1)^{r+1}K_{0r}.$$

The contribution to the partial-fraction expansion of **Od** $Z(p)$ from two poles of order r at p_0 and $-p_0$ is

$$\left[\frac{K_{01}}{p - p_0} + \frac{K_{02}}{(p - p_0)^2} + \frac{K_{03}}{(p - p_0)^3} + \cdots + \frac{K_{0r}}{(p - p_0)^r}\right]$$

$$+ \left[\frac{K_{01}}{p + p_0} + \frac{-K_{02}}{(p + p_0)^2} + \frac{K_{03}}{(p + p_0)^3} + \cdots + \frac{(-1)^{r+1}K_{0r}}{(p + p_0)^r}\right].$$

$$(8.18\text{–}13)$$

As with simple poles, reversing the sign of p in the second bracket gives the negative of the first one, and the previous procedure is still valid. In the partial-fraction expansion of **Od** $Z(p)$ those terms due to left-half-plane poles (doubled) and the imaginary-pole terms exactly make up $Z(p)$.

Here is an independent demonstration of the existence of a definite minimum resistance corresponding to a given reactance. The calculation procedure is summed up below in terms of reactance and impedance, but applies equally well to the calculation of admittance from susceptance.

A suitable reactance $X(\omega)$ being given, the Bode procedure is to

1. obtain **Od** $Z(p)$ by substituting p/j for ω in $jX(\omega)$;
2. factor the denominator of **Od** $Z(p)$, i.e., find the poles;
3. calculate the coefficients of the terms in the partial-fraction expansion of **Od** $Z(p)$ that correspond to left-half-plane and imaginary poles;
4. form $2Z_L(p)$, the sum of these terms with coefficients doubled for the left-half-plane pole term but untouched for the imaginary-pole terms;
5. determine $R_{\min}$, the minimum value of **Re** $2Z_L(j\omega)$, which will be negative, or zero;
6. add $-R_{\min}$ to $2Z_L(p)$ to obtain the desired $Z(p)$. $(8.18\text{–}14)$

To this result can be added any positive resistance, of course. The illustrative examples below have the same data as those of § 8.12, but are worked by the Bode method.

Example 1. From the datum function

$$X(\omega) = \frac{-3}{\omega^3 + 4\omega} \quad \text{ohms}$$

(cf. Fig. 8.12–A), we find

$$\mathbf{Od}\ Z(p) = \frac{3}{-p^3 + 4p} = \frac{-\frac{3}{8}}{p + 2} + \frac{-\frac{3}{8}}{p - 2} + \frac{\frac{3}{4}}{p},$$

$$2Z_L(p) = \frac{-\frac{3}{4}}{p + 2} + \frac{\frac{3}{4}}{p} = \frac{\frac{3}{2}}{p^2 + 2p},$$

$$\mathbf{Re}\ 2Z_L(j\omega) = \frac{3}{2}\left(\frac{p^2}{p^4 - 4p^2}\right)_{p = j\omega} = \frac{\frac{3}{2}}{-\omega^2 - 4}.$$

To $2Z_L(p)$ we must add 0.375, with the result

$$Z(p) = \frac{\frac{3}{2}}{p^2 + 2p} + 0.375 = 0.375 \frac{p^2 + 2p + 4}{p^2 + 2p} \quad \text{ohms}$$

as the minimum-resistance associated impedance function.   See Fig. 8.18–A.

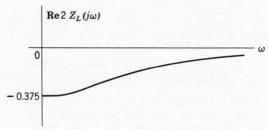

Fig. 8.18–A

Example 2.

$$X(\omega) = \frac{2\omega^5 - 3\omega^3}{5\omega^8 - 2\omega^2 + 4} \quad \text{ohms.}$$

Here

$$\mathbf{Od}\, Z(p) = 0.4 \frac{p^5 + 1.5p^3}{p^8 + 0.4p^2 + 0.8}$$

which has the following poles (obtained not without labor; cf. Appendix A):

$$p_1 = -0.9221 + j0.4207,$$

$$p_2 = -0.3142 + j0.8786.$$

See Fig. 8.18–B.

Fig. 8.18–B

In the partial-fraction expansion we find (again not without considerable labor)

$$K_1 = 0.05 \frac{p_1{}^4 + 1.5p_1{}^2}{p_1{}^6 + 0.1} = 0.02995 + j0.1145,$$

$$K_2 = 0.05 \frac{p_2{}^4 + 1.5p_2{}^2}{p_2{}^6 + 0.1} = -0.02995 - j0.05283,$$

and so

$$2Z_L(p) = 2 \left(\frac{K_1}{p - p_1} + \frac{\bar{K}_1}{p - \bar{p}_1} + \frac{K_2}{p - p_2} + \frac{\bar{K}_2}{p - \bar{p}_2} \right)$$

$$= \frac{-0.07984p^2 + 0.2026p + 0.08049}{p^4 + 2.473p^3 + 3.057p^2 + 2.251p + 0.8944}.$$

This is clearly not p-r, but does have the correct imaginary part at real frequencies. To make it p-r we need only add an appropriate constant. The work of determining the minimum of $\mathbf{Re}\ 2Z_L(j\omega)$ was performed in Example 2 of § 8.12 (q.v.); it is $(-0.4 \times 0.4338) = -0.1735$, and when 0.1735 is added in we obtain

$$Z(p) = \frac{0.1735p^4 + 0.4291p^3 + 0.4506p^2 + 0.5933p + 0.2537}{p^4 + 2.473p^3 + 3.057p^2 + 2.251p + 0.8944} \quad \text{ohms}$$

as the minimum-resistance function we seek.

8.19 Review

This chapter has been quite lengthy. Before going on we ought to look back over it, place it in our general scheme, and chart our immediate course.

Our first concern is with network properties: these we must know, otherwise intelligent attack on synthesis problems is impossible. In this chapter we have concentrated on the rather important properties of driving-point immittance functions that tie their real and imaginary parts together. There are integral relations, useful in theoretical discussion and also because they lead to a practical graphical method of calculating one part from another; there are algebraic processes too, and these may be the more useful in calculations of the exact immittance function from a knowledge of one part. Every one of these points out the relations between the parts and the limitations to their generality. With this discussion we have completed our investigation of properties of driving-point immittance functions.

Our second concern is with the approximation problem—and our third with the realization proper. We shall still postpone our discussion of approximation, and turn next to realization. For networks with one or two kinds of elements only, we have an adequate knowledge of realization procedures already (Chapters 6, 7). There remains only the general (*R-L-C*) case, and to this we turn next.

8.20 References

Minimum immittance and immittance reduction: BO 3, BR 1, BR 4.

Integral relations between parts of immittance functions: BA 1, BA 3, BO 1, BO 2, BO 3, CA 5, GU 3, KU 1, LE 1, MU 1.

Methods of computation of parts: Tables and graphical methods based on the integral relations: BO 3, CO 2, TH 1.   The Brune-Gewertz method: BR 4, GE 1. The Bode method: BO 3.

Additional references: AD 2, DA 1, NO 2, SE 2.

PROBLEMS

8-1. Show that any (p-r) impedance function $Z(p)$ can be written as the sum of (a) a reactance (odd, p-r) function; (b) a minimum-reactance, minimum resistance function; (c) a constant (that is real and positive, or zero).

8-2. For each of the networks shown, are the input immittance functions minimum-resistance? Minimum-reactance? Minimum-susceptance? Minimum-conductance?

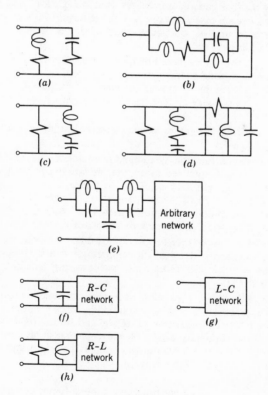

(a)   (b)

(c)   (d)

Arbitrary network

(e)

R-C network

(f)

L-C network

(g)

R-L network

(h)

Prob. 8-2

8-3. Show that the function

$$Z(p) = \frac{p^2 + 7p + 9}{p^2 + 7p + 10}$$

is p-r. As an impedance function, in which of the four ways is it minimum? Repeat for the admittance functions

$$Y(p) = \frac{p^3 + p^2 + 3p}{p^3 + 2p^2 + p + 2} \qquad Y(p) = \frac{p^2 + 3p + 2}{2p^3 + 7p^2 + 4p + 2}.$$

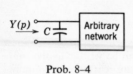

Prob. 8-4

8-4. Measurements made on the network shown give a very-high-frequency behavior for $Y(p)$ of 6 mhos conductance and susceptance equal to that of a 3-f capacitor. On the basis of this information and the diagram, how far can you go in answering the following questions? What is the value of C? In which of the four ways is the admittance function $Y(p)$ minimum? Explain your reasoning.

8-5. Prove that (8.01-5) is p-r, in general. Verify the expansion (8.01-9) and show also that both (8.01-8) and (8.01-10) are p-r.

8-6. Review the four canonic procedures used in L-C, R-C, and R-L network realization, and in each case point out how the removal of reactance, of susceptance, of resistance, and of conductance was used. Is the maximum amount of each removed at each stage?

8-7. In testing a given immittance function to determine whether it is minimum-resistance (minimum-conductance), the primary task is to find whether the numerator of the even part vanishes at any real frequencies. Under what circumstances is it necessary to consider the denominator, and when may it be ignored?

8-8. Verify in detail the rather sketchy demonstration in § 8.02 that $Z_2(p)$ is p-r. (Cf. Prob. 8-5.)

8-9. An immittance function is minimum-reactance and minimum-susceptance, but neither minimum-resistance nor minimum-conductance. Let the minimum value of its resistance be R_{min}, occurring at ω_r, and the minimum value of its conductance be G_{min}, occurring at ω_g. In general $\omega_r \neq \omega_g$. What must be true of the immittance function if these two frequencies are to be equal? If $\omega_r = \omega_g$, are R_{min} and G_{min} necessarily reciprocals?

8-10. Consider the impedance function (8.02–14). At what frequency is the *conductance* a minimum? How much conductance can be removed from the admittance (as parallel resistance), still leaving a p-r remainder? Contrast your answer with (8.02–17).

8-11. Let $E = \text{Ev } F(j\omega)$, $F(p)$ being an immittance function under investigation for minimum-resistance and minimum-conductance properties. Show that substitution of x for ω^2, calculation of dE/dx, and setting $dE/dx = 0$ gives the locations of all the stationary points of E except that at the origin (zero frequency). Why is there always a stationary point at the origin, and why is it not a root of $dE/dx = 0$ above? What is the meaning of "extraneous" roots such as $x = -1$ in (8.02–16)?

8-12. The following immittance functions, though requiring all three kinds of elements, are realizable by removal of reactance and susceptance; no additional techniques are necessary. Show this by obtaining network realizations, considering each to be first an impedance, and then an admittance.

(a) $\dfrac{144p^5 + 72p^4 + 88p^3 + 26p^2 + 9p + 1}{36p^4 + 18p^3 + 19p^2 + 5p + 1}$

(b) $\dfrac{p^2 + 3p + 2}{2p^3 + 7p^2 + 4p + 2}$

(c) $\dfrac{120p^4 + 64p^3 + 38p^2 + 2p + 1}{120p^4 + 90p^3 + 10p^2 + 5p}$

(d) $\dfrac{18p^3 + 9p^2 + 2p + 1}{15p^2 + 3p + 1}$ (Cf. Prob. 10–2)

(e) $\dfrac{36p^3 + 18p^2 + 5p + 1}{48p^4 + 24p^3 + 14p^2 + 4p + 1}$

(f) $\dfrac{112p^4 + 56p^3 + 40p^2 + 2p + 1}{192p^5 + 96p^4 + 84p^3 + 6p^2 + 3p}$

(g) $\dfrac{1840p^6 + 440p^5 + 1570p^4 + 203p^3 + 239p^2 + 16p + 3}{1920p^7 + 960p^6 + 3008p^5 + 1264p^4 + 794p^3 + 151p^2 + 18p + 3}$

8-13. Show, in terms of the impedance function below, how susceptance reduction may be possible after resistance reduction has been performed, even though it is not originally possible. How does this aid the synthesis? State and explain the dual statement.

$$Z(p) = \frac{12p^4 + 46p^3 + 28p^2 + 15p + 5}{10p^3 + 5p^2 + 3p + 1}.$$

8-14. Prove (8.11–4) by showing that if $Z(p)$, which is p-r, has a pole at $j\omega_0$, so that $(p^2 + \omega_0{}^2)$ is a factor of the denominator of $Z(p)$, this factor appears in both numerator and denominator of (8.11–2) in such a fashion that it cancels out when $R(\omega)$, or $\mathrm{Ev}\ Z(p)$, is brought to lowest terms.

8-15. The discussion of § 8.04 shows that a given resistance function determines the associated reactance, but only within an arbitrary pure reactance

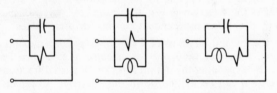

Prob. 8–15

(L-C immittance) function. It is possible, by considering the inevitable dissipation present in all real reactive network elements, and looking on the pure L and C elements only as limits, to state that a given resistance function *completely* determines the associated reactance.

Show, by evaluating the limit of the resistance function as dissipation disappears in each of the cases given in the figure, that a pole of impedance on the imaginary axis then does actually contribute to the resistance in the form of an impulse function (of frequency). Show that in (8.04–9) if a given resistance function does have impulse components, they do contribute the reactance associated with nondissipative resonant combinations. (GU 7.)

Discuss the effect this has on the validity of (8.11–4) and how important it is or is not in synthesis based on constructing resistance functions (as the important feature of a network) and then realizing them.

Is there a parallel statement that can be made as to the complete determination of resistance associated with given reactance?

8-16. Show that (8.04–2), and hence (8.04–8) and subsequent formulas also, give the same result for $R(\omega)$ if the $X(\omega)$ used is not minimum-reactance (but the impedance in question is still p-r, and has no pole at infinity), provided the integration through the additional imaginary poles is performed in the limiting fashion, giving the principal values, (a) by evaluating the contributions of the added (p-r) imaginary poles in (8.04–2); (b) by recalculating the original contour integral of § 3.23, allowing for (p-r) poles of $F(p)$ on the imaginary axis.

8-17. What difficulty arises in extending the discussion of Prob. 8-16 to an impedance function with a pole at infinity? For such a function obtain formulas similar to (8.04–2) and (8.04–3) by evaluating $\oint \dfrac{Z(p)}{p(p - j\omega_1)} dp$ around a suitable contour. In what way(s) do your results differ from (8.04–2) and (8.04–3)? Show that your results can be written in forms which contain the right-hand sides of these two equations, with suitable additive corrections.

8-18. It can be said that (8.04–6) is true simply by inspection. Explain this by using a symmetry property of the integrand.

8-19. The integral relations of § 8.04 apply to the real and imaginary parts of any function that is analytic in the right half plane and on the boundary. Show that they imply that (a) if the real part is even, then the imaginary part is odd (as functions of ω), and if the imaginary part is odd, the real part is even; (b) if the real part is odd, then the imaginary part is even, and if the imaginary part is even, the real part is odd (with one additional restriction).

Show, from (8.07–9) and (8.07–10) that the same is true of logarithms.

Which of (a) and (b) applies to p-r functions? Show from the integral relations that if the function is p-r, the imaginary part vanishes at both the origin and infinity. Give independent reasons for these values.

8-20. Use the integral relations of § 8.04 to establish a method of calculating reactance from resistance (and one for calculating resistance from reactance) that proceeds by expanding the datum function in partial fractions, from which the other function can be written down immediately. Compare this with the Bode procedure of § 8.17.

8-21. Show that positive reality is not necessary for the valid application of the integral relations (§ 8.04), by explaining why they may legitimately be applied to these two functions:

$$F_1(p) = \frac{p - 3}{p + 6} \qquad F_2(p) = \frac{1}{p^2 + 6p + 10}.$$

Give two examples that show that positive reality alone is not sufficient for validity of the relations.

8-22. Derive (8.05–7).

8-23. In the derivation of (8.05–17) and (8.05–18) certain terms vanish at the limits, as indicated in the text. Show in detail that this is so in each case. Give the complete derivation of (8.05–18).

8-24. From (8.05–6), by integration by parts, obtain the relation

$$R(\omega) = \frac{1}{\pi} \int_0^\infty \frac{dX}{d\lambda} \ln |\lambda^2 - \omega^2| \, d\lambda + R(\infty).$$

To what extent does the validity of this relation depend on the assumption of minimum reactance?

From (8.05–7), by integration by parts, obtain the relation

$$X(\omega) = - \frac{\omega}{\pi} \int_0^\infty \frac{d(R/\lambda)}{d\lambda} \ln |\lambda^2 - \omega^2| \, d\lambda,$$

carefully pointing out the restrictions necessary on the resistance function for its validity.

Compare these two relations with those derived in § 8.05 that also involve derivatives.

8-25. Show from (8.05–11) that if the resistance is small except at large values of frequency, the associated reactance is approximately linear at small values of frequency; and that if the resistance is small except at small values of frequency, the associated reactance varies approximately as ω^{-1} at large values of frequency. From (8.05–21) obtain the same result by investigating the behavior of the weighting function.

8-26. Obtain (8.05–21) by making the substitution $u = \ln (\lambda/\omega)$ in (8.05–11) and then integrating by parts. Similarly obtain (8.05–20) from (8.05–10).

8-27. A resistance function consists of a series of horizontal line segments, with discontinuities at their ends, as in the figure. With the use of (8.05–18) find the associated minimum reactance in terms of the locations and amounts of the discontinuities.

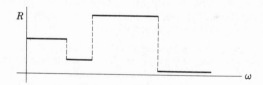

Prob. 8–27

Discuss and illustrate the use of your (general) result as a means of rapidly obtaining a rough approximation to the minimum reactance associated with a given resistance function. In what way is the method inferior to that of §8.09? Can you extend the principle to the calculation of resistance from reactance?

8-28. Derive (8.06–1) from (8.05–17). Derive (8.06–1) and (8.06–5) directly from a suitable contour integral.

8-29. For the network shown express the area under the curve of the reactance plotted against frequency on a logarithmic scale in terms of the three element values, using the reactance integral theorem. Show that the impedance function, measured in units of R_0, can be normalized so that

$Z = R + jX \longrightarrow$

Prob. 8–29

it contains only one parameter, $\alpha = R_0/\sqrt{L/C}$, and plot both the reactance and the resistance against (logarithmic) frequency for various values of α. Compare the areas in the various cases.

8-30. Prove (8.06–8) by using a suitably indented contour, contour integration, and the properties of positive-real functions. Illustrate by evaluating the resistance integral for the three networks shown in the figure. What is the effect of adding a resistance in parallel with the L-C combination?

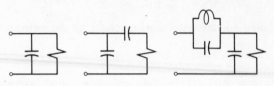

Prob. 8–30

Somewhat more generally, show that if $Z(\infty)$ is finite and not zero, but the high-frequency reactance is that of a capacitor, (8.06–8) holds with only a slight modification. If the high-frequency reactance vanishes more rapidly than ω^{-1}, what is the value of the resistance integral? Illustrate, by sketches of resistance versus frequency, how this result is possible in physical networks.

8-31. Show that the function $\ln Z(p)$ is analytic except at points where Z becomes zero or infinite. Where are the branch points of the function? If $Z(p)$ is p-r, with several zeros and poles on the imaginary axis (but neither at infinity), sketch a possible branch-cut pattern that may be used to define the single-valued function $F(p)$ used in § 8.07. Show clearly why $F(p)$ is analytic on and within the contour C of Fig. 8.07–A.

8-32. Show that $\beta(0)$, $\beta(\omega)$ being defined by (8.07–8), is necessarily zero if $Z(p)$ has neither pole nor zero at the origin. If it has one or the other, what is the limit of $\beta(\omega)$ as $\omega \to 0$ through positive values of ω? Through negative values? Explain in terms of a p-plane sketch the behavior of β at the origin in these cases.

Give a corresponding discussion of possible behavior of $\beta(\omega)$ at infinity.

8-33. Suppose (8.07–9) and (8.07–10) are to be applied to a p-r function $Z(p)$ with a pole or zero at infinity. Show how the device of dividing (or multiplying) $Z(p)$ by p yields a function whose logarithm is regular at infinity so that the relations can be applied to this function without further argument. Explain how to correct the magnitude or angle so determined, to return to the magnitude or angle of the function actually of interest.

8-34. Illustrate the discussion in § 8.07 about the logarithmic singularity at infinity by changing the variable to ω^{-1} (moving the singularity to the origin) and showing what happens then as frequency becomes large in the original equations.

8-35. Consider each of the functions below in turn. In each case determine the associated angle or magnitude function, and explain the necessary corrections to be made in applying (8.07–9) and (8.07–10). Verify your results by comparison with appropriate network immittance functions.

$$|Z(j\omega)| = K\omega \qquad \beta(\omega) = \pm\pi/2, \quad \omega < 0$$
$$|Z(j\omega)| = K/\omega \qquad \qquad = \mp\pi/2, \quad \omega < 0$$

8-36. Given the angle function $\beta(\omega)$ shown, with the additional information that β is an odd function, find the corresponding $|Z(j\omega)|$, using (8.07–9). Show, by means of a p-plane sketch, why $\beta(\omega)$ behaves in this fashion. Give the schematic diagram of a network realization of $Z(p)$. When small amounts of dissipation are added in the network, in the form of small resistors in series with inductors, and large resistors in parallel with capacitors, how do the curves of magnitude and angle of $Z(j\omega)$ change? Repeat the above for an angle function with discontinuities at two frequencies rather than one.

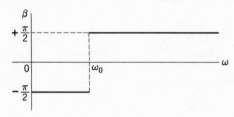

Prob. 8–36

Explain how a rough method of calculating magnitude from angle might be based on the results above, somewhat in the manner of Prob. 8-27. What is the corresponding method of calculating, approximately, angle from given magnitude?

8-37. The functions shown (p. 478) represent idealized resistance functions and are, of course, even. Using the most suitable of the various integral relations (§ 8.08) in each case, determine and plot the associated minimum reactance. Effectively remove numerical parameters by normalization as far as possible; where a numerical parameter must be specified, obtain literal results and make plots for several representative numerical values thereof. (Cf. Prob. 3-47.) Note that these functions have singularities on the imaginary axis, but that the integral relations may still be applied. Why is this so? (The complete functions may be assumed analytic in the right half plane.)

Repeat on the assumption that the functions shown represent conductance to find associated susceptance. Repeat on the assumption that the functions shown represent magnitude of immittance to find associated angle.

8-38. The functions shown in the figure for Prob. 8-37 are here to be interpreted as idealized reactance functions; they are then, of course, odd functions. Using the most suitable of the integral relations, as in Prob. 8-37, determine and plot in each case the associated minimum resistance.

Repeat on the assumption that the functions represent susceptance to find associated conductance, and on the assumption that they represent angle to find associated magnitude.

What is the effect on your results of changing the sign of the functions, i.e., of reflecting them in the ω axis? Does this lead to physically meaningful (though idealized) functions here? In the cases of Prob. 8-37?

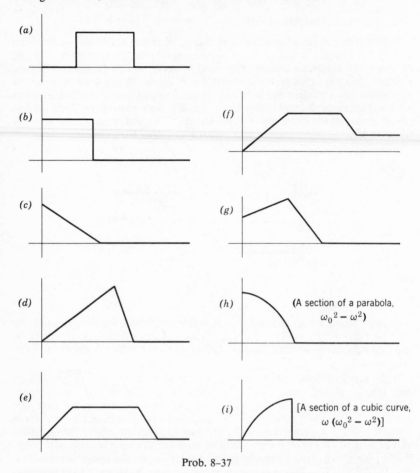

(a)

(b)   (f)

(c)   (g)

(d)   (h)   (A section of a parabola, $\omega_0{}^2 - \omega^2$)

(e)   (i)   [A section of a cubic curve, $\omega(\omega_0{}^2 - \omega^2)$]

Prob. 8–37

8-39. What is the minimum reactance associated with a resistance that is constant with frequency? Illustrate this by (a) adding constants to each of the functions in Prob. 8-37 and (b) subtracting these functions from constants, showing in each case how the results are thereby changed. Repeat for constant conductance, for constant magnitude of immittance.

8-40. A given resistance function $R(\omega)$ determines the corresponding or associated minimum-reactance impedance function $Z(p)$, as the text demonstrates in several ways. Explain why a given $R(\omega)$ does not determine a corresponding or associated minimum-conductance or minimum-susceptance admittance function.

8-41. The resistance function $R(\omega) = (1 + \omega^4)^{-1}$ is an example of a rather simple function.   Contrast the work of finding the associated minimum reactance by the integral methods, by the Brune-Gewertz method, and by the Bode (algebraic) method.   (Cf. Prob. 8-77.)

Repeat for the calculation of (8.02–14), taking (8.02–15) as data, and again, taking the reactance $X(\omega)$ as data.

8-42.   Given the resistance function

$$R(\omega) = \frac{1}{1 + \omega^{2s}},$$

in which s is a positive integer, find the associated minimum reactance from (8.05–11).   Does this particular one of the integral formulas offer advantages, in this case, over the others?   Reconstitute $Z(j\omega)$ from $R(\omega)$ and $X(\omega)$ and finally obtain $Z(p)$.

The formula

$$\int_0^\infty \frac{x^{2m}}{x^{2n} + 1}\, dx = \frac{\pi}{2n \sin\left(\dfrac{2m + 1}{2n}\,\pi\right)},$$

which may be established by contour integration, will be helpful.

8-43.   It may occasionally be advantageous to have the integral relations of Fig. 8.08–A expressed in terms of the variable $1/\omega$ rather than ω.   Change the variable accordingly and obtain the forms which the integral relations take in terms of the reciprocal frequency variable.   Explain in a general way the circumstances under which such transformed relations may be preferable.

8-44.   In the table of integral relations, Table 8.08–A, the left column expresses real part in terms of integrals of imaginary part and the constant $H_1(\infty)$.   Recast these expressions for the real part in forms which involve integrals of imaginary part and the constant $H_1(0)$ rather than $H_1(\infty)$.   [*Suggestion:* In each case determine the difference between these two constants by setting $\omega = 0$ in the formula; then substitute for $H_1(\infty)$ and combine terms.]   Show that the most important change is to replace $H_2(\lambda)$ by $H_2(\lambda)/\lambda$ or by $H_2(\lambda)/\lambda^2$, with appropriate other minor changes.

8-45.   In addition to the formulas of § 8.06, many other definite-integral relations between resistance and reactance, or functions thereof, exist.   By letting ω take the values zero and infinity in the various relations of Table 8.08–A, derive some of these other relations.

8-46.   Many additional integral relations can be obtained by changing the integrand in the fundamental contour integral of § 3.23 from which came the relations of § 8.08.   To what relations between resistance and reactance, both in the arbitrary-frequency form (as in § 8.08) and in the definite-frequency form (as in § 8.06) do the following integrands in place of $F(p) \times (p - j\omega_1)^{-1}$ lead?

$$\frac{F(p)}{p(p - j\omega_1)} \qquad \frac{pF(p)}{(p - j\omega_1)^2} \qquad \frac{F(p)}{(p - j\omega_1)^2} \qquad \frac{F(p)}{p(p - j\omega_1)^2} \qquad \frac{F(p)}{p^2(p - j\omega_1)^2}.$$

8-47.   Section 8.09 describes a very useful approximate method of calculating one part from the other, making use of plots on logarithmic frequency scales. It is also possible, though not generally as convenient, to make use of arithmetic frequency scales.

Using the most appropriate form in Table 8.08–A, determine formally the reactance associated with the resistance function shown, and plot it against ω. What difficulty arises if this is made a semi-infinite slope, i.e., if ω_2 is increased indefinitely? Why does this difficulty not arise when a logarithmic frequency scale is used? Do difficulties arise as ω_1 approaches zero?

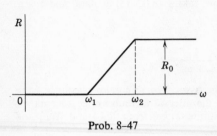

Prob. 8–47

Explain how an approximate method of calculating resistance from reactance based on straight-line approximations to the resistance could be built on your results above. Construct a small family of the necessary curves, and explain and illustrate their use. (Cf. BO 3.)

Extend your results to the calculation of reactance from resistance, and to the other possibilities listed in Table 8.08–B.

8-48. Let $Z(p)$ represent a positive-real, minimum-reactance impedance function, with $Z(j\omega) = R(\omega) + jX(\omega)$. Derive the following formulas which in the right half plane express $Z(p)$ and its parts in terms of the values of Z on the boundary of the right half plane, for any right-half-plane value of p.

(a) $\quad Z(p) = Z(\infty) + \dfrac{j}{\pi} \displaystyle\int_{-\infty}^{\infty} \dfrac{(\lambda - \omega)Z(j\lambda)}{\sigma^2 + (\lambda - \omega)^2} \, d\lambda,$

(b) $\quad Z(p) = \dfrac{\sigma}{\pi} \displaystyle\int_{-\infty}^{\infty} \dfrac{Z(j\lambda)}{\sigma^2 + (\lambda - \omega)^2} \, d\lambda,$

(c) $\mathbf{Re}\, Z(p) = Z(\infty) - \dfrac{1}{\pi} \displaystyle\int_{-\infty}^{\infty} \dfrac{(\lambda - \omega)X(\lambda)}{\sigma^2 + (\lambda - \omega)^2} \, d\lambda,$

(d) $\mathbf{Re}\, Z(p) = \dfrac{\sigma}{\pi} \displaystyle\int_{-\infty}^{\infty} \dfrac{R(\lambda)}{\sigma^2 + (\lambda - \omega)^2} \, d\lambda,$

(e) $\mathbf{Im}\, Z(p) = \dfrac{1}{\pi} \displaystyle\int_{-\infty}^{\infty} \dfrac{(\lambda - \omega)R(\lambda)}{\sigma^2 + (\lambda - \omega)^2} \, d\lambda,$

(f) $\mathbf{Im}\, Z(p) = \dfrac{\sigma}{\pi} \displaystyle\int_{-\infty}^{\infty} \dfrac{X(\lambda)}{\sigma^2 + (\lambda - \omega)^2} \, d\lambda.$

[*Suggestion:* Integrate $Z(p) \times (p - p_1)^{-1}$ around the usual contour enclosing the right half plane, first when p_1 is an arbitrary right-half-plane point, and second when p_1 is negative of the conjugate of that point; combine the results by addition and subtraction.]

Let $\sigma = 0$ and compare your results with those of the text. Under what conditions will the results be valid in the left half plane?

Let p be real in (c) above. Obtain the following formula for $Z(p)$ in terms of $X(\omega)$:

$$Z(p) = Z(\infty) - \frac{2}{\pi} \int_0^{\infty} \frac{\omega X(\omega)}{p^2 + \omega^2} \, d\omega.$$

Can this formula be extended to arbitrary values of p? Explain. Repeat the process, using (b), to obtain

$$Z(p) = \frac{2p}{\pi} \int_0^\infty \frac{R(\omega)}{p^2 + \omega^2} \, d\omega.$$

By considering $F(p) = \ln Z(p)$, $Z(p)$ being p-r (but not necessarily minimum-reactance), derive the following formulas for $Z(p)$ in terms of the magnitude and of the angle of $Z(j\omega)$.

$$\ln Z(p) = \ln Z(\infty) - \frac{2}{\pi} \int_0^\infty \frac{\lambda \beta(\lambda)}{p^2 + \lambda^2} \, d\lambda,$$

$$\ln Z(p) = \frac{2p}{\pi} \int_0^\infty \frac{\ln |Z(j\lambda)|}{p^2 + \lambda^2} \, d\lambda.$$

8-49. By using the definite integral (to be found in tables)

$$\int_0^\infty \ln \left(\frac{e^x + 1}{e^x - 1} \right) dx = \frac{\pi^2}{4},$$

obtain the relation for reactance in terms of resistance

$$X(\omega) = \frac{\pi}{2} \left(\frac{dR}{du} \right)_0 + \frac{1}{\pi} \int_{-\infty}^\infty \left[\left(\frac{dR}{du} \right) - \left(\frac{dR}{du} \right)_0 \right] \ln \coth \frac{|u|}{2} \, du$$

in which $u = \ln (\lambda/\omega)$ and the subscript zero means calculation at $u = 0$. Discuss the importance of the slope of the resistance at any given frequency (on a logarithmic frequency scale) in determining the reactance at that frequency. What symmetry is required in the resistance for the integral to vanish? What is the physical interpretation of this case? Considering the nature of the weighting function, what property of the resistance function is most important, and at what frequencies, in determining the reactance at some particular frequency?

8-50. The integral relations of § 8.08 express one part (reactance, e.g.) in terms of the other (resistance, e.g.) given at all frequencies. If one part is known only in certain frequency bands and the other at the remaining frequencies, the gaps can be filled by integral relations.

Suppose, for example, that of a minimum-reactance (p-r) impedance function $Z(p)$ the real-frequency resistance is known only in the band $0 \leq \omega \leq \omega_0$, and the reactance only in the band $\omega_0 \leq \omega$. Derive, by contour integration of the function

$$\frac{Z(p)}{(p - j\omega_1) \overset{+}{\sqrt{p^2 + \omega_0^2}}},$$

expressions for the missing parts. (Take the branch cut in the left half plane and use the traditional sort of contour.) Explain fully why this particular integrand gives these two-band relations, whereas that of § 3.23 does not. Check your results against formulas of § 8.08 for the cases $\omega_0 \to 0$ and $\omega_0 \to \infty$; then normalize the frequency scale so $\omega_0 = 1$ to obtain the results below, in which the integrals are not improper but are to be interpreted in the usual limiting (principal-value) sense, and all square roots are positive.

$$R(\omega) = -\frac{2\omega}{\pi}\sqrt{\omega^2 - 1}\left[\int_0^1 \frac{R(\lambda)\,d\lambda}{(\lambda^2 - \omega^2)\sqrt{1 - \lambda^2}} + \int_1^\infty \frac{X(\lambda)\,d\lambda}{(\lambda^2 - \omega^2)\sqrt{\lambda^2 - 1}}\right], \quad \omega > 1,$$

$$X(\omega) = \frac{2\omega}{\pi}\sqrt{1 - \omega^2}\left[\int_0^1 \frac{R(\lambda)\,d\lambda}{(\lambda^2 - \omega^2)\sqrt{1 - \lambda^2}} + \int_1^\infty \frac{X(\lambda)\,d\lambda}{(\lambda^2 - \omega^2)\sqrt{\lambda^2 - 1}}\right], \quad 0 < \omega < 1.$$

If the resistance is known only in the band $1 \le \omega$ and the reactance only in the band $0 \le \omega \le 1$, obtain the formulas

$$R(\omega) = \frac{2}{\pi}\sqrt{1 - \omega^2}\left[-\int_0^1 \frac{\lambda X(\lambda)\,d\lambda}{(\lambda^2 - \omega^2)\sqrt{1 - \lambda^2}} + \int_1^\infty \frac{\lambda R(\lambda)\,d\lambda}{(\lambda^2 - \omega^2)\sqrt{\lambda^2 - 1}}\right], \quad 0 < \omega < 1,$$

$$X(\omega) = \frac{2}{\pi}\sqrt{\omega^2 - 1}\left[-\int_0^1 \frac{\lambda X(\lambda)\,d\lambda}{(\lambda^2 - \omega^2)\sqrt{1 - \lambda^2}} + \int_1^\infty \frac{\lambda R(\lambda)\,d\lambda}{(\lambda^2 - \omega^2)\sqrt{\lambda^2 - 1}}\right], \quad \omega > 1.$$

8-51. Show, by using the results of Prob. 8-50, that when resistance is known in one part of the frequency spectrum, and reactance in the other, unit normalized frequency being the dividing point, that the extreme-frequency unknown value of resistance is given by

$$R(\infty) = \frac{2}{\pi}\left[\int_0^1 \frac{R(\omega)\,d\omega}{\sqrt{1 - \omega^2}} + \int_1^\infty \frac{X(\omega)\,d\omega}{\sqrt{\omega^2 - 1}}\right]$$

or

$$R(0) = \frac{2}{\pi}\left[-\int_0^1 \frac{X(\omega)\,d\omega}{\omega\sqrt{1 - \omega^2}} + \int_1^\infty \frac{R(\omega)\,d\omega}{\omega\sqrt{\omega^2 - 1}}\right].$$

What values do the formulas of Prob. 8-50 give for $X(0)$ and $X(\infty)$? Explain. Derive also the following integral relations:

$$\int_0^1 \frac{R(\omega) - R(\infty)}{\sqrt{1 - \omega^2}}\,d\omega + \int_1^\infty \frac{X(\omega)\,d\omega}{\sqrt{\omega^2 - 1}} = 0,$$

$$-\int_0^1 \frac{X(\omega)\,d\omega}{\omega\sqrt{1 - \omega^2}} + \int_1^\infty \frac{R(\omega) - R(0)}{\omega\sqrt{\omega^2 - 1}}\,d\omega = 0.$$

8-52. Find the (idealized) immittance functions that have the following parts:

(a) $R = 0,\ 0 \le \omega \le 1;\ X = $ constant, $1 \le \omega$.
[Partial-fraction expansion of $(\lambda^2 - \omega^2)^{-1}$ and inversion of the frequency scale may be helpful.] (GU 3.)

(b) $|Y| = 1,\ 0 \le \omega \le 1;\ \overline{Y} = 90°,\ 1 \le \omega$.

(c) $R = \sqrt{1 - \omega^2},\ 0 \le \omega \le 1;\ X = \sqrt{\omega^2 - 1},\ 1 \le \omega$.

(d) $G = \dfrac{\sqrt{1 - \omega^2}}{\omega_1^2 - \omega^2},\ 0 \le \omega \le 1;\ B = \dfrac{\sqrt{\omega^2 - 1}}{\omega^2 - \omega_1^2},\ 1 \le \omega,\ \omega_1 > 1.$

(e) $X = a\omega,\ 0 \le \omega \le 1;\ R = b,\ 1 \le \omega$. (BO 3.)

8-53. Following the general procedure of Prob. 8-50, but using two square-root factors, find formulas for filling the gaps when, for example, resistance is known at low and high frequencies but not in an internal band (where, however, reactance is known). Repeat for the complementary situation. What changes occur in the results when one square-root factor is placed in the numerator, and one in the denominator, rather than both in the denominator?

8-54. If (for example) resistance is known in the band $0 \leq \omega \leq 1$ and reactance in the band $1 \leq \omega$, the determination of the missing parts can be carried out formally as discussed in the foregoing problems. Develop now an approximate method, similar to that of § 8.09, that may be applied to this situation. The approximations used may be (a) horizontal line segments, (b) linear segments on an arithmetic frequency scale, (c) linear segments on a logarithmic scale. Compare your method(s) as to practicality with that of using the method of § 8.09 in successive approximations: assume a form for the resistance at frequencies where it is not known, compute the associated reactance and compare with the datum reactance, revise the assumption and repeat, etc. Simultaneous treatment of the datum reactance will also be helpful.

8-55. Demonstrate the equivalence of the rectangular and polar forms of the definition of positive reality (§ 4.04) by starting from (d) and (e) of Prob. 8-48 and comparing the tangents of the angles of $Z(p)$ and of p. Do this first for minimum-reactance functions and then discuss the modifications necessary to include other p-r functions.

8-56. Among the various alternate approaches to the relations between real and imaginary parts, an especially interesting (and not complicated) one depends on the transformation generated by $w = u + jv = (p - 1)/(p + 1)$. Describe this mapping briefly; in particular, sketch the w-plane mapping of the (normalized) ω axis and of the right and left half planes.

Consider now a minimum-reactance (p-r) impedance (or minimum-susceptance admittance) function, $Z(p) = F(w)$. Show that the power-series expansion of $F(w)$ about $w = 0$,

$$F(w) = A_0 + A_1 w + A_2 w^2 + A_3 w^3 + \cdots$$

is valid at least inside and on the circle $|w| = 1$. Show further that all the A's are real.

Let w now be on the unit circle, $w = e^{j\theta}$. Show that

$$F(e^{j\theta}) = (A_0 + A_1 \cos \theta + A_2 \cos 2\theta + \cdots) + j(A_1 \sin \theta + A_2 \sin 2\theta + \cdots)$$

in which the two parentheses are real, so that F has been split into its real and imaginary parts (which are respectively even and odd functions of θ). What is the functional relation between ω and θ?

Let $Z(j\omega) = R(\omega) + jX(\omega)$. From the foregoing deduce an independent proof that resistance and reactance are related, and derive the following method of calculation of one part, given the other.

(a) Given $R(\omega)$, transform it and expand in a Fourier series in θ,

$$R(\omega) = A_0 + A_1 \cos \theta + A_2 \cos 2\theta + \cdots .$$

Then

$$X(\omega) = A_1 \sin \theta + A_2 \sin 2\theta + \cdots$$

and

$$Z(j\omega) = A_0 + A_1 e^{j\theta} + A_2 e^{j2\theta} + \cdots$$

and

$$Z(p) = A_0 + A_1 \left(\frac{p-1}{p+1}\right) + A_2 \left(\frac{p-1}{p+1}\right)^2 + \cdots .$$

(b) Given $X(\omega)$, transform it and expand in a Fourier series in θ,

$$X(\omega) = A_1 \sin \theta + A_2 \sin 2\theta + \cdots$$

and then proceed essentially as in (a).

Illustrate by calculating the minimum-reactance $Z(p)$, given

$$(1)\ R(\omega) = \frac{1}{1 + \omega^2} \qquad (2)\ R(\omega) = \frac{1}{1 + \omega^2 + \omega^4}.$$

Contrast and explain the difficulties of calculation in the two cases. Does $Z(p)$ necessarily have a singularity at $p = -1$ in general, as the series $Z(p) = \sum_k A_k (p - 1)^k/(p + 1)^k$ seems to imply? Explain.

Extend the method to the calculation of immittance, given magnitude or angle. (LE 1, RE 2.) (Cf. also Prob. 13-104.)

8-57. Devise an approximate method of calculating one part of an immittance given the other, by plotting the given part versus θ (Prob. 8-56), approximating it with straight-line segments, and obtaining the Fourier series for the succession of linear segments. (Determine in literal form the Fourier-series coefficients for the function shown, both as an odd function and as an even function, and show why no further Fourier-series coefficient calculations are necessary.) What considerations determine the best choice of frequency-scale normalization in the p plane? (Consider the effect on the θ plot of various choices.)

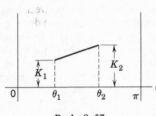

Prob. 8–57

Illustrate by determining the minimum reactance associated with the resistance function $R(\omega) = (1 + \omega^2)^{-1}$, using one, two, and three segments. Plot this reactance against frequency and compare with the true function, $X(\omega) = -\omega/(1 + \omega^2)$. Contrast the work required with that of the method of § 8.09 (cf. Appendix B).

8-58. An interesting extension of the integral relations between parts of an immittance is the discussion of the extent to which both resistance and reactance (for example) can be specified, independently of each other, in a band of frequencies, neither being specified outside this band. Generally there are no unreasonable limitations here (cf. RE 2).

To illustrate the possibilities, determine and plot the family of reactance curves associated with the family of resistance curves given in (a) of the figure, using the transformation of Prob. 8-56. Discuss briefly, in their light, the range of possibilities for reactance in the band $0 < \omega < 1$, given only that the resistance is constant in the same band. What light does this shed on the possibility of independent specification of R and X in a band of frequencies, provided that no specifications are laid down outside the band?

For purposes of calculating R and X in the band $\omega > 1$, given R and X in the band $0 < \omega < 1$, consider the following procedure. Let

$$R = A_0 + A_1 \cos \theta + A_2 \cos 2\theta + \cdots$$

and

$$X = B_1 \sin \theta + B_2 \sin 2\theta + \cdots$$

be the Fourier series for the R and X functions.   When the unknown parts have been properly determined, and the gaps filled, then of course $B_1 = A_1$, $B_2 = A_2$, etc. (Prob. 8-56).   Show that this requires

$$\int_0^\pi (R \cos n\theta - X \sin n\theta)d\theta = 0, \qquad n = 0, 1, 2, 3, \cdots .$$

We may proceed to an estimate of the unknown parts by a succession of step-function approximations as is to be illustrated next.   Here the functions are assumed known in $0 < \theta < \pi/2$ and unknown in $\pi/2 < \theta < \pi$.   As a first approximation in the latter region, the steps of heights R_1 and X_1 are laid down

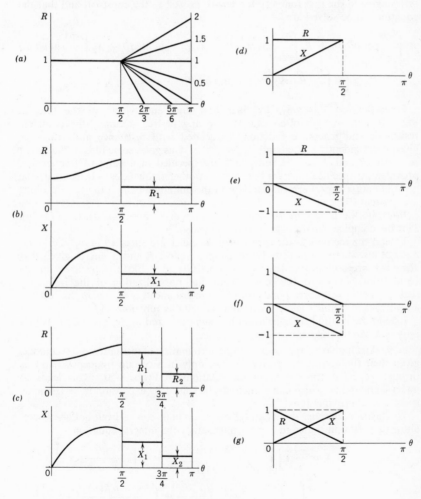

Prob. 8–58

in (b). Show that their heights can be so determined that $B_1 = A_1$ and $B_2 = A_2$ by solving the pair of simultaneous linear equations

$$R_1 \int_{\pi/2}^{\pi} \cos \theta \, d\theta - X_1 \int_{\pi/2}^{\pi} \sin \theta \, d\theta = - \int_{0}^{\pi/2} (R \cos \theta - X \sin \theta) d\theta,$$

$$R_1 \int_{\pi/2}^{\pi} \cos 2\theta \, d\theta - X_1 \int_{\pi/2}^{\pi} \sin 2\theta \, d\theta = - \int_{0}^{\pi/2} (R \cos 2\theta - X \sin 2\theta) d\theta.$$

Explain why the constant term may be considered automatically correct.

As a second approximation we lay down in (c) two steps in the unknown interval. Show that their heights can be determined so that now the Fourier series agree in the first four varying terms, as well as the constant, and that the equations to be solved are

$$R_1 \int_{\pi/2}^{3\pi/4} \cos n\theta \, d\theta + R_2 \int_{\pi/2}^{3\pi/4} \cos n\theta \, d\theta - X_1 \int_{\pi/2}^{3\pi/4} \sin n\theta \, d\theta - X_2 \int_{\pi/2}^{3\pi/4} \sin n\theta \, d\theta$$

$$= \int_{0}^{\pi/2} (R \cos n\theta - X \sin n\theta) d\theta, \qquad n = 1, 2, 3, 4.$$

Proceeding in this way, by finer and finer subdivision of the interval $\pi/2 < \theta < \pi$, we can often calculate to any desired accuracy the complete resistance and reactance functions associated with resistance and reactance given independently in the band $0 < \omega < 1$. This gives some idea of the extent to which R and X can be independently specified in a band of frequencies, provided no specifications are laid down at other frequencies. In general, one must of course expect erratic behavior in the unknown band if the specifications are unusual (RE 2).

Illustrate the procedure by completing the curves given in (d), (e), (f), (g). Plot the complete curves against frequency also.

Extend the method to the case where R and X are specified in $\omega_1 < \omega < \omega_2$ but not elsewhere. Illustrate by plotting complete R and X curves given that R and X are constant at the values $+600\,\Omega$ and $-100\,\Omega$ respectively in the band from 25 kcps to 100 kcps. Note that normalization of the frequency scale so that $\omega = 1$ corresponds to the geometric mean of ω_1 and ω_2 has certain advantages in symmetrically laying out the data as functions of θ.

Extend the method to calculation of magnitude and angle, given their values only in a certain frequency band.

8-59. An alternative approach to the determination of resistance and reactance, given their (independent) specified values only in a certain frequency band, is through repeated application of the relations of Prob. 8-50. This leads to integral equations, which can sometimes be solved by expansion in series or by successive approximations.

To illustrate, suppose that R and X are given in $0 < \omega < 1$ but not elsewhere. Show that $R(\omega)$ in the band $1 < \omega$ must satisfy the integral equation

$$R(\omega) = - \frac{2\omega}{\pi} \sqrt{\omega^2 - 1} \left\{ \int_{0}^{1} \frac{R(\lambda) \, d\lambda}{(\lambda^2 - \omega^2)\sqrt{1 - \lambda^2}} + \frac{2}{\pi} \int_{1}^{\infty} \frac{d\lambda}{\lambda^2 - \omega^2} \times \right.$$

$$\left. \left[- \int_{0}^{1} \frac{\mu X(\mu) \, d\mu}{(\mu^2 - \lambda^2)\sqrt{1 - \mu^2}} + \int_{1}^{\infty} \frac{\mu R(\mu) \, d\mu}{(\mu^2 - \lambda^2)\sqrt{\mu^2 - 1}} \right] \right\}.$$

8-60. An alternate approach to relations between real and imaginary parts is through network analysis, the calculation of *time* response to given driving functions (of time). For example, if a unit impulse (a pulse of extremely short duration but large enough in amplitude that its integral during its existence is unity) of current is applied to a network whose (minimum-reactance) driving-point impedance is $Z(p)$, assumed to contain no energy at the instant of application ($t = 0$), then the response voltage at the driving point is

$$v(t) = \frac{1}{\pi} \int_0^\infty [R(\omega) \cos t\omega - X(\omega) \sin t\omega] \, d\omega, \qquad t \neq 0.$$

Verify this, as by (bilateral) Fourier- or Laplace-transformation analysis. One integral relation,

$$\int_0^\infty R(\omega) \cos t\omega \, d\omega + \int_0^\infty X(\omega) \sin t\omega \, d\omega = 0,$$

follows because $v(t) = 0$ for $t < 0$. Verify this and explain how the response $v(t)$ can therefore be calculated with a knowledge of only the resistance *or* the reactance, giving the formulas for $v(t)$. Finally, obtain the specific resistance-reactance relations

$$X(\omega) = \frac{2}{\pi} \int_0^\infty \left[\int_0^\infty R(\lambda) \cos t\lambda \, d\lambda \right] \sin \omega t \, dt,$$

$$R(\omega) = -\frac{2}{\pi} \int_0^\infty \left[\int_0^\infty X(\lambda) \sin t\lambda \, d\lambda \right] \cos \omega t \, dt,$$

which determine one part in terms of the other in another fashion different from those of the text. To what extent is the foregoing analysis dependent on a minimum-resistance character for $Z(p)$? Is there any inherent assumption as to the value of $R(\infty)$? (LE 1.)

8-61. Another approach to integral relations through network analysis (cf. Prob. 8-60) is to assume temporarily that the driving-point impedance $Z(j\omega) = R(\omega) + j0$, i.e., that the resistance R has *no* associated reactance. Then the response to the unit impulse of current is

$$v(t) = \frac{1}{2\pi} \int_{-\infty}^\infty R(\omega) e^{jt\omega} \, d\omega, \qquad t \neq 0,$$

which generally has values for both positive and negative time. Verify the formula and illustrate this statement by plotting $v(t)$ against t for $R(\omega) = (1 + \omega^2)^{-1}$. Since negative-time response is absurd, there must be an error in prescribing $Z(j\omega) = R(\omega) + j0$. To find the error, write $v(t) = 0$ for $t < 0$ and $v(t)$ equal to the expression above for $t > 0$, as being more reasonable. Show by transforming $v(t)$, assuming that the order of integration can be changed and being careful of the evaluation of improper integrals by using an appropriate limiting process in approaching the imaginary axis, that then

$$Z(j\omega) = \int_0^\infty \left[\frac{1}{2\pi} \int_{-\infty}^\infty R(\lambda) e^{jt\lambda} \, d\lambda \right] e^{-j\omega t} \, dt$$

$$= \frac{1}{2} \left[R(\omega) + j \frac{1}{\pi} \int_{-\infty}^\infty \frac{R(\lambda) \, d\lambda}{\lambda - \omega} \right],$$

or, in words, that the associated reactance is thereby specifically determined (cf. the appropriate form of § 8.08).

The factor $\frac{1}{2}$ may be explained by correlating the development above with the Bode (algebraic) method of calculation of $Z(p)$ from $R(\omega)$ of § 8.17. If $R(\omega)$ is first converted to $\mathrm{Ev}\, Z(p)$ and expanded in partial fractions, as in (8.17–6), and $v(t)$ is then calculated as above, the terms corresponding to $Z_R(p)$ will have value for negative time and should be discarded. There remains only $Z_L(p)$, which is $\frac{1}{2}Z(p)$, as in (8.17–10). Verify these statements and illustrate by determining $Z(p)$, given $R(\omega) = (1 + \omega^2)^{-1}$.

8-62. Show, by the use of the appropriate formula of § 8.08, that if a resistance function continually decreases (increases) with frequency, the associated minimum reactance is never positive (negative), nor is it zero at any frequency except zero and infinity. Is the converse necessarily true? Show further that if the product of reactance and frequency increases (decreases) continually with frequency, then the associated resistance is maximum (minimum) at infinity. Can you find a corresponding statement relative to $R(0)$?

Give the corresponding statements for conductance and susceptance, and for magnitude and angle of immittance.

8-63. Calculate the scale factors to be applied to the function F_0 when the method of § 8.09 is to be used to determine $\log_{10}|Z|$ from angle given in degrees, from angle given in radians, and $\ln|Z|$ from the same data.

8-64. Show how the *quotient* of the given reactance and frequency may be used in place of their product in (8.09–11) in determining resistance from reactance. For what sort of (given) reactance functions would each procedure be appropriate? Make corresponding statements for the determination of magnitude from angle.

8-65. Show that the integral in (8.09-8) is convergent, for all values of x_0. Evaluate $F_0(\infty)$ by dividing the integration into two parts (from 0 to 1 and from 1 to ∞), showing the contributions to be equal, and then using the definite integral given in Prob. 8-49. Verify your result by comparison with the tables of Appendix B.

8-66. Derive the series

$$F_0\left(\frac{\omega}{\omega_0}\right) = \frac{2}{\pi}\left(x_0 + \frac{x_0^3}{9} + \frac{x_0^5}{25} + \frac{x_0^7}{49} + \cdots\right), \quad 0 \le x_0 \le 1,\ x_0 = \omega/\omega_0 = f/f_0,$$

for the function (8.09-8), to be compared with (B–3). Calculate F_0 for $\omega/\omega_0 = 0.1$ and 0.2 and compare with the values in Table B–1. Derive the symmetry relation

$$F_0\left(\frac{\omega}{\omega_0}\right) = \frac{\pi}{2} - F_0\left(\frac{\omega_0}{\omega}\right)$$

to be compared with (B–2). Use it to calculate F_0 for $\omega/\omega_0 = 5$ and 10, and compare with the values in Table B–1.

8-67. Show that the tables of Appendix B could also be constructed by tabulating first the function

$$\int_1^{w_0} \frac{\ln w}{w - 1}\, dw.$$

[*Suggestion:* Break (8.09–8) or (B–1) into the sum of two integrals; then replace $(1 + x)$ and $(1 - x)$ respectively by new symbols.]   (For tabulations of this function see FL 2; this is due to B. A. Kingsbury.)

8-68. Show that the function F_0 given by (8.09–8) can be written

$$F_0 = \frac{2}{\pi} \int_0^{x_0} \frac{\tanh^{-1} x}{x} \, dx$$

which can also, of course, be computed from the series given in Prob. 8-66 (CO 2).

8-69. Compute and plot carefully the resistance function $R(\omega)$ of the network shown. (Element values are normalized ohms, henrys, farads.) From the plot, using the method of § 8.09 and Appendix B, determine and plot the reactance function $X(\omega)$. Use enough line segments to give reasonably accurate results. Compare your result with the actual reactance, determined from the original network.

$Z = R + jX$

Prob. 8–69

8-70. For each of the following resistance functions, make a plot against frequency on a logarithmic scale and determine, by the method of § 8.09 and Appendix B, the associated minimum reactance in the form of a curve.

$$(a) \;\; \frac{1}{1 + \omega^{10}} \qquad (b) \;\; \frac{\omega^2}{1 + \omega^{10}} \qquad (c) \;\; \frac{\omega^4}{1 + \omega^{10}}$$

$$(d) \;\; \frac{\omega^6}{1 + \omega^{10}} \qquad (e) \;\; \frac{\omega^8}{1 + \omega^{10}} \qquad (f) \;\; \frac{\omega^{10}}{1 + \omega^{10}}$$

In each case do this (1) with the smallest reasonable number of line segments, (2) with a somewhat larger number, to improve the accuracy of your result; compare the results with the actual reactance (to be obtained by analytical methods). Discuss your results.

Starting from the reactance, as determined analytically above, determine the associated minimum resistance in analogous fashion, and discuss your results.

Show that the principles of removing reactance and susceptance in the form of series or shunt *L-C* networks (described in § 8.01) are enough to realize these particular functions, by actually obtaining network realizations from the analytical expressions for $Z(p)$.

Repeat on the dual basis.

8-71. Determine the resistance associated with the reactance

$$X(\omega) = - \frac{\omega}{1 + \omega^2},$$

using a three-segment approximation, and so verify Figs. B–E and B–F of Appendix B. Repeat with a five-segment approximation.

Repeat the two calculations, approximating X/ω rather than ωX. Compare the results in each case with the exact resistance (to be obtained analytically). Discuss the relative merits, in respect to errors, of the two methods.

State and solve the dual problems.

8-72. Given

$$\beta = -\tan^{-1}\frac{\omega}{1 + 2\omega^2},$$

which is the real-frequency angle of a driving-point impedance function $Z(p)$, obtain an approximate plot of $|Z(j\omega)|$ by the method of § 8.09. Obtain the actual function $Z(p)$ and plot its real-frequency magnitude for comparison. Realize the function as a driving-point impedance, and as a driving-point admittance (only two kinds of elements are necessary).

8-73. In § 8.13 it is pointed out that even if $|Z|^2$ is an even function of ω with real coefficients, not negative for any ω, with imaginary zeros and poles double, it does not necessarily follow then that the $Z(p)$ extracted by the method of § 8.13 is p-r. Nevertheless the function $|Z|^2$ determines, by itself, the answer to the question: *is $Z(p)$ p-r?* Use the graphical method of § 8.09 to emphasize this fact by predicting, solely on the basis of plots of $|Z(j\omega)|$, whether the following proposed $|Z|^2$ functions will give p-r functions $Z(p)$. Verify your conclusions analytically.

(a) $\dfrac{\omega^2}{1 + \omega^4}$ (b) $\dfrac{1 + \omega^4}{1 + \omega^6}$ (c) $\dfrac{(\omega^2 - 1)^2}{\omega^2(\omega^2 + 1)}$

(d) $\dfrac{\omega^2(\omega^2 + 8)^2}{(\omega^4 - 19\omega^2 + 100)(\omega^4 - 33\omega^2 + 289)}$

For what range of the parameter a will the function $[(1 + a\omega^2)/(1 + \omega^4)]$, interpreted as the square of the magnitude of an admittance function, lead to a p-r function $Y(p)$?

8-74. As stated in § 8.13 (cf. Prob. 8-73) it is not immediately apparent on inspection of a given *magnitude* function whether the corresponding function of p is p-r. One may say, however, that abrupt changes in the function $|Z|$, i.e., large values ($\pm$) of its slope when plotted against frequency, tend to make $Z(p)$ unrealizable. Discuss this statement both analytically, drawing upon § 8.08, and in terms of the approximate graphical procedure (Prob. 8-73). The functions $(1 + \omega^2)^{-1}$ and $(1 + \omega^{10})^{-1}$, both being interpreted as $|Z|^2$, may be used for illustration.

~ 8-75. The pairs of curves shown represent rough sketches of resistance and reactance desired of one-terminal pairs. Which of them represent reasonably possible situations and which do not? Explain.

8-76. The pairs of functions given below represent driving-point conductance and susceptance desired of one-terminal pairs. Discuss the possibility of realizing each, explaining your reasoning fully. If changes have to be made, of what nature are they?

(a) $G = \dfrac{7 + 6\omega^{10}}{1 + \omega^{10}}$ $B = \dfrac{-\omega}{1 + \omega^{10}}.$

(b) $G = \dfrac{\omega^4}{(1 + \omega^2)^3}$ $B = \dfrac{-3\omega^5 + 6\omega^3 + \omega}{(1 + \omega^2)^3}.$

8-77. The evaluation of integrals required for the determination of (for example) reactance from resistance according to the formulas of § 8.08 can be a lengthy process. When the datum resistance function is rational, factoring of a polynomial into two subpolynomials (Appendix A) and calculation of residues for the application of contour integration suffice, however, and the work can be formalized and in part tabulated once for all. Show that the appropriate integral of § 8.08 can in this case be cast in the form

$$X(\omega) = f(\omega) \int_{-\infty}^{\infty} \frac{g(\lambda, \omega)}{h(\lambda)h(-\lambda)} \, d\lambda$$

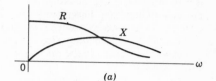

(a)

in which f is rational, g is a polynomial in λ whose coefficients depend on ω, and the zeros of $h(\lambda)$, a polynomial of degree n, all have positive imaginary parts. In terms of the (literal) coefficients of g and h, evaluate the integral for $n = 1, 2, 3$, and indicate how such a table can be extended. (See JA 4, pp. 333 ff. and 369, and ME 2.) Illustrate the use of the table by calculating the minimum reactance corresponding to

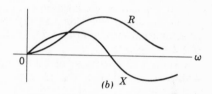

(b)

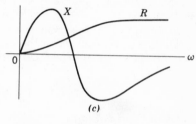

(c)

$$R(\omega) = \frac{(4 - \omega^2)^2}{(1 + \omega^2)(2 + \omega^2)(3 + \omega^2)}.$$

(Due to M. Tobak and G. A. Smith.)

8-78. Consider the appearance of real-frequency poles in the resistance function (8.11-2). If $Z(p)$ is p-r and has a pole at $j\omega_0$, show that the denominator of (8.11-2) has a double zero at that point, the numerator has at least a double zero at that point, and that consequently $R(\omega)$ has no real-frequency poles, as (8.11-4) states.

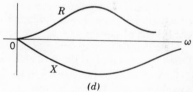

(d)

Prob. 8–75

8-79. An alternative algebraic process for calculating (for example) reactance from resistance, due to Miyata (MI 3), determines the denominator of the complete impedance function (8.11–1) exactly as in § 8.11, but the numerator somewhat differently. Let

$$F(p) = N(-p^2) \frac{M_3 + N_3}{M_2 + N_2}$$

in which $(M_2 + N_2)$ is the (Hurwitz) polynomial obtained by factoring the denominator of the datum (resistance) function $D(-p^2)$ as in § 8.11, $N(-p^2)$ is the numerator of this datum function, and $(M_3 + N_3)$ is another polynomial whose calculation is explained below, as is the relation of $F(p)$ to the desired impedance function $Z(p)$.

Show that if $M_2 M_3 - N_2 N_3 = 1$, then Ev $F(p)$ is equal to the datum function $N(-p^2)/D(-p^2)$. Show now that if we write $N_3 = e_1 p + e_3 p^3 + \cdots$ of sufficiently high degree, then an even polynomial M_3, also with real coefficients, can be found to satisfy $M_2M_3 - N_2N_3 = 1$, the e's being suitably determined, and hence that $F(p)$ has the datum even part. Finally show that $F(p)$, although it may not be p-r, can be made p-r without altering its even part, by subtracting an odd polynomial. This modified function is $Z(p)$, the (p-r) minimum-reactance impedance function whose resistance function is that given.

Illustrate by determining $Z(p)$, given $R(\omega) = \omega^4/(1 + 2\omega^2 - 3\omega^4 + \omega^6)$.

Extend the process to the calculation of impedance from reactance. (See also Prob. 10-79.)

8-80. For the set of simultaneous equations that must be solved in the Brune-Gewertz method of determining impedance from resistance, (8.11–10), show that the determinant of the coefficients does not vanish, and hence the set can be solved. (*Suggestion:* Compare this determinant with those of the Hurwitz criterion mentioned in Prob. 5-37; do the integral relations, or the Bode method of § 8.17, assist?)

8-81. In the discussion of § 8.11 show that $a_0 = b_0c_0/d_0$ and reconcile this with $a_0 = c_0/b_0$ of (8.11–10). Similarly, show that $a_m = b_mc_{2m}/d_{2m}$ and reconcile with $a_m = c_{2m}/b_m$.

8-82. Discuss the possibility of proceeding in the following manner in the Bode method of calculating $Z(p)$ from $R(\omega)$ of § 8.17.

(a) Form $\mathrm{Ev}\, Z(p)$ from $R(\omega)$.

(b) Factor the denominator thereof into two polynomials, one Hurwitz and one anti-Hurwitz, $P_1(p)$ and $P_2(p)$ respectively.

(c) Write

$$\mathrm{Ev}\, Z(p) = \left(\frac{Q_1}{P_1} + \frac{K_0}{2}\right) + \left(\frac{Q_2}{P_2} + \frac{K_0}{2}\right)$$

in which $Q_1 = a_0 + a_1p + \cdots + a_{n-1}p^{n-1}$, the order of $R(\omega)$ being $2n$.

(d) It remains to determine Q_1. Find the a's from a set of simultaneous equations obtained by manipulation of the expression in (c) to a point where coefficients of powers of p can be equated.

Note that this avoids complex numbers when the poles of $\mathrm{Ev}\, Z(p)$ are complex. Discuss its relation to the Brune-Gewertz method. (Due to W. R. Davis.)

8-83. A class of functions suitable for driving-point resistance or conductance functions (§ 8.16) is defined by

$$F(\omega) = \frac{\omega^{2m}}{1 + \omega^{2n}}, \quad n = 1, 2, 3, \cdots ; \quad m = 0, 1, 2, \cdots n.$$

They provide good exercise in the determination of associated minimum reactance (susceptance) and complete impedance (admittance) without difficult computation, because of the simplicity of the denominator. Furthermore, the resulting immittance functions are all realizable with no tools beyond the ideas of § 8.01. Verify these remarks and obtain network realizations of $F(\omega)$, both as driving-point resistance and as driving-point conductance, for the various cases corresponding to $n = 1, 2, 3, 4, 5$.

8-84. Find the reactance, $X(\omega)$, that corresponds to the resistance

$$R(\omega) = \frac{\omega^4 - 2\omega^2 + 1000}{\omega^4 - 54\omega^2 + 2025} \quad \text{ohms.}$$

What arbitrariness is there in your answer?

8-85. Find the complete impedance function $Z(p)$ that corresponds to the resistance function

$$R(\omega) = \frac{\omega^2}{\omega^4 + 8\omega^2 + 16}.$$

What arbitrariness is inherent in your result?

Repeat for the function

$$R(\omega) = \frac{\omega^4 - 4\omega^2 + 4}{(\omega^2 + 1)(\omega^4 + 2\omega^2 + 2)}.$$

8-86. The function

$$G(\omega) = \frac{2\omega^2}{\omega^4 + 4}$$

represents the real-frequency conductance at the input of a network. Calculate the real-frequency angle of this admittance and sketch its behavior versus frequency. Is there any arbitrariness in your result? If there is, give only the simplest answer, but explain why there may be others.

8-87. Each of the functions given below meets the requirements for realizability as a driving-point resistance or conductance function (§ 8.16), on the assumption (to be verified in Chapter 9) that positive reality implies realizability. Obtain, in each case, the corresponding minimum-reactance impedance function or minimum-susceptance admittance function, and plot both real and imaginary parts versus frequency.

(a) $\dfrac{4 + \omega^2}{1 + \omega^2}$ (b) $\dfrac{(\omega^2 - 4)^2}{1 + \omega^4}$ (c) $\dfrac{\omega^4 + 2.8\omega^2 + 16.8}{\omega^4 + 13\omega^2 + 36}$ (d) $\dfrac{\omega^2(1 - \omega^2)^2}{1 + \omega^6}$

(e) $\dfrac{(\omega^2 - 6)^2}{1 + \omega^6}$ (f) $\dfrac{\omega^4}{1 + 2\omega^2 + \omega^4}$ (g) $\dfrac{(1 - \omega^2)^4}{1 + \omega^8}$ (h) $\dfrac{\omega^4(1 - \omega^2)^2}{1 + \omega^8}$

(i) $\left(\dfrac{\omega^2 - 4}{\omega^2 + 4}\right)^4$ (j) $\dfrac{(\omega^2 - 1)^2(\omega^2 - 2)^2}{1 + \omega^8}$ (k) $\dfrac{\omega^{10} + \omega^8 + 33\omega^4 - 40\omega^2 + 17}{1 + 10\omega^6 + \omega^{10}}$

(l) $\dfrac{\omega^2(\omega^2 - 3)^2}{(1 + \omega^2)(2 + \omega^2)(3 + \omega^2)}$ (m) $\dfrac{46 - 18\omega^2 + 2\omega^4}{10 - 6\omega^2 + \omega^4} + 4.73$

8-88. Consider the function

$$H(p) = \frac{1}{1 - G^2},$$

in which $G(p)$ is a reactance function (Chapter 6). Show that if $H(j\omega)$ is interpreted as a driving-point resistance (conductance) function, the corresponding impedance (admittance) is p-r and realizable in a particularly simple fashion. Show that if $H(j\omega)$ is interpreted as the square of the magnitude of a driving-point immittance function, that function is p-r and realizable in a particularly simple fashion. What is the difference between the realizations?

8-89. Starting from the form (8.11–1), show that the coefficients c_{2s} in (8.11–2) can be expressed in the form

$$\sum_{k=-\infty}^{+\infty} a_{s+k} b_{s-k} (-1)^k$$

in which negative-subscript a's and b's are to be taken as zero. Show that this formula is the same as (8.11–11). Similarly, show that the formulas

$$\sum_{k=-\infty}^{\infty} b_{s+k}b_{s-k}(-1)^k \quad \text{and} \quad \sum_{k=-\infty}^{\infty} a_{s+k}b_{s-k+1}(-1)^{k+1}$$

give the coefficients d_{2s} in (8.11–2) and the numerator coefficients of (8.12–4) (BR 4).

Show that, if $R(\omega)$ is given, the coefficients a_m and a_0 in (8.11–1) can be written immediately from the values $R(\infty)$ and $R(0)$ and the coefficient d_0 (with $b_m = 1$).

8-90. In the Brune-Gewertz method of determining $Z(p)$ from a knowledge of only the real-frequency resistance or reactance, it is necessary to determine a polynomial whose zeros are the left-half-plane zeros of a given even polynomial. Let p_k^2 represent a zero of the given even polynomial and write

$$p_k^2 = a + jb = re^{j\theta} = r\underline{/\theta};$$

this is of course accompanied by its conjugate. Show that the corresponding factor of the polynomial desired is

$$[p^2 + 2\sqrt{r}\cos{(\theta/2)} + r] \quad \text{or} \quad [p^2 + \sqrt{2(r + a)}p + r]$$

and hence that the numerical evaluation of the square roots of complex numbers can be avoided, even if the p^2 zeros of the denominator of the datum function are used rather than a polynomial-splitting method (Appendix A).

8-91. In the Bode method of computing $Z(p)$ from $R(\omega)$ of § 8.17, we get

$$2Z_L(p) = \sum_i \frac{K_i}{p - p_i} + \cdots + K_0 \tag{8.17–10}$$

in which the p_i are the left-half-plane poles of the datum function, and the dots represent multiple-pole terms. Prove that this function $2Z_L(p)$ is p-r. Show by contour integration that if $K_0 = 0$, then

$$\int_{-\infty}^{\infty} R(\omega)\,d\omega = \pi(\sum_i K_i)$$

and hence that as $p \to \infty$, $Z_L(p) \to K/p$, in which $K > 0$. Correlate this with Bode's resistance integral, § 8.06.

8-92. Prove (8.17–17). This may be done by a differentiation process, or by writing (8.17–18) with arbitrary coefficients and showing that (8.17–17) must hold if it is to be truly even. Repeat the problem for the corresponding relations of § 8.18.

8-93. Let $G(p)$ be an even rational function of p with real coefficients. Answer the following questions with a general discussion and illustrative examples, letting the function $F(p)$ be defined by Ev $F(p) = G(p)$. How many answers are there to the question: what is $F(p)$? How many of these answers are p-r functions?

Now let $G(p)$ be odd rather than even. Repeat, with the definition Od $F(p) = G(p)$.

8-94. Review the calculation of $X(\omega)$ or $Z(p)$ from $R(\omega)$ by each of the methods discussed in the text. Explain in each case the effect of using a non-minimum-resistance function instead of a minimum one, i.e., the effect of adding a constant to the data. Repeat for the calculation of $R(\omega)$ or $Z(p)$ from $X(\omega)$, by explaining the effect of using a nonminimum-reactance datum function for $X(\omega)$.

8-94. Show that in (8.12-3) and (8.12-4) *any a* may arbitrarily be set equal to zero, the equations solved, and that the resulting $Z(p)$ is correct within an additive real constant. If a_0 is set equal to zero, show that $Z(p)$ so determined must be augmented by adding a constant equal to $R(0)$ in the final result. How is $R(0)$ to be determined?

8-96. Consider the even function

$$\text{Ev } Z(p) = K \frac{(p - p_1)(\cdot \cdot \cdot)}{(p - p_2)(\cdot \cdot \cdot)}.$$

What restriction does the positive reality of $Z(p)$ place on the poles of Ev $Z(p)$? What restriction on the zeros of Ev $Z(p)$? On the multiplier K? Is this set of restrictions sufficient to insure that an even function is the even part of a p-r function? Repeat for an odd function, Od $Z(p)$. What relations are there between the poles (and between the zeros) of $Z(p)$, Ev $Z(p)$, Od $Z(p)$?

8-97. Show that the residues at real-frequency poles of any reactance expression $X(\omega) = -j$ Od $Z(j\omega)$, in which $Z(p)$ is p-r, are real and negative when ω is considered the variable.

8-98. A class of functions suitable for driving-point reactance or susceptance functions (§ 8.16) is defined by

$$F(\omega) = \frac{\omega^{2m+1}}{1 + \omega^{2n}}, \qquad n = 1, 2, 3, \cdot \cdot \cdot \; ; \; m = 0, 1, 2, \cdot \cdot \cdot, n,$$

Because the denominator is simple, they provide good exercise in the determination of associated minimum resistance (conductance) without difficult computation. Verify these remarks and obtain immittance functions (both impedance and admittance) that have $F(\omega)$ as their imaginary parts at real frequencies, for the various cases corresponding to $n = 1, 2, 3, 4, 5$. Discuss the possibility of changing the sign of $F(\omega)$ in each case and show the effect thereof.

8-99. The function $[(\omega - \omega^3)/(\omega^4 + 2\omega^2 + 1)]$ is the susceptance of a certain driving-point admittance. Find the corresponding driving-point conductance function and explain the arbitrariness of the result.

8-100. Find a (p-r) impedance function that corresponds to each of the reactance functions given below, if that is possible. If not possible, explain why not. In each case consider both possibilities as to sign.

$$\frac{2}{\omega(\omega^2 - 1)} \qquad \frac{2\omega}{(\omega^2 - 1)} \qquad \frac{2\omega^3}{(\omega^2 - 1)} \qquad \frac{(1 - \omega^2)^2}{\omega(\omega^2 - 3)}$$

8-101. Convert each of the functions of Prob. 8-87 into an odd function by (*a*) multiplying by ω, (*b*) dividing by ω. Where the resulting function meets the requirements for realizability as a driving-point reactance (susceptance) function as stated in § 8.16, on the assumption that positive reality implies realizability, obtain the corresponding minimum-resistance and minimum-conductance immittance functions, and plot both real and imaginary parts versus frequency.

Repeat for the functions

$$\frac{\omega(1 - \omega^2)(4 - \omega^2)(9 - \omega^2)}{1 + \omega^8} \qquad \frac{\omega(\omega^2 - 1)^4}{1 + \omega^8}$$

8-102. Consider the function

$$H(p) = \frac{jG}{1 - G^2},$$

in which $G(p)$ is a reactance function (Chapter 6). Show that if $H(j\omega)$ is interpreted as a driving-point reactance (susceptance) function, the corresponding (impedance) admittance is p-r and realizable in a particularly simple fashion. In what way do your results change if the sign of $H(p)$ is reversed?

8-103. Each of the functions below represents the square of the real-frequency magnitude of a function $Z(p)$. Find $Z(p)$ in each case, making all choices to tend to p-r character for $Z(p)$. Does any arbitrariness remain in the results? In which cases is $Z(p)$ p-r? In the remaining cases, if it is possible to add a constant to $|Z(j\omega)|^2$ to make $Z(p)$ p-r, do so; if not possible, explain why not.

$$(a) \ \frac{1 + 3\omega^2}{\omega^4} \qquad (b) \ \frac{\omega^2 + 0.3}{4\omega^4 + 7\omega^2 + 0.3} \qquad (c) \ \frac{\omega^2 - 4}{\omega^2 + 4}$$

$$(d) \ 72\frac{\omega^4 + 6\omega^2 + 25}{\omega^4 - 6\omega^2 + 25} \qquad (e) \ \frac{(1 - \omega^2)^2\omega^2}{1 + \omega^8} \qquad (f) \ \frac{\omega^2 + 16}{\omega^4 + 10\omega^2 + 9}$$

$$(g) \ \frac{\omega^4(\omega^2 + 1)^4}{1 + \omega^8} \qquad (h) \ \frac{1 - 1.75\omega^2 + \omega^4}{1 + \omega^2}$$

8-104. Show that the real-frequency magnitude and angle of a p-r function are essentially the even and odd parts of the (natural) logarithm of that function. Relate these to the product and quotient of $Z(p)$ and $Z(-p)$. Compare the general problems of § 8.13 and § 8.14 with those of § 8.11 and § 8.12 in this light.

8-105. Define the function $\beta(p)$ by the relation $\exp(j2\beta) = Z(p)/Z(-p)$. Then calculate $\tan \beta$ and show that for $p = j\omega$, β is the angle of Z. What is β in terms of $Z(p)$ for arbitrary values of p?

8-106. Given a rational, p-r function $Z(p)$, show that the zeros of $\text{Ev } Z(p)$ and of $\text{Od } Z(p)$ may lie anywhere, provided certain symmetry requirements are met, hence that the zeros and poles of $\tanh(j\beta)$ of § 8.14 are unrestricted in location. It does not follow, of course, that any arbitrary (but properly symmetrical) set of points can be laid down as these zeros. What sort of additional zeros may be necessary to make the derived function $Z(p)$ p-r? How arbitrary are the poles of $\text{Ev } Z(p)$ and of $\text{Od } Z(p)$ once the zeros have been fixed as above?

8-107. Anent the discussion following (8.14–10), assuming $Z(p)$ is p-r, plot the locus of $Z(j\omega) = R + jX$ in a complex plane in the vicinity of the following points (all to be on the imaginary axis):

(a) a zero of $Z(p)$;
(b) a pole of $Z(p)$ where $R = 0$;
(c) a pole of $Z(p)$ where $R \neq 0$;
(d) a point where $R = 0$ and $X \neq 0$;
(e) a point where $R \neq 0$ and $X = 0$.

Use indentations to explain anomalies as limits, where necessary. From these plots sketch tan β versus ω in the same regions and hence explain the lack of restrictions on zeros and poles of tan β, as stated in the paragraph following (8.14–11). Plot $\beta(\omega)$ also.

8-108. Given an angle function $\beta(\omega)$ that is odd, and such that tan β is rational with real coefficients, prove the following.

(a) If $|\beta| \leq \pi/2$ for all ω, the corresponding (immittance) function is rational, p-r, and has no real-frequency zeros or poles, including infinity.

(b) If $|\beta| > \pi/2$ in some ranges of ω, the corresponding function is rational but not p-r.

In (b) how can the function be patched up to make it p-r without altering tan β? What change in β is necessary?

Now examine carefully the discussion of § 8.14 and fill in any gaps you find in the proof of the statement: "any odd rational function of ω with real coefficients is the real-frequency tangent of the angle of a p-r function that is thus determined uniquely except for the multiplier."

8-109. Prove that any quotient of Hurwitz polynomials, though not necessarily p-r, can be made so by adding suitable real-frequency zeros and poles.

8-110. Show how a change of sign of a datum angle or tangent-of-angle function operates to invert the final function $Z(p)$ determined therefrom according to § 8.14, by carefully examining the effect of this sign change at each step in (8.14–27).

8-111. Given the rational (but not necessarily p-r) function

$$F(p) = \frac{A_1 + pB_1}{A_2 + pB_2},$$

and the polynomial $(A + pB) = (A_1 + pB_1)(A_2 - pB_2)$, explain the conditions under which the generalized tangent of angle of $F(p)$, pB/A, is an odd polynomial divided by an even one, and the conditions under which it becomes an even polynomial divided by an odd one.

In § 8.14 the datum tangent function is assumed to be in the first of these two forms. Carry through the details of the development for the second case and show that the procedure summarized on pp. 447–8 is equally valid then. Explain this alternatively by the 90° shift mentioned in § 8.14.

8-112. If the datum function (8.14–11) is not in lowest terms, explain in detail the effect of the common factors in numerator and denominator on the determination of $Z(p)$, when they are not canceled out before starting.

8-113. Show that (8.14–23) and (8.14–24) both lead to the correct tangent of angle. Explain why both do and why only one is appropriate. If a mistake is made in the choice between them, show that a factor of p^2 or p^{-2} must be inserted and that this is a limiting case of the usual procedure. Why is a minus sign prefixed in (8.14–22)?

8-114. If the tangent of a given angle function is never positive (or never negative) at any frequency, it suffices to treat $(A + pB)$ alone and finally multiply by p or $1/p$; further, $Z(p)$ so derived has no internal real-frequency poles or zeros. Prove these statements (§ 8.14).

8-115. Consider the polynomial $Q(p) = p^3 + p^2 - 2$. Write all the rational functions with real coefficients (not necessarily p-r) whose real-frequency angle is the same as that of $Q(j\omega)$. (Functions obtained by multiplication or division by even polynomials that do not contribute to the angle are to be excluded.)

If $Q(p)$ is a polynomial of degree n with real coefficients, none of whose zeros are imaginary, how many such rational functions have the same real-frequency angle? How many of these will automatically be p-r?

If you are not restricted to real coefficients, how do your answers change?

8-116. If the datum tangent function in § 8.14 is such that $Q(p)$ is a Hurwitz polynomial, show (a) that the derived $Z(p)$ or $Y(p)$ is realizable by a very simple form of network and (b) the converse. How important is the correction process (introduction of imaginary zeros and poles) in this case? Where are the poles of $Z(p)$ or $Y(p)$?

8-117. Show that when β, the angle of $Q(j\omega)$, is increasing and passes through 90°, and a pair of imaginary poles is added as directed in § 8.14, that the residue of $Z_2(p)$, the new function, is there real and positive. Show in detail why $Z(p)$ as determined in § 8.14 is p-r.

8-118. Show how Fig. 8.14–D is obtained by sketching the angle of $[(p - p_1)(p - \bar{p}_1)]_{p=j\omega}$, $p = -\epsilon + j1$, versus ω for $\epsilon = 1, 0.5, 0.1, 0$. Do this also for a single real zero at $(-\epsilon, 0)$ and for the corresponding cases where poles rather than zeros are involved.

8-119. Consider Example 4 of § 8.14. Sketch the loci of $Q(j\omega)$, $Z_1(j\omega)$, and $Z(j\omega)$. Explain, in terms of these, the non-p-r behavior, how this is corrected, and how the discontinuities in the angle of $Z(j\omega)$ are to be interpreted. (Use portions of large and small circles and indent the imaginary axis to the right where necessary.)

More generally, considering step 5 of (8.14–27), show that this procedure is the proper one by examining the locus of $Q(j\omega)$, or of $Q_1(j\omega)$ or $Q_2(j\omega)$, and that every change in tangent from positive to negative represents a counterclockwise crossing of the ω axis (every change from negative to positive a clockwise crossing), so that the procedure stated is correct.

8-120. An alternative view of the process of calculating $Z(p)$, given only its real-frequency angle, is the following. Given, in the language of § 8.14, $\tanh (j\beta) = pB/A$, we may write

$$Z(p) = (A + pB)\frac{C_2}{C_1},$$

in which C_1 and C_2 are even polynomials (possibly constants, though not generally so). The role of C_1 is to transform right-half-plane zeros of $(A + pB)$ into left-half-plane poles of $Z(p)$, and to add real-frequency poles as necessary; C_2 adds real-frequency zeros as necessary. For $p = j\omega$, C_1 and C_2 affect the angle only by adding steps of $\pm 180°$ at certain frequencies, and together they in effect insure the correct choice among the many values of the arctangent function.

Verify the statements made above and correlate them with the procedure of § 8.14. Explain what happens in the case of a 90° angle at the origin.

Show how the direct process of "rationalizing" a given rational function $Z(p)$, by multiplying and dividing by the Hurwitz conjugate of its denominator, gives exactly the expression above.

8-121. In § 8.14 the polynomial $Q(p)$, say of degree n, has zeros generally in both left and right half planes. Let m be the number of right-half-plane zeros, so that $(n - m)$ is the number of left-half-plane zeros. Explain how the value of m can be determined by each of the procedures below.

(a) Plotting the angle of $Q(j\omega)$, $\beta(\omega)$, versus ω; starting from zero at $\omega = 0$, this angle must approach $(n - 2m)\pi/2$ radians at high frequencies.

(b) Applying the test of § 5.14 to $Q(p)$; the number of negative coefficients must be m (cf. Prob. 5-41).

(c) Applying the method of § 3.22; as by plotting $j \tan \beta(\omega)$ with reference to the point $(1, 0)$; cf. Prob. 5-36.

In what part of the procedure of § 8.14 may Sturm's theorem (§ 5.15) be useful?

8-122. Show that if in $\tan \beta = N/D$ the degree of D is greater than the degree of N, and D has no real-frequency zeros, then the zeros of $Q(p)$ of § 8.14 are equally divided between the left and right halves of the p plane.

8-123. Let $Q(p) = A + pB$ be an arbitrary polynomial, except that the even polynomials A and B have no common factors. Form the polynomial $Q_1(p) = A_1 + pB_1$ in which $A_1 = KA$ or $B_1 = KB$, K being a real, positive constant. Show that the distribution of the zeros of $Q_1(p)$ between the left and right halves of the p plane is the same as that of $Q(p)$. Form the polynomial $Q_2(p)$ exactly as $Q_1(p)$ except that K is negative. Show that the distribution of zeros is now reversed.

8-124. The following functions represent real-frequency tangents of angle desired for driving-point immittance functions. In each case determine a p-r impedance (or admittance) function to meet the requirements.

(a) ω^n, $n = 1, 3, 5, 7$ (b) ω^n, $n = -1, -3, -5, -7$ (c) $\omega(\omega^2 - 6)$

(d) $\omega(1 - \omega^2)(4 - \omega^2)$ (e) $3\omega(\omega^2 - 1)^3$ (f) $\omega(1 + \omega^2 + \omega^4 + \omega^6)$

(g) $\dfrac{\omega}{1 + \omega^6}$ (h) $\dfrac{\omega^5}{(\omega^2 - 3)^4}$ (i) $\dfrac{(\omega^2 - 2)^3}{\omega^5}$ (j) $\dfrac{\omega}{(1 - \omega^2)^4}$

(k) $\dfrac{2\omega^2 + 1}{\omega}$ (l) $\dfrac{8 - 5\omega^2}{10\omega - \omega^3}$ (m) $\dfrac{3\omega - \omega^3}{1 - 3\omega^2}$ (n) $\dfrac{\omega}{\omega^4 + \omega^2 + 1}$

(o) $\dfrac{4\omega - \omega^3}{\omega^2 + 20}$ (p) $\dfrac{4\omega + \omega^3}{6 - \omega^2}$ (q) $\dfrac{1.6(\omega^2 - 1)(\omega^2 - 9)}{\omega(\omega^2 - 4)^2}$

(r) $\dfrac{-63\omega + 15\omega^3}{16 - 16\omega^2 + 4\omega^4}$ (s) $\dfrac{-24\omega + 9\omega^3 - 3\omega^5}{8 - 24\omega^2 + 3\omega^4 - \omega^6}$

8-125. Repeat Prob. 8-124 for the functions obtained by changing the sign in the functions given there. What change does this make in the result? Repeat Prob. 8-124 for the functions obtained by inverting the functions given there. What changes does this make?

8-126. If the tangent of the real-frequency angle of an immittance function is multiplied by a real, positive constant, what changes are made, in general, in the plot of $\tan \beta(\omega)$, in the locus of $Q(j\omega)$, in the plot of $\beta(\omega)$, in the zeros and poles of the immittance function?

Find the impedance function corresponding to the following tangent of angle. Compare your work and results with Example 3 of § 8.14. Explain why certain zeros and poles are much closer to the imaginary axis in one case.

$$\tan \beta = -\frac{3(\omega^2 - 1)(\omega^2 - 4)}{\omega(\omega^2 - 2)^2}.$$

8-127. In Prob. 7-37 it is to be demonstrated that the even and odd parts of an *R-C* impedance (*R-L* admittance) function of order *n* are subject to the following necessary conditions.

Even part: order = 2n (or 2n − 2 if the complete function has a pole at the origin);
neither pole nor zero at the origin;
at infinity *may* have a zero (not a pole) which must there be double;
all zeros and poles real, simple (with exception above), alternating in half the plane, with a symmetrical set in the other half plane; the pair nearest the origin are poles;
multiplier is arbitrary in magnitude, but not in sign.

Odd part: order = 2n (or 2n − 1 if the complete function has a pole at the origin);
either pole or zero at the origin;
simple zero at infinity;
all zeros and poles real, simple, alternating straight across the plane (symmetrically);
multiplier is arbitrary in magnitude but not in sign.

Show that these are also *sufficient*, in that the complete function derived from such data will be realizable as an *R-C* impedance or *R-L* admittance function.

Show that the only significant change when it is an *R-C* admittance (*R-L* impedance) that is considered is an interchange of the words *zero* and *infinity* as applied to frequency.

8-128. What must be the pattern of zeros and poles for $[F(p)F(-p)]$ in which $F(p)$ is an *R-C* impedance or *R-L* admittance function of order *n*? How is this function related to the magnitude of $F(j\omega)$?

Demonstrate the sufficiency of your set of characteristics. Why is this case so much simpler to describe than those of Prob. 8-127?

Repeat for $F(p)$ an *R-C* admittance or *R-L* impedance function.

8-129. Let $F(p)$ represent an *R-C* impedance (or *R-L* admittance) function of order *n*. Show that

$$G(p) = \frac{F(p)}{F(-p)} = \frac{Q(p)}{Q(-p)}$$

in which $Q(p)$ is the polynomial of § 8.14, and relate this function to the angle of $F(j\omega)$. Show that the function $G(p)$ is subject to the necessary conditions:

order = 2n in general, (2n − 1) if $F(p)$ has a pole at the origin *or* zero at infinity, (2n − 2) if $F(p)$ has both pole at the origin and zero at infinity;
neither pole nor zero at the origin;
neither pole nor zero at infinity;
all poles and zeros real, simple, alternating straight across the plane (symmetrical as to location but antisymmetrical as to kind);
multiplier is unity.

How are the zeros of $Q(p)$ then restricted?

Show that these conditions are also sufficient in that the complete impedance function derived from such a $Q(p)$, with the same real-frequency angle, will be realizable as an *R-C* impedance or *R-L* admittance function.

What changes are necessary if $F(p)$ is to represent an R-C admittance or R-L impedance?

Illustrate by accomplishing the realizations for

$$G(p) = \frac{(1 + p)(2 - p)(3 + p)(4 - p)}{(1 - p)(2 + p)(3 - p)(4 + p)}.$$

8-130. Occasionally the *slope* of the angle (phase) characteristic of a driving-point immittance, $d\beta/d\omega$, is of importance in design problems. Show that in the notation of § 8.14 this is, in generalized form,

$$F(p) = \frac{AB + p(AB' - A'B)}{A^2 - p^2 B^2}$$

in which the primes denote differentiation, with

$$F(j\omega) = \frac{d}{d\omega} \left[\tan^{-1} \left(\frac{pB}{jA} \right)_{p=j\omega} \right].$$

What is the connection between this function and the polynomial $Q = A + pB$?

Show that not *all* even, rational functions may be taken for $d\beta/d\omega$ by demonstrating that the following conditions are necessary for $F(j\omega)$ to be realizable as the derivative of the angle of a driving-point immittance function:

(a) that denominator of $F(j\omega)$ be an even polynomial with real coefficients, none of whose zeros occur for real values of ω;

(b) that the numerator of $F(j\omega)$ be a certain function of the denominator, i.e., the numerator is (within limits) determined, once the denominator is known.

Outline a procedure for the calculation of the numerator according to (b), given the denominator, and illustrate by so constructing $F(p)$, given for the denominator of $F(j\omega)$

$$(1) \ (1 + \omega^2)^n, \quad n = 1, 2, 3, 4,$$

$$(2) \ (1 + \omega^{2n}), \quad n = 2, 3, 4, 5,$$

$$(3) \ (4 + 4\omega^2 + \omega^4 + \omega^6).$$

Indicate carefully any arbitrariness in the procedure, and if more than one possibility exists, give them all.

Show that any function that meets the necessary conditions (a) and (b) above can be realized in the sense that a p-r immittance function $Z(p)$ can be found, whose real-frequency angle is given by

$$\tan \beta = \left(\frac{pB}{jA} \right)_{p=j\omega}$$

Explain how to determine such a function through the intermediary of $Q(p)$, and illustrate with the specific functions above. In which cases is the realization exact in the sense that $d\beta/d\omega$ is exactly as postulated? In which cases is a modification necessary through the introduction of imaginary zeros or poles in $Z(p)$ and how does this affect the derivative of the angle, $d\beta/d\omega$? Illustrate with sketches of $\beta(\omega)$ and $\beta'(\omega)$ both for the ideal case and for that in which these imaginary zeros and poles are displaced slightly to the left (as by parasitic dissipation, § 12.02).

Under what conditions is $d\beta/d\omega = 0$ at $\omega = 0$? As $\omega \to \infty$? At internal frequencies?

What effect does the presence of a zero or pole at the origin in $Z(p)$ have on $d\beta/d\omega$? Will such a zero or pole ever appear in a $Z(p)$ constructed from a given $d\beta/d\omega$ according to the process above?

What sort of value must $\displaystyle\int_0^\infty F(j\omega)\, d\omega$ have? Explain and illustrate in terms of the two integrals

$$\int_0^\infty \frac{d\omega}{1 + \omega^2} = \frac{\pi}{2},$$

$$\int_0^\infty \frac{d\omega}{1 + \omega^4} = \frac{\pi}{2\sqrt{2}}.$$

9.

The R-L-C
One-Terminal Pair—I

Reflectere noli, ad terminum ubi perveneris
—(attributed to Publilius Syrus)

Our topic in this volume is the synthesis of one-terminal pairs. We have learned a good deal about the properties of network driving-point impedance functions, what must be true of them if the network exists—primarily their property of positive reality. We have also developed methods for realizing those particular functions that characterize networks with only two kinds of elements. We have progressed from Fig. 5.03–A to Fig. 7.15–A; there remains only the shaded area, representing those rational p-r functions that cannot be realized as driving-point impedance functions of networks with only two kinds of elements. If these functions are realizable, all three kinds of elements are required to realize them. These functions *are* realizable—any p-r rational function has at least one network realization—and it is the objective of this chapter to demonstrate by actual synthesis that positive reality is sufficient, as well as necessary, for physical realizability.

Of the three logical steps in solving a synthesis problem (1: a study of network properties to see what networks are capable of doing; 2: solution of the approximation problem; 3: realization or synthesis proper) we have taken the first in some detail, and the third for certain special cases. To sidestep the critically important approximation problem and merely to realize given p-r functions is not logical, for the data are not often given the designer in neat functional form, as $Z(p)$ or $Y(p)$; the approximation cannot be avoided. Nevertheless we shall postpone consideration of approximation until we have treated the most general case of p-r functions and know how to proceed to a realization, given any rational p-r function. So we turn now to the realization of a general immittance function, rational and p-r but otherwise arbitrary. We have

503

no proof as yet that this can be made, though we do know that in many special cases positive reality is sufficient.

9.01 An inventory

We have not built up our present stock of realization methods solely for the special cases to which they have been so far applied; they are more useful than that. A given p-r function can be reduced in four ways (if it is not minimum to begin with) without destroying positive reality: by removal of series resistance, series reactance, shunt conductance, and shunt susceptance, as discussed in Chapter 8. We can continue to apply these reduction techniques in various sequences, each reduction making the function simpler, until we reach a stage at which we have a *minimum* p-r function left. (This stage may be very early, or no reduction at all may be possible, or it may be very late, or these techniques may even suffice for the complete job.) From this we can extract nothing by any method yet developed without leaving a non-p-r (and therefore unrealizable) remainder function. If positive reality is actually sufficient for realizability in the general case, we must develop some new technique, some procedure for realizing any p-r function which is free of real-frequency poles and zeros (including zeros and poles at infinity) and whose real part vanishes at one or more real frequencies. Several such techniques are known; these we shall describe, and thereby complete our proof of the sufficiency of positive reality. There may well be others, not yet known, but any one such method is enough to prove this point. We shall find that the known techniques leave something to be desired in practicability of the resulting networks—which indicates a need for research in these matters.

We have also found expansion in partial fractions, and in continued fractions, very useful in the special cases where two kinds of elements suffice for realization. These expansions are not very serviceable in general, but we shall later discuss them a little (BO 3, FR 2, DA 1, CA 2). At present, then, the tactical situation is this: by the four processes of reduction we can (in general) simplify a given p-r function, thereby gaining some ground. When we reach a stage where the function is *minimum* (and this might be at the very beginning, though usually it is not) we are stuck. New strategy is needed, and to develop it we must use imagination.

9.02 Brune's realization

Brune's original work (BR 4, BR 1) on the one-terminal pair included much more than the discovery of the p-r property and that it is a necessary condition for realizability; he also was the first to demonstrate its sufficiency. To show this he merely went ahead and developed a canonic form in which any p-r function could be realized: he found a network which realized any rational p-r function as a driving-point immittance. We shall follow his original method, seeking to design such a network and expecting, of course, to have to use all three kinds of elements. When we have obtained it we shall have proved the sufficiency of positive reality, and (equally important) shall have one solution to the general realization problem for the one-terminal pair. There may, of course, be many other solutions too (and we shall find some later).

Two basic ideas are presented in Brune's classic synthesis. With one we are already familiar: the idea of simplification by removal of resistance, reactance, conductance, and susceptance. When the possibilities of these techniques are exhausted, when all changes have been rung on this idea, we come down to a minimum immittance function—for which the second idea is needed. (We may be lucky and find the realization complete at this stage, but in general we shall not.) This second technique represents a novel idea, yet one which, with the benefit of hindsight, will seem only a logical continuation of the reduction process. As with any new method, it will probably be clearer if first presented through a fairly simple example, and so we postpone generalities.

We start with the function

$$Z(p) = \frac{5p^2 + 18p + 8}{p^2 + p + 10} \quad \text{ohms.} \quad (9.02\text{--}1)$$

This, we suppose, is what is left from some original (normalized) p-r function (supposed to be a driving-point impedance function) after the possibilities of reduction by removal of resistance, reactance, conductance, and susceptance have been exhausted. We can simplify the arithmetic a little by further normalization in division by the leading coefficient, to obtain

$$Z_0(p) = \frac{p^2 + 3.6p + 1.6}{p^2 + p + 10}. \quad (9.02\text{--}2)$$

The poles and zeros of this function are shown in Fig. 9.02–A. The resistance function is

$$R_0(\omega) = \mathbf{Re}\, Z_0(j\omega) = \left[\frac{(p^2 + 1.6)(p^2 + 10) - (3.6p)(p)}{(p^2 + 10)^2 - (p)^2}\right]_{p=j\omega}$$

$$= \frac{\omega^4 - 8\omega^2 + 16}{\omega^4 - 19\omega^2 + 100} = \frac{(\omega^2 - 4)^2}{\omega^4 - 19\omega^2 + 100}, \quad (9.02\text{--}3)$$

whose behavior is shown in Fig. 9.02–B. By inspection we see that the function is p-r, and that it has indeed been stripped of all possible resistance, reactance, conductance, and susceptance. The function is truly minimum and the positive frequency at which the resistance is zero (there is only one) is $\omega = 2$. (The numbers in this example are as usual made conveniently simple; in practice, to reach this stage may require the expenditure of considerable labor in computation.) We can remove no further immittance by any process of reduction we have yet found.

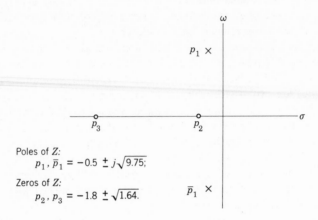

Poles of Z:
$$p_1, \bar{p}_1 = -0.5 \pm j\sqrt{9.75};$$

Zeros of Z:
$$p_2, p_3 = -1.8 \pm \sqrt{1.64}.$$

Fig. 9.02–A

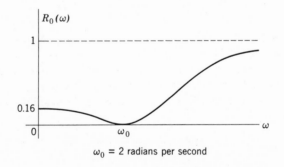

$\omega_0 = 2$ radians per second

Fig. 9.02–B

Instead we now take the second step in the Brune process, a bold step requiring imagination to conceive, and representing a brilliant idea.

The step is simply to disregard the minimum-reactance character of $Z_0(p)$ and to remove some reactance anyway. This will of course make the remainder nonphysical, but we shall ignore that. As to what reactance to remove, we have no guide in real-frequency poles, for there are none. The one outstanding fact is that at a certain frequency (ω_0), Z_0 is purely imaginary—and this we seize on. We now attempt to remove a simple reactive element, an inductor of the proper value to account for the reactance (and hence the whole impedance) at this particular frequency. At this frequency

$$Z_0(j\omega_0) = \left(\frac{p^2 + 3.6p + 1.6}{p^2 + p + 10}\right)_{p=j2} = \frac{-2.4 + j7.2}{6 + j2} = 0 + j1.2. \quad (9.02\text{--}4)$$

Luckily the reactance is positive, so that an inductor of $1.2/2 = 0.6$ henry will fill the bill. We are assuming now the development indicated in Fig. 9.02–C in which, somehow or other, $Z_1(j2) = 0$ (as caused, perhaps,

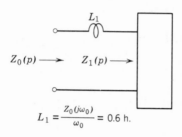

$$L_1 = \frac{Z_0(j\omega_0)}{\omega_0} = 0.6 \text{ h.}$$

Fig. 9.02–C

by a resonance). Although the inductor L_1 is a perfectly good, realizable element, the remaining impedance function $Z_1(p)$ is not p-r and therefore certainly not realizable by itself. Ignoring this for the moment, let us examine $Z_1(p)$. We have

$$Z_1(p) = Z_0 - L_1 p = \frac{-0.6p^3 + 0.4p^2 - 2.4p + 1.6}{p^2 + p + 10} \quad (9.02\text{--}5)$$

which consists of the given (p-r) function $Z_0(p)$ and a pole at infinity corresponding to a negative inductor. Since we removed a nonexistent pole, the remainder has naturally a "negative" pole to compensate, and the order of Z_1 is one more than the order of Z_0; Z_1 is definitely not realizable. But $Z_1(p)$ has a zero at $\omega = 2$, for we made it so (L_1 accounts for the whole impedance, at this frequency). Accordingly, $1/Z_1$ has there a pole, which we now remove, ignoring the possibility of negative elements and other possible consequences of the nonpositive-reality of Z_1. This step is one of ordinary susceptance reduction.
We have

$$Y_1 = \frac{1}{Z_1} = \frac{p^2 + p + 10}{-0.6p^3 + 0.4p^2 - 2.4p + 1.6}$$

$$= \frac{p^2 + p + 10}{-0.6(p^2 + 4)(p - \tfrac{2}{3})} \quad (9.02\text{--}6)$$

in which the denominator factor $(p^2 + 4)$ is known, for there must also be a pole at $-j2$ because the coefficients are real, and the other factor is obtained by division. The partial-fraction expansion of Y_1 is

$$Y_1 = \frac{K_1}{p - j2} + \frac{\bar{K}_1}{p + j2} + \frac{K_2}{p - \frac{2}{3}} \qquad (9.02\text{–}7)$$

in which

$$K_1 = \left[\frac{p^2 + p + 10}{-0.6(p + j2)(p - \frac{2}{3})}\right]_{p=j2} = 1.25,$$

$$\bar{K}_1 = 1.25,$$

$$K_2 = \left[\frac{p^2 + p + 10}{-0.6(p^2 + 4)}\right]_{p=\frac{2}{3}} = -\frac{25}{6}. \qquad (9.02\text{–}8)$$

Hence

$$Y_1 = \frac{2.5p}{p^2 + 4} + \frac{-\frac{25}{6}}{p - \frac{2}{3}} \qquad (9.02\text{–}9)$$

in which the first term is familiar, and the second emphasizes the non-p-r character of Y_1. The first term (luckily) represents a simple L-C combination, with positive elements, that gives the pole of Y_1 (zero of Z_1) at the frequency ω_0. This we now remove, reaching the stage shown in Fig.

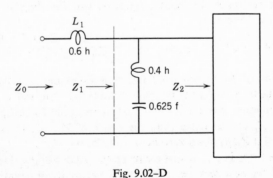

Fig. 9.02–D

9.02–D. The nonphysical character of this network, which we introduced when we first removed L_1, is relegated to the final box, for which

$$Z_2(p) = -0.24p + 0.16. \qquad (9.02\text{–}10)$$

This is the impedance of a (negative) inductor and a (positive) resistor, so that the nonreality is confined to one element, this last inductor.

The complete schematic diagram is shown in Fig. 9.02–E.   The network of Fig. 9.02–E has on paper the driving-point impedance function we set out to realize, (9.02–2).   Its only flaw is the inductor L_3, which is negative

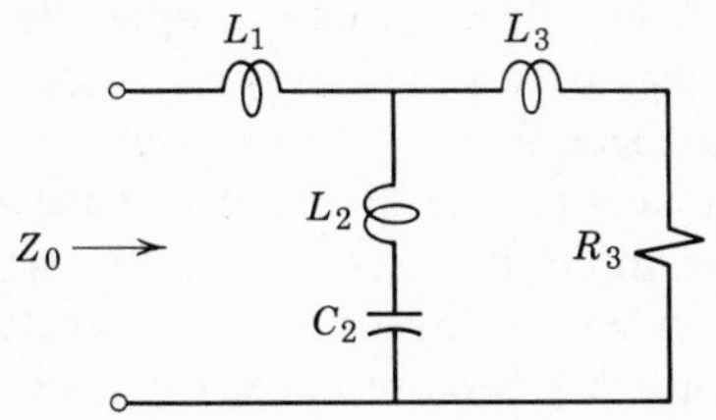

$$L_1 = 0.6 \text{ h}, \qquad C_2 = 0.625 \text{ f},$$
$$L_2 = 0.4 \text{ h}, \qquad R_3 = 0.16 \,\Omega.$$
$$L_3 = -0.24 \text{ h},$$

Fig. 9.02–E

in inductance.   But now let us look at this more closely.   Although a negative inductance is by itself impossible to realize (except perhaps over limited frequency ranges by complicated circuits involving active elements), the *combination* of the three inductors, the set of coils forming a T network, may be realizable through the use of mutual inductance, i.e., of coupled inductors or a transformer.   This is actually possible, the negative

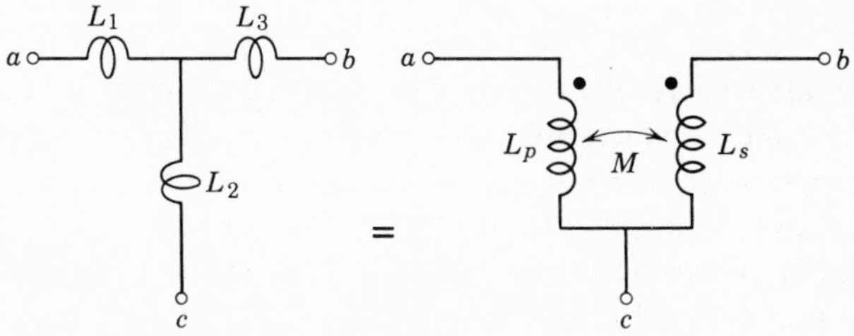

$$L_p = L_1 + L_2 = 1 \text{ h}, \qquad M = L_2 = 0.4 \text{ h},$$
$$L_s = L_2 + L_3 = 0.16 \text{ h}, \qquad k = \frac{M}{\sqrt{L_p L_s}} = \frac{0.4}{\sqrt{1 \times 0.16}} = 1.$$

Fig. 9.02–F

inductance is no flaw at all, and Brune's procedure has succeeded, as demonstrated in Fig. 9.02–F.   The equivalence holds because in writing the loop-basis equations of analysis (§ 2.07–1), Z_{11} (the impedance on the left-hand loop), Z_{22} (that on the right-hand loop), and Z_{12} (the negative of the common impedance) are indistinguishable in the two cases. The transformer shown is realizable, although the coefficient of coupling required is *unity*, which is the upper limit for physical realizability (cf. § 2.01 and § 4.11). Aside from practical difficulties of construction (perfect coupling is rather hard to achieve) the design is complete and a physical realization has been found. The presence of a pair of perfectly coupled inductors is characteristic of the Brune network and the chief reason that it is seldom found in practical circuits except as a last resort.

The Brune process, which continues to remove reactance even when the minimum-reactance stage has been reached, has been found to work for this particular example. The final result is the network of Fig. 9.02–G,

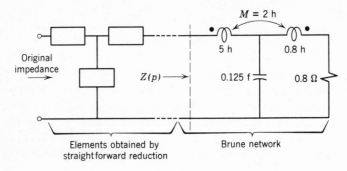

Fig. 9.02–G

which includes the results of any reductions made prior to the work of this section, and in which the proper scale of impedance is restored.

We must now consider the possibility of generalizing the Brune procedure to cover all possible cases. The particular function (9.02–1) happens to be realizable in this manner, but this of course proves nothing about the generality of the Brune process.

Of the many questions which naturally arise, one of the first is: Of what value is the realization technique if the reactance at the frequency ω_0 is not positive but *negative*? To investigate this, let us consider the reciprocal of (9.02–1), the new p-r impedance function

$$Z(p) = \frac{p^2 + p + 10}{5p^2 + 18p + 8} \quad \text{ohms} \tag{9.02–11}$$

or, more convenient,

$$Z_0(p) = 5Z(p) = \frac{p^2 + p + 10}{p^2 + 3.6p + 1.6}. \tag{9.02–12}$$

The resistance function

$$R_0(\omega) = \mathrm{Re}\, Z_0(j\omega) = \frac{\omega^4 - 8\omega^2 + 16}{\omega^4 + 9.76\omega^2 + 2.56} \qquad (9.02\text{–}13)$$

behaves much as the curve in Fig. 9.02–B; the resistance is zero at $\omega = \omega_0 = 2$ and there only—and this is the important characteristic. Again the function $Z_0(p)$ is minimum in all four respects, but we proceed to remove a reactive element whose value will give the correct reactance at the frequency ω_0. We have

$$Z_0(j\omega_0) = \left(\frac{p^2 + p + 10}{p^2 + 3.6p + 1.6}\right)_{p=j2} = 0 - j\frac{5}{6} \qquad (9.02\text{–}14)$$

which represents a negative reactance, as expected. It might then seem more reasonable to remove a capacitor this time—but this does not give the most useful network. Since we have found a negative inductor to be realizable once, it may be again, and we accordingly remove an inductor,

$$L_1 = \frac{Z_0(j\omega_0)}{j\omega_0} = -\frac{5}{12}\text{ h.} \qquad (9.02\text{–}15)$$

Figure 9.02–C represents our progress so far. We now have

$$Z_1(p) = Z_0(p) - L_1 p = \frac{\tfrac{5}{12}p^3 + 2.5p^2 + \tfrac{5}{3}p + 10}{p^2 + 3.6p + 1.6} \qquad (9.02\text{–}16)$$

which is p-r and has a zero at $j\omega_0$. On inverting Z_1 and expanding in partial fractions we obtain

$$Y_1(p) = \frac{1}{Z_1} = \frac{p^2 + 3.6p + 1.6}{\tfrac{5}{12}(p^2 + 4)(p + 6)}$$

$$= \frac{1.44p}{p^2 + 4} + \frac{0.96}{p + 6}. \qquad (9.02\text{–}17)$$

It happens then that the developments of Figs. 9.02–D and 9.02–E proceed exactly as before, but with a positive value for L_3 this time, as well as positive values for L_2, C_2, and R_3. The complete development is shown in Fig. 9.02–H.

As before, we examine the possibility of realizing the T network of three inductors by a pair of coupled inductors. In the notation of Fig. 9.02–F we have

$$L_p = L_1 + L_2 = \tfrac{5}{18}\text{ h,}$$

$$L_s = L_2 + L_3 = \tfrac{125}{72}\text{ h,}$$

$$M = L_2 = \tfrac{1}{1.44}\text{ h,} \qquad (9.02\text{–}18)$$

$$k = \frac{M}{\sqrt{L_p L_s}} = 1.$$

Again the Brune technique has produced a realization and again it has required a pair of perfectly coupled (but theoretically realizable) inductors

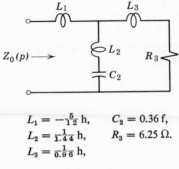

$$L_1 = -\tfrac{5}{12}\,\text{h}, \qquad C_2 = 0.36\,\text{f},$$
$$L_2 = \tfrac{1}{1.44}\,\text{h}, \qquad R_3 = 6.25\,\Omega.$$
$$L_3 = \tfrac{1}{0.96}\,\text{h},$$

Fig. 9.02–H

to succeed. With the scale of impedance restored, and indication of previous reduction by straightforward immittance removal, the realization is shown in Fig. 9.02–I.

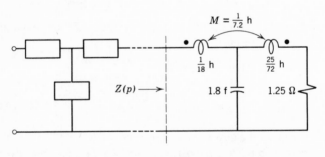

Fig. 9.02–I

However strong the practical objection to unity-coupled coils, the fact remains that the Brune technique has succeeded in finding a realization for each of two p-r immittance functions which are not amenable to previously developed realization techniques. But, although everything essential in Brune's process is contained in these two examples, they do not, of course, prove that the technique can always be used. Before discussing alternative methods of realization, we ought first to decide whether the Brune technique will succeed in general, i.e., whether it will realize *any* p-r function as a driving-point immittance.

9.03 Generalization

Although the two simple examples in § 9.02 do not prove the general validity of the Brune process, they nevertheless indicate the fundamental ideas of the technique and point out what must be proved in general. Suppose now that we have a p-r function $Z(p)$, of order n, which is minimum in all respects and is to represent a driving-point impedance. Then

$$Z(p) = K\frac{p^n + a_{n-1}p^{n-1} + \cdots + a_0}{p^n + b_{n-1}p^{n-1} + \cdots + b_0} \qquad (9.03\text{--}1)$$

has no imaginary zeros or poles, and at some frequency ω_0 (and possibly at others as well) the resistance vanishes, i.e.,

$$\mathbf{Re}\, Z(j\omega_0) = 0. \qquad (9.03\text{--}2)$$

For convenience we deal with the function

$$Z_0(p) = \frac{Z(p)}{K} = \frac{p^n + a_{n-1}p^{n-1} + \cdots + a_0}{p^n + b_{n-1}p^{n-1} + \cdots + b_0} \qquad (9.03\text{--}3)$$

and define its value at $p = j\omega_0$ by

$$Z_0(j\omega_0) = 0 + jX_0. \qquad (9.03\text{--}4)$$

The number X_0 may be positive or negative, but will not be zero.

Let us deal first with the case in which X_0 is positive. Then, guided by the first example of § 9.02, we remove an inductor of inductance

$$L_1 = \frac{Z_0(j\omega_0)}{j\omega_0} = \frac{X_0}{\omega_0} \qquad (9.03\text{--}5)$$

which is positive and therefore realizable. We then have (see Fig. 9.03–A)

$$Z_1(p) = Z_0(p) - L_1 p \qquad (9.03\text{--}6)$$

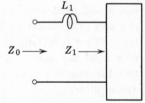

Fig. 9.03–A

which is not p-r. The function $Z_1(p)$ has a zero at the point $j\omega_0$ because we have forced it to: the removal of L_1 has created this zero in $Z_1(p)$—or, better, the zero has been moved from some point off the imaginary axis to the point $j\omega_0$ on this axis. The corresponding admittance function, $Y_1 = 1/Z_1$, has a pole at this frequency, which we hope to remove in the form of a shunt-connected series-L-C network, as before. To show that this can be done we have to demonstrate that this pole in Y_1 is simple and that its residue is real and positive. Then we must show that from the impedance remaining after removal of this shunt branch an inductor (negative) can be removed; that the combination of three inductors can be realized by a pair of unity-coupled inductors; and finally that this procedure results in a simpler remaining impedance (p-r) function, to which the Brune process can be applied again and again until the realization is complete. In order to demonstrate these things it is appropriate to digress a little and discuss the properties of functions of the form of $Z_1 = Z_0 - L_1 p$; such functions are evidently quite important in the Brune development. We shall thereby prove the general validity of the Brune process, and shall go on to possible variations on it and to certain rather important extensions. Much of the argument is lengthy and tedious, and the reader interested only in conclusions may do well to jump now to § 9.14.

9.04 Pseudo-p-r functions

Consider now functions of the general type encountered in § 9.03. Specifically, let

$$F(p) = Z(p) - Lp \qquad (9.04-1)$$

in which $Z(p)$ is rational and p-r, and L is real and positive. We also require that $Z(p)$ either be regular at infinity or, if it has a pole there, that the "strength" of this pole be limited by the condition $Z'(\infty) < L$, i.e., that for large values of $|p|$, $Z(p) = K_1 p + K_0 + K_{-1}/p + \cdots$ where $K_1 < L$. We further require either that $Z(p)$ not have a zero at the origin or, if it does, that $Z'(0) > L$. The reasons for these restrictions will shortly appear.

Such a function $F(p)$ is more general than the function met in § 9.03, but it will be convenient to know something about its properties. This is a sort of "pseudo-p-r" function, for in many respects its properties are those of p-r functions, though it is definitely not p-r itself (it has one pole of a kind not admissible in p-r functions). Following the items in the test for positive reality of (5.13–5), we observe that because of our assumptions,

1. $F(p)$ has real coefficients and is therefore real when p is real;
2(a). at infinity $F(p)$ behaves as $-L'p$, i.e., for very large values of $|p|$,

$$F(p) = K_1 p - Lp + K_0 + \frac{K_{-1}}{p} + \cdots$$
$$= -L'p + \text{(insignificant terms)},$$

in which $L' = (L - K_1) > 0$ by hypothesis ($L' = L$ if Z has no pole at infinity); $F(p)$ has, in effect, a "negative" simple pole at infinity;
2(b). $F(p)$ is analytic in the right half plane;
2(c). any imaginary poles $F(p)$ may have are simple, with real, positive residues;
3. $\text{Re } F(j\omega) \geq 0$. $(9.04-2)$

It is in test 2(a), and only there, that $F(p)$ fails to meet the requirements of positive reality. As a consequence we know that $F(p)$ is not necessarily free of right-half-plane zeros—and it is rather important to know exactly how many such zeros $F(p)$ has. This we now investigate.

The theorem of § 3.22 offers a convenient method for determining this number. It states that if p traces out a closed contour [on which $F(p)$ has no zeros or poles], the net number of revolutions the radius vector $F(p)$ makes about the origin is equal to the number of zeros of $F(p)$ within that contour, reduced by the number of poles of $F(p)$ in the same region. Since we are interested here in the entire right half plane, we let p traverse the contour C_1 of Fig. 9.04–A. In the limit as ϵ approaches

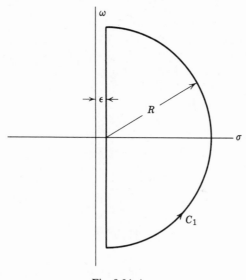

Fig. 9.04–A

zero and R (the radius of the large semicircle) becomes infinite, C_1 encloses the entire right half plane.

The important behavior of $F(p)$ as p traverses C_1, i.e., of the mapping of C_1 by the function $F(p)$, is easy to calculate. Since $F(p)$ behaves as does $-L'p$ for large $|p|$, the mapping of the large semicircle into the F plane is another large semicircle, but one around the *left* half plane. And when p is imaginary we have

$$\mathbf{Re}\, F(j\omega) = \mathbf{Re}\, Z(j\omega) \geqq 0 \qquad (9.04\text{–}3)$$

so that in the limit as ϵ vanishes every point on the imaginary axis of the

p plane maps into a point in the right half of the F plane, except those points where $\mathbf{Re}\, Z(j\omega) = 0$. Those map to the imaginary axis of the F plane. [At the imaginary poles of $F(p)$ we consider C_1 to be indented to the right, i.e., ϵ not to vanish until the behavior of $F(p)$ is established; the mapping of such small semicircles is to large semicircles in the right half plane, traversed in the counterclockwise direction, because of the nature of these poles.] Consequently all of the straight portion of C_1 maps to the imaginary axis or to points in the right half plane, while the large semicircle maps to another large semicircle, but one rotated through $180°$. Figure 9.04–B illustrates our knowledge to this point: C_2 is the

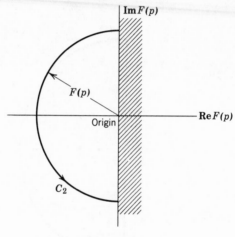

Fig. 9.04–B

mapping of C_1, and except for the large semicircle, lies entirely on or to the right of the imaginary axis.

Since we need to know the number of revolutions which the vector $F(p)$ makes, we must also investigate carefully the behavior of $F(p)$ near any points where $F(p) = 0$ (at which the contour C_1 must be indented into the right half plane, or ϵ must not become zero until the behavior is established), for this will determine whether the contour C_2 passes to the left or the right of the origin, an important matter in determining the number of revolutions of $F(p)$. Zeros of $F(p)$ may well occur for imaginary values of p. Near such a point, say $p = j\omega_1$,

$$F(p) = 0 + F'(j\omega_1)(p - j\omega_1) + F''(j\omega_1)(p - j\omega_1)^2 + \cdots$$
$$= [Z'(j\omega_1) - L](p - j\omega_1) + \cdots. \tag{9.04-4}$$

If we write $Z(j\omega)$ in terms of its real and imaginary parts as

$$Z(j\omega) = R(\omega) + jX(\omega), \qquad (9.04\text{-}5)$$

then

$$Z'(j\omega) = \left\{\frac{d}{dp}\left[R(\omega) + jX(\omega)\right]\right\}_{p=j\omega}$$

$$= -jR'(\omega) + X'(\omega). \qquad (9.04\text{-}6)$$

At an imaginary zero of $F(p)$ we have

$$F(j\omega_1) = 0 = R(\omega_1) + jX(\omega_1) - jL\omega_1, \qquad (9.04\text{-}7)$$

hence

$$R(\omega_1) = 0,$$

$$X(\omega_1) = L\omega_1. \qquad (9.04\text{-}8)$$

Since zeros of $R(\omega)$ must be of even order (to prevent R from becoming negative), we also have

$$R'(\omega_1) = 0; \qquad (9.04\text{-}9)$$

consequently

$$Z'(j\omega_1) = 0 + X'(\omega_1) \qquad (9.04\text{-}10)$$

from (9.04-6). Thus we have, near $p = j\omega_1$,

$$F(p) = [X'(\omega_1) - L](p - j\omega_1) + \cdots. \qquad (9.04\text{-}11)$$

The relative values of $X'(\omega_1)$ and L are evidently extremely important. We can quickly discover a relation between them, as follows.

Suppose first that $Z(p)$ is free of imaginary poles (is minimum-reactive if it represents an impedance). We can then apply (8.05-11) to it to obtain

$$X(\omega) = \frac{2\omega}{\pi}\int_0^\infty \frac{R(\lambda) - R(\omega)}{\lambda^2 - \omega^2}\, d\lambda. \qquad (9.04\text{-}12)$$

The integrand and the integral are uniformly continuous and we may differentiate under the integral sign to obtain the following expression for $X'(\omega)$:

$$X'(\omega) = \frac{2}{\pi}\int_0^\infty \frac{R(\lambda) - R(\omega)}{\lambda^2 - \omega^2}\, d\lambda$$

$$+ \frac{2\omega}{\pi}\int_0^\infty \frac{-(\lambda^2 - \omega^2)R'(\omega) + [R(\lambda) - R(\omega)]2\omega}{(\lambda^2 - \omega^2)^2}\, d\lambda. \qquad (9.04\text{-}13)$$

Since we know that $R(\omega_1) = 0$ and $R'(\omega_1) = 0$, we have

$$X'(\omega_1) = \frac{X(\omega_1)}{\omega_1} + \frac{4\omega_1^2}{\pi}\int_0^\infty \frac{R(\lambda)}{(\lambda^2 - \omega_1^2)^2}\, d\lambda. \qquad (9.04\text{-}14)$$

Now $R(\lambda)$ is never negative and is not identically zero (in immittance terms, we are not dealing with a reactance function). Hence, if we exclude zero and infinite values of ω_1, the second term in (9.04–14) is positive, so that

$$X'(\omega_1) > \frac{X(\omega_1)}{\omega_1}. \qquad (9.04\text{–}15)$$

But at all the imaginary zeros of $F(p)$, we have

$$\frac{X(\omega_1)}{\omega_1} = L \qquad (9.04\text{–}16)$$

by (9.04–8) and thus, finally,

$$X'(\omega_1) > L. \qquad (9.04\text{–}17)$$

This states that in (9.04–11) the coefficient of the leading term in the expansion of $F(p)$ near one of its imaginary zeros is a (real) positive number when $Z(p)$ has no imaginary poles. This includes behavior at the origin, if that is a zero of $F(p)$, by hypothesis; at infinity there can be no zero, also by hypothesis.

It is not difficult to show that if $Z(p)$ has poles on the imaginary axis then relation (9.04–17) still holds. In fact, we can say generally (Problems 9-59, 9-60) that if $Z(p)$ is p-r, and $Z(j\omega) = R(\omega) + jX(\omega)$, then at any real-frequency zero of R (or at any real frequency where R reaches its minimum value, if Z is not minimum-resistance), say ω_1,

$$X'(\omega_1) > \left| \frac{X(\omega_1)}{\omega_1} \right|. \qquad (9.04\text{–}18)$$

The only exceptions occur when ω_1 is zero or infinity and in the special cases where $Z(p)$ is the sum of a constant (perhaps zero) and either Kp or K/p—then the inequality becomes an equality. Relation (9.04–17) is always valid here, however, for these exceptions do not arise in the present application.

This means then that the part of C_1 around one of the imaginary zeros of $F(p)$ maps into another small semicircle, indented to the *right* around the origin of the F plane (Fig. 9.04–C) and traversed in the clockwise direction. With C_1 indented at every imaginary zero (and pole) of $F(p)$, as shown specifically for four such frequencies in Fig. 9.04–C(a), then C_2, the locus of the tip of the $F(p)$ vector, consists of the large semicircle and points lying in the shaded region or on its boundary, as in Fig. 9.04–C(b). We can now say immediately that the number of revolutions of the vector $F(p)$ about the origin is *one*, and therefore (since F has no right-half-plane poles) $F(p) = Z(p) - Lp$ has one (and only one) right-half-plane zero.

(The radii of the small semicircles shrink to zero, and those of the large ones increase indefinitely, of course, in the limiting process necessary to

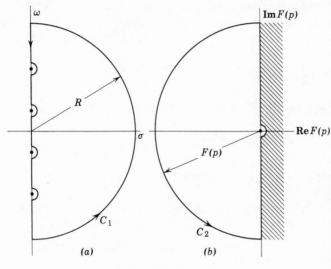

Fig. 9.04–C

insure that the whole right half of the *p* plane is covered.) This zero must also be real, and we could have stated its existence as soon as the function $F(p)$ was defined, by drawing a sketch like Fig. 9.04–D. This is

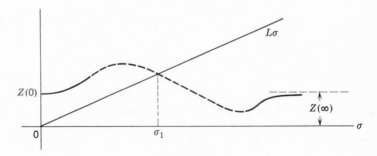

Fig. 9.04–D

a plot of $Z(\sigma)$ and of $L\sigma$ for positive values of σ. Since $Z(p)$ is p-r, $Z(\sigma)$ must have only real, positive, finite values, with behavior something like that shown. [If $Z(0) = 0$, the slope of $Z(\sigma)$ will be greater than that of

$L\sigma$, so that the Z curve rises above the straight line; $Z(\infty)$ may, of course, be zero.] There must evidently be at least one intersection with the line $L\sigma$ (as at the value σ_1), for these reasons alone. Our argument based on the Cauchy theorem shows further that there are no other zeros in the right half plane; $p = \sigma_1$ is the only right-half-plane zero of $F(p)$. From Fig. 9.04–D we note that at this zero the slope is (real and) negative, i.e.,

$$F'(\sigma_1) = \left\{\frac{d}{dp}\left[Z(p) - Lp\right]\right\}_{p=\sigma_1} < 0. \tag{9.04–19}$$

We have also learned that at all of its imaginary zeros, as at $j\omega_1$,

$$F'(j\omega_1) = Z'(j\omega_1) - L = \left[X'(\omega_1) - \frac{X(\omega_1)}{\omega_1}\right] > 0. \tag{9.04–20}$$

In words, the imaginary zeros of $F(p)$ are simple, with real, positive derivatives there.

To sum up our discoveries, the pseudo-p-r function $F(p) = Z(p) - Lp$ has the properties of (9.04–2) and, as corollaries of these,

$F(p)$ has one (and only one) right-half-plane zero; at this (simple, real) zero, $F'(p)$ is real and negative;
all the imaginary zeros of $F(p)$ are simple, and at them $F'(p)$ is real and positive. $\tag{9.04–21}$

We need also to know the properties of the reciprocals of these functions, for they too enter into the Brune process. Let

$$G(p) = \frac{1}{F(p)} = \frac{1}{Z(p) - Lp} \tag{9.04–22}$$

in which L is (real) and positive, $Z(p)$ is p-r and either regular at infinity or $Z'(\infty) < L$, and $Z(p)$ either has no zero at the origin or $Z'(0) > L$. The function $G(p)$ evidently has the following properties, in the light of the properties of $F(p)$:

1. $G(p)$ has real coefficients and is therefore real when p is real;
2(a). at infinity $G(p)$ behaves as $-1/L'p$, i.e., for large $|p|$,

$$Z(p) = K_1 p + K_0 + \frac{K_{-1}}{p} + \cdots,$$

and

$$G(p) = \frac{1}{Z(p) - Lp} = \frac{1}{(K_1 - L)p + K_0 + (K_{-1}/p) + \cdots}$$

$$= \frac{-1}{L'p} - \frac{K_0}{L'^2 p^2} + \cdots.$$

in which $L' = L - K_1 = [L - Z'(\infty)] > 0$ and the terms following the first are negligible in comparison; $G(p)$ has, in effect, a "negative" simple zero at infinity;

2(b). $G(p)$ has one (and only one) pole in the right half plane, which is simple and has a real, negative residue;

2(c). the imaginary poles of $G(p)$ are simple, with real, positive residues;

3. Re $G(j\omega) \geq 0$.   (9.04–23)

Such a function we also call pseudo-p-r, for it too has many of the properties of p-r functions though it is not p-r itself—it contains one pole of a kind not admissible in p-r functions.

More properties of $G(p)$ are revealed by its partial-fraction expansion. This expansion we need to make only in part, as

$$G(p) = \frac{-K}{p - \sigma_1} + G_1(p) \tag{9.04–24}$$

in which K and σ_1 are real and positive and the specific value of K is given by

$$(-K)^{-1} = \left[\frac{dG}{dp}\right]^{-1}_{p=\sigma_1} = Z'(\sigma_1) - L. \tag{9.04–25}$$

It is convenient to add a symmetrical term $-K/(p + \sigma_1)$, the same being simultaneously subtracted from G_1 to form G_2, so that

$$G(p) = \frac{-K}{p - \sigma_1} + \frac{-K}{p + \sigma_1} + G_2(p)$$

$$= \frac{-2Kp}{p^2 - \sigma_1^2} + G_2(p). \tag{9.04–26}$$

The function $G_2(p)$ may or may not actually have a pole at $-\sigma_1$, depending on the circumstances; that is not important. It *is* rather important that $G_2(p)$, so defined, is p-r, as we now show.

1. $G_2(p)$ has real coefficients and is therefore real when p is real;

2(a). at infinity the behavior of $G_2(p)$, from (9.04–26) and (9.04–23), is

$$G_2(p) = G(p) + \frac{2Kp}{p^2 - \sigma_1^2}$$

$$= -\frac{1}{L'p} - \frac{K_0}{L'^2 p^2} + \cdots + \frac{2K}{p} + \frac{2K\sigma_1^2}{p^3} + \cdots$$

$$= \left[-\frac{1}{L'} + \frac{2}{L - Z'(\sigma_1)}\right]\frac{1}{p} + \text{(insignificant terms)}$$

$$= \frac{K_2}{p} + \cdots$$

in which K_2 is positive, for $L' \geq L > Z'(\sigma_1)$;

2(b). $G_2(p)$ is analytic in the right half plane, for the only pole that $G(p)$ has there has been removed in forming $G_2(p)$;

2(c). the imaginary poles of $G_2(p)$ are the same as those of $G(p)$, by (9.04–26), and are therefore simple, and the residues are real and positive;

3. **Re** $G_2(j\omega) = $ **Re** $G(j\omega) \geq 0$, by (9.04–26) and (9.04–23).   (9.04–27)

The above analysis demonstrates that $G_2(p)$ is p-r, and we emphasize this now by writing $G_2(p) = Y(p)$. With the aid of this fact we can find additional properties of $G(p)$.

Consider now the zeros of $G(p)$, especially those in the right half plane (if any) and on the imaginary axis. We have

$$G(p) = Y(p) - \frac{2Kp}{p^2 - \sigma_1^2} \qquad (9.04\text{–}28)$$

in which $Y(p)$ is p-r and has a zero at infinity. To begin with, consider imaginary values of p and write

$$Y(j\omega) = \Gamma(\omega) + jB(\omega). \qquad (9.04\text{–}29)$$

At an imaginary zero of $G(p)$, say $j\omega_1$, we have

$$G(j\omega_1) = 0,$$

$$\Gamma(\omega_1) = 0, \qquad B(\omega_1) + \frac{2K\omega_1}{\omega_1^2 + \sigma_1^2} = 0, \qquad (9.04\text{–}30)$$

and further, since $Y(p)$ is p-r,

$$\Gamma'(\omega_1) = 0. \qquad (9.04\text{–}31)$$

At such a zero of $G(p)$, the derivative is

$$
\begin{aligned}
G'(j\omega_1) &= \left[Y'(p) - 2K\frac{(p^2 - \sigma_1^2) - p(2p)}{(p^2 - \sigma_1^2)^2} \right]_{p=j\omega_1} \\
&= \left[Y'(p) + 2K\frac{(p^2 - \sigma_1^2) + 2\sigma_1^2}{(p^2 - \sigma_1^2)^2} \right]_{p=j\omega_1} \\
&= B'(\omega_1) + \frac{B(\omega_1)}{\omega_1} + \frac{4K\sigma_1^2}{(\omega_1^2 + \sigma_1^2)^2}.
\end{aligned}
\qquad (9.04\text{–}32)
$$

Since $Y(p)$ is p-r, we can apply to it the reasoning of (9.04–12) through (9.04–18) and state that

$$B'(\omega_1) \geq \left| \frac{B(\omega_1)}{\omega_1} \right|. \qquad (9.04\text{–}33)$$

Consequently, from (9.04–32), the derivative of $G(p)$ at one of these zeros (including the zero at the origin, if there is one) is not only real but positive. In other words,

the imaginary zeros of $G(p)$ are simple, and at them $G'(p)$ is real and positive.   (9.04–34)

Now consider values of p in the right half plane. Whether there are any right-half-plane zeros of $G(p)$ we can quickly determine by again using the Cauchy theorem of § 3.22, with p again traversing the contour of Fig. 9.04–A. For large $|p|$, $G(p)$ behaves as $-1/L'p$, and accordingly the large semicircle maps into a small semicircle in the G plane, centered on the origin, lying in the left half plane, and traversed in the clockwise direction. The mapping of the imaginary axis will be entirely in the right half of the G plane or on the imaginary axis, since $\mathbf{Re}\, G(j\omega) \geqq 0$. We have found that all imaginary poles and zeros of $G(p)$ are simple, with residues and derivatives that are real and positive; consequently the corresponding large and small semicircles lie in the right half plane. With this information we can draw Fig. 9.04–E, in which (a) represents

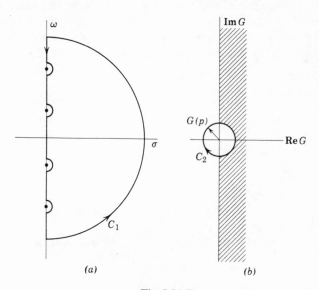

Fig. 9.04–E

the p-plane contour, suitably indented at any imaginary zeros and poles that $G(p)$ has, and (b) represents the mapping of this contour. The locus of the tip of the $G(p)$ vector consists of the small semicircle in the left half plane (traversed once) and points lying in the shaded region or on its boundary. We can say immediately that the number of revolutions of the vector $G(p)$ about the origin is *one*, in the *clockwise* (negative) direction. This shows that the number of right-half-plane poles of $G(p)$ is one more than the number of right-half-plane zeros of $G(p)$. Since $G(p)$ has one (and only one) such pole, it follows that

$$G(p) \text{ has } \textit{no} \text{ right-half-plane zeros.} \qquad (9.04\text{–}35)$$

To recapitulate, when $G(p)$ is defined by (9.04–22), it has the properties (9.04–23) and also these:

$$G(p) = \frac{-K}{p - \sigma_1} + \frac{-K}{p + \sigma_1} + Y(p),$$

where K and σ_1 are real and positive; $Y(p)$ is p-r and has a zero at infinity; $G(p)$ has no zeros in the right half plane, imaginary zeros of $G(p)$ are simple, and $G'(p)$ is there real and positive.   (9.04–36)

We observe also that if a rational function $H(p)$ (with real coefficients) has the form

$$H(p) = \frac{-K}{p - \sigma_1} + \frac{-K}{p + \sigma_1} + Y(p) = \frac{-2Kp}{p^2 - \sigma_1^2} + Y(p) \quad (9.04\text{–}37)$$

in which K and σ_1 are real and positive and $Y(p)$ is p-r and has a zero at infinity [restricted in "strength" as in 2(a) below], the symbols not necessarily being related to any of the foregoing, then its reciprocal falls in the first class of pseudo-p-r functions. For

1. the function $1/H(p)$ is real when p is real;

2(a). for large $|p|$ we have

$$H(p) = -\frac{K}{p}\left(1 + \frac{\sigma_1}{p} + \cdots\right) - \frac{K}{p}\left(1 - \frac{\sigma_1}{p} + \cdots\right) + \left(\frac{K_{-1}}{p} + \frac{K_{-2}}{p^2} + \cdots\right)$$

in which the last parenthesis represents an expansion of $Y(p)$; accordingly

$$H(p) = \frac{-2K + K_{-1}}{p} + \frac{K_{-2}}{p^2} + \cdots ;$$

we now assume $K_{-1} < 2K$ (we have no interest in other cases)—then $1/H(p)$ behaves at infinity as $-(2K - K_{-1})^{-1}p$;

2(b). the reasoning of (9.04–28) through (9.04–35) can be applied to $H(p)$, and demonstrates that $H(p)$ has no right-half-plane zeros; therefore $1/H(p)$ is analytic in the right half plane;

2(c). similarly we find that the imaginary zeros of $H(p)$ are simple, at them $H'(p)$ is real and positive, and consequently the imaginary poles of $1/H(p)$ are simple, with real positive residues;

3. since $\operatorname{Re} H(j\omega) = \operatorname{Re} Y(j\omega) \geqq 0$, and the imaginary zeros of $H(p)$ are of the required type,

$$\operatorname{Re}\left[\frac{1}{H(j\omega)}\right] \geqq 0. \qquad (9.04\text{–}38)$$

The nature of $1/H(p)$ evidently depends on the behavior of $Y(p)$ at infinity, in particular on the size of K_{-1}. Our assumption that $2K > K_{-1}$ requires that $1/H(p)$ not be p-r; but

$$Z(p) = \frac{1}{H(p)} + Lp \qquad (9.04\text{–}39)$$

is p-r if

$$L \geqq (2K - K_{-1})^{-1}. \qquad (9.04\text{-}40)$$

If the lower limit value of L is chosen [the $=$ sign used in (9.04-40)], then it develops that we must also have $K_{-2} < 0$ for $Z(p)$ to be p-r. Accordingly, under these circumstances,

$$\frac{1}{H(p)} = Z(p) - Lp \qquad (9.04\text{-}41)$$

belongs to the first class of pseudo-p-r functions: $Z(p)$ is p-r, L is real and positive, and $1/H(p)$ has the properties listed in (9.04-2) and (9.04-21). The function $Z(p)$ may have a pole at infinity, but if so, $Z'(\infty) < L$; and $Z(p)$ may have a zero at the origin, but if so, $Z'(0) > L$.

We have now obtained all the results necessary for our discussion of the Brune process. The derivation has been somewhat involved; it is well to recapitulate what we have discovered. All of the statements below have been proved in this section (specifically, for rational functions).

1. If a function $F(p)$ has the form $[Z(p) - Lp]$, in which L is a (real) positive constant, $Z(p)$ is p-r, Z is either regular at infinity or, if not, $Z'(\infty) < L$, and Z either does not have a zero at the origin or, if it does, $Z'(0) > L$, then $F(p)$ has one (and only one) zero in the right half plane, and at this (simple, real) zero $F'(p)$ is real and negative; in addition any imaginary zeros of $F(p)$ are simple, and at them $F'(p)$ is real and positive. (9.04-42)

2. If $G(p)$ is the reciprocal of such a function, $G(p) = [Z(p) - Lp]^{-1}$, then $G(p)$ has the expansion

$$G(p) = \frac{-K}{p - \sigma_1} + \frac{-K}{p + \sigma_1} + Y(p)$$

in which K is real and positive, σ_1 represents the real, positive zero of $[Z(p) - Lp]$, and $Y(p)$ is p-r; further, $G(p)$ has no zeros in the right half plane, any imaginary zeros of $G(p)$ are simple, and at them $G'(p)$ is real and positive. (9.04-43)

3. If a function $H(p)$ has the form

$$H(p) = \frac{-K}{p - \sigma_1} + \frac{-K}{p + \sigma_1} + Y(p)$$

in which K and σ_1 are real and positive, and $Y(p)$ is p-r and behaves at infinity as $K_{-1}/p + K_{-2}/p^2 + \cdots$, in which $K_{-1} < 2K$, then its reciprocal, $1/H(p)$, has the properties of the functions of statement 1, in particular

$$\frac{1}{H(p)} = Z(p) - Lp$$

in which $Z(p)$ is p-r, and L is real and positive, and bound by (9.04-40). (9.04-44)

Most of these results can be derived in different fashion (BR 1, RI 2).

We now resume the discussion of the Brune synthesis process in the general case, and with these results can rapidly demonstrate its validity.

9.05 Brune's realization, continued

In § 9.03 we began a discussion of the application of the Brune synthesis process to a p-r, minimum (impedance) function $Z_0(p)$ of order n, (9.03–3).   From the value of $Z(p)$ at the frequency ω_0, where the resistance is zero, we obtained L_1 (assumed positive) and removed a corresponding inductor.   The situation is represented in Fig. 9.03–A, in which

$$Z_1(p) = Z_0(p) - L_1 p \qquad (9.05\text{–}1)$$

represents the impedance remaining after the inductor L_1 has been removed.

The function $Z_1(p)$ falls in the first class of pseudo-p-r functions discussed in § 9.04 so that we can immediately write the following expansion of the admittance to the right of L_1 in Fig. 9.03–A, by (9.04–42) and (9.04–43).

$$Y_1(p) = \frac{1}{Z_1(p)} = Y_a(p) + \frac{-K}{p - \sigma_1} + \frac{-K}{p + \sigma_1} \qquad (9.05\text{–}2)$$

in which K and σ_1 are real and positive and Y_a is p-r. Since we have carefully chosen L_1 to account for the whole of the impedance Z_0 at the frequency ω_0, $Z_1(p)$ has a zero at $j\omega_0$ and its reciprocal, $Y_1(p)$, has a pole there.   In (9.05–2) this pole must be in Y_a and is accordingly simple, with a real, positive residue.   In symbols, we have

$$Y_1(p) = \frac{\Gamma_2 p}{p^2 + \omega_0^2} + Y_b(p) + \frac{-K}{p - \sigma_1} + \frac{-K}{p + \sigma_1} \qquad (9.05\text{–}3)$$

which exhibits the pole at $j\omega_0$ (and its conjugate).   Here Y_b is p-r, for the removal of the pole under discussion and its conjugate leaves a p-r remainder.   The residue is

$$\tfrac{1}{2}\Gamma_2 = [Z_1{}'(j\omega_0)]^{-1} = [Z_0{}'(j\omega_0) - L_1]^{-1}$$

$$= [X_0{}'(\omega_0) - L_1]^{-1} = \left[X_0{}'(\omega_0) - \frac{X_0(\omega_0)}{\omega_0} \right] \qquad (9.05\text{–}4)$$

which is of course positive.   The first term in (9.05–3) represents the shunt-connected series L-C network we had hoped for, and this we now remove (Fig. 9.05–A).

We have now to consider the remaining admittance,

$$Y_2(p) = \frac{1}{Z_2(p)} = Y_1(p) - \frac{\Gamma_2 p}{p^2 + \omega_0^2}$$

$$= Y_b(p) + \frac{-K}{p - \sigma_1} + \frac{-K}{p + \sigma_1} \qquad (9.05\text{–}5)$$

in which Y_b is p-r, and K_1 and σ_1 are real and positive. In order to apply the results of § 9.04 we need to know the behavior of Y_b at infinity, and this is not difficult to calculate. By (9.05–3), Y_b clearly has a zero at infinity and so we may write, for large $|p|$,

$$Y_b = \frac{K_{-1}}{p} + \frac{K_{-2}}{p^2} + \cdots \tag{9.05–6}$$

and also, because Z_0 has no pole at infinity,

$$Z_0(p) = A_0 + \frac{A_{-1}}{p} + \cdots. \tag{9.05–7}$$

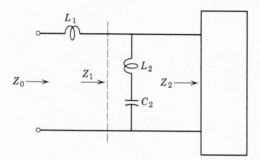

$$L_2 = \Gamma_2^{-1} = \tfrac{1}{2}[X_0'(\omega_0) - L_1] = \frac{1}{2}\left[X_0'(\omega_0) - \frac{X_0(\omega_0)}{\omega_0}\right].$$

$$C_2 = \frac{1}{L_2\omega_0^2}.$$

Fig. 9.05–A

Then, for large $|p|$,

$$
\begin{aligned}
Y_1(p) &= \frac{1}{Z_0(p) - L_1 p} = \frac{1}{-L_1 p + A_0 + A_{-1}/p + \cdots} \\
&= \frac{-1}{L_1 p}\left(1 + \frac{A_0}{L_1 p} + \cdots\right) \\
&= \frac{\Gamma_2}{p}\left(1 - \frac{\omega_0^2}{p^2} + \cdots\right) + \left(\frac{K_{-1}}{p} + \frac{K_{-2}}{p^2} + \cdots\right) \\
&\qquad\qquad - \frac{2K}{p}\left(1 + \frac{\sigma_1^2}{p^2} + \cdots\right). \tag{9.05–8}
\end{aligned}
$$

From the coefficients of p^{-1}, with the notation $\Gamma_1 = 1/L_1$, we obtain

$$K_{-1} - 2K = -\Gamma_1 - \Gamma_2 \tag{9.05–9}$$

and from the coefficients of p^{-2}

$$K_{-2} = -\frac{A_0}{L_1{}^2}. \tag{9.05-10}$$

By (9.05–9) $2K > K_{-1}$ so that (9.04–44) may be applied to $Y_2(p)$. Further, because $Z_0(p)$ is p-r, A_0 is positive and consequently K_{-2} is negative; we may therefore use the $=$ sign in (9.04–40) if we wish. We conclude that

$$Z_2(p) = \frac{1}{Y_2(p)} = Z(p) - Lp \tag{9.05-11}$$

in which Z is p-r and L is real, positive, and arbitrary except that its reciprocal Γ must obey

$$\Gamma \leqq 2K - K_{-1}, \quad \text{i.e., } \Gamma \leqq \Gamma_1 + \Gamma_2. \tag{9.05-12}$$

We may evidently consider Z_2 to represent the series combination of an inductor (negative) and the p-r impedance $Z(p)$, a result not at all surprising in view of the numerical example we first worked in § 9.02.

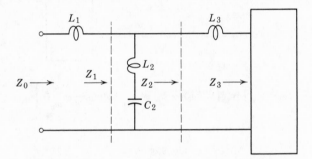

Fig. 9.05–B

We must now consider whether the range of values of L permitted by (9.05–12) includes any physically realizable value(s). The realization we expect is shown in Fig. 9.05–B, in which

$$Z_2(p) = L_3 p + Z_3(p) = Z(p) - Lp \tag{9.05-13}$$

and we have to show that the T network of inductors, with suitable choice(s) for L, is realizable (and then that Z_3 is a simpler impedance, so that definite progress has actually been made). For the T network composed of L_1, L_2, and L_3 to be realizable, we must generally have both $(L_1 + L_2)$ and $(L_2 + L_3)$ positive (§ 2.01), and

$$k^2 = \frac{L_2{}^2}{(L_1 + L_2)(L_2 + L_3)} \leqq 1 \tag{9.05-14}$$

or

$$(L_1 + L_2)(L_2 + L_3) - L_2{}^2 = (L_1 L_2 + L_2 L_3 + L_3 L_1) \geqq 0. \quad (9.05\text{--}15)$$

This last condition is somewhat simpler in terms of reciprocal inductance; if any one of the three inductances is a negative number, the other two being positive, then condition (9.05–15) can be expressed (by dividing through by $L_1 L_2 L_3$) as

$$\Gamma_1 + \Gamma_2 + \Gamma_3 \leqq 0. \quad (9.05\text{--}16)$$

Then if this is true, the T network is realizable by a pair of coupled inductors [for L_1 and L_2 are positive, and from (9.05–16), $(L_2 + L_3)$ is also positive, L_3 being negative].

If we now identify L_3 with $-L$ in (9.05–13), and Z_3 with $Z(p)$ there, then the limitation imposed on L_3 by the previous theoretical development is, by (9.05–12),

$$\Gamma_3 \geqq - (\Gamma_1 + \Gamma_2), \quad \text{or} \quad \Gamma_1 + \Gamma_2 + \Gamma_3 \geqq 0. \quad (9.05\text{--}17)$$

Evidently we can satisfy both (9.05–16) and (9.05–17) only by the choice for L, or L_3, given by

$$\Gamma_3 = -(\Gamma_1 + \Gamma_2) \quad (9.05\text{--}18)$$

which represents the smallest value of $|L_3|$ that keeps Z_3 p-r and also the largest value of $|L_3|$ that results in a physical network.   So far the Brune process has worked exactly as in the first numerical illustration (§ 9.02) and still requires a pair of perfectly coupled inductors.

It remains to investigate the nature of $Z_3(p)$, the remainder impedance function.   We know that $Z_3(p)$ is p-r, and if it is also less complicated than was $Z_0(p)$ we have made definite progress toward the realization of Z_0.   Consider then the order of each of the immittance functions in the sequence; Table 9.05–A results.

Table 9.05–A

Function	Order
Z_0	n
$\left.\begin{array}{c} Z_1 \\ Y_1 \end{array}\right\}$	$n + 1$
$\left.\begin{array}{c} Y_2 \\ Z_2 \end{array}\right\}$	$n - 1$
Z_3	$n - 2$

In removing the inductor L_1 from Z_0 to form Z_1 we add one pole, since Z_0 had no pole at infinity; consequently the order increases by one.   The L_2-C_2 branch removes two poles from the admittance, reducing the order by two.   With the choice for L, or for L_3, made necessary by physical realizability, we find that Z_3 has no pole at infinity, though Z_2 clearly does; consequently removal of L_3 reduces the order by one. We conclude that the Brune process, carried through one cycle as here, reduces the order by *two*.

We must now re-examine the restrictions imposed on Z_0 before we can generalize completely. The assumption that the datum immittance function is minimum in all four respects does not restrict us, for we can reduce any immittance function to this form. The only important restriction is the assumption we have made that the number X_0 (the reactance at the frequency ω_0, where the resistance is zero) is positive. Although X_0 cannot be zero, it may very well be negative (as in the second example of § 9.02), and we must consider the general application of the Brune process in such a case.

We start with the function (9.03–3) and the definition (9.03–4) in which X_0 is now a *negative* number. Guided by the second numerical example in § 9.02 we remove an inductor of inductance

$$L_1 = \frac{Z_0(j\omega_0)}{j\omega_0} = \frac{X_0}{\omega_0}. \tag{9.05–19}$$

Although L_1 is negative, we hope to be able to realize it by the use of mutual inductance, as before. We then have (as in Fig. 9.03–A)

$$Z_1(p) = Z_0(p) - L_1 p \tag{9.05–20}$$

which *is* p-r, for L_1 is negative. Since $Z_1(p)$ also has a zero at $j\omega_0$, we can immediately invert Z_1 and remove the series L-C combination of L_2 and C_2 (Fig. 9.05–A) with the assurance that the elements are positive; the values are given in Fig. 9.05–A. The remaining function, $Z_2(p)$, is still p-r; we have only to investigate its behavior at infinity, remove the pole we expect, investigate the realizability of the T network of inductors, and check that the impedance finally remaining is simpler than the original impedance function.

We have

$$Y_1(p) = \frac{1}{Z_1(p)} = \frac{1}{Z_0(p) - L_1 p}$$

$$= -\frac{1}{L_1 p}\left[1 + \frac{Z_0(p)}{L_1 p} + \cdots\right] \tag{9.05–21}$$

for large $|p|$, since $Z_0(p)$ is regular at infinity; in this, $L_1 = X_0(\omega_0)/\omega_0$ is negative. Also

$$Y_2 = Y_1 - \frac{\Gamma_2 p}{p^2 + \omega_0{}^2} = \left(-\frac{1}{L_1 p} - \cdots\right) - \frac{\Gamma_2}{p}\left(1 - \frac{\omega_0{}^2}{p^2} + \cdots\right)$$

$$= -\frac{(\Gamma_1 + \Gamma_2)}{p} + \cdots = \frac{\Gamma}{p} + \cdots \tag{9.05–22}$$

in which $\Gamma = -(\Gamma_1 + \Gamma_2)$ is *positive*, for Y_2 is p-r. Accordingly, $Z_2(p)$ has a pole at infinity, corresponding to an inductance $L = 1/\Gamma$. If we now write, as before,

$$Z_2(p) = L_3 p + Z_3(p) \qquad (9.05\text{-}23)$$

then we must have $L_3 \leq L$ for Z_3 to be p-r. (If the choice is $L_3 = L$, then Z_3 has no pole at infinity.) In terms of reciprocal inductance, this condition is $\Gamma_3 \geq \Gamma = -(\Gamma_1 + \Gamma_2)$, i.e.,

$$\Gamma_1 + \Gamma_2 + \Gamma_3 \geq 0. \qquad (9.05\text{-}24)$$

But for the T network of inductors to be realizable we must also have

$$\Gamma_1 + \Gamma_2 + \Gamma_3 \leq 0 \qquad (9.05\text{-}25)$$

by (9.05-16), which insures that $k \leq 1$, and also that $(L_1 + L_2)$ as well as $(L_2 + L_3)$ be positive. As before, in order to satisfy both requirements we must take the $=$ sign in both conditions, which requires that $L_3 = L$ and that the coupling be perfect $(k = 1)$. Then the Brune cycle proceeds satisfactorily, for the remaining impedance, $Z_3(p)$, is p-r, and Table 9.05-A applies to this situation without change, so that again a reduction in order of two is accomplished by the Brune cycle.

We have now demonstrated that if $Z_0(p)$ is a minimum function the Brune cycle may always be carried through, with realizable results, and a reduction in order of two. Schematically, the result is shown in Fig. 9.05-B, in which *either* L_1 or L_3 is negative, but L_2 and C_2 are positive and the T network of inductors is realizable by a pair of perfectly coupled inductors; Z_3 is p-r, and if Z_0 is of order n, Z_3 is of order $(n - 2)$. The three inductors and the capacitor form what we shall call a *Brune network*, representable as in Fig. 9.05-C.

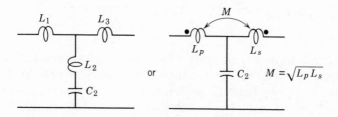

Fig. 9.05-C

In (9.05-26) are collected the formulas we have found for the elements together with expressions for L_3 and for the inductance parameters of the transformer formed by the two coupled inductors, in terms of the original function $Z_0(p)$. Notice that only the values of its reactance and the derivative of this reactance, at the frequency ω_0, appear in these. The formulas apply whether L_1 is positive (and L_3 negative) or L_1 is negative (and L_3 positive).

$$L_1 = \frac{Z_0(j\omega_0)}{j\omega_0} = \frac{X_0(\omega_0)}{\omega_0} = \frac{1}{\Gamma_1},$$

$$L_2 = \tfrac{1}{2}[X_0'(\omega_0) - L_1] = \tfrac{1}{2}\left[X_0'(\omega_0) - \frac{X_0(\omega_0)}{\omega_0}\right] = \frac{1}{\Gamma_2},$$

$$L_3 = -(\Gamma_1 + \Gamma_2)^{-1} = -L_1 \frac{X_0'(\omega_0) - L_1}{X_0'(\omega_0) + L_1}$$

$$= -\frac{X_0(\omega_0)}{\omega_0} \times \frac{X_0'(\omega_0) - \dfrac{X_0(\omega_0)}{\omega_0}}{X_0'(\omega_0) + \dfrac{X_0(\omega_0)}{\omega_0}} = \frac{1}{\Gamma_3},$$

$$\Gamma_1 + \Gamma_2 + \Gamma_3 = 0, \quad \text{i.e.,} \quad k = \frac{M}{\sqrt{L_p L_s}} = 1, \qquad (9.05\text{--}26)$$

$$C_2 = \frac{1}{L_2 \omega_0{}^2},$$

$$L_p = L_1 + L_2 = \tfrac{1}{2}[X_0'(\omega_0) + L_1] = \tfrac{1}{2}\left[X_0'(\omega_0) + \frac{X_0(\omega_0)}{\omega_0}\right] > 0,$$

$$M = L_2 = \tfrac{1}{2}[X_0'(\omega_0) - L_1] = \tfrac{1}{2}\left[X_0'(\omega_0) - \frac{X_0(\omega_0)}{\omega_0}\right] > 0,$$

$$L_s = L_2 + L_3 = -\frac{L_2 L_3}{L_1} = \frac{M^2}{L_p} = \frac{1}{2}\frac{\left[X_0'(\omega_0) - \dfrac{X_0(\omega_0)}{\omega_0}\right]^2}{\left[X_0'(\omega_0) + \dfrac{X_0(\omega_0)}{\omega_0}\right]} > 0.$$

The implications of this general applicability of the Brune process are considerable. We can now synthesize a network whose driving-point impedance (or admittance) is any given p-r function, $Z(p)$ or $Y(p)$. The procedure is first to reduce the immittance function as far as possible by removal of resistance, reactance, conductance, and susceptance; this can be done in various sequences, possibly with a considerable reduction in order after repeated reduction, and possibly with little or no simplification, depending on the nature of the given immittance function and on the sequences in which the four reduction processes are applied. When the immittance is reduced to minimum character, then the Brune cycle (operating on the reduced impedance function) is to be carried through (as is always possible), with a further reduction in order of two. Then we begin again with the remaining impedance function (which is not necessarily minimum) and remove resistance, reactance, conductance, and susceptance as far as possible, and finally apply the Brune process once more. This cycle we repeat as often as necessary, as indicated in Fig. 9.05–D. Since the order of the impedance function is reduced by each

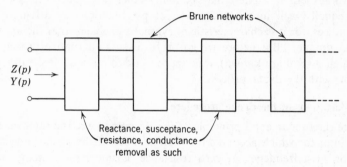

Fig. 9.05–D

operation, we shall eventually reduce the order to two (when if straightforward reduction fails a Brune network, terminated in a resistor, will complete the realization), or to one (when a simple *R-C* or *R-L* network will complete the realization), or to zero (when a resistor completes the realization). It is possible, of course, that only a part of this apparatus may be necessary: straightforward reduction alone may suffice, or the realization may contain Brune networks alone except for a resistor at the end, or various mixtures may appear. The Brune technique is only a somewhat broader, more imaginative kind of reduction by removal of reactance, so one could say that the devices of removing series resistance and reactance and shunt susceptance are always enough for realization.

And so we have finally demonstrated (at least for rational functions) a property many times predicted: that

positive reality is not only *necessary* for the realizability of driving-point immittance functions; it is also *sufficient*.   (9.05–27)

The abbreviation "p-r" can henceforth be freely interpreted as meaning either "positive-real" or "physically realizable"; for our network functions the two terms are synonymous. The shaded area in Fig. 7.15–A we now know to contain only realizable functions—and every function in the region of overlap of Fig. 5.03–A is realizable as the driving-point immittance of one or more networks, and no other functions are.

Our demonstration has also furnished us with a definite method of actual realization of given driving-point immittance functions—not a very practical one, because of the perfectly coupled inductors that may be required, but nevertheless a theoretically acceptable one, and one of great historical importance, for it was the first to demonstrate the sufficiency of positive reality.

We must realize that the Brune process is not necessarily the only realization method. There may be many other techniques which would work equally well in the realization of p-r functions as driving-point immittances, for it is characteristic of synthesis problems that the answers are not unique. But before we go on to discuss alternative procedures (of which several are known), it is appropriate to discuss some variations possible with the Brune process.

9.06 Variations of the Brune procedure

Once the fundamental principle of the Brune process, the removal of a series inductor which accounts for the reactance of the given impedance function at a frequency of zero resistance, is understood, many other possibilities suggest themselves. The removed element might be a capacitor in series, for example. Or the dual approach might be investigated, by removing a capacitor or an inductor in shunt. Of these four possibilities, only the series-inductor case is of great interest in the general case, for the other three lead to "Brune networks" which are realizable only through the use of ideal transformers (Problem 9-57). The fundamental Brune cycle, developed above and requiring only perfectly coupled inductors, is closer to reality and of more interest in general. We might also consider the possibility of removing a more complicated reactance network (of two or more elements), but this we shall not investigate (except in § 9.13). The principal objective of the Brune theory, a proof that positive reality is equivalent to physical realizability, has been attained.

The Brune process has considerable practical importance, however, in spite of the basic need for at least perfectly coupled inductors. It is not necessary to reduce the impedance function to minimum-reactance form before entering the Brune cycle: part or all of any real-frequency poles of impedance may be left in the impedance function to which the Brune process is applied. A review of the analysis of the preceding sections will show that the only essential characteristic of the impedance function $Z_0(p)$ is that it be minimum-resistance, i.e., that it be possible to find a real frequency ω_0 at which $\text{Re } Z_0 = 0$. If this frequency is zero or infinity, straightforward reactance or susceptance reduction will simplify the impedance function; if ω_0 is not zero or infinity, then the Brune process can be applied exactly as before, with similar results: a Brune network, terminated in a simpler impedance—and if it happens that $\mathbf{Im}\,Z_0$ also vanishes at the frequency ω_0, i.e., that $Z_0(j\omega_0) = 0$, this Brune network degenerates into the ordinary shunt *L-C* combination we might have removed by straightforward susceptance reduction. This opens up a vast number of equivalent realizations in cases where the given impedance function is not minimum-reactance.

An important case is the occurrence of a pole of impedance at infinity, for then the corresponding inductor can be utilized to reduce the required coupling. If this pole is first removed, and the Brune process then applied, in the ordinary manner, the realization of Fig. 9.06–A results, in which

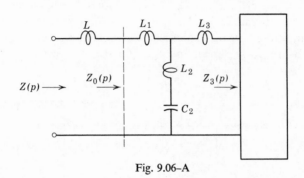

Fig. 9.06–A

$Z(p)$ is the given impedance function (minimum-resistance, or previously reduced to minimum-resistance). Its pole at infinity is removed by the usual process, in the inductor L. Then the Brune process yields a Brune network (Fig. 9.06–A) in which either L_1 or L_3 is negative. If we now consider the two inductors L and L_1 to be a single inductor (as of course we may do), then the coefficient of coupling required in the realization is given by

$$k^2 = \frac{L_2{}^2}{(L + L_1 + L_2)(L_2 + L_3)}. \tag{9.06–1}$$

The number k is clearly less than unity now, because of the addition of L to one factor of the denominator. If L_1 is negative, and $L \geqq |L_1|$, then no coupling at all is required, for all the inductances become positive. Notice that the same result will be obtained whether or not the pole at infinity is consciously removed, for if it is not, then the first inductance of the Brune cycle, "L_1," will automatically have the value $(L + L_1)$ of Fig. 9.06–A. [The reason that perfect coupling is not required by the theory in such a case is that (9.05–7) and (9.05–9) do not apply when the function $Z_0(p)$ has a pole at infinity.] If the pole at infinity is ignored (not removed), then in the resulting Brune network all the inductors in the T network may be individually realizable; if not, the T network is realizable by a pair of coupled inductors, with coupling less than unity: from any one of the three a positive inductor may be removed, up to a point, without destroying the physical realizability of the remainder. Thus poles at infinity may be ignored in the development and no attractive equivalent network will be overlooked; in the resulting Brune network(s) all the equivalents can be examined easily. This case is rather important in certain kinds of filter networks (for which often no coupled inductors at all are required), so that the Brune realization process is not academic.

The Brune process we have been describing, based on removal first of the inductor L_1, we call the *standard* Brune process. In addition, the *dual* process can be extremely helpful. If the Brune process is carried through in dual form, without regard to physical realizability, the "Brune network" resulting has the form shown in Fig. 9.06–B. No further analysis is

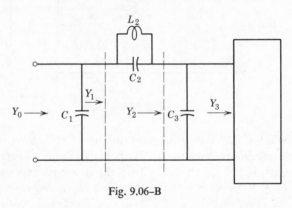

Fig. 9.06–B

necessary to demonstrate this, for it would be exactly dual to that already performed. Here either C_1 or C_3 is negative, and the network is not realizable. (An equivalent network, realizable with an ideal transformer, is discussed in Problem 9-57.) But if the given admittance function $Y(p)$ has a pole at infinity, then the Brune process (in dual form) may yield only positive capacitances, and the network is then realizable. Again it makes no difference whether the pole at infinity in $Y(p)$ is consciously removed before applying the Brune technique or not: the resulting network will be the same (if the two capacitors in shunt at the input, in the first case, are combined). The Brune process, applied to admittance functions (as here) rather than to impedance functions, is extremely useful. Since it is exactly dual to the previously discussed method, no detailed remarks are necessary. But it is important to recognize that inversion of the impedance function, removal of a shunt capacitor (to supply all of the susceptance at the frequency ω_0 where the conductance is zero), and removal of the pole of impedance thereby created, in the form of a parallel *L-C* network in series, followed by removal of another shunt capacitor is a process that constitutes another useful realization method, different only in that it is dual to the first method discussed. For practical reasons (Chapter 12) this attack may well be preferable, for the parasitic capacitance of physical inductors can be very troublesome. Here the inductor is connected across a capacitor which can often be adjusted in value to compensate for this parasitic capacitance; in the first type of Brune realization this is not possible, for the inductors are not so connected.

The two other possible versions of the Brune process, in which either a series capacitor or a shunt inductor is removed to account for the immittance at the frequency ω_0, are not important in general. But here again in certain cases they can lead to useful realizations. They differ from the two cases discussed above only in inversion of the frequency scale, which interchanges the rôles of inductance and capacitance. If a

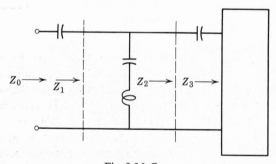

Fig. 9.06–C

series capacitor is removed first, as in Fig. 9.06–C, one of the series capacitors will be negative; but if the given impedance is not minimum and has a pole at the origin, this technique may yield only positive elements. If a shunt inductor is removed, as in Fig. 9.06–D, one of the shunt inductors will be negative; but if the given impedance has a zero at the origin, the realization may contain only positive elements.

The importance of these variations of the Brune procedure is much greater than the space given their discussion would indicate. They involve no new ideas, however, for the removal of reactance and susceptance from a minimum-resistance (minimum-conductance) function, followed by application of the basic Brune technique of removal of an element to account for the whole immittance at a frequency of zero resistance (conductance), of then removing the pole so created, and finally of removing the remaining pole at infinity or the origin is all that need be remembered. The device of removing susceptance by a shunt L-C network corresponding to imaginary zeros of an impedance is only a special case of the Brune technique, in fact, where $L_1 = 0$ (and removing reactance by a series L-C network is a special case of the dual technique).

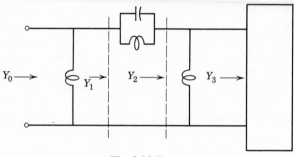

Fig. 9.06–D

If the frequency of zero resistance is zero or infinity, the Brune technique reduces again to this special form. In fact, all the techniques of Chapter 6 and some of those of Chapter 7 are special cases of the Brune technique.

That synthesis is not a unique process should be extremely clear by now. But the Brune process suggests still more possibilities for alternative realizations. If the given immittance function has internal (not zero or infinite) real-frequency poles, these need not be removed before applying the Brune technique: some may be removed, some not, or parts of some may be removed. The same is true of a pole at the origin when the first technique (removal of a series inductor first) is used, and for its dual, and for poles at infinity for the other two techniques. The variety of equivalent networks thus made possible is great. The presence of these internal real-frequency poles in the given impedance or admittance function does not, however, relax the coupling-coefficient requirement (or remove the need for a negative element or an ideal transformer in the alternative forms).

Another important source of equivalent networks (which generally differ among themselves) is present when the resistance of the given impedance function has several minima, all of the same value. Then, after reduction to minimum resistance (and possibly a Brune cycle or two), an impedance function arises in which the resistance is zero at several different (real) frequencies. We may choose any one of these as ω_0 for the first Brune cycle. The reduced impedance function will have zeros of resistance at all the other zeros of the original resistance function, any one of which will serve for the ω_0 of the next Brune cycle. In such a case there are a number of different sequences in which the Brune realization can be carried out, for the zeros of the original resistance function can be "removed" in any order. Some of the corresponding networks (which will be different in general) may be vastly superior to others, because in some the coupled inductors (negative elements) may not be necessary, whereas in others they may be required. Similar variations may be possible in the three other versions of the Brune technique.

We have seen, in this section, that the Brune technique is often of great practical value. This is true because many important immittance functions are not of the minimum type that requires coupled inductors or ideal transformers. Nor is simple reduction by removal of reactance, resistance, susceptance, and inductance enough to realize them. Yet for them the Brune technique may yield quite practical realizations. In later discussions, after we have become acquainted with some approximation procedures and familiar with some of the immittance functions often used, we shall come to appreciate this fact.

A completely general theory that explains when the Brune technique can be expected to yield practical network forms (without coupled inductors, for example) seems not yet to have been developed. There are many gaps in the known theory of *R-L-C* driving-point immittance realization in fact, but research in the theory of transformation between equivalent networks may fill these.

9.07 A new point of view

All of our discussion of the Brune process so far has assumed that we first reduce the given immittance function to a minimum-resistance (minimum-conductance) function. Reactance and susceptance reduction to minimum are not necessary, but our analysis has so far required that there be a real frequency, ω_0, at which the resistance (conductance) is zero. But even this is not necessary.

To extend the Brune technique it is necessary now to generalize our thinking a little. While we think of the given impedance function at real frequencies, it is very appropriate to consider it as made up of resistance and reactance (and correspondingly for the dual case). But the important division in general is not into real and imaginary parts, but rather into *even* and *odd* parts. The two divisions are equivalent at real frequencies (§ 5.11) so that the analysis of this chapter, so far, would be unaffected by such a revised point of view. In the extension we are about to consider this will no longer be true—hence we now turn our attention from the resistance function to the even part of the given impedance function $Z(p)$, to

$$\text{Ev } Z(p) = \tfrac{1}{2}[Z(p) + Z(-p)]. \qquad (9.07\text{-}1)$$

At real frequencies, of course,

$$\text{Ev } Z(j\omega) = \text{Re } Z(j\omega) = R(\omega) \qquad (9.07\text{-}2)$$

represents the resistance function we have been concerned with, which we previously caused (by resistance reduction) to have a zero (of even order) at some frequency ω_0. In such a situation $\text{Ev } Z(p)$ evidently also has a zero (of even order) at $j\omega_0$ (and at $-j\omega_0$). It is instructive to consider what the process of resistance reduction has done to these zeros of $\text{Ev } Z(p)$, for they were surely not on the imaginary axis prior to the resistance reduction. In general, if $Z(p)$ is p-r (and rational), its even part may have zeros of the following kinds, and of these only:

(a) imaginary zeros (of even order);
(b) real zeros (if located symmetrically about the origin);
(c) complex zeros (if with quadrantal symmetry, as in Fig. 5.14–C). $(9.07\text{-}3)$

The fundamental requirement is that on the imaginary axis $\text{Ev } Z(p)$, i.e., the resistance, should not be negative at any point (including infinity); from this stems requirement (a). The other requirements are concerned with symmetry and follow from the even-function nature of $\text{Ev } Z(p)$; § 8.11 and § 8.16 discussed these matters. These requirements are the only ones, for from any even function which is zero or positive all along the imaginary axis we can obtain a p-r function $Z(p)$ whose even part is the given even function (cf. Chapter 8—§ 8.11, for example).

The synthesis process we have been discussing is concerned with this function, $\text{Ev } Z(p)$, more than we have realized. For the first process, reactance reduction, removes from the impedance that part which is not related to (derivable from) the even part, i.e., reduces the function to one whose even and odd parts are consistent with the fundamental relations of Chapter 8. These relations connect resistance and reactance (for example), and hence imply corresponding relations between even and odd parts. (Susceptance reduction is not necessary; it is merely convenient.) If the reduced function is not minimum-resistance, then none of the zeros of its even part lie on the imaginary axis. In order to apply the Brune technique, we reduced the function further by removal of enough resistance to make the remaining resistance function vanish at a frequency ω_0 (and possibly others). The constant removed is an even function, and affects only the even part of the impedance, not the odd part. If $Z(p)$ represents the impedance function before resistance reduction and $Z_0(p)$ the function after reduction by removal of a resistance R_0, then

$$\mathbf{Od}\, Z_0(p) = \mathbf{Od}\, Z(p), \qquad (9.07\text{--}4)$$

but

$$\mathbf{Ev}\, Z_0(p) = \mathbf{Ev}\, Z(p) - R_0. \qquad (9.07\text{--}5)$$

The zeros of $\mathbf{Ev}\, Z_0(p)$ and of $\mathbf{Ev}\, Z(p)$ are certainly not the same (though the poles are). What has happened is illustrated in Fig. 9.07–A. Before

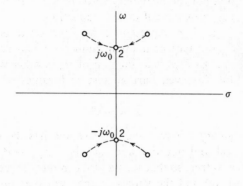

Fig. 9.07–A

reduction to minimum-resistance, the zeros of $\mathbf{Ev}\, Z(p)$ were off the imaginary axis; the four zeros shown in Fig. 9.07–A represent possible locations of some of them. (There can be variations: they could lie on the real axis; they could coincide and be multiple zeros.) As resistance is removed, these zeros of the even part of the impedance move, and when R_0 has been removed, some at least have reached the imaginary axis, by paths of some sort. Generally they arrive in pairs at points such as $\pm j\omega_0$ in Fig. 9.07–A, though they could assemble in larger groups (so long as the number of coincident zeros is even), and of course the origin and infinity are possible situations, although very special ones.

The aim of the Brune process is, in this light, first to move zeros of the even part of the impedance (or dually of the admittance) function to be realized to the imaginary axis. Then the fundamental technique of removing a reactive element to account for the impedance at such a frequency, i.e., of also moving a zero of the odd part to the same point so that the impedance itself has a zero there, etc., can be applied. Such forced motion of zeros can be extremely useful in network theory (in both approximation and realization problems). If the given impedance function is minimum-resistance (conductance) to begin with, then some zeros of the even part are already on the imaginary axis and no forced motion is necessary. If it is not, then we have to induce such a motion by subtracting resistance. As we do so, we can not expect to find any simply describable sort of motion of the zeros. They are, in the beginning, on the real axis or on neither axis, though always with quadrantal symmetry. And as they move those not originally on either axis may go fairly directly to the imaginary axis or they may move to the real axis—there are various possibilities. What we shall consider next is the feasibility of using not the imaginary zeros of the even part of an immittance but the real zeros thereof in the realization.

Suppose then that $Z(p)$ represents a p-r function to be realized, as an impedance. Its even part contains in numerator and denominator only even powers of p; $\mathrm{Ev}\,Z(p)$ is a function of p^2, in other words. We may conveniently plot this even part against real values of a new variable defined by

$$x = -p^2. \tag{9.07-6}$$

When p is imaginary x is real and positive and has the value ω^2; when p is real x is real and negative and has the value $-\sigma^2$. The converse statements are also true, so that such a plot exhibits the resistance function (when x is positive) and the values of the even part on the real p axis (when x is negative). The plot can show no poles for $x \geqq 0$ or for infinite x, by (8.11–4), though it may for negative (finite) x. Figure 9.07–B illustrates a few possibilities, but there are many more. Neither

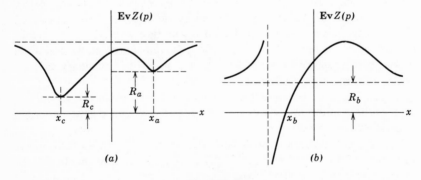

Fig. 9.07–B

of these impedance functions is minimum-resistance. The first could be reduced by removing as much resistance as R_a, the second by removing as much as R_b—and these reductions would make the functions minimum-resistance. Removal of a smaller amount of resistance, R_c, would cause the even part of the first to have double zeros on the real axis at $p = \pm\sqrt{-x_c}$; further reduction would split these double zeros apart into simple zeros, as in Fig. 9.07–C. The second already has a simple

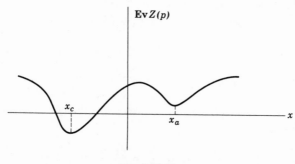

Fig. 9.07–C

zero (at $p = \pm\sqrt{-x_b}$). The order of these zeros, when p is considered the variable rather than x, is unchanged (except at the origin and at infinity). Evidently we can sometimes create both simple and double (and even higher order) zeros of the even part of an impedance on the real axis (if they are not there already). We shall now investigate the possibility of realizations based on these zeros.

9.08 A further variation of the Brune process

Suppose now that the given impedance function $Z(p)$ has been reduced by reactance and susceptance removal (at least that the pole at infinity and zero at the origin, if originally present, have been removed) and by

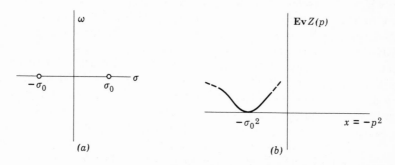

Fig. 9.08–A

resistance removal to the point where the even part has zeros on the real axis; these may be of any order. Let the function (so reduced) be $Z_0(p)$. Figure 9.08–A shows a pair of such zeros as well as the behavior of Ev $Z_0(p)$ as a function of $-p^2$ nearby, when the order of the zeros is even. This situation could well exist in the original $Z(p)$, of course, and it may be possible to continue the resistance reduction beyond this point. We shall be content for the present with this. We have

$$\text{Ev } Z_0(-\sigma_0) = \text{Ev } Z_0(\sigma_0) = 0 \qquad (9.08\text{–}1)$$

and

$$Z_0(-\sigma_0) = \text{Od } Z_0(-\sigma_0) = -\text{ Od } Z_0(\sigma_0) = -Z_0(\sigma_0). \quad (9.08\text{–}2)$$

Since $Z_0(p)$ is p-r, $Z_0(\sigma_0)$ is real and positive. Proceeding along a course similar to that followed when the zeros of the even part were imaginary, we remove an inductor of inductance

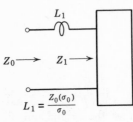

$$L_1 = \frac{1}{\Gamma_1} = \frac{Z_0(\sigma_0)}{\sigma_0} = \frac{Z_0(-\sigma_0)}{-\sigma_0} > 0, \quad (9.08\text{–}3)$$

$$L_1 = \frac{Z_0(\sigma_0)}{\sigma_0}$$

with the aim of creating a zero at σ_0. See Fig. 9.08–B.

Fig. 9.08–B

The reduced impedance function is

$$Z_1(p) = Z_0(p) - L_1 p \qquad (9.08\text{–}4)$$

and this is again in the first class of pseudo-p-r functions discussed in § 9.04. (It may have no real-frequency zeros, but that does not affect the properties derived in § 9.04.) Accordingly, $Z_1(p)$ has one right-half-plane zero and its reciprocal has the expansion

$$Y_1(p) = \frac{1}{Z_1(p)} = Y_a(p) + \frac{-K}{p - \sigma_1} + \frac{-K}{p + \sigma_1} \qquad (9.08\text{–}5)$$

in which σ_1 represents this right-half-plane zero, K is real and positive, and Y_a is p-r. Since the chosen value of L_1 reduces Z_1 to zero at σ_0 (and at $-\sigma_0$) by (9.08–3), $Y_1(p)$ has a pole at σ_0. But Y_1 has only one right-half-plane pole, so that σ_1 and σ_0 must be identical. Since Y_1 also has a pole at $-\sigma_0$ (i.e., at $-\sigma_1$), the pole at $-\sigma_1$ in Y_a (if present) cannot completely cancel the pole at $-\sigma_1$ exhibited in (9.08–5). If the zero of Ev Z_0 at $-\sigma_1$ is double, or of higher order, then this pole is not present in Y_a at all, though it is if the zero is simple.

We cannot now remove an ordinary series L-C network in shunt, for Y_a in general will have no real-frequency pole. But we can remove the last two terms in (9.08–5) as a similar network in which the inductance is negative—for they add to $-2Kp/(p^2 - \sigma_1^2)$, which is the admittance of the combination of a negative inductor and a positive capacitor in series. Since Y_a is p-r, the third inductance of the T network, if we can develop the realization in that fashion, will be positive and we hope again to realize the T network by means of coupled inductors. The present situation is shown in Fig. 9.08–C.

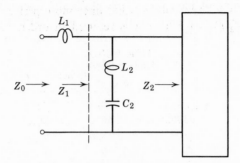

$$L_2 = \Gamma_2^{-1} = \frac{1}{-2K} = \tfrac{1}{2}[Z_0{}'(\sigma_1) - L_1] = \frac{1}{2}\left[Z'(\sigma_1) - \frac{Z_0(\sigma_1)}{\sigma_1}\right] < 0 \text{ by (9.04–25)},$$

$$C_2 = \frac{-1}{L_2\sigma_1{}^2} > 0.$$

Fig. 9.08–C

Here

$$Y_2 = Y_1 - \frac{\Gamma_2 p}{p^2 - \sigma_1{}^2} = Y_1 + \frac{2Kp}{p^2 - \sigma_1{}^2} = Y_a \qquad (9.08\text{–}6)$$

and is p-r. At infinity Y_2 has a zero, by (9.08–5) and (9.08–4), and in fact

$$\begin{aligned}
Y_2 &= \frac{1}{Z_0 - L_1 p} + \frac{2Kp}{p^2 - \sigma_1{}^2} \\
&= -\frac{1}{L_1 p}\left(1 + \frac{Z_0}{L_1 p} + \cdots\right) + \frac{2K}{p}\left(1 + \frac{\sigma_1{}^2}{p^2} + \cdots\right) \\
&= \frac{1}{p}(-\Gamma_1 + 2K) - \frac{Z_0}{L_1{}^2 p^2} + \cdots \qquad (9.08\text{–}7) \\
&= \frac{1}{p}(-\Gamma_1 - \Gamma_2) - \cdots
\end{aligned}$$

for we have assumed that Z_0 is regular at infinity. Since Y_2 is p-r, $(-\Gamma_1 - \Gamma_2)$ must be positive—which implies that $(L_1 + L_2)$ is positive. Accordingly, Z_2 has the desired pole at infinity and we have

$$Z_2 = \frac{1}{Y_2} = L_3 p + Z_3(p) \qquad (9.08\text{–}8)$$

in which Z_2 is p-r. We must have

$$\Gamma_3 \geqq (-\Gamma_1 - \Gamma_2) \quad \text{or} \quad \Gamma_1 + \Gamma_2 + \Gamma_3 \geqq 0 \qquad (9.08\text{-}9)$$

for $Z_3(p)$ to be p-r, and as before [cf. (9.05–16)] we must also have

$$\Gamma_1 + \Gamma_2 + \Gamma_3 \leqq 0 \qquad (9.08\text{-}10)$$

for the T network of inductors to be physically realizable. Again we must take the = sign in both, so that once more perfect coupling is required. But $Z_3(p)$ is p-r, and it is reduced in order, as Table 9.08–A

Table 9.08–A

Function	Order (a)	(b)
Z_0	n	n
$\left.\begin{array}{c} Z_1 \\ Y_1 \end{array}\right\}$	$n + 1$	$n + 1$
$\left.\begin{array}{c} Y_2 \\ Z_2 \end{array}\right\}$	$n - 1$	n
Z_3	$n - 2$	$n - 1$

shows, so that the Brune process has succeeded once more. The cycle is shown in Fig. 9.08–D. In Table 9.08–A column (a) applies when the

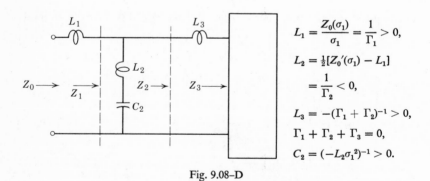

$$L_1 = \frac{Z_0(\sigma_1)}{\sigma_1} = \frac{1}{\Gamma_1} > 0,$$

$$L_2 = \tfrac{1}{2}[Z_0'(\sigma_1) - L_1]$$

$$= \frac{1}{\Gamma_2} < 0,$$

$$L_3 = -(\Gamma_1 + \Gamma_2)^{-1} > 0,$$

$$\Gamma_1 + \Gamma_2 + \Gamma_3 = 0,$$

$$C_2 = (-L_2\sigma_1^2)^{-1} > 0.$$

Fig. 9.08–D

zero of **Ev** $Z_0(p)$ at σ_0 is of order two or more, and the pole at $-\sigma_0$ is completely removed in L_2 and C_2; column (b) applies when the zero is simple and only part of this pole is removed, the balance remaining in Y_2. Notice that the reduction in order may here be only *one*, in contrast to the original Brune cycle; in fact, the process may be applied even if **Ev** $Z_0(\sigma_0) \neq 0$, but then there is no reduction in order. The Brune network proper is realizable by a pair of perfectly coupled inductors, as in Fig. 9.08–E.

$$L_p = \tfrac{1}{2}[Z_0'(\sigma_1) + L_1] > 0,$$

$$M = \tfrac{1}{2}|Z_0'(\sigma_1) - L_1|,$$

$$L_s = \frac{1}{2}\frac{[Z_0'(\sigma_1) - L_1]^2}{[Z_0'(\sigma_1) + L_1]} > 0,$$

$$k = \frac{M}{\sqrt{L_p L_s}} = 1,$$

$$C_2 = (-L_2\sigma_1^2)^{-1} > 0.$$

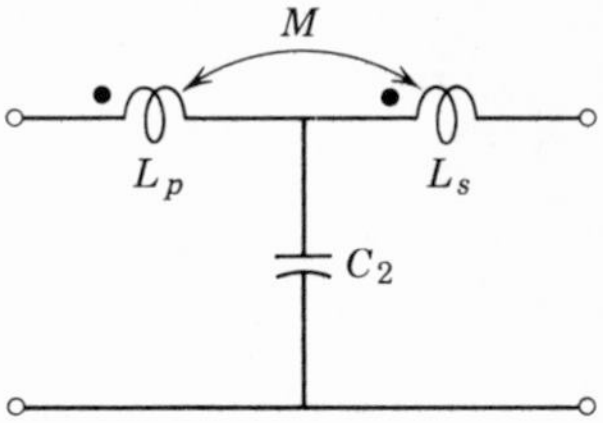

Fig. 9.08–E

Evidently we have here another method of possible use in network realization. If **Ev** $Z(p)$ has real zeros, or can be made to have them by resistance reduction, the Brune cycle can be based on these real zeros. We shall not discuss the dual approach here, nor the possibility of removing a capacitor in place of an inductor, nor its dual; variations made by leaving part of the original excess reactance in we also pass over. Even by the technique described above, we cannot hope to avoid the need for inductor coupling when this method is used. A pole at infinity in the impedance function can be used to relax the requirement of *perfect* coupling, but because it is L_2 that is negative, rather than L_1 or L_3, some coupling will always be required. Networks of this type are occasionally necessary in practice, though to be avoided if possible. The aspect of Brune synthesis just described is chiefly of theoretical interest.

We shall conclude our discussion with an illustrative numerical example. Let the impedance function to be realized, normalized and reduced (by resistance removal) to a form in which the even part has double real zeros, be given by

$$Z_0(p) = \frac{p^2 + 9p + 8}{p^2 + 2p + 2} \quad \text{ohms.} \tag{9.08–11}$$

We find

$$\mathbf{Ev}\, Z_0(p) = \frac{(p^2 + 8)(p^2 + 2) - (9p)(2p)}{(p^2 + 2)^2 - (2p)^2}$$

$$= \frac{p^4 - 8p^2 + 16}{p^4 + 4} = \frac{(p^2 - 4)^2}{p^4 + 4} \tag{9.08–12}$$

with the behavior shown in Fig. 9.08–F. Here

$$\sigma_0 = \sigma_1 = 2 \text{ radians per sec,}$$

$$Z_0(\sigma_1) = Z_0(2) = 3 \text{ ohms,} \qquad (9.08\text{–}13)$$

$$L_1 = \frac{Z_0(\sigma_1)}{\sigma_1} = 1.5 \text{ h.}$$

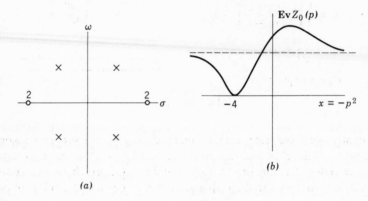

Fig. 9.08–F

Then

$$Y_1 = \frac{1}{Z_0 - L_1 p} = \frac{p^2 + 2p + 2}{-1.5 p^3 - 2p^2 + 6p + 8}$$

$$= -\frac{2}{3} \frac{p^2 + 2p + 2}{p^3 + \frac{4}{3} p^2 - 4p - \frac{16}{3}} \quad \text{mhos.} \qquad (9.08\text{–}14)$$

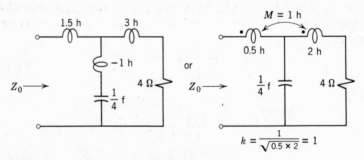

Fig. 9.08–G

Since this has poles at ± 2, the denominator is easily factored and the partial-fraction expansion made; it is

$$Y_1 = \frac{-\frac{1}{2}}{p + 2} + \frac{-\frac{1}{2}}{p - 2} + \frac{\frac{1}{3}}{p + \frac{4}{3}}$$

$$= \frac{-p}{p^2 - 4} + \frac{\frac{1}{3}}{p + \frac{4}{3}} \quad \text{mhos.} \qquad (9.08\text{--}15)$$

From this expansion the network to be connected to L_1 is readily seen to have the expected form, and we have the realization of Fig. 9.08–G.

9.09 The Brune method in retrospect; Darlington's extension

Here in Chapter 9 we are attempting to develop realization methods for the most general type of driving-point immittance functions, that where all three kinds of elements are required: L, R, and C. We have so far discussed in some detail the method due to Brune, and have reached the conclusion that if a rational function of p is p-r, it is realizable—as either the driving-point impedance or driving-point admittance function of a one-terminal pair.   Not only is positive reality required of all driving-point immittance functions (Chapter 4) but it is sufficient for realizability of a given function.   We have then, in the property of positive reality, a compact gauge for measurement of functions proposed for network driving-point immittances: if a function is p-r, it is suitable; if it is not p-r, then it is a waste of time to attempt realization.

Of the Brune process several things should be said again for emphasis. In the first place, although it will realize any given p-r function, and that in a variety of (equivalent) networks in general, we have no reason to consider this to be the only possible realization method.   And it suffers from two disadvantages, both of which urge us on to look for other methods.   The first is the presence of resistance, scattered in general through the network (between the canonic Brune networks) along with reactance networks representing reactance (susceptance) reduction.   The second is the requirement of perfect coupling between two inductors (or, worse, of ideal transformers).   The impracticality of Brune networks, because of the second difficulty, is self-evident.   The first matter is objectionable for reasons less evident at this point.   Suffice it to say that it may be very useful to be able to realize driving-point immittance functions in a form in which resistors appear as infrequently as possible, for the sake of reduction in power dissipation.   (Section 11.04 illustrates this.) A general realization in which only *one* resistor is required will, in fact, be extremely useful in Volume II.   Accordingly, we shall discuss next the possibility of such a one-resistor realization (leaving for discussion in Chapter 10 the possibility of realization without mutual inductance).

Such a one-resistor realization process can be set up, and one approach is in fact nothing but a logical extension of the Brune process which we have been discussing. Let us rapidly review this Brune process (for its true character may well have been lost in the maze of detail we have developed). Its first principle is reduction by removal of reactance, susceptance, resistance, and conductance. These straightforward processes, which result in series- and shunt-connected one-terminal pairs each of which contains a pure L-C network (or else a single resistor) are now very familiar. Often they suffice for the complete realization, a very happy situation.

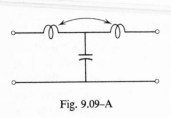

Fig. 9.09–A

But if they do not, if a stage is reached in which the immittance functions have no zeros or poles on the imaginary axis, and their real parts vanish at one or more pairs of (real) frequencies, then the second principle must be invoked. The second principle is reduction by removal of a Brune network (shown in Fig. 9.09–A) in which, generally, perfect coupling is required of the mutual inductance. This Brune network is developed essentially not by any new principle, but by reactance and susceptance removal—with the additional freedom given by a visionary attitude that permits a negative (unrealizable) element in the network, and then shows this to be realizable after all, through the use of mutual inductance. With these two principles, applied repeatedly, any p-r function can be realized. It is in the resistance (conductance) reduction stages that the intermediate resistors appear; it is in the Brune networks that the perfectly coupled inductors appear. We shall discuss

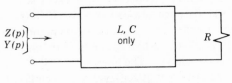

$$\left.\begin{array}{l} Z(p) \\ Y(p) \end{array}\right\} \longrightarrow$$

L, C only

R

Fig. 9.09–B

first the possibility of one-resistor realization, and later the possibility of realizations that never require mutual inductance.

Not many years after Brune's discovery, Darlington developed an extension of the process, in which resistance reduction is not used (DA 1).

If this Darlington process is completely general, it must of course use some resistance, but we shall find that only *one* resistor is needed, however complicated the immittance function may be. Pictorially, Fig. 9.09–B shows the form of network which the Darlington realization produces. From the beginning we should realize the probable need for rather complicated nature of the *L-C* network and be willing to accept this; it is the price paid for concentration of the network's resistance in one resistor, *R*.

9.10 The zeros of Ev $Z(p)$

Before discussing the actual one-resistor realization process, let us review the Brune process again, with particular emphasis on the parts in which resistance and conductance reduction are not used. We shall find that the Brune process goes further toward the goal of a one-resistor realization than we may have thought.

The appropriate focus of the discussion here is the zeros of Ev $Z(p)$, $Z(p)$ being the p-r impedance function to be realized. In § 9.07 and § 9.08 we had a hint of this, for there we found that the fundamental Brune procedure is based on imaginary zeros of Ev $Z(p)$, created if necessary by removing resistance. And we found also that if zeros of Ev $Z(p)$ lie on the real axis, or can be moved there by resistance reduction, the Brune process can again be used, with only slight modification. We may profitably examine these zeros of the even part more closely. How, in a realization of the type we have been discussing in this chapter, do these zeros come about?

Consider first what reactance reduction accomplishes from this point of view. Figure 9.10–A shows such a step, $Z(p)$ being the original function,

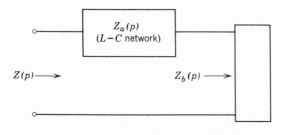

Fig. 9.10–A

and $Z_b(p)$ the result of removing the series *L-C* network of impedance $Z_a(p)$. We see that

$$Z(p) = Z_a + Z_b \qquad (9.10\text{–}1)$$

so that

$$\text{Ev } Z(p) = \text{Ev } (Z_a + Z_b) = \text{Ev } Z_b, \qquad (9.10\text{-}2)$$

for $Z_a(p)$ is an odd function. Reactance removal has no effect on the even part of the impedance, though it does reduce the order of the function. Correspondingly, resistance removal has no effect on the odd part, nor on the poles of the even part, though it does alter the zeros of the even part (as discussed in § 9.07).

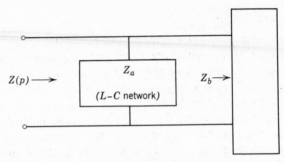

$Z(p) \longrightarrow$

Z_a

$(L\text{-}C \text{ network})$

$Z_b \rightarrow$

Fig. 9.10–B

Consider next the effect of susceptance reduction, illustrated in Fig. 9.10–B. Here

$$Z(p) = \frac{Z_a Z_b}{Z_a + Z_b} = \frac{Z_a(E_b + O_b)}{E_b + (Z_a + O_b)} \qquad (9.10\text{-}3)$$

in which E_b and O_b represent respectively the even and odd parts of $Z_b(p)$. Since the function Z_a is odd, we find that

$$\text{Ev } Z(p) = \text{Ev } \left[\frac{Z_a(E_b + O_b)(E_b - Z_a - O_b)}{(E_b)^2 - (Z_a + O_b)^2} \right]$$

$$= - \frac{Z_a^2 E_b}{(E_b)^2 - (Z_a + O_b)^2}. \qquad (9.10\text{-}4)$$

The effect of susceptance removal on the even part of the impedance is considerable, even though the network removed contains no resistance. On the (reasonable) assumption that the susceptance reduction is complete, i.e., that no real-frequency zeros of impedance remain in Z_b, we can see what Z_a and Z_b individually contribute to the zeros of $\text{Ev } Z(p)$. From (9.10–4) it is clear that these zeros come in general from zeros of $Z_a(p)$, zeros of $E_b(p)$, and poles of $Z_b(p)$.

Consider first the zeros of $Z_a(p)$. These are all at real frequencies, and at none of them does Z_b vanish. Since at such a point the denominator of (9.10–4) reduces to $(E_b^2 - O_b^2)$, and there E_b is real and O_b imaginary, the denominator could vanish only if Z_b were zero—which it is not. The same situation exists at infinity. Consequently, *all* the zeros of Z_a contribute zeros to **Ev** $Z(p)$. These zeros are all at real frequencies (and possibly infinity); they are simple in Z_a and therefore double in **Ev** Z, because Z_a is squared in (9.10–4). Physically, the fact that a zero of Z_a produces a zero of **Ev** Z is apparent from Fig. 9.10–B, for then Z_a is a short circuit and Z must vanish; since this occurs only at real frequencies, the even and odd parts of Z must also vanish individually, i.e., the resistance and reactance are separately zero at such a point. Figure 9.10–C

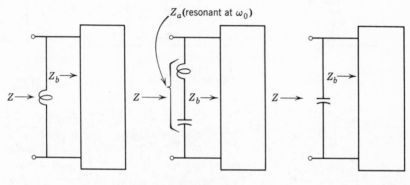

Fig. 9.10–C

illustrates this with three simple examples, in which the zeros of **Ev** Z introduced by the shunt-connected *L-C* network are respectively at the frequencies 0, ω_0, ∞. More complicated examples are represented by Fig. 9.10–B, Z_a being an arbitrary *L-C* network.

Consider next the zeros of $E_b(p)$. These may occur anywhere, though they are subject to the general symmetry requirements of even functions, and those at real frequencies must be of even order. If the denominator of (9.10–4) is not zero at these points, then the zeros of E_b contribute directly to the zeros of **Ev** Z. Such zeros may be off the imaginary axis, or may be at real frequencies (including infinity), and may even coincide with zeros of Z_a, in which case the multiplicities of the consequent zeros of **Ev** Z are increased by the zeros contributed by E_b. Physically, the real-frequency zeros of E_b cause Z_b to be purely reactive (though not zero) at such points, and since $Z_a(j\omega)$ is reactive, the parallel combination of Z_a and Z_b is also purely reactive—or the resistance (the even) part of Z

is zero. Figure 9.10–D gives an illustrative example. There $\mathrm{Ev}\, Z_d(p)$ has a double zero at the frequency ω_1 (from the discussion of the effect of susceptance reduction just given). If Z_c is an $L\text{-}C$ network, then $\mathrm{Ev}\, Z_b = E_b$ has these same zeros; i.e., Z_b is purely reactive at the frequency ω_1. Then Z is also purely reactive at this frequency, or $\mathrm{Ev}\, Z(p)$ has zeros at $\pm j\omega_1$, whose origin is in the zeros of E_b.

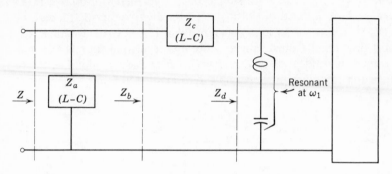

Fig. 9.10–D

It is possible for the denominator of (9.10–4) to vanish simultaneously with E_b. But this can occur only at real frequencies—and it produces a pole in $Z(p)$ (Problem 9-49). The even part of $Z(p)$ then may or may not be zero, depending on the order of the zero of E_b. If a represents the order of the zero of E_b, then $\mathrm{Ev}\, Z$ has no zero at this point when $a = 2$, but has a zero there of order $(a - 2)$ when $a > 2$. In this special circumstance, the zeros of E_b contribute to the zeros of $\mathrm{Ev}\, Z$ not directly, but with a reduction in order of two. In the example of Fig. 9.10–D, this special circumstance could arise, for instance, if Z_a were simply a capacitor, Z_c simply an inductor, and these two elements resonated at the frequency ω_1. In general, however, the zeros of E_b appear directly in $\mathrm{Ev}\, Z(p)$.

Consider finally the points at which the denominator of (9.10–4) becomes infinite. Although such points may lie off the imaginary axis, they then are not zeros of $\mathrm{Ev}\, Z(p)$ (Problem 9-45). When such a point is imaginary, the denominator becomes infinite only because Z_a or O_b becomes infinite, for E_b cannot become infinite at real frequencies. A pole of Z_a does not alone cause $\mathrm{Ev}\, Z$ to vanish, as inspection of (9.10–4) indicates. Nor does a pole common to Z_a and O_b, for such a pole must be simple (with a residue that is real and positive) in Z_a, in Z_b, and hence in O_b, and consequently in $(Z_a + O_b)$. But if O_b alone has the (simple) pole, then it produces a double zero in $\mathrm{Ev}\, Z$. (The behavior may occur at infinity also.) The mechanism of this is illustrated by Fig. 9.10–E, in which a pole of Z_b at the frequency ω_2 is exhibited in Z_c. At this frequency Z is purely reactive (in fact, $Z = Z_a$), Z_a is finite, and so **Ev** $Z = 0$. Similar behavior may occur at zero and infinite frequencies, as illustrated in Fig. 9.10–F. The networks Z_a and Z_c may of course be more complicated also. And the zeros contributed to E_b by these (real-frequency) poles of Z_b may coincide with, and augment, zeros produced by vanishing of Z_a, and by zeros of **Ev** Z_c (Fig. 9.10–E).

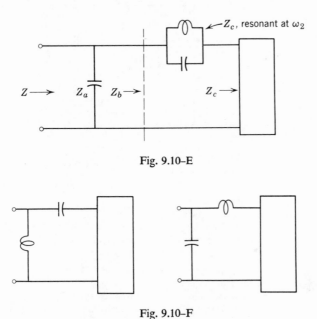

Fig. 9.10–E

Fig. 9.10–F

We might also consider the effect of conductance removal, when the network Z_a of Fig. 9.10–B would become a resistor alone. This process may appear sometimes to remove zeros of the even part of the impedance, but actually it merely shifts zeros caused by Z_b. In any event, we are concerned with finding one-resistor realizations, so that intermediate conductance removals are of no interest here.

In the process of removing reactance (Fig. 9.10–A) no change is made in the even part of the impedance function. But in the process of removing susceptance (Fig. 9.10–B) a considerable change is made. We must now review our findings and correlate these with the Brune process in general. Figure 9.10–G summarizes the results of this section; in it are listed the various origins of the zeros of **Ev** $Z(p)$.

In Fig. 9.10–G we have a summary of the physical causes of the zeros of Ev $Z(p)$. From another point of view, the removal of Z_a removes some of the zeros of Ev $Z(p)$, so that Ev Z_b is less complicated. We might discuss this inverse point of view in the same detailed fashion, computing the zeros of Ev Z_b and observing that they are those of Ev $Z(p)$ except for some that have dropped out because of the Z_a stage of realization (Problem

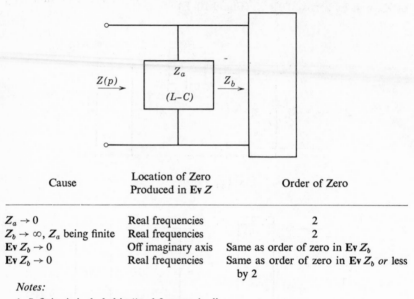

Cause	Location of Zero Produced in Ev Z	Order of Zero
$Z_a \rightarrow 0$	Real frequencies	2
$Z_b \rightarrow \infty$, Z_a being finite	Real frequencies	2
Ev $Z_b \rightarrow 0$	Off imaginary axis	Same as order of zero in Ev Z_b
Ev $Z_b \rightarrow 0$	Real frequencies	Same as order of zero in Ev Z_b *or* less by 2

Notes:
1. Infinity is included in "real frequencies."
2. Poles of Z_b off the imaginary axis do not cause zeros in Ev $Z(p)$.
3. Coincidence of (real-frequency) zeros from different causes is possible.

Fig. 9.10–G.   Origin of the zeros of Ev $Z(p)$.

9-50). The details are implicit in the discussion above, however. Instead we now go on to generalize and discuss the various stages of the Brune realization in the light of Fig. 9.10–G.

9.11 The ladder-network point of view

The Brune process leads to a realization in the form aptly called a *ladder network* (Fig. 9.11–A). Each box here represents one stage of reduction; its contents will be a number of L and C elements (and possibly one resistor), and in some of the boxes it may be necessary to use negative inductance. In the one-resistor realization we seek, resistors are not allowed (except for one), but the negative inductance (realizable by pairs of coupled inductors) should certainly be considered reactance, just as ordinary inductance, and used as necessary. We may use reactance reduction—which gives a series *L-C* network to the ladder, a component which we shall call a *section* of *Type A* (Fig. 9.11–B); and we may use susceptance reduction—which gives a shunt *L-C* network to the ladder,

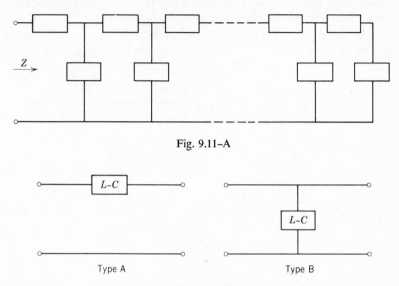

Fig. 9.11–A

Type A   Type B

Fig. 9.11–B

which we shall call a *Type-B* section (Fig. 9.11–B). These two components may be used to reduce the order of the given impedance function $Z(p)$ (by removing real-frequency zeros and poles), up to the point where the reduced impedance function has no imaginary zeros or poles. The network development so far contains no resistance; it is in ladder form, each section being a series- or shunt-connected *L-C* network, to which the theory of Chapter 6 may be applied to yield equivalent networks. Still other alternative realizations may be based on removing zeros and poles in different sequences, and on partial removals (with accompanying increases in the number of elements).

A Type-A section in itself has no effect on the zeros of the even part of the impedance function. A Type-B section, we have found, however, to have a considerable effect. Each zero of Z_a (the impedance of the *L-C* network in the Type-B section) removes two zeros from the even part of the impedance function. That is (Fig. 9.11–C), while

$$\text{Ev } Z_1(p) = \text{Ev } Z_2(p), \qquad (9.11\text{–}1)$$

still $\mathbf{Ev}\, Z_2(p)$ is definitely not the same as $\mathbf{Ev}\, Z_3(p)$. Among the zeros of $\mathbf{Ev}\, Z_2(p)$ are all the zeros of Z_a (doubled) and these do not appear in $\mathbf{Ev}\, Z_3(p)$ which contributes its own zeros to $\mathbf{Ev}\, Z_2(p)$. We may look on Z_a (the Type-B section) then as an agent that removes some zeros from $\mathbf{Ev}\, Z_2$, as well as an instrument that reduces the order of the impedance function: the Type-B sections remove some (real-frequency) zeros from the even part of the impedance function.

A Type-A section following a Type-B section also is instrumental in removing zeros, as Z_b in Fig. 9.11–C. In Z_b are real-frequency poles of

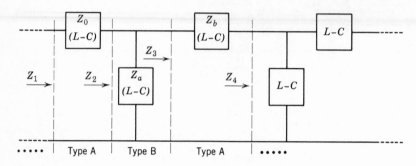

Fig. 9.11–C

the impedance $Z_3(p)$, and these we have found generally to produce zeros in $\mathbf{Ev}\, Z_2(p)$; if the previous reactance reduction made by Z_0 is complete, then Z_2 has no real-frequency poles and every such pole of Z_b will contribute two zeros to $\mathbf{Ev}\, Z_2(p)$. Hence Type-A sections (acting in conjunction with Type-B sections) not only reduce the order of impedance functions but also remove some (real-frequency) zeros from the even part of the impedance functions.

We are interested now in developing a one-resistor realization process. Evidently the Type-A and Type-B sections, used in alternation until a minimum-reactance, minimum-susceptance stage is reached, not only remove excess reactance and susceptance and hence reduce the order of the impedance function but also remove many of the real-frequency zeros of its even part. We shall use "$\mathbf{Ev}\, Z(p)$" generically now, to refer to the impedance at various stages of the realization, not necessarily to the driving-point impedance to be realized.

Our immediate problem, then, is to remove the remaining zeros of $\mathbf{Ev}\, Z(p)$, and to do so without using more than one resistor. The zeros yet to be removed may be complex, real—or even imaginary. For it is perfectly possible that at this minimum-reactance, minimum-susceptance stage **Ev** $Z(p)$ should vanish at some real frequency ω_0. There **Od** $Z(p)$ will not vanish (for Z is now minimum-susceptance); in other words, we have $R(\omega_0) = 0$, $X(\omega_0) \neq 0$. Removal of this zero of **Ev** $Z(p)$ by ordinary susceptance reduction is not possible. But this is exactly the situation the Brune network was devised to handle. If **Ev** $Z(j\omega_0) = 0$, the Brune technique may be applied immediately, and adds to the ladder development a Brune network, or what we now designate a *Type-C* section (Fig. 9.11–D). (We shall broaden the definition of Type-C section later.) In

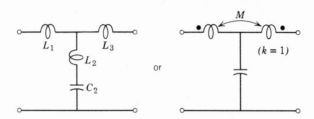

Fig. 9.11–D

this network either L_1 or L_3 is negative, but otherwise the section amounts merely to two Type-A sections, separated by a Type-B section. The inductor L_1 has in itself no effect in removing zeros of **Ev** $Z(p)$, be it positive or negative, for $L_1 p$ is purely odd. Nor (if Z has been reduced to minimum-reactance) does L_1 produce a zero at infinity in conjunction with a Type-B section preceding it—for the input impedance to the Brune network has no pole at infinity. In the series combination of L_2 and C_2 we have a Type-B section which clearly removes four zeros of **Ev** $Z(p)$, two at $+j\omega_0$ and two at $-j\omega_0$. The inductor L_3 again has no effect on the zeros of **Ev** $Z(p)$, for both it and the shunt arm become infinite at the same point, infinity—and, as previously discussed, there is then no consequent zero in **Ev** $Z(p)$. Hence the Brune or Type-C section removes zeros of the even part of the impedance function at real frequencies. When the odd part is also zero at such points, the Brune network degenerates into L_2 and C_2 alone (a case of ordinary susceptance reduction); when the odd part is not zero a true Brune network does the job.

We now observe that

sections of Types A, B, and C are sufficient to remove all real-frequency zeros of **Ev** $Z(p)$.   (9.11–2)

There are usually several different sequences in which the sections can be removed, but only these three types are required to reduce the given impedance function to one whose even part has no imaginary zeros.

In many practical networks the zeros of the even part of the given $Z(p)$ are confined to the imaginary axis (because of the network's application and use). For those networks these sections suffice: repeatedly applied, they will reduce the even part of the impedance to a function with no zeros, and therefore with no poles, i.e., to a constant. This constant represents the one resistor necessary in this case. The associated minimum reactance is zero, and any excess reactance appearing at this stage can be realized by a Type-A section. We can say then that

if the zeros of the even part of a given (p-r) impedance function are all on the imaginary axis, the function can be realized by a ladder network (made up of L-C sections of Types A, B, and C) terminated in one resistor.   (9.11–3)

For such impedance functions, then, a one-resistor realization is always possible. It will take the form shown in Fig. 9.11–E, in which the ladder

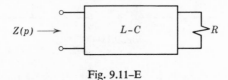

Fig. 9.11–E

network (including sections of all three types in general) is represented by the box.

If the datum function represents admittance (say Y), rather than impedance, it is similarly realizable. This we might justify simply by duality—but then ideal transformers would be required in the realization of the network dual to the Type-C section (cf. § 9.06 and Problem 9-57). These we may avoid by inverting the admittance function at the appropriate point in the development and proceeding, as before, on an impedance basis with the Type-C section. Or, since the zeros of **Ev** $(1/Y)$, i.e., of the even part of the corresponding impedance, are the same as the zeros of **Ev** Y except possibly for additions or subtractions at real frequencies (Problem 9-45), we can immediately make the following statement (the realization being made, if necessary, by considering $Z = 1/Y$ in place of Y):

if the zeros of the even part of a given (p-r) admittance function are all on the imaginary axis, the function can be realized by a ladder network (made up of L-C sections of Types A, B, and C) terminated in one resistor. (9.11–4)

For any p-r function whose even part vanishes only on the imaginary axis (including infinity), then, we can find both impedance and admittance realizations in the form shown in Fig. 9.11–E. This realization uses ordinary L and C elements, and may require perfectly coupled inductors, but it requires only *one* resistor. And if we permit the use of an ideal transformer (Fig. 9.11–F), this resistor may be given any arbitrary value, R_0. All that is necessary is that the transformer ratio satisfy

$$\frac{R_0}{a^2} = R, \qquad (9.11\text{–}5)$$

for then the resistance terminating the L-C network is still effectively R. Since (9.11–5) determines the required ratio a, R_0 is actually arbitrary.

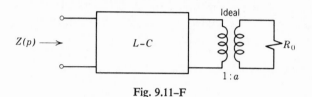

Fig. 9.11–F

We have found that the three types of ladder-network section are enough to realize the real-frequency zeros of the even part of the given immittance function. Of these the Type-C section, with its perfectly coupled inductors, is practically undesirable though theoretically satisfactory. Hence it would be of value to be able to determine by inspection of the datum function whether Type-C sections are required. Unfortunately, only certain sufficient conditions appear to be known (DA 1); we do not have satisfactory knowledge of necessary and sufficient conditions (on Z or Y) for realizability with only Type-A or Type-B sections. One interesting case is that in which all the zeros of **Ev** Z (or of **Ev** Y) lie at the origin, at infinity, or are distributed between these two points. Then the Type-C section will not be required and the Type-A and Type-B sections will consist of single L or C elements only—since the "resonances" required occur only at zero and infinite frequency—or possibly of two such elements when two adjacent sections are combined in one. Then (9.11–3) and (9.11–4) can be modified to read:

> if the zeros of the even part of a given (p-r) immittance function lie only at the origin or infinity (or at both), the function can be realized by an L-C ladder network (each of whose arms contains only one or two elements) terminated in a resistor. (9.11–6)

When the zeros are distributed between the origin and infinity, various different realizations can be obtained by changing the sequence in which the zeros are removed (Problems 9-7, 9-8). In (9.11–6) it is assumed that the function is minimum-reactance or minimum-susceptance; if it is not, an additional Type-A or Type-B section (of more complicated nature, perhaps) will be required.

There are probably many other methods of realization, different from that we have developed, but we shall not attempt to discuss even the known ones, for the Brune process is satisfactory for our purposes. With it we are able to strip $\text{Ev } Z(p)$ of all its real-frequency zeros.

At this stage in the general case, we have left an impedance function (reduced), none of the zeros of whose even part are on the imaginary axis (or at infinity). Suppose we turn our attention now to zeros of $\text{Ev } Z(p)$ on the *real* axis. These we have already seen (§§ 9.07, 9.08) can be the basis for reduction by a modified Brune network. In the light of our present discussion, we rather expect this Brune network actually to remove these real zeros of $\text{Ev } Z(p)$. That this action does occur we can demonstrate by applying our previous analysis (§ 9.10) to the reduction process of § 9.08, illustrated again in Fig. 9.11–G. Here the inductor L_1

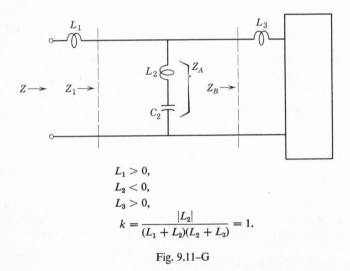

$$L_1 > 0,$$
$$L_2 < 0,$$
$$L_3 > 0,$$
$$k = \frac{|L_2|}{(L_1 + L_2)(L_2 + L_3)} = 1.$$

Fig. 9.11–G

constitutes a Type-A section, and (exactly as with the standard Brune network above) it has no effect on the zeros of $\text{Ev } Z(p)$. The shunt branch (L_2, C_2) constitutes a Type-B section in effect (though L_2 is negative). To investigate its effect, we observe (much as before, since Z_A is an odd function even though L_2 is negative) that

$$\text{Ev } Z = \text{Ev } Z_1 = -\frac{Z_A{}^2 E_B}{(E_B)^2 - (Z_A + O_B)^2} \qquad (9.11\text{-}7)$$

in which E_B and O_B respectively represent the even and odd parts of $Z_B(p)$. The zeros of Z_A are simple and are two in number, occurring at

$$p = \pm \frac{1}{\sqrt{-L_2 C_2}} = \pm \sigma_1 \qquad (9.11\text{--}8)$$

as illustrated in Fig. 9.11–H. Unless the denominator of (9.11–7) also vanishes at these points, each contributes a double zero to $\mathbf{Ev}\, Z(p)$. But the denominator may well vanish; it will do so at $-\sigma_1$ if (and only if) Z_B also vanishes there, but this zero of the denominator will be simple, so that $\mathbf{Ev}\, Z(p)$ still has a simple zero at $-\sigma_1$, and the same will be true at $+\sigma_1$ (Problems 9-48, 9-62). If the design of this Brune network is based (as in § 9.08) on a zero of $\mathbf{Ev}\, Z(p)$, Z_A will remove one or two zeros at this point. The

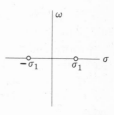

Fig. 9.11–H

inductor L_3 constitutes another Type-A section, but one with no effect on the zeros of $\mathbf{Ev}\, Z(p)$, for both it and Z_A become infinite at the same frequency.

The Brune network used here (in which L_2 is negative) would be realized by a pair of perfectly coupled inductors, as in Fig. 9.11–I. Since this network differs from what we have called a Type-C section only in the "polarity" of the mutual inductance, we shall now consider both

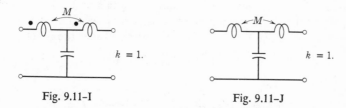

Fig. 9.11–I   Fig. 9.11–J

networks to be Type-C sections. By definition, then, a Type-C section is that shown in Fig. 9.11–J in which either polarity of coupling is permitted. With this definition and the discussion preceding it, we can now say that

> sections of Types A, B, and C are sufficient to remove all zeros of $\mathbf{Ev}\, Z(p)$ that lie on either axis.   (9.11–9)

These zeros may generally be removed in a variety of different sequences, leading to different networks, but in no case is it necessary to use a resistor in this part of the realization.

If the zeros of the even part of the given $Z(p)$ are confined to the axes of the p plane, the three types of sections that we have developed are sufficient to reduce the impedance to a minimum-reactance impedance whose even part has no zeros, i.e., to a constant, a resistor. Hence,

if the zeros of the even part of a given (p-r) impedance function are confined to the real and imaginary axes, the function can be realized by an L-C network (made up of sections of Types A, B, and C) terminated in one resistor. (9.11–10)

Figure 9.11–E illustrates the realization. A corresponding statement holds for p-r admittance functions [cf. (9.11–4) and the discussion preceding it], and if an ideal transformer is permitted, the single resistor may have arbitrary resistance (Fig. 9.11–F).

To return to our general case, we have left, after using sections of these three types to remove axial zeros of $\mathrm{Ev}\, Z(p)$, an impedance function whose even part vanishes only at complex points located off the axes. Although resistance removal would move these zeros to points on the axes, our immediate objective is a realization that uses only one (final) resistor. We must find a method of removing complex zeros of $\mathrm{Ev}\, Z(p)$ without using resistance—and do this our present types of network cannot.

9.12 Pseudo-p-r functions again

To demonstrate that these complex zeros of $\mathrm{Ev}\, Z(p)$ can be removed without using resistance, an additional type of network "section" must be devised. But it is helpful, before discussing this network, to develop the properties of pseudo-p-r functions further than was done in § 9.04.

Let $Z(p)$ be a (rational) p-r function and consider the function

$$F(p) = Z(p) - Z_R(p) \qquad (9.12–1)$$

in which

$$Z_R(p) = \frac{S_0}{p} + \sum_{k=1}^{M} \frac{S_k p}{p^2 + \omega_k{}^2} + L_0 p \qquad (9.12–2)$$

is a general reactance function; i.e., those of the numbers

$$S_0, S_1, S_2, \cdots, \omega_1{}^2, \omega_2{}^2, \cdots, L_0 \qquad (9.12–3)$$

that are not zero are real and positive (there may be as many as $2M + 2$ poles in Z_R). To avoid trivial cases we further require that if any pole of $Z(p)$ coincides with a pole of $Z_R(p)$, the net residue of $F(p)$ there be negative; otherwise these (imaginary) poles of $Z_R(p)$ would effectively be swallowed up in $Z(p)$ and might just as well not be in $Z_R(p)$. At infinity we impose the corresponding requirement, $Z'(\infty) < L_0$ if $L_0 \neq 0$.

Now $F(p)$ is not p-r, for it contains improper imaginary poles. It does have many of the properties of p-r functions, however; in fact, following the items in our test for positive reality in (5.13–5) we observe that

1. $F(p)$ has real coefficients and is therefore real when p is real;

2(a). at infinity $F(p)$ may be regular or may behave as $L_\infty p$, in which L_∞ is negative;

2(b). $F(p)$ is analytic in the right half plane;

2(c). the imaginary poles of $F(p)$ are simple, with real residues; such a residue is positive if the pole does not appear in Z_R, and negative if the pole does appear in Z_R;

3. Re $F(j\omega) \geq 0$.   (9.12–4)

It is only in its imaginary poles (including that at infinity) that $F(p)$ fails to meet the requirements of positive reality. These are not all of the proper kind, so that $F(p)$ is not p-r and may have right-half-plane zeros— and the number of these that $F(p)$ has will be of great interest to us.

Let p trace out again the contour C_1 of Fig. 9.04–A. The mapping of C_1 in the plane of $F(p)$ is a curve C_2, describable much as in § 9.04. All of the straight portion of C_1 maps to the imaginary axis or to points in the right half plane, except for some of the imaginary poles of $F(p)$. Around each imaginary pole we imagine a small indentation to the right half plane, as in Fig. 9.04–C(a). These small semicircles map into infinite semicircles (traversed in the counterclockwise direction), in the right half plane if the residue of $F(p)$ is positive, in the left half plane if the residue is negative. At all imaginary poles of $F(p)$ due to $Z(p)$ alone (where Z_R has no pole), the mapping is in the right half plane; at all such poles where Z_R has a pole, the mapping is in the left half plane; included in one of these categories is the pole at infinity if present. If N is the order of the function $Z_R(p)$, then there will be N such left-half-plane large semicircles. Consequently the mapping is as shown in Fig. 9.04–B: it lies entirely on the imaginary axis or in the right half plane, except for the portion represented by the large semicircle in the left half plane, which is traversed N times, always in the counterclockwise direction.

We must now examine the mapping in the vicinity of any zeros of $F(p)$ that occur on C_1, i.e., for imaginary values of p. Since $Z_R(p)$ is odd, $\mathbf{Re}\, Z_R(j\omega) = 0$ and these zeros can occur only when $\mathbf{Re}\, Z(j\omega) = 0$. If we designate such a zero of $F(p)$ as $j\omega_0$, and write

$$Z(j\omega) = R(\omega) + jX(\omega),$$
$$Z_R(j\omega) = 0 + jX_R(\omega),$$ (9.12–5)

then $R(\omega_0) = 0$, $R'(\omega_0) = 0$ (for Z is p-r), and $X_R(\omega_0) = X(\omega_0)$. Now

$$F'(j\omega_0) = Z'(j\omega_0) - Z_R'(j\omega_0)$$
$$= X'(\omega_0) - X_R'(\omega_0).$$ (9.12–6)

Unfortunately the simple relation (9.04–18) does not here show that
$F'(j\omega_0)$ is positive, for $X_R'(\omega_0) \neq X(\omega_0)/\omega_0$. In fact, it is possible that
$F'(j\omega_0)$ is negative, or even zero. A small indentation in C_1 made at such
an imaginary zero of $F(p)$, as in Fig. 9.04–C(a), will map into a small
semicircle about the origin, but it may lie in the right half plane as in
Fig. 9.12–A(a) [if $F'(j\omega_0)$ is positive], or it may lie in the left half plane

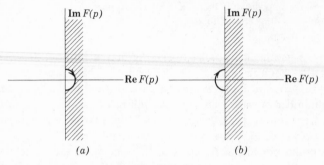

Fig. 9.12–A

as in Fig. 9.12–A(b) [if $F'(j\omega_0)$ is negative]. It will be traversed in the
clockwise direction in either case. If $F'(j\omega_0) = 0$, then the zero is multiple
and the mapping will consist of at least a full circle, but still traversed
in the clockwise direction. If $F(p)$
has a zero at infinity, corresponding
analysis shows that the large semicircle in C_1 maps similarly.

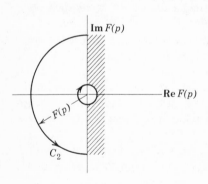

Fig. 9.12–B

Our conclusion is that the mapping
of C_1 [properly indented to the
right around any zeros and poles
that $F(p)$ has on the imaginary axis]
consists of a left-half-plane large
semicircle traversed N times in the
counterclockwise direction, of sections lying entirely in the right half
plane or on the imaginary axis,
and possibly of small left-half-plane
semicircles about the origin traversed in the clockwise direction. Figure
9.12–B sums this up. The number of positive revolutions of the vector $F(p)$
about the origin is evidently N if there are no small left-half-plane semicircles; but if such are present, then the net number of revolutions is less
than N. Since $F(p)$ has no right-half-plane poles, it follows that

$$F(p) \text{ has } at \text{ } most \text{ } N \text{ right-half-plane zeros,} \qquad (9.12\text{–}7)$$

N being the order of $Z_R(p)$. This result should be contrasted with the precise result (9.04–21); the introduction of additional elements in Z_R alters the conclusion considerably. But (9.12–7) will be sufficient for our purposes. The statement still holds if our restrictions are relaxed [some of the numbers in (9.12–3) allowed to be negative, or poles in $Z(p)$ allowed to overcome those in Z_R], but with the bars so let down it is less important.

We shall also need a complement to (9.12–7) which follows from the same kind of argument. Let $Z(p)$ be a (rational) p-r function as before, but now let Z_R, expressed by (9.12–2), be only *formally* a reactance function; i.e., those of the numbers (9.12–3) that are present are still to be real but not necessarily positive. Again let N be the order of $Z_R(p)$ and consider the function $F(p)$ defined by (9.12–1). A review of the reasoning above shows that

if $F(p)$ has N right-half-plane zeros, then the numbers in (9.12–3) are *positive*.   (9.12–8)

For if S_0, L_0, or any of the S_k were negative (the $\omega_k{}^2$ being positive), then the number of left-half-plane large semicircles in C_2 would be less than N; if an $\omega_k{}^2$ were negative, then the two corresponding poles would not lie on the imaginary axis and would contribute no left-half-plane large semicircles, though $F(p)$ would have *one* right-half-plane pole. In any case $F(p)$ cannot have N right-half-plane zeros unless all N of the numbers (9.12–3) are positive. In other words,

if $F(p)$ has N right-half-plane zeros, then $Z_R(p)$ is a reactance function and represents a realizable *L-C* driving-point impedance of order N.   (9.12–9)

Corollary conclusions can be drawn for special cases, of which one in particular will be useful. Suppose that Z_R has the special form

$$Z_R(p) = \frac{S'p}{p^2 + \omega_1{}^2} + Lp.   (9.12\text{–}10)$$

Here $N = 3$ and we know that $F(p)$ has at most three right-half-plane zeros. By the arguments above we can also say that

if $F(p)$ has (at least) two right-half-plane zeros, and $\omega_1{}^2$ is known to be positive, then S' is positive, but L may be positive, negative, or zero. (9.12–11)

In addition, we can now say something (with the assumptions above) about the behavior of $F(p)$ at imaginary zeros of $F(p)$. If $L \leq 0$, then C_2 must contain the large semicircle, traversed twice and only twice; and since $F(p)$ has two right-half-plane zeros there can be no left-half-plane small semicircles in C_2, for they would reduce the number of right-half-plane zeros below two. Consequently, C_2 passes the origin to the *right* at all imaginary zeros of $F(p)$, these zeros are simple, and at them $F'(p)$ is real and positive. On the other hand, if $L > 0$, then C_2 may traverse the large semicircle thrice; there might be *one* left-half-plane small semi-circle in C_2 for then $F(p)$ would still have two right-half-plane zeros. This could occur only at the origin and we rule it out by requiring further that either $Z(0) \neq 0$ or that if $Z(0) = 0$ then $Z'(0) > Z_R'(0)$ [and of course $Z'(0) > 0$, for $Z(p)$ is p-r]. There will then be no left-half-plane small semicircles in C_2, the imaginary zeros of $F(p)$ will again be simple, and $F'(p)$ real and positive thereat. To summarize, we have found that in this special case,

all the imaginary zeros of $F(p)$ are simple and at them $F'(p)$ is real and positive.   (9.12–12)

We now have apparatus sufficient to proceed to the one-resistor realization.

9.13 One-resistor realization

To show that realization with only one resistor is always possible, it remains only to devise an *L-C* network that realizes the complex zeros of **Ev** $Z(p)$ with the aid of only one resistor (in the whole network). Such an additional type of "section" was contributed by Darlington (DA 1); it can be developed along lines similar to our previous work. Somewhat later alternative developments have been made by Cauer (CA 2), Leroy (LE 2), Ville (VI 1), and others.

Suppose that a p-r impedance function $Z_0(p)$ is in hand, and that **Ev** $Z_0(p)$ has a zero at the point $p_0 = \sigma_0 + j\omega_0$, in the first quadrant (i.e., $\sigma_0 > 0$ and $\omega_0 > 0$); see Fig. 9.13–A. (Then three symmetrically placed zeros also occur, but we need not deal with these for the moment.)

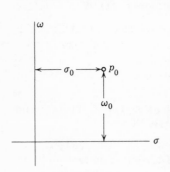

Fig. 9.13–A

Prompted by our previous experience, we shall remove a small reactance network Z_a, such that $Z_a(p_0) = Z_0(p_0)$. This will create a zero of the remaining impedance function at p_0 (and probably at other symmetric points also). Then we hope to remove these poles of admittance in a reactance network Z_b, and finally to remove some poles remaining in the impedance, in the reactance network Z_c. (See Fig. 9.13–B.) All this we hope to do within the restrictions of physical realizability of the resultant T network and of removal of the zero of **Ev** $Z_0(p)$ on which the process is based, with consequent reduction in order of the impedance function. That is, we expect the network composed of Z_a, Z_b, and Z_c to be realizable (though very likely only with the aid of perfectly coupled inductors), and the impedance Z_3 to be p-r, of order less than that of Z_0, and that $\text{Ev } Z_3(p)$ will lack the zero at p_0.

Our first concern is with Z_a. This cannot be a simple inductor now, for $Z_0(p_0)$ is generally a complex number, with angle different from that of p_0. To meet the requirement

$$Z_a(p_0) = Z_0(p_0) \qquad (9.13\text{--}1)$$

we must use at least an inductor and a capacitor in Z_a. These can be shown to suffice, if an ideal transformer is also used (Problem 9-77);

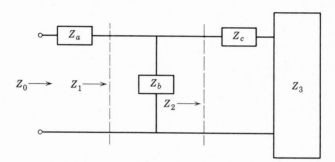

Fig. 9.13–B

generally two elements are not enough to accomplish the realization without the ideal transformer. But we shall avoid discussion of this by postponing specific statement as to the nature of $Z_a(p)$—except, of course, that it is an odd function (with real coefficients), for there is to be no resistance in this T network. The question of realizability we shall answer in due course. If Z_a is so designed that (9.13–1) holds, then

$$Z_1(p) = Z_0(p) - Z_a(p) \qquad (9.13\text{--}2)$$

has a zero at p_0, presumably simple. Since only real coefficients are involved, $Z_1(p)$ also has a zero at the conjugate point, $\bar{p}_0$. Consequently, the admittance function

$$Y_1 = \frac{1}{Z_1} = \frac{1}{Z_0 - Z_a} \qquad (9.13\text{--}3)$$

has poles at these points and may be written

$$Y_1 = \frac{K_0}{p - p_0} + \frac{\bar{K}_0}{p - \bar{p}_0} + Y_d \qquad (9.13\text{--}4)$$

in which Y_d represents the admittance remaining after extraction of these two poles. The residue K_0 is given by

$$K_0 = [Z_1'(p_0)]^{-1} = \left[\frac{d}{dp}(Z_0 - Z_a)\right]^{-1}_{p=p_0} \tag{9.13-5}$$

Suppose that these two poles are removed in Z_b, along with whatever others may later be found necessary or useful. Then Z_b has zeros at p_0 and $\bar{p}_0$, and

$$Y_b = \frac{1}{Z_b} = \frac{K_0}{p - p_0} + \frac{\bar{K}_0}{p - \bar{p}_0} + Y_e \tag{9.13-6}$$

in which Y_e represents the additional terms in Y_b, and

$$K_0 = [Z_b'(p_0)]^{-1}. \tag{9.13-7}$$

We have now the relations

$$Z_0(p_0) = Z_a(p_0) + Z_b(p_0) \tag{9.13-8}$$

and

$$Z_0'(p_0) = Z_a'(p_0) + Z_b'(p_0) \tag{9.13-9}$$

which are required to hold if our process is to succeed. These two equations are merely variations of (9.13–1) and (9.13–5), in which (9.13–7) and the fact that Z_b has a zero at p_0 have been used.

We may temporarily limit our discussion to the impedance function

$$z_{11}(p) = Z_a(p) + Z_b(p) \tag{9.13-10}$$

which is to be an *odd* function (no resistance is to be used). It must also be p-r, for if the T network is to be realizable, then z_{11} represents the driving-point impedance of this (L-C) T network when the connection to its termination Z_3 is broken. In other words, $z_{11}(p)$ is to be a reactance function that matches the datum function at p_0—and the derivatives must also agree there:

$$\begin{aligned} z_{11}(p_0) &= Z_0(p_0), \\ z_{11}'(p_0) &= Z_0'(p_0). \end{aligned} \tag{9.13-11}$$

We shall now look for the simplest reactance function $z_{11}(p)$ that satisfies the two equations in (9.13–11). It must be of order four at least (the corresponding network must contain at least four elements), for the real and imaginary parts of $Z_0(p_0)$ and of $Z_0'(p_0)$ constitute four requirements to be met. At the origin we certainly do not want a zero, for if $z_{11}(0) = 0$, then the input impedance Z_0 in Fig. 9.13–B will also vanish at the origin, and we want no such restriction on Z_0. The frequency pattern of z_{11} must then be as shown in Fig. 9.13–C, and

$$z_{11}(p) = H \frac{p^4 + a_2 p^2 + a_0}{p(p^2 + \omega_1{}^2)} \qquad (9.13\text{–}12)$$

$$= \frac{S}{p} + \frac{S'p}{p^2 + \omega_1{}^2} + Lp \qquad (9.13\text{–}13)$$

in which the form shown in Fig. 9.13–D is assumed (since z_{11} is eventually

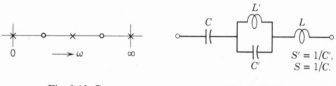

Fig. 9.13–C   Fig. 9.13–D

to be split into the series combination of Z_a and Z_b). The element values in $z_{11}(p)$ are now to be determined, according to (9.13–11), by

$$z_{11}(p_0) = \frac{S}{p_0} + \frac{S'p_0}{p_0{}^2 + \omega_1{}^2} + Lp_0 = Z_0(p_0),$$

$$\qquad (9.13\text{–}14)$$

$$z_{11}'(p_0) = -\frac{S}{p_0{}^2} - \frac{S(p_0{}^2 - \omega_1{}^2)}{(p_0{}^2 + \omega_1{}^2)^2} + L = Z_0'(p_0),$$

which amount to four equations in the four (real) unknowns S, S', L, $\omega_1{}^2$, in terms of $Z_0(p_0)$ and $Z_0'(p_0)$ as data. Now these four numbers, so determined, must be positive. For if we let

$$F(p) = Z_0(p) - z_{11}(p) \qquad (9.13\text{–}15)$$

then

$$F(p_0) = 0 \quad \text{and} \quad F'(p_0) = 0 \qquad (9.13\text{–}16)$$

because we have so stipulated. Hence $F(p)$ has at least a double zero at p_0, and another double zero at $\bar{p}_0$, i.e., at least four right-half-plane zeros. But by (9.12–8) it follows then that S, S', $\omega_1{}^2$, and L are all *positive* numbers and that $z_{11}(p)$ represents a reactance function, realizable, for example, in the form shown in Fig. 9.13–D.

We turn now to $Z_a(p)$, for which we assume the form shown in Fig. 9.13–E (if two elements should suffice for the network we want in special cases, our analysis will reveal this; we do not consider other possibilities for Z_a). Since this is a part of z_{11}, the resonant frequency of L_1 and C_1 we take to be ω_1 as calculated from (9.13–14); i.e.,

$$\frac{1}{L_1 C_1} = \omega_1{}^2, \qquad (9.13\text{–}17)$$

and since $\omega_1{}^2$ has been shown to be positive, L_1 and C_1 must have the same sign. We shall now determine the values of the elements in Z_a and investigate their individual signs.

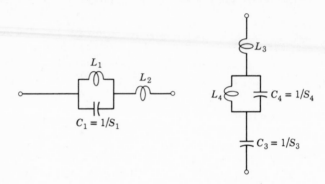

Fig. 9.13–E   Fig. 9.13–F

From Fig. 9.13–E we have

$$Z_a(p) = \frac{S_1 p}{p^2 + \omega_1{}^2} + L_2 p \qquad (9.13\text{–}18)$$

and from (9.13–1)

$$Z_a(p_0) = \frac{S_1 p_0}{p_0{}^2 + \omega_1{}^2} + L_2 p_0 = Z_0(p_0) \qquad (9.13\text{–}19)$$

which represents two equations in the two (real) unknowns S_1 and L_2, in terms of $Z_0(p_0)$ as data. Now the function

$$F(p) = Z_0(p) - Z_a(p) \qquad (9.13\text{–}20)$$

has two right-half-plane zeros (one at p_0 and one at $\bar{p}_0$), $\omega_1{}^2$ is positive, and consequently, by (9.12–11), S_1 is positive (though L_2 may be positive, negative, or zero). By (9.13–17) L_1 is also positive.

Let us turn our attention now to Z_b. From our discussion of $z_{11}(p)$ and the relation (9.13–10) we know that the form of Z_b should still be that of Fig. 9.13–D. In particular let Fig. 9.13–F represent Z_b. Since

$$Z_b(p) = z_{11}(p) - Z_a(p), \qquad (9.13\text{–}21)$$

we have

$$S_3 = S,$$
$$S_4 = S' - S_1,$$
$$L_3 = L - L_2, \tag{9.13-22}$$
$$\frac{1}{L_4 C_4} = \omega_1{}^2,$$

in which at least S_3 and $\omega_1{}^2$ are positive. As to the signs of S_4 and L_3, we can reason as follows.

By (9.12–7) we know that $Z_b(p)$ can have at most three right-half-plane zeros (for z_{11} is p-r and Z_a has only three poles). Now Z_b has two such zeros (at p_0 and $\bar{p}_0$) so that these zeros must be simple (else Z_b would have four right-half-plane zeros); hence

$$Z_b'(p_0) \neq 0. \tag{9.13-23}$$

Further, $Z_b(p)$ is odd and of order four, so that it can have only two right-half-plane zeros (the other two must be symmetrically located in the left half plane, at $-p_0$ and $-\bar{p}_0$). Now S_4 cannot be positive (or zero), for then we should have

$$Z_b(p) = \left(\frac{S_3}{p} + \frac{S_4 p}{p^2 + \omega_1{}^2} \right) + L_3 p \tag{9.13-24}$$

in which the parenthesis represents a reactance function, and Z_b could have at most one right-half-plane zero (L_3 then being negative). Hence S_4 is negative. If we rewrite (9.13–24) as

$$Z_b = - \left[\left(\frac{-S_4 p}{p_2 + \omega_1{}^2} \right) - \left(\frac{S_3}{p} + L_3 p \right) \right] \tag{9.13-25}$$

we see also that L_3 must be positive, else Z_b could have at most one right-half-plane zero. To summarize, we have found that in Z_b, L_3 and C_3 are positive, while L_4 and C_4 are negative. We can also write

$$Z_b(p) = \frac{S_3}{p} + \frac{S_4 p}{p^2 + \omega_1{}^2} + L_3 p = L_3 \frac{p^4 + a_2 p^2 + a_0}{p(p^2 + \omega_1{}^2)} \tag{9.13-26}$$

and

$$Y_b(p) = \frac{1}{Z_b(p)} = \frac{p(p^2 + \omega_1{}^2)}{L_3(p^4 + a_2 p^2 + a_0)}$$

$$= \frac{K_0}{p - p_0} + \frac{\bar{K}_0}{p - \bar{p}_0} + \frac{K_0}{p + p_0} + \frac{\bar{K}_0}{p + \bar{p}_0}. \tag{9.13-27}$$

We return now to our original plan, to develop $Z_0(p)$ in the manner shown in Fig. 9.13–B. The first small network Z_a we have determined to have the form shown in Fig. 9.13–D, with element values determined by (9.13–14) and (9.13–19), in which L_1 and C_1 are positive, while L_2 may have either sign or be zero. On removing Z_a we have left

$$Z_1(p) = Z_0(p) - Z_a(p) \qquad (9.13\text{--}2)$$

which has zeros at p_0 and $\bar{p}_0$. These zeros are simple, for

$$Z_1'(p_0) = Z_0'(p_0) - Z_a'(p_0) = z_{11}'(p_0) - Z_a'(p_0)$$
$$= Z_b'(p_0) \neq 0 \qquad (9.13\text{--}28)$$

by virtue of (9.13–11), (9.13–10), and (9.13–23). We now use these two zeros of Z_1, exactly as in the Brune process, to remove elements in shunt. Much as in the Brune process, however, Z_1 also has zeros at the negatives of these points. For $\mathbf{Ev}\, Z_0(-p_0) = 0$ since $\mathbf{Ev}\, Z_0(p_0) = 0$ and this function is even, and $Z_a(p)$ is odd, so that

$$Z_1(-p_0) = Z_0(-p_0) - Z_a(-p_0)$$
$$= -\mathbf{Od}\, Z_0(p_0) + Z_a(p_0)$$
$$= -Z_1(p_0) = 0. \qquad (9.13\text{--}29)$$

We shall accordingly attempt to remove all four of these zeros of Z_1 (Fig. 9.13–G) in a shunt branch.

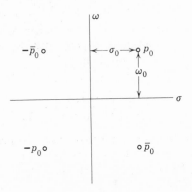

Fig. 9.13–G

The residue of $Y_1 = 1/Z_1$ at p_0 we have designated

$$K_0 = \frac{1}{Z_1'(p_0)} = \left[\frac{d}{dp}(Z_0 - Z_a) \right]_{p=p_0}^{-1} = \frac{1}{Z_b'(p_0)}; \qquad (9.13\text{--}30)$$

this is a (generally complex) number easily calculated from the datum function and our previously computed $Z_a(p)$, which we also write as

$$K_0 = K_r + jK_i. \qquad (9.13\text{--}31)$$

The residue of Y_1 at $\bar{p}_0$ will be $\bar{K}_0 = K_r - jK_i$. Note that the residues of Y_1 at the left-half-plane poles are K_0 at $-p_0$ and $\bar{K}_0$ at $-\bar{p}_0$ if the zero of Ev $Z_0(p)$ at p_0 is of multiplicity two or more, but not if the zero is simple. We now write

$$\frac{1}{Z_b} = Y_b = \frac{K_0}{p - p_0} + \frac{\bar{K}_0}{p - \bar{p}_0} + \frac{K_0}{p + p_0} + \frac{\bar{K}_0}{p + \bar{p}_0} \quad (9.13\text{–}32)$$

as the admittance to be removed, and observe that it is exactly the same function $Z_b(p)$ as that discussed earlier in connection with $z_{11}(p)$. Hence the previously determined network Z_b is the shunt branch we want to remove. If the zero of Ev $Z_0(p)$ at p_0 is multiple, then in

$$Y_2 = Y_1 - Y_b \quad (9.13\text{–}33)$$

there will be no poles at $-p_0$ and $-\bar{p}_0$; if the zero is simple, then Y_2 still has poles at these points. In any event the poles at p_0 and $\bar{p}_0$ are removed (in Y_b) and Y_2 has no poles at these two points.

We have now determined Z_a and Z_b, and found that L_4 and C_4 are negative and that L_2 may be negative (which elements we hope to realize by some sort of transformer connection). Next we consider Z_2, and thus Z_c and Z_3 (Fig. 9.13–B). For convenience we assume that $Z_0(p)$ has no pole at infinity, or at $\pm j\omega_1$, and that either $Z_0(0) \neq 0$ or if $Z_0(0) = 0$ then $Z_0'(0) > Z_a'(0)$, though these restrictions are not necessary. We now examine

$$Y_2(p) = Y_1 - Y_b = \frac{1}{Z_0 - Z_a} - Y_b \quad (9.13\text{–}34)$$

and ask first, is it p-r? Following the standard test (5.13–5) we observe first that Y_2 has the required real coefficients, for nowhere have we removed any but real elements.

Second, we investigate the behavior of $Y_2(p)$ at infinity. This depends on whether L_2 (in Z_a) is positive or not. If $L_2 > 0$ then the important terms in the behavior at infinity are given by

$$Y_2 \to \left(\frac{1}{Z_0(\infty) - L_2 p} - \frac{1}{L_3 p} \right) \to -(\Gamma_2 + \Gamma_3)\frac{1}{p} = \frac{\Gamma_5}{p} \quad (9.13\text{–}35)$$

in which $\Gamma_2 = 1/L_2 > 0$, $\Gamma_3 = 1/L_3 > 0$, $\Gamma_5 = 1/L_5 = -(\Gamma_2 + \Gamma_3) < 0$. This is the behavior of a negative inductor, but our experience with the corresponding case in the Brune procedure is ground for hope that this will still be realizable. If $L_2 < 0$ then again (9.13–35) applies, and

$$\Gamma_5 = -\left(\frac{1}{L_2} + \frac{1}{L_3} \right) = \left(-\frac{L_2 L_3}{L_2 + L_3} \right) > 0 \quad (9.13\text{–}36)$$

for $L_2 < 0$, $L_3 > 0$, and $(L_2 + L_3) = L > 0$ by our analysis of $z_{11}(p)$. In either case

$$\Gamma_2 + \Gamma_3 + \Gamma_5 = 0 \qquad (9.13\text{–}37)$$

which corresponds to the relation $(\Gamma_1 + \Gamma_2 + \Gamma_3 = 0)$ of the Brune procedure and is due to the fact that $Z_0(p)$ has no pole at infinity. And if $L_2 = 0$, then

$$Y_2 \to \frac{1}{Z_0(\infty)} \qquad (9.13\text{–}38)$$

which is a real, positive number (or else Y_2 has a pole of the proper kind there). Notice that in each of the three cases

$$(L_2 + L_3) > 0 \qquad \text{and} \qquad (L_3 + L_5) > 0, \qquad (9.13\text{–}39)$$

the latter relation being derivable from (9.13–37).

Consider now whether $Y_2(p)$ has any right-half-plane poles. If $L_2 > 0$ then the function

$$Z_1(p) = Z_0(p) - \left(\frac{S_1 p}{p^2 + \omega_1{}^2} + L_2 p \right) \qquad (9.13\text{–}40)$$

has at most three right-half-plane zeros and $Y_1(p)$ has at most three right-half-plane poles. There are certainly two poles (at p_0 and $\bar{p}_0$) but these are removed in Y_b so that $Y_2(p)$ has at most one right-half-plane pole. Because of our assumptions as to the behavior of $Z_0(p)$ near the origin, by an argument similar to that leading up to (9.12–12), Y_2 definitely has one right-half-plane pole, at some (real, positive) point σ_1. Further, $Z_1'(\sigma_1) < 0$; this may be shown by drawing a sketch much like Fig. 9.04–D, to show the two parts of Z_1 exhibited in (9.13–40). If $L_2 \leqq 0$ then $Z_1(p)$ has at most two right-half-plane zeros, the corresponding poles in Y_1 are removed in Y_b, and Y_2 has no right-half-plane poles.

By (9.12–12), which applies here, all the imaginary poles of $Y_1(p)$ are simple, with real, positive residues. These poles appear unchanged in Y_2, so that the imaginary poles of $Y_2(p)$ are of the proper kind for positive reality.

Finally we observe that

$$\mathbf{Re}\ Y_2(j\omega) = \mathbf{Re}\ Y_1(j\omega) - \mathbf{Re}\ Y_b(j\omega) = \mathbf{Re}\ Y_1(j\omega), \qquad (9.13\text{–}41)$$

that

$$\mathbf{Re}\ Z_1(j\omega) = \mathbf{Re}\ Z_0(j\omega) - \mathbf{Re}\ Z_a(j\omega) = \mathbf{Re}\ Z_0(j\omega) \geqq 0, \qquad (9.13\text{–}42)$$

and hence that

$$\mathbf{Re}\ Y_2(j\omega) \geqq 0. \qquad (9.13\text{–}43)$$

In sum, our testing of $Y_2(p)$ for positive reality shows that if $L_2 \leqq 0$, then Y_2 is p-r. But if $L_2 > 0$, then Y_2 has a "negative" pole at infinity and a right-half-plane zero. Then (9.04–44) applies and we can write

$$Y_2(p) = \frac{1}{Z(p) + L_5 p} \qquad (9.13\text{–}44)$$

in which $Z(p)$ is p-r and L_5 is real and negative.

Our progress toward accomplishing the realization of Fig. 9.13–B is: Z_a has been found (Fig. 9.13–E), as has Z_b (Fig. 9.13–F), and $Z_2(p)$ has been shown to be either p-r or the sum of a p-r function and the impedance of a negative inductor. From Z_2 we now remove Z_c. For its form we expect the same as that of Z_a, and we let Fig. 9.13–H represent Z_c, removing in it the poles of Z_2 at $\pm j\omega_1$ and infinity (if present).

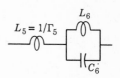

Fig. 9.13–H

We have already found L_5 in our discussion of the behavior of $Y_2(p)$ at infinity:

$$\text{if } L_2 > 0, \ \Gamma_5 = -(\Gamma_2 + \Gamma_3) < 0,$$
$$\text{if } L_2 = 0, \ L_5 = 0, \qquad (9.13\text{–}45)$$
$$\text{if } L_2 < 0, \ \Gamma_5 = -(\Gamma_2 + \Gamma_3) > 0.$$

We can easily determine L_6 and C_6 by a similar examination of the behavior of $Y_2(p)$ or, better, of $Z_2(p)$ at $\pm j\omega_1$. Since $Z_0(p)$ has no poles at $\pm j\omega_1$, $Z_1(p) = Z_0 - Z_a$ does have them; and since $Z_b(p)$ has such poles, so also must $Z_2(p)$. These poles in $Z_2(p)$ must be simple, with real positive residues, for (except possibly for L_5) $Z_2(p)$ is p-r; hence S_6 and L_6 are positive (and resonate at the frequency ω_1). In the vicinity of $\pm j\omega_1$ we have

$$Z_0(p) = \left(S_1 + \frac{S_4 S_6}{S_4 + S_6} \right) \frac{p}{p^2 + \omega_1{}^2} + \cdots \qquad (9.13\text{–}46)$$

whence, because $Z_0(j\omega_1)$ is finite,

$$\frac{S_1 S_4 + S_4 S_6 + S_6 S_1}{S_4 + S_6} = 0 \qquad (9.13\text{–}47)$$

or

$$S_1 S_4 + S_4 S_6 + S_6 S_1 = 0.$$

Alternatively,

$$C_1 + C_4 + C_6 = 0 \qquad (9.13\text{–}48)$$

so that

$$C_6 = -(C_1 + C_4). \qquad (9.13\text{–}49)$$

From (9.13–46) we have

$$(S_4 + S_6) = -\frac{S_4 S_6}{S_1} > 0 \qquad (9.13\text{–}50)$$

because of the known signs of the individual S's. Similarly, or from the discussion of $z_{11}(p)$,

$$(S_1 + S_4) > 0. \qquad (9.13\text{–}51)$$

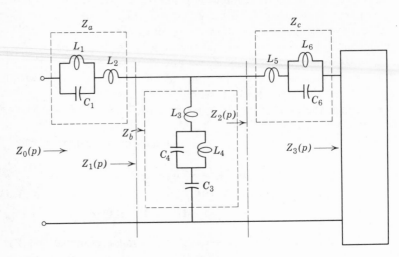

Fig. 9.13–I

We have now obtained the development shown in Fig. 9.13–I. We have yet to show that this is realizable, but before doing this, let us recapitulate. The design procedure for the T network is

to determine the elements of $z_{11} = Z_a + Z_b$ from (9.13–14), then those of Z_a from (9.13–19), then those of Z_b by subtraction ($Z_b = z_{11} - Z_a$), and finally those of Z_c from (9.13–45), (9.13–49), and $L_6 C_6 = 1/\omega_1{}^2$,   (9.13–52)

which is a tedious, but straightforward process. It is only of theoretical interest, so no detailed procedure or example will be given here. Of the resulting element values, all are positive except L_4, C_4, and L_2 or L_5. That this T network is actually realizable we shall demonstrate in a moment. The remaining impedance function $Z_3(p)$ is p-r, for $Z_2(p)$ was shown to be p-r except possibly for L_5, which has been removed. And $Z_3(p)$ is less complicated than $Z_0(p)$, i.e., a reduction has been accomplished, as Table 9.13–A shows. In it are listed (on the assumption that L_2 and L_5 are not zero) the orders of each of the immittance functions in the development, (a) when the zero of $\text{Ev } Z_0(p)$ at p_0 is multiple and (b) when it is simple.   [If $\text{Ev } Z_0(p_0) \neq 0$ the development is still possible, but no reduction in order is achieved.]   If $L_2 = L_5 = 0$, the orders in the second and third lines are less by one than those shown in Table 9.13–A, but Z_3 still has the order shown.

Table 9.13–A

Order

Function	(a)	(b)
Z_0	n	n
$\left.\begin{array}{l} Z_1 \\ Y_1 \end{array}\right\}$	$n + 3$	$n + 3$
$\left.\begin{array}{l} Y_2 \\ Z_2 \end{array}\right\}$	$n - 1$	$n + 1$
Z_3	$n - 4$	$n - 2$

Furthermore, the T network has removed the zeros of $\text{Ev } Z_0(p)$ on which the development was based, for (Problem 9-75)

$$\text{Ev } Z_0(p) = -\frac{Z_b{}^2 E_3}{(E_2)^2 - (Z_b + O_2)^2} \tag{9.13–53}$$

in which

$$\begin{aligned} E_2 &= \text{Ev } Z_2(p), \\ O_2 &= \text{Od } Z_2(p), \\ E_3 &= \text{Ev } Z_3(p). \end{aligned} \tag{9.13–54}$$

Casual inspection of (9.13–53) suggests that these zeros of $\text{Ev } Z_0(p)$ are removed in Z_b and are not present in E_3; careful examination (Problem 9-75) shows that if the zeros of $\text{Ev } Z_0(p)$ are multiple, two are indeed removed by the T network at each of the points p_0, $\bar{p}_0$, $-p_0$, $-\bar{p}_0$ (eight in all)—while if the zeros are simple, this one zero is removed at each point (four in all).

Since Z_3 is realizable, and of order less than that of $Z_0(p)$, by four or two, definite progress has been made in the realization, if the T network is indeed realizable.   We shall now show that it is.

Our "realization" is now in the form shown generally in Fig. 9.13–B and in detail in Fig. 9.13–I.   In the T network are certain elements (L_4, C_4, probably L_2 or L_5) that are negative and themselves not realizable. The Brune expedient of using perfectly coupled inductors would take care of the small network L_2-L_3-L_5, though not of L_4 and C_4—but a similar device will. Suppose the T network Z_a-Z_b-Z_c to be enclosed in the box N of Fig. 9.13–J. There are probably many other networks equivalent to our T network in that the driving-point impedance remains $Z_0(p)$ when they are substituted for N in Fig. 9.13–J. The full discussion of this

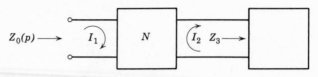

Fig. 9.13–J

possibility is evidently in the domain of two-terminal-pair network theory (to be discussed in Volume II), but we can by similar analysis easily demonstrate two possible equivalent networks which are here satisfactory. If a voltage source E_1 is connected to the input terminals in Fig. 9.13–J, loop currents I_1 and I_2 will flow, and the equations of analysis (2.07–1) are

$$Z_{11}I_1 + Z_{12}I_2 = E_1,$$
$$Z_{21}I_1 + Z_{22}I_2 = 0,$$

(9.13–55)

in which

$$Z_{11} = z_{11} = Z_a + Z_b,$$
$$Z_{12} = Z_{21} = -Z_b,$$
$$Z_{22} = Z_b + Z_c + Z_3,$$

(9.13–56)

and of course

$$Z_0(p) = \frac{E_1}{I_1}.$$

(9.13–57)

If some other network is substituted for N and analysis shows I_1 to be unaltered, then this network is equivalent for our purposes. Such a network may have more internal meshes, and the equations of analysis may be more than two in number; but we can manipulate them by eliminating the internal loop currents until only the two equations in (9.13–55) remain. If the new Z_{11}, Z_{12}, Z_{21}, Z_{22} are unchanged from the (old) values given in (9.13–56), then I_1 is unaltered and the new network is equivalent for our purposes to the old one.

As such a possible equivalent network, consider that shown in Fig. 9.13–K for which the element values are given by (9.13–58).

$$L_9 = L_2 + L_3 = I,$$

$$L_{10} = L_3 + L_5,$$

$$M_2 = L_3,$$

$$k_1{}^2 = \frac{L_3{}^2}{(L_2 + L_3)(L_3 + L_5)} = \frac{L_3}{L_3 + L_2 L_5(\Gamma_2 + \Gamma_3 + \Gamma_5)} = 1,$$

$$S_7 = S_1 + S_4 = S',$$

$$L_7 = \frac{S_7}{\omega_1{}^2} = \frac{S_1 + S_4}{\omega_1{}^2}, \qquad\qquad (9.13\text{--}58)$$

$$M_1 = \frac{S_4}{\omega_1{}^2},$$

$$L_8 = \frac{S_4{}^2}{\omega_1{}^2(S_1 + S_4)},$$

$$k_2{}^2 = \frac{M_1{}^2}{L_7 L_8} = 1.$$

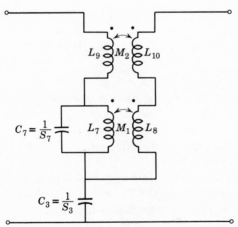

Fig. 9.13–K

On the basis of previous discussion we can say that L_9, L_{10}, M_2, S_7, L_7, L_8 are positive, that M_1 is negative, and that the coupling between inductors in each of the two cases is perfect. The genesis of such a network is more properly discussed in Volume II. But analysis of this network, terminated in Z_3 at the right-hand terminals, gives for the parameters of (9.13–55), on elimination of the internal loop currents,

$$Z_{11} = L_9 p + \frac{S_4 p}{p^2 + \omega_1{}^2} + \frac{S_3}{p},$$

$$Z_{12} = Z_{21} = L_3 p + \frac{S_4 p}{p^2 + \omega_1{}^2} + \frac{S_3}{p}, \qquad (9.13\text{–}59)$$

$$Z_{22} = L_{10} p + \frac{S_4{}^2}{(S_1 + S_4)^2} \times \frac{S_7 p}{(p^2 + \omega_1{}^2)} + \frac{S_3}{p} + Z_3,$$

which are exactly the same as those for the T network Z_a-Z_b-Z_c. This network is realizable, and is an equivalent then, in which two pairs of perfectly coupled inductors in effect realize the negative elements.

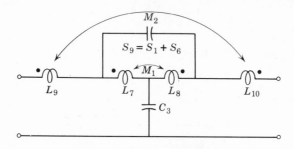

Fig. 9.13–L.   The Type-D Section.

Another equivalent is shown in Fig. 9.13–L. The only new element value is $S_9 = S_1 + S_6$, which is positive, for both S_1 and S_6 are positive. The coupling in each of the two cases is again perfect; indeed, the two pairs of coupled inductors are unchanged, as is C_3. The network is realizable and analysis gives the same set of "Z" parameters, so that this is actually equivalent.

The particular equivalent shown in Fig. 9.13–L we call a section of *Type D*, after Darlington (DA 1), and it completes a family of *L-C* "sections" sufficient for the one-resistor realization we have been discussing. For with its use we can remove complex zeros of **Ev** $Z(p)$ without using resistance, and we have already seen how to do this for purely real and purely imaginary zeros of **Ev** $Z(p)$. When all the zeros of **Ev** $Z(p)$ have been removed (with reduction by removal of reactance as appropriate) we have left nothing but a constant, in other words a resistor. And since this is the *only* resistor used, we can now state definitely that

any p-r function can be realized as a driving-point immittance by a network that uses only one resistor,   (9.13–60) sometimes called *Darlington's theorem*. Figure 9.09–B illustrates the realization schematically. This one resistor can be made to have an arbitrary value, of course, if an ideal transformer is permitted.

Our particular method of reaching conclusion (9.13–60) shows also that

any p-r function can be realized as a driving-point immittance by a cascade connection of (*L-C*) sections of Types A, B, C, D, terminated in a resistance.

$$(9.13–61)$$

These four building blocks are sufficient for the realization of any p-r function in a form that uses but one resistor. In general, however, the realization does employ perfectly coupled inductors. Yet we cannot say that these coupled inductors are necessary, for we have developed only one approach; presumably there are many other (equivalent) realizations, in other forms.

9.14 Recapitulation

In the maze of detail of the preceding sections one is apt to lose sight of the objectives and even to be confused about the results; a recapitulation is in order.

The Brune process accomplishes the realization of a p-r function, say $Z(p)$, as a driving-point impedance by removing first the imaginary poles, in other words, the excess reactance, i.e., **Od** $Z(p)$ is exploited as much as possible; then **Ev** $Z(p)$ is utilized, a resistor is removed, and the resistance reduced to minimum, which amounts to shifting some of the zeros of **Ev** $Z(p)$ to the imaginary axis. On these zeros is then based the removal of a "Brune network," a section of Type C. The impedance remaining is of reduced order, and the entire process is repeated until finally the

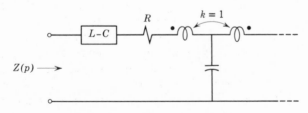

Fig. 9.14–A

realization is complete; Fig. 9.14–A shows the process, to be repeated as necessary. On the basis of this we made the important statement (9.05–27)

positive reality is *sufficient* for realizability of a driving-point immittance function

$$(9.14–1)$$

toward which we have been traveling for some time. The Brune process demonstrates this by actually accomplishing the realization, but it does not give the *only* realization.

For even in the Brune process itself variations are possible: imaginary poles (Type-A sections) need not be removed in the beginning, nor at any particular point, and this leads to a variety of networks in general. [Imaginary zeros (Type-B sections) will be removed automatically as degenerate Brune networks or Type-C sections.] Resistance must be removed at certain points, but here again there may be options. For we have found that the foundations of the Brune cycle is in the zeros of Ev $Z(p)$, and the Type-C section can remove *real* zeros of Ev $Z(p)$ also. Additional freedom may be had in removing these (if present at any stage) in place of the imaginary zeros, or by removing only enough resistance to create them. And by using Type-D sections, complex zeros of Ev $Z(p)$ may be removed without removing resistance at all. From this we found (§ 9.13) that

a realizable (p-r) driving-point immittance function can be realized with the use of only *one* resistor. (9.14–2)

We now see additional possibilities, for the zeros of Ev $Z(p)$ may be removed *in any sequence*, and they may be moved about at any stage by removing some resistance (up to a certain limit). These, together with the freedom of removing imaginary poles or not at any stage, show that the Brune–Darlington process in general will yield a number of different network realizations of any given p-r function, as a driving-point immittance. Some of these will require only one resistor, but all, in general, will make use of perfectly coupled inductors.

But there are many types of practical networks for which the sections of Types C and D are not necessary, which we shall find in Volume II to be a rather fortunate circumstance. If, for example, all the zeros of Ev $Z(p)$ are at the origin, or at infinity, or some are at the origin and some at infinity (none elsewhere), then no mutual inductance is required in this (one-resistor) realization; if some of the zeros lie elsewhere on the imaginary axis, then mutual inductance *may* be necessary in this particular realization, and if zeros lie off the imaginary axis, then *certainly* it will be.

To illustrate the utility of the Brune process in practical cases, suppose we are to realize a network whose (normalized) driving-point impedance is given by the p-r function

$$Z(p) = \frac{19.5p^4 + 33p^3 + 60p^2 + 84p + 24}{13p^3 + 22p^2 + 20p + 24} \quad \text{ohms.} \quad (9.14–3)$$

From this we obtain

$$\text{Ev } Z(p) = \frac{36(p^2 + 4)^2}{D(p)D(-p)} \qquad (9.14\text{--}4)$$

in which $D(p)$ represents the denominator of $Z(p)$. Since the zeros of $\text{Ev } Z(p)$ are all on the imaginary axis (two each at $\pm j2$, two at infinity) we expect that sections of Types A, B, and possibly C will suffice for a one-resistor realization, which we seek.

There are no real-frequency zeros or poles except the pole at infinity. This pole and the zeros of $\text{Ev } Z(p)$ are the clues to the various Brune realizations. Suppose we first remove the pole at infinity, leaving an impedance Z_1 whose even part has zeros at $\pm j2$ and at infinity. In fact, Z_1 itself has a zero at infinity which we next remove, leaving an impedance Z_2 whose even part has zeros at $\pm j2$. To this we apply the standard Brune process and thus complete the realization of Fig. 9.14–B. (Notice

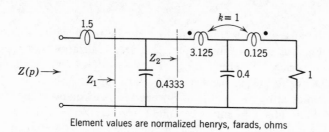

Element values are normalized henrys, farads, ohms

Fig. 9.14–B

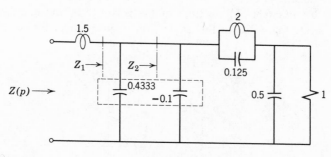

Fig. 9.14–C

that removing the zero of Z_1 at infinity amounts to a degenerate Brune cycle in which $L_1 = L_2 = L_3 = 0$.) As an alternative, we can remove the zeros of $\text{Ev } Z_2$ at $\pm j2$ by the dual Brune process, shown in Fig. 9.14–C. In this case the negative capacitance can be combined with the adjacent positive capacitance to give a single realizable capacitor. We obtain still another equivalent network if we go back to Z_1 and remove not the zero at infinity, but the zeros of Ev Z_1 at $\pm j2$ (by the Brune process), i.e., adopt a different sequence of removing the zeros of the even part. The result is shown in Fig. 9.14–D. Here the T form of the Type-C section

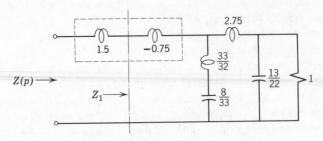

Fig. 9.14–D

is shown because it is possible here to combine the negative inductance with the adjacent positive inductance to give a realization not requiring mutual inductance. The remaining zero of Ev Z_1 (at infinity) is removed in the capacitor following the Type-C section. If these zeros of Ev Z_1 at $\pm j2$ are removed by the dual Brune process, no new network but that of Fig. 9.14–C results. Finally, we might try removal of the zeros of Ev $Z(p)$ directly without first removing the pole at infinity; but this leads again to the networks we have already found. In them we have three different realizations of (9.14–3), two of which require no mutual inductance, but use in effect only sections of Types A and B, and one resistor. These illustrate the utility of the Brune process in a practical case.

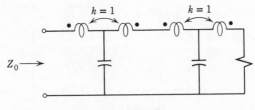

Fig. 9.14–E

Variations of the sequence in which the zeros of Ev $Z(p)$ are removed, and of the type of Brune process used (standard or dual), lead to a large number of possible realizations in more complicated cases. The impedance $Z_0(p)$ of the network shown in Fig. 9.14–E, for example, can thus be realized (on paper) in eight different forms. Some will require perfectly coupled inductors, some negative capacitors (realizable only with the aid of ideal transformers), and some both. But if the actual impedance to be realized has a pole or zero at infinity, previously removed and not shown, there might then be a number of practical realizations without the objectionable features in these eight. Additional realizations could be found by postponing the removal of the pole or zero at infinity. Further illustrations will be found in the problems, a large number of which must be worked to appreciate the power of the Brune process.

What this chapter has presented is (1) a proof that positive reality is sufficient (as well as necessary) for realizability of driving-point immittance functions, (2) a proof that realization can moreover be accomplished, if desired, with only one resistor, and (3) a method of realization that is often extremely useful, academic though it may be in the general case. There are other methods of realization; some we shall discuss in Chapter 10, though no complete study of all possible methods has yet been made.

We have now not only completed our study of driving-point-immittance *properties* (Chapters 4, 5, 8), the first step in synthesis (§ 1.01), but also have here a general method of *realization* (as well as the special methods of Chapters 6, 7), which is the third step in the synthesis process. The important second step, *approximation*, we shall postpone again while we look further into realization, in Chapter 10.

9.15 References

BA 3, BO 6, BR 4, BR 1, CA 2, DA 1, LE 2, RI 2, VI 1.

Brune's paper is one of those classics that ought to be read; Darlington's paper is of fundamental importance, but more difficult to read. Ville gives a very compact and readable treatment of one-resistor realization in ladder form.

PROBLEMS

9-1. Consider the four canonic realizations of *R-C* immittance functions; show that the standard Brune procedure leads to one of them. To which does the Brune procedure on the dual basis lead? Where are the frequencies of zero resistance?

All four realizations use a number of resistors, in general. Give a "canonic" form for one-resistor realization of *R-C* immittance functions based on the use of Type-C sections (cf. Prob. 8-127 for the location of the zeros of the even part). Repeat for *R-L* immittance functions, and for *L-C* functions.

9-2. To illustrate *R-L-C* network synthesis for which the simpler techniques of Chapters 6, 7, and 8 suffice, realize the following immittance functions, both as given and in dual form. Use in each case primarily the technique indicated; the symbols have their customary meanings.

(a) $R(\omega) = \dfrac{1}{1 + \omega^6}$, continued-fraction expansion (of impedance) with attention focused on low frequencies.

(b) $R(\omega) = \dfrac{\omega^6}{1 + \omega^6}$, continued-fraction expansion (of impedance) with attention focused on high frequencies.

(c) $Z(p) = \dfrac{288p^4 + 31.2p^3 + 76.6p^2 + 5.4p + 2}{96p^3 + 10.4p^2 + 12.2p + 1}$, partial-fraction expansion.

(d) $Z(p) = \dfrac{25p^3 + 19p^2 + 7p + 1}{6p^4 + 6p^3 + 6p^2 + 6p}$, reactance and susceptance removal.

(e) $Z(p) = \dfrac{4.8p^2 + 4.2p + 1.4}{0.48p^2 + 1.62p + 0.34}$, resistance and conductance removal.

(f) $Z(p) = \dfrac{6p^3 + 6.8p^2 + 4.82p + 1.12}{2p^2 + 2.2p + 1.2}$, all four reduction processes.

(g) $Z(p) = \dfrac{p^2 + 2p}{p^3 + 3p^2 + 2p + 4}$, susceptance removal, and R-C synthesis.

(h) $Z(p) = \dfrac{336p^3 + 876p^2 + 126.4p + 1.6}{144p^2 + 362.4p + 6}$, combinations (successive applications) of R-C and R-L synthesis.

(i) $Z(p) = \dfrac{p^6 + 3.158p^5 + 5.628p^4 + 5.020p^3 + 2.722p^2 + 0.6121p + 0.01687}{p^7 + 4.779p^6 + 11.326p^5 + 15.06p^4 + 11.23p^3 + 3.226p^2 + 0.2906p + 0.0066}$.

Show by counter examples drawn from the above cases that each of the methods mentioned is not of *general* utility (i.e., that additional realization techniques are necessary).

9-3. Let $Z(p)$ be a p-r function whose poles are located as shown. (The numbers indicate the orders of the poles.) What are the requirements on the

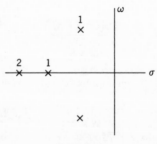

Prob. 9–3

coefficients in the partial-fraction expansion of $Z(p)$, that each pair of conjugate-pole terms and each real-pole term be individually realizable? In the complex-pole case, express the restriction on the residues geometrically by delimiting the area of a complex plane in which they must lie (cf. WE 8, WE 9). Does the positive reality of $Z(p)$ guarantee that these requirements will be met? What is the *general* utility of partial-fraction expansion in driving-point-immittance realization?

9-4. Consider a p-r function of order two,

$$Z(p) = K\frac{p^2 + a_1 p + a_0}{p^2 + b_1 p + b_0}.$$

(*a*) Show that its real-frequency resistance function $R(\omega)$ may have any of the general forms illustrated. [Use diagrams showing the locations of the zeros and poles of **Ev** $Z(p)$ as well as algebra.] Can you extend the series?

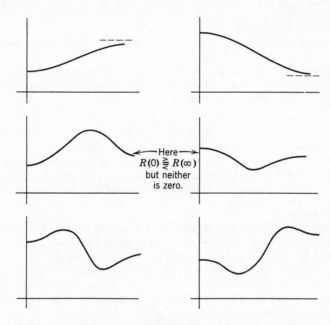

Prob. 9-4

(*b*) Resistance may be removed in all the cases illustrated. In which cases will the remainder of the realization be straightforward, requiring only the four basic removal techniques? Why do these not suffice in the other cases?

(*c*) For each of the following specific cases, delineate the portion of the *p* plane within which the zeros of $Z(p)$ must fall to give each of the cases of (*a*) and (*b*).

(1) $b_1 = 2, b_0 = 1,$

(2) $b_1 = 2, b_0 = 2,$

(3) $b_1 = 4, b_0 = 3.$

(*d*) Repeat on the dual basis. (Cf. BR 1, FO 4, KU 2, MA 12.)

9-5. Consider the function $F(p) = [(p + \alpha)/(p + 1)]^n$ for $n = 1, 2, 3, 4$. In each case, what are the ranges of α that make $F(p)$ p-r? When are simple reduction techniques sufficient for the realization of $F(p)$ as impedance and as admittance?

9-6. Let the function $Z(p)$ of Prob. 9-4 be a (p-r) function that is *minimum* (in all four respects). Normalize the frequency scale so that the frequency of zero resistance is unity.

May the poles lie *anywhere* in the left half plane? To what extent are the zeros independent of the poles? For poles situated as follows, trace curves that delimit the possible locations of the zeros.

(a) Complex, on circles of radius ω_0, and on the real axis such that $b_0 = \omega_0$ = constant, $\omega_0 > 1$.

(b) Ditto, with $\omega_0 = 1$.

(c) Ditto, with $\omega_0 < 1$.

If only one resistor is to be used in realizations of this function, what form may the network take? (Cf. FO 4, MA 12.)

9-7. Show that if the zeros of Ev $Z(p)$ or of Ev $Y(p)$ are distributed between the origin and infinity (none are elsewhere), i.e., if the real-frequency resistance (or conductance) functions have the form

$$\frac{\omega^{2m}}{b_0 + b_2\omega^2 + \cdots + b_{2n}\omega^{2n}},$$

then no Brune network is necessary in the Brune realization, i.e., sections of Types A and B suffice for realization. How does the Brune network degenerate into a form that does not have a negative element in such cases? Alternatively, show that such a function is necessarily capable of realization by reactance or susceptance removal or both until the reduced immittance is a constant, only one resistor being used.

Give the schematic form of the network for each of the following cases.

(a) Ev $Z(p)$ has n pairs of zeros at infinity and no other zeros,

(b) Ev $Z(p)$ has n pairs of zeros at the origin and no other zeros,

(c) Ev $Y(p)$ has n pairs of zeros at infinity and no other zeros,

(d) Ev $Y(p)$ has n pairs of zeros at the origin and no other zeros,

Explain how the element values would be calculated in the above realizations if the even part were the actual data.

Repeat for the following cases, pointing out in each the various different possibilities. The zeros indicated are the *only* zeros that the even part has.

Number of Pairs of Zeros of Ev $Z(p)$ or of Ev $Y(p)$

Case	At the Origin	At Infinity
(e)	1	1
(f)	1	2
(g)	2	1
(h)	2	2
(i)	1	3
(j)	3	1
(k)	1	4
(l)	2	3
(m)	3	2
(n)	4	1

How do these numbers of zeros compare with the numbers of inductors and of capacitors used?

If $Z(p)$ is not minimum-reactance, or $Y(p)$ is not minimum-susceptance, how would your realizations above be modified? Explain the nonuniqueness of your answer carefully.

9-8. In realizations such as those discussed in Prob. 9-7, if there are $2m$ zeros of Ev $Z(p)$ at the origin and $2(n - m)$ at infinity, and n and m are large, there will be a large number of possible realizations, different in schematic form. Discuss the following two methods for obtaining a complete set of the various schematic diagrams in any given case:

(*a*) Consider all possible sequences of removing the zeros of Ev $Z(p)$.

(*b*) Draw the schematic diagram of a prototype network of order $(n - m)$, with all the zeros of Ev $Z(p)$ at infinity. Then list the possible networks formed by inserting m inductors and capacitors into this network in the various appropriate ways.

(*c*) Draw the schematic diagram of a prototype network of order m with all zeros of Ev $Z(p)$ at the origin. Then list the possible networks formed by inserting $(n - m)$ inductors and capacitors into this network in the various appropriate ways.

Show that the final realization always reduces, in effect, to the prototype network of (*b*) at high frequencies, and to that of (*c*) at low frequencies. A slightly different approach would then be to draw both prototype networks and examine the various possibilities of "interleaving" them. Explain.

Repeat on the dual basis.

9-9. Explain how, in the cases

$$R(\omega) = \frac{1}{1 + \omega^{2n}} \qquad R(\omega) = \frac{\omega^{2n}}{1 + \omega^{2n}}$$

and their duals, it should be possible to obtain literal values for the elements of network realizations, as functions of n. The trigonometry required is generally complicated but has been carried out (GR 2, NO 2).

9-10. (*a*) For the network shown demonstrate that

$$R(\omega) = \frac{1}{b_0 + b_2\omega^2 + b_4\omega^4 + b_6\omega^6 + b_8\omega^8}$$

and evaluate the b's in terms of the literal element values.

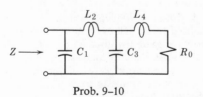

Prob. 9–10

(*b*) Discuss the relative merits of the two following proposals for synthesizing the network, given the resistance function, i.e., the values of the b's:

(1) Determine the associated $Z(p)$ and develop it in a continued fraction.

(2) Write and solve simultaneous equations for the element values, using the results of (*a*).

9-11. Give, with literal coefficients, the input resistance and input conductance functions for each of the eight networks shown. State specifically where the zeros of these functions are. Conversely, what, in general terms, are the

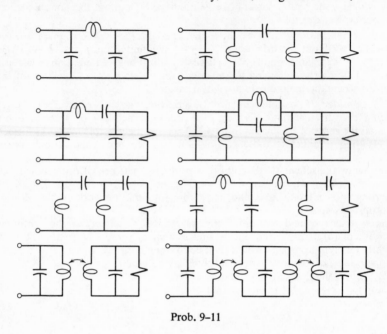

Prob. 9–11

limitations on your coefficients that such functions be so realizable? Illustrate with functions whose denominators are of the form (a) $(1 + \omega^{2n})$, (b) $(1 + \omega^2 + \omega^4 + \omega^6 + \cdot \cdot \cdot)$. Where equivalent but different one-resistor realizations can be obtained, give the others also.

9-12. Obtain two one-resistor realizations of the driving-point resistance

$$R(\omega) = \frac{\omega^2}{\omega^2 + 0.3(\omega^2 - 1)^4}$$

for which the scale factors are 20 mcps and 1200 Ω, corresponding to $\omega = 1$ and $R = 1$ in normalized form. Show how it would be possible, in both networks, to prevent the passage of any direct current from the input to the resistor (in a practical realization in which the inductors would contain some resistance) by converting an L-shaped network of two inductors to a transformer. What possibilities does this offer of changing the value of the resistor and of other elements without affecting $R(\omega)$? (Such networks are of use in vacuum-tube amplifiers; cf. §§ 11.04-5.)

9-13. Obtain two one-resistor realizations of the driving-point resistance

$$R(\omega) = \frac{\omega^6}{\omega^6 + (1 - \omega^2)^4}$$

with the same scale factors as in Prob. 9-12.   Is the transformer necessary here (on the assumption that the capacitors are perfect but the inductors contain some resistance)?

9-14. Select, from the data of the problems listed below, those cases in which realizability in the form of an *L-C* ladder network that terminates in a single resistor (no mutual inductance being used) can be guaranteed a priori.   Carry out the realizations in both the given and the dual forms.

Probs. 5-54, 8-3, 8-70, 8-73, 8-76, 8-83, 8-84, 8-85, 8-87, 8-98, 8-99, 8-100, 8-101, 8-103, 8-124, 8-125, 8-126, 8-130.

9-15. Carry out realizations of those realizable functions mentioned in Prob. 9-14 in which the guarantee cannot be made.

9-16. Find networks that realize each of the following datum functions, in which the symbols have their usual meanings.   Repeat on the dual basis. Where you have used more than one resistor, find additional realizations that use only one resistor.

$$(a)\ R(\omega) = \frac{\omega^4}{1 + \omega^8}, \qquad (b)\ X(\omega) = \frac{\omega^5}{1 + \omega^8},$$

$$(c)\ |Z(j\omega)|^2 = \frac{\omega^2(1 - \omega^2)^2}{1 + \omega^8} + K, \qquad K \text{ having the minimum possible value,}$$

$$(d)\ \beta = \tan^{-1}\left[\frac{\omega^9}{(1 - \omega^2)^2(2 - \omega^2)^2}\right].$$

9-17. The network shown is proposed as a form for realization of the resistance function of Prob. 9-12.   Explain why, although this might at first glance be

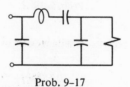

Prob. 9-17

considered a possibility, it is not.   (Cf. Prob. 9-8.)   For what sort of resistance functions is this a suitable realization?

9-18. Consider a (p-r) driving-point impedance function with the properties (*a*) all its zeros are imaginary, (*b*) all its poles lie to the left of the imaginary axis. Show that the numerator can be simply expressed in terms of the denominator; write the impedance in a form that sets this forth clearly.   What form does the resistance function take?   What is a simple form for its realization?   Draw a schematic diagram showing all elements for such an impedance of order six. What changes in the schematic would you expect if the resistance function had the same poles, but its zeros coalesced so that the numerator was $(\omega^2 - 1)^6$? Explain.

9-19. It is desired to realize a network whose input resistance, as a function of frequency, has the form shown.   Which of the six diagrams given can immediately be ruled out as a possible realization? Explain. Using the corresponding impedance function,

$$Z(p) = \frac{4p^3 + 3p^2 + 4p + 1}{12p^4 + 9p^3 + 14p^2 + 4p + 2},$$

investigate the remaining diagrams and either obtain the element values or explain why such a realization is impossible.

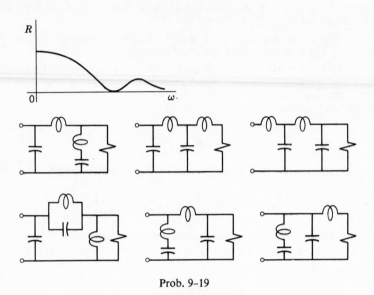

Prob. 9-19

9-20. Find realizations, both as impedance and as admittance, of the following functions.

(a) $\dfrac{11p^3 + 6p^2 + 4p + 2}{5p^2 + 2p + 1}$

(b) $\dfrac{0.586p^2 + 0.414p + 1}{p^3 + 2.414p^2 + 2.414p + 1}$

(c) $\dfrac{p^2 + 7p + 9}{p^2 + 7p + 10}$

(d) $\dfrac{16p^4 + 8p^3 + 8p^2 + 3p}{8p^3 + 4p^2 + 3p + 1}$

(e) $\dfrac{9p^2 + 4p + 9}{2p^2 + p + 2}$

(f) $\dfrac{p^2 + 9p + 2}{2p^2 + p + 1}$

(g) $\dfrac{2p^3 + p^2 + p}{p^3 + 3p^2 + 3p + 1}$

(h) $\dfrac{54p^3 + 399p^2 + 160p + 31}{54p^2 + 21p + 4}$

(i) $\dfrac{p^2 + 4p + 1}{p^2 + p + 1}$

(j) $\dfrac{48p^3 + 52p^2 + 27p + 8}{8p^3 + 8p^2 + 4p + 1}$

(k) $\dfrac{23p^2 + 34p + 42}{9p^2 + 5p + 6}$

(l) $\dfrac{p^2 + 3p + 2}{2p^3 + 7p^2 + 4p + 2}$

(m) $\dfrac{2p + 1}{p^2 + p + 1}$

(n) $\dfrac{3.16p^3 + 2.6p^2 + 2.2p + 1}{1.6p^2 + p + 1}$

(o) $\dfrac{15p^2 + 3p + 1}{18p^3 + 9p^2 + 2p + 1}$

(p) $\left(\dfrac{p + 3}{p + 1}\right)^3$

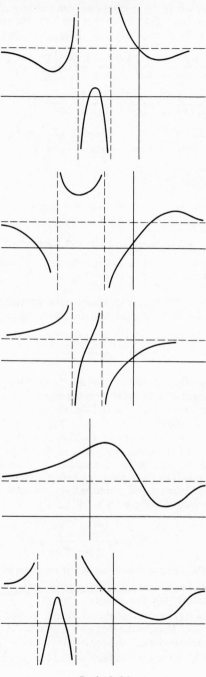

Prob. 9–26

9-21. In those cases where the realizations found in Prob. 9-20 use more than one resistor, find additional realizations that use only one resistor.

9-22. Find network realizations, both as admittance and as impedance, of

(a) $$\frac{19.2p^5 + 24p^4 + 12.4p^3 + 10.4p^2 + 1.2p + 1}{128p^4 + 40p^3 + 26p^2 + 6p + 1}$$

(b) $$\frac{281.5p^5 + 63p^4 + 1462p^3 + 276p^2 + 1800p + 240}{55.5p^4 + 11p^3 + 244p^2 + 32p + 240}$$

(c) $$\frac{204.8p^5 + 460.8p^4 + 156.8p^3 + 57.6p^2 + 12.8p + 1.2}{1024p^5 + 384p^4 + 144p^3 + 48p^2 + 4p + 1}$$

(d) $$\frac{24p^4 + 124p^3 + 114p^2 + 27p + 6}{20p^3 + 20p^2 + 5p + 1}$$

(e) $$\frac{180p^6 + 300p^5 + 324p^4 + 203p^3 + 53p^2 + 20p + 1}{60p^5 + 100p^4 + 104p^3 + 61p^2 + 11p + 3}$$

9-23. Realize, both as resistance and as conductance,

(a) $\dfrac{(1 - \omega^2)^6}{1 + \omega^{12}}$ (b) $\dfrac{(1 - \omega^2)^2(4 - \omega^2)^2}{1 + \omega^{12}}$ (c) $\dfrac{\omega^2(1 + \omega^2)^2}{1 + \omega^{12}}$

9-24. Find at least two different realizations of the function $(\omega^2 - 1)^2/(1 + \omega^8)$ as a driving-point resistance. Repeat as a driving-point conductance.

9-25. Given

$$R(\omega) = \frac{\omega^4 + 2\omega^2 + 1}{\omega^4 + 6\omega^2 + 1},$$

plot this resistance function against ω^2. From the sketch explain the possibility of realizing the corresponding impedance in the Brune fashion in two ways, one of which begins by removing a resistor and the other of which does not. Obtain the two networks and compare them.

9-26. The curves on p. 595 represent Ev $Z(p)$ plotted against $x = -p^2$ for x real. Construct such functions in each case of the lowest order possible and realize them. In cases where different constants may be subtracted to move zeros of Ev $Z(p)$ to an axis of the p plane, give the different networks that result from each possible subtraction and compare them. Repeat on the assumption that the sketches represent Ev $Y(p)$. (Cf. BR 1.)

9-27. Realize

$$Z(p) = \frac{p^2 + p + 1}{p^2 + 2p + 1}$$

(a) by the Brune method and (b) with the use of only one resistor.

9-28. Find networks equivalent in driving-point impedance to those shown on p. 597, but containing only one resistor.

9-29. Realize (9.08–11) by the standard Brune procedure. Compare the result with Fig. 9.08–G. Discuss the two with regard to the number of elements used, the number of resistors used, the practicality of each.

9-30. Carry out in detail the realizations of (9.14–3) given in § 9.14.

9-31. Obtain realizations of the impedance function

$$Z(p) = \frac{3p^2 + 2p + 4}{p^3 + p^2 + 4p + 4}$$

by following each of these three procedures, and compare the three networks:

(a) Remove the pole of impedance at $\omega = 2$ and then realize the remainder.

(b) Remove the pole of admittance at infinity and then make the standard Brune development of the remaining impedance.

(c) Remove the pole of admittance at infinity and then make the dual Brune development of the remaining admittance.

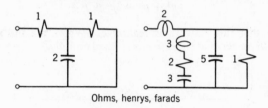

Ohms, henrys, farads

Prob. 9–28

9-32. Using only the principles of reactance and susceptance removal and the standard Brune procedure, in the various sequences possible, how many realizations of the impedance function

$$Z(p) = \frac{126p^4 + 452p^3 + 192p^2 + 112p + 24}{54p^5 + 194p^4 + 129p^3 + 218p^2 + 75p + 24}$$

can you obtain? Compare the networks, particularly with respect to the manner in which the various zeros of Ev $Z(p)$ are realized, and the number of Type-C sections (Brune networks) used. Explain, in the light of your results, how it may happen that the shunt L-C branch in a Brune network will not give rise to zeros in Ev $Z(p)$.

9-33. In order that an impedance function $Z(p)$ have a realization in the form given, show that it is necessary but not sufficient that (a) minima of resistance

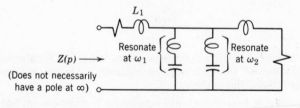

Prob. 9–33

occur at ω_1 and ω_2 and have the same value, $R_{\min}$, and (b) at both frequencies $Z = R_{\min} + jL_1\omega$. (A counter example in schematic form, not necessarily involving numerical values, may be useful.)

9-34. If all the zeros of a given $\mathrm{Ev}\,Z(p)$ are imaginary, how many resistors does the standard Brune realization of the corresponding minimum-reactance $Z(p)$ use in general? If none of the zeros are imaginary but all the minima of $\mathrm{Ev}\,Z(j\omega)$ have the same value, and correspond in number to the zeros of $\mathrm{Ev}\,Z(p)$, how many are used?

If the zeros of $\mathrm{Ev}\,Z(p)$ fall at $\pm j\omega_0$ and there only, how many different networks can be obtained by the standard Brune process? How does your answer change if the zeros of $\mathrm{Ev}\,Z(p)$ are all imaginary but not necessarily coincident?

Illustrate the different character of the different networks by realizing the function

$$Z(p) = \frac{5p^4 + 6p^3 + 8p^2 + 3p + 2}{p^4 + p^3 + 3p^2 + p + 1}.$$

9-35. Show that this network is realizable. Where are the zeros of Z_A? Does $\mathrm{Ev}\,Z(p)$ have zeros at these points? Explain fully.

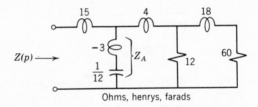

Ohms, henrys, farads

Prob. 9–35

9-36. Show that if, in the standard Brune cycle, $Z(j\omega_1) = (A + jB)/(C + jD)$, then the first inductor L_1 has the value $B/(\omega_1 C) = -A/(\omega_1 D)$.

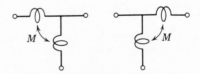

Prob. 9–36

Show also that in this cycle the two variations illustrated are alternative forms for the realization of the T network of inductors. Discuss the possibility of autotransformer realization thereof.

9-37. Obtain one-resistor networks equivalent in driving-point impedance to those shown on p. 599. Take all element values as unity, for simplicity.

9-38. Consider the input impedance of the network on p. 599, in which L_2 is negative, but $Z(p)$ is p-r. What is the maximum possible order of $Z(p)$? What other possible values exist for the order of $Z(p)$? Explain in each case how the reduction in order comes about.

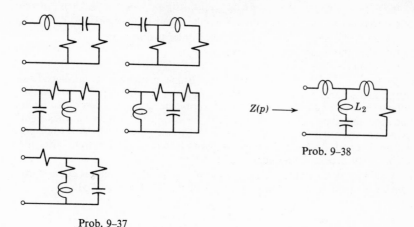

$Z(p) \longrightarrow$

Prob. 9-38

Prob. 9-37

9-39. Show that any realization of an immittance function of order n must contain at least n reactive (L, C) elements, though it need not always contain resistors. Show that the Brune realization of an impedance uses only the minimum possible total number of elements. (*Suggestion:* The number of elements must at least equal the number of parameters in the impedance function; ideal transformers, if used, count as single elements; a start with a simple case followed by a generalization may be the best attack; cf. Prob. 10-92.)

9-40. Show that the Type-C section can be drawn in the equivalent form given, and determine the values of L and a in terms of L_1, L_2, L_3. Compare this form with the networks obtained by those variations of the Brune procedure

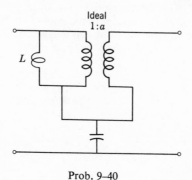

Ideal
1:a

L

Prob. 9-40

that begin by removing (*a*) a shunt capacitor, (*b*) a shunt inductor, (*c*) a series capacitor, all of which require, in general, an ideal transformer for realizability. (See Prob. 9-57.)

9-41. Show that if the $=$ sign is taken in (9.04-40), then K_{-2} must be negative for $Z(p)$ to be p-r.

9-42. In the Brune cycle of § 9.08, applied to an initial impedance function $Z_0(p)$ of order n, give (with explanations) the orders of the functions Y_1, Y_2, Y_3,

(a) when the zero of Ev $Z_0(p)$ at σ_0 is of order two or more,

(b) when the zero of Ev $Z_0(p)$ at σ_0 is simple,

(c) when Ev $Z_0(\sigma_0) \neq 0$.

9-43. Consider the application of the Brune procedure to an impedance function $Z_0(p)$ that is in all four respects minimum. Let the impedance remaining after one Brune cycle be $Z_3(p)$; i.e., Z_3 terminates a Type-C section to realize the input impedance $Z_0(p)$. Is it possible for $Z_3(p)$ to have a zero at the origin? A pole at the origin? A zero at infinity? A pole at infinity? A zero or pole at an internal frequency? Explain your answers. Demonstrate also that $Z_3(p)$ is not necessarily minimum in any respect.

9-44. Plot the loci of the zeros of Ev $Z(p)$ as resistance is subtracted, and thus show their motion in the complex plane, for the following Ev $Z(p)$:

$$(a) \quad \frac{2 - 2\omega^2 + \omega^4 + \omega^6}{1 + \omega^6} \qquad (b) \quad \frac{1 + \omega^4}{4 + 5\omega^2 + \omega^4}$$

$$(c) \quad \frac{2 - 4\omega^2 + 6\omega^4 - 4\omega^6 + \omega^8 + \omega^{10}}{1 + \omega^{10}} \qquad (d) \quad \frac{2 + \omega^4}{1 + \omega^4}$$

$$(e) \quad \frac{1 + 3\omega^2 + 4\omega^4 + \omega^6}{1 + 3\omega^2 + 3\omega^4 + \omega^6} \qquad (f) \quad \frac{2 + 4\omega^2 + 6\omega^4 + 4\omega^6 + 2\omega^8}{1 + \omega^8}$$

Is it possible for zeros of Ev $Z(p)$ to go first to the real axis, as resistance is removed, and then (as more resistance is removed) to the imaginary axis? Explain fully. (Sketches of the resistance function versus ω^2 will be helpful in this problem.) Note that the orders of zeros of Ev $Z(p)$, regarded first as a function of $x = -p^2$ and second as a function of p, are the same, unless the zero is at the origin or infinity. What is the relation between the orders then?

9-45. Show that if $Z(p)$ and $Y(p)$ are p-r functions, one the reciprocal of the other, the zeros of Ev $Z(p)$ are the same as the zeros of Ev $Y(p)$ with the following possible exceptions, and no others: at real-frequency zeros of $Y(p)$ the order of the zero of Ev $Z(p)$ is two less than the order of the zero of Ev $Y(p)$, and at real-frequency poles of $Y(p)$ the order of the zero of Ev $Z(p)$ is two more than the order of the zero of Ev $Y(p)$. Illustrate these exceptions with simple networks and explain the physical action. Give also the dual statement, with illustrations. Show also that at poles of the denominator of (9.10–4) not at real frequencies, Ev $Z(p) \neq 0$. (Suggestion: At such poles both even and odd parts have poles of the same order, and their Laurent expansions effectively cancel.)

9-46. Discuss the effect of removing conductance on the zeros of Ev $Z(p)$. Show that none are actually removed, they are merely shifted, in general. Are there any exceptions?

9-47. Show that if the real zero of Ev $Z_0(p)$ used in § 9.08 is double (or of higher order), then Y_a [see (9.08–5)] has no pole at this point. Show also that if this real zero of Ev Z_0 is simple, then Y_a does have a pole there, and that the effect of this is to cancel one of the two zeros of Ev Z introduced by the L_2-C_2 branch.

9-48. Show that the denominator of (9.11–7) can vanish at $-\sigma_1$ (Fig. 9.11–H) only if Z_B has a zero there, and that then $E_B = 0$. Show that if

$Z_B(-\sigma_1) = 0$ this zero of the denominator must be simple, so that a simple zero remains in Ev Z. [Remember that L_1 was chosen to make $Z_1(-\sigma_1) = 0$.] Explain the action at the point $+\sigma_1$, where Ev Z must also have a simple zero, because it is an even function.

9-49. Complete the discussion in § 9.10 of the contribution of the zeros of E_b to those of Ev Z along the following lines. Show (*a*) that the denominator of (9.10–4) can vanish simultaneously with E_b only at imaginary values of p, and that where this happens Z has a pole; (*b*) that the order of the zero produced in Ev Z by a zero of E_b, under these conditions, is less by two than the order of the zero in E_b. Can this reduction of order (of the zero of Ev Z in comparison with the zero of E_b) occur at infinity?

9-50. Consider the removal of zeros of Ev Z by a Type-B section, and by a Type-B and a Type-A section in combination, along the following lines. Correlate your discussion with that in the text. Write Ev Z_b in terms of Ev Z, Od Z, Z_a. Investigate the zeros of Ev Z_b and show (in comparison with those of Ev Z) that there are no additions, but that there are subtractions: zeros of Z_a remove two apiece, some are converted into (real-frequency) poles of Z_b to be removed in Z_c, some remain in zeros of Ev Z_b.

9-51. Demonstrate steps 2(*b*) and 2(*c*) of (9.04–38) by careful application of the reasoning referred to.

9-52. Show that the Brune process (§§ 9.03–9.05) can be carried through equally well if the given impedance function is not first reduced to minimum reactance, i.e., if $Z_0(p)$ has one or more poles on the imaginary axis. If $Z_0(p)$ is not minimum-susceptance, i.e., $Z_0(p)$ has one or more real-frequency zeros, in what way does this affect the Brune development of $Z_0(p)$?

9-53. Show that the first inductor of the Brune cycle has the value

$$L_1 = \frac{2}{\pi} \int_0^\infty \frac{R(\lambda)}{\lambda^2 - \omega_0{}^2} \, d\lambda$$

and explain from this why it may be positive or negative.

9-54. Under what conditions may it be possible to remove an *L-C* network more complicated than a mere capacitor in the Brune cycle, in the fashion

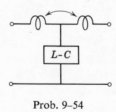

Prob. 9–54

indicated? (An interpretation in terms of degenerate or coalescing successive Type-C sections may be helpful.)

9-55. Review the analysis of § 9.05 and point out the changes that there occur when Z_0 has a pole at infinity. In particular, explain why the perfect coupling is no longer required between the two inductors of the Brune network. Show that if Z_0 has an *internal* real-frequency pole, this property is of no assistance in relaxing the perfect coupling requirement of the Brune process.

Show also that if $Z_0(p)$ has zero resistance at several different real frequencies, then after the first Brune cycle the resistance of the reduced impedance Z_3 is zero at all of these frequencies except that used in the Brune cycle, in general. Demonstrate this by physical reasoning alone, and then by expressing the input impedance Z_0 in terms of Z_3 (the reduced impedance) and the elements of the Brune network; find an expression for $R_0(\omega) = \mathbf{Re}\, Z_0(j\omega)$.

9-56. Show that it is possible to modify the Brune synthesis process as follows. Given $Z(p)$, with pole at infinity and zero at the origin removed if present originally, remove an *arbitrary* inductor L in series. Then remove a shunt branch (or branches). Show that a pair of perfectly coupled inductors is required, and that a reduction in order results, and a valid synthesis procedure. Comment on the number of elements generally required and illustrate with an example.

9-57. The basic Brune cycle of §§ 9.03–9.05 proceeds by initially removing a series inductor. Show that it is possible to remove initially a series capacitor

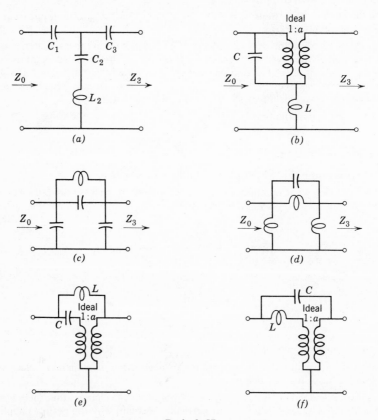

Prob. 9–57

(instead of the inductor), which procedure yields the network (*a*) in which either C_1 or C_3 is negative, C_2 and L_2 are positive, $C_1 + C_2 + C_3 \geq 0$, and Z_3 is of order two less than the order of Z_0. This network is not immediately realizable, of course; demonstrate that the network (*b*) is equivalent and realizable; determine the values of *a* and the elements *L* and *C*. Is C_3 still arbitrary? (Most of the analysis of the text is applicable if the frequency scale is inverted, i.e., if the variable $s = 1/p$ is considered; the network equivalence may be demonstrated by the method used in § 9.13.)

Show that the dual approaches (to the standard Brune development, and to that described above) lead to networks (*c*) and (*d*) and determine the element values. Show that although these networks are not immediately realizable, they possess the realizable equivalents (*e*) and (*f*) respectively. Discuss the possibility of realizing (*f*) by means of a pair of perfectly coupled inductors and show how this network differs from the standard Brune network.

Suppose that the same frequency of zero resistance is used in each of the four developments. Does the *same* remainder impedance $Z_3(p)$ generally result in each case?

9-58. Given a (realizable) resistance function $R(\omega)$, show that the realization of the corresponding minimum-reactance impedance can be accomplished without actually calculating the impedance function $Z(p)$. Use formulas from § 9.05 and the integral relations between reactance and resistance. If the data consist of the reactance $X(\omega)$, can a similar procedure be devised?

9-59. Prove that if $Z(p)$ is p-r, $Z(j\omega) = R + jX$, then at a real frequency where $R = 0$, $dX/d\omega \geq |X/\omega|$. (This is done in § 9.04 for the minimum-reactance case; here imaginary poles must be taken into account.)

Show that the = sign holds only when $Z(p)$ is of the form $(R + Lp)$ or $(R + 1/Cp)$, and at the origin and at infinity. Then prove that (9.04–15) holds in general at an imaginary zero of $F(p)$, i.e., that $F'(j\omega_1)$ is real and positive, except for the trivial case $Z(p) = 0 + Lp$ where no imaginary zero exists anyway. For reactance (*L-C*) functions show that $dX/d\omega > |X/\omega|$ for all frequencies, with two exceptional cases.

Show that none of the exceptions to (9.04–18) there mentioned can occur to upset the arguments leading up to (9.04–20).

9-60. Show that if $Z(p)$ is minimum-reactance but not minimum-resistance, then at a true minimum of $R(\omega)$, $dX/d\omega > X/\omega$ but at a local minimum or maximum this is not necessarily true, and at a true maximum it is definitely not true.

9-61. Verify those relations in (9.05–26) that are not completely derived in the text. From the formula for L_3 demonstrate that L_1 and L_3 have opposite signs.

9-62. (*a*) Discuss the application of the Brune process (§ 9.08) to a pair of *simple* real zeros of Ev $Z(p)$. Show that the process works but that the reduction in order accomplished is only one, though the same number of elements are still used. Explain how the shunt branch L_2-C_2 does not actually produce a double zero of Ev $Z(p)$ in this case, though it does in § 9.08.

(*b*) Realize the function below by the method of (*a*), first removing R_0; then realize it by the method of § 9.08, removing only enough of R_0 to create a double zero of Ev $Z(p)$; finally realize it by straightforward reduction and the normal Brune process. Contrast the realizations.

$$Z(p) = \frac{p^2 + 4.5p + 2}{p^2 + 2p + 2} + R_0.$$

9-63. Show that the Brune development based on a zero of Ev $Z(p)$ at a point σ_0 on the real axis can be made even if $Z(p) = R$, i.e., that a Type-C section terminated in a resistor can be a network of purely constant (resistance) input impedance. Show that the procedure works in general, even if Ev $Z \neq 0$ at σ_0, though no reduction in order results.

9-64. Explain why L_1 can be zero in the Brune process when the zero of Ev $Z(p)$ considered is on the imaginary axis, but that the series arm of the Type-C or Type-D section cannot be zero when the zero of Ev $Z(p)$ is off the imaginary axis.

9-65. Consider the function $F(p) = Z(p) - Lp$, in which $Z(p)$ is p-r and of order n and L is a real, positive constant. How many zeros does $F(p)$ have in the right half plane

  (a) when $Z'(0) > L$,
  (b) when $Z'(0) = L$,
  (c) when $Z'(0) < L$?

Explain your answers. In which cases is $F(p)$ p-r?

9-66. If $Z(p)$ is p-r and behaves as $1/Cp$ near the origin, how many right-half-plane zeros has $F(p) = Z(p) - S_0/p$? (Consider all positive values of S_0.) If $Z(p)$ has no pole at the origin, for what values of S_0 will $F(p)$ have the same properties as the function $(Z - Lp)$ of § 9.04?

9-67. Let $F(p) = Z(p) - Z_R(p)$ in which $Z(p)$ is p-r, of order m, and $Z_R(p)$ is a reactance function of order n. None of the poles of Z_R appear in Z, and Z is not minimum-resistance. How many right-half-plane zeros does $F(p)$ have? If $Z(p)$ is minimum-resistance, to what extent can the question be answered?

9-68. Show that (9.12–7) is still valid if some of the numbers in (9.12–3) are negative, or if the residues of $Z(p)$ at poles coincident with those of $Z_R(p)$ are not restricted.

9-69. Let $Z(p)$ be a p-r function, and $Z_R = (S_0/p) + [S_1p/(p^2 + \omega_1^2)] + L_0p$ be a particular reactance function. The poles of Z coincident with those of Z_R do not have larger residues. Show how the four constants in Z_R might be chosen so that $F(p) = Z - Z_R$ has (a) four right-half-plane zeros, (b) two and only two right-half-plane zeros, (c) no right-half-plane zeros. What are the requirements on $Z(p)$ that this be possible?

9-70. With reference to (9.12–6) derive an expression for $F'(j\omega_0)$ in the form

$$F'(j\omega_0) = \left[X'(\omega_0) - \frac{X(\omega_0)}{\omega_0} \right] - G$$

in which G is positive, and thus show how $F'(j\omega_0)$ can be positive, zero, or negative.

9-71. Show that the procedure for developing the Type-D section (§ 9.13) is in no way dependent on the vanishing of Ev $Z(p)$ at the point p_0, and may be carried through whether or not Ev $Z_0(p_0) = 0$. What effect on the order of $Z(p)$ does the removal of the Type-D section have, if Ev $Z_0(p_0) \neq 0$? Illustrate by developing the impedance function $Z_0(p) = R = $ constant in a Type-D section terminated in a resistor. (Cf. Prob. 10-94.)

9-72. Derive (9.13–51).

9-73. Apply (d) and (e) of Prob. 8-48 to the solution of Prob. 9–79.

9-74. In § 9.13 certain restrictions are imposed on $Z_0(p)$ for convenience. Show that these are not necessary and that the Type-D section can always be removed (though zeros of Ev Z_0 are needed if any reduction in order is to be accomplished). What is the corresponding statement for the Brune process?

9-75. Show that the Type-D development of § 9.13 does remove the zeros of Ev Z_0 on which the development is based, both for the case of multiple zeros of Ev Z_0 and of simple zeros of Ev Z_0. If Ev $Z_0(p_0) \neq 0$, explain in terms of (9.13–53) why no zeros of Ev Z_0 are removed. Explain fully the development of Table 9.13–A, including the case where Ev $Z_0(p_0) \neq 0$.

9-76. Show that in Fig. 9.13–F (a) $L_3 = 1/(4K_r)$ and hence **Re** $Z_1'(p_0) > 0$, (b) $C_3 = -4$ **Re** (K_0/p_0^2) and hence **Re** $[p_0^2 Z_1(p_0)] < 0$.

9-77. Show that a section of the type illustrated in (a) will remove four complex zeros of the even part of an impedance, as does the Type-D section

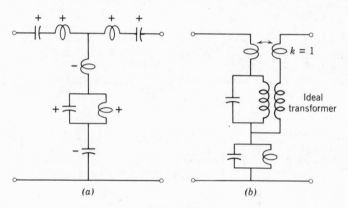

(a)   (b)

Prob. 9–77

(VI 1). Is $z_{11}(p)$ altered from that of § 9.13? Show that (b) is a realizable equivalent of (a).

9-78. Show, by analysis, that the network of Fig. 9.13–K leads to the parameters given in (9.13–59) and that these are the same as those in (9.13–56). (*Suggestion:* Make the calculation with Z_3 disconnected and insert Z_3 only at the end of the work; justify this procedure.) Repeat for Fig. 9.13–L.

9-79. From (9.13–19) derive formulas for S_1 and L_2. From the positive reality of $Z_0(p)$ show now that S_1 and L_1 are positive. Can you draw any conclusions as to the sign of L_2?

9-80. Show that if $L_2 = L_5 = 0$, the Type-D section can be reduced to the form shown, which still realizes four complex zeros of Ev $Z_0(p)$. Is this a general possibility? Give a numerical example (of order two) to illustrate, and realize the same impedance by the standard Brune procedure.

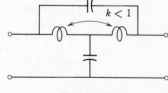

Prob. 9–80

9-81. Carry out the solution of (9.13–14) for the four element values of z_{11} and show that each is positive because $Z_0(p)$ is p-r.

9-82. Show that the series combination of an R-C network and a single inductor forms an impedance (a) all of whose poles are real and not more than two of whose zeros are complex. (*Suggestion:* Plot the impedance of the R-C network alone versus σ, then $L\sigma$, then their sum.)

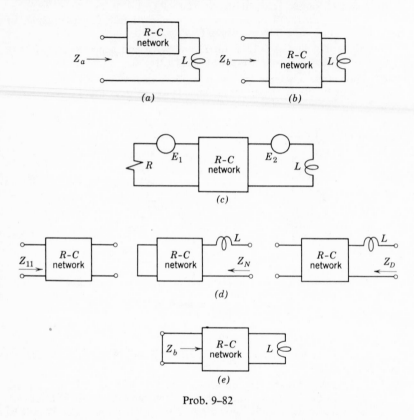

(a)   (b)

(c)

(d)

(e)

Prob. 9–82

Show that the impedance (b) of a network that contains only one inductor has at most two complex zeros and at most two complex poles. [*Suggestion:* Write the equations of analysis (2.07–7) for the situation (c) and from these show by manipulation of determinants that $Z_b = Z_{11}Z_N/Z_D$, the symbols being defined in (d). An alternative approach is to consider the natural modes of the system (e) that correspond to the roots of $Z_b(p) = 0$ and generally also make the impedance of the loops that contains L vanish.]

Show that although any p-r immittance function can be realized with only one resistor, in general it *cannot* be realized with only one inductor, nor with only one capacitor. (DE 2, PA 4.)

10.

The *R-L-C*
One-Terminal Pair—II

· · · but the end is not yet.
Matt. 24:6

Before proceeding to the (extremely important) matter of *approximation*, it is appropriate to investigate some other methods of realization of driving-point immittance functions. Our study of *properties* showed that positive reality was necessary for realizability, and the *realization* processes of Chapter 9 showed it also to be sufficient. The Brune technique of realization demonstrated this with a general process using resistance in various places and requiring perfectly coupled inductors. In Darlington's extension we found a proof that only one resistor is necessary, but this still makes use of perfectly coupled inductors, a practically undesirable feature. Yet this does not mean that mutual inductance is *necessary* in the realization of any driving-point immittance functions: it merely shows that this particular approach to the one-terminal-pair realization problem leads in general to networks with coupled inductors. And for nearly 20 years after Brune's work no alternative appeared to demonstrate conclusively that mutual inductance is never necessary. It is perfectly possible to realize any p-r function without mutual inductance, however, and to the demonstration of this we turn next.

10.01 Realization without mutual inductance

It was found almost simultaneously by Bott and Duffin (BO 4) and by Darlington (in unpublished work) that realization without mutual inductance is possible, and not difficult, once the point of view is changed properly. Resistors, capacitors, and (isolated) inductors are enough to realize any p-r function, although it seems at present that to avoid mutual inductance one may have to use a larger number of these elements than the processes of Chapter 9 require.

We shall again begin our discussion with a simple numerical example, to illustrate the process, before undertaking any general discussion. Consider again the p-r function (9.02–1) whose Brune realization as an impedance is shown in Fig. 9.02–G. This function is minimum in all respects, which is convenient (though not necessary) for our purposes here. Faced with the impossibility of further reduction by removal of ordinary elements, Brune removed an inductor L_1, sufficient to account for the whole impedance at the frequency of zero resistance, ω_0. The Brune technique proceeds then to complete the realization with a fairly complicated network (Z_1) in series with L_1 (Fig. 9.02–C), and it is here, in the nonpositive reality of Z_1, that the need for mutual inductance can be said to arise. We might be able to avoid this by completing the realization by adding something in parallel with L_1 as well, Fig. 10.01–A(a), or in

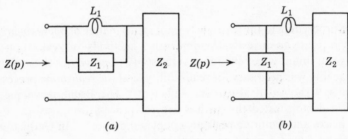

(a)   (b)

Fig. 10.01–A

parallel at the input, Fig. 10.01–A(b). These are alternative ways of "patching up" the network L_1 in an attempt to realize $Z(p)$; we do not yet know whether they are actually possible, nor if mutual inductance can thereby be avoided. But let us try.

Starting from the same datum impedance function,

$$Z(p) = \frac{5p^2 + 18p + 8}{p^2 + p + 10} \quad \text{ohms}, \quad (10.01\text{–}1)$$

we write

$$Z_0(p) = \frac{Z}{5} = \frac{p^2 + 3.6p + 1.6}{p^2 + p + 10} \quad (10.01\text{–}2)$$

for convenience, and then observe that the function is minimum-reactance and minimum-susceptance (Fig. 9.02–A) and also minimum-resistance and minimum-conductance (Fig. 9.02–B), exactly as we did in Chapter 9. The only outstanding characteristic of $Z_0(p)$ is that at $p = \pm j2$ the resistance is zero, as shown by (9.02–3), i.e., that $\mathrm{Ev}\, Z(p)$ has (double) zeros at $\pm j2$. At these points an inductance

$$L_1 = \frac{Z_0(j2)}{j2} = \frac{j1.2}{j2} = 0.6 \text{ h} \qquad (10.01\text{–}3)$$

will supply the whole impedance, and this inductance we put down. Now let us consider how to patch up this primitive network L_1 so that we have the impedance $Z_0(p)$. There must be a shunt of some sort around L_1, to prevent the appearance of a pole at infinity in the input impedance (the Brune process avoided this by means of a subsequent negative inductance, which we do not wish to use), and there must be something in series to prevent the appearance of a zero at the origin. Let us follow the suggestion in Fig. 10.01–A(a) for the present. More or less arbitrarily, we also split the second box up into the parallel combination of a capacitor and another network (it then appears more symmetrical), which gives us the

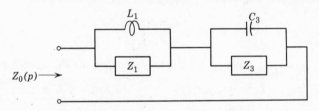

Fig. 10.01–B

network of Fig. 10.01–B as a possible realization. If this attack is to succeed, we must have

$$Z_3(0) = Z_0(0),$$
$$Z_1(\infty) = Z_0(\infty),$$
$$Z_1(\pm j2) \to \infty, \qquad (10.01\text{–}4)$$
$$Z_3(\pm j2) = 0.$$

With these stipulations, the network of Fig. 10.01–B is a realization of $Z_0(p)$ at four points: 0, ∞, $\pm j2$. Whether it can be made a realization for all values of p we have yet to see.

The inverse behavior of Z_1 and Z_3 at $\pm j2$ suggests that we might reduce the number of variables by making these two impedances have inverse behavior at *all* values of p; and so we let

$$Z_1 Z_3 = R_0^2, \qquad (10.01\text{–}5)$$

in which R_0 is a real positive constant with the dimensions of resistance.

This is not unreasonable, since if Z_1 is p-r, then so also is Z_3, defined by (10.01–5). We have now to determine C_3, $Z_1(p)$, and R_0—and to do this so that the input impedance is indeed $Z_0(p)$, and that the network is realizable in a reasonably simple fashion, without mutual inductance. To see whether this is possible, we write out the input impedance from Fig. 10.01–B, making use of (10.01–5) to eliminate Z_3:

$$Z_0(p) = \frac{1}{1/L_1 p + 1/Z_1} + \frac{1}{C_3 p + 1/Z_3}$$

$$= \frac{L_1 p Z_1}{Z_1 + L_1 p} + \frac{R_0{}^2}{Z_1 + R_0{}^2 C_3 p}.$$

$$(10.01–6)$$

This expression would be simpler if the two denominators were the same, so we also require

$$L_1 = R_0{}^2 C_3 \qquad (10.01–7)$$

which reduces our unknowns to $Z_1(p)$ and C_3. Now we have

$$Z_0(p) = \frac{L_1 p Z_1 + L_1 S_3}{Z_1 + L_1 p} \qquad (10.01–8)$$

in which $S_3 = 1/C_3$. We now solve this equation for Z_1, to obtain

$$Z_1 = \frac{L_1 S_3 - L_1 p Z_0(p)}{Z_0(p) - L_1 p} = -L_1 p \, \frac{Z_0(p) - 1/C_3 p}{Z_0(p) - L_1 p}. \qquad (10.01–9)$$

The burning question is, can C_3 be so chosen that $Z_1(p)$ is p-r? And if so, is $Z_1(p)$ simpler to realize than is $Z_0(p)$?

It is apparent in (10.01–9) that Z_1 has poles at $\pm j2$, which may make the answer to the second question *yes*; but it is also clear that Z_1 has a pole in the right-half plane, for its denominator is one of the pseudo-p-r functions discussed in § 9.04, which has one (and only one) right-half-plane zero—and this might make it difficult to answer the first question affirmatively. But if C_3 is positive the numerator has the same property (Problem 9-66). It follows that C_3 must certainly be given that value which makes these two zeros coincide; then $Z_1(p)$ will be free of right-half-plane poles and zeros, and to that extent will be p-r. It is not difficult to apply the remainder of the test for positive reality to show that Z_1 is then actually p-r, but we shall not stop here to do this. Instead we shall actually calculate Z_1.

Let the right-half-plane root of

$$Z_0(p) - L_1 p = 0 \qquad (10.01–10)$$

be σ_1. Its numerical value is easily found, for (10.01–10) is

$$\frac{p^2 + 3.6p + 1.6}{p^2 + p + 10} - 0.6p = \frac{-0.6p^3 + 0.4p^2 - 2.4p + 1.6}{p^2 + p + 10} = 0,$$

$$(10.01\text{--}11)$$

and we already know that two of the three roots are $p = \pm j2$, since L_1 was chosen in effect to satisfy (10.01–10) at these two points. Ordinary division then gives us

$$-0.6p^3 + 0.4p^2 - 2.4p + 1.6 = (p^2 + 4)(-0.6p + 0.4) = 0 \quad (10.01\text{--}12)$$

so that

$$\sigma_1 = \tfrac{2}{3}. \qquad (10.01\text{--}13)$$

We now determine C_3, which must satisfy

$$Z_0(\sigma_1) - \frac{1}{C_3\sigma_1} = 0 \qquad (10.01\text{--}14)$$

or

$$\frac{1}{C_3\sigma_1} = Z_0(\sigma_1) = L_1\sigma_1 \qquad (10.01\text{--}15)$$

or

$$C_3 = \frac{1}{L_1\sigma_1^{\,2}} = \frac{1}{0.6(\tfrac{2}{3})^2} = 3.75 \text{ f.} \qquad (10.01\text{--}16)$$

Then, from (10.01–9),

$$\begin{aligned} Z_1 &= \frac{-0.6p^3 - 2p^2 - 0.8p + 1.6}{-0.6p^3 + 0.4p^2 - 2.4p + 1.6} \\[6pt] &= \frac{(-0.6p + 0.4)(p^2 + 4p + 4)}{(p^2 + 4)(-0.6p + 0.4)} \end{aligned}$$

$$(10.01\text{--}17)$$

in which we have factored out the known right-half-plane zero in both numerator and denominator. The cancellation we have planned is evident, and

$$Z_1 = \frac{p^2 + 4p + 4}{p^2 + 4} \qquad (10.01\text{--}18)$$

which is readily realized, for it is not minimum-reactance and

$$Z_1 = \frac{4p}{p^2 + 4} + 1. \qquad (10.01\text{--}19)$$

It is not an accident that Z_1 has poles at $\pm j2$, as we noticed before, for we so chose L_1 that it made up the whole impedance Z_0 at these points; therefore the shunt Z_1 (Fig. 10.01–B) must become infinite there. And it is these poles that make it possible to reduce the order of Z_1 (which is unchanged from that of the original function Z_0) without using mutual inductance. Our realization is now complete, for a realization of (10.01–19) can be written by inspection—and we also have

$$Y_3 = \frac{1}{Z_3} = \frac{Z_1}{R_0{}^2} = \frac{Z_1}{L_1/C_3} = \frac{1}{0.16}\left[\frac{4p}{p^2 + 4} + 1\right], \quad (10.01\text{–}20)$$

a realization of which can again be written by inspection. The result, after restoring the scale factor 5, is given in Fig. 10.01–C.

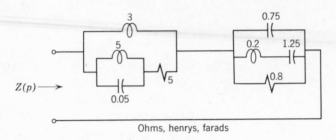

Ohms, henrys, farads

Fig. 10.01–C

We have thus found a realization that *does not require mutual inductance* for the function $Z(p)$. A good many matters must be investigated before we can make any general statements, but the basic idea of the technique is given in this example (and in its dual): to set up the inductance L_1 and then to build up the network with complementary elements, to make up Z. (Perhaps there are other ways of looking at this, but it will do for the moment.) Notice the increase in number of elements over the Brune realization of the same function (Fig. 9.02–E).

Before investigating the generality of this approach, let us determine whether the alternate approach, suggested in Fig. 10.01–A(b), will also give us a realization. It is more convenient here to start with

$$Y_0 = \frac{1}{Z_0} = \frac{p^2 + p + 10}{p^2 + 3.6p + 1.6} \quad \text{mhos}, \quad (10.01\text{–}21)$$

for we expect to obtain a parallel combination of component networks rather than the series combination of Fig. 10.01–C. At the important points $p = \pm j2$, we have $Y_0 = 1/j1.2$ which is the admittance of an inductor L_1 defined by

$$L_1 = \frac{1}{j2\,Y_0(j2)} = 0.6\text{ h} \quad (10.01\text{–}22)$$

as before. We proceed to build a network around this in the form shown in Fig. 10.01–D. Here an impedance Z_a is necessary to prevent

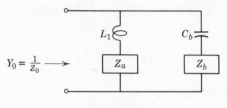

$$Y_0 = \frac{1}{Z_0} \longrightarrow$$

Fig. 10.01–D

a short circuit at zero frequency; a shunt path is necessary to prevent an open circuit at infinity, and this path we arbitrarily split into C_b and Z_b as shown. The symbols have meanings different to those of the first Bott–Duffin realization, of course. But, much as before, we must have

$$\begin{aligned}
Z_a(0) &= Z_0(0), \\
Z_b(\infty) &= Z_0(\infty), \\
Z_a(\pm j2) &= 0, \\
Z_b(\pm j2) &\to \infty.
\end{aligned} \qquad (10.01\text{–}23)$$

We now require also that

$$Z_a Z_b = R_c^2 \qquad (10.01\text{–}24)$$

which leaves $Z_a(p)$, R_c, and C_b to be determined, if possible, so that the network of Fig. 10.01–D is realizable, and without great difficulty. Then from Fig. 10.01–D,

$$\begin{aligned}
Y_0 &= \frac{1}{L_1 p + Z_a} + \frac{1}{1/C_b p + Z_b} \\
&= \frac{1}{Z_a + L_a p} + \frac{C_b p Z_1}{Z_a + R_c^2 C_b p} \qquad (10.01\text{–}25)
\end{aligned}$$

and for simplicity we again set the denominators equal. With

$$L_1 = R_c^2 C_b \qquad (10.01\text{–}26)$$

we have

$$Y_0(p) = \frac{C_b p Z_a + 1}{Z_a + L_1 p}. \qquad (10.01\text{–}27)$$

Solution for Z_a gives

$$Z_a = \frac{1 - L_1 p Y_0(p)}{Y_0(p) - C_b p} = -L_1 p \, \frac{Y_0(p) - 1/L_1 p}{Y_0(p) - C_b p} \qquad (10.01\text{–}28)$$

which is not greatly different from (10.01–9) in character. The numerator is a pseudo-p-r function, with one (and only one) right-half-plane zero; if C_b is positive, so is the denominator, and we shall determine C_b to cancel the right-half-plane zero of Z_a. The resemblance to (10.01–9) is more evident in

$$Y_a = \frac{1}{Z_a} = -C_b p \, \frac{Z_0(p) - 1/C_b p}{Z_0(p) - L_1 p}; \qquad (10.01\text{–}29)$$

in fact, we now observe that

$$Y_a(p) = \frac{C_b}{L_1} Z_1(p) = \frac{Z_1(p)}{R_c^2} \qquad (10.01\text{–}30)$$

in which (10.01–9) and (10.01–26) have been used to relate Y_a of this development to Z_1 of the previous realization. We need calculate no more, for the realization of Y_a will be essentially the same as that of Z_1, and we should find

$$C_b = C_3, \qquad R_c = R_0, \qquad (10.01\text{–}31)$$

so that

$$Y_a = \frac{Z_1(p)}{R_0^2} = \frac{1}{Z_3}, \qquad (10.01\text{–}32)$$

and

$$Z_b = R_0^2 Y_a = Z_1. \qquad (10.01\text{–}33)$$

Hence the realization proposed in Fig. 10.01–D is possible, and in fact it can be obtained immediately from that of Fig. 10.01–C by placing the impedance Z_1 in series with $C_b = C_3$, and Z_2 in series with L_1, as Fig. 10.01–E shows.

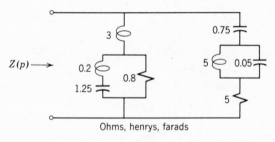

Ohms, henrys, farads

Fig. 10.01–E

We have thus found two different (though closely related) realizations of the impedance function $Z(p)$ of (10.01–1). Whether the process is truly general we do not yet know, and a careful investigation is in order. Before embarking thereon, let us consider the other possibility, the case in which at the frequency of zero resistance the reactance is *negative* rather than positive. For illustration we take again the reciprocal of the function used above, i.e.,

$$Z(p) = \frac{p^2 + p + 10}{5p^2 + 18p + 8} \quad \text{ohms} \tag{10.01-34}$$

or

$$Z_0(p) = 5Z = \frac{p^2 + p + 10}{p^2 + 3.6p + 1.6}. \tag{10.01-35}$$

This function is in all respects minimum, and we know that its even part vanishes at $p = \pm j2$. Since

$$Z_0(j2) = \frac{1}{j1.2} = -j0.8333 \tag{10.01-36}$$

we cannot use an inductor to represent the impedance at this frequency. We can, however, use a capacitor, whose reactance is negative. This would be C_3 if we seek the form of realization of Fig. 10.01–B, or C_b if that of Fig. 10.01–D. We need not calculate at all, however, for every step would be dual to one taken before. Our example here is numerically the same in terms of admittance as that one was in terms of impedance, so that we can immediately write down two realizations of (10.01–34)—another instance of the power of the duality principle. They are shown in Fig. 10.01–F (dual to Fig. 10.01–C) and in Fig. 10.01–G (dual to

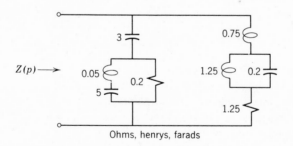

Ohms, henrys, farads

Fig. 10.01–F

Fig. 10.01–E). Had the numerical work not been done previously in another connection, it would of course be necessary to go through it— but the only change from that of the first example, aside from numbers, would be in the replacement of each electrical quantity by its dual.

The numerical examples of this section indicate that the Bott–Duffin technique gives two different realizations of driving-point immittance functions, the forms being those of Figs. 10.01–C and –E, or of Figs. 10.01–F and –G, the choice depending on the sign of the reactance at the frequency of zero resistance. The two realizations are not really different, however, as one might expect from the resemblances of the second development to the first, evidenced in (10.01–31), (10.01–32),

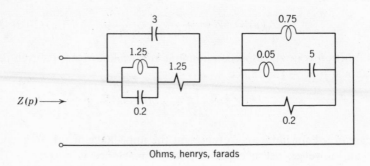

Ohms, henrys, farads

Fig. 10.01–G

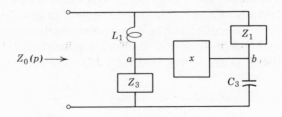

Fig. 10.01–H

(10.01–33). If we redraw Fig. 10.01–B as Fig. 10.01–H, their common character becomes evident. If the network x is a short circuit, this is Fig. 10.01–B again; if x is an open circuit, it is Fig. 10.01–D again. Simple analysis in the latter case shows that the points a and b are always at the same potential, so that no current will flow in x, regardless of the nature of x. This is in effect a balanced-bridge structure, x representing the "detector" arm, and x may be any network whatever. The two simplest possibilities are of course the short circuit and the open circuit of the original developments; more complicated x networks are entirely academic, yet in theory the Bott–Duffin technique on this account leads to an infinite number of realizations. Their common nature justifies the statement, however, that even the two primitive realizations are not really different.

Since no mutual inductance is required in these examples, it becomes of great interest to know whether the technique will succeed in general when applied to *any* p-r function. It is not at all difficult to retrace the arguments of this section in general terms, with $Z_0(p)$ now representing an arbitrary (minimum) p-r function. The principal step is the demonstration that $Z_1(p)$, as given by (10.01–9) with C_3 determined by (10.01–15), is p-r and of at most the same order as Z_0. That it has poles at the basic frequencies of zero resistance is evident, and when these poles are removed a new impedance, reduced in order by at least two in comparison with $Z_0(p)$, appears. This reduced impedance and its inverse in Z_3 (Z_4 and Z_5 in Fig. 10.01–I) we can reduce to minimum; and we can then apply the

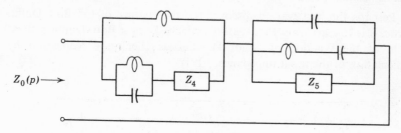

Fig. 10.01–I

entire Bott–Duffin procedure again, etc., until the realization is complete. It will take a branching form, not at all like the Brune ladder structure, but nowhere will it use mutual inductance. Assuming this work done, we can now say that

any p-r function can be realized as a driving-point immittance without the use of mutual inductance.   (10.01–37)

The number of elements used in the Bott–Duffin process increases rapidly with the order of the function, which is apparently the price to be paid for the absence of mutual inductance. But we see now that just as in the *L-C* (and *R-C* and *R-L*) cases, M is not necessary in the general (*R-L-C*) case.

The original function need not be reduced to minimum-reactance and minimum-susceptance form, except that sometimes poles and zeros at the origin and infinity must be removed before applying the Bott–Duffin technique (Problem 10-13). It need not even be reduced to minimum-resistance (minimum-conductance) form: then L_1 is to be determined by new means, and sometimes it can be chosen so that Z_1 is more readily realized and progress is made. Still more possibilities for different realizations appear at each stage of reduction, in choosing the technique to be applied next to Z_1 and Z_3, for our previously developed methods could also be used. That synthesis is not unique has been abundantly demonstrated, but the fact is emphasized again and again as we discover new techniques. Indeed, we have not yet seen all the possibilities of the Bott–Duffin technique.

In order to understand the basic principle of this process, we must adopt a different point of view. The development presented above is entirely too arbitrary at many points to be satisfactory, although it yields a perfectly general procedure. We shall now discard this approach and investigate the real character of this new realization process.

10.02 Another point of view

Perhaps the best way to discover the true nature of the Bott–Duffin process is to start from Fig. 10.01–C, which shows a Bott–Duffin realization of the function of (10.01–1). Let us check the realization by calculation of the input impedance. It is

$$Z(p) = \cfrac{1}{\cfrac{1}{3p} + \cfrac{1}{\cfrac{1}{0.05p + \cfrac{1}{5p}} + 5}} + \cfrac{1}{0.75p + \cfrac{1}{0.2p + \cfrac{1}{1.25p}} + \cfrac{1}{0.8}}$$

$$= \frac{5p(p^2 + 4p + 4)}{p^3 + \frac{5}{3}p^2 + \frac{32}{3}p + \frac{20}{3}} + \frac{\frac{4}{3}(p^2 + 4)}{p^3 + \frac{5}{3}p^2 + \frac{32}{3}p + \frac{20}{3}} \qquad (10.02-1)$$

$$= \frac{5p^3 + \frac{64}{3}p^2 + 20p + \frac{16}{3}}{p^3 + \frac{5}{3}p^2 + \frac{32}{3}p + \frac{20}{3}}$$

$$= \frac{5(p^2 + 3.6p + 1.6)(p + \frac{2}{3})}{(p^2 + p + 10)(p + \frac{2}{3})} \qquad (10.02-2)$$

$$= \frac{5p^2 + 18p + 8}{p^2 + p + 10} \quad \text{ohms}$$

which agrees with (10.01–1). It should, of course—but notice the manner in which the agreement is forced: the impedance of the network of Fig. 10.01–C should generally be of order six, but two things reduce it. First, the poles of the two networks in series are the same, as (10.02–1) shows, and this reduces the order to three; second, when the terms are written over their common denominator as in (10.02–2), a cancellation occurs and the order is brought down to two. And with these observations the light dawns: the Bott–Duffin realization procedure amounts really to

1. multiplying and dividing the given immittance by a *surplus factor*, in this example $(p + \frac{2}{3})$ as in (10.02–2), and
2. separating the augmented impedance into two terms, each of which is then easier to realize, as in (10.02–1).   (10.02–3)

The first function has a zero at the origin, and after this has been removed, the remaining impedance function has poles at $\pm j2$; the second function has zeros at infinity and at $\pm j2$. The increase in the number of elements over the number used in the Brune realization (Fig. 9.02–E) is due to this increase in the order of the function when the surplus factor is introduced and when the separation into two series-connected networks is made. This new factor of numerator and denominator does not actually affect the impedance function, but it evidently is of great value in the realization process. This is a device new to us, the introduction of surplus or unnecessary factors, and it is the heart of the Bott–Duffin technique. Let us now examine this device in general, for it appears to be a valuable tool, and with it we can indeed jettison the clumsy approach of § 10.01 (PA 1).

Suppose $Z(p)$ an arbitrary p-r impedance function to be realized. We can first reduce it to minimum, usually in various ways; let $Z_0(p)$ be the minimum function so obtained. On introducing a surplus factor $(p + \alpha)$, α being real and positive, we have

$$Z_s(p) = \frac{(p + \alpha)Z_0(p)}{(p + \alpha)} \qquad (10.02\text{–}4)$$

to realize. This is now to be split into two (or more) additive components, each of which must be p-r and capable of reduction in some simple fashion without the use of mutual inductance, as by the removal of imaginary zeros or poles:

$$Z_s = Z_A + Z_B. \qquad (10.02\text{–}5)$$

It is convenient again to consider the even part, so we divide the impedance function into even and odd parts and write

$$Z_0(p) = E_0 + O_0. \qquad (10.02\text{–}6)$$

Then

$$Z_s(p) = \frac{(\alpha + p)(E_0 + O_0)}{(\alpha + p)} \qquad (10.02\text{–}7)$$

and

$$\mathrm{Ev}\, Z_s(p) = \frac{(\alpha^2 - p^2)E_0}{\alpha^2 - p^2} = E_A + E_B, \qquad (10.02\text{–}8)$$

in which E_A and E_B represent the even parts of the two components. A natural identification to make is

$$E_A = \frac{\alpha^2 E_0}{\alpha^2 - p^2},$$

$$E_B = \frac{-p^2 E_0}{\alpha^2 - p^2}.$$

(10.02–9)

Both of these are positive (or zero) at all real frequencies as required (§ 8.16). From them we can calculate O_A and O_B, i.e., Z_A and Z_B (for Z_A and Z_B must be minimum-reactance), each of which is to be p-r and capable of simple reduction (at least in part). The order of each has been increased by one over that of $Z_0(p)$; but Z_A will evidently have a zero at infinity, and Z_B a zero at the origin, whose removal will restore the original order. The main problem is to insure that, on removal of these, each function will have additional imaginary zeros or poles for simple reduction. And since the even parts have zeros not only at infinity and the origin respectively but also at the frequencies of zero resistance of Z_0, this is likely to be possible.

To do this we must obtain Z_A and Z_B themselves, and fortunately this can be done without the involved calculations of Chapter 8. We write the odd part of Z_A as

$$O_A = \frac{\alpha^2 O_0}{\alpha^2 - p^2} + \frac{f(p)}{\alpha^2 - p^2}$$

(10.02–10)

in which the first term represents simply a hopeful guess at the major part of O_A, suggested by the form of E_A, and the second term represents whatever is necessary to complete O_A. Clearly $f(p)$ must be rational and *odd*. Now

$$Z_A = E_A + O_A = \frac{\alpha^2(E_0 + O_0) + f(p)}{\alpha^2 - p^2} = \frac{\alpha^2 Z_0(p) + f(p)}{\alpha^2 - p^2}$$

(10.02–11)

is to be p-r. And $f(p)$ can have no right-half-plane poles, for there can be none in Z_A, and Z_0 has none to cancel any in $f(p)$. Hence $f(p)$ can have only imaginary poles and may be a reactance function in form, though possibly with some negative residues. Each such negative-residue pole gives the numerator of (10.02–11) a right-half-plane zero by the reasoning of § 9.12, and of these we want one (at $p = \alpha$) and only one, so we write

$$f(p) = -Kp \qquad \text{or} \qquad -K/p$$

(10.02–12)

in which $K > 0$. With the second choice Z_A would not be p-r (it would have a second-order zero at infinity), so we take $f(p) = Kp$. We now have

$$Z_A = \frac{\alpha^2 Z_0(p) - Kp}{\alpha^2 - p^2} \qquad (10.02-13)$$

and, by subtraction from Z_0,

$$Z_B = \frac{-p^2 Z_0(p) + Kp}{\alpha^2 - p^2} = \frac{-p^2(Z_0 - K/p)}{\alpha^2 - p^2}. \qquad (10.02-14)$$

Evidently K and α must be related by

$$K = \alpha Z_0(\alpha), \qquad (10.02-15)$$

for this removes the right-half-plane pole from both Z_A and Z_B by giving each of them a zero at the same point. (If the pole at $p = \alpha$ is removed from Z_A, it is automatically removed from Z_B also, for Z_0 has no such pole.) Both Z_A and Z_B are now p-r, as routine testing will show, so long as (10.02-15) is fulfilled. We can give to K (or to α) any positive value we wish, but probably progress in the realization will not be made if K is arbitrarily chosen. But it can always be chosen so that simple reduction is possible; for there is at least one real frequency, ω_0, at which Z_0 is purely reactive,

$$Z_0(j\omega_0) = 0 + jX_0. \qquad (10.02-16)$$

If $X_0 > 0$ we can give Z_A a zero there by the choice

$$K = \frac{\alpha^2 X_0}{\omega_0} = \alpha^2 L_1 > 0 \qquad (10.02-17)$$

in which

$$L_1 = \frac{X_0}{\omega_0}. \qquad (10.02-18)$$

Here L_1 is known, and K and α are determined by simultaneous solution of (10.02-17) and (10.02-15); this amounts to finding the right-half-plane zero of $[Z_0(p) - L_1 p]$, which is α and can always be found.

Then

$$Y_A = \frac{1}{Z_A} = \frac{\alpha^2 - p^2}{\alpha^2(Z_0 - L_1 p)}$$

$$= C_3 p + (-C_3 p)\frac{Z_0 - 1/C_3 p}{Z_0 - L_1 p}, \qquad (10.02-19)$$

in which

$$C_3 = \frac{1}{\alpha^2 L_1}. \qquad (10.02-20)$$

And

$$Y_B = \frac{1}{Z_B} = \frac{\alpha^2 - p^2}{-p^2 Z_0 + \alpha^2 L_1 p}$$

$$= \frac{(1/L_1)}{p} + \frac{Z_0 - L_1 p}{(-L_1 p)(Z_0 - 1/C_3 p)}. \qquad (10.02\text{–}21)$$

In each case the expected pole (at infinity or the origin) has been removed; and it is evident that Y_A also has poles at $\pm j\omega_0$, as does the impedance remaining after removal of L_1 from Y_B. Thus the realization of Fig. 10.02–A is obtained, in which the impedances remaining, indicated by

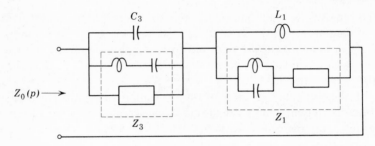

Fig. 10.02–A

boxes, are reduced in order by two from that of Z_0. This is identical with a realization of § 10.01, that shown in Fig. 10.01–B and the accompanying analysis, and the symbols have the same meanings and interrelations.

If $X_0 < 0$, we can give Z_B zeros at $\pm j\omega_0$ by the choice

$$K = -\omega_0 X_0 = \frac{1}{C_3} > 0 \qquad (10.02\text{–}22)$$

which defines C_3. Then

$$Y_A = \frac{1}{Z_A} = \frac{\alpha^2 - p^2}{\alpha^2 Z_0 - (1/C_3)p}$$

$$= C_3 p + (-C_3 p)\frac{Z_0 - 1/C_3 p}{Z_0 - L_1 p}, \qquad (10.02\text{–}23)$$

in which

$$L_1 = \frac{1}{\alpha^2 C_3}$$

and α is determined by (10.02–15).

And

$$Y_B = \frac{1}{Z_B} = \frac{\alpha^2 - p^2}{-p^2 Z_0 + (1/C_3)p}$$

$$= \frac{(1/L_1)}{p} + \frac{Z_0 - L_1 p}{(-L_1 p)[Z_0 - 1/C_3 p]} \qquad (10.02\text{–}24)$$

and the realization of Fig. 10.02–B is obtained. This is again identical with a realization of § 10.01, that shown in Fig. 10.01–G for the example considered there, and the symbols again have the same meanings.

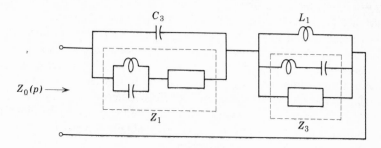

Fig. 10.02–B

Thus the use of a surplus factor and the separation of Z_s indicated in (10.02–9) lead again to the Bott–Duffin realization (the process being repeated with the reduced impedances as necessary). A similar treatment of admittance (rather than impedance) leads to the networks of Fig. 10.01–D, as is immediately evident by duality. The remarks of §10.01 on the common nature of the two realizations apply equally well here also, of course. So far, then, the surplus-factor approach has produced no new realizations. But it has indeed given us some insight and has placed the Bott–Duffin technique on a somewhat more logical foundation than did the heuristic approach of § 10.01. And it is more powerful still, as we shall see.

Before continuing this investigation we should consider the possibility of giving to L_1 (or equivalently, to C_3 or α or K, for any one of the four determines the others) a value different from that determined by (10.02–18) or (10.02–22). The components Z_A and Z_B will be p-r for any real, positive choice, and the elements L_1 and C_3 can be removed, leaving two immittance functions of the same order as the original function,

$$Y_A = C_3 p + (-C_3 p) \frac{Z_0 - 1/C_3 p}{Z_0 - L_1 p} \qquad (10.02\text{–}25)$$

$$= C_3 p + Y_3,$$

$$Y_B = \frac{(1/L_1)}{p} + \left(\frac{-1}{L_1 p}\right) \frac{Z_0 - L_1 p}{Z_0 - 1/C_3 p}$$

$$= \frac{(1/L_1)}{p} + Y_1,$$

(10.02–26)

exactly as before. This is illustrated in Fig. 10.01–B. If progress is to be made, these new functions Y_1 and Y_3 must be capable of simple reduction—and our previous choices are quite clearly those which create an appropriate real-frequency pole or zero: either $(Z_0 - L_1 p)$ or $[Z_0 - 1/C_3 p]$ then vanishes at $\pm j\omega_0$. And if $Z_0(p)$ is minimum-resistance (as assumed above), these are the only useful choices.

But if the datum impedance function is *not* minimum-resistance, then additional possibilities arise. Instead of first removing series resistance to reduce the function, and then using the surplus-factor technique as previously described, we can immediately apply this technique to obtain (10.02–25) and (10.02–26), with an arbitrary value of L_1. Then neither Z_1 nor Z_3 is minimum-resistance. By then reducing either or both to minimum-resistance we may (or may not) obtain functions with real-frequency zeros or poles that can then be removed. Since the value of L_1 is arbitrary here, it may well be possible to choose it so that a useful realization can thus be obtained. And the dual possibility of removing conductance (rather than resistance) may be helpful. It is difficult to generalize this and we shall not attempt to do so. But there is here a possibility of obtaining additional realizations.

If the datum impedance function is not minimum-resistance, the zeros of its even part lie on the real axis or in complex tetrads. Since the original approach to the Bott–Duffin realization was based on determining L_1 (or C_3) to give the value of Z_0 at the zero of Ev Z_0 at $j\omega_0$, it is only natural to attempt the same thing when the zeros of the even part are not imaginary—especially since this technique was so successful in Chapter 9. For complex zeros, two elements (rather than L_1 or C_3 alone) are of course necessary, and this requires the use of two surplus factors rather than one (Problem 10-15). For real zeros, however, only one element is necessary to give the value of Z_0 and this possibility we now investigate.

Regardless of the value given L_1 we have (almost exactly as before)

$$Z_A = \frac{\alpha^2}{\alpha^2 - p^2}(Z_0 - L_1 p),$$

(10.02–27)

$$Z_B = \frac{-p^2}{\alpha^2 - p^2}\left(Z_0 - \frac{1}{C_3 p}\right),$$

(10.02–28)

in which $Z_0(p)$ is the datum (nonminimum-resistance) impedance function,

$-\alpha$ is the zero of the surplus factor, and the terms $(-L_1 p)$ and $(-1/C_3 p)$ are those required to obtain the impedance functions Z_A and Z_B when $\mathrm{Ev}\, Z_s(p)$ is separated as in (10.02–9). All three of these constants are for the moment arbitrary (except that they must be positive and are inter-related). If they are so chosen that Z_A and Z_B are p-r, the developments of (10.02–25) and (10.02–26) are then possible. Since $\mathrm{Ev}\, Z_0(p)$ has a real zero, say at p_0 in the right half plane (and of course at $-p_0$, and possibly elsewhere too), let us determine L_1 by

$$Z_0(p_0) = L_1 p_0 \quad \text{or} \quad L_1 = \frac{Z_0(p_0)}{p_0}. \qquad (10.02\text{–}29)$$

(This is equivalent, in the heuristic approach of § 10.01, to choosing L_1 in Fig. 10.01–A to represent the whole of Z_0 at the point p_0.) Since $Z_0(p)$ is p-r, L_1 determined by (10.02–29) is positive, and $(Z_0 - L_1 p)$ has only one right-half-plane zero, that at p_0. If Z_A is to be p-r then we must take

$$\alpha = p_0 \qquad (10.02\text{–}30)$$

to remove the right-half-plane zero in (10.02–27). Then to remove the right-half-plane pole in (10.02–28) we must set

$$C_3 = \frac{1}{Z_0(p_0) \times p_0} = \frac{1}{Z_0(\alpha) \times \alpha}. \qquad (10.02\text{–}31)$$

Then both Z_A and Z_B are p-r, and we can expand the admittances as in (10.02–25) and (10.02–26). If the order of Z_0 is n we expect the order of Z_A (and of Z_B) to be $(n + 1)$, because of the surplus factor, and the order of Z_3 (and of Z_1) to be n again. But in this case there is a further reduction in order which is apparent in (10.02–25) and (10.02–26). For the two functions $(Z_0 - L_1 p)$ and $(Z_0 - 1/C_3 p)$ have zeros at p_0 (by design) and *also* at $(-p_0)$. These left-half-plane zeros arise because $\mathrm{Ev}\, Z_0(p_0) = 0$ and hence the terms $L_1 p$ and $1/C_3 p$ (which are odd) take the value of $\mathrm{Od}\, Z_0(p_0)$ at p_0; when the functions are evaluated at $(-p_0)$ the even parts are again zero, and so also are the odd parts. Hence the order of Z_3 (and of Z_1) is $(n - 1)$ rather than n, for two cancellations occur. Furthermore, the additional factor that cancels is $(p + \alpha)$, i.e., the surplus factor disappears. In other words, this particular decomposition does not actually use the surplus factor but could have been made without it. And in retrospect this possibility is quite clear: we need only write

$$E_0 = \mathrm{Ev}\, Z_0(p) = \frac{N_0}{D_0} = \frac{(p_0^2 - p^2)N_{01}}{D_0} \qquad (10.02\text{–}32)$$

in which the real zero has been factored out for emphasis, and compare this with (10.02–7) and (10.02–9). Here we need no surplus factor because the factor $(p_0{}^2 - p^2)$ already present in $\mathrm{Ev}\, Z_0(p)$ will serve just as well.   We separate E_0 into

$$E_A = \frac{p_0{}^2 N_{01}}{D_0} \tag{10.02-33}$$

and

$$E_B = \frac{-p^2 N_{01}}{D_0}, \tag{10.02-34}$$

and observe that both fulfil the requirements on the even part of a p-r function (§ 8.16), hence that when the corresponding impedance functions $Z_A(p)$ and $Z_B(p)$ are calculated they will be p-r.   The order of each is the same as that of Z_0, but Z_A will have a zero at infinity and Z_B a zero at the origin;   these can be immediately removed (as in Fig. 10.02–C) so that

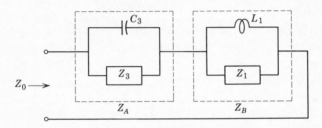

Fig. 10.02–C

the order is reduced by one in each case, and both Z_3 and Z_1 are of order $(n-1)$.   Real zeros of the even part then can be used as a basis for the separation into parts, even with no surplus factor;   and each different real zero leads to a different realization.   The realizations obtainable thereby may be preferable in some cases (because they require a smaller number of elements) to those obtained by first removing resistance and then applying the Brune or Bott–Duffin technique to the resulting minimum-resistance function.   In all of this, as usual, the dual point of view could be adopted, but no essentially new network results (cf. the discussion associated with Fig. 10.01–H).   Nor will a matching of the value of $Z_0(p_0)$ with a capacitor rather than an inductor yield anything new; it is already included in the above discussion, for here both L_1 and C_3 supply the value of Z_0 at p_0—in marked contrast to the case where the zero of $\mathrm{Ev}\, Z_0(p)$ is imaginary.

  In retrospect, the ideas proposed in § 10.01 have led us to the Bott–Duffin realization technique, and even further.   For we now have before us a vast field of possible realization devices, which we cannot completely explore. The basic principle of all of these is

> to separate the even part of an immittance into two or more (additive) terms, each of which is the even part of a p-r function that is capable of simple reduction.   (10.02–35)

We have seen that this may occasionally be done with the original function, that sometimes it is necessary first to multiply and divide by a surplus factor, and we expect that at times it will be helpful to use two or even more surplus factors.   It is not particularly difficult to determine whether an even function is actually the even part of a p-r function: the principal requirement is that it not take any negative values on the imaginary axis (§ 8.16), and this is our guide in the separation process.   We seek also to make a separation such that one part has zeros at the origin and the other at infinity, so that reduction by removal of an inductor or a capacitor, or of several of these, is immediately possible.   (Sometimes zeros at internal real frequencies will lead to zeros or poles in the partial immittances that are easily removed, also.)   If a surplus factor is used, we must also insure that further simple reduction is possible after we return to the order of the original function.

One may ask: could the *odd* part of the given immittance also serve as a basis for decomposition?   Since either part (odd or even) determines a minimum immittance function, the answer must in theory be *yes*.   But use of the odd part is awkward, for an odd function determines its corresponding whole function only within an additive constant (resistance or conductance); this constant must have a certain minimum value if the function is to be p-r, obtainable only by calculation of the even part of the whole function, and only then do we know whether the decomposition is possible.   The even part, on the other hand, determines the corresponding whole function uniquely (if imaginary poles are excluded) and we know *in advance* whether or not it will be p-r.   Hence it is the even part that should be used in these decomposition procedures, as a practical matter.   One might well use the immittance function itself, of course, but the even parts must be investigated anyway (in checking realizability) and they might as well be employed *ab initio*.

We cannot completely investigate the manifold possibilities of our new technique (it is too broad), but we can discuss a few, enough to point out the important possibilities.

10.03 Separation without surplus factors

In the two preceding sections we have encountered a new basis for realization, that summed up in (10.02–35).   This separation of the even part into additive components can often be accomplished in a large number of different ways; it is not at all unique. But to prepare a detailed catalog of the various possible partitions, with statements of the utility of each, is not a simple matter; we shall not attempt it here, but shall only mention some of the realizations that can be made. One reason for this wide variety is that these realizations generally use more elements than are absolutely necessary: the Brune realization of a minimum immittance of order two, for example, uses three reactive elements (and one resistor); the Bott–Duffin realization requires six reactive elements (and two resistors). This increase in number of elements appears in general to be the price of the elimination of mutual inductance, though this has not actually been demonstrated.

We found, in § 10.02, that the separation could sometimes be performed directly on the datum function without a surplus factor. Let us consider this possibility in more detail, taking

$$E_0 = \frac{a_0 + a_2 p^2 + a_4 p^4 + \cdots + a_{2n} p^{2n}}{b_0 + b_2 p^2 + b_4 p^4 + \cdots + b_{2n} p^{2n}} = \frac{N_0}{D_0} \qquad (10.03\text{–}1)$$

as the even part of the given (p-r) impedance function $Z_0(p)$ reduced to minimum-reactance—or, with dual interpretation of all that follows, of the given admittance function—of order n. Then E_0 has no imaginary poles, by (8.11–4), its denominator is positive, and its numerator is zero or positive for all imaginary values of p. We seek to partition it, requiring each part to have these same properties and to lend itself fairly simply to reduction.

One simple possibility occurs if

$$\left.\begin{matrix} a_0 \\ a_4 \\ a_8 \\ \cdot \\ \cdot \\ \cdot \end{matrix}\right\} \geqq 0 \quad \text{and} \quad \left.\begin{matrix} a_2 \\ a_6 \\ a_{10} \\ \cdot \\ \cdot \\ \cdot \end{matrix}\right\} \leqq 0. \qquad (10.03\text{–}2)$$

For then each individual term in the numerator of E_0 is zero or positive at all real frequencies; and we can separate E_0 into n components, all with the denominator of E_0 and with numerators consisting each of a single term from the numerator of E_0; the zeros of each of these components occur only at the origin or only at infinity (or at both). As discussed in § 9.11, the realization of such functions is particularly simple, requiring only a ladder structure (in which each arm is a single inductor or capacitor, with several possible arrangements in general) terminated in a resistor.   For example, if we have a minimum-reactance function $Z_0(p)$ to realize, whose even part is

$$E_0 = \frac{a_0 + a_4 p^4 + a_8 p^8}{b_0 + b_2 p^2 \cdots + b_8 p^8} = \frac{N_0}{D_0} \qquad (10.03\text{–}3)$$

(in which the a's are all positive), we may write

$$E_0 = \frac{a_0}{D_0} + \frac{a_4 p^4}{D_0} + \frac{a_8 p^8}{D_0}$$
$$= E_A + E_B + E_C. \qquad (10.03\text{–}4)$$

When the corresponding minimum-reactance impedances Z_A, Z_B, and Z_C are found (as by the techniques of Chapter 8 or that of Problem 10-79), they can immediately be developed as shown in Fig. 10.03–A.   In developing Z_A (and Z_C) the procedure offers no choice, for all the zeros of E_A

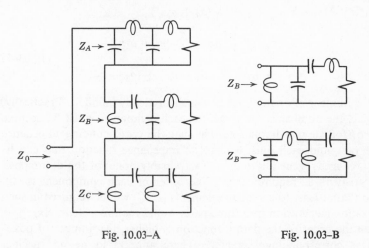

Fig. 10.03–A   Fig. 10.03–B

(and of E_C) are at one point (infinity and the origin, respectively); but in developing Z_B we may remove the zeros of E_B (located half at the origin and half at infinity) in various sequences, leading to the additional possibilities for Z_B shown in Fig. 10.03–B.   Under certain circumstances this method may require fewer elements than the other methods we have discussed, except the Brune method (which requires mutual inductance, not needed here).   In general, however, it will require more elements than the other methods.

It may be possible to economize on elements by separating E_0 into a smaller number of components, i.e., to take the terms of N_0 in groups, at least some of which contain more than one term. Each term in N_0 may be assigned entirely to one of these groups, or may be divided between several; the possibilities are in general numerous, since the only requirements are that no group become negative at any real frequency, and that each group have a zero at the origin, or be of degree less than that of D_0, or have zeros at internal real frequencies that lead to zeros in the corresponding component impedance. If the datum function is of order two, for example, we have

$$N_0 = a_0 + a_2 p^2 + a_4 p^4. \qquad (10.03\text{--}5)$$

This could be partitioned into

$$\left.\begin{array}{c} (a_0) + (a_2 p^2 + a_4 p^4) \\[2mm] \text{or} \\[2mm] (a_2 p^2) + (a_0 + a_4 p^4) \\[2mm] \text{or} \\[2mm] (a_4 p^4) + (a_0 + a_2 p^2) \end{array}\right\} \qquad (10.03\text{--}6)$$

or into

$$\left.\begin{array}{c} (a_0 + a_2' p^2) + [(a_2 - a_2')p^2 + a_4 p^4] \\[2mm] \text{or} \\[2mm] (a_0' + a_2' p^2 + a_4 p^4) + [(a_0 - a_0') + (a_2 - a_2')p^2] \end{array}\right\} \qquad (10.03\text{--}7)$$

etc.; the number of possibilities here is theoretically infinite. Practically, of course, the number is not large, for each component must be positive (or zero) for all real frequencies (so that the corresponding impedance will be p-r), and each must lead to an impedance function that can be readily reduced; generally only a few (possibly none) of the decompositions satisfy these requirements. The order of each component is still two, so that at least four reactive elements (L, C) will be required in such a realization (separation into three parts would require at least six).

When the order of the datum function is higher, the number of possibilities is correspondingly greater. There appears to be no succinct method of cataloging the possible partitions, for most of them are valid only if the datum function meets certain requirements and not in general. (The method illustrated in Fig. 10.02–C, however, is an example that is always valid when the even part of the datum function has real zeros.) In any particular case, the attractive possibilities can be examined numerically. The problems at the end of this chapter will give some idea of the possibilities; Problems 10-57, 10-58, 10-59 are particularly interesting. Furthermore, the number of elements can sometimes be appreciably reduced by partitioning into fewer parts and repeating the process (KU 2).

If the datum function is minimum-resistance (minimum-conductance) with a zero value of resistance (conductance) at $\omega = \omega_0$, say, then the factor $(p^2 + \omega_0{}^2)^2$, and perhaps more like it, is necessarily common to all the components; it may be temporarily ignored and the possibility of partition of only the balance of N_0 considered. Similarly, any factor or group of factors of N_0 that is not negative at any real frequency may be temporarily excluded from the partitioning and later restored to the parts.

The number of possible realizations employing the technique of dividing up the even part of an impedance or admittance function into parts for separate realization is obviously large in general. It may well happen that some of these realizations require fewer elements than do the other known methods of realization without the use of mutual inductance; but in general one may expect to use at least as many elements in this kind of realization, and often more than, for example, do the methods of Pantell (§ 10.05) and Bott and Duffin. Notice that an examination of the possible partitions of the even part of either the impedance *or* the admittance function is sufficient; the possibilities are the same, but any particular partition may lead to two different realizations, one if it is **Ev** Z_0 that is so divided, and one if it is **Ev** Y_0.

One interesting possibility that should not be overlooked is partitioning N_0 in such a way that some cancellation occurs between the numerator and denominator in some of the com-
ponent parts of E_0. For example, if the datum impedance function has a zero on the (negative) real axis, it may be possible to remove a simple *R-C* network, as in Fig. 10.03–C. This possibility could be investigated by expanding $(1/pZ_0)$ in partial fractions (§ 7.08); if the residue at the corresponding pole is positive, and if the

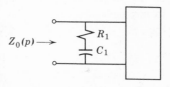

$Z_0(p) \longrightarrow$

Fig. 10.03–C

admittance remaining after removal of the corresponding term in the expansion is p-r, then the branch R_1-C_1 may be removed. To apply the present technique, on the other hand, since the even part of the admittance corresponding to the branch R_1-C_1 is

$$\mathbf{Ev}\left(\frac{1}{R_1 + 1/C_1 p}\right) = \frac{-R_1 C_1{}^2 p^2}{1 - R_1{}^2 C_1{}^2 p^2} = \frac{-(1/R_1)p^2}{(1/R_1 C_1) - p^2}, \quad (10.03\text{--}8)$$

we should so seek to partition N_0 (of the admittance) that one of the parts consists of all the factors of D_0, except one like $(p_0{}^2 - p^2)$, and the factor $(-p^2)$; then the desired cancellation will occur, the *R-C* branch is immediately removable, and one may proceed to the realization of the reduced network. Corresponding devices lead to the removal (when possible) of shunt *R-L* branches—and of simple series or parallel *R-C* or *R-L* networks in general (cf. MO 1).

It is clear now that examination of the even part of the datum immittance function, with a view to partitioning it, may be a useful technique, even without considering the use of a surplus factor. Every possible ladder realization can in fact be obtained in this manner, including as special cases the canonic forms of L-C, R-C, and R-L networks (Chapters 6, 7), mixtures thereof, and the Brune and Darlington techniques of Chapter 9.

10.04 Separation with surplus factors

The use of surplus factors in immittance realizations has the primary advantage of making the number of successful partitions of the even part larger than when no surplus factor is used. If all the zeros of the even part lie on the imaginary axis, for example, no useful partition of the original function is possible; but the introduction of one surplus factor immediately makes possible the Bott–Duffin partition (§10.02).

Again it does not seem feasible to make a detailed catalog of the various possible partitions, as they depend too much on the characteristics of the particular immittance function in hand. Essentially the partition problem here differs from that of § 10.03 only in that there is a parameter α, corresponding to the surplus factor $(p + \alpha)$, whose value may be adjusted to any desired positive value—and often with very useful results. With the notation of (10.03–1) we write

$$E_s = \frac{(\alpha^2 - p^2)}{(\alpha^2 - p^2)} E_0 = \frac{(\alpha^2 - p^2)N_0}{(\alpha^2 - p^2)D_0} = \frac{N_s}{D_s} \qquad (10.04\text{–}1)$$

for the even part after the introduction of the surplus factor $(p + \alpha)$ into the datum immittance function. The modified even part has of course no imaginary poles, its denominator is positive, and its numerator zero or positive, for all imaginary values of p. Its numerator is

$$N_s = (\alpha^2 - p^2)(a_0 + a_2 p^2 + a_4 p^4 + \cdots + a_{2n} p^{2n})$$
$$= (\alpha^2 a_0) + (\alpha^2 a_2 - a_0)p^2 + (\alpha^2 a_4 - a^2)p^4 + \cdots$$
$$+ (\alpha^2 a_{2n} - a_{2n-2})p^{2n} + (-a_{2n})p^{2n+2}. \qquad (10.04\text{–}2)$$

Since α is adjustable, the possibilities for partition clearly are numerous. Each partial immittance will now be of order $(n + 1)$, in comparison with the order n of the original immittance function, so that the number of elements used will naturally be larger than in a realization obtained without using a surplus factor.

Perhaps the most straightforward partition is to take the terms of N_s individually as numerators of the components (all with denominator D_s).

This will be possible if α can be so chosen that

$$
\left.\begin{array}{c}
\alpha^2 a_0 \\
(\alpha^2 a_4 - a_2) \\
(\alpha^2 a_8 - a_6) \\
\cdot \\
\cdot \\
\cdot
\end{array}\right\} \geqq 0
\quad \text{and} \quad
\left.\begin{array}{c}
(\alpha^2 a_2 - a_0) \\
(\alpha^2 a_6 - a_4) \\
(\alpha^2 a_{10} - a_8) \\
\cdot \\
\cdot \\
\cdot
\end{array}\right\} \leqq 0, \quad (10.04\text{–}3)
$$

for then each term in N_s will be zero or positive all along the imaginary axis, and each corresponding immittance will be p-r. Exactly as before (§ 10.03) each of these components is readily realized as a ladder network, each arm of which is a single inductor or capacitor (with several possibilities in general) terminated in a resistor.

For example, suppose $Z_0(p)$ is p-r and of order two. Then

$$
E_0 = \frac{1 + 2ap^2 + p^4}{b_0 + b_2 p^2 + b_4 p^4} = \frac{N_0}{D_0} \quad (10.04\text{–}4)
$$

in which $a \leqq 1$. Negative values of a (and zero) are of no interest here, for then each term in N_0 already leads, individually, to a realization. If a is positive, however, (10.03–2) is violated and the partition there indicated cannot be made. But a surplus factor can be introduced; and to satisfy (10.04–3) we then need

$$
\begin{array}{cc}
\alpha^2 \geqq 0, & (2a\alpha^2 - 1) \leqq 0, \\
(\alpha^2 - 2a) \geqq 0, & (-1) \leqq 0.
\end{array} \quad (10.04\text{–}5)
$$

That is, α must satisfy

$$
2a \leqq \alpha^2 \leqq \frac{1}{2a} \quad (a > 0) \quad (10.04\text{–}6)
$$

which is possible if

$$
(4a^2) \leqq 1 \quad \text{or} \quad a \leqq \tfrac{1}{2}. \quad (10.04\text{–}7)
$$

If this requirement is met, then we have a range of possible values for α, and

$$
E_s = \frac{\alpha^2}{D_s} + \frac{(2a\alpha^2 - 1)p^2}{D_s} + \frac{(\alpha^2 - 2a)p^4}{D_s} + \frac{(-p^6)}{D_s} \quad (10.04\text{–}8)
$$

$$
= E_A + \quad E_B \quad + \quad E_C \quad + \quad E_D
$$

in which $D_s = (\alpha^2 - p^2)D_0$; this leads to the realization of Fig. 10.04–A. (Alternative configurations for two of the components are also shown.) It is interesting to interpret requirement (10.04–7) geometrically. If we designate the four zeros of $\text{Ev } Z_0(p)$ by

$$
p_0 = \sigma_0 + j\omega_0 = r_0 e^{j\theta_0} \quad (10.04\text{–}9)
$$

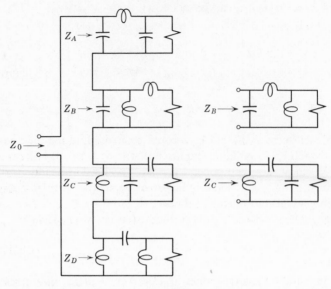

Fig. 10.04–A

(Fig. 10.04–B) and the three symmetrically located points (p_0 being assumed complex for the moment), then

$$
\begin{aligned}
N_0 &= (p - p_0)(p - \bar{p}_0)(p + p_0)(p + \bar{p}_0) \\
&= (p^2 - 2\sigma_0 p + r_0{}^2)(p^2 + 2\sigma_0 p + r_0{}^2) \\
&= p^4 + (2r_0{}^2 - 4\sigma_0{}^2)p^2 + r_0{}^4 \\
&= p^4 - 2(r_0{}^2 \cos 2\theta_0)p^2 + r_0{}^4.
\end{aligned}
\tag{10.04–10}
$$

Evidently

$$
r_0 = 1 \quad \text{and} \quad a = -\cos 2\theta_0
\tag{10.04–11}
$$

and requirement (10.04–7) amounts to $\theta_0 \leqq 60°$. If $\theta_0 \leqq 45°$ (including the case of real zeros), then E_0 meets the requirements of (10.03–2) without a surplus factor, and we have found that if θ_0 exceeds 45° but not 60°, one surplus factor will make this partition possible. (Additional surplus factors will make realization by this technique possible in cases where θ_0 exceeds 60° and is less than 90°; no finite number will suffice if $\theta_0 = 90°$.)

In more complicated cases, the determination of α may not be so simple a matter, but the principle should be clear. Generally these realizations required an excessive number of elements. But, exactly as before, the partitioning of N_s as given by (10.04–2) into a smaller number of components, by assigning parts or all of *several* terms of N_s to each component, may reduce the number of elements required. The partitioning must be made, of course, so that each component is not negative at any point on the imaginary axis, that it has some real-frequency zeros, and that these lead to real-frequency zeros in the corresponding component immittances. At one extreme is the Bott–Duffin technique in which N_0 is left undisturbed and the partition made as

$$N_s = (\alpha^2 N_0) + (-p^2 N_0); \quad (10.04\text{--}12)$$

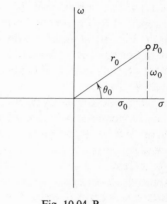

Fig. 10.04–B

at the other extreme is the technique just described, in which each term in (10.04–2) is considered a separate component. In between lie a large number of possibilities, in which the terms of (10.04–2) are arranged in various groupings to make up the components of N_s (cf. the corresponding discussion in § 10.03); these may be investigated individually. Alternatively (though equivalently), we may factor N_0 and write

$$
\begin{aligned}
N_s &= (\alpha^2 - p^2)N_0 \\
&= (\alpha^2 - p^2)[(p_0 - p)(p_0 + p)][(p_1 - p)(\bar{p}_1 - p)(p_1 + p)(\bar{p}_1 + p)] \\
&\qquad \times [(\omega_2{}^2 + p^2)^2] \times \cdots \quad (10.04\text{--}13)
\end{aligned}
$$

in which p_0 typifies a real zero of N_0, p_1 a complex zero, $j\omega_2$ an imaginary zero, and the corresponding factors shown in brackets are required by symmetry and the positive reality of the original immittance function. We may now take any number of the brackets, each of which is zero or positive for all real frequencies, and temporarily set it aside while we partition the remaining polynomial. The factors corresponding to real-frequency zeros must be common to all components and so treated; with the others we have freedom. If real zeros are present, they may often be used to advantage as a basis of partition without a surplus factor (§ 10.03). In complex zeros we have additional interesting possibilities. For example, suppose

$$N_0 = (1 + 2ap^2 + p^4)N_{01} \quad (10.04\text{--}14)$$

in which $-1 < a < 1$ so that the parenthesis represents a tetrad of complex zeros; N_{01} represents all the other zeros of N_0. If $a \leqq 0$, partitions of the parenthesis are possible without a surplus factor (§ 10.03).

If $0 < a < 1$, we may introduce a surplus factor and then proceed exactly as in the treatment of (10.04–4) above; all the discussion there applies here also, with the multiplication of each component of (10.04–8) by N_{01} (and the use of the appropriate denominator) and the corresponding increase in complexity of the component networks (in each the resistance is replaced by a more complicated network, but reactive elements arranged as in Fig. 10.04–A are again obtained, for the zeros of the even parts at the origin and at infinity are still present). The geometrical requirement on the location of the complex zeros on which this is based is again that $\theta_0 \leqq 60°$.

When real-frequency zeros, i.e., factors like $(\omega_2{}^2 + p^2)^2$, are present it may be possible to choose α so that some of the component immittances have zeros at $\pm j\omega_2$, or have zeros or poles at $\pm j\omega_2$ after the removal of some single reactive elements (corresponding to zeros of the even part at the origin and infinity, which are conveniently removed first). This choice is advantageous because *two* reactive elements can then be removed, with a reduction in order of two. Phrased differently, the object here is so to choose α that in the Brune development of one or more of the component immittances no mutual inductance (but only Type-A and Type-B sections) will be required in removing the factor $(\omega_2{}^2 + p^2)^2$ from the even part; this is a basic problem in the general application of the separation method.

Generally a partition into more than two components is inefficient and will require more elements than a partition into two parts (but there are exceptions). The Bott–Duffin approach always gives a two-component partition immediately; others are often feasible too, but it does not seem possible to generalize—each case is best investigated individually.

There are further illustrations in the problems at the end of this chapter; one more is given here. Suppose we have to realize a (p-r) minimum impedance function $Z_0(p)$ of order n, whose even part has the form

$$E_0 = \frac{N_0}{D_0} = \frac{(p^2 + \omega_0{}^2)^2(p^4 + a_2 p^2 + a_0)N_{01}}{D_0}, \qquad (10.04\text{–}15)$$

in which $a_0 > 0$, and we assume $a_2 > 0$ also (else the problem is of less interest). Although such a function may successfully be realized in other ways, let us here consider the use of a surplus factor, and write

$$E_s = \frac{\alpha^2 - p^2}{\alpha^2 - p^2} E_0$$

$$= \frac{(-p^6 - a_2 p^4 + \alpha^2 p^4 - a_0 p^2 + a_2 \alpha^2 p^2 + a_0 \alpha^2)(p^2 + \omega_0{}^2)^2 N_{01}}{(\alpha^2 - p^2)D_0}.$$

$$(10.04\text{–}16)$$

This we partition into two parts, E_A and E_B, with

$$E_A = \frac{a_0 \alpha^2 (p^2 + \omega_0^2)^2 N_{01}}{(\alpha^2 - p^2) D_0},$$

$$E_B = \frac{(-p^6 - a_2 p^4 + \alpha^2 p^4 - a_0 p^2 + a_2 \alpha^2 p^2)(p^2 + \omega_0^2)^2 N_{01}}{(\alpha^2 - p^2) D_0}.$$

$$(10.04\text{--}17)$$

The purpose of this form of partition is to achieve the realization shown in Fig. 10.04–C. If the partition is successful, E_A will have six zeros at

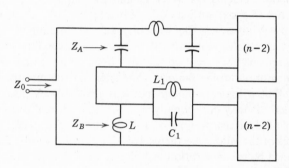

Fig. 10.04–C

infinity, so that the capacitors and the inductor shown can be removed from Z_A, leaving an impedance of order $(n-2)$. Since E_B will have a zero at the origin, the inductor L may be removed, and we hope to be able to choose α so that the elements L_1 and C_1 (resonant at ω_0) may also be removed, as shown.

To determine whether this partition can be successfully made, we have to insure (α being at our disposal) that both Z_A and Z_B are p-r, and further that

$$\lim_{p \to 0} \frac{Z_B(p)}{p} = \frac{Z_B(j\omega_0)}{j\omega_0}, \qquad (10.04\text{--}18)$$

for then Z_B can be developed as shown in Fig. 10.04–C. Now E_A meets all the requirements of the even part of a p-r function, so that $Z_A(p)$, determined therefrom, will be p-r, regardless of the value of α; the calculation of Z_A and its development in the form shown is a routine matter. In Z_B we have a more difficult problem. In the first place, to insure that Z_B will be p-r, we must have

$$\alpha^2 \leqq \frac{a_0}{a_2} \quad \text{and} \quad \alpha^2 \leqq (2\sqrt{a_0} - a_2). \qquad (10.04\text{--}19)$$

In the second place we must insure that (10.04-18) is satisfied.   From

$$Z_B = Z_0 - Z_A \qquad (10.04\text{-}20)$$

we may calculate both of the quantities in (10.04-18) in terms of Z_A, and equate them.   A rather complicated equation for α^2 results; and it is not true in general that it has a real positive root, nor that (10.04-19) is also satisfied if it has.   But in some cases one or more usable values of α may be found (only numerical investigation will tell), and then the realization of Fig. 10.04-C can be made.   The number of elements used, in the reduction from order n to order $(n-2)$, is the same as in the Bott-Duffin method, but the elements are different and the reduced impedances are different; hence this method may offer advantages.

This example illustrates the difficulty of categorizing the possible realization methods available with the use of a surplus factor, and also shows that such methods may be useful.   It may also be helpful to use *two* (or even more) surplus factors.   We shall not discuss this, for the procedure is but a logical (though perhaps involved) extension of our previous ideas.   It may occasionally result in efficient realizations.

All possible ladder realizations of a given immittance (including those in which arms of the ladder are themselves developed in ladder form, etc.) can be obtained by this separation technique.   This includes the majority of known realization methods (most of which use no surplus factor), but not all—for realizations in nonladder forms are possible.

10.05 But the end is not yet

A really complete theory of realization of driving-point immittance functions has not yet been developed, for there is at least one other known method, quite different from those we have discussed—and probably there are many that are not known.   In illustration of this method, let us return to Fig. 10.01-A.   In more general form it becomes Fig. 10.05-A in which

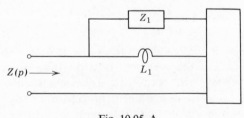

Fig. 10.05-A

the purpose of Z_1 is to prevent the occurrence of a pole at infinity in $Z(p)$, and the three-terminal network is as yet arbitrary.   A completely new type of realization may be found by exercise of the imagination (PA 1) in visualizing possible forms for this three-terminal network. For example, consider again the function (10.01–1) or (10.01–2),

$$Z_0(p) = \frac{Z(p)}{5} = \frac{p^2 + 3.6p + 1.6}{p^2 + p + 10} \text{ ohms.} \quad (10.05\text{--}1)$$

We again determine the key inductance (whose symbol is now changed to L_0) so that it represents the value of $Z_0(j2)$, by (10.01–3); then $L_0 = 0.6$ h. We may now put down the element R_0 (Fig. 10.05–B) with

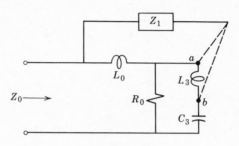

Fig. 10.05–B

the purpose of representing thereby the zero-frequency behavior of $Z_0(p)$ (so that $R_0 = 0.16 \, \Omega$), and the elements L_3 and C_3 (resonant at $\omega = 2$) to short-circuit R_0 at the frequency of zero resistance. Then Z_1 must become an open circuit at $\omega = 2$. We may connect the right-hand terminal of Z_1 either to the point a (in which case we have only a series

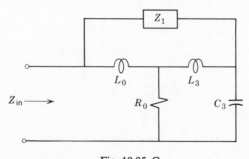

Fig. 10.05–C

combination of two networks, whose possibilities we have already discussed) or to the point b; in the latter case we have a new type of network, that shown in Fig. 10.05–C. Regardless of what is in the box Z_1, the input impedance Z_{in} clearly agrees with Z_0 at $p = 0$, and if $Z_1(p)$ has poles at $p = \pm j2$, then Z_{in} agrees with Z_0 at $p = \pm j2$ also. It is now of great interest to answer the question: can Z_1 be so designed that $Z_{\text{in}}(p)$ and $Z_0(p)$ are identical, so that we obtain a new, different realization of $Z_0(p)$?

Since at infinity Z_1 clearly must have the same value as $Z_0(p)$ (because of the connection made), and must have poles at $\pm j2$, it seems that the simplest possible form Z_1 can take is that indicated in Fig. 10.05–D. For

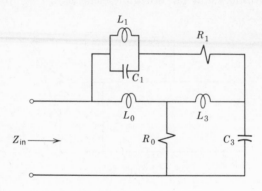

Fig. 10.05–D

the seven elements shown, five relations have been established; with the use of ω_0 for the frequency of zero resistance ($\omega_0 = 2$), these are

$$L_0 = \frac{Z_0(j\omega_0)}{j\omega_0} = 0.6 \text{ h},$$

$$R_0 = Z_0(0) = 0.16 \ \Omega,$$

$$R_1 = Z_0(\infty) = 1.00 \ \Omega, \tag{10.05-2}$$

$$L_1 C_1 = \frac{1}{\omega_0^2} = \frac{1}{4},$$

$$L_3 C_3 = \frac{1}{\omega_0^2} = \frac{1}{4}.$$

It remains now to determine whether the two parameters remaining can be so adjusted that $Z_{\text{in}}(p)$ is in fact $Z_0(p)$, with positive values for L_1, C_1, L_3, and C_3. That this is possible is not difficult to show, though the calculation is tedious. On calculating $Z_{\text{in}}(p)$ we obtain a rational function of order five in which these two parameters appear in literal form. By requiring that the numerator have a factor $(p^2 + 3.6p + 1.6)$, or that the denominator have a factor $(p^2 + p + 10)$, i.e., that the remainders on division by these polynomials be zero, we can determine values for these parameters, and it develops that the same values satisfy both requirements. The result is

$$Z_{in}(p) = \frac{(p^2 + 3.6p + 1.6)(p + \frac{2}{3})^2(p + 6)}{(p^2 + p + 10)(p + \frac{2}{3})^2(p + 6)} \qquad (10.05\text{–}3)$$

which, on cancellation of the common factors, becomes $Z_0(p)$ as desired. The realization (with the scale factor 5 restored) is shown in Fig. 10.05–E.

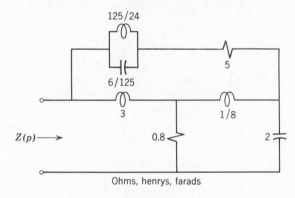

Fig. 10.05–E

Notice that this realization uses one less element than does the Bott–Duffin realization (Fig. 10.01–C), and is evidently obtained through the use of three surplus factors.

The success of this approach in this particular example leads us now to investigate its general possibilities.   To begin with, we replace R_0 in Fig. 10.05–C by a general impedance Z_2, for we expect both this branch and Z_1 to take more complicated forms in general if the process is valid. For $Z_2(p)$ in Fig. 10.05–F we now arbitrarily write

$$Z_2(p) = \frac{L_0\alpha^2}{z_R(p) - [(Ap)/(p^2 + \omega_0^2)]} \qquad (10.05\text{–}4)$$

in which

$$z_R(p) = (-p)\frac{Z_0(p) - [(L_0\alpha^2)/p]}{Z_0(p) - L_0 p}. \qquad (10.05\text{–}5)$$

This function $z_R(p)$, already familiar to us for it appeared in § 10.02, was first discussed by Richards (RI 2) and was used by Bott and Duffin

(BO 4). In it $Z_0(p)$ is the minimum (but otherwise arbitrary) impedance function to be realized, of order n, with a zero of resistance at frequency ω_0; L_0 is again determined by

$$L_0 = \frac{Z_0(j\omega_0)}{j\omega_0}, \qquad (10.05\text{--}6)$$

and for the present we assume L_0 to be positive. Here α is the right-half-plane root of

$$Z_0(p) - L_0 p = 0 \qquad (10.05\text{--}7)$$

so that $z_R(p)$ is easily shown to be p-r. Finally, A represents a constant, as yet undetermined. A logical development of (10.05–4) has not yet

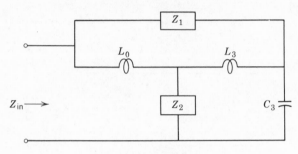

Fig. 10.05–F

been made; it was found by experiment (PA 1) that this value for $Z_2(p)$ is a useful one, and we simply proceed to use it on that basis. On the same basis we write

$$L_3 = \frac{\alpha^2 L_0}{\omega_0^2 + A} \qquad (10.05\text{--}8)$$

and choose C_3 so that $L_3 C_3 = 1/\omega_0^2$.

We have now several things to do: we must

1. demonstrate that $Z_2(p)$ is p-r if A is properly chosen, and that L_3 is then positive;
2. find $Z_1(p)$ such that $Z_{in} = Z_0(p)$;
3. demonstrate that $Z_1(p)$ so found is p-r;
4. investigate the utility of this realization procedure.   (10.05–9)

For the first item, consider the reciprocal of $Z_2(p)$. We have already demonstrated in essence (§ 10.02) that $z_R(p)$ is a p-r function, but an independent check of its positive reality is a straightforward calculation. If $1/Z_2(p)$, and hence $Z_2(p)$, is to be p-r, we must require A either to be negative or, if positive, not to be so large that the poles of $z_R(p)$ at $\pm j\omega_0$ are overcome and negative residues result there for $1/Z_2$. In addition, if L_3 is to be positive, $(\omega_0^2 + A)$ must be positive. In other words, if $Z_2(p)$ is to be p-r and L_3 positive, then we must have

$$-\omega_0^2 < A \leq K_0, \tag{10.05–10}$$

in which

$$K_0 = [2 \times \text{residue at } p = j\omega_0 \text{ of } z_R(p)]. \tag{10.05–11}$$

If (10.05–10) is fulfilled, then $Z_2(p)$ is p-r and L_3 is positive (as is C_3). Since one of these limits on A is negative and the other is positive, a rather wide range of values for A is available, at least so far as item 1 is concerned.

For the second item in (10.05–9) we consider $Z_{\text{in}}(p)$ of Fig. 10.05–F, in which Z_1 is unknown but all the other branches are known (as functions of A). It is a lengthy but straightforward calculation to obtain $Z_{\text{in}}(p)$ as a function of Z_1, A, and known quantities; the result may be set equal to $Z_0(p)$ and the equation solved for $Z_1(p)$. We then find that if the network of Fig. 10.05–F is to have $Z_0(p)$ as its input impedance function,

$$Z_1(p) = L_0 \left(z_R(p) + \frac{\alpha^2 A}{\omega_0^2 + A} \times \frac{p}{p^2 + \omega_0^2} \right). \tag{10.05–12}$$

Our third task is to show that $Z_1(p)$, as given above, is p-r. Since $z_R(p)$ is p-r (as previously discussed), it is necessary and sufficient for this that

$$\left(\frac{\alpha^2 A}{\omega_0^2 + A} + K_0 \right) \geq 0, \tag{10.05–13}$$

i.e., that

$$A \geq \frac{-K_0 \omega_0^2}{\alpha^2 + K_0}. \tag{10.05–14}$$

This requirement does not conflict with that of (10.05–10) and we may now write

$$\frac{-K_0 \omega_0^2}{\alpha^2 + K_0} \leq A \leq K_0 \tag{10.05–15}$$

as the condition on A that will make L_3 and C_3 positive, and both $Z_1(p)$ and $Z_2(p)$ p-r (Fig. 10.05–F). Thus realization in this form *can* be accomplished.

It remains to investigate the utility of this procedure. The order of $z_R(p)$ is n, the same as that of $Z_0(p)$, because α is so chosen that the right-half-plane zeros of numerator and denominator cancel. The order of both $Z_1(p)$ and $Z_2(p)$ in general is also n [for the terms added to $z_R(p)$ contain no new poles], and no particular progress has been made. But if A is given either of the extreme values permitted by (10.05–15), then either $Z_1(p)$ or $Z_2(p)$ will be of order $(n-2)$; the other will be of order n, but immediately reducible, by removal of a pair of real-frequency poles or zeros, to order $(n-2)$.

Figure 10.05–G illustrates the reductions accomplished in the two cases; the numbers in parentheses indicate the orders of the impedance functions.

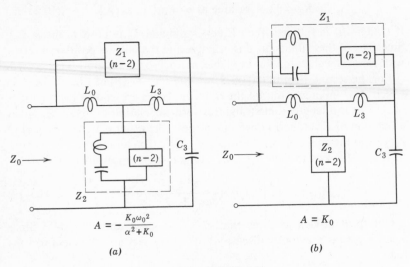

$$A = -\frac{K_0\omega_0^2}{\alpha^2 + K_0}$$

$$(a)$$

$$A = K_0$$

$$(b)$$

Fig. 10.05–G

In Fig. 10.05–G(b) we recognize the realization of (10.05–1) achieved in Fig. 10.05–D; the realization of the same function with the alternate value of A, i.e., according to Fig. 10.05–G(a), is given in Fig. 10.05–H. The design procedure is a straightforward calculation in sequence and from the foregoing formulas of

$$L_0, \ \alpha, \ z_R(p), \ K_0, \ A, \ Z_1(p), \ Z_2(p), \ L_3, \ C_3, \qquad (10\text{–}05.16)$$

followed by removal of the two reactive elements from Z_1 or Z_2. There will remain two impedance functions, each reduced in order by two from that of the original function, whose realization can be continued by this method or by any of the other methods.

We must now return to the beginning of the development of this new method and consider the case where $Z_0(j\omega_0)/j\omega_0$ is *negative* (so that L_0 in the above would not be realizable). We might now replace L_0 by a capacitor and carry through a similar development, but it is simpler to make use of the principle of duality. Suppose we temporarily consider the impedance function $R^2/Z_0(p)$, with $R = 1\ \Omega$. This is of course p-r, and its realization according to the foregoing method will proceed as above, for its reactance at the frequency ω_0 (where its resistance is zero)

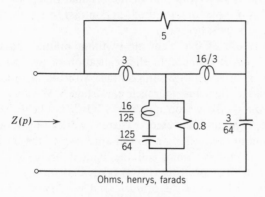

$$Z(p) \longrightarrow$$

Ohms, henrys, farads

Fig. 10.05–H

will be positive. We may then find the network dual to each of the resulting realizations (Problem 10-83) and adjust the element values so that the input impedance is actually $Z_0(p)$. The results are shown in

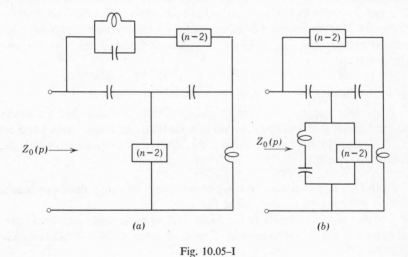

(a)   (b)

Fig. 10.05–I

Fig. 10.05–I. There is no need to set down formulas, as each would correspond exactly to one given previously in this section—in fact, one may just as well carry out the realization of the impedance function

$1/Z_0(p)$ and at the last step interpret the numerical results in terms of Fig. 10.05–I rather than Fig. 10.05–G. The conclusion is the same as for the case where L_0 is positive: there remain two impedance functions, each reduced in order by two from that of the original function. Here three capacitors and two inductors are used, in contrast to the three inductors and two capacitors used before.

Thus with the use of five elements (without mutual inductance) the realization of $Z_0(p)$ is reduced to the realization of two p-r impedance functions each of order $(n - 2)$, in contrast with the method of § 10.02 which requires *six* elements to reach this stage. Whether even more efficient techniques exist we do not know, but it is likely that there are other methods, as yet undiscovered. There is work to be done in searching for them and in establishing a logical approach to the method of this section. This method we may call the Pantell bridge (or bridged-T) method, for Pantell's realization (PA 1) takes that form, L_3 (or its dual) being the "detector" arm of the bridge. Independent work on this was also done by Fialkow and Gerst (FI 4) and Reza (RE 3).

There is one additional possibility that should be investigated. The heuristic approach used does not really indicate whether L_3 and C_3 should be connected as in Fig. 10.05–F or interchanged. If they are interchanged, however, an additional element will in general be required—so that this method is of less interest. Apparently, then, we have exhausted the useful possibilities of this method of realization. Yet we cannot state definitely that there are no other useful methods closely or distantly related to this; the subject is by no means closed, and the field is open for research.

10.06 Realization of the general one-terminal R-L-C pair

It is most appropriate here to stop and recapitulate what we have learned about step 3 of the solution of a synthesis problem. In Chapters 6, 7, 9, and 10 we have discussed this matter of realization, with the following results.

1. If $F(p)$ is p-r, it can be realized both as a driving-point impedance and as a driving-point admittance function.

2. Certain special kinds of p-r functions are realizable with two kinds of elements only, as L-C networks (Chapter 6) or as R-C (or R-L) networks (Chapter 7).

3. In general, all three kinds of elements are required, and for the general case we have the methods of:

a. Brune (Chapter 9), perhaps requiring perfect coupling between inductors and using resistors in various places;

b. Darlington (Chapter 9), usually requiring perfect coupling but only one resistor;

c. partition of the even part (Chapter 10), requiring no mutual inductance, but usually requiring surplus factors and an increased number of elements (including resistors), of which the Bott–Duffin method is the outstanding example of general applicability;

d. Pantell (Chapter 10), requiring no mutual inductance, but using surplus factors (though fewer elements than the Bott–Duffin method).

Since each method accomplishes the realization in stages, at each of which the order of the immittance function(s) is reduced, it is possible to use more than one of the techniques in a realization problem. This means that for immittance functions of even moderate order, a large number of realizations are possible; mixing the techniques at various stages will produce many different networks that are yet equivalent as to driving-point immittance. Reduction to minimum form (as to reactance, susceptance, resistance, conductance) may be performed at various points, partially or wholly, and the various techniques may be applied in various sequences and at various points. In many cases partial-fraction or continued-fraction expansion will yield useful results—or such results can be obtained by methods such as those discussed at the end of § 10.03. All ladder networks can be obtained by partition of the even part.

We have no evidence that the number of techniques is exhausted by those discussed here. There may be many more basic techniques, as yet unknown, and some of them may be very useful; it remains for future research to investigate these matters, and to develop a general approach that will give *all* realizations: this is a fertile, untilled field.

What we have definitely accomplished is to demonstrate, many times over, that positive reality is indeed sufficient for realization, and to assemble a set of techniques that will give a variety of realizations, from which the engineer must choose on the basis of practicability and economy.

We have essentially concluded our discussion of the realization problem now, but before continuing our journey (to the study of the approximation problem) there are certain related matters to be discussed, in the balance of this chapter and in Chapters 11 and 12.

10.07 Equivalent and inverse networks

Beginning with our first real synthesis (of *L-C* networks) in Chapter 6, we have often used the term *equivalent network*. Applied to the one-terminal pair it means simply that a network has the same driving-point immittance function as some other network. The two networks of Fig. 10.07–A are *equivalent* in this respect if the identity

$$Z_1(p) = Z_2(p) \qquad (10.07\text{–}1)$$

holds (for all values of p). Since synthesis is not unique, since there are usually a great many different realizations of any given immittance (p-r)

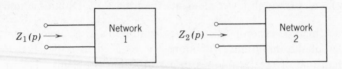

Fig. 10.07–A

function, there are usually a great many different networks that are yet equivalent as to driving-point impedance and driving-point admittance. Their existence is a matter for thanksgiving by the engineer, for among them are probably some that are much more practical than others, and in these lies his primary interest. Such things as the sizes of elements, their relative locations with respect to parasitic capacitance, the influence of parasitic dissipation, affect practicability and cost—and possibly quite differently for different realizations of the same immittance function, since the structures may be quite dissimilar. These matters he must consider (§ 6.09, Chapter 12) in making a choice from all the equivalent networks that his various realization techniques yield.

A related concept that has suggested itself, especially in the discussion of *L-C* networks (§ 6.09), is that of *inverse* networks. Since positive reality is sufficient for realization, the same (p-r) function can be realized either as a driving-point impedance or as a driving-point admittance (with proper adjustment of dimensions), in a variety of equivalent forms in each case. Any network from one category is then said to be *inverse* as to driving-point immittances to any network from the other category, with respect to some reference resistance R_0. If in Fig. 10.07–A

$$Z_1(p) = \frac{R_0^2}{Z_2(p)} = R_0^2 Y_2(p) \qquad (10.07\text{–}2)$$

i.e.,

$$Z_1(p)Z_2(p) = R_0^2, \qquad (10.07\text{–}3)$$

then the two networks are inverse, with respect to R_0 (ohms). If a network exists, its input impedance $Z(p)$ is p-r; so also is the reciprocal function $1/Z(p)$, and the function $R_0^2/Z(p)$, so that an inverse network can always be constructed, and usually in a variety of forms (all of which are equivalent to each other). The Bott–Duffin technique made good use of this fact for the *R-L-C* case. In *L-C* networks we found the inverse networks again to be *L-C* networks; in *R-C* networks we found the inverse networks to be *R-L* networks and vice versa. The concept will prove to be very useful in later work also, as in § 10.08 and in many places in Volume II.

Since much design work is conveniently carried out in terms of normalized immittance functions, we shall often find it convenient to take $R_0 = 1\ \Omega$, so that

$$Z_1(p)Z_2(p) = 1. \qquad (10.07\text{–}4)$$

In this case the networks are said to be *reciprocal* as to driving-point immittance. Inverse networks are always potentially reciprocal, and are actually reciprocal if $R_0 = 1\ \Omega$.

Evidently *duality* (§ 2.06) has something to do with the concept of inverse networks, because the impedance function of one is identical, except for a scale factor, to the admittance function of the other. One might be tempted to say that if two networks are inverse, they must be dual networks. But this clearly cannot be true, for if it were, all the various realizations of $R_0^2/Z_1(p)$ would be dual to any one realization of $Z_1(p)$—and the dual of a network (if it exists at all) is unique. Yet the dual to any one realization of $Z_1(p)$ has a driving-point admittance that behaves functionally exactly as does $Z_1(p)$, and is therefore a realization of the inverse impedance, though surely not the only one. What singles out this particular inverse-impedance realization?

A little thought will show that of all the (equivalent) networks whose driving-point immittances are inverse to those of a given network, only the dual network is the *structural* inverse of the original network. That is, not only is its driving-point impedance inverse but its whole structure, its entire schematic form, is also "inverse" (i.e., dual) to that of the original network. The geometric method of finding the dual (Problem 10-83) makes this evident: the dual network is inverse *everywhere*, not merely with respect to driving-point immittances. There are many realizations of $R_0^2/Z_1(p)$ in general, but the internal structure of most of these is not related to that of the original network, whose input impedance is $Z_1(p)$; only the dual is related internally, as well as externally, by the inverseness property. A given network need not have a dual (if it is not planar, no dual exists); nevertheless inverse networks always exist, and usually in profusion. If the dual does exist, it represents a particularly easy way to find an inverse network, which makes it valuable; an instance of this occurred in § 10.05. Other inverse networks must be obtained by a complete realization process, but the dual can be obtained with very little effort. This is a principle of particular value in the design of constant-resistance networks (§ 10.08) and in two-terminal-pair synthesis.

10.08 Constant-resistance networks

An interesting variety of network results from what may at first seem a trivial application of the technique of § 10.02. Suppose we take $Z_0(p)$ to be simply the (real, positive) constant R_0. Then we write

$$E_s(p) = R_0 = R_0 \frac{\alpha^2 - p^2}{\alpha^2 - p^2} = \frac{\alpha^2 R_0}{\alpha^2 - p^2} + \frac{(-p^2)R_0}{\alpha^2 - p^2}$$

$$\text{(10.08–1)}$$

$$= E_A(p) + E_B(p)$$

in which α is arbitrary (but real and positive). Clearly each of the two terms into which Z_s is partitioned, Z_A and Z_B, will be p-r. As before, we find

$$Z_A(p) = \frac{\alpha^2 R_0 - Kp}{\alpha^2 - p^2}$$

and $\hspace{8cm}$ (10.08–2)

$$Z_B(p) = \frac{(-p^2)(R_0 - K/p)}{\alpha^2 - p^2}$$

or

$$Z_A(p) = \frac{-K[p - (\alpha^2 R_0)/K]}{-(p - \alpha)(p + \alpha)}$$

and $\hspace{8cm}$ (10.08–3)

$$Z_B(p) = \frac{-R_0 p(p - K/R_0)}{-(p - \alpha)(p + \alpha)}.$$

We must determine K by

$$K = R_0 \alpha;$$ $\hspace{4cm}$ (10.08–4)

then

$$Z_A = \frac{\alpha R_0}{p + \alpha}$$

and $\hspace{8cm}$ (10.08–5)

$$Z_B = \frac{p R_0}{p + \alpha}$$

which add to form Z_0. In fact, we might simply have written directly

$$Z_s = R_0 \frac{p + \alpha}{p + \alpha} = \frac{\alpha R_0}{p + \alpha} + \frac{p R_0}{p + \alpha}$$

$$\text{(10.08–6}$$

$$= Z_A + Z_B.$$

The realization is shown in Fig. 10.08–A.

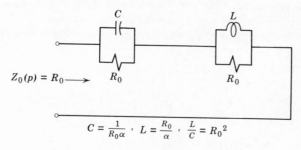

$$C = \frac{1}{R_0 \alpha} \; , \; L = \frac{R_0}{\alpha} \; , \; \frac{L}{C} = R_0{}^2$$

Fig. 10.08–A

As a means of realizing a purely resistive impedance, this is a rather silly procedure; to make use of two reactive elements, two resistors and two surplus factors, when one resistor would do alone. But it may happen that an impedance exists, and for some reason or other (as, e.g., to eliminate reflections at the terminal of a transmission line) it is desired to combine with it a network (in series or in parallel) such that the impedance of the combination is a pure resistance. The device discussed above immediately suggests that this may be possible, and it requires very little analysis to discover exactly when it can be done. If $Z_A(p)$ in Fig.

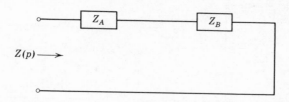

Fig. 10.08–B

10.08–B represents the extant impedance, then $(R_0 - Z_A)$ is the impedance required in $Z_B(p)$ to make the series combination present a pure resistance, so that $Z(p) = R_0$. By straightforward application of our standard test, we find that if $Z_A(p)$ has no pole at infinity and no poles on the imaginary axis, and if R_0 is at least equal to the maximum value of $\mathbf{Re}\, Z_A(j\omega)$, then $Z_B(p) = [R_0 - Z_A(p)]$ is p-r. The dual statement is that if $Y_A(p)$ in Fig. 10.08–C has no imaginary poles (infinity included), and if G_0 is at least equal to the maximum value of $\mathbf{Re}\, Y_A(j\omega)$, then $Y_B(p) = [G_0 - Y_A(p)]$ is p-r. Under these very reasonable conditions,

then, it is possible to "build out" the given impedance or admittance to
a constant, resistive value, for the required immittance will be p-r. Each
such design represents, from a different point of view, the application of
a number of surplus factors to the impedance function $Z_0(p) = R_0$ (or
its dual), followed by one of the various possible partitions into two parts.

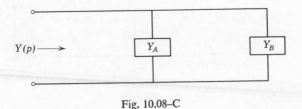

Fig. 10.08–C

In the choice of the surplus factors and of the partitions here, the possibilities are legion indeed. The realization of $Z_B(p)$ or $Y_B(p)$ can be
accomplished by any of the various realization methods we have discussed
in this and previous chapters.

An interesting and useful special case occurs when Z_A in Fig. 10.08–B
takes the form of an arbitrary impedance Z_1 shunted by a resistor, or
when Y_A in Fig. 10.08–C takes the form of an arbitrary admittance Y_1 in

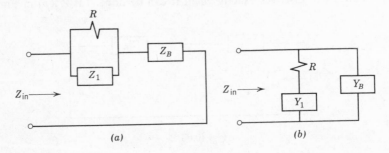

Fig. 10.08–D

series with a resistor, as in Fig. 10.08–D. Then if $Z_{\text{in}}(p)$ is to be simply
the constant R_0, the required impedance is

$$Z_B = R_0 - \frac{1}{1/R + 1/Z_1} = \frac{R_0 R + (R_0 - R)Z_1}{Z_1 + R} \qquad (10.08\text{–}7)$$

(or the dual) and it is certainly appropriate to take $R_0 = R$. (A larger value would represent building out more than is necessary, though this is possible; a smaller value may make Z_B non-p-r.)   Then

$$Z_B = \frac{R_0^2}{Z_1 + R_0} = \frac{1}{Z_1/R_0^2 + 1/R_0} \qquad (10.08\text{-}8)$$

which represents the parallel combination of R_0 and the impedance inverse to Z_1 with respect to R_0 (or the dual).   The resulting networks are shown in Fig. 10.08–E.   These two networks have much in common,

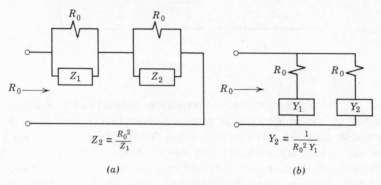

$$Z_2 = \frac{R_0^2}{Z_1}$$

(a)

$$Y_2 = \frac{1}{R_0^2\, Y_1}$$

(b)

Fig. 10.08–E

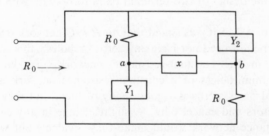

Fig. 10.08–F

as Fig. 10.08–F shows.   Here the second network is redrawn and a network x connected between the points a and b.   If x is an open circuit, we have the original network, and if x is a short circuit, the other structure. And (as in Fig. 10.01–H) *any* form may be given to x, for the structure is a balanced bridge and no current will flow in x in any case.   In addition to the two extreme values given x above, it is often useful to make x a resistor R_0; then the network has certain useful properties as a two-terminal pair, in the "bridged-T" form shown in Fig. 10.08–G (to be discussed in § 11.02 and in Volume II).

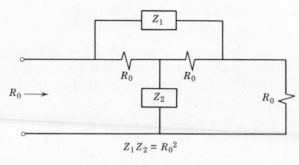

$$Z_1 Z_2 = R_0^2$$

Fig. 10.08–G

All of the foregoing constant-resistance networks are essentially obtained by the application of surplus factors to the impedance R_0, followed by partition. The partitioning need not be limited to two parts, however. If the surplus factors are properly chosen, a series (or parallel) combination of three or more networks may be constructed, whose over-all impedance (admittance) is a constant; Figs. 10.03–A and 10.04–A indicate some of the many possibilities. This principle will be of use in Volume II in the design of two-terminal pairs to operate with a common input.

At the end of § 7.15 it was stated that an *R-L-C* network driving-point immittance function need not have any zeros or poles; this we have just substantiated in the constant-resistance network. To be sure, the driving-point immittances of a constant-resistance network actually do have zeros and poles, perhaps a good many of them, but they all appear in surplus factors and cancel out. A slight change in any element of a constant-resistance network would make these evident, but with proper adjustment of the elements they are not evident at the input.

That there are other constant-resistance networks, not obtainable by partitioning of the even part (but still using surplus factors, of course), is evidenced by the symmetrical network of Fig. 10.08–H. (This type of network will be developed in Volume II, as a two-terminal pair in which the "output" or "load" is at R_0.) In it we require $Z_1 Z_2 = R_0^2$; it follows then, by analysis, that the input impedance is a pure resistance, as indicated. Z_1 may have any form whatever, and Z_2 is inverse to it with respect to R_0. The existence of this network, not obtainable by partitioning of E_s, nor by application of the method of § 10.05, indicates the existence of additional (unknown) realization methods whose application to the simple impedance function R_0 would presumably result in this network. There

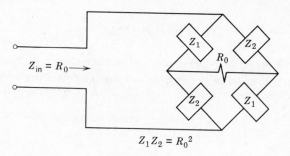

$$Z_{in} = R_0 \longrightarrow$$

$$Z_1 Z_2 = R_0{}^2$$

Fig. 10.08–H

is indeed much about synthesis of which we are ignorant.   (Two-terminal-pair theory can, to be sure, obtain this network—but the statement still stands as to one-terminal-pair theory.)

10.09 Conclusion

At this point we terminate our discussion of the realization part of one-terminal-pair synthesis.   We have completed our exploration of the sections of Figs. 5.03–A and 7.15–A and established conclusively that any function lying in the region of overlap is realizable as a driving-point immittance, as well as that the immittance functions of all networks lie therein.   The demonstration has ranged through several chapters (§ 10.06) and covered a good deal of ground, and a real understanding of the material can be gained only by considerable practice and experience in actual realization.

It is appropriate now to consider some of the uses to which one-terminal pairs are actually put, before entering on a discussion of the approximation problem.   In Chapter 11 we shall do this, and in Chapter 12 we shall consider another hitherto neglected matter: the practicability of some of our paper realizations and the annoying effects of practical network elements in general.   Then in Chapter 13 we shall begin our discussion of the remaining part of synthesis: the matter of *approximation*.

10.10 References

The Bott–Duffin process: BA 3, BO 4, DU 1, GI 1, GU 4, NI 1, RI 2.
Partitioning the even part: KU 2, MI 3, PA 1.
Bridge-circuit realizations: FI 4, KI 5, PA 1, RE 3, VA 5.
Other expansions: BO 3, FR 2.
Résumés: DA 5, GI 1, GU 4.

Constant-resistance networks: BA 5, JO 1, NO 2, ZO 1.
Duality: see § 2.11.
Inverse networks: BA 3, BO 3, GU 2, JO 1, TE 1, ZO 1.

PROBLEMS

10-1. Verify (as far as possible) and explain the following statements.

(a) Any p-r function can be realized as a driving-point immittance with the use of only one resistor (though mutual inductance or transformers may be necessary).

(b) Any p-r function can be realized as a driving-point immittance without the use of mutual inductance or transformers (though more than one resistor may be necessary).

(c) Only certain special p-r functions can be realized as driving-point immittances with the use of only one resistor and without the use of mutual inductance or transformers.

10-2. Realize the admittance function

$$Y(p) = \frac{18p^3 + 9p^2 + 2p + 1}{15p^2 + 3p + 1}$$

by removing the pole at infinity and then applying (a) the Brune procedure, (b) the Bott–Duffin procedure. Contrast these two realizations with that obtained by first removing the real-frequency pole of impedance. (Cf. Prob. 8-12.)

10-3. Find network realizations of the driving-point resistance function given below in the Brune, Bott–Duffin, Pantell forms. Find also a one-resistor realization.

$$R(\omega) = \frac{16\omega^4 - 96\omega^2 + 144}{\omega^4 + 8\omega^2 + 16}.$$

10-4. Find several different realizations of the driving-point resistance functions given, at least one of which uses only one resistor and at least one of which uses no mutual inductance.

(a) $\dfrac{(\omega^2 - 4)^4}{(\omega^2 + 4)^4}$ (b) $\dfrac{(\omega^2 - 6)^2}{1 + \omega^6}$ (c) $\dfrac{(\omega^2 - 1)^2}{1 + \omega^8}$ (d) $\dfrac{\omega^2(\omega^2 - 3)^2}{1 + \omega^6}$

(e) $\dfrac{1 + \omega^2}{2 + \omega^2}$ (f) $\dfrac{(\omega^2 - 1)^2(\omega^2 - 2)^2}{1 + \omega^8}$ (g) $\dfrac{\omega^2(\omega^2 - 3)^2}{(1 + \omega^2)(2 + \omega^2)(3 + \omega^2)}$

(h) $\dfrac{(\omega^2 - 4)^2}{1 + \omega^4}$

10-5. Repeat Prob. 10-4 on the assumption that functions given represent driving-point conductance functions.

10-6. Obtain realizations that do not use mutual inductance of those immittance functions of Chapter 9 (examples and problems) for whose realization mutual inductance was there used.

10-7. Consider the impedance function

$$Z(p) = \frac{2p^3 + 10p^2 + 41p + 38}{p^2 + p + 10}.$$

(*a*) Realize this without using mutual inductance, by the use of one surplus factor, after reduction to minimum character.

(*b*) Repeat the realization, but without first reducing the function to minimum-reactance. Discuss the various possibilities here and compare them with the realization of (*a*).

(*c*) Repeat the realization but without first reducing the function to minimum-resistance. Contrast your result with those previously found.

10-8. The input impedance of the network shown has zero resistance at a certain frequency. Explain how the mutual inductance acts to produce this effect. Obtain a realization of the same driving-point impedance without mutual inductance (*a*) by first reducing the impedance to minimum-reactance and then using the Bott–Duffin technique, (*b*) by applying the Bott–Duffin technique without the preliminary reduction to minimum-reactance. Compare the resulting networks. What happens to the network realizations you have found if the coupling coefficient in the original network becomes unity? (DU 1.)

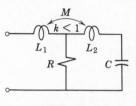

Prob. 10–8

10-9. Consider those impedance functions of order two whose even parts have four finite, real zeros, but are otherwise general (unrestricted). Show in schematic form the realization of such an impedance (*a*) by the Brune method, (*b*) using only one resistor, (*c*) by the normal Bott–Duffin procedure (first reducing the impedance to minimum-resistance), (*d*) by a modified Bott–Duffin method procedure (not reducing to minimum-resistance, but following the discussion that accompanies Fig. 10.02–C).

Compare the number of elements used in each. Under what particular circumstances might an even smaller number be sufficient?

10-10. Consider the p-r impedance function

$$Z(p) = \frac{a_2 p^2 + a_1 p + a_0}{b_2 p^2 + b_1 p + b_0}.$$

What is the number of coefficients that are independent, in the sense that they can be varied (at least to some extent) without rendering $Z(p)$ non-p-r? What is the number of elements required in general in the Brune realization thereof? Illustrate with a schematic diagram. What is the number of elements required in general in the Bott–Duffin realization of this function? Illustrate with a schematic diagram. Discuss the relations between the three numbers found above and the minimum possible number of elements in any realization of $Z(p)$. (Cf. Prob. 9-39.)

10-11. A number of low-order networks are given by Foster in an early discussion of realizations (FO 4). Give the schematic diagrams of Brune and Bott–Duffin realizations of these networks where they differ from Foster's. Explain why they differ.

10-12. Show that the value of the resistor R_0 with respect to which Z_1 and Z_3 of the Bott–Duffin realization process (§ 10.01) are inverse is given by $R_0 = Z_0(\sigma_1)$.

10-13. Show that $Z_1(p)$ in (10.01–9), with C_3 determined by (10.01–7), is p-r (a) if $Z_0(p)$ is a minimum (p-r) function of arbitrary order, the determination of L_1 being made at any one of the frequencies of zero resistance, as in (10.01–3); (b) if $Z_0(p)$ is an arbitrary p-r function (except that it has neither zero nor pole at infinity or at the origin) and L_1 has an arbitrary positive value. Discuss the possible positive reality of $Z(p)$ in (b) if it has a zero or pole at the origin or at infinity.

10-14. Realize the following impedance functions in the Bott–Duffin manner, (a) first reducing them to minimum-reactance and (b) without so first reducing them. Discuss the various possibilities in the second case.

$$(1) \quad \frac{2p^3 + 5p^2 + 2.5p + 4}{p^2 + 2p + 1} \qquad (2) \quad \frac{p^4 + 0.5p^3 + 5p^2 + 0.5p + 4}{p^4 + 2p^3 + 2p^2 + 2p + 1}$$

$$(3) \quad \frac{p^3 + 2.5p^2 + 8p + 2}{p^3 + 2p^2 + p}.$$

10-15. Given a p-r function $Z_0(p)$ with neither zero nor pole at the origin nor at infinity, discuss the possibilities of basing the Bott–Duffin procedure on zeros of Ev $Z_0(p)$ (a) at real frequencies, (b) at real values of p, (c) at complex values of p.

10-16. Discuss the realization of impedance functions with these resistance functions:

$$(a) \quad \frac{(\omega^4 + 4)(\omega^4 - 6\omega^2 + 25)}{(\omega^2 + 2)^4} \qquad (b) \quad \frac{(\omega^4 + 4)(\omega^2 - 5)^2}{(\omega^2 + 2)^4}.$$

10-17. The treatment of the Bott–Duffin technique in this chapter makes use of one surplus factor per "stage" or "cycle" of the realization. It might be said that this technique actually uses *four* surplus factors for the realization of an immittance of order two, since *six* reactive elements are used. Explain and illustrate this statement.

If the order of the original immittance function is n, how many surplus factors are used in one application of the Bott–Duffin technique, on the assumption that the reduced immittances are each realized with the minimum possible number of elements?

From this point of view criticize the title of § 10.03.

10-18. The function

$$F(p) = -p \frac{Z(p) - 1/Cp}{Z(p) - Lp},$$

in which $Z(p)$ is p-r, and L and C are real positive numbers so related that numerator and denominator of $F(p)$ each have a zero at the same right-half-plane point, which appears first in (10.01–9) and many times thereafter, is sometimes called the *Richards function* (RI 2). Show that it is p-r (a) by application of the standard test and (b) by adding p to $F(p)$ and treating the sum. Is the second method any shorter? Can you obtain an independent proof of (9.04–20) by it?

10-19. Realize the resistance function $(3 - \omega^2)^2/(3 + \omega^2)^2$ in the Brune, Bott–Duffin, and Pantell fashions, and compare the number of elements used in each realization. Demonstrate that the Brune method uses the minimum possible number of elements.

10-20. Give the schematic form of every realization of the resistance function

$$R(\omega) = \frac{(1 - \omega^2)^2(2 + \omega^2)}{256 + \omega^8}$$

that can be obtained by the methods discussed in this and previous chapters, including those obtained by mixtures of the techniques.

10-21. In realizing a minimum impedance function of order n,

$$Z_0(p) = \frac{A_1 + pB_1}{A_2 + pB_2}$$

whose resistance is zero at $p = j\omega_0$, with the use of a surplus factor $(p + \alpha)$ by the method of § 10.02, α is determined by finding the right-half-plane zero of $(Z_0 - L_1 p)$ or of $[Z_0 - 1/C_3 p]$. But α may be given *any* positive value (§ 10.02).

Show that if α is determined from

$$(A_2\alpha + p^2 B_2)_{p=j\omega_0} = 0$$

or from

$$(B_2\alpha + A_2)_{p=j\omega_0} = 0,$$

one of which always gives a positive value for α, then for $n = 2$ this value for α is the same as that mentioned above.

For $n > 2$ the value is generally different, and may often be used to obtain another realization (by a different partition of the even part). Illustrate this in the case $n = 3$. How does the number of elements used compare with the number used in the standard Brune method?

10-22. Show that with the choice of K given by (10.02–15), Z_A and Z_B of (10.02–13) and (10.02–14) are p-r.

10-23. Show that both Z_A and Z_B as defined by (10.02–27) and (10.02–28) are p-r when p_0 is in the right half plane and (10.02–29), (10.02–30), and (10.02–31) are fulfilled. Show also that Z_A and Z_B obtained from (10.02–33) and (10.02–34) will be p-r.

10-24. Show that if $Z_0(p)$ is not minimum-resistance, neither Z_1 nor Z_3 in (10.02–25) and (10.02–26) is minimum-resistance.

For a case where in Fig. 10.02–A L_1 has the value 2 and $R_1(\omega)$ is the function

$$\mathrm{Re}\, Z_1(j\omega) = 3 + \frac{\omega^2}{1 + \omega^6},$$

give the complete realization and explain how this illustrates the discussion of the paragraph following (10.02–26). If $Z_1(p)$ has real-frequency poles, may $Z_0(p)$ be nonminimum-resistance?

Find also the standard Bott–Duffin and Brune realization of this impedance function and compare the three networks.

10-25. Realize the function

$$Z(p) = \frac{9p^2 + 29p + 30}{p^2 + 6p + 6}$$

(a) by the Brune process, (b) by the Bott–Duffin process, (c) by partition of the even part. Do (c) in two ways: (1) using the surplus-factor idea and (10.02–27) and (10.02–28), (2) not using it, but rather (10.02–33) and (10.02–34).

10-26. If

$$R(\omega) = \frac{a_0 + a_2\omega^2 + a_4\omega^4 + \cdots + a_{2n}\omega^{2n}}{1 + b_2\omega^2 + b_4\omega^4 + \cdots + b_{2n}\omega^{2n}}$$

is a realizable driving-point resistance function in which all the a's are positive (or zero), the corresponding minimum-reactance impedance can be realized without the use of mutual inductance by a series connection of ladder networks, each of which uses only one resistor.

Prove this statement. How general is the technique it implies? How many surplus factors does it use? Illustrate by so realizing the resistance function

$$R(\omega) = \frac{2 + 3\omega^2 + 5\omega^6}{1 + \omega^6}.$$

Compare this realization with those obtained by other methods. (Cf. Probs. 9-7 and 9-8; MI 3.)

State the dual process. (See also Prob. 10-57.)

10-27. Realize the function

$$Z(p) = \frac{2p^3 + 15p^2 + 59p + 20}{5p^3 + 21p^2 + 20p + 50}$$

by partitioning the even part repeatedly, making maximum use of the zeros of the even part of the function (FI 3).

10-28. Draw an arbitrary two-loop network, on each loop of which, and in the mutual arm, all three elements (in series) may appear. Mutual inductance may exist between the inductors. Find the element values of a network without mutual inductance equivalent in driving-point impedance to the given network, opened at any point to form two terminals, in terms of those of the original network (DU 2).

10-29. Consider the realization of a p-r impedance function of order two. Draw the Brune and Bott–Duffin realizations for the general case in which no degeneracy occurs. Find formulas that express the element values of the Bott–Duffin network in terms of those of the Brune network (RE 3). Consider both possibilities as to the sign of L_1 in the Brune network, and point out what happens in the particular case $L_1 = 0$, in both networks. Extend your formulas to one cycle of the realization process when the given impedance is of arbitrary order. (RE 3.)

10-30. Consider the realization of the (p-r) impedance function

$$Z(p) = \frac{A_1 + pB_1}{A_2 + pB_2}$$

of order n ($n \geq 2$) which has no real-frequency zeros or poles, and the numerator of whose even part has the special form

$$(p^2 + \omega_0^2) \sum_{s=0}^{s=n-2} a_s(-p^2)^s$$

in which all $a_s > 0$. Demonstrate the following propositions (MI 3). (See also Prob. 10-58.)

(1) If one of the four even polynomials A_1, B_1, A_2, B_2 has a factor $(p^2 + \omega_0^2)$, then the impedance may be realized by the series connection of $(n - 1)$ networks,

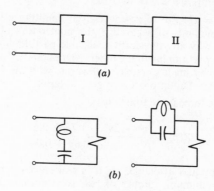

(a)

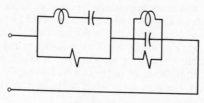

(b)

Prob. 10–30

each of which has the form shown in (a) in which network I is a ladder each of whose arms contains one or two reactive elements and nothing more, and network II has one of the two forms shown in (b); the dual arrangement is also allowed. [*Suggestion:* Show that $(p^2 + \omega_0^2)$ is a factor of one of the A's or B's of each constituent impedance, remains so as the elements of network I are removed, and is so still for the impedance of network II.]

(2) If none of the four polynomials has a factor $(p^2 + \omega_0^2)$, then by the use of a surplus factor $(p + \alpha)$ a similar realization can be obtained, using n of the constituent networks. [*Suggestion:* Determine α so that the property used in (1) is obtained.]

Prob. 10–31

10-31. An impedance function of order two has been realized (by partitioning the even part) in the form shown. Demonstrate that it can be realized more simply by following the Brune procedure (or its dual).

10-32. In what part of the p plane must the zeros of the even part of R-C impedance functions lie? (Cf. Prob. 8-127.) Discuss the realization of such functions by the process of partitioning the even part and compare the results with the canonic forms of Chapter 7.

10-33. Consider the general (p-r) impedance function of order one. Show that it can always be realized by partitioning the even part according to (10.02–32) without the use of surplus factors, and give the realization. Show that it can be realized more simply by the methods of Chapter 7, and explain these methods in terms of partitioning the even part.

Repeat on the dual basis.

10-34. Let $Z_0(p) = 1/Y_0(p)$ represent a given immittance function and consider the possible methods of separating the numerators of $\mathrm{Ev}\, Z_0(p)$ and of $\mathrm{Ev}\, Y_0(p)$. Explain why any physically realizable partitioning of one is also a physically realizable partitioning of the other. Does this mean that two different realizations are thereby made possible? Illustrate with the function (10.03–3), and also with the Bott–Duffin process in general terms.

10-35. Realize the impedance function

$$Z(p) = \frac{p^3 + 2p^2 + 1.7p + 0.6}{p^3 + 2p^2 + 0.6p + 0.04}$$

by the various techniques available. If it is realized by partitioning the even part, what is the minimum number of reactive elements required if mutual inductance is not used?

10-36. Consider a (p-r) impedance function of order two that is minimum but otherwise unrestricted. It is to be realized with the use of one surplus factor by separating the numerator of the even part into two parts, one of which is one term of this numerator, the other the remaining three terms. Discuss each possibility, indicating necessary conditions on the numerator of the given even part and the zero of the surplus factor; give schematic diagrams in as much detail as possible. Illustrate with the functions

$$(a)\ E_0 = \frac{p^4 + 1.64p^2 + 1}{p^4 + p^2 + 1} \qquad (b)\ E_0 = \frac{9p^4 + 20p^2 + 16}{p^4 + 4p^2 + 16}.$$

10-37. Consider a minimum impedance function of order three. Discuss the various ways in which realization may be accomplished by partitioning the even part, both with and without the use of a surplus factor. Give your results as schematic diagrams with as much detail as possible in the absence of specific numerical data. Where a reduction to order two is made, indicate what would be necessary for the impedance of order two to be readily realizable with two reactive elements and one resistor; what parameter(s) is (are) available to attempt to meet the requirement?

10-38. Discuss the conditions under which a p-r function of order three can be realized by the series connection of two networks, each of which contains three reactive elements and one resistor, and possibly an additional resistor. Give the schematic diagram of the realization. Show also the Brune and one-resistor realizations.

10-39. Realize the impedance function

$$\frac{p^3 + 6p^2 + 11p + 12}{p^3 + 2p^2 + 2p + 1}$$

by partitioning the even part, both with and without the use of a surplus factor, in various forms. Contrast these with the Brune and one-resistor realizations.

10-40. It is desired to realize the impedance function whose even part is

$$E_0 = \frac{(1 - p^2)(2 - p^2)}{1 + p^4}.$$

Contrast the realizations obtained by partitioning E_0 on the basis of its real zeros with the realization obtained by the Brune method.

10-41. Obtain networks whose driving-point conductance is

$$\frac{(4 + \omega^2)^2}{4 + \omega^4},$$

(*a*) by partitioning the even part in various ways, (*b*) with the use of only one resistor, (*c*) by the Brune method. Contrast the results.

10-42. Let $Z_0(p)$ represent a minimum-reactance impedance function to be realized, and $E_0(p)$ its even part.

(*a*) If

$$E_0 = \frac{a_0 + a_2p^2 + a_4p^4 + a_6p^6}{b_0 + b_2p^2 + b_4p^4 + b_6p^6}$$

in which a_0 and a_4 are positive, and a_2 and a_6 negative, give the schematic diagrams of realizations obtained by separating E_0 into four components (cf. Fig. 10.03-A). How many alternatives are there for each of the four (cf. Fig. 10.03-B)?

(*b*) Repeat (1) but interpreting E_0 as the even part of a given minimum-susceptance *admittance* function.

Illustrate both discussions with numerical examples.

10-43. Realize the admittance function whose even part is

$$\frac{1 - p^2 - p^6}{2 - p^2 + 2p^4 - p^6}$$

in various ways. Do not overlook the possibilities suggested in Fig. 10.03–C, but do not confine yourself to them.

10-44. Discuss realizations of the impedance function whose even part is

(*a*) $\dfrac{p^4 + a_2p^2 + a_0}{1 + p^4}$ (*b*) $\dfrac{p^4 + a_2p^2 + a_0}{1 - p^6}$,

for positive, zero, and negative values of the constant a_2, i.e., for various locations of the zeros of the even part. Collect the results in the form of schematic diagrams, for comparison. Under what conditions (as to the given immittance function of order n) could one expect to obtain branches like those shown, as part of the realization process? (The orders of the reduced immittances are shown in their boxes.) Outline a method of accomplishing such realizations.

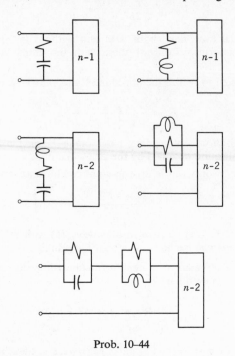

Prob. 10–44

10-45. It is sometimes possible to extract from an impedance function a term representing a dissipative resonant circuit, as in the diagram, with a consequent reduction in order of two (BR 4).

(a) Let the corresponding two terms in the partial-fraction expansion of $Z_0(p)$ be $K_1/(p) - p_1$ and $K_2/(p - p_2)$. Determine relations between the residues

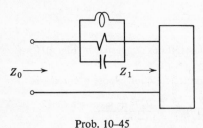

Prob. 10–45

(K_1 and K_2) and the poles (p_1 and p_2) necessary for these two terms to represent the impedance of the resonant circuit. (Consider in turn real and distinct, real and coincident, complex poles; in the complex case, what simple geometric relation exists between the complex numbers that represent K_1 and p_1?) Show that these relations are also sufficient for the realization of the small R-L-C network. What is required if $Z_1(p)$ is also to be p-r? Summarize the properties required of $Z_0(p)$ for this step in its realization to be possible. Correlate these with the requirements in the special case where p_1 and p_2 are purely imaginary.

(*b*) Discuss the dual process.

(*c*) Discuss (*a*) and (*b*) as examples of realization by partitioning of the even part. How is the partition to be made?

10-46. Discuss the realization of an arbitrary (p-r) impedance function $Z(p)$, or admittance function $Y(p)$, by utilizing its expansion in partial fractions. *Suggestion* (BO 3): If

$$Z(p) = \frac{K_1}{p - p_1} + \frac{K_2}{p - p_2} + \cdots + \frac{K_{2a}}{(p - p_a)^2} + \frac{K_{1a}}{p - p_a} + \cdots + K_0 + K_\infty p$$

in which p_1, p_2, $\cdots$ are simple poles, p_a, $\cdots$ are second-order poles, etc., and the K's are constants, show that each term that corresponds to a simple real pole is realizable within an additive real constant, that each pair of terms corresponding to a pair of conjugate-complex simple poles is so also, that a term like $K_{2a}(p - p_a)^{-2}$ is so also if p_a is real, and the combination of it and the corresponding term for $\bar{p}_a$ is so if p_a is complex, etc. What must be true of K_0 if the process is to succeed? What sort of network realizations would be used for each of the various kinds of terms? How is this approach related to partitioning of the even part?

Show that partial-fraction expansion of an arbitrary p-r function will not necessarily lead to a realization (by separate realization of each term or of pairs of terms). If this technique is successful in a given case, explain how the realization could also have been obtained by partition of the even part.

10-47. Any realization obtained by partitioning of the even part could equally well be obtained by partial-fraction expansion. Discuss this statement carefully; explain why it is true and give the advantages and disadvantages of the two approaches.

10-48. Expand the function

$$\frac{3p^3 + 14p^2 + 24p + 21}{p^4 + 5p^3 + 13p^2 + 19p + 10}$$

in partial fractions and discuss the possibility of separate realization of each term (or pair of terms associated with conjugate-complex numbers) as an impedance. Is any simpler realization obtainable by combining the terms in small groups? Compare your results with realizations obtained by the methods of the text (without using partial-fraction expansion). Repeat, with the interpretation of the function as an admittance.

10-49. (*a*) Explain why all possible ladder realizations of a given immittance function (including those in which the arms of the ladder are themselves of ladder form) may be obtained by partitioning of the even part, perhaps with surplus factors. Illustrate with schematic diagrams.

(*b*) Show that continued-fraction expansion of an arbitrary p-r function will not necessarily lead to a realization (by separate realization of each term). If this technique succeeds in a given case, explain how the realization could also have been obtained by partitioning of the even part. Show that if all the zeros of the even part of the function lie at the origin, or all at infinity, continued-fraction expansion of the function will lead immediately to a simple realization. Correlate this with the theory of Chapter 9.

10-50. Show that the fact that $a_0 = 1$ and $a_4 = 1$ in (10.04-4) in no way restricts the generality implied, for these values can be obtained by normalization.

Go through the discussion of the function (10.04-4) and explain all points not specifically explained there. Illustrate with a numerical example, carried through to element values. What happens to the realization if $\theta_0 = 60°$?

10-51. Realize the (minimum-reactance) impedance function whose even part is

$$\frac{(1 + p^2 + p^4)(1 + p^2)^2}{(1 - p^2)^4}$$

with the use of a surplus factor as indicated in the discussion following (10.04-14). Realize the same function by Brune's method and by the Bott-Duffin method for comparison.

10-52. Consider the realization of $Z_0(p)$ whose even part has the form (10.04-15), by the method there discussed. Explain all statements made there and indicate in detail how the equation that determines α^2 is obtained. Illustrate with an example. Would you expect that the zeros of E_B at $\pm j\omega_0$ could be realized by the connection of an inductor and a capacitor (in series) across L rather than by L_1 and C_1 as shown in Fig. 10.04-C? Explain. If $a_2 < 0$ what other method suggests itself immediately? If $a_2 = 0$?

10-53. Discuss the use of *two* surplus factors for the realization of minimum immittance functions. Include remarks on the various methods in which the numerator of E_s may be partitioned and explain why the Bott-Duffin procedure does not have this range of possible partitions. Is there any particular advantage in placing the zeros of the surplus factors on the 45° lines of the p plane? Explain. Illustrate the reduction as far as possible in the general case, and then with specific examples. Does the method have advantages over the use of only one surplus factor?

If E_0 has a tetrad of complex zeros, and the above method is applied to the realization of Z_0, the zeros of the surplus factors being placed at these zeros of E_0, to what does this method reduce?

10-54. The following resistance function is to be realized.

$$R(\omega) = \frac{6(1 + \omega^2)^2(6 - 7\omega^2 + 4\omega^4)}{(2 + \omega^2)^4} + 2 \quad \text{ohms.}$$

Obtain networks with this driving-point resistance function in as many different forms as you can; compare and discuss them. Note in particular the effect of removing various amounts of resistance before using the Brune, Bott-Duffin, or other techniques.

Repeat, on the assumption that the function above is a conductance function (mhos).

10-55. Realize the function

$$Z(p) = \frac{p^3 + 7p^2 + 6p + 2}{p^3 + 3p^2 + 8p + 4}$$

in each of the various ways discussed in Chapters 9 and 10. Include in particular (a) a realization that partitions the even part into four terms, the numerator of each being one term of the numerator of the whole even part, and (b) a realization that partitions the even part into two terms, each numerator being the sum of two terms of the whole numerator (MI 3), and compare these realizations carefully with your others.

Repeat on the dual basis.

10-56. Obtain realizations of the function

$$Z(p) = \frac{6p^2 + 9p + 9}{p^2 + 3p + 4}$$

by the Brune, Bott–Duffin, and Pantell methods, and compare them with the realization obtained by partitioning the even part so that only six reactive elements are used (MI 3).

10-57. Consider the realization of impedance functions whose even parts meet the conditions of Prob. 10-26, by partitioning into two parts, with numerators $(a_0 + a_2\omega^2 + \cdots + a_{2k}\omega^{2k})$ and $(a_{2k+1}\omega^{2k+1} + \cdots + a_{2n}\omega^{2n})$ respectively. Show that these parts may be realized by simple *L-C* ladder networks terminated in impedances of order (k) and $(n - k - 1)$ respectively. Show further that the numerators of the even parts of these reduced impedances still have nonnegative coefficients, so that the process can be repeated for each. What form does the complete realization take? Discuss briefly the various possibilities as to choice of k in each cycle. Compare the number of elements used in general in this realization with that required for Brune, Bott–Duffin, Pantell synthesis of such functions. Illustrate with the resistance function

$$\frac{1 + 2\omega^2 + 3\omega^4 + \omega^8}{1 + \omega^8}.$$

Give the dual synthesis. (KU 2.)

10-58. Discuss the application of the method of Prob. 10-57 to the realization of functions with the properties stated in Prob. 10-30. Show in particular that no other technique is necessary until the remainder impedances are of order two (KU 2). Can elements be saved by applying the Bott–Duffin or Pantell technique sooner? Illustrate with examples (KU 2).

10-59. Discuss the possibility of realizing impedance functions with the properties stated in Prob. 10-30, except that now some a_s may be negative. The technique of Probs. 10-57 and 10-58 is to be used. Illustrate with examples (KU 2).

10-60. Realize the function

$$Z(p) = \frac{p^2 + p + 3}{p^2 + 2p + 1}$$

(*a*) by Brune's method, (*b*) by separating the even part (without a surplus factor) into parts, one of which has internal real-frequency zeros (cf. § 10.03; how arbitrary is this zero?), (*c*) by Pantell's method, (*d*) by the Bott–Duffin method. Tabulate the number of elements used in each realization, for comparison. Is Kuh's method (Prob. 10-59) of help in reducing the number?

Repeat for the inverse function and discuss any differences in procedure that appear.

10-61. Consider the impedance function

$$Z(p) = \frac{6p^2 + 14p + 20}{p^2 + 4p + 6}.$$

(*a*) Realize $Z(p)$ by the Brune method. (*b*) Show that (10.03–2) is satisfied here and realize the impedance by the method there described. (*c*) Realize $Z(p)$ by the Pantell method. (*d*) Realize $Z(p)$ by the Bott–Duffin method.

Compare the numbers of elements used in each realization. If some additional resistance is added to $Z(p)$, what happens to the realization of (b)? If some resistance is subtracted from $Z(p)$, what happens to the realization of (b)?

The form of network obtained in (b) resembles that obtained in Fig. 10.02–C. Is it possible to obtain the network of (b) by the method associated therewith? By the Bott–Duffin method if some appropriate value is is given L_1?

10-62. Realize the function

$$F(p) = \frac{p^2 + 1.4p + 1}{p^2 + 3p + 4}$$

as an impedance (a) by the method of Fig. 10.04–A, (b) by the Bott–Duffin method, (c) by Pantell's method, (d) by Brune's method, and also as an admittance, by each method. Are there additional advantageous methods?

10-63. Let $Z(p)$ be an impedance function of order n. Tabulate the number of reactive elements and the number of resistors used (for $n = 1, 2, 3, 4$) by each of the following techniques of realization in general: (a) Brune's technique, (b) Pantell's technique, (c) partition of the even part into one term for each term of its numerator (if this can be made), (d) partition of the even part in some other fashion, without surplus factors (if this can be done), (e) partition with one surplus factor in the Bott–Duffin fashion, (f) partition with one surplus factor in other ways.

What may happen if special cases occur?

How does the table change if $Z(p)$ is an *admittance* function?

10-64. Following the line of reasoning used in the discussion following (10.04–4), determine the upper limit on a if *two* surplus factors are used and the same type of partition of E_s is made. What form does E_s take when a has this limiting value?

Explain why no finite number of surplus factors will make it possible to realize a *minimum* impedance function ($a = 1$) by this method of partitioning the even part so that each power of p becomes the numerator of a separate component.

10-65. Write out the detailed steps (including formulas) for the realization of $Z_0(p)$ by the method of § 10.05 in the case where $L_0 = Z_0(j\omega_0)/(j\omega_0)$ is *negative*. Illustrate by so realizing the function

$$Z_0(p) = \frac{6p^2 + 6p + 60}{p^2 + 3.6p + 1.6}.$$

10-66. Derive (10.05–10).

10-67. Derive (10.05–12). [A modification of the procedure suggested in the text can be based on the fact that, in the determinant notation of § 2.07 with loop 1 as the input loop and loop 3 as that containing Z_1, we want $Z_{in} = \Delta/\Delta_{11} = Z_0$, i.e., $\Delta - \Delta_{11}Z_0 = 0$. This means that the determinant Δ' of the network formed by attaching $(-Z_0)$ to the input terminals must be zero. Hence Z_1 may be determined from $\Delta' = \Delta_0' + Z_1\Delta_{33}' = 0$, or $Z_1 = -\Delta_0'/\Delta_{33}'$ in which Δ_0' is the value of Δ' when $Z_1 = 0$.]

10-68. Show that $Z_1(p)$ defined by (10.05–12) is p-r if and only if (10.05–14) is satisfied, and that (10.05–15) expresses both (10.05–10) and (10.05–14).

10-69. Discuss the use of values of A lying between the extremes given by (10.05–15). Give the orders of the functions involved and explain the limiting cases. Are the intermediate values of A useful?

10-70. Realize the function (10.05–1) in each of the two forms shown in Fig. 10.05–G by calculating $Z_1(p)$ and $Z_2(p)$ with the appropriate values of A. Check your results with Figs. 10.05–E and –H.

10-71. Carry through the realization of (10.05–1) in the manner discussed after (10.05–2), to obtain the network of Fig. 10.05–E. Contrast the calculations with those of Prob. 10-70.

10-72. Consider the possibility of realizing the function (10.05–1) in the form shown in Fig. 10.05–D, except that L_3 and C_3 are to be interchanged. Demonstrate that this cannot be done. (Cf. Prob. 10-73.)

10-73. Realize the function (10.05–1) in the form shown, which corresponds to Fig. 10.05–C with the interchange of L_3 and C_3 and the addition of C_2. Compare the element values and the number of elements used with the realization of Fig. 10.05–E and with those of Figs. 10.01–C and –E.

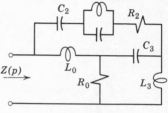

Prob. 10–73

Discuss the possibility of obtaining a realization somewhat like that of Fig. 10.05–H, but with L_3 and C_3 interchanged and an appropriate additional element.

10-74. In Prob. 10-73, if $R_0 = Z(0)$, as in § 10.05, why is the additional element C_2 necessary? Compare the value obtained here for R_2 with the value of R_1 of the realization of Fig. 10.05–D and with $Z(\infty)$.

If this method is to be valid for *any* driving-point function $Z(p)$ of order two, how must $Z(0)$ and $Z(\infty)$ be related? Show that they are so related if $L_0 > 0$. Develop the general procedure. For the case $L_0 < 0$ develop a corresponding general procedure. What happens if $L_0 = 0$?

If the order of $Z(p)$ is greater than two, does the relation between $Z(0)$ and $Z(\infty)$ necessarily hold if $L_0 > 0$? Need it, for this realization method to succeed?

10-75. In § 10.05 it is assumed that $Z_0(p)$ is *minimum*, i.e., that it has no imaginary zeros or poles and that at one frequency (at least) **Re** $Z_0(j\omega) = 0$. Discuss the need for these restrictions and, if some are not necessary, the utility of the method in those cases.

10-76. Draw the schematic diagrams of realizations of the function (10.05–1) by Brune's method, by the Pantell (bridge) method, and by the Bott–Duffin method. State the number of each kind of element used in each realization and compare them. Discuss the relative merits of the three methods as to practicality and efficiency in the number of elements used.

In general, what is the minimum number of reactive elements required in the realization of a p-r function of order two? Of resistors? If the function is minimum, does the Brune realization use any more elements than are absolutely required? Do the Bott–Duffin and Pantell methods? (Cf. Probs. 10-92, 9-39.)

Discuss the possibility of answering the question "What is the minimum number of elements required in the realization of such a function without using mutual inductance?" on the basis of the various methods presented in the text.

10-77. Discuss the possibility of converting a Bott–Duffin realization of a given impedance into a Pantell realization by inserting an appropriate element in a current-free branch and performing the classical Y-Δ or star-mesh transformation (RE 3, ST 5).

10-78. A somewhat different (largely mathematical) approach to the Pantell realization was given, independently, by Fialkow and Gerst (FI 4). Verify their development and that it leads to the same bridge realization.

10-79. Calculation of the minimum-reactance impedance function corresponding to a given even function, required in the methods of § 10.03 and § 10.04, may be carried out by the Brune-Gewertz method (§ 8.11) or other methods discussed in Chapter 8, by Miyata's method (Prob. 8-79), or by the somewhat different method given below, due to Pantell (PA 1). Verify this last process in detail.

Let $E_0(p)$ and $O_0(p)$ be the even and odd parts of the impedance function that is sought, $Z_0(p) = N_0/D_0$, so that $Z_0 = E_0 + O_0$. Only E_0 is known; let its numerator and denominator be N_{0e} and $D_0(p)D_0(-p)$ respectively, the usual factoring into left-half-plane and right-half-plane parts being implied for the latter. Let the (unknown) numerator of the odd part be N_{00}; the denominator is of course $D_0(p)D_0(-p)$. Now form $Z_0(p)$ by adding these:

$$Z_0(p) = E_0 + O_0 = \frac{N_{0e} + N_{00}}{D_0(p)D_0(-p)}$$

in which only the odd polynomial $N_{00} = a_1 p + a_3 p^3 + \cdots + a_n p^n$ is unknown; n is a known odd integer.

(a) The coefficients a may be determined by requiring that, at each zero of $D(-p)$, $N_{0e} + N_{00} = 0$, and solving the resulting simultaneous equations.

(b) The coefficients a may alternatively be determined by dividing $(N_{0e} + N_{00})$ by $D(-p)$, requiring that the remainder be identically zero, and solving the resulting simultaneous equations.

(c) An alternative process is to factor N_{0e}, to separate out a small factor such as $(\alpha^2 - p^2)$ or $(b_0 + b_2 p^2 + b_4 p^4)$, and to write, for example,

$$Z_0(p) = \frac{\left(\dfrac{N_{0e}}{\alpha^2 - p^2}\right) [(\alpha^2 - p^2) + c_1 p + c_3 p^3 + \cdots]}{D_0(p)D_0(-p)}.$$

The coefficients c are then determined as in (a) or (b), and the cancellation(s) made. Then another factor is separated, brought into the bracket, and the new coefficients found. The process is repeated until all factors of N_{0e} have been used, and $Z_0(p)$ has been found. In some cases the solution of simultaneous equations may be avoided by using this device.

For illustration:

(1) Obtain $Z_A(p)$ and $Z_B(p)$ below by this and by the other two methods mentioned, and compare the techniques,

$$E_s(p) = \frac{1}{4 + p^4} + \frac{p^4}{4 + p^4} = E_A + E_B.$$

(2) Similarly, obtain the minimum-reactance impedance function that corresponds to the resistance function

$$\frac{(p^2 + 3)^2(p^2 + 5)^2}{(p^4 + 6p^2 + 10)(p^4 + 8p^2 + 16)}.$$

Extend the method to the calculation of impedance, given the odd part only, and to the dual applications.

10-80. Some immittance functions that require all three kinds of elements can be realized by taking a number of networks, all of driving-point impedance proportional to some p-r function $Z(p)$ or its reciprocal, treating them as network elements, and appropriately connecting them in series, parallel, and in more complicated fashion.

By using the theory of Chapter 6, with p replaced by $Z(p)$, show that if such a realization is possible, the datum immittance function must have the following properties: (*a*) it is a reactance function in which p is replaced by $Z(p)$; (*b*) its zeros and poles lie on the curve(s) **Re** $Z(p) = 0$. Show that the first of these properties is sufficient for realization in canonic forms in which $Z(p)$ and its inverse are the "building blocks."

What is the parallel case based on the theory of Chapter 7? (Cf. RE 4.)

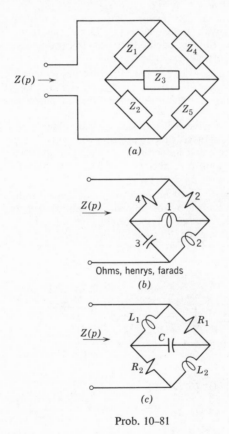

(*a*)

(*b*)

Ohms, henrys, farads

(*c*)

Prob. 10–81

10-81. The general realization methods of Chapters 9 and 10 do not exhaust the number of possible realization techniques, which are not all known. Nor do they all necessarily give the realization with the smallest number of elements. For example, some functions can be realized in the bridge form shown in (*a*) which is not the immediate result of any method discussed in the text (KI 5, PA 4, VA 5.)

(1) To illustrate this, determine by analysis the driving-point impedance $Z(p)$ of the network of (*b*). Realize this according to the Brune, Bott–Duffin, and Pantell techniques, and also with one resistor. Contrast the various realizations.

(2) From the literal form for $Z(p)$ of the network shown in (*c*) as a function of the five elements, determine conditions necessary and sufficient that a third-order immittance function be so realizable. How general is the realization? Illustrate with a numerical example and contrast this realization with those of the same function obtained by other techniques.

(3) If in (2) the two inductance values are equal, and the two resistance values are equal, what happens to the function $Z(p)$? What kinds of p-r functions are realizable by such a network (VA 5)?

(4) Many other forms of the network of (*a*) exist with only five elements, not to mention those with more elements. Draw one such, determine its driving-point impedance function, delimit the class of p-r functions so realizable, and illustrate with a numerical example (KI 5).

10-82. Give an example of a (p-r) driving point immittance function, all of whose zeros and poles are on the real axis, that requires all three kinds of elements in its realization. Explain how the function differs from those discussed in Chapter 7.

Is it possible for the driving-point impedance (admittance) of a given R-L-C network to meet the requirements for realization with only resistors and capacitors? With only resistors and inductors? Explain and illustrate.

Explain why any constant-resistance network must contain all three kinds of elements.

10-83. Networks dual to given networks that contain no mutual inductance (if they exist) may be obtained by the following graphical process (GA 1).

(1) On the schematic diagram of the original network place a node (dot) within each loop, and one node "outside" the network.

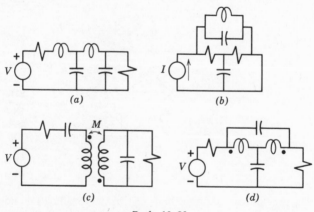

Prob. 10–83

(2) Connect these new nodes by branches drawn to cross each element of the original network once (only) and containing the dual element in each case. These form the dual network desired.

Demonstrate the validity of this from the basic definition of the dual network: its equations of analysis are mathematically identical with those of the original network, but physical quantities are interchanged according to the table of § 2.06. If mutual inductance is present, how must the procedure be modified? Illustrate by finding networks dual to those of Figs. 10.05–E, –G, –H, and those shown here.

10-84. Find networks whose input admittance (with proper element values)

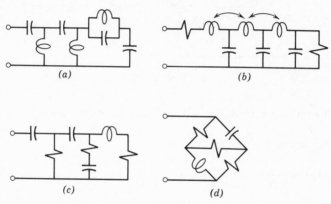

(a)   (b)

(c)   (d)

Prob. 10–84

will be numerically identical (as functions of p) with the input impedance of the networks shown.

10-85. Give the details of the derivation of the network dual to that of Fig. 10.08–A, developed in the same fashion. Correlate both of these with the development of (10.02–25) and (10.02–26); what values may L_1 have? Compare the number of reactive elements in the realizations with the order of $Z_0(p)$ here, and reconcile their differences.

10-86. Derive the conditions under which a given impedance (admittance) may be "built out" to a pure resistance, as in Figs. 10.08–B, –C. In terms of the zeros and poles of the given immittance function, what surplus factors are used in the process?

In Fig. 10.08–B let Z_A be an R-C network (arbitrary except that Z_A does not have a pole at the origin); Z_B is to be designed so that $Z(p) = R_0$, R_0 being the minimum constant resistance to which Z_A can be built out. Show that $Z_B(p)$ can be realized as an R-L network. Must it necessarily be realized without capacitance?

Discuss the corresponding matters when Z_A is an R-L network, and the two corresponding cases for building out in the manner of Fig. 10.08–C.

Build out networks with the following driving-point immittance functions, where possible, (a) to the minimum possible constant resistance, (b) to the

minimum possible constant conductance.   Where not possible, explain why not.
Realize the complementary networks.

(1) $Z(p) = \dfrac{p^2 + 1}{p^2 + p + 1}$ (2) $Z(p) = \dfrac{4p^2 + 3p + 4}{p^2 + p + 1}$

(3) $Y(p) = \dfrac{p^2 + 1}{(p + 1)^2}$ (4) $Y(p) = \dfrac{p^2 + 4p + 4}{p^2 + 2p + 1}$

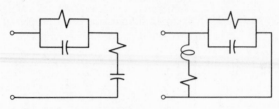

Prob. 10–86

(5) The minimum-reactance impedance corresponding to $R(\omega) = \dfrac{1}{1 + \omega^{10}}$,

$\left.\begin{array}{c}(6)\\(7)\end{array}\right\}$ See figure,

(8) $Z(p) = \dfrac{2}{p + 6}$.

10-87. Find four (equivalent) networks for the realization of each driving-point function below, and four networks inverse to each in driving-point impedance, with respect to R_0.   What value should R_0 have to make the networks reciprocal?   Point out examples of duality.

(a) $Z(p) = \dfrac{(p^2 + 2)(p^2 + 6)}{p(p^2 + 4)}$ (b) $Y(p) = \dfrac{p(p + 4)}{(p + 2)(p + 6)}$

(c) $R(\omega) = \dfrac{(\omega^2 - 4)^2}{1 + \omega^6}$ (d) $X(\omega) = \dfrac{-\omega}{1 + \omega^6}$ (e) $\beta(\omega) = \tan^{-1}(\omega^7)$

10-88. Show that if the dual of network 1 is found, the terminals a-a' being open, there are terminals b-b' in the dual (network 2), easily recognized, at which the driving-point impedance is inverse to that at a-a'.

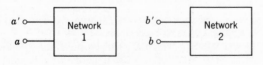

Prob. 10–88

10-89. Suppose that in Figs. 10.08–E, –G, –H the structure of Z_1 is given, containing no mutual inductance.   Explain how the structure and element values of Z_2 may immediately be written down. Explain the utility of the formulas $L/C = R_0^2$ and $R_1 R_2 = R_0^2$ here. Is this the only realization of Z_2? Explain. If Z_1 contains mutual inductance, what difficulty may arise?

10-90. Obtain constant-resistance networks by the use of the surplus factors in $(p^4 + Ap^2 + 1)$, partitioning $1 = (p^4 + Ap^2 + 1)/(p^4 + Ap^2 + 1)$ into two parts in various ways. Explain why $A \leq 0$ is required. Show the forms the networks take when $A = 0$ and when $A < 0$. Illustrate with numerical values. Use the same surplus factors in the realization of $Z_0(p)$, a minimum impedance of order n, and indicate the first reduction cycle; correlate it with the realization of the constant resistance.

10-91. Find constant-resistance networks by using the surplus factors given below. In each case use each of the various nontrivial partitions possible (including those into more than two parts) and contrast the results; give also the dual results. Where numerical data are not given, indicate the schematic form of the networks.

(a) $1 + p^4$ (b) $1 + p^6$ (c) $1 + p^{2n}$ (d) $1 - 2p^2 + p^4$

(e) $1 + 2p^2 + p^4$ (f) $1 + 2p^4 + p^8$ (g) $1 - p^2 + p^4 - p^6 + p^8$

(h) $1 + p^2 + p^4 - p^6$

10-92. Show that if an $R\text{-}L\text{-}C$ network contains m inductors and n capacitors, the order N of any driving-point immittance function is in general given by $N = m + n$. Discuss the exceptions (in which m or n does not truly represent the number of elements of that kind because of series, parallel, T, or Π connection of elements of the same kind).

Discuss the statement: the true order of the driving-point immittance functions of a constant-resistance network containing m inductors and n capacitors is $(m + n)$, even though the input impedance is simply the constant R_0.

Discuss the statement: a network whose driving-point impedance is of order N must contain *at least* N reactive elements; it may contain many more, as well as resistors. (Cf. Probs. 9-39, 10-10, 10-63, 10-76.)

10-93. Show that any first-order p-r rational function can be realized as the driving-point impedance of an $R\text{-}C$ or $R\text{-}L$ network. Discuss the various possibilities. *Must* a realization of such a function contain only two kinds of elements? Explain.

10-94. Develop a constant-resistance network in the bridged-T form shown by using the Type-D section of § 9.13. Take the input impedance to be unity,

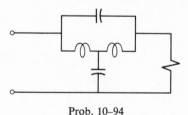

Prob. 10–94

and p_0 to be $1/\underline{60°}$. What surplus factors appear in the input impedance? (Cf. Prob. 9-75.)

10-95. What surplus factors (in terms of the zeros and poles of Z_1 or Y_1) are used in the realizations of Fig. 10.08–E?

10-96. Explain the statements that the networks of Figs. 10.01–F and –H are of the "balanced-bridge" type, and that no current flows in the network x. Use these facts to determine the ratio of the various voltages in the network, when x is a resistor R_0 as in Fig. 10.08–G, to the voltage at the input (driving point) to the network.

10-97. Show by analysis that, in Fig. 10.08–H, $Z_{\text{in}} = R_0$ if $Z_1 Z_2 = R_0^2$. (Contrast the straightforward solution of mesh- or node-basis equations with a solution based on symmetry and working backward from currents x and y in Z_1 and Z_2.) How many surplus factors appear in Z_{in}? How are they related to the zeros and poles of Z_1 or Z_2? Determine also the ratio of the output voltage (that across R_0) to the input voltage. Do surplus factors appear in it?

10-98. Show how a realization of any driving-point immittance function that contains a resistor may be extended indefinitely without affecting the

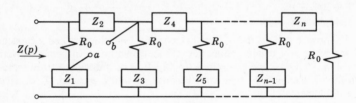

Prob. 10–98

driving-point immittances by replacing resistors by constant-resistance networks.

In particular, explain what relations must exist between the impedances in this network, so that $Z(p) = R_0$.

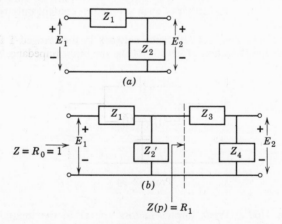

Prob. 10–99

Show how this network can be converted into a chain or cascade connection of networks of the constant-resistance bridged-T form (Fig. 10.08–G) by adding $n/2$ resistors R_0 connected between a and b, and between corresponding pairs of points. Does this affect the input impedance $Z(p)$? Explain.

What is the ratio of the voltage across the final right-hand resistor of the network without the added resistors, to the voltage at the input, when the network is driven by a current or voltage source? (It is in this manner as a two-terminal pair that this network is useful.)

How does this ratio change when the additional resistors are added? Explain.

10-99. Certain impedances may be built out by the series connection of a second impedance to form a constant-resistance impedance R_0 (Prob. 10-86). Let $Z_1(p)$ be such an impedance function, normalized so $R_0 = 1$, and $Z_2(p)$ the complementary function. Show that in (a) the voltage ratio $E_2/E_1 = Z_2(p)$.

Explain how the network can be continued by repeating the process as in (b), so that $E_2/E_1 = Z_2 Z_4$. How is Z_2' related to Z_2? What determines allowable values for R_1? In what way is the choice of Z_3 restricted?

Discuss briefly the requirements on a voltage ratio that it be so realizable. Extend to networks formed by three or more "cycles" of this process.

Give the dual discussion.

11.

Some Applications

It is only logical that collection of tools and of material precede the application of the one to the other. We have tools now in our knowledge of properties and realization methods; we have our material in the network elements. True, we have not yet studied the matter of approximation; still we can here at least illustrate the application of networks to the performance of actual engineering tasks. It is fitting to do so, both to show the utility of our knowledge, and to give us some feeling for practical problems, the better to approach the subject of approximation.

11.01 Uses of one-terminal pairs

Practically all two-terminal networks exist as component parts of four-terminal or more complicated networks. It is the chief function of one-terminal pairs to make up two-terminal pairs, i.e., *transmission* networks, which have separate input and output terminals. Such networks will be discussed in detail in Volume II; here we merely hint at some of them in order to illustrate the application of the one-terminal pair. We can consider but a sample, as the field is broad indeed.

All networks with more than two terminals are of necessity composed of smaller networks with two terminals only (and possibly transformers), suitably interconnected. This means that the design of these networks may reduce largely to the design of one-terminal pairs: in some cases the design can almost immediately be broken down into that of one or more one-terminal pairs; in others the division of the problem into one-terminal-pair subproblems is not as clear. For the examples of this chapter we shall confine ourselves to those in which the breakdown is clear.

Networks seldom play leading roles in engineering works—they usually have small parts not apparent when one looks at the system as a whole.

Their parts, though small, are often important and must be carefully fitted into the performance of the complete system, doing the particular jobs assigned them. Consequently network design is usually a subordinate item in the design of a more complicated system; the requirements laid down for the networks are determined by system considerations. Hence each of the following illustrations represents only a part of some system design problem.

11.02 Distortion correction

The design of a communication or control system involves many essential parts that incidentally produce distortion: transmission lines, amplifiers, other apparatus provide essential services but also have transmission characteristics that are not ideal. Many network design problems arise from the need for networks to be introduced into such systems to counteract this distortion, i.e., for distortion-correcting or compensating networks (equalizers).

One learns in network analysis that for the accurate transmission of signals, for the preservation of the important characteristics of waveshapes as functions of time, the steady-state transmission characteristic of the system must have

(a) amplitude that is constant as a function of frequency, at least over all important frequency ranges;

(b) phase shift that is linear as a function of frequency, at least over all important frequency ranges. (11.02–1)

The problem of distortion correction is often posed as the problem of compensating for the departures of system-apparatus characteristics from these ideals, over certain frequency ranges that are the most important. The problem is thus made into a steady-state network problem that may be phrased:

Given a system amplitude (or phase) transmission characteristic, design a network with a complementary characteristic such that when the network is introduced into the system, the over-all characteristic will be tolerably good. (11.02–2)

This is of course a two-terminal-pair problem, but it is often reduced to a one-terminal-pair problem by the use of special network configurations. Amplitude and phase equalization are frequently carried out independently (either because one is not as important, or because one is more conveniently done first), and we shall discuss only these special networks and the independent equalization of each characteristic.

Consider first the correction of amplitude distortion, without regard to phase. (We shall find in Volume II that these two are related, much as resistance and reactance, or conductance and susceptance, or magnitude and angle of immittance are—and that equalization of one may automatically tend to equalization of the other.) A commonly used type of equalizer is the constant-resistance bridged-T network of Figs. 10.08–G and 11.02–A. It is easily shown by analysis (Problem 10-96) that if this

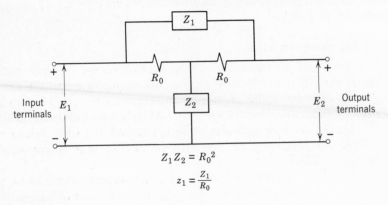

$$Z_1 Z_2 = R_0{}^2$$

$$z_1 = \frac{Z_1}{R_0}$$

Fig. 11.02–A

network is properly terminated (i.e., if the output terminals are closed through a resistor R_0), then

$$\frac{E_1}{E_2} = 1 + \frac{Z_1}{R_0} = 1 + z_1. \qquad (11.02\text{–}3)$$

This represents the transmission characteristic of the network (inverted, for simplicity), remarkable because the whole behavior of the network depends only on z_1, i.e., on Z_1 measured in units of R_0. If a point can be found in the system where the impedance (looking either to the left or to the right, but preferably in both directions) is substantially a constant resistance R_0, then the effect of inserting this network at that point will be simply to alter the system transmission function by the factor $(1 + z_1)$. The design of the network then amounts to the design of a one-terminal pair, the network Z_1, such that $(1 + z_1)$ has the desired magnitude-versus-frequency characteristic. This problem is simply that of designing a one-terminal pair (having the desired magnitude characteristic) that is *not* of the minimum-resistance type (Problem 11-2). It is highly desirable, of course, that the network Z_1 be realizable in a simple fashion, without the use of mutual inductance, for example, and that it be in a practical form. For this reason these equalizers are often designed on a trial-and-error basis, guided by experience: a promising network Z_1 is assumed, the parameters adjusted by trial, Z_1 revised if necessary, and further trials made, until a satisfactory design is obtained. Charts that facilitate this process are easy to construct (Problem 11-5) and may be very useful. The process can be so organized that an experienced designer can quickly produce an equalizer for almost any given characteristic. Realizability and practicality present no problems here, as the design proceeds from an assumed (trial) network.

A more sophisticated approach would be to start with a literal form for Z_1, to determine appropriate values for the coefficients in the two polynomials, as by specifying the magnitude of $(1 + z_1)$ at certain frequencies, and solving the resulting simultaneous equations. Unfortunately there is no a priori guarantee that this will lead to a realizable network (§ 8.13), but the technique may sometimes be useful. Still more elaborate approaches have been devised, but these are really matters of approximation proper and lead us somewhat afield.

Although the bridged-T network of Fig. 11.02–A is widely used, it is not by any means the only one. Simple insertion of a one-terminal pair in series or in parallel may be satisfactory (Problem 11-4), and there are many other forms of equalizers (ZO 1). One such is the *lattice* network of Fig. 10.08–H. This is more flexible than the bridged-T network, but may consequently be more expensive and less convenient in practice. A detailed theory of equalization can be developed, building on the lattice (GU 2). Amplitude equalization can be accomplished by less direct means, as by designing the transmission characteristics of the system's amplifiers so that they provide equalization as well as gain. But here too, as in the examples above, the problem very often reduces to that of designing a two-terminal network, a one-terminal pair—whose properties, and methods for realizing which, we have been developing.

Consider now the correction of phase distortion. The original phase characteristic of the system is altered, of course, by the addition of the amplitude (or loss) equalizer. In fact, if the $(1 + z_1)$ type of network is used, the change in the phase characteristic is determined immediately by the amplitude characteristic, through the relations between resistance and reactance (and so in general, as discussed in Volume II). This change may (and usually will) tend to improve the linearity of the system phase characteristic, but there may remain substantial nonlinearities that must be corrected. For this purpose the type of network discussed above is not suitable. In the first place, if Z_1 is designed so that $(1 + z_1)$ has the desired phase characteristic, then $(1 + z_1)$ will also have an amplitude characteristic, and the insertion of the network will upset the amplitude equalization. In the second place, the maximum amount of phase shift obtainable from such a network is 90° in magnitude, which may be insufficient (though of course a number of networks could be used). But a different type of network exists that has the remarkable property of introducing phase shift without affecting the magnitude of the transmission function. This network is the lattice of Fig. 10.08–H, redrawn

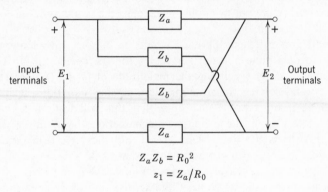

$$Z_a Z_b = R_0{}^2$$
$$z_1 = Z_a / R_0$$

Fig. 11.02–B

in Fig. 11.02–B. For this network, if the output terminals are closed through a resistance R_0, then analysis shows that

$$\frac{E_1}{E_2} = \frac{1 + z_1}{1 - z_1} \qquad (11.02\text{–}4)$$

which is reminiscent of (11.02–3). Here z_1 represents the normalized impedance of one arm of the lattice; the other arms do not appear because of the symmetry and constant-resistance property. On the assumption again that a point in the system can be found at which the impedance (looking either to the left or to the right, but preferably in both directions) is a resistance R_0, then it can be shown by analysis that the effect of inserting this network is to multiply the system transmission function (in inverse form, i.e., input divided by output) by

$$F(p) = \frac{1 + z_1}{1 - z_1}. \qquad (11.02\text{–}5)$$

This again depends only on the one-terminal-pair impedance function $z_1(p)$. The network may be undesirable, to be sure, because we cannot ground both input and output terminals (to do so would short-circuit one of the boxes). For systems in which this common grounding is required, however, there are usually equivalent networks (to be discussed in Volume II), and for systems of a balanced (to ground) nature the network is suitable.

Suppose now that the network Z_1 is made an L-C network (which requires that Z_2 also be nondissipative). Then at real frequencies

$$z_1 = 0 + jx_1, \tag{11.02-6}$$

numerator and denominator in (11.02–5) are conjugates, and we find

$$|F(j\omega)| = 1. \tag{11.02-7}$$

This shows the remarkable property, for introducing this network has no effect on the magnitude of the system function (at real frequencies), but it does affect the phase characteristic, since

$$\beta = \overline{F(j\omega)} = 2 \tan^{-1} x_1. \tag{11.02-8}$$

The problem then is to design an L-C one-terminal pair, of (normalized) real-frequency reactance x_1, according to

$$x_1(\omega) = \tan\left[\tfrac{1}{2}\beta(\omega)\right] \tag{11.02-9}$$

in which β represents the desired phase characteristic. Since the behavior of reactance functions at real frequencies is very much like the behavior of the tangent function (§ 6.03), we may reasonably expect to be able to do this. The phase shift produced by such a network (defined, as above, as the angle of lag of the output with respect to the input) must steadily increase with frequency. The poles and zeros of the reactance x_1 determine the frequencies at which β passes through multiples of 180° or π radians (conveniently called "π points"). One design technique is thus to determine z_1 immediately from the π points of the characteristic desired (the multiplier is fixed by some additional information). Then the resulting phase is to be calculated at intermediate frequencies and compared with that desired, with subsequent readjustment and improvement as indicated. An alternative would be the point-matching technique mentioned above—but the determination of z_1 is again in the field of approximation.

Phase equalization is often carried out in terms of the *slope* of the phase characteristic, i.e., one concentrates on $d\beta/d\omega$ (which should ideally be constant) instead of β. But this involves only minor modifications of the remarks above. Notice that we can only *add* to the slope of the phase characteristic; we cannot subtract therefrom. Since $d\beta/d\omega$ is associated with the "delay" experienced by a signal in passing through the system (though not in any simple fashion—and we shall not examine the meaning of the word *delay* here), it seems only reasonable that we should not be able to decrease the delay, but only to add to it. (In fact, networks of this type may be designed solely to retard signals; they are then called *delay networks*.) Similarly, with the $(1 + z_1)$ type of network we can introduce attenuation but not remove it.

These brief remarks on the subject of equalization (which is a vast one) only hint at the techniques used. But they do point out a field in which the synthesis of two-terminal pairs very often reduces immediately to that of one-terminal pairs, i.e., of driving-point immittances. Similar problems arise in sound recording and reproduction, in frequency-modulation and television work, and in many other places.

11.03 Impedance correction and simulation

We have already pointed out (§ 10.08) how the "correction" of extant impedance to a constant resistance leads to a one-terminal-pair problem. Similarly, the "building out" of an impedance to any impedance function is a one-terminal-pair problem.

A similar problem is encountered when it is necessary to simulate or match some known immittance (e.g., that of a transmission line) that is not rational in form. Such an occasion arises in the construction of an amplifier or "repeater" for a two-wire system that transmits in both directions (JO 1). In bare essentials, Fig. 11.03–A illustrates the problem.

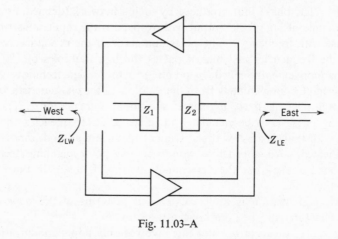

Fig. 11.03–A

Here a transmission system, running east and west, is interrupted in order to provide amplification. To accomplish the bidirectional amplification desired, two amplifiers are provided (the arrowhead-like symbols), which individually are of necessity one-way devices. These cannot be simply connected to the lines at the blank points, however, for an incoming signal would then not only be amplified and sent on, it would also (in part) enter the other amplifier and proceed around the closed loop. In such a loop, including active elements (the amplifiers) the possibility of self-oscillation or "singing" is apparent, presents a real danger, and something has to be done to prevent it. The two one-terminal pairs Z_1 and Z_2, together with an appropriate scheme of interconnection in the spaces left blank, do this. At the left-hand blank, where the line west, the top amplifier output, the lower amplifier input, and the leads to Z_1 all meet, we insert a coupling device (it is simply a multiwinding transformer, called a "hybrid coil") in such a manner that a bridge is formed, which is balanced when $Z_{LW} = Z_1$. The output of the top amplifier is the generator arm, and the input to the bottom amplifier is the detector arm of this bridge. Then, insofar as we can make $Z_1 = Z_{LW}$ the bridge is balanced, and no transmission around the loop can occur. Exactly the same thing is done at the other end of the repeater, to make doubly sure.

Here then is a straightforward one-terminal-pair design problem. The data are given as immittances (Z_{LW}, Z_{LE}); the problem is to design Z_1 and Z_2 to match closely. The resulting networks are known as *balancing* networks for obvious reasons.

11.04 One-resistor realizations

That any p-r function can be realized as a driving-point immittance with the use of only one resistor was demonstrated in Chapter 9; that this is an extremely useful fact we here demonstrate. Suppose such a realization of an impedance $Z(p)$ is driven by a current source I_0 at the input (Fig. 11.04–A). The single resistor is R_0; the balance of the

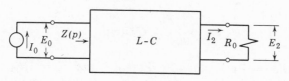

Fig. 11.04–A

network contains reactive elements only. In the steady state we can write the average power input to the network as

$$P_{in} = |I_0|^2 R(\omega) \qquad (11.04–1)$$

in which I_0 is in rms terms and $R(\omega) = \mathbf{Re}\, Z(j\omega)$. We can write the average power delivered to R_0, i.e., the output power if this is regarded now as a two-terminal pair terminated in R_0, in terms of the rms output voltage as

$$P_{out} = \frac{|E_2|^2}{R_0}. \qquad (11.04–2)$$

But these must be equal, because there is no element within the box (the two-terminal pair) that can dissipate energy; hence

$$\left| \frac{E_2}{I_0} \right|^2 = R_0 R(\omega). \qquad (11.04\text{--}3)$$

In words: the (magnitude) transmission characteristic of the two-terminal pair is proportional to the input resistance function. This immediately reduces a large number of two-terminal-pair design problems to the design of resistance functions and their realization in the one-resistor form (DA 1). The importance of this can hardly be exaggerated, for this principle is of tremendous value in two-terminal-pair synthesis, both in the cases described here and in the more general cases in which a resistor appears also in the source; the matter will be discussed in detail in Volume II.

If it is the output current that is of interest in Fig. 11.04–A, the relation corresponding to (11.04–3) is

$$\left| \frac{I_2}{I_0} \right|^2 = \frac{R(\omega)}{R_0}, \qquad (11.04\text{--}4)$$

whereas if the source is a voltage generator E_0 (rather than a current generator), then we have, by duality,

$$\left| \frac{E_2}{E_0} \right|^2 = \frac{G(\omega)}{G_0} \qquad (11.04\text{--}5)$$

and

$$\left| \frac{I_2}{E_0} \right|^2 = G_0 G(\omega), \qquad (11.04\text{--}6)$$

in which $G(\omega) = \mathbf{Re}\, Y(j\omega) = \mathbf{Re}\, [Z(j\omega)]^{-1}$, and $G_0 = 1/R_0$. Hence if our interest is confined to synthesis for a prescribed magnitude of transmission function, and if the system in which the network is to operate can provide a zero- or infinite-impedance source (as is done, to a good approximation, by some vacuum-tube circuits), and if the network can operate into a resistor R_0, then the synthesis problem is essentially a one-terminal-pair problem. It is to devise an appropriate resistance function $R(\omega)$, to find the corresponding $Z(p)$, and to realize $Z(p)$ in a one-resistor form. We recognize here, as far as we know, that mutual inductance may be required, and perhaps perfect coupling between inductors, but that if the zeros of $\mathbf{Ev}\, Z(p)$ are confined to the imaginary axis, then there is a good chance that mutual inductance will not be needed, and if these zeros occur only at the origin or at infinity (or both), then mutual inductance certainly will not be necessary (§ 9.14). In solving the approximation problem, then, we should use discretion in locating the zeros of **Ev** $Z(p)$, i.e., of the resistance function.

Here then is another two-terminal-pair problem that is in essence only a one-terminal-pair problem. In this case only the resistance (conductance) is of interest and designers would pay no attention to the corresponding reactance (susceptance) but would work only with the real part during the approximation process; in the actual realization the associated minimum reactance (susceptance) would automatically be obtained.

By way of illustration, consider the common "double-tuned" amplifier interstage network of Fig. 11.04–B. If the first vacuum tube is a pentode,

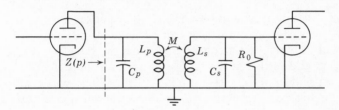

Fig. 11.04–B

its small-signal equivalent circuit for alternating currents is substantially a current generator, which we identify with I_0 of Fig. 11.04–A. Then the capacitors C_p and C_s, and the transformer L_p and L_s (or an equivalent network with self-inductance only) form the nondissipative network, and R_0 provides the termination. (These capacitances are to include parasitic capacitance effects, and R_0 may be considered to account for the parasitic dissipation effects.) Then we may proceed to design the interstage network by formulating a resistance function of the form

$$R(\omega) = \frac{a_2\omega^2}{\omega^8 + b_6\omega^6 + b_4\omega^4 + b_2\omega^2 + b_0}. \qquad (11.04\text{–}7)$$

If $R(\omega) \geqq 0$ and is finite for all frequencies, then the synthesis can be completed in the form shown. This form for $R(\omega)$ is merely illustrative; in other applications it may of course be quite different.

11.05 Interstage and feedback networks

The example given in Fig. 11.04–B is the first to bring active elements (the vacuum tubes) into our calculations. These are not really parts of our networks, so our basic assumption of passivity is not violated. But this suggests that the active-network designer may have other uses for passive one-terminal pairs. And so he does—in many places.

One method of connecting together two successive tubes in a vacuum-tube amplifier is by means of a one-terminal-pair interstage network, as in Fig. 11.05–A. [Here again the usual restriction to small (a-c) signals

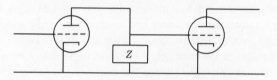

Fig. 11.05–A

is made, linearity is assumed, and it is also assumed that the requisite blocking capacitor and grid leak can be ignored, i.e., that we are not concerned with very low frequencies.] Then the ratio of the voltage at the second grid to that at the first is a simple function of Z; if the first tube is a pentode, in fact, this ratio is substantially proportional to $Z(p)$. Hence the function $Z(p)$ is a measure of the transmission of this "stage" of the amplifier, and this part of the amplifier design is practically a one-terminal-pair problem. Here, of course, Z must have a capacitor at its terminals (part or all of this capacitance is actually supplied by tube and wiring capacitance), and Z may have to provide a path for the direct current supplied to the plate. We shall discuss this design problem later (Chapters 14, 15) in illustration of some basic approximation procedures. In some applications the use of a two-terminal pair may be preferred, but there are many applications indeed in which amplifier interstage network design is actually, as here, one-terminal-pair design. Similar designs may be required in transistor circuits, in servomechanisms, or in any active network.

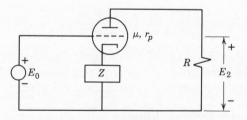

Fig. 11.05–B

Another use of the passive one-terminal pair is to provide prescribed feedback characteristics in amplifiers of that type. A very simple jllustration is in Fig. 11.05–B, in which the one-terminal pair Z is inserted in the cathode connection, and the input and output connections of the amplifier have been simplified. With the usual assumptions, we find by analysis that

$$\frac{E_2}{E_0} = \frac{-[(\mu R)/(Z + r_p + R)]}{1 + [(\mu Z)/(Z + r_p + R)]} \tag{11.05-1}$$

in which μ represents the amplification factor of the tube, and r_p its dynamic plate resistance. If the amplification factor is large, then (approximately)

$$\frac{E_2}{E_0} = -\frac{R}{Z}, \tag{11.05-2}$$

whereas if this is not so,

$$\frac{E_2}{E_0} = \frac{-[(\mu R)/(r_p + R)]}{1 + Z[(\mu + 1)/(r_p + R)]}. \tag{11.05-3}$$

In either case we have again a one-terminal-pair problem, that of designing and realizing $Z(p)$ to provide the desired feedback. In (11.05-2) the transmission is simply inversely proportional to (normalized) $Z(p)$. In (11.05-3) we see again (11.02-3) in essence: the transmission is proportional to $(1 + z)^{-1}$, z being a normalized $Z(p)$. Thus some of the discussion of § 11.02 applies here also.

The uses to which one-terminal pairs are put in active networks are many, but these two are perhaps representative. The literature describing these applications is vast, so that any attempt to list illustrative works can be only superficial; a few are given below.

11.06 Conclusion

This brief chapter has had only one purpose: to present a few specific applications of one-terminal pairs. It does not pretend to be a catalog of uses of these networks, nor a guide thereto. Its moral is simply that even networks with only two terminals are extremely useful and widely employed, and that time spent on the study of their synthesis is time well spent, even without regard to its value as preparation for the study of two-terminal pairs. The meager sampling presented here can rapidly be broadened to any desired extent merely by turning the pages of any contemporary journal that deals with electrical engineering.

11.07 References

The references listed here are merely illustrative; the literature of applications of one-terminal-pair theory is so vast that it were folly to even consider anything like a complete list. The issues of journals like the *Bell System Technical Journal, Electrical Communication,* the *Proceedings* of the Institution of Electrical Engineers and of the Institute of Radio Engineers, the *R C A Review*, and many others will yield innumerable additional examples—these are merely typical.

Distortion correction (equalization): BO 3, GU 2, JO 1, LA 3, ME 1, SH 1, ZO 1.
Impedance simulation and compensation (correction): BO 6, HO 2, HO 3, PA 2, SH 1, VA 4.
One-resistor realizations (used as two-terminal pairs): BR 7, CA 2, DA 1, NO 2.
Vacuum-tube circuits: BO 3, MO 1 (an excellent specific illustration of several different uses of the one-terminal pair in a vacuum-tube amplifier), ST 3, VA 1, VA 6.

PROBLEMS

11-1. Explain why the bridged-T network discussed in § 11.02 can introduce attenuation but cannot remove it (i.e., cannot provide *gain*).

11-2. Show that if a p-r function $F(p)$ can be found, such that (*a*) $|F(j\omega)|$ is tolerably close to the desired magnitude characteristic in an amplitude equalization problem, and (*b*) Re $F(j\omega) > 0$ for all ω, then it is always possible to find a (p-r) impedance function $Z(p)$ such that

$$1 + Z_1/R_0 = KF(p),$$

in which K is a real, positive constant.

If an equalizer is constructed, based on this Z_1, its *amplitude equalization* mission will be fulfilled, regardless of the value of K. Explain this statement. What is the physical effect of large values of K?

11-3. Show that if the constant-resistance bridged-T network of Fig. 11.02–A is inserted at some point in a two-wire transmission system at which the impedance, looking *either* to the right or to the left, is a resistance R_0, the system

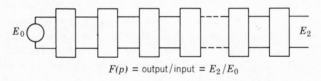

$F(p) =$ output/input $= E_2/E_0$

Prob. 11–3

transmission function $F(p)$ is modified merely by division by $(1 + z_1)$. [See figure.] (*Suggestion:* The theorems of § 2.09 may be useful.) Explain why it is that of all the elements in the network it is essentially only $Z_1(p)$ that appears in this factor.

11-4. Show that if a one-terminal pair of impedance $Z(p)$ is inserted in the two-wire system of Prob. 11-3 in series, or in parallel, its effect on the system transmission function is of the same general sort as that of the insertion of the bridged-T, provided the impedances to the left and to the right are both resistances. Obtain the actual formulas and show how any techniques useful for the design

(a) (b)

Prob. 11–4

of $Z_1(p)$ in the bridged-T can then immediately be applied to the design of $Z(p)$ in each of the two cases shown here.

11-5. For the amplitude equalizers of Probs. 11-3 and 11-4, the design problem is to find a one-terminal pair of normalized impedance $z_1(p)$ such that $|1 + z_1(j\omega)|$ has a behavior tolerably close to that desired. A practical design method is to assume a reasonable network form for z_1 and then to calculate $|1 + z_1|$ as a

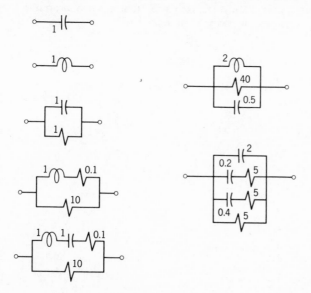

Prob. 11–5

function of frequency for comparison with the requirements, as a guide to subsequent improvement. A great deal of effort can be saved by drawing up charts with which one can obtain the value of $|1 + z_1|$ directly from the (complex) value of z_1 or of $1/z_1$. Show that if $z_1 = r_1 + jx_1$ then the curves of constant $|1 + z_1|$ in the plane of coordinates r_1 and x_1 are circles. Give the coordinates of their centers, their radii, and construct a chart made up of these circles.

(*Note:* Magnitude or amplitude characteristics are usually discussed in logarithmic terms, so that the circles should be identified not by the value of $|1 + z_1|$ but by the value of $x = 20 \log_{10}|1 + z_1|$. Here x represents the *loss* introduced by the network, in decibels.)

The chart obtained above is convenient if z_1 is constructed by the series combination of a number of small networks. In practice it is usually more convenient to construct z_1 by placing small networks in parallel; then it is appropriate to draw up the charts in terms of g_1 and b_1, given by $y_1 = g_1 + jb_1$. Show that in the plane of coordinates g_1 and b_1 the curves of constant $|1 + z_1|$ are again circles, give the coordinates of centers, the radii, and construct a design chart.

Illustrate the use of the chart by calculating the values of the admittance y_1 in the cases given (p. 691) at a number of frequencies; then plot the insertion loss (loss introduced by inserting the network into the system) against frequency. (In the figure, in each case the network Z_1 is shown, with element values in normalized ohms, henrys, farads, on the basis $R_0 = 1$.) Show also the *gain* (the negative of x) against frequency.

11-6. Construct equalizers to provide the following insertion-loss characteristics. In each case use as simple a network for z_1 as possible, determining its general character by the resonances that seem appropriate, and adding resistors and adjusting element values by trial. Make use of the results of Prob. 11-5.

	Frequency (Normalized)	Insertion Loss Desired (db)	Tolerance (db)
(*a*)	0	10	±0.5
	0.5	9	±0.5
	1	5	±0.5
	1.5	1	±0.5
	2	0	±0.5
(*b*)	0	5	±0.5
	1	2	±0.5
	2	0	±0.5
	3	2	±0.5
	4	5	±0.5
(*c*)	0	5	±0.8
	1	8	±0.8
	1.5	5	±0.8
	2	8	±0.8
	2.5	5	±0.8
	3	2	±0.8
	3.5	1	±0.8

(*d*) The desired loss is represented by a straight line from 6 db at zero frequency to 10 db at unit frequency, by a second line from the last point to 0 db at frequency 2, thereafter zero loss; the tolerance is ±0.4 db at all frequencies.

11-7. On the assumption that a constant attenuation (loss in decibels) may be added if necessary, design amplitude equalizers for the following systems. Each system characteristic is to be made approximately flat over the frequency range specified, by the insertion of a constant-resistance equalizer. (Cf. Probs. 11-5, 11-6.)

(a) The system loss is $\sqrt{\omega}$ db in the range $1 < \omega < 4$. The tolerance is ±0.2 db.

(b) The system loss is expressible by the function $12(\omega - 1)^2$ db. The frequency range is from $\omega = 1$ to $\omega = 2$, the tolerance ±0.7 db.

(c) The system loss is outlined by the following measured points that cover the important frequency range. The tolerance is ±1/4 db.

Frequency	Loss (db)	Frequency	Loss (db)
1	0	2.0	−2.5
1.2	−4	2.2	−3
1.4	−4	2.4	−2.5
1.6	−2.5	2.6	−0.5
1.8	−2	2.8	+2
		3.0	+4

11-8. Suppose the network Z_1 of a constant-resistance bridged-T equalizer has the form shown, in which Z_a is an L-C impedance of order n. Sketch the magnitude of the insertion-effect factor $(1 + z_1)$ as a function of frequency for small values of n for the various possible cases. What distinguishing characteristics does it have? For what kinds of equalization problems might this structure be useful?

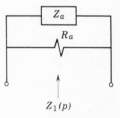

Prob. 11-8

11-9. Suppose one of the networks with transmission function $F(p) = E_{\text{in}}/E_{\text{out}} = (1 + z_1)$ is to be used for amplitude equalization purposes. Explain in the language of Chapter 8 how the phase shift it will introduce is automatically determined by its amplitude or magnitude characteristic. Explain why this phase shift is bounded by ±90°. Sketch the phase shift to be expected from equalizers which provide (approximately) the amplitude (loss) characteristics shown on p. 694.

11-10. A constant-resistance network is desired to have approximately the idealized characteristic shown (p. 694), when properly terminated. Determine by trials how closely this can be done with a constant-resistance bridged-T network in which Z_1 has the form (a) or (b).

11-11. The transmission loss (attenuation) of a coaxial cable is closely proportional to the square root of frequency, when measured logarithmically. Consider the problem of designing an equalizer to compensate for this amplitude distortion, so that cable and equalizer together will have approximately a constant attenuation in a prescribed frequency band. From the following data obtain equalizer designs, using the constant-resistance bridged-T network(s).

The transmission function of the cable and its terminations, without equalization, is given by

$$\left| \frac{E_{\text{out}}}{E_{\text{in}}} \right| = 10^{-\sqrt{\omega}/20}$$

on a normalized frequency scale. On this scale the frequencies of interest run from zero to $\omega = 400$.

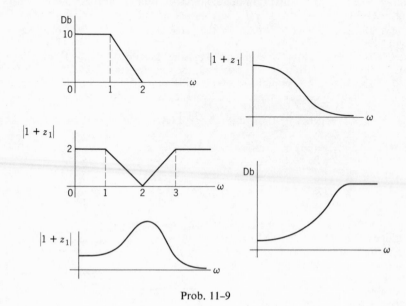

Prob. 11–9

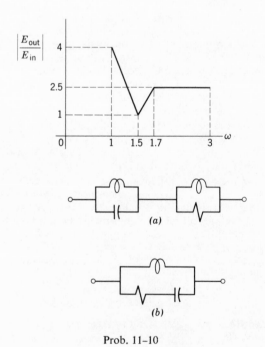

Prob. 11–10

(a) Using a single network with Z_1 simply the parallel combination of a resistor and a capacitor, determine by trial the quality of equalization that can be accomplished. Try several values for the constant loss that is to be approximated by cable and equalizer together; determine the resistor to give this value at zero frequency and adjust the capacitor for appropriate behavior at higher frequencies. Discuss your results and illustrate with plots of the over-all attenuation against frequency.

(b) Repeat, using for Z_1 an R-C network of order two.

(c) Repeat, using for Z_1 an R-C network of order three.

11-12. Attack Prob. 11-11 by the following method. Write a literal expression for $Z_1(p)$, of order three. Determine the coefficients by requiring that exactly the desired magnitude be obtained at selected frequencies and solving the resulting simultaneous equations. Find the corresponding $Z_1(p)$ and realize it (if possible). Plot the characteristic. Discuss the general utility of this approach.

11-13. A useful form of equalizer design chart (AL 1), different from those of Prob. 11-5, can be based on the bilinear transformation of (3.24–5). In the plane of $\rho = (z_1 - 1)/(z_1 + 1)$ what are the loci of constant attenuation? of constant r_1? of constant x_1? of constant g_1? of constant b_1? What relation does this chart have with the Smith chart of transmission-line theory?

Draw up such a chart and use it to plot loss versus frequency for the networks of the figure for Prob. 11-5. Illustrate its use in the design problems of Prob. 11-6.

11-14. Design a simple filtering network in the constant-resistance bridged-T form, to meet the following specifications: system impedance level is 600 Ω; no signal is to be transmitted at the frequency 1000 cps; no attenuation is to be introduced at the frequency 3000 cps; a 50% reduction in voltage magnitude is to be made at the frequency 2000 cps.

In the interests of simplicity, use an L-C network for Z_1. What changes in the attenuation curve might be expected when the network is actually built?

11-15. Demonstrate by analysis the validity of (11.02–5). (The theorems of § 2.09 may be helpful.)

11-16. Explain why the phase characteristic expressed by (11.02–8) must have a positive slope at all frequencies. Why can such a network only *add* to the slope of a system phase characteristic and not subtract therefrom? Explain also the connection between the frequencies at which x_1 is zero or infinity, and the frequencies at which β is a multiple of π radians. Illustrate by designing networks of this type to meet the following requirements. Plot the phase characteristics against frequency.

(a) Order of z_1 is to be three; $\beta = 0°$ at $\omega = 0$,

$$\beta = 180° \text{ at } \omega = 1,$$
$$\beta = 360° \text{ at } \omega = 3,$$
$$\frac{d\beta}{d\omega} = \pi \text{ at } \omega = 0.$$

(b) Order of z_1 is to be five; $\beta = 0°$, $180°$, $360°$, $540°$, $720°$ at

$$\omega = 0, 1, 2, 3, 4 \text{ respectively, and}$$
$$\frac{d\beta}{d\omega} = 0.2\pi \text{ at } \omega = 0.$$

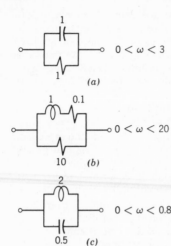

$0 < \omega < 3$

(a)

$0 < \omega < 20$

(b)

$0 < \omega < 0.8$

(c)

Prob. 11–17

11-17. The networks shown are the Z_1 arms of a bridged-T constant-resistance amplitude equalizer with element values in ohms, henrys, farads on the basis $R_0 = 1$. For each calculate and plot the phase characteristic versus frequency, and design a phase equalizer such that the two networks in combination will have approximately linear phase characteristics in the frequency ranges indicated. Use one- or two-element lattice arms first; then indicate the improvement to be gained by adding more elements.

11-18. A network for the purpose of retarding or delaying signals may be constructed in the L-C lattice form of Fig. 11.02–B. Ideally such a delay network has a phase characteristic linear with frequency, i.e., $\beta = T_0\omega$, and a constant amplitude characteristic.

Design a set of such networks by requiring that β agree with the ideal linear phase at the values $180°, 360°, 540°, \cdots$ as far as possible, for the cases $n =$ order of $Z_a = 1, 2, 3, 4, 5$. Adjust the multiplier to give the correct phase slope at zero frequency.

In each case plot the actual phase β and its departure from linearity (i.e., the error) versus frequency. For the $n = 5$ case find actual element values for your network, in various equivalent forms, for $R_0 = 600 \ \Omega$ and $T_0 = 1$ millisec.

It is an interesting exercise in network analysis to compute and plot the response of such a delay network to a step function of time, and to contrast this response with the ideal. Why do they differ?

11-19. The constant-resistance bridged-T structure is useful for other purposes than equalization. Within certain limitations (cf. Prob. 11-20) any transmission function can be realized by the use of a number of these networks

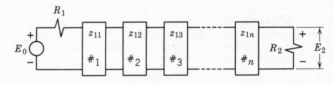

Prob. 11–19

in a cascade (tandem) connection. The work of this problem is to illustrate this fact.

(a) Show that if a number of these networks are connected as shown, R_0 being the same throughout, then

$$F(p) = \frac{E_2}{E_0} = \frac{\text{constant}}{(1 + z_{11})(1 + z_{12})(1 + z_{13}) \cdots (1 + z_{1n})}.$$

(b) Each of the factors of the denominator of $F(p)$ has the properties of a nonminimum-resistance p-r impedance function; why? Where must the zeros and poles of $F(p)$ lie? What restrictions are there on their multiplicities?

(c) Show how such a realization is possible for each of the following functions and obtain the networks. It may be necessary to introduce surplus factors; if so, explain why, and discuss the freedom you have. It is permissible to alter the constant multiplier in the realization if this is desirable.

$$(1)\ \frac{p}{p+1} \qquad (2)\ \frac{p^2+1}{p^2+3p+1} \qquad (3)\ \frac{p^2}{p^2+p+1}$$

$$(4)\ \frac{1}{(p+2)^3} \qquad (5)\ \frac{p^3}{(p+1)(p^2+2p+10)}$$

$$(6)\ \frac{p^6+10.4p^5+48.6p^4+134.4p^3+232.6p^2+236p+105}{p^5+3p^4+7p^3+15p^2+10p}$$

(d) Discuss the realization of these same transmission functions, and of functions like that of (a) in general, in the form of the networks of Probs. 10-98 and 10-99.

11-20. Under certain rather general conditions any reasonable transmission function can be realized by a chain of constant-resistance networks, as in the figure for Prob. 11-19, so that the design problem is essentially reduced to one-terminal-pair terms. This problem is to demonstrate this.

Let $F(p)$ be a transmission function, proportional to E_2/E_0, i.e., a rational function of p with real coefficients, all of whose poles are in the left half plane and none of whose zeros are in the right half plane. Some zeros, but no poles, may be at real frequencies, including infinity. Show that it is always possible to factor $1/F(p)$ into a finite number of factors of the form $(1 + z)$ in which z is a p-r function of p, if one is permitted to alter the multiplier and to introduce surplus factors. Explain why this proves the point.

11-21. Pairs of wires in common types of local lead-sheathed telephone cables may be used for short-distance transmission of television signals, but this requires rather careful design of equalizing networks and associated networks (RO 3). One of the networks needed is an impedance-simulating (impedance-matching) one-terminal pair whose impedance is to match closely the cable pair's impedance, Z_0. The following table of measured data illustrates the nature of the impedance to be matched.

Frequency (kcps)	Z_0 (ohms)	Frequency (kcps)	Z_0 (ohms)
0.1	1140	6	185
0.2	800	10	165
0.4	570	20	150
0.6	470	40	135
1.0	360	60	130
2	260	100	125
4	200	1000	120

From the trend of these measurements it seems only reasonable to use the simple and practical R-C kind of network. Design, by adjusting critical frequencies and multipliers by trial, a series of R-C networks (of orders one, two, three, four) of impedance $Z(p)$ to match the data in the table in the frequency range from 100 cps to 1000 kcps. In each case plot the magnitude of the reflection coefficient $\rho(p) = (Z - Z_0)/(Z + Z_0)$ as an indication of the quality of simulation. What is the ideal value of ρ?

On the assumption that at frequencies below 100 cps the cable impedance Z_0 varies as $(\sqrt{p})^{-1}$, and at frequencies above 1000 kcps it is constant, determine by a method from Chapter 8 the resistance and reactance of the cable. Compare these with those of your designs.

11-22. A long open-wire transmission line has substantially the impedance $Z_0(p) = D\sqrt[+/]{(r + lp)(g + cp)}$ in which

$$r = 12 \, \Omega \text{ per mile,}$$

$$g = 1.4 \, \mu\text{mhos per mile,}$$

$$l = 4 \text{ mh per mile,}$$

$$c = 0.009 \, \mu\text{f per mile,}$$

$$D = 175 \text{ miles (length of the line).}$$

Design for use with this line several impedance-simulating networks of increasing complexity, confining your attention to the frequency range from 40 cps to 10 kcps. Discuss the quality of your results.

11-23. Derive (11.04–4), (11.04–5), (11.04–6).

11-24. Explain why (11.04–7) is necessarily the form taken by the driving-point resistance function $R(\omega) = \text{Re } Z(j\omega)$ of Fig. 11.04–B. Explain why, if the constants are so chosen that $R(\omega) \geq 0$ and is finite for all frequencies, the form of network shown is a realization of the corresponding minimum-reactance $Z(p)$.

Illustrate by synthesizing the interstage network for the case

$$R(\omega) = \frac{20\omega^2}{(\omega^2 - 1)^4 + 20\omega^2} \quad \text{(normalized).}$$

Is there any arbitrariness in the construction of the transformer from the equivalent circuit of inductors that you first obtain? Find the element values if the frequency of maximum transmission is 1.5 mcps and R_0 is to be 5000 Ω. Sketch the magnitude of the transmission characteristic of the amplifier stage versus frequency. (Cf. Prob. 9-12.)

11-25. Which of the networks of the figure for Prob. 9-11 are suitable for vacuum-tube interstage networks? Outline the steps in their realization when the magnitude of the transmission characteristic of this part of the amplifier is given.

11-26. Realize the resistance function

$$R(\omega) = \frac{1}{1 + [(1 - \omega^2)^4/\omega^6]} \quad \text{(normalized)}$$

using only one resistor. Your realization is to be suitable for use as a vacuum-tube-amplifier interstage network, in which the input is supplied by a signal from a driving tube (a pentode) and the grid of the next (driven) tube is connected across the resistor. There must be provision for supplying direct current through the network to the plate of the driving tube without applying any direct voltage to the grid of the driven tube. Do not forget parasitic plate-cathode and grid-cathode capacitance; grid-plate capacitance may be neglected. (*Suggestion:* It is not necessary to remove *all* of a pole in reactance or susceptance reduction, if a useful purpose is served.)

Give actual element values, taking $\omega = 1$ to correspond to 15 mcps, and obtaining as high a gain as possible with some reasonable choice of tubes. Calculate and plot the gain (magnitude of transmission) characteristic of the amplifier stage. Give the schematic diagrams of any equivalent forms you may be able to find by removing the zeros of $\mathbf{Ev}\,Z(p)$ in different sequences. (Cf. Prob. 9-13.)

11-27. Is the resistance function

$$R(\omega) = \frac{\omega^4}{b_0 + b_2\omega^2 + b_4\omega^4 + b_6\omega^6 + b_8\omega^8}$$

of practical value in the design of interstage networks in the fashion of Prob. 11-26? Explain your answer fully.

11-28. Each of the networks shown represents a possible interstage network configuration. For each determine the form of the driving-point resistance

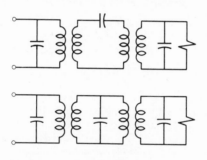

Prob. 11–28

function and explain how the element values could be obtained if this resistance function alone were known. Illustrate with numerical examples.

11-29. Design a network which, when driven by a current source and terminated in a resistor, will realize the transmission function

$$\left|\frac{\text{output voltage}}{\text{input current}}\right|^2 = \frac{1}{1 + \omega^{10}}.$$

Plot this transmission function. Explain how the phase (angle of the complex transmission function) can be determined (*a*) analytically and (*b*) by the approximate method of § 8.09. Plot the phase characteristic also.

Defining *filter* as a network that transmits well at some frequencies and poorly at others, explain why the function above can be said to lead to a filter. Repeat for the function (constant $\times\ \omega^4)/(1 + \omega^{10})$, contrasting the two. Realize this second filter function with a network in which the maximum transmission occurs at 200 kcps and the terminating resistor is 500 Ω.

11-30. For networks of the type shown, the real-frequency magnitude of the transmission function $T(p) = E_{out}/I_{in}$ is simply related to the driving-point resistance $R(\omega)$. In filtering application it may be desirable to have as good transmission as possible at some frequencies, say from ω_1 to ω_2, and as little as possible at others. Since the area under the resistance curve is limited (§ 8.06)

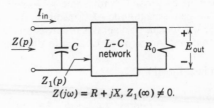

$$Z(j\omega) = R + jX, \quad Z_1(\infty) \neq 0.$$

Prob. 11–30

by C, which is prescribed (e.g., by parasitic capacitance), the shaping of the $R(\omega)$ curve determines the efficiency with which this result is attained. To express this numerically we may define an efficiency

$$\eta = 100 \frac{\displaystyle\int_{\omega_1}^{\omega_2} |T|^2 \, d\omega}{\displaystyle\int_0^\infty |T|^2 \, d\omega} \quad \text{per cent.}$$

This is sometimes called *resistance efficiency* (BO 3).

Explain why this term is appropriate by deriving an expression for η in terms of $R(\omega)$. Evaluate the resistance efficiency for the following examples (approximate answers are satisfactory). The actual frequency that corresponds to $\omega = 1$ below is 8 mcps; the minimum value permitted for C is 12 $\mu\mu f$. The functions are normalized driving-point resistances; $\omega_1 = 0$, $\omega_2 = 1$.

$$\frac{1}{1 + \omega^2} \qquad \frac{1}{1 + \omega^4} \qquad \frac{1}{1 + \omega^6} \qquad \frac{1}{1 + \omega^8} \qquad \frac{(\omega^2 - 1.44)^2}{1 + \omega^{10}}$$

As an idealized ($\eta = 100\%$) case suppose $R(\omega) = 0$ for $0 < \omega < \omega_1$ and for $\omega_2 < \omega$. Suppose further that in the transmission band $\omega_1 < \omega < \omega_2$, $R(\omega)$ is constant at the value R_m. Sketch the resulting $|T|$ versus ω. How is the value of R_m limited by C? What is the maximum possible constant gain achievable in a band of (frequency) width w in terms of a prescribed value of C? Explain how one can in this idealized case "trade" gain for bandwidth, but the *product* of the two is fixed by C. In broad terms what are the practical consequences of this gain-bandwidth limitation (BO 3)?

11-31. Derive (11.05–1), (11.05–2), and (11.05–3) by straightforward analysis. Also derive (11.05–1) by determining the forward amplification A and the feedback transmission β and using these in the standard feedback formula

$$\frac{E_2}{E_0} = \frac{A}{1 - A\beta}.$$

11-32. Determine the ratio of the voltage at the second grid to that at the first, in terms of the tube parameters, in Fig. 11.05–A, ignoring grid-plate capacitance. Show how this function becomes simply a constant times $Z(p)$, if Z includes the parasitic capacitance and the tube resistance.

Design such an interstage network to operate between two 6AK5 tubes with the functional behavior for this ratio

$$\text{constant} \times \frac{p^2 + 3p + 2}{p^3 + 5p^2 + 8p + 6}.$$

The constant is to be as large as possible; unit normalized frequency is to correspond to 10 mcps.

11-33. Another feedback-amplifier configuration is that shown, in which the arrowhead (triangle) symbol represents an ideal amplifier for which $E_2 = AE_1$, A being a real constant. The one-terminal pair Z provides feedback. Show by analysis that the transmission function is

$$\frac{E_2}{E_0} = - \frac{A}{1 + y}$$

in which y is a normalized form of $1/Z$. Discuss the relation of the design problem here to others described in the text.

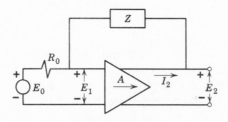

Prob. 11–33

Show that if A is large in magnitude the transmission becomes approximately

$$\frac{E_2}{E_0} = - \frac{Z}{R_0}$$

and compare this with the transmission of the active network of Fig. 11.05–B.

With A large this network is used in computing devices, with a single element in Z; it is called an *operational amplifier*. For each of the three possibilities give the transmission characteristic as a function of frequency. Then explain the action to be expected upon an input wave of arbitrary shape, regarded as a function of time; explain the pertinence of the term "operational."

Repeat the above calculations on the assumption that the ideal amplifier has the characteristic $I_2 = BE_1$, B being a real constant, and no current being drawn from the E_2 terminals. Is the ratio E_2/E_0 the same as before in general? if $|B|$ is large?

12.

Some Practical Matters

The best laid schemes o' mice an' men,
Gang aft agley
—R. Burns

It is a rather imposing structure that we have built on the foundation of our postulates, that we have three kinds of linear, lumped, constant elements to use, characterized by the laws set forth in Table 2.01–A. (We have also assumed that these can be connected together by wires whose effects are negligible.) To continue building much higher without testing its strength is foolish if our work is to be regarded as engineering work; for weaknesses in our foundations and the inevitable perversity of Nature make it improbable that our realizations, once constructed and tested, will perform exactly as these networks were intended to do. In fact, it is often necessary to add to our three subproblems of network synthesis (§ 1.01) a fourth: the problem of actually making the network perform properly. In this fourth part there is need for a good deal of practical skill, gained only by experience—much of it is art rather than science— yet it is possible to anticipate some of the practical difficulties of network construction and to guide the theoretical design to compensate for them. In the present chapter we descend from the ivory tower to examine briefly some of these matters.

12.01 Actual element behavior

We are able now to carry a one-terminal-pair design to the point where we have a schematic diagram; on that diagram appear a number of symbols (for inductors, capacitors, resistors), suitably marked with element values and suitably interconnected by lines (wires). The network presumably performs beautifully, as would be evidenced by analysis. But this assumes that in the actual network every element is lumped, behaves linearly, and is constant with time—and that the wiring connecting the elements and the container holding them have

702

no effect at all. None of these desirable hypotheses actually holds in practice.

It is not appropriate here to describe in detail how actual elements depart, in their characters, from those assumed. The subject is an involved one, requires experimental work and makes great use of empirical knowledge, and can be well understood only after much practical experience. In fact, the design of network *elements* as such, of inductors, resistors, capacitors, is an art in itself; in large organizations there may be groups whose sole occupation is the design and construction of these elements as a service to the network engineer. This book makes no attempt to describe these matters adequately; yet to attain any perspective at all in network synthesis we must know something about them.

Concerning *linearity*, there is little to say. As long as voltages and currents are kept small in amplitude, and as long as the use of nonlinear materials (e.g., in inductor cores) is kept within bounds, network elements behave quite linearly. When high inductance values are needed, iron, one of the magnetic alloys, or other material may be used as a core (form); in such elements saturation can occur, and voltage and current must be limited to reasonable values.

About *constancy*, again there is little that can be said here. Network elements tend to vary in value with time because of changes in environment, e.g., in temperature, humidity, mechanical position (with vibration). If the system in which the network operates is subject to these perturbations, appropriate care must be used in the design of the mechanical structure of the network to offset their effects. Many networks are not subjected to them.

The assumption of *lumped* character is perhaps the weakest. All inductors (and even connecting wires) have some external magnetic field in practice, and electric-field (capacitive) effects exist between all elements, wiring, and the container used to house the network. These parasitic effects are phenomena of the electromagnetic field, i.e., they are due to the *distributed* characteristics of the network. Very often, however, they can be considered as the effects of small lumped L and C elements. An additional parasitic effect is due to the distributed dissipation of energy in wiring, because of its finite conductivity; this may often be thought of as the effect of small additional lumped resistors.

Consider first the *inductor*, symbolized in Fig. 12.01–A(a). Such an element, as actually constructed, is essentially a coil of wire, and its behavior differs from the ideal: it is not a nondissipative element, and its reactance is not linear with frequency. The first effect noticed is usually the dissipation of energy in heat, the effect of the finite conductivity. Hence we may take as a second approximation for a description of the actual coil, using only ideal elements but now additional ones to account for parasitic effects, the network of Fig. 12.01–A(b); presumably r will be small in comparison with the reactance, at the frequencies of interest. The second effect noticed may be the departure of the reactance-versus-frequency curve from linearity, usually by rising to a high value at some frequency, an effect of self-resonance. This may be taken into account,

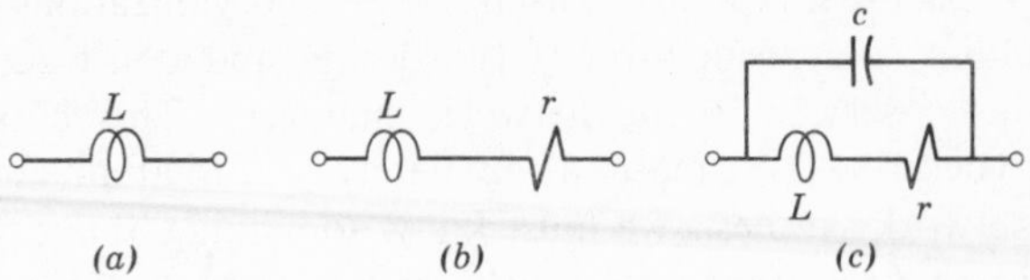

(a)   (b)   (c)

Fig. 12.01–A

as in the third approximation, the network of Fig. 12.01–A(c). This three-element network offers a fairly accurate description of most coils at frequencies where they are designed to operate, and considerably higher. In it L predominates, but r and c may seldom be neglected—though c is not important at low frequencies. None of the three is an exact equivalent to the actual inductor. Better representations can be made by adding more elements to get more complicated networks; these equivalents, necessary at very high frequencies, point out the limitations of the assumption of lumped character. But we shall consider only the dissipation (r) and capacitance (c). These are the most important parasitic effects; both can be considered in making the network design, and both ought to be.

The inevitable dissipation, represented above by r, depends on frequency and hence cannot be represented exactly by a simple lumped resistor. It is usually described in terms of the reactance-resistance ratio, or quality factor Q, of the coil (ideally infinite). If r were constant with frequency, the plot of Q would be a straight line, like the top curve of Fig. 12.01–B. But this resistance varies with frequency because the distribution of current in the conductor changes appreciably (even though the magnetic field changes little), so that the Q curve is linear over only a limited range of frequencies; the lower curve, showing a maximum value of Q, is more realistic. Linear variation of Q with frequency is desirable, for the effects of dissipation can then be more easily compensated for (§12.02); hence the coil designer tries to make the linear portion occur in the important frequency range, as well as to make Q as large as possible. (The maximum value obtainable depends not only on materials and construction but also on the frequency at which it is to occur; values of 100 or so can usually be got without difficulty, and values of 500 or so can be got, by careful design, at some frequencies.)

The inevitable parasitic capacitance represented in Fig. 12.01–A(*c*) by *c* behaves in contrast more as a lumped element. At low frequencies it may often be neglected. If a network is to operate at frequencies where this capacitance cannot be neglected, it is important to choose from the

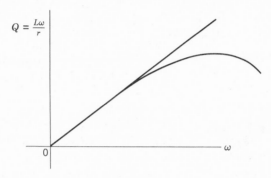

Fig. 12.01–B

various equivalent network forms that one in which parasitic capacitance is least important. As between the two Foster canonic forms for an *L-C* network, for example, that form in which capacitors appear in parallel with inductors wherever possible is certainly preferable. For then the effect can be cancelled by reducing the size of the capacitor; the parasitic capacitance then makes up for the reduction.

Consider next the *resistor*, symbolized in Fig. 12.01–C(*a*). In such an element, as actually constructed, we again notice effects suggestive of the other two kinds of elements. We find inductive effects due to the winding of the resistance wire, and capacitive effects due to the proximity of various parts of the resistor, so that Fig. 12.01–C(*b*) is a more accurate representation. The former effect may be greatly reduced by bifilar winding— or no wire at all may be used, but rather some resistive material deposited on an appropriate surface. The latter effect may also be reduced by careful construction, and one would again choose that network form, from the various equivalents, in which capacitors appear in parallel with resistors as far as possible. The network

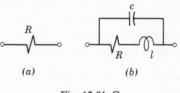

Fig. 12.01–C

of Fig. 12.01–C(*b*) resembles that of Fig. 12.01–A(*c*) superficially, but is quite different in that here the *resistor* predominates and the other two elements are incidental.

We have also the *capacitor* to consider; see Fig. 12.01–D(*a*). Because there are losses in the dielectric, capacitors too have dissipation; and the leads may have enough inductance to introduce that effect too, so that Fig. 12.01–D(*b*) provides a better representation. The amount of dissipation is again conveniently described by a quality factor Q, defined here as the ratio of susceptance to conductance, $C\omega/g$. Generally, capacitor Q values are much higher than inductor Q values (ideally, of course, they are infinite) because the physical dissipation is of different character. Sometimes capacitor dissipation may be completely neglected even though inductor dissipation is rather important. But it may be advisable, other considerations permitting, to select a network form in which resistors appear in parallel with capacitors as far as possible.

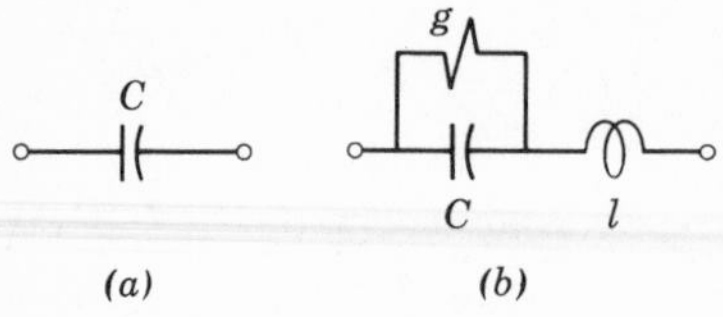

(a)   (b)

Fig. 12.01–D

The parasitic effects present in the three kinds of actual network elements are not the only ones. Wire must be used to connect the elements, the elements must be supported, and a container of some sort must be used. All of these introduce additional parasitic capacitance, and perhaps inductance (both "self-inductance" of leads and "mutual inductance" in the coupling of fields of elements and leads), and perhaps dissipation (when current flows in container walls). The alleviation of these effects is a matter of importance in many cases, calling for careful attention to the manner and locations in which elements are mounted and to the general "mechanical design" of the network.

Of the various parasitic effects discussed here, that of dissipation is often the most important. It can be provided for, to a certain extent, in the network synthesis; this we shall discuss. The other parasitic effects require more of the constructor's art, and about them we shall say little.

12.02 Parasitic dissipation

In practice it often happens that the most important parasitic effect is that of dissipation. We shall ignore here all field (distributed) effects and consider that the dissipation can be represented by lumped resistors that are, then, merely additional network elements (though undesired ones). We have to consider now what happens when the ideal elements of Fig. 12.02–A(*a*) are replaced by the networks of Fig. 12.02–A(*b*). This brings us closer to reality, though we still have only approximations; in particular, we ignore the departure of the Q curves from linearity with frequency.

The immittance functions are now

$$Z_L(p) = Lp + r = L(p + d_L)$$

and $\qquad\qquad\qquad\qquad\qquad\qquad\qquad\qquad$ (12.02–1)

$$Y_C(p) = Cp + g = C(p + d_C),$$

in which $d_L = r/L$ and $d_C = g/C$ are the *dissipation constants* of the inductor and capacitor respectively. These numbers (assumed constant)

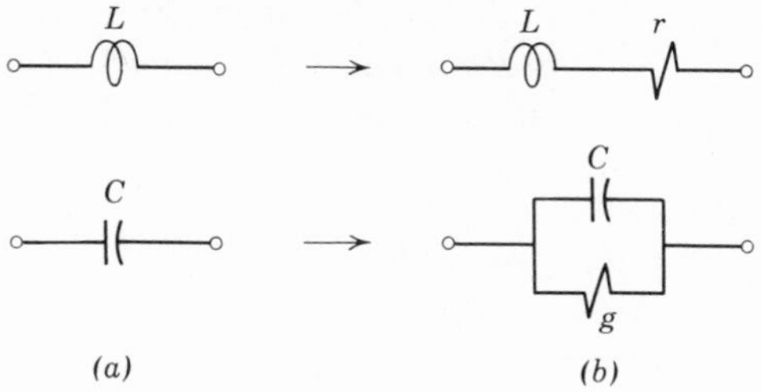

Fig. 12.02–A

are usually rather small (but not necessarily negligible), for they represent ω/Q and Q is presumably fairly large. In the absence of dissipation the immittance functions would be simply Lp and Cp, corresponding to zero values of the dissipation constants. The effect of the dissipation is simply to replace p by $(p + d)$, d being the appropriate dissipation constant in each case. If d were the same in numerical value for all inductors and capacitors, then the effect of dissipation would be very easily calculated: instead of $Z(p)$ we should obtain $Z(p + d)$. Although it is likely that Q will have about the same value for all the inductors, and also an approximately constant value for all the capacitors, these two values may differ considerably. The condition $d_L = d_C$ throughout the network is called *uniform dissipation*; it simplifies the mathematics of dissipation, an advantage that makes it occasionally desirable actually to degrade capacitor Q's to achieve it.

In general, however, $d_L \neq d_C$, nor is d_L actually the same for all the inductors (or d_C for all the capacitors). Yet the mathematical simplification attending uniform dissipation makes it very appealing. (If d_L is the same for all inductors, and d_C the same for all capacitors, some simplification can still be made, even though $d_L \neq d_C$, as discussed in Problem 12-1.) Since the effects of dissipation are small, one would expect that the use of an *average* value of dissipation constant as an "equivalent" uniform dissipation would give fairly good results. This expectation is verified by experience, so we now take

$$d = \frac{\Sigma\, d_L + \Sigma\, d_C}{N} \tag{12.02-2}$$

as our dissipation constant, uniformly for all inductors and capacitors. Here the summations cover all inductors and all capacitors respectively, and N is the total number of reactive elements (L and C). If now $Z(p)$ is the designed impedance function (which assumes ideal, nondissipative L and C elements), then $Z(p + d)$ is the impedance function obtained when dissipation appears in the reactive elements; i.e., $Z(p + d)$ is a good approximation to the impedance actually obtained when the network is built (if we neglect parasitic capacitance and inductance effects). Remembering that d is small, we write

$$Z(p + d) = Z(p) + Z'(p) \times d + Z''(p) \times \frac{d^2}{2!} + \cdots \tag{12.02-3}$$

as the Taylor-series expansion of Z about any regular point p. In this series the first term is the impedance function in the absence of dissipation, and the second term gives the principal effect of dissipation, since d is small; i.e.,

$$Z(p + d) = Z(p) + dZ'(p) \tag{12.02-4}$$

gives the actual impedance at any frequency (represented by p), in terms of the nondissipative impedance at that frequency, and its derivative. At real frequencies, where our primary interest lies, with the usual notation for resistance and reactance, we obtain

$$(R + jX)_{\text{actual}} = (R + jX)_{d=0} + d\left[\frac{1}{j}\frac{d}{d\omega}(R + jX)_{d=0}\right]$$

$$= (R_0 + jX_0) + d(X_0' - jR_0'). \tag{12.02-5}$$

Here $R_0(\omega)$ and $X_0(\omega)$ represent the nondissipative ($d = 0$) resistance and reactance functions corresponding to $Z(j\omega)$, and $R_0'(\omega)$ and $X_0'(\omega)$ their derivatives. Evidently the principal effect on the resistance is an increase proportional to d and to the slope of the (nondissipative) reactance-frequency curve. The reactance increase is negatively proportional to d and to the slope of the (nondissipative) resistance-frequency curve. In symbols, the actual resistance and reactance, as functions of frequency, are

$$R(\omega) = R_0(\omega) + dX_0'(\omega)$$

and

$$\tag{12.02-6}$$

$$X(\omega) = X_0(\omega) - dR_0'(\omega).$$

By duality, the corresponding admittance quantities are

$$G(\omega) = G_0(\omega) + dB_0{}'(\omega)$$

and

$$B(\omega) = B_0(\omega) - dG_0{}'(\omega).$$

(12.02–7)

These pairs of equations give a very convenient method of estimating the effect of the parasitic dissipation that will be present, whether anticipated or not, in any actual network. It is primarily the slope of the reactance curve that determines the change in resistance (for a given amount of dissipation), and the slope of the resistance curve that determines the change in reactance. The approximation made by taking only one term of (12.02–3) is usually quite good; in view of our other approximations (use of an equivalent uniform dissipation, ignoring parasitic inductance and capacitance), it would be inappropriate to take additional terms even if the calculations were simple.

In (12.02–6) and (12.02–7) we have statements of the effect of parasitic dissipation. We might apply these to our finished design, looking at the reactance-frequency and resistance-frequency curves to estimate the changes that will be produced by dissipation, and if the changes are objectionable, go back and rework the design. With more foresight, we would obtain an estimate of the Q values to be expected, and use them in the course of our design, especially if it proceeds on a trial-and-error basis (§ 11.02 and § 13.03). For this we may imagine all our elements to be dissipative and use only such elements in the design. Or we may design with nondissipative L and C elements, but try to anticipate the effect of dissipation by designing for resistance, for example, that is not exactly what is desired but will become so when affected by dissipation, as indicated by (12.02–6). This requires using an estimate of the expected slope of the reactance curve when forming the resistance function; the principles and techniques of Chapter 8 may be helpful here. Alternatively, we may sometimes be able to make the correction in a more elegant way, discussed in § 12.03.

12.03 Predistortion

It is sometimes possible to operate on a desired immittance function $Z(p)$ (designed on the basis of nondissipative elements), before carrying out the realization, in such a fashion that the effects of dissipation are anticipated and largely offset by appropriate changes in the network. The basis of this technique is the fact that when the dissipation is uniform, its only effect is to replace (p) by $(p + d)$ in the nondissipative immittance function. We again use an average dissipation constant d, defined by (12.02–2), and assume uniform dissipation of this amount.

In graphical terms, the introduction of dissipation then moves all the zeros and poles of our (rational) immittance function horizontally to the left, through a distance d. The multiplier is unaffected, but a factor such as $(p - p_0)$ undergoes the transformation

$$(p - p_0) \rightarrow (p + d - p_0) = (p - p_0'). \qquad (12.03\text{--}1)$$

Here $p_0' = (p_0 - d)$, which represents the horizontal motion of the zero (or pole) shown in Fig. 12.03–A. If the dissipation is not uniform, the zeros and poles move in varying amounts, and not necessarily horizontally—though the general nature of the motions is leftward. (If the variation of Q with frequency is also to be considered, then we no longer have rational functions to deal with and the picture is clouded.) The use of an average value of d represents an approximation, but one that is still usefully good; to improve on it requires more elaborate techniques (DA 1, GU 2) into which we shall not go here. (An alternative point of view here is to keep the zeros and poles fixed, but to consider the axis of real frequencies to be displaced a distance d to the right; if the dissipation is not uniform, the axis is also deformed into some sort of curve.)

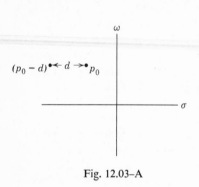

Fig. 12.03–A

From the fact that dissipation moves all the zeros and poles a distance d to the left, a remedy suggests itself: to move all the zeros and poles a distance d to the *right* before realizing $Z(p)$. That is, after obtaining a suitable function $Z(p)$ whose behavior it is desired to realize, we realize instead the function $Z(p - d)$—if we can. This process of *predistortion* (DA 1) may very well make the p-r function $Z(p)$ into a non-p-r function, $Z(p - d)$, for it is equivalent to inserting negative resistors at certain points; but if it does not, and we realize the function $Z(p - d)$ in schematic form, then in the actual network the zeros and poles will be shifted to the left by dissipation and the actual immittance function will become $Z(p)$, as desired. The name "predistortion" signifies distortion deliberately introduced in the realization process, but of a kind that will later be offset by the distortion that dissipation produces in the actual network. The net effect should be nearly complete cancellation of the effects of dissipation, something that we instinctively feel is too good to be true. We must then examine very carefully the conditions under which the predistorted function $Z(p - d)$ is still p-r and hence realizable.

Certainly no zero or pole of the undistorted (desired) function $Z(p)$ can lie to the right of the line $\sigma = -d$ (Fig. 12.03–B). For the predistortion process would move such a zero or pole into the right half plane and $Z(p - d)$ would not be p-r. The shaded area is a forbidden zone in which no zero or pole of $Z(p)$ may lie if predistortion is to be accomplished. It is a necessary condition that the real part of every zero and every pole of $Z(p)$, typified by p_1, obey

$$\mathbf{Re}\, p_1 \leqq -d. \qquad (12.03\text{--}2)$$

But this is not sufficient, for even though predistortion moves no zero or pole into the right half plane it may still transform $Z(p)$ into an unrealizable function; the function $Z(p - d)$ must still be tested for positive reality.

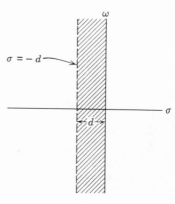

Fig. 12.03–B

If all the zeros and poles of $Z(p)$ are well to the left of the imaginary axis, then predistortion can often be accomplished. What this means is that the realization of $Z(p)$ would contain a large amount of dissipation anyway; in effect, predistortion merely reduces resistance (conductance) values, and dissipation restores them. This may actually occur, if there is a realization of $Z(p)$ that has resistors in the correct places; if not, an equivalent redistribution of resistance takes place. The R-C and R-L cases show this clearly, for in certain of the canonic forms resistors appear exactly where needed, and predistortion amounts merely to reducing the resistance (conductance) values on the final schematic diagram to allow for the contributions of dissipation. But in other realizations the resistors do not appear where needed and predistortion will produce a different network (which, on the addition of dissipation, will become equivalent). In the R-L-C case either may occur. Even without considering parasitic dissipation, it may be advisable to predistort (if possible), realize the predistorted function, and then shift back by introducing appropriate uniform dissipation. In this way the occurrence of purely reactive elements in the network is prevented. Parasitic dissipation may then be compensated for, if necessary, simply by reducing the deliberate dissipation by appropriate amounts. This in effect amounts to reducing an impedance function to minimum-resistance, not by removing resistance in series, but by shifting the imaginary axis on the p plane. The end results of the two approaches may be quite different.

In the L-C case we can never carry out the predistortion process, for all zeros and poles are already on the imaginary axis. And in many R-L-C (and even R-C and R-L) cases zeros and poles will be imaginary or too close to the imaginary axis to permit predistortion. A minimum-resistance function, for example, cannot be predistorted, nor can most nonminimum-reactance impedance functions. In these cases we must be content with only partial predistortion. We move those zeros and poles that are off the imaginary axis to the right as much of the distance d as we can: some we may be able to move the whole distance, and some only part of it, the limits being set by the requirement that the predistorted function still be p-r. We may often have to be content with moving only the most important zeros and poles (those closest to the most important parts of the imaginary axis); the others may be forced, by the p-r requirement, to move to other definite positions, over which we have no control. (And occasionally no motion at all may be possible.) The result is only a partial correction for the effects of dissipation, but one that may still be acceptable. If the dissipation is small, the principal effects may be only to replace theoretically infinite values of impedance by finite but acceptably large values, and theoretically zero values of impedance by nonzero but acceptably small values, for example. Or the important characteristics may be almost completely preserved in the important frequency ranges at the cost of changes outside these ranges. This is about all we can do to offset the dissipation, and it is fortunate that the results may be quite acceptable in practice. Predistortion is even more useful in two-terminal-pair synthesis, and we shall also find there (e.g., in filters) that this partial correction is often adequate.

12.04 Q and resonance

Parasitic dissipation makes itself strikingly evident in the effect it has at points of *resonance*. For our purposes we shall consider a resonance (in the driving-point immittance functions of a one-terminal pair) to occur ideally at an imaginary zero or pole, where either the impedance or admittance becomes infinite. The effect of dissipation cannot be avoided at such points; they will move off the imaginary axis into the left half plane when the inevitable dissipation is considered. But if the original zero or pole is not too close to other zeros or poles, and if the dissipation is small, there will still be a pronounced maximum in the magnitude of the impedance or admittance (and a corresponding minimum in the other) at a real frequency close to the location of the original zero or pole; this we shall still consider to be a resonance, though the maximum is not infinite and the minimum is not zero. In Fig. 12.04–A, which illustrates such a resonance, only the pole of impedance causing the resonance is shown; the other poles, and the zeros, are assumed to be far enough away that the only important variation in $Z(p)$ near the frequency ω_0 is that of the factor $(j\omega - p_0)^{-1}$. The quality or sharpness of the resonance is dependent on the amount of dissipation and may be described by a quality factor Q for the network. This we now discuss.

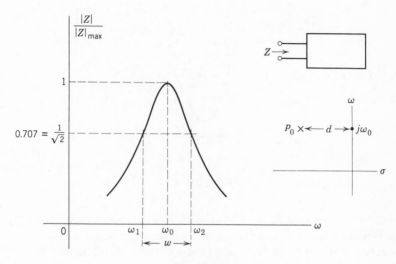

Fig. 12.04–A

In § 12.01 we defined quality factors Q for the inductor and the capacitor as the magnitude of the ratio of reactance to resistance (or of susceptance to conductance, which is equivalent). This is a convenient figure of merit for discussing the effect of parasitic dissipation on the quality of individual inductors and capacitors, particularly for specifications on the individual elements to be used in building a network. But such a definition is not appropriate for the driving-point immittance functions of a one-terminal pair in general. In its place we shall define a quality factor Q in terms of the sharpness of the resonance curve, i.e., of the plot of $|Z|$ or $|Y|$ versus frequency. We may arbitrarily define a *bandwidth* w by the points at which the curve has dropped to 70.7% of its peak value, as shown in Fig. 12.04–A. Then a convenient measure of the sharpness of the resonance is

$$Q = \frac{\omega_0}{w} = \frac{\omega_0}{\omega_2 - \omega_1}. \tag{12.04–1}$$

In words, this quality factor is the reciprocal of the bandwidth measured in units of ω_0. For high Q the curve is sharp; for low Q it becomes less peaked. Q as so defined is a constant, and applies only to the resonance in question; the same network may have different Q's at different resonances, occurring at different frequencies. The definition could equally well be based on a plot of $|Y|$ (see Fig. 12.04-B), in which there

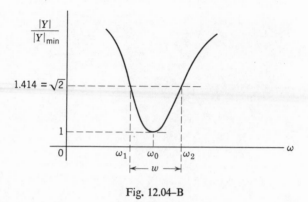

Fig. 12.04-B

would be a *minimum* at ω_0, and ω_1 and ω_2 would be defined as the frequencies at which $|Y|$ has risen to 1.414 times the minimum value. And of course it might be $|Y|$ that had the maximum, $|Z|$ the minimum.

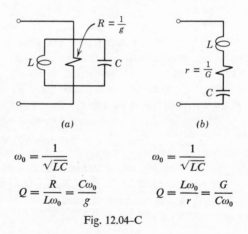

$$\omega_0 = \frac{1}{\sqrt{LC}} \qquad\qquad \omega_0 = \frac{1}{\sqrt{LC}}$$

$$Q = \frac{R}{L\omega_0} = \frac{C\omega_0}{g} \qquad\qquad Q = \frac{L\omega_0}{r} = \frac{G}{C\omega_0}$$

Fig. 12.04-C

For simple illustrations, consider the two "tuned circuits" of Fig. 12.04-C. Here the bandwidth definition of Q given above leads (exactly) to the formulas given. Note the correlation, in the first case, between the circuit (network) Q at resonance, and the Q of the capacitor (r being considered to represent the dissipation of the capacitor); in the second case there is a dual correlation. Another illustration is given in Fig. 12.04–D, in which, for simplicity, r is assumed small, so that Q is large

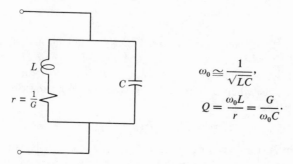

$$\omega_0 \cong \frac{1}{\sqrt{LC}},$$

$$Q = \frac{\omega_0 L}{r} = \frac{G}{\omega_0 C}.$$

Fig. 12.04–D

and the simple approximate formulas given result. Note again the correlation with the inductor Q. These correlations between the Q of the network immittances and Q's of individual elements occur only because the network has very few elements; in general there is no simple relation.

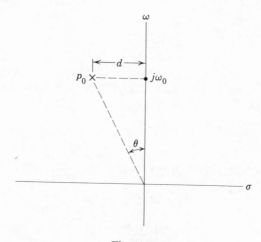

Fig. 12.04–E

In the general case Q is most easily understood in terms of the p-plane diagram shown in Fig. 12.04–A. This is reproduced on larger scale in Fig. 12.04–E, which shows only the pole of $Z(p)$ that causes the resonance,

$p_0 = -d + j\omega_0$; the other poles and the zeros are assumed to be relatively distant. (If it is $|Y|$ rather than $|Z|$ that has the peak, all quantities here are to be replaced by their duals.) Let $F(p)$ represent the factors of $Y(p) = 1/Z$ due to these other critical points, so that

$$Y(p) = F(p) \times (p - p_0)$$
$$= F(p)(d + p - j\omega_0). \qquad (12.04\text{--}2)$$

If d were zero, then, since $Z(p)$ is p-r, $F(j\omega_0)$ would be a real, positive number, $Y'(j\omega_0)$, which we call H. In the vicinity of $j\omega_0$, $F(p)$ will not vary appreciably, since its zero and poles are distant. Nor will it be altered appreciably when d is introduced, for the same reason. Hence for values of p near $j\omega_0$,

$$Y(p) = Hd + H(p - j\omega_0). \qquad (12.04\text{--}3)$$

(The same conclusion could be reached by assuming the displacement of p_0 to the left to be due to the introduction of dissipation and using the analysis of § 12.02.) Now the minimum value of $|Y|$ at real frequencies is Hd. The frequencies at which $|Y|$ is increased by a factor $\sqrt{2}$ are given by

$$H^2(\omega - \omega_0)^2 = H^2 d^2 \qquad (12.04\text{--}4)$$

so that

$$\omega_2 = \omega_0 + d \quad \text{and} \quad \omega_1 = \omega_0 - d. \qquad (12.04\text{--}5)$$

Hence, from (12.04–1),

$$Q = \frac{\omega_0}{2d} \qquad (12.04\text{--}6)$$

which expresses Q in terms of the resonant frequency and the horizontal displacement of the causative pole of $Z(p)$. An alternative expression in terms of the angle θ (Fig. 12.04–E) is, for small d,

$$Q = \frac{1}{2\theta}. \qquad (12.04\text{--}7)$$

Let us indicate by subscript 0 that quantities are to be evaluated at ω_0. Then

$$Y_0 = Y(j\omega_0) = Hd,$$
$$Z_0 = Z(j\omega_0) = \frac{1}{Hd},$$
$$Y'(j\omega_0) = \left(\frac{dB}{d\omega}\right)_0 = H, \qquad (12.04\text{--}8)$$
$$Z'(j\omega_0) = \left(\frac{dX}{d\omega}\right)_0 = -\frac{1}{Hd^2}$$

and we accordingly express Q as

$$Q = \frac{1}{2}\omega_0 Z_0 \left(\frac{dB}{d\omega}\right)_0 = -\frac{1}{2}\omega_0 Y_0 \left(\frac{dX}{d\omega}\right)_0. \tag{12.04-9}$$

This formula for Q is useful when information on the slope of the susceptance or reactance curve and the value of the immittance, at the resonant frequency, is available.

Still another expression for Q is in terms of the ratio of stored energy and the rate of dissipation of energy. To obtain it, we use some of the analysis of Chapter 4, which was based on energy considerations. From (4.12–16), written for real frequencies, we have

$$Y(j\omega) = \left(F_0 + V_0 p + \frac{T_0}{p}\right)_{p=j\omega}$$

$$= F_0 + j\left(V_0\omega - \frac{T_0}{\omega}\right)$$

$$= F_0 + j\frac{V_0}{\omega}(\omega - \sqrt{T_0/V_0})(\omega + \sqrt{T_0/V_0})$$

$$= F_0 + j2V_0(\omega - \omega_0). \tag{12.04-10}$$

In the manipulation above we have set

$$\sqrt{\frac{T_0}{V_0}} = \omega_0. \tag{12.04-11}$$

The quantities T_0, F_0, and V_0, defined in (4.12–17), are functions of p, but always real and positive. In the vicinity of the resonance they are evidently stationary, as we see by comparing (12.04–11) with (12.04–3). Within the approximations used here (which do very well, since Q is not generally considered a precise quantity) we may consider these three quantities to be constant near the resonance, whose frequency is then defined by (12.04–11). Their relations to d and H are

$$H = 2V_0,$$
$$d = \frac{1}{2}\frac{F_0}{V_0}, \tag{12.04-12}$$

so that

$$Q = \omega_0 \frac{V_0}{F_0} = \frac{\sqrt{T_0 V_0}}{F_0}. \tag{12.04-13}$$

This expression for Q is not in terms of energy, for T_0, F_0, and V_0 are in general only distantly related to energy. In the sinusoidal steady state, however (with which we are concerned here), they have simple relations to energy functions. Then all currents and voltages are sinusoidal functions of time, with a frequency ω_0 equal to that of the source(s). In particular, the voltages across capacitors are given by

$$v_r = \mathbf{Re}\, E_r e^{j\omega_0 t} = |E_r| \cos (\omega_0 t + \phi_r)$$

$$= \tfrac{1}{2}(E_r e^{j\omega_0 t} + \bar{E}_r e^{-j\omega_0 t}) \tag{12.04-14}$$

in which

$$E_r = |E_r|\, e^{j\phi_r} \tag{12.04-15}$$

is the complex-number (phasor) representation of $v_r(t)$. The instantaneous value of the total electrical stored energy (the energy in the capacitors) is then, by (4.09–3),

$$
\begin{aligned}
V &= \tfrac{1}{2}\sum_{r,s} C_{rs} v_r v_s \\
&= \tfrac{1}{8}\sum_{r,s} C_{rs}(E_r e^{j\omega_0 t} + \bar{E}_r e^{-j\omega_0 t})(E_s e^{j\omega_0 t} + \bar{E}_s e^{-j\omega_0 t}) \\
&= \tfrac{1}{8}\sum_{r,s} C_{rs}(E_r E_s e^{j2\omega_0 t} + \bar{E}_r \bar{E}_s e^{-j2\omega_0 t} + E_r \bar{E}_s + \bar{E}_r E_s) \tag{12.04-16} \\
&= \tfrac{1}{4}\,\mathbf{Re}\sum_{r,s} C_{rs}(\bar{E}_r E_s + E_r E_s e^{j2\omega_0 t}) \\
&= \tfrac{1}{4}\,\mathbf{Re}\sum_{r,s} C_{rs}\bar{E}_r E_s + \tfrac{1}{4}\,\mathbf{Re}\sum_{r,s} C_{rs} E_r E_s e^{j2\omega_0 t}.
\end{aligned}
$$

The *average* value of the total electrical stored energy is easily extracted from this. The second sum varies sinusoidally with time (at double frequency) and hence contributes nothing to the average energy. In the first sum every term is accompanied by its conjugate, the imaginary part of the sum is zero, and the sign $\mathbf{Re}$ may be dropped; this sum is *constant* with time and therefore represents the average value of V. Denoting it V_{avg}, we have

$$V_{\text{avg}} = \tfrac{1}{4}\sum_{r,s} C_{rs}\bar{E}_r E_s \tag{12.04-17}$$

which is very close to V_0 as defined in § 4.12. In (4.12–17) the symbol E_r represents the Laplace transform of v_r, while in (12.04–17) the same symbol is the complex-number representation of v_r. But these two quantities are proportional, so that we may write (4.12–17) again,

$$V_0 = \frac{\displaystyle\sum_{r,s} C_{rs}\bar{E}_r E_s}{|E_1|^2} \tag{12.04-18}$$

in which the E's are now the complex-number representations used here, for the proportionality factors cancel out in the ratios. Hence V_{avg} and V_0 are proportional.

For the dissipation functions F_{avg} (similarly defined and representing half the average rate of energy dissipation) and F_0, a parallel analysis (which involves only replacement of C_{rs} by G_{rs}) gives

$$F_{avg} = \tfrac{1}{4} \sum_{r,s} G_{rs} \bar{E}_r E_s \qquad (12.04\text{--}19)$$

and

$$F_0 = \frac{\sum_{r,s} G_{rs} \bar{E}_r E_s}{|E_1|^2}. \qquad (12.04\text{--}20)$$

Hence we can write

$$\frac{V_0}{F_0} = \frac{V_{avg}}{F_{avg}} \qquad (12.04\text{--}21)$$

and so, from (12.04–13),

$$Q = \omega_0 \frac{V_{avg}}{F_{avg}}. \qquad (12.04\text{--}22)$$

For the sort of high-Q network we are considering, the phase relations between the important (large) currents and voltages are substantially as they would be in the absence of dissipation. That is, with a suitable reference, all the E's may be considered to be nearly real. Then (12.04–16) becomes, very closely,

$$V = \tfrac{1}{2} V_{peak}(1 + \cos 2\omega_0 t). \qquad (12.04\text{--}23)$$

Here V_{peak} represents the maximum value attained by V, and clearly

$$V_{peak} = 2V_{avg}. \qquad (12.04\text{--}24)$$

The total instantaneous stored energy W, the sum of the energy stored in capacitors and inductors, must be constant since we are concerned with a resonance, at which frequency no reactive power is taken from the source. Hence $W = T + V$ is a constant. Now

$$T = W - V = W - \tfrac{1}{2} V_{peak} (1 + \cos 2\omega_0 t). \qquad (12.04\text{--}25)$$

But there must be an expression similar to (12.04–23) for T, by a similar argument, showing that here also the peak value of the stored energy is twice the average value. Hence we must have

$$W = V_{peak} \qquad (12.04\text{--}26)$$

and

$$T = \tfrac{1}{2} V_{peak} (1 - \cos 2\omega_0 t). \qquad (12.04\text{--}27)$$

Thus

$$T_{peak} = V_{peak},$$
$$T_{avg} = V_{avg}, \qquad (12.04\text{--}28)$$
$$W = T_{peak} = V_{peak} = 2V_{avg} = 2T_{avg}.$$

The stored energy oscillates completely between the capacitors and the inductors.

The energy loss due to dissipation in the resistors is small, but not negligible in calculating the Q (as it was immediately above). In one cycle this loss is

$$W_d = (2F_{\text{avg}}) \frac{2\pi}{\omega_0}, \tag{12.04-29}$$

since $2F_{\text{avg}}$ represents the average dissipation rate. By combining these results we obtain

$$
\begin{aligned}
Q &= \omega_0 \frac{V_{\text{avg}}}{F_{\text{avg}}} \\[2mm]
&= \omega_0 \frac{\text{total stored energy}}{\text{average rate of dissipation of energy}} \\[2mm]
&= 2\pi \frac{W}{W_d} \\[2mm]
&= 2\pi \frac{\text{total energy stored}}{\text{energy dissipated per cycle}}.
\end{aligned} \tag{12.04-30}
$$

With this expression of Q in terms of stored energy and energy dissipation rate, we conclude our discussion of Q. The particular expression to use, out of all those given above (which are equivalent for high-Q networks), depends in each application on the most interesting or most easily calculated or measured quantities.

12.05 Miscellaneous matters

The three preceding sections have dealt with the effects of parasitic dissipation, which can often be anticipated and compensated for to some extent. Parasitic capacitance and parasitic inductance do not lend themselves to the same treatment.

If one has a choice between several equivalent network realizations, those in which parasitic capacitance will be effectively in parallel with designed capacitance are naturally to be preferred. For then the parasitic capacitance can not only be compensated for but actually used as a network element. Networks to be associated with vacuum tubes ought to have capacitance across their terminals; networks using inductors ought to use them in parallel combinations with capacitors; networks using resistors would do well to have capacitors connected across them. Although this sort of thing can often be done, naturally there are limits, and one can only do one's best.

Parasitic mutual inductance ("pickup") may become important at high frequencies, but can be avoided to some extent by careful physical orientation of inductors or by placing them in shields. But the shields may introduce additional problems of parasitic capacitance and dissipation in the conducting material of the shields.

Another sort of parasitic effect can arise in the self-inductance of wiring, or in general from the impedance of wiring that is common to two or more meshes of the network. The Cauer canonic forms of L-C networks, for example, may behave in a completely unexpected fashion if the bottom leads from the shunt elements are not brought to a common (grounding) point, as the worker with radio frequencies well knows. In all of these matters art may become more important than science, and there is no substitute for experience in handling the difficult problem of making a network perform properly at high frequencies. It is surprising, however, how high in frequency lumped-element network designs can be made to perform usefully: the vicinity of 50 mcps is about the upper limit. At low frequencies many of these effects can of course be ignored.

There are other matters to plague the network designer, too. In choosing between equivalent networks, one must examine the range of element values required by each. The ease of building an element, the value of Q obtainable, the amount of parasitic effects, all depend on the size of the inductance, capacitance, or resistance desired. Hence one network may be preferable because of the values of its elements. Another matter to be considered is the sensitivity of the network performance to small changes in element values. This may be better in one equivalent network than in others. And it must be investigated in any case to determine the precision required in the realization of each element. Tolerances on each element must be determined, generally by the tolerances set on the performance of the network as a whole by the system of which it is to be a part. The cost of a network may be greatly influenced by these allowed limits, so that some compromise must be made between quality of performance and cost. The investigation of the sensitivity to element changes is a matter of network analysis, requiring, in general, calculation of network impedance (for example) for many situations, in each of which a small change is made in an element value. For very precise work one may use some variable elements, to be adjusted at the last stage, the final measurement of the network's characteristic. Variable capacitors and variable resistors are common elements; variable inductors can be made by inserting movable slugs (of Permalloy or copper, e.g.) in the coil form, or by providing sliding contacts on the coil itself. Finally, when all possible precautions have been taken and the network constructed, there remains the matter of *measurement* of the network's performance. This is a complicated science (and art) in its own right.

12.06 Summary

This chapter is far from complete. But it does not aim to discuss the troublesome effects of the practical difficulties of network construction in detail. Its sole purpose is to point out the existence of these problems, in which compensation for dissipation and careful construction can be extremely important. One may conclude that the elaborate structure of network synthesis that we have developed is not seriously imperiled by these practical difficulties. In many important cases all the work is justified; in many other cases a great deal of it is still extremely useful.

12.07 References

Network elements: BL 1, BR 5, GR 1, MA 3, MA 4, PE 2, ST 1, ST 6, TE 1, WE 3.
Effects of dissipation: BO 3, DA 1, GU 2, KO 1, MA 6.
Predistortion: BO 3, DA 1, DE 3, MI 1, NI 1, WE 8.
Q and resonance: GR 3, GU 5, KA 1, MA 3, MA 4, MO 5, RY 1, SE 1, TE 1.

PROBLEMS

12-1. (a) Let $Z(p)$ be an odd p-r (impedance) function. Show that if dissipation is added in any realization of this function such that $d_L = r/L$ is the same for all inductors and $d_C = g/C$ is the same for all capacitors, but $d_L \neq d_C$, then the input impedance function becomes

$$\sqrt{\frac{p + d_L}{p + d_C}} \times Z(s),$$

in which $s = \sqrt{(p + d_L)(p + d_C)}$, and the p-r square roots are to be taken. (*Suggestion:* Show that this is true for individual L and C elements; then consider combinations thereof. An alternate approach is through the determinants of network analysis.)

(b) If d_L and d_C are nearly equal, the modified expression for (dissipative) impedance above can be simplified by taking only the leading terms of appropriate expansions. Obtain this simplified form, given below, with the notation $d_{\text{avg}} = \frac{1}{2}(d_L + d_C)$, $\delta = \frac{1}{2}(d_L - d_C)$.

$$Z(p) + d_{\text{avg}} Z'(p) + \frac{\delta}{p} Z(p) + \cdots$$

and for real frequencies,

$$Z(j\omega) = jX(\omega) + dX'(\omega) + \delta \frac{X(\omega)}{\omega} + \cdots.$$

Give the dual relations.

(c) Show how the expression in (a) approaches that of (12.02–3) as d_L and d_C approach equality.

(d) Let $Z(p)$ now be *any* p-r function and let dissipation be added in a realization thereof, under the conditions of (a). Explain why the modified expression for impedance given in (a) is no longer valid. Explain why it *is* valid if $d_L = d_C$.

12-2. By the use of the result of Prob. 12-1 only, demonstrate that for L-C networks

$$\frac{dX}{d\omega} \geq \left| \frac{X}{\omega} \right|$$

except at the poles.

12-3. Calculate and plot the actual input resistance of this network, (a) with elements as shown; (b) with dissipation corresponding to $d_{L1} = 0.02$, $d_{L2} = 0.01$, $d_{C1} = 0.001$, $d_{C2} = 0.005$.

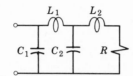

Normalized ohms, henrys, farads

$C_1 = 1$	$L_1 = 2$	$R = 1$
$C_2 = 2$	$L_2 = 1$	

Prob. 12–3

Calculate the input resistance, using approximate methods as indicated below, and compare with the results above, (c) assuming d_L the same for all inductors (at an average value), and d_C the same for all capacitors (at an average value); (d) assuming uniform dissipation d throughout (at an average value).

12-4. Sketch the (real-frequency) reactance and resistance of the impedance function

$$Z(p) = H \frac{p(p^2 + \omega_2^2)(p^2 + \omega_4^2)}{(p^2 + \omega_1^2)(p^2 + \omega_3^2)(p^2 + \omega_5^2)}, \qquad 0 < \omega_1 < \omega_2 < \omega_3 < \omega_4 < \omega_5.$$

From these sketches estimate the effect of incidental dissipation in inductors and capacitors on the reactance and resistance.

12-5. Determine and plot the zeros and poles of $Z(p)$ of the network shown (a) when no dissipation is present; (b) when L_1 alone has dissipation, in amount

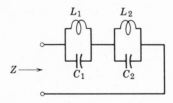

$$L_1 = L_2 = 1\ \text{h} \qquad C_1 = C_2 = 1\ \text{f}$$

Prob. 12–5

corresponding to $d_{L1} = 0.05$; (c) when L_1 has dissipation corresponding to $d_{L1} = 0.06$ and L_2 has dissipation corresponding to $d_{L2} = 0.10$; (d) when both L_1 and L_2 have dissipation corresponding to $d = 0.05$, the capacitors being considered to have negligible dissipation throughout.

Discuss the behavior of the zeros and poles under these circumstances. In each case determine at what frequencies resonance occurs and give the Q for each.

12-6. Show that the immittances of the networks illustrated can be realized in forms in which a resistor appears in series with each inductor and in parallel with each capacitor.

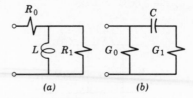

(a)   (b)

Prob. 12–6

Discuss the same proposition if R_1 (or G_1) is replaced by an arbitrary network. What properties must the "arbitrary" network have if such realizations are still to be possible?

12-7. Calculate the driving-point impedance function $Z(p)$ of the network shown in (a). Obtain the impedance function that results if the inductor dissipation is $d_L = 0.06$ (for all inductors) and there is no dissipation in the capacitors. Obtain the impedance function that results if *uniform* dissipation is added to the original network, d having the average value for the foregoing case.

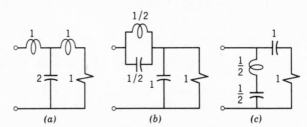

(a)   (b)   (c)

Element values are (normalized) ohms, henrys, farads

Prob. 12–7

Plot the zeros and poles of the impedance function for the three cases and compare the motions produced by the two sorts of dissipation. Plot the resistance and the reactance for the three cases and compare them.

Repeat for the networks of (b) and (c).

12-8. Suppose it is desired to realize a network with the driving-point resistance function

$$R = \frac{(1 - \omega^2)^2}{1 + \omega^4}.$$

By the graphical method of § 8.09 obtain the corresponding reactance curve.

From this make an estimate of the increase in resistance to be expected when uniform dissipation corresponding to an average inductor and capacitor Q of 100 at $\omega = 1$ is added.

Realize the given resistance function, using ideal L and C elements. Now compute the driving-point resistance of your network, assuming a capacitor Q of infinity and an inductor Q of 200 at $\omega = 1$. Compare this actual resistance with the original estimate.

Use the original estimate to alter the resistance function to anticipate the effect of the dissipation: keep the difference between $R(0)$ and $R(1)$ equal to 1 Ω and retain the general shape as best you can, by altering the multiplier and using a term in ω^2 in the denominator. Now recalculate the estimate of the effect of dissipation; realize the network and compare its actual resistance with this, using the Q data above.

In contrast, accomplish the result desired by predistortion.

12-9. (a) Show that at a frequency where Re $Z(j\omega)$ attains its minimum value, $Z(p)$ being a p-r impedance function, the introduction of dissipation will *increase* the resistance.

(b) Is this necessarily true at frequencies where Re $Z(j\omega)$ is not at its minimum value? Explain and illustrate.

(c) Does the introduction of dissipation necessarily move driving-point-immittance zeros and poles to the *left*? Explain and illustrate.

12-10. Show that the two networks given are practically equivalent at frequencies well below the resonant frequency, if r is small, so that either may be used as an equivalent for the inductor (cf. Fig. 12.01–A).

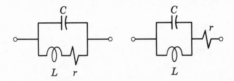

Prob. 12–10

12-11. In Fig. 12.01–D(b) assume l is negligible and calculate the capacitor Q as the reactance-resistance ratio of the equivalent network. Does your result correlate with the definition of Q for the inductor (Fig. 12.01–B) as to duality?

12-12. In the equivalent T network for a pair of coupled inductors, a negative inductance may appear, as in (b) of the figure. When dissipation, equivalent

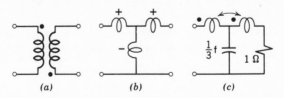

(a)   (b)   (c)

Prob. 12–12

to resistance independent of frequency (due to energy dissipation in the wire) is taken into account, how do the equivalent resistors appear in (a) and in (b)? Illustrate with the numerical values for a transformer with primary inductance 2 h, secondary inductance 3 h (normalized), and coupling coefficient 0.8.

The pair of coupled inductors form part of a network as in (c). Evaluate and plot $R(\omega) = \text{Re } Z(j\omega)$, (1) neglecting dissipation; (2) assuming uniform dissipation with $d = 0.06$ (normalized); (3) with inductor dissipation corresponding to $d_L = 0.12$ for both primary and secondary windings, and negligible capacitor dissipation. Compare and discuss the curves.

12-13. Consider problems in which the only important criterion is the *resistance* part of the impedance, i.e., design is solely for $R(\omega)$, though probably carried out in terms of $\text{Ev } Z(p)$.

(a) Show that when uniform dissipation in amount d is added in a realization of $\text{Ev } Z(p)$: (1) the left-half-plane poles move horizontally a distance d to the left, and the right-half-plane poles move horizontally a distance d to the right; (2) the zeros move along curves of complicated nature in general, and usually *not* horizontally.

Illustrate this by plotting the motions of the zeros and poles of the even part of the impedance when dissipation is added to the impedance corresponding to

$$R(\omega) = \frac{(1 - \omega^2)^2}{25 + 6\omega^2 + \omega^4}.$$

Repeat for the following resistance functions:

$$\frac{1}{1 + \omega^2} \qquad \frac{\omega^2}{1 + \omega^2} \qquad \frac{\omega^4}{1 + \omega^4} \qquad \frac{\omega^2}{1 + \omega^4}$$

(b) Show that if interest is confined to parts of the imaginary axis relatively close to the poles of $\text{Ev } Z$ and distant from the zeros of $\text{Ev } Z$, then predistortion accomplished by moving all poles of $\text{Ev } Z(p)$ horizontally toward the imaginary axis a distance d, the zeros being left as they are, will offset the major effects of dissipation in the network realization. When would it be possible also to predistort the zeros of $\text{Ev } Z$?

Illustrate this by calculating the resistance of realizations of the functions of (a) with and without the use of predistortion.

12-14. Repeat Prob. 12-13, but considering problems in which the only important criterion is the *reactance* part of the impedance. Give a discussion with appropriate changes, and illustrative examples.

12-15. Discuss the possibility of predistortion to offset the effects of dissipation when $|Z(j\omega)|$ is the design criterion.

12-16. Discuss the possibility of predistortion to offset the effects of dissipation when $\overline{Z}$ is the design criterion.

12-17. (1) Calculate and plot resistance and reactance versus ω on the assumption of infinite Q for the inductor and the two capacitors. (The resistors shown do not represent dissipation in the elements, but are part of the design.)

(2) Repeat, taking account of the finite Q of the inductor and capacitors as given by the curves.

(3) Repeat, assuming constant resistors to represent the dissipation in each element (use values determined from the Q curves at low frequencies).

(4) Predistort the network, using a d equal to the average d in (3).   Repeat the calculations above, using the actual Q curves, for this new network. Compare and discuss your results.

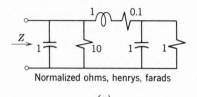

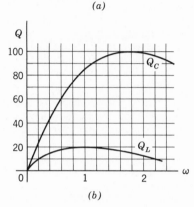

Normalized ohms, henrys, farads

(a)

(b)

Prob. 12–17

12-18. For the first network shown calculate and plot resistance and reactance versus ω on the assumption of infinite Q for the inductor and capacitors.   From

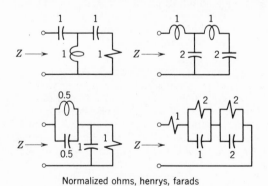

Normalized ohms, henrys, farads

Prob. 12–18

these curves and (12.02–6) estimate the effect of incidental dissipation corresponding to $d_L = 0.02$, $d_C = 0.01$.   Insert corresponding constant resistors with each reactive element and calculate actual resistance and reactance. How good was your estimate?

Repeat for each of the other three networks.

12-19. In estimating the effect of incidental dissipation on resistance, where only the resistance is at hand to begin with, it is necessary to determine a curve of the derivative of reactance versus frequency. Discuss how tables similar to those developed in § 8.09 might be drawn up to assist in this task.

12-20. If a driving-point immittance function $F(p)$ has no imaginary zeros or poles (it may have either at infinity, however) and the minimum value of $\text{Re } F(j\omega)$ is $R_{\min} \neq 0$, then $F(p)$ may be predistorted to account for dissipation. Prove this statement and discuss the amount of dissipation d that can be compensated for.

P-r immittance functions $F(p)$ with the following properties are to be predistorted to anticipate the effects of dissipation. In each case state whether this can be done, and if so to what extent. Explain. (a) No zeros or poles of $F(p)$ are imaginary. The minimum value of $\text{Re } F(j\omega)$ is zero. (b) No zeros or poles of $F(p)$ are imaginary. The minimum value of $\text{Re } F(j\omega)$ is greater than zero. (c) $F(p)$ has one pair of imaginary zeros.

12-21. Let $Z(p)$ be a p-r function, all of whose zeros and poles lie on or to the left of the line $\sigma = -d$. Of the five requirements of the test for positive reality (5.13–5), which are certainly still met by the predistorted function $Z(p - d)$, and which may not be?

12-22. Let $F(p)$ be p-r and have imaginary zeros and a number of left-half-plane zeros and poles. By considering the derivative of $F(p)$ at an imaginary zero, show that predistortion of all the left-half-plane zeros and poles will in general give a non-p-r function. (From this it follows that in general only a part of the left-half-plane zeros and poles may be predistorted; the remainder must move in a different fashion to retain the p-r character.)

12-23. Show that if an immittance function $Z(p)$ is p-r, the following conditions are necessary and sufficient for successful predistortion of $Z(p)$ in amount d: (a) No poles of $Z(p)$ lie in the strip $-d < \sigma \leq 0$. (b) Any poles of $Z(p)$ on the line $\sigma = -d$ are simple, with residues that are real and positive. (c) $\text{Re } Z(-d + j\omega) \geq 0$ for all ω (poles on $\sigma = -d$ excepted).

Explain why it is not necessary to consider the locations of the zeros of $Z(p)$ in the above.

12-24. Suppose that an immittance function $Z(p)$ is p-r, and the curve C that represents the locus of points at which $\text{Re } Z(p) = 0$ is drawn. Let $-a$ be the real part of the point (or points) on this locus that is farthest to the right (has maximum real part), infinity (if it is or appears to be on the locus) being very carefully considered. Demonstrate that (a) a is positive (or zero); (b) all poles and zeros of $Z(p)$ lie on C; (c) predistortion in amount d can be successfully accomplished if $d < a$. If d is to be equal to a, what additional information is necessary?

Note that the property of minimum resistance (conductance) requires $a = 0$, as does (independently) the presence of any imaginary poles, except possibly at infinity. Explain this.

12-25. A p-r impedance function $Z(p)$ is minimum-reactance and minimum-susceptance, but not minimum-resistance or minimum-conductance. Discuss the following statements.

(*a*) Realization of this function by Brune's method will require ideal (non-dissipative) L and C elements (and often perfect coupling between inductors).

(*b*) Realization by the Bott-Duffin or any similar method based upon zeros of resistance at finite frequencies still requires nondissipative L and C elements.

(*c*) Predistortion can be performed, and if this is done before realization, then there will be no nondissipative elements in the final design; the inherent resistance of the function is thus distributed among the reactive elements.

(*d*) Sometimes additional predistortion can be performed at various stages of the subsequent realization, leading to a different (and perhaps more desirable) distribution of the dissipation.

Note that this removes the need for ideal (nondissipative) reactance elements in cases falling in the above category.

12-26. In the following assume that no zeros or poles of the immittance functions occur on the imaginary axis, and that the dissipation of reactive elements is not large.

(*a*) In which of the canonic forms of R-C networks is it immediately evident that predistortion can be accomplished? How does predistortion alter these schematic diagrams?

(*b*) In the other canonic forms, what happens when predistortion is performed?

(*c*) Illustrate these points with the impedance functions

$$Z(p) = K\frac{(p + 2)}{(p + 1)(p + 3)} \qquad Z(p) = K\frac{(p + 2)(p + 4)}{(p + 1)(p + 3)}.$$

Repeat the above for the R-L case. The given functions are here to be interpreted as admittance functions.

12-27. Consider the admittance function

$$Y(p) = \frac{(p^2 + 16)(p + 1)(p + b)}{(p^2 + 2p + 2)(p + a)},$$

for which the important frequency range is from 0 to 2 radians per sec.

(*a*) Show that this function is p-r only if a and b are related in a certain fashion. What is the specific relation?

(*b*) Show that the function can be partially predistorted to compensate for (small) dissipation by moving the three critical points (zeros, poles) nearest the origin to the right a corresponding distance d, provided a and b are readjusted. What is the new relation required between a and b? Can the pole at $-a$ also be predistorted?

Now let (uniform) dissipation of amount d be added in the predistorted function. Show that the result is a p-r function. Give the function that expresses the net effect of predistortion *and* dissipation, i.e., the ratio of this last admittance to the original admittance.

(*c*) Take $a = 2$ and $d = 0.1$. Plot the resistance and reactance for (1) the original admittance function (in which dissipation is ignored), (2) the original admittance function with the addition of dissipation without predistortion (i.e., all zeros and poles are simply moved a distance d to the left), (3) the dissipative admittance function that had been predistorted, from (*b*).

Discuss the value of this particular predistortion as evidenced by the three sets of curves. Give network realizations for each of the three cases.

12-28. An R-C driving-point impedance function $Z(p)$ has a pole at the origin. Show that if all the nonzero zeros and poles are predistorted (by a reasonable amount) the new impedance function is still p-r and R-C realizable. Illustrate in terms of the impedance function of Example 1 of § 7.13, by calculating and plotting the reactance versus frequency, (a) in the absence of dissipation, (b) when uniform dissipation ($d = 0.1$) is added, (c) when the function is first predistorted as indicated above and uniform dissipation is then added.

Repeat, using the admittance function of Example 2 of § 7.13, and calculating the angle.

Discuss the benefits obtained in the important part of the frequency spectrum by this technique, assuming that the dissipation cannot be avoided when the network is built.

12-29. Consider the realization of the impedance function

$$Z(p) = \frac{2p^2 + p + 1}{p^2 + p + 2}.$$

(a) Show that $Z(p)$ is p-r and obtain realizations, using ideal (nondissipative) L and C elements as necessary.

(b) Suppose dissipation equivalent to an average dissipation constant $d = 0.1$ is present in the actual reactive elements. Discuss the possibility of predistorting the function $Z(p)$ and of realizing the function so obtained. Obtain a realization that, using dissipative elements, will give the desired impedance function, if possible. If not possible, discuss the reasons therefor.

(c) Plot the resistance and reactance versus frequency for the realization of (a) and for the same with uniform dissipation added. What corrections can you make either in the light of (b), or in the schematic diagrams, to offset the dissipation?

(d) If $d_L = 0.2$ and $d_C = 0$ for all the reactive elements, are the various realizations all affected in the same manner by dissipation? Explain and illustrate with curves.

12-30. Consider the impedance function

$$Z(p) = \frac{p + 2}{p^2 + 2p + 2}.$$

(a) Show that $Z(p)$ is p-r.

(b) From examination of the locations of the zeros and poles of $Z(p)$ alone, to what extent would you think that predistortion might be accomplished (i.e., for how large a value of d, the average dissipation constant)? Determine the actual limitation on d, and explain your result.

(c) If the dissipation of capacitors can be neglected, to what extent can dissipation be compensated for?

12-31. Realize the function

$$Z(p) = \frac{p + 2}{p^2 + 3p + 3}$$

both without regard to dissipation and with predistortion to take account of an average dissipation $d = 0.05$. Discuss the possibility of correcting the first network for dissipation without using the formal predistortion process. Does this depend on the particular realization chosen?

12-32. The action of the predistortion process is to place resistors in series with inductors, and in parallel with capacitors. A more complicated process is based on "predistortion" by replacing p in $Z(p)$ by w, defined by

$$w = \frac{p + a}{p + b}, \qquad a \text{ and } b \text{ real, and } 0 < a < b,$$

whence p is also determined as a function $f(w)$. Then the new function $Z_1(w) = Z(p) = Z[f(w)]$ may be p-r, and if so can be realized in various ways in general. On completion of the realization, each inductor is replaced by a network of the form shown, with dual procedure for the capacitor. This results in a different distribution of the function's inherent dissipation, possibly of value if the Q-versus-frequency characteristics of the elements are not linear.

Prob. 12–32

Under what conditions will the function $Z_1(w)$ be p-r? [*Suggestion:* On the p plane sketch both the mapping of the w-plane imaginary axis and the curve defined by **Re** $Z(p) = 0$.]

Show that if $Z_1(w)$ is p-r, and is realized in some form, then the corresponding realization of $Z(p)$ does have dissipation associated with each inductor and each capacitor in the manner indicated above.

Illustrate with the function

$$Z(p) = 5\frac{p^2 + 3.6p + 1.6}{p^2 + p + 10} + 1.$$

Contrast realizations obtained thus with those obtained by the ordinary predistortion method (with the maximum amount of predistortion), and by the Brune, Bott–Duffin, Pantell methods (after reduction to minimum resistance).

12-33. If in predistortion the use of a single (average) dissipation constant does not give sufficiently accurate results, the following procedure may be used. Realize the desired impedance function $Z(p)$ with nondissipative L and C elements; add to the network parasitic dissipation corresponding to the expected Q's (different among the various elements); compute the impedance of this dissipative network and note the changes that have taken place in the positions of the zeros and poles; now predistort the original impedance function by giving its zeros and poles the contrary changes; realize this new impedance function, if it is possible to do so. This modified network, on the addition of dissipation with the Q's assumed, will have very closely the desired impedance (except possibly for a multiplier, which is easily adjusted).

Explain in general terms why this procedure should give better results than predistortion with an average dissipation d assumed constant among the various L and C elements. If this predistortion can be accomplished, will it completely (exactly) compensate for dissipation? If not, will it be helpful to repeat the process in an iterative fashion?

In carrying out this more exact predistortion process, it is often satisfactory to use the following first-order formula for the changes in the zeros and poles of the given impedance function when dissipation is added.

$$\Delta p_k = -\frac{Z(p_k, d)}{Z'(p_k, 0)}.$$

Here $Z(p_k, 0) = Z(p_k) = $ the datum function $Z(p)$ evaluated at one of its zeros, p_k; in the argument "0" indicates absence of parasitic dissipation.

$Z'(p_k, 0) = Z'(p_k) = $ the derivative of $Z(p)$ evaluated at this zero, p_k.

$Z(p_k, d) = $ the impedance at $p = p_k$ of the network designed from $Z(p)$, with the use of nondissipative L and C elements, after the addition of parasitic dissipation with the various Q's.

$\Delta p_k = $ the change in the position of the zero p_k that is due to the addition of this dissipation.

Use of this formula replaces the determination of the zeros of the dissipative impedance (which may be a lengthy job) with the calculation of the value of the dissipative impedance at p_k and of the derivative of the nondissipative impedance there.

Derive this formula, using appropriate series expansions, on the assumption that the dissipation is small (though not uniform) and that the motion of the zeros is also small. Give the corresponding formula for the motion of the poles, in terms of the admittance function. (Cf. DE 3.)

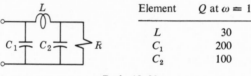

Element	Q at $\omega = 1$
L	30
C_1	200
C_2	100

Prob. 12–33

Illustrate by calculating and plotting the impedance obtained on realizing the function

$$Z(p) = \frac{p^2 + 0.7p + 2.8}{p^3 + 0.7p + 6.8p + 2.8}$$

with dissipative elements as given in the figure, (a) using an average value of d and (b) using the method above and the various Q's given. The important frequency range is $0 < \omega < 5$; the parts of the impedance of importance are its magnitude and its angle.

12-34. What are the implications of the formula given in Prob. 12-33, modified if necessary to fit the circumstances, with regard to desirable values of the derivative of an immittance function at a zero or pole, when it is desired that the immittance be relatively insensitive to changes in the network that cause the zeros or poles to move? (The motion may be due to dissipation, as in Prob. 12-33, or to variations in element values caused by manufacturing deviations, or by misadjustment, or by aging, or the like.)

12-35. Let $F(p)$ represent a p-r function, and $F_1(s)$ with $s = p + d$ its predistorted equivalent. For each of the following cases determine the amount of predistortion possible in terms of salient characteristics of the function $F(p)$, give the form of the indicated realizations of $F_1(s)$, and the form taken when dissipation is added, i.e., when s is replaced by $p + d$ (cf. WE 8).

(a) $F(p)$ is an R-C impedance function, finite at the origin; discuss the four canonic realizations.

(b) $F(p)$ is an R-C admittance function, not zero at the origin; discuss the four canonic realizations.

(c) $F(p)$ is an R-L impedance function not zero at the origin; discuss the four canonic realizations.

(d) $F(p)$ is an R-L admittance function finite at the origin; discuss the four canonic realizations.

(e) $F(p)$ is an R-L-C impedance function with complex poles, capable of partial-fraction expansion such that the (pairs of) terms are p-r; discuss the realization of each pair of terms (cf. Prob. 9-3).

(f) $F(p)$ is an R-L-C admittance function with similar properties, for similar discussion.

(g) $F(p)$ is an impedance function of order two that is minimum-reactance and minimum-susceptance but not minimum-resistance; discuss the Brune realization.

Illustrate each case with a numerical example.

12-36. Show that for the quality factor Q of an inductor, these two definitions are equivalent:

$Q =$ reactance/resistance,

$Q =$ susceptance/conductance.

Use Fig. 12.01–A(b) for the equivalent circuit of the inductor and ignore any negative signs that appear.

Explain why a definition of Q as the ratio of reactance to resistance, or of susceptance to conductance, is not generally appropriate for driving-point immittances of networks; in particular, what does such a definition give when there is a pronounced resonance at the terminals?

12-37. Derive the various expressions for Q given in § 12.04 for and in terms of the elements of the network shown, in which R is large. Point out how the

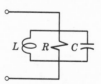

Prob. 12–37

approximations made in § 12.04 amount largely to replacing the arbitrary high-Q network, in the vicinity of resonance, by one of this sort. Could you thus derive the general relations of § 12.04?

12-38. Derive (12.04–3) by starting with a network in which $p_0 = 0 + j\omega_0$, introducing a small amount of dissipation, and using the analysis of § 12.02.

12-39. Derive the relations in (12.04–8).

12-40. Show that when a voltage (or current) is sinusoidal with time, its Laplace transform and its usual complex-number or phasor representation are proportional, as assumed in writing (12.04–18).

12-41. Show that the energy expression for Q given by (12.04–29), which was derived on the basis of resonance, is also valid for the Q of a single inductor or capacitor, if the *average* value of stored energy is used. What is the relation between the Q of such a single element and the power factor thereof?

12-42. For network (*a*) of Fig. 12.04–C express $Z(p)$ in terms of Q (as there defined), $\delta = (\omega - \omega_0)/\omega_0$, and as few additional symbols as possible. Show the approximate form that results when δ is small and only first-power terms are retained. Discuss the next approximation (using δ^2 terms) and the exact behavior.

12-43. Derive the relations given in Fig. 12.04–C.

12-44. Express the driving-point impedance and admittance functions of the networks of Figs. 12.04–C and –D in terms of L, C, and Q as there defined. Point out how, for large Q, these become simple (approximate) expressions that show the effect of Q on resonance sharpness.

12-45. The use of the number $\sqrt{2}$ in Figs. 12.04–A and –B is arbitrary, but convenient because it corresponds to a simple number, 2, in discussing $|Z|^2$ or $|Y|^2$. Why is the square of the magnitude more convenient to work with than the magnitude itself?

The frequencies ω_1 and ω_2 are sometimes referred to as "half-power" frequencies. Suppose a resonant network (of fairly high Q) driven (*a*) by a current source and (*b*) by a voltage source. Compute the (average) power taken by the network at frequencies ω_1, ω_0, ω_2 and compare the results. Under what conditions are these numbers in the ratio $0.5 : 1 : 0.5$?

12-46. Find the relation between the Q (defined in terms of sharpness of resonance) and the dissipation constant(s) d of appropriate reactive elements,

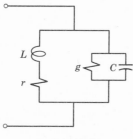

Prob. 12–46

in the networks of Figs. 12.04–C and –D and the one shown here. Use suitable approximations, all dissipation being small.

12-47. Consider the four canonic realizations of the impedance function

$$Z(p) = \frac{Hp(p^2 + 1)}{(p^2 + 0.64)(p^2 + 1.44)}.$$

If capacitors with negligible dissipation can be provided, but inductors having dissipation corresponding to $d_L = 0.01$ are the best available, evaluate the highest Q obtainable in each realization at each resonance. Explain the variations.

12-48. On a reproduction of Fig. 12.04–E show also the positions of the "half-power" points $j\omega_2$ and $j\omega_1$. Draw the triangle with vertices at p_0, $j\omega_1$, $j\omega_2$. What are its angles? How is it related to the circle centered at $j\omega_0$, of radius d?

12-49. Verify (12.04–12) and (12.04–13) and show also that there

$$\left(\frac{dB}{d\omega}\right)_0 = 2V_0, \qquad \left(\frac{dX}{d\omega}\right)_0 = -2\frac{V_0}{F_0^2}.$$

12-50. Show that in the vicinity of a marked maximum of $|Z|$,

$$Y = F_0[1 + j2Q(\omega/\omega_0 - 1)],$$

$$Z = \frac{1}{F_0}[1 - j2Q(\omega/\omega_0 - 1)].$$

12-51. For some typical high-Q network verify the phase relations mentioned just after (12.04–22) in the text.

12-52. Show that for a purely reactive network (12.04–23) and a similar expression for T hold exactly, so that $T_{\text{peak}} = 2T_{\text{avg}}$ and $V_{\text{peak}} = 2V_{\text{avg}}$. If the network also contains some resistance, but is only slightly dissipative, are the relations still valid?

12-53. In this network the inductors are slightly dissipative ($d_L = 0.01$); dissipation in the capacitors may be neglected. It is driven by a sinusoidal source connected to the driving terminals.

Sketch the reactance versus frequency (*a*) in the absence of dissipation, (*b*) in the presence of dissipation. Repeat for the resistance. Calculate the Q of the network at each resonance.

At one of the resonances determine the relative sizes of the currents in the inductors and the voltages across the capacitors. Determine also their phases (angles). Show how (12.04–23) and (12.04–25) result from the general expressions, and indicate the amount of error in (12.04–27).

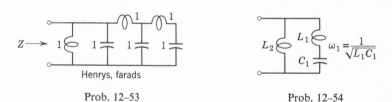

Prob. 12–53   Prob. 12–54

12-54. In this network the inductors are dissipative, with $d_L = 0.02$; the capacitor dissipation may be neglected.

(*a*) If L_2 and L_1 are of the same order of magnitude, and C_1 is numerically in the same (normalized) range, the network has a resonance at $j\omega_1$ of the usual kind. Calculate the network Q there. Calculate also the instantaneous energy functions T and V, showing the energy distribution, as a function of time when the network is driven at the frequency ω_1. How nearly true are (12.04–23), (12.04–26), (12.04–27)?

(*b*) Show that if L_2 is now permitted to vary it is possible to choose L_2 so that (still at ω_1) $T_{avg} = T_{peak}$ and $T =$ constant. Reconcile this with the equations mentioned above, pointing out where the assumptions made in this chapter are not fulfilled in this case. Discuss the "resonances" with this choice of L_2.

12-55. Find the Q's of the networks shown at their resonances. Assume that *all* reactive elements are slightly dissipative.

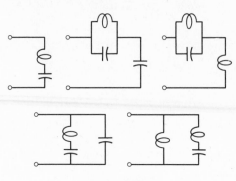

Prob. 12–55

12-56. Determine the Q at the input of the network shown in (a) at each resonant frequency. Compare these values and explain their agreement or disagreement.

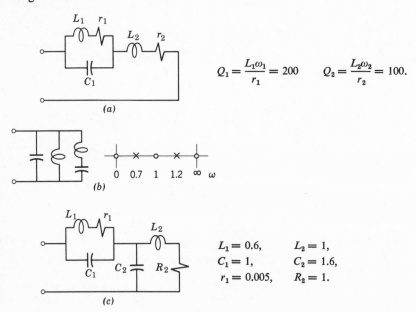

$$Q_1 = \frac{L_1\omega_1}{r_1} = 200 \qquad Q_2 = \frac{L_2\omega_2}{r_2} = 100.$$

(a)

(b)

$$0 \quad 0.7 \quad 1 \quad 1.2 \quad \infty \quad \omega$$

$$L_1 = 0.6, \qquad L_2 = 1,$$
$$C_1 = 1, \qquad C_2 = 1.6,$$
$$r_1 = 0.005, \qquad R_2 = 1.$$

(c)

Prob. 12–56

Repeat for the network shown in (b). Capacitor dissipation may be neglected; inductor dissipation corresponds to inductor Q's that are linear with frequency, with the value 150 at $\omega = 1$ (normalized).

Repeat for the network shown in (c). (Element values are normalized.)

12-57. (1) Plot the conductance and susceptance of the network of (a) in the vicinity of its resonant frequency ω_1. Determine, from these curves alone, the position of the maximum of $|Z|$.

(2) Now connect at the points a-a' the network of (b). Add its contributions to the conductance and susceptance in the vicinity of ω_1. Explain the change

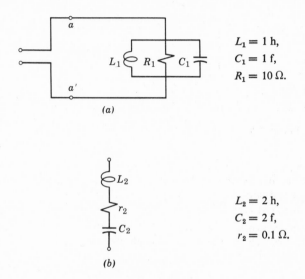

$L_1 = 1$ h,
$C_1 = 1$ f,
$R_1 = 10 \, \Omega.$

(a)

$L_2 = 2$ h,
$C_2 = 2$ f,
$r_2 = 0.1 \, \Omega.$

(b)

Prob. 12-57

in location of the peak of $|Z|$ considered in (a) and determine its new location. Where is the peak according to the analysis of § 12.04? What relation here exists between G, B and derivatives at this peak?

(3) Discuss the resonance of the L_2-C_2 branch alone, i.e., in the absence of L_1, R_1, and C_1, in the manner of (1).

(4) Now restore the L_1-R_1-C_1 network and discuss its effect on the resonance of (3), in the manner of (2).

12-58. Take $L = 1$ h and $C = 1$ f in the network shown and plot the loci of the zeros and poles of $Z(p)$ as r varies from 0 to 1. Plot the Q of the network as a function of r.

Determine the following frequencies, each of which is somehow related to the idea of resonance, and plot each as a function of r:
(a) the frequency at which $|Z|$ is a maximum;
(b) the frequency at which the angle of Z is

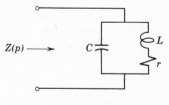

$Z(p) \longrightarrow$

Prob. 12-58

zero; (c) the frequency "opposite" the pole of $Z(p)$, i.e., the imaginary part of the pole; (d) the frequency at which the network is resonant in the absence of dissipation.

Discuss the relations between these frequencies and the suitability of each as a definition of *resonant frequency*; illustrate their relative positions on the p plane, for a Q of 100, a Q of 10. In the (approximate) analysis of § 12.04, how are these four frequencies related? Explain.

12-59. Discuss the resonance(s) of this network, on the assumption that both R_1 and C_2 are small. What happens if C_2 becomes rather large? If R_1 does so?

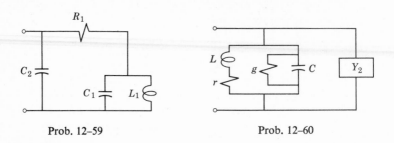

Prob. 12–59   Prob. 12–60

12-60. Consider a network across whose terminals a slightly dissipative "tuned circuit" appears in parallel with another network whose admittance Y_2 (see figure) is substantially constant in the vicinity of the resonance. Find the Q of the network at $\omega_0 = 1/\sqrt{LC}$.

12-61. In the network shown take $C_1 = C_2 = 1$ f, $L_1 = L_2 = 1$ h, $R_2 = 20\ \Omega$, $k = 0.7$ (the coupling coefficient). Calculate the Q of this network at each of

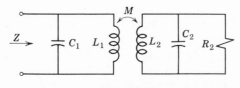

Prob. 12–61

its resonances (a) with no dissipation other than R_2, (b) with additional dissipation in L_1 and L_2 of 0.1 Ω each. Compare and explain your results.

12-62. Consider an L-C network, to which dissipation is added uniformly in small amount, d. Show that the Q of the network at each resonance is given by $Q = \omega/2d$, in which ω is the frequency of resonance, if the two adjacent critical frequencies are not too close. Discuss the validity of this formula when one or both of the adjacent critical frequencies is very close.

12-63. Consider the natural behavior of a network, i.e. (for example) the transient voltage appearing at the (open-circuited) input to a two-terminal network after an impulse of current has been applied. Show that if one of the poles of the input impedance produces a high-Q resonance at the frequency ω_0, then in this natural behavior the term corresponding to this pole is damped by the factor $e^{-(\omega_0 t/2Q)}$, in which Q is the quality factor of the resonance. What is the time constant associated with this term?

12-64. Discuss the effect of parasitic dissipation on realizations of the functions

$$Z(p) = \frac{(p^2 + 1)}{p(p^2 + 2)} \quad \text{and} \quad Y(p) = \frac{(p^2 + 1)}{p(p^2 + 2)},$$

(a) if the dissipation is uniform with $d = 0.005$, (b) if the capacitor dissipation is negligible and $d_L = 0.010$. Illustrate with curves of resistance and of reactance versus frequency.

12-65. Discuss the effect on driving-point immittance of incidental dissipation in the inductor and capacitor of the constant-resistance networks of Fig. 10.08–E (with, e.g., Z_1 or Y_1 a single inductor), (a) if the dissipation is uniform, (b) if only the inductors are dissipative.

12-66. Discuss the effect on driving-point immittance of a small change (misadjustment) in one of the element values of the constant-resistance networks of Fig. 10.08–E. Illustrate with sketches showing the locations of zeros and poles in a specific case, as when Z_1 is a single reactive element, and correlate with Prob. 12-65. Can you point out generally similar phenomena in other branches of engineering or of physics?

12-67. A nondissipative driving-point impedance function is defined by

$$Z(p) = H\frac{p(p^2 + \omega_2{}^2)}{(p^2 + \omega_1{}^2)}.$$

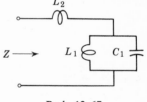

Prob. 12-67

Suppose that dissipation in the inductor L_1 makes the Q of the L_1-C_1 combination equal to 150 at ω_1; see the figure. Discuss the effect of increasing L_2 (representing, e.g., parasitic inductance in wiring) on the Q of Z at ω_1. Explain what happens at ω_1 when L_2 is very large.

Discuss the effect on the resonance at ω_1 as the inductor dissipation in realizations of $Z(p)$ is increased from zero to large values. Is there a difference in behavior between the various canonic realizations?

12-68. It is desired to build a network with the driving-point impedance function

$$Z(p) = H\frac{p(p^2 + \omega_2{}^2)}{(p^2 + \omega_1{}^2)(p^2 + \omega_3{}^2)}$$

in which $f_1 = 1.2$ mcps, $f_2 = 1.5$ mcps, $f_3 = 2$ mcps. It is also desired to make the slope of the reactance-frequency curve as small as reasonably possible at 1.5 mcps. Obtain the four canonic realizations and discuss the practicability of realizing each. Which one do you prefer?

Devise and work out a similar problem involving an R-C network.

12-69. Discuss the practical advantages and disadvantages of each of the three equivalents for Z_B shown in Figs. 10.03–A and –B.

12-70. Discuss the effects on the input resistance and reactance of this network of (a) mutual inductance between the inductors, (b) parasitic capacitance from inductor to inductor, (c) parasitic capacitance in the inductors themselves,

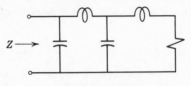

Prob. 12–70

(d) parasitic capacitance from inductors to ground. For numerical illustration, take unit values for the elements and representative values for the parasitic effects, the normalization factors being 10 mcps and 75 Ω.

12-71. In this network the element values are chosen so that $Z(p) = R_0$ = constant (§ 10.08). Discuss the effect on the input impedance of variations

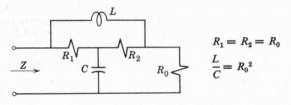

$$R_1 = R_2 = R_0$$
$$\frac{L}{C} = R_0{}^2$$

Prob. 12–71

in R_2 from its nominal value, (a) when the other elements have the correct values, (b) when one of the other elements is slightly misadjusted. In each case, how useful is the element R_2?

12-72. In the design of a high-precision resistor for low-frequency use it is sometimes necessary to compensate for the parasitic inductance of the resistor

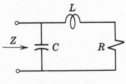

Prob. 12–72

by adding a small capacitor. The network then becomes that shown, in which L and C are small, and ideally $Z(p) = R$. For fixed R and L discuss the optimum choice of C. Illustrate with curves of driving-point resistance and reactance.

If it is the parasitic *capacitance* of a resistor that must be compensated, discuss and illustrate a corresponding method.

13.

Approximation

$\cdots$ *tous les problèmes qui se réduisent à des approximations, et conséquemment presque toutes les applications des Mathématiques à la nature* $\cdots$
—P. S. Laplace

Of the three important parts of network synthesis (§ 1.01) we have discussed two in detail: *properties* and *realization*. It remains to discuss *approximation*, and the problems one faces when data given for network synthesis are not realizable as they stand. Then the additional problem of devising a function that is both realizable and acceptably close to what is wanted must be solved. To this we now turn.

13.01 Approximation

The etymological meaning of the word *approximation* is *to come near, to approach*, with implications of "almost, but not quite." This is what engineers are always doing, for they are seldom able to achieve *exactly* the result desired, nor does it matter if they don't: so long as they come fairly close to the goal, and do so at reasonable cost, the job is satisfactorily done. Jobs must be done within a limited time, after all, and no practical man expects perfection—nor would he pay for it if it were attainable.

The approximation problem we have to solve is to determine a function $Z(p)$, or $Y(p)$, that is rational and positive-real, and whose behavior as a function of frequency is acceptably close to the requirements laid down by the "customer." Since networks usually form only small parts of systems, these requirements (data for the synthesis) are determined by considerations foreign to the network problem. It is the network engineer's job to approximate them in network form, within the tolerances and cost limits laid down by the system, as best he can. The approximation process amounts to fitting a (p-r) rational function to the desired function, i.e., to the determination of the coefficients of the two polynomials that are the numerator and denominator of the immittance function, or of its zeros, poles, and multiplier. They must be so determined that the immittance function behaves closely, in one or more of its properties, as the requirements. Interest may be confined to the resistance-frequency curve, or the reactance-frequency curve, or to the behavior of magnitude or of angle with frequency, or some combination of these may be important. In all cases the problem is basically the same: to determine a function that is both realizable and acceptable in its behavior with frequency.

The need for approximation arises in that system requirements are often conveniently expressed in idealized form, as by segments of straight lines. These may form a curve, in a general sense, but the sharp corners (discontinuities in derivatives) are impossible to achieve with rational functions. (Or it may be that the requirements, though realizable, are so only at prohibitive expense.) Rational functions are versatile, and if of high enough order can do remarkable things, but only within a certain approximation. They cannot remain linear or even constant over a band of frequencies (except in the usually trivial case of functions that are simply linear or constant), but they can be made to approximate to such behavior. In illustration, consider Fig. 13.01–A. In (a) the line segments show a requirement for the magnitude of an impedance (or admittance) function; the dashed curve shows what might be an approximation thereto that is both acceptable and realizable. (Only positive frequencies need be considered, because of the inevitable symmetry.) Or this might represent requirements and solution for a resistance, or some other function. In (b) a problem and possible solution for, say, a resistance (or conductance) function are shown. In (c) is shown what might be done if the requirement is, for example, a reactance (or susceptance) that is constant with frequency; here the realizability requirement that the function be odd forces us to be content with a good approximation in only a certain range of frequencies, and a much poorer approximation elsewhere. A similar situation would exist if (c) represented a requirement on the angle of an immittance function, as it might. In situations like these we can only try to adjust the parameters of the rational function so that the corresponding (smooth) curve follows the same general course as the requirement, probably crossing and recrossing it, yet never getting too far away.

This matter of approximation is not solely the concern of the engineer. It is a problem that has long interested mathematicians, and there is an extensive literature on it, some under the heading *interpolation*. Some of this can be exceedingly helpful to us, though we shall also find good use for an engineering approach through analogs with familiar physical systems. But the basic problem is always the determination of a rational p-r function whose behavior on at least some parts of the imaginary axis is in some respect (as real part, or magnitude, or angle, or imaginary part, or even whole value) reasonably close to that desired. The function

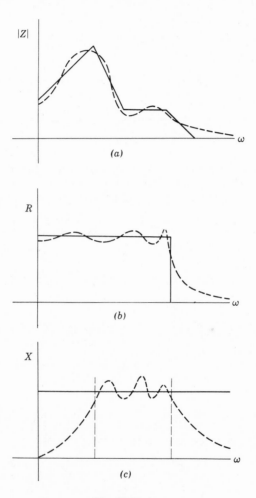

Fig. 13.01–A

should also be of fairly low order, to be economical of realization, and as easy to realize as possible; it should not, for example, require the complications of a Brune or Bott–Duffin or similar network, if they can be avoided. But we must first consider rather carefully the words "reasonably close."

13.02 Error

Although "the act of coming reasonably close" may be satisfactory as a general definition of approximation, it is still rather vague and offers little hope for precise mathematical treatment. We can be more exact if we introduce the following definition of the *error*: the difference between what is actually obtained and what is desired. Even more precisely, let

error $= \Delta(\omega)$

$\qquad = $ (approximating function) $-$ (function approximated).   (13.02–1)

The quality of the approximation is certainly expressed by the magnitude of Δ: where Δ is small the approximation is good; where Δ is large the approximation is poor. (The sign of the error is often relatively unimportant.) The terms "small" and "large" are still vague, to be sure, but become precise whenever a specific application is considered, for then the tolerances laid down by the system requiring the network will state definitely what errors are tolerable. These may be constant limits over the (frequency) band of approximation or they may vary because smallness of error is more important to the system at some frequencies than at others. It is in the behavior of the error, of the function $\Delta(\omega)$, with respect to these limits that we can find a measure of the approximation.

The size of the error at the points where $|\Delta|$ is maximum is of course important; but equally so may be the manner in which Δ varies with frequency. In defining the sort of approximation achieved, both as to method of obtaining it and as to the quality thereof, we shall consider both things. To illustrate the many possibilities, Fig. 13.02–A presents

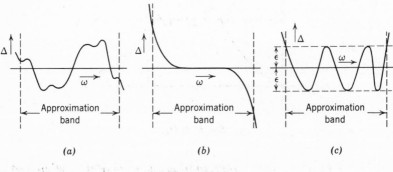

(a) $\qquad\qquad\qquad\qquad (b)$ $\qquad\qquad\qquad\qquad (c)$

Fig. 13.02–A

three rather different error functions in graphical form. Each of the three curves is a plot of error versus frequency, in the region where the approximation is made, the *approximation band*. Each may well have been determined by some definite criterion of approximation, yet each has distinctly different character.   In (*a*) the error oscillates back and forth between positive and negative values, in an apparently haphazard fashion, with minor fluctuations entirely on one side or the other of the axis, and never becomes exceedingly large.   In (*b*) the error is quite close to zero in the central part of the approximation band, and varies smoothly towards large values at the ends of the band.   In (*c*) the error again oscillates back and forth between positive and negative values, but this time without minor fluctuations, and every one of the maxima of $|\Delta|$ has the same value, ϵ.   One might suppose that if the horizontal dashed lines show the allowable limits of error, this last type of error curve represents a very efficient manner of approximation, for in it the allowed deviation seems to have been exploited as much as possible, probably with attendant gains in width of the approximation band, or perhaps in behavior outside the band.   This supposition is indeed valid in many cases.   It is often convenient (though not always accurate) to think of the error curve as a length of (water) hose, flexible but of unchanging length, that can be bent into various patterns, though room must always be found for the whole of it.   It may be laid closely along the desired line over part of the band, as in (*b*), but then the error must become large at the band end(s).   Or it may be wound back and forth in some arbitrary fashion as in (*a*), or systematically as in (*c*) in an effort to keep the maximum magnitude of the error a minimum by making all maxima alike.

To define or measure the quality of approximation achieved we might simply state the maximum value of the magnitude of Δ.   But this single number gives no information on the variation of Δ with frequency.   A more informative single-number criterion is some integrated or *average* value.   This cannot be simply the average value of Δ itself, for that could easily be zero; even in the presence of large errors, positive and negative values could cancel each other out, as in any of the curves in Fig. 13.02–A. An alternative would be to average the magnitude of Δ, but this is inconvenient because $|\Delta|$ is not mathematically tractable.   We can obtain an average that is both meaningful and tractable if we average the *square* of the error and take the rms (root-mean-square) error as a criterion (or, for that matter, we might average any even power of Δ).   Such criteria, in the form of single numbers, still do not give much information on the *distribution* of the error.   The rms errors for the three cases in Fig. 13.02–A might be nearly equal numbers, for example, though the distribution of error is radically different in the three cases: in (*c*) it is quite uniform, whereas in (*b*) it is far from uniform.   Evidently we must in general consider not only how large the error gets, or its average in some sense, but also how the error is distributed over the approximation band. Which is most important will depend on the requirements of the particular problem in hand.

Of equal or greater importance to us is the manner in which the approximation is obtained. Both technique of approximation and kind or quality of approximation obtained are important, and often inseparable. We shall now discuss some techniques of approximation, and the sorts of approximation obtained.

13.03 A very straightforward method

Perhaps the most straightforward approximation technique is that of trial and error. It uses no elaborate mathematics, as a rule, but only common sense and arithmetic. In its simplest form, it guesses at a suitable network function, i.e., it arbitrarily chooses a set of numbers for the zeros and poles, or the coefficients, in the function being set up (perhaps even chooses the values of the elements on a schematic diagram). The error is then computed; and after consideration thereof, a new trial function is set up. The process continues in stages like this until an acceptable and realizable result is obtained. Of great importance here is clearly a background of experience and judgment on the part of the approximator. With the perspective given by such a background the method can be extremely useful. The process of successive improvement can, in fact, be made very efficient, and the method can be powerful indeed.

In more systematic form, the trial-and-error method may proceed to determine the first approximation by setting the error equal to zero at certain selected frequencies. This leads to a set of simultaneous equations which can usually be solved for the unknown parameters of the network function; if not, the points (frequencies) at which the error is set equal to zero can be altered, or certain nonzero errors can be stipulated at some points.

For example, if the problem is to determine an impedance function approximating certain requirements (resistance and reactance), we may set up the function

$$Z(p) = \frac{a_0 + a_1 p + a_2 p^2 + \cdots + a_n p^n}{b_0 + b_1 p + b_2 p^2 + \cdots + b_n p^n}, \tag{13.03-1}$$

in which the order n is probably determined at first by economic considerations; if the first choice proves inadequate, the value of n may be raised later. One of the coefficients, such as b_n, may be taken as unity with no loss of generality. At a number of judiciously selected frequencies $(p = j\omega_1, j\omega_2, \cdots)$ we now equate the function (13.03-1) and the data or requirements. There is some algebraic work to be done: clearing of fractions and separation of each equation into two equations in real numbers only by separating real and imaginary parts (the a's and b's being assumed real). Then we have a set of linear simultaneous equations in the unknown a's and b's. The number of points at which the data are matched (error set equal to zero) is of course chosen so that the number of these equations is equal to the number of unknowns. Since these equations are linear, and involve only real numbers, their solution is straightforward, either with the use of determinants or by successive elimination. (In those rare cases where they are not all independent, some change in the matching points, or addition of one or more such points, can be made to make the equations soluble.) This determines the function (13.03–1). Of it two important things must be said. In the first place there is no guarantee that $Z(p)$ is positive-real; it must be tested, and if found wanting, the locations of the matching points must be altered, or else some nonzero errors specified, so that $Z(p)$ becomes realizable. In the second place, even if $Z(p)$ is realizable, the error will probably be zero (or as specified) only at the matching points; the function $\Delta(\omega)$ must be computed at a number of other points, until a good knowledge of the error function is obtained. If this error is acceptable, the job may be considered done; if it is not, as is likely, then revisions must be made.

This can be done by looking at the error curve(s) and readjusting the values that $Z(p)$ is to take at the matching points. (Here the hose concept of the error may be utilized to suggest what error specification at certain points may improve the over-all error.) The equations are solved again, the error obtained, and the whole process repeated until a satisfactory result is obtained. A further systematization is to calculate, individually, the effect of small changes in each parameter on the error-frequency curves. With a set of these first-order-effect curves (presumably superposable) one can quickly determine a new set of parameters to try. Experience, and the exercise of judgment at each step, are invaluable, however.

An alternative approach is to work directly in terms of the zeros and poles of $Z(p)$, rather than the a and b coefficients. For a first trial, a set of zeros and poles is chosen on the basis of experience or standard (normalized) curves illustrating the effects of zeros and poles at various locations. The error is computed, and then the zeros and poles are adjusted to reduce the error, by using the standard curves. These may be augmented by standard curves illustrating individually the effects of small changes in the positions of zeros and poles. With a collection of these curves one can rapidly determine zero and pole changes to improve the first approximation (TR 1). If the problem warrants the work, more elaborate techniques may be used: the required changes in zero and pole location may be determined by reducing the error to zero at specified points, much as discussed above, but using these incremental-effect curves —or the required changes may be determined by an orthogonal-function and least-mean-square-error use of these curves (LI 1, TR 1). The function obtained must of course still be tested for positive reality before the approximation problem can be considered to be solved.

As another illustration, consider the problem of determining a *resistance* function to approximate certain data. The procedure is the same in essence, but the function is to be of the form

$$R(\omega) = \frac{a_0 + a_2\omega^2 + a_4\omega^4 + \cdots + a_{2n}\omega^{2n}}{b_0 + b_2\omega^2 + b_4\omega^4 + \cdots + b_{2n}\omega^{2n}} \qquad (13.03\text{--}2)$$

and of course we must insure that $R(\omega)$ is not negative (or infinite) at any real frequency. The problem is simpler because, if these requirements are met, the corresponding impedance function will automatically be positive-real and no further test is necessary, as it was in the preceding case (§ 8.16). Determination of the coefficients a and b can be made by matching at selected frequencies (leading again to simultaneous linear equations), calculating the $\Delta(\omega)$ curve, and subsequently revising as indicated. Or one may work in terms of the zeros and poles of the resistance function or, better, of the (corresponding) function $\mathrm{Ev}\,Z(p)$. In any event the error curve is "pushed around" in successive readjustments, either with the exercise of judgment or the use of curves indicating the effects of small changes in coefficients, or in zeros or poles, until a satisfactory result is obtained. In the interests of simplifying the realization, one may also require that the zeros of $R(\omega)$ be confined to the ω axis, perhaps even to the origin and infinity (§ 9.11). Approximation of a desired *conductance* function is of course merely the dual problem.

If *reactance* (or susceptance) is the important characteristic, similar procedures may be followed, starting with an *odd* function of frequency, as

$$X(\omega) = \frac{a_1\omega + a_3\omega^3 + \cdots + a_{2n+1}\omega^{2n+1}}{b_0 + b_2\omega^2 + \cdots + b_{2n}\omega^{2n}} \qquad (13.03\text{--}3)$$

or its reciprocal, depending on the data. So long as the coefficients are real, and any real-frequency poles are simple with residues that are real and negative (ω being considered the independent variable), the corresponding impedance function is realizable and no further test is necessary (§ 8.16).

If the *angle* of an immittance is the important characteristic, we deal in like fashion with an odd rational function of ω (with real coefficients) that represents its tangent, thus insuring realizability. The angle is of course confined to the range from $-90°$ to $+90°$, for positive reality.

Since the various parts of an immittance function (R, X, G, B, magnitude, angle) are not independent (Chapter 8), we may choose to work in terms of one part only, even if the whole (complex) immittance is to be approximated. For example, we may solve the approximation problem in terms of the resistance function alone, having first made certain by the methods of Chapter 8 that the desired reactance is consistent with the desired resistance (i.e., is very closely the associated minimum reactance, except possibly for real-frequency poles realizable with an L-C network). If the behavior of the immittance function outside the (finite) approximation band is not important, we can specify the parts independently in the approximation band, but often with results at frequencies outside the band that are rather curious (Problem 8-58).

Another approach is a modification of that used in § 8.09. It consists in approximating with a succession of straight lines, a process not too difficult of accomplishment graphically, when moderate accuracy suffices (BA 2, TR 1). This approach, and others, are mentioned in the problems.

Although such trial-and-error methods may lack something in mathematical elegance, they are very practical. The approximator using these methods is in close touch with his function, can see the whole problem clearly and develop a strong feeling for "what is going on," and closely control the manner in which the error is distributed; in mathematically more elegant methods (to be described) there is sometimes a danger of losing this touch, in the mechanics of the operations. Unusual constraints, unusual data, unusual variation of tolerances with frequency, all are handled as easily as common ones with these "cut-and-try" methods, and not usually so with the more formal mathematical methods. The general applicability and power of trial-and-error methods make them invaluable, in spite of the amount of numerical work required (which is inevitable in most network-synthesis problems).

Of these methods the inherent flexibility and opportunity for varied attacks makes adequate discussion and illustration difficult. For practice and experience there is no real substitute. We shall briefly discuss an illustrative example, however, to make some of the ideas concrete.

Consider the problem of designing a network whose input resistance varies inversely as the square root of frequency (a problem presumably posed by some system requirement). With appropriate normalization, the approximation problem is then to fit the function $F(\omega) = 1/\sqrt{\omega}$ with a function of the form (13.03–2). The approximation cannot be good at extremely low frequencies, for R must remain finite; we shall assume that the (normalized) frequency band of most importance is from $\omega = 1$ to $\omega = 4$. For our first trial we take $n = 2$ and

$$R(\omega) = \frac{1}{b_0 + b_2\omega^2 + b_4\omega^4}, \qquad (13.03\text{–}4)$$

i.e., we place all the zeros of $\text{Ev}\, Z(p)$ at infinity so that the result will be a simple ladder network. We may conveniently determine a preliminary set of b's by matching $R(\omega)$ to $F(\omega)$ at the three points $\omega = 1, 2, 3$, which more or less cover the approximation band; the result will give us some feeling for what can and cannot be done, and we may then proceed to refine it. Because of the form of $R(\omega)$ here (the numerator is merely a known constant) we can very quickly determine the coefficient b's in terms of literal symbols for the values $R(\omega)$ is to take at these three points; such a determination is convenient because later improvements can then be made without solving the simultaneous equations for the b's again. In fact, a general tabulation could be made for approximation of any function by a resistance function of the form (13.03–4). With the notation

$$R(1) = 1/A, \qquad R(2) = 1/B, \qquad R(3) = 1/C \qquad (13.03\text{–}5)$$

for the specified values, the equations for the b's are

$$b_0 + b_2 + b_4 = A,$$
$$b_0 + 4b_2 + 16b_4 = B, \qquad (13.03\text{–}6)$$
$$b_0 + 9b_2 + 81b_4 = C.$$

These may readily be solved by successive elimination (Appendix A), or with the use of determinants. In the solution below, given to illustrate the simplicity of the elimination process, b_0 (whose coefficients are all unity already) is first eliminated by subtracting the first equation from the second, and the second from the third. Then the coefficients of b_2 are made unity by division, and the equations subtracted again to give an equation for b_4. Then b_2 is obtained from one of the preceding pair of equations, and finally b_0 from one of the original equations. The results should, of course, be checked by substitution in all of the original equations. The schematic form is almost self-explanatory: only the coefficients of the b's and of A, B, and C are written, for these are the only numbers actually used.

	b_0	b_2	b_4	A	B	C
Original equations	1	1	1	1	0	0
	1	4	16	0	1	0
	1	9	81	0	0	1
By subtraction	0	3	15	−1	1	0
	0	5	65	0	−1	1
By division		1	5	−0.333 · · ·	0.333 · · ·	0
		1	13	0	−0.2	0.2
By subtraction		0	8	0.333 · · ·	−0.533 · · ·	0.2

From the equation above: (13.03–7)

$$b_4 = 0.041667A - 0.066667B + 0.025C,$$

from the second or third equation above:

$$b_2 = -0.541667A + 0.666667B - 0.125C,$$

from one of the three original equations:

$$b_0 = 1.54A - 0.6B + 0.1C.$$

We next determine the b's when the function $R(\omega)$ is matched to $F(\omega)$ at these three points, i.e., when $A = \sqrt{1}$, $B = \sqrt{2}$, $C = \sqrt{3}$. When these numbers are substituted in (13.03–7) we obtain

$$b_0 = \quad 0.8247,$$
$$b_2 = \quad 0.1846, \qquad (13.03\text{–}8)$$
$$b_4 = -0.0093.$$

This represents an unrealizable result, for $R(\omega)$ becomes negative at high frequencies; in fact, $R(\omega)$ has a pole at $\omega = 4.9$. Figure 13.03–A shows the behavior of both R and F, exhibiting a fairly good approximation in the band from $\omega = 1$ to $\omega = 3$, as one would reasonably expect. The unrealizability of the result should not be surprising, for forcing the function (13.03–4) through these three points (the approximation technique used here) is not in any way related to physical realizability of the function in network form. But it is imperative that the approximation produce a realizable function. With hindsight it is now easy to see where we have erred: if the denominator of $R(\omega)$ is a polynomial of degree four, as in (13.03–4), and the coefficients are determined by matching $F = 1/\sqrt{\omega}$ at three points, it is inevitable that this unrealizable behavior result (as graphical consideration of the reciprocal functions will show).

Instead of relaxing the requirement that three points be matched, let us increase the order of the impedance function to three, so that

$$R(\omega) = \frac{1}{b_0 + b_2\omega^2 + b_4\omega^4 + b_6\omega^6}. \qquad (13.03\text{–}9)$$

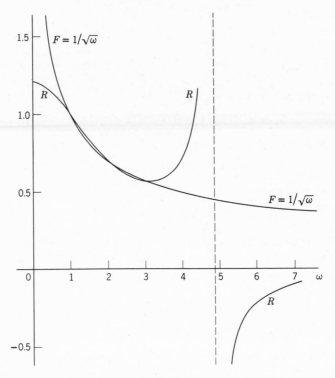

Fig. 13.03–A

We shall now determine the b's by specifying R at $\omega = 1, 2, 3, 4$. With the notation

$$R(1) = 1/A, \qquad R(2) = 1/B, \qquad R(3) = 1/C, \qquad R(4) = 1/D, \qquad (13.03\text{–}10)$$

the simultaneous equations in schematic form are

b_0	b_2	b_4	b_6		A	B	C	D	
1	1	1	1	=	1	0	0	0	
1	4	16	64	=	0	1	0	0	
1	9	81	729	=	0	0	1	0	$(13.03\text{–}11)$
1	16	256	4096	=	0	0	0	1	

whose solution is

$$b_6 = -0.002778A + 0.005556B - 0.003571C + 0.000794D,$$
$$b_4 = 0.080556A - 0.144444B + 0.075000C - 0.011111D,$$
$$b_2 = -0.677778A + 0.938889B - 0.300000C + 0.038889D,$$
$$b_0 = 1.600000A - 0.800000B + 0.228571C - 0.028571D.$$

(13.03–12)

On setting $A = \sqrt{1}$, $B = \sqrt{2}$, $C = \sqrt{3}$, $D = \sqrt{4}$, i.e., on matching R to $F = 1/\sqrt{\omega}$ at $\omega = 1, 2, 3, 4$, we obtain the values

$$b_0 = 0.807383,$$
$$b_2 = 0.208175,$$
$$b_4 = -0.016038,$$
$$b_6 = 0.000480.$$

(13.03–13)

The nature of the arithmetic of these and similar calculations usually makes it advisable to carry more significant figures than in ordinary

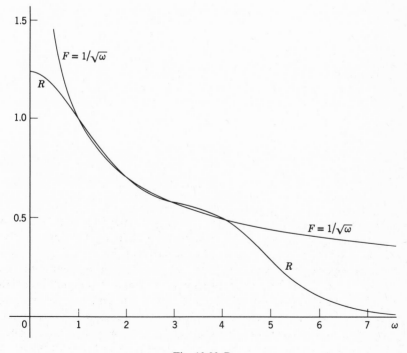

Fig. 13.03–B

calculations; b_6 above, for example, can be determined to three significant figures only by using six significant figures in (13.03–12). For this reason, the calculations of the approximation process must often be performed with more than slide-rule accuracy unless some ingenious special method of solution is available.

The values in (13.03–13) appear reasonable from the point of view of realizability—at least there is no obvious flaw—so we proceed to calculate $R(\omega)$. Figure 13.03–B shows its behavior, as well as that of $F(\omega)$. The approximation in the band $1 \leq \omega \leq 4$ is good, as would be expected, and at frequencies above and below, $R(\omega)$ departs appreciably from F. Since R clearly does not go negative, it is realizable.

To illustrate the quality of approximation in the approximation band, an expanded plot of the error is shown in the solid curve of Fig. 13.03–C.

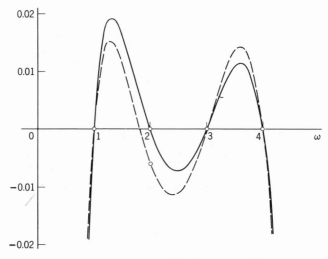

Fig. 13.03–C

Although the result is quite good as it stands, we may improve the approximation somewhat, toward the equal-ripple type, by revising the four specified values of R. We retain the matching of F at $\omega = 1$ and $\omega = 4$, since the error curve is so steep there, and this more or less determines the location and extent of the approximation band. Examination of the (solid) curve of Fig. 13.03–C suggests that nearly equal-ripple behavior would result if the error were dropped about 0.006 at $\omega = 2$ and the match kept at $\omega = 3$. Then presumably the first loop would drop, as would the second, and the third would probably rise (in a sort of pivoting action about $\omega = 3$), the three then being about equal in magnitude. Accordingly, we now specify

$$A = \sqrt{1}, \qquad B = \left(\frac{1}{\sqrt{2}} - 0.006\right)^{-1}, \qquad C = \sqrt{3}, \qquad D = \sqrt{4}.$$

$$(13.03\text{--}14)$$

The new values of the b's are quickly obtained, since (13.03–12) is in a form suited for convenient revision of the specified values; they are

$$
\begin{aligned}
b_0 &= 0.797702, \\
b_2 &= 0.219537, \\
b_4 &= -0.017786, \\
b_6 &= 0.000548.
\end{aligned}
$$

$$(13.03\text{--}15)$$

On calculating R and the error, we obtain the dashed curve of Fig. 13.03–C. [The plot of $R(\omega)$ itself is not sufficiently different to warrant replotting.] The error is not exactly equal in the magnitude of its loops, but is probably quite good enough, though evidently a change of about 0.007 would have been better than 0.006. (For extremely accurate work, one would plot the difference between these two curves and use it as a measure of the effect of changing B; this could be used, with similar curves corresponding to changes in the other parameters, to accurately determine the most desirable changes.)

Before proceeding to the realization, in fact even before making the refinement above, we should determine the parasitic effects to be expected. Of these we shall consider only dissipation. A very rough estimate of the effect of parasitic dissipation can be quickly obtained by recognizing that the resistance curve of Fig. 13.03–B is somewhat like that of a network composed of a resistor and a capacitor in parallel. For such a network the resistance function is of the form

$$R = \frac{1}{a + b\omega^2}.$$

$$(13.03\text{--}16)$$

By trial we find that $a = 0.8$ and $b = 0.11$ give a fair fit. The corresponding reactance function, found by the methods of Chapter 8, is

$$X = \frac{-3.4\omega}{7.3 + \omega^2},$$

$$(13.03\text{--}17)$$

whose derivative does not exceed 0.2 in magnitude in the frequency range of interest. If we may expect inductor Q's of 100 and capacitor Q's that are essentially infinite, then the maximum effect of dissipation upon the resistance will be about $0.005 \times 0.2 = 0.001$, by (12.02–6). A more precise estimate could be obtained by the method of § 8.09, but the effect of dissipation is negligible. If it were not, we might apply the pre-distortion technique of § 12.03 in the realization. Or, more carefully, we might proceed to calculate the error curve by realizing the network and calculating its resistance function, taking into account the actual element Q's. Then we should alter the specified values in the nondissipative resistance function as the dissipative error dictates, and recalculate the error. In this way, by successive trials, we can include the effect of dissipation in the design, at the cost of additional computation. For the particular example given here, the realization is inherently dissipative, and the slope of the resistance function desired is not large enough for the impedance to have enough associated reactance (strictly slope of react-ance; cf. § 8.05) to appreciably affect the non-dissipative design.

Additional possibilities exist in resistance functions whose numerators are not constant, and of course in the use of larger n. We shall not consider these, for the illustration above is sufficient. In general, the possibilities of this method of approximation are enormous, far beyond simple description; but they usually become evident in any particular example as the approximator proceeds.

13.04 Least-mean-square-error approximation

In direct contrast to trial-and-error methods is the "method of least squares." Instead of a succession of trials, it uses a straightforward, precisely defined procedure that leads, in theory, directly to the approx-imating function. From this point of view it appears ideal; unfortu-nately its application to network approximation problems usually presents certain difficulties that preclude its wide use.

The least-mean-square-error method of approximation makes use of the single-number error criterion mentioned in § 13.02: the average (over the approximation band) of the square of the error. We might use, to obtain such a single-number criterion, the integral of any power of $|\Delta|$; but only the even powers are representable by mathematically tractable functions, and of these the square is the simplest. Higher powers intro-duce a weighting effect that tends to reduce the larger errors at the expense of the smaller, which may sometimes be useful—but we shall discuss only the use of the square.

The basic principle of this method is to minimize this single number that represents the error. All parameters in the approximating function are varied through all possible values and the particular set of values that minimizes the mean-square error is taken as the solution. In it we accordingly have both a precise technique (method) of approximation and a precise *sense* (mode), the least-mean-square-error sense, in which the approximation is made. The theory is elegant and has many extremely important applications, though the network-synthesis applications usually lead to computational difficulties.

If we write

$F(\omega)$ = function to be approximated (the desired behavior of R, X, $|Z|$, or the like),

and

$$G(\omega, a_0, a_1, a_2, \cdots, b_0, b_1, b_2, \cdots) \tag{13.04–1}$$

= approximating (network) function, in which the a's and b's represent the parameters to be determined,

then the error is $\Delta(\omega) = (G - F)$ and the mean-square error is

$$E = \frac{1}{\omega_2 - \omega_1} \int_{\omega_1}^{\omega_2} \Delta^2 \, d\omega, \tag{13.04–2}$$

in which ω_1 is the lower limit and ω_2 the upper limit of the approximation band. Now E is to be minimized by selecting that set of values for the a's and b's that reduces (13.04–2) (which is of course positive) to the minimum possible value. If the parameters have these values it necessarily follows that

$$\frac{\partial E}{\partial a_0} = 0, \qquad \frac{\partial E}{\partial b_0} = 0,$$

$$\frac{\partial E}{\partial a_1} = 0, \qquad \frac{\partial E}{\partial b_1} = 0, \tag{13.04–3}$$

$$\cdot \quad \cdot \quad \cdot \quad \cdot \quad \cdot \quad \cdot \quad \cdot$$

From the simultaneous equations in (13.04–3), of which there is one for each unknown parameter, we can presumably obtain the solution, the set of parameter values desired. (We shall not discuss the question whether this solution represents a minimum or a maximum of E; usually E is quite clearly minimized.) Somewhat more specifically, these equations take the form, obtained by application of (13.04–3) to (13.04–2),

$$\int_{\omega_1}^{\omega_2} (G - F)G' \, d\omega = 0, \tag{13.04–4}$$

which represents the whole set of equations, the prime being taken to represent a partial differentiation with respect to each parameter in turn. If the parameters enter only linearly into G, then (13.04–4) yields a set of linear simultaneous equations for the parameters, not difficult to solve; the theory of expansion in orthogonal functions presents a particularly simple example, in which the solution may be written immediately, for each equation contains only one parameter (Problem 13-20). But in general the parameters enter in more complicated fashion and the equations symbolized in (13.04–4) are impossible or at least extremely difficult to solve. Nor would there be any guarantee of realizability of the solution if it could be found. (Laborious approximate methods may sometimes be used, but for our purposes it would be more appropriate to apply them to the determination of the parameters directly in terms of error, as in § 13.03.) It is for this reason that the least-mean-square-error method is not often used in the solution of network-synthesis approximation problems.

To illustrate this point, let us attempt the solution of the illustrative problem posed in § 13.03 by this method. Specifically, we again take $F = 1/\sqrt{\omega}$, $1 < \omega < 4$ as the approximation band, and for the approximating (resistance) function

$$G(\omega) = R(\omega) = \frac{1}{b_0 + b_2\omega^2 + b_4\omega^4 + b_6\omega^6}. \qquad (13.04\text{–}5)$$

The equations for least-mean-square-error determination of the b parameters, from (13.04–4), are here

$$\int_1^4 \left(\frac{1}{b_0 + b_2\omega^2 + b_4\omega^4 + b_6\omega^6} - \frac{1}{\sqrt{\omega}}\right)\frac{\omega^m \, d\omega}{(b_0 + b_2\omega^2 + b_4\omega^4 + b_6\omega^6)^2} = 0,$$

$$m = 0, 2, 4, 6. \qquad (13.04\text{–}6)$$

In (13.04–6) we have a set of four simultaneous equations in the four unknown b's. Because of the nonlinear manner in which the b's enter, these equations are impossible of straightforward solution: they illustrate the reason that the least-mean-square-error method is generally of no great help to us.

At the same time they form a set of which we can obtain a useful approximate solution, because the b's enter only in the denominator of G, and there linearly. We rewrite (13.04–6) as

$$\int_1^4 \frac{\omega^{m-\frac{1}{2}}[\sqrt{\omega} - (b_0 + b_2\omega^2 + b_4\omega^4 + b_6\omega^6)]}{(b_0 + b_2\omega^2 + b_4\omega^4 + b_6\omega^6)^3} \, d\omega = 0, \qquad m = 0, 2, 4, 6$$

$$(13.04\text{–}7)$$

and observe that the integrand will be changed by only a small amount if we substitute $\sqrt{\omega}$ for $(b_0 + b_2\omega^2 + b_4\omega^4 + b_6\omega^6)$ in the *denominator*. We then have

$$\int_1^4 \omega^{m-2}[\sqrt{\omega} - (b_0 + b_2\omega^2 + b_4\omega^4 + b_6\omega^6)] \, d\omega = 0, \qquad m = 0, 2, 4, 6$$

$$(13.04\text{–}8)$$

as the set of four equations determining the four b's. They are now linear, and easily solved. The results are

$$b_0 = 0.842440,$$
$$b_2 = 0.195186,$$
$$b_4 = -0.014799,$$
$$b_6 = 0.000456,$$

(13.04–9)

which are not greatly different from those in (13.03–13) or (13.03–15). The corresponding resistance curve is substantially that of Fig. 13.03–B, and therefore realizable; the error is plotted in detail in Fig. 13.04–A,

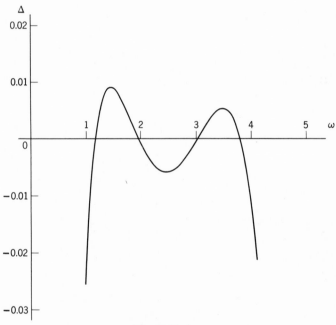

Fig. 13.04–A

which is to be compared with Fig. 13.03–C. Notice that the only appreciable change caused by adoption of the least-mean-square-error criterion is a general reduction of the size of the error in the interior of the band (where it is "spread out" and correspondingly influences the mean-square error) at the expense of larger errors confined to small regions at the band ends.

In the particular example discussed above, the least-mean-square-error technique was readily applicable only because of the special form of the resistance function: it had no parameters in its numerator. If the numerator contains parameters to be determined, the approximation made above is no longer valid and the simultaneous equations become too involved to warrant discussion. And so it is in general in network-synthesis approximation problems: only special ones are amenable to least-mean-square-error treatment.

13.05 Taylor approximation

Another, very useful, method of approximation is one that still makes use of a single-number error criterion, but focuses attention on *a single point* in the approximation band, on one frequency at and near which the approximation is to be excellent, perhaps at the expense of the quality of approximation elsewhere. The sort of approximation achieved is illustrated in Fig. 13.02–A(*b*). In contrast to the method of § 13.04, this method concentrates on one frequency, and there makes the error, and as many of its derivatives as possible, equal zero. An error that is zero at this frequency, and increases in magnitude very slowly (and smoothly) in the immediate vicinity, is the result. Generally the price paid for this desirable behavior is a much larger error towards the ends of the band of approximation, away from the focusing point. The technique used here again presents a straightforward, precisely defined procedure that leads in theory directly to the approximating function. For rational approximating functions the calculations involved may become lengthy, but they remain direct. There is no guarantee of realizability of the result, but at least the approximating function is defined and obtainable.

The basic principle of this method is so to determine the parameters of the approximating function that at the center of interest, ω_0, the error and as many of its derivatives as possible are zero. Formally, the equations that determine the parameters are

$$\Delta(\omega_0) = 0,$$
$$\Delta'(\omega_0) = 0,$$
$$\Delta''(\omega_0) = 0, \qquad\qquad (13.05\text{–}1)$$
$$\cdot \quad \cdot \quad \cdot \quad \cdot \quad \cdot$$
$$\Delta^{(N)}(\omega_0) = 0.$$

The single number that characterizes the approximation is N, the order of the highest derivative that is made to vanish at ω_0. From another point of view, this procedure forces an agreement between the first $(N + 1)$ terms of (*a*) the Taylor series about ω_0 for the approximating function, and (*b*) the series for the function to be approximated; from this comes the name given this type of approximation. That is, the error is made to be

$$\Delta(\omega) = \Delta^{(N+1)}(\omega_0) \frac{(\omega - \omega_0)^{N+1}}{(N+1)!} + \Delta^{(N+2)}(\omega_0) \frac{(\omega - \omega_0)^{N+2}}{(N+2)!} + \cdots$$

$$(13.05\text{--}2)$$

in the vicinity of ω_0. It may also be called *maximal* approximation, since the approximation is in maximal agreement with the function approximated at the frequency ω_0. When it is important that the error be kept small in a narrow band of frequencies, but larger errors are tolerable as we depart from this critical band, this method of approximation is useful. The actual determination of parameters can be purely mathematical (algebraic), as discussed below; it can also often be conveniently carried out by means of an analogy with certain physical problems depending on Laplace's equation, a method to be discussed later (Chapter 14). This type of approximation is related, as a limiting case, to the uniform type of approximation illustrated in Fig. 13.02–A(c), and to approximations based on matching the desired function at specified points (frequencies): when the width of the approximation band approaches zero, the Taylor type of approximation results (§ 14.15).

To determine the parameters in the approximating function we have the equations (13.05–1) to solve. Although these may become complicated in general, when the approximating function is rational (the case of interest to us) their solution reduces to that of a set of simultaneous linear algebraic equations. In this case of rational approximation functions the process is also called *Padé* approximation after the author of its first extensive investigation (PA 3); it is related to continued-fraction expansion and has been mathematically investigated in some detail (BE 1, FR 5, PE 1, WA 2). Various alternative devices are available that are useful in certain cases, but we shall consider only the algebraic, simultaneous-equation method of determining the parameters. This we shall first illustrate by means of an example, and then discuss in more general terms.

Consider again the illustrative problem first posed in § 13.03, and treated again in § 13.04, the design of a resistance function that approximates the reciprocal of the square root of frequency in the band $1 < \omega < 4$. For definiteness we again take

$$R(\omega) = \frac{1}{b_0 + b_2\omega^2 + b_4\omega^4 + b_6\omega^6} \qquad (13.05\text{--}3)$$

and use this to approximate the function $F = 1/\sqrt{\omega}$ in the Taylor sense. Our first problem is the choice of ω_0. We might well take ω_0 as the arithmetic mean of the approximation band limits, but it frequently happens that the geometric mean is an equally good choice. Here we arbitrarily set $\omega_0 = 2$ and shall later consider other possibilities. It is convenient to normalize the frequency scale once more, to simplify the arithmetic, by taking $\omega' = \omega/\omega_0 = \omega/2$ as a new variable. Since we are concerned only with the immediate vicinity of $\omega' = 1$, it is even more convenient to work in terms of $x = \omega' - 1$, the departure from the point of primary interest. Then we have

$$x = \omega' - 1 = \frac{\omega}{\omega_0} - 1 = \frac{\omega}{2} - 1$$

and

$$\omega = \omega_0(1 + x) = 2(1 + x).$$

(13.05–4)

The function to be approximated is then

$$F(\omega) = \frac{1}{\sqrt{\omega}} = \frac{1}{\sqrt{2(1 + x)}} = \frac{1}{\sqrt{2}} \times \frac{1}{\sqrt{1 + x}} = G(x)$$

(13.05–5)

and the approximating function is

$$R(\omega) = \frac{1}{b_0 + b_2\omega_0^2(1 + x)^2 + b_4\omega_0^4(1 + x)^4 + b_6\omega_0^6(1 + x)^6}.$$

(13.05–6)

In terms of the variable x the approximation process is still to match terms in the Taylor series for R to corresponding terms in that for F, but the expansions are made about the point $x = 0$. Our data are

$$G(0) = \frac{1}{\sqrt{2}} (1 + x)^{-1/2} \bigg]_{x=0} = \frac{1}{\sqrt{2}},$$

$$G'(0) = \frac{1}{\sqrt{2}} \left(-\frac{1}{2}\right) (1 + x)^{-3/2} \bigg]_{x=0} = -\frac{1}{\sqrt{2}} \times \frac{1}{2},$$

$$G''(0) = \frac{1}{\sqrt{2}} \left(\frac{3}{4}\right) (1 + x)^{-5/2} \bigg]_{x=0} = \frac{1}{\sqrt{2}} \times \frac{3}{4},$$

(13.05–7)

$$G'''(0) = \frac{1}{\sqrt{2}} \left(-\frac{15}{8}\right) (1 + x)^{-7/2} \bigg]_{x=0} = -\frac{1}{\sqrt{2}} \times \frac{15}{8}.$$

That is, we write

$$F(\omega) = G(x) = \frac{1}{\sqrt{2}} (1 - \tfrac{1}{2}x + \tfrac{3}{8}x^2 - \tfrac{5}{16}x^3 + \cdots), \quad (13.05–8)$$

which could of course have been obtained immediately from a table of series expansions or by using the binomial theorem. We write only the four terms shown because we have only four parameters in $R(\omega)$; hence only these terms in the series can be matched.

We now have to obtain the values of R and its derivatives at ω_0, in terms of the unknown parameters; these expressions we shall equate to the numbers in (13.05–7). Straightforward calculation of R and its derivatives leads immediately to very cumbersome expressions in which the parameters do not enter linearly. Fortunately a simple device will avoid this difficulty. We have

$$R = \frac{1}{b_0 + b_2\omega_0^2(1 + x)^2 + b_4\omega_0^4(1 + x)^4 + b_6\omega_0^6(1 + x)^6}$$

$$= \frac{1}{\sqrt{2}}(1 - \tfrac{1}{2}x + \tfrac{3}{8}x^2 - \tfrac{5}{16}x^3 + \cdots) + \Delta, \tag{13.05–9}$$

in which $\Delta(\omega)$ represents the error. The power series for Δ about the point $x = 0$ begins with a term in x^4 if the parameters in R are properly determined; i.e., in

$$\Delta = \varepsilon_0 + \varepsilon_1 x + \varepsilon_2 x^2 + \varepsilon_3 x^3 + \varepsilon_4 x^4 + \cdots \tag{13.05–10}$$

we wish to make ε_0, ε_1, ε_2, and ε_3 vanish. We can obtain simultaneous equations in the unknown parameters, the b's, that lead to values that will accomplish this simply by multiplying through by the denominator of R, collecting terms in like powers of x (which must be the same on the two sides), and then setting ε_0, ε_1, ε_2, and ε_3 equal to zero.

It is convenient first to simplify the algebra by letting

$$c_n = \frac{\omega_0^n b_n}{\sqrt{\omega_0}}, \qquad n = 0, 2, 4, 6. \tag{13.05–11}$$

We have also to make use of the binomial theorem (or the Pascal triangle or just ordinary multiplication) to expand the powers of ω, i.e., to obtain

$$\omega = 1 + x,$$
$$\omega^2 = (1 + x)^2 = 1 + 2x + x^2,$$
$$\omega^3 = (1 + x)^3 = 1 + 3x + 3x^2 + x^3,$$
$$\omega^4 = (1 + x)^4 = 1 + 4x + 6x^2 + 4x^3 + x^4, \tag{13.05–12}$$
$$\omega^5 = (1 + x)^5 = 1 + 5x + 10x^2 + 10x^3 + 5x^4 + x^5,$$
$$\omega^6 = (1 + x)^6 = 1 + 6x + 15x^2 + 20x^3 + 15x^4 + 6x^5 + x^6.$$

Then after sorting out the various powers of x in the denominator of R, (13.05–9) becomes

$$\frac{1}{\begin{aligned}[(c_0 + c_2 + c_4 + c_6) + (2c_2 + 4c_4 + 6c_6)x + (c_2 + 6c_4 + 15c_6)x^2 \\ + (4c_4 + 20c_6)x^3 + (c_4 + 15c_6)x^4 + 6c_6x^5 + c_6x^6]\end{aligned}}$$
$$= (1 - \tfrac{1}{2}x + \tfrac{3}{8}x^2 - \tfrac{5}{16}x^3 + \cdots) + (\varepsilon_0 + \varepsilon_1 x + \varepsilon_2 x^2 + \varepsilon_3 x^3 + \cdots)$$

$$(13.05\text{-}13)$$

On cross multiplication (an operation we assume valid if x is small), we obtain

$$\begin{aligned}
1 = {}& (1 + \varepsilon_0)(c_0 + c_2 + c_4 + c_6) \\
& + [(1 + \varepsilon_0)(2c_2 + 4c_4 + 6c_6) + (-\tfrac{1}{2} + \varepsilon_1)(c_0 + c_2 + c_4 + c_6)]x \\
& + [(1 + \varepsilon_0)(c_2 + 6c_4 + 15c_6) + (-\tfrac{1}{2} + \varepsilon_1)(2c_2 + 4c_4 + 6c_6) \\
& \quad + (\tfrac{3}{8} + \varepsilon_2)(c_0 + c_2 + c_4 + c_6)]x^2 \\
& + [(1 + \varepsilon_0)(4c_4 + 20c_6) + (-\tfrac{1}{2} + \varepsilon_1)(c_2 + 6c_4 + 15c_6) \\
& \quad + (\tfrac{3}{8} + \varepsilon_2)(2c_2 + 4c_4 + 6c_6) + (-\tfrac{5}{16} + \varepsilon_3)(c_0 + c_2 + c_4 + c_6)]x^3 \\
& + \cdots.
\end{aligned}$$

$$(13.05\text{-}14)$$

If this is to hold for x at and near zero, then the coefficients of like powers of x on the left and right sides must be equal. We can evidently determine the parameters now so that four of the ε's are zero—and of course it is ε_0, ε_1, ε_2, and ε_3 that we cause to vanish. The first four powers of x give us our equations; with these ε's set equal to zero, these equations are, in detached-coefficient form,

c_0	c_2	c_4	c_6	
1	1	1	1	$= 1,$
$-\tfrac{1}{2}$	$\tfrac{3}{2}$	$\tfrac{7}{2}$	$\tfrac{11}{2}$	$= 0,$
$\tfrac{3}{8}$	$\tfrac{3}{8}$	$\tfrac{35}{8}$	$\tfrac{99}{8}$	$= 0,$
$-\tfrac{5}{16}$	$-\tfrac{1}{16}$	$\tfrac{35}{16}$	$\tfrac{231}{16}$	$= 0.$

$$(13.05\text{-}15)$$

Their simultaneous solution, obtained by the usual methods (cf. Appendix A), is

$$
\begin{aligned}
c_0 &= 0.601563, & b_0 &= 0.850738, \\
c_2 &= 0.601563, & b_2 &= 0.212684, \\
c_4 &= -0.257813, &\text{or}\quad b_4 &= -0.022788, \\
c_6 &= 0.054688, & b_6 &= 0.001208,
\end{aligned}
$$

$$(13.05\text{-}16)$$

in which (13.05–11) has been used to obtain the b's. These are the numerical values to be used in (13.05–3) for the desired resistance function. They should be checked by careful calculation of $R(\omega_0)$, $R'(\omega_0)$, $R''(\omega_0)$, $R'''(\omega_0)$ and comparison of the results with $F(\omega_0)$, $F'(\omega_0)$, $F''(\omega_0)$, $F'''(\omega_0)$. When the error, $\Delta = R - F$, is computed, we obtain the curve of Fig. 13.05–A. It exhibits exactly the behavior expected: extremely small

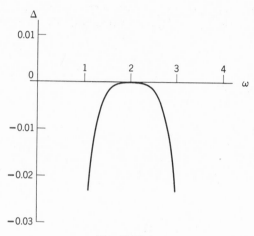

Fig. 13.05–A

error at and near $\omega = 2$, smoothly increasing to large values as we move away from the focus point. Figure 13.05–B, which shows both R and F, makes the character of the approximation even clearer: osculation at ω_0 and steady drawing apart as frequency departs from ω_0 in both directions. Evidently the choice $\omega_0 = 2.5$ would have been better in this example; one learns by experience. It is here a simple matter however to adjust the b's for any choice of ω_0: (13.05–11) gives them, and the error curve can in this case be shifted and expanded in a simple manner to suit any choice of ω_0. Since $R(\omega)$ does not go negative at any frequency, the function is realizable.

This example illustrates the essential principles of Taylor approximation. Because the function $1/\sqrt{\omega}$ falls off rather slowly, the rational-function approximation does not cling to it over a wide band. But this is exactly the behavior we find if we determine the coefficients by matching at specified points, or by the method of least squares: it is intrinsic in the use of a *rational* approximating function, to which we are bound. The Taylor approximation concentrates the approximation at a point, as of course it must; the others distribute the error over the approximation band but lack the fine quality of approximation at any one point. For many applications we want the largest possible width of approximation band attainable within the requirement that the magnitude of the error not exceed a prescribed limit. But for some applications it may be more important to have the high quality of approximation over a narrow band that Taylor or maximal approximation gives. The width of the band of approximation can be increased if more terms are placed in the numerator of the approximating function, or if a function of higher order is used.

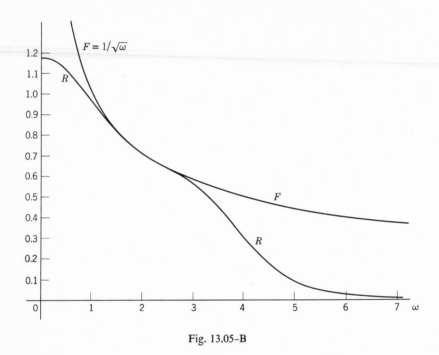

Fig. 13.05–B

When the approximating function is *even* in frequency (as for resistance, conductance, or square of magnitude of immittance), and the approximation is to be maximal at the frequency ω_0, the general process is that summarized below. Here $R(\omega)$ is the approximating (rational, even) function and $F(\omega)$ is the function to be approximated; the order of R, and the degrees of its numerator and denominator (i.e., its behavior at infinity), are determined by considerations of economy and form of network desired. Generally, once the order has been decided upon, we might put down a complete denominator and a complete numerator of corresponding degree. It may be advantageous to specify the locations of some of the zeros, however, as in the example above where they were all placed at infinity to insure a simple form of network. Then too, specifying that the approximating function be zero at certain points removed from the focus point may be helpful in improving the general trend of the error over a large band, though it will deteriorate the approximation at the focus itself. For example, if the function to be approximated vanishes at the origin, and the approximation is to be maximal at $\omega_0 = 1$, it may be desirable to specify that the numerator have a zero of a certain order at the origin; this fixes certain coefficients and therefore reduces the number of derivatives that can be matched at ω_0. Yet the result may be good, in that no very large error appears between the origin and ω_0. These are modifications of the Taylor approximation, however, and truly maximal approximation is obtained only when all terms are considered present in numerator and denominator, and all coefficients are used to match derivatives at ω_0, without other constraint. This general procedure we shall now describe; if any preliminary constraints are applied, the procedure is essentially the same (cf. § 13.10).

We first convert $R(\omega)$ to the corresponding function of x, the fractional departure from ω_0, using (13.05–4). Thus

$$
\begin{aligned}
R(\omega) &= \frac{a_0 + a_2\omega^2 + a_4\omega^4 + \cdots}{b_0 + b_2\omega^2 + b_4\omega^4 + \cdots} \\[2mm]
&= \frac{a_0 + a_2\omega_0^2(1 + x)^2 + a_4\omega_0^4(1 + x)^4 + \cdots}{b_0 + b_2\omega_0^2(1 + x)^2 + b_4\omega_0^4(1 + x)^4 + \cdots} \quad (13.05\text{–}17) \\[2mm]
&= \frac{c_0 + c_1x + c_2x^2 + c_3x^3 + c_4x^4 + \cdots}{d_0 + d_1x + d_2x^2 + d_3x^3 + d_4x^4 + \cdots}
\end{aligned}
$$

in which the c's and d's are the linear combinations of the a's and b's respectively that result from collecting terms in like powers of x. With the notation

$$a_m' = a_m\omega_0^m$$

and

$$b_m' = b_m\omega_0^m \qquad (13.05\text{–}18)$$

these are

$$
\begin{aligned}
c_0 &= a_0' + a_2' + a_4' + a_6' + \cdots, \\
c_1 &= \qquad 2a_2' + 4a_4' + 6a_6' + \cdots, \\
c_2 &= \qquad a_2' + 6a_4' + 15a_6' + \cdots, \\
c_3 &= \qquad\qquad 4a_4' + 20a_6' + \cdots, \\
c_4 &= \qquad\qquad a_4' + 15a_6' + \cdots, \\
&\quad\cdots\cdots\cdots\cdots\cdots\cdots
\end{aligned}
\qquad (13.05\text{–}19)
$$

The expressions for the d's are exactly those of (13.05–19) with the c's replaced by the d's and the a's by the b's. Note that the coefficients in the sth column are simply those in the expansion of $(1 + x)^{2(s-1)}$, so that (13.05–19) is easily written out completely for any particular case.

We now write the function to be approximated as

$$F(\omega) = F(\omega_0) + F'(\omega_0)(\omega - \omega_0) + F''(\omega_0)\frac{(\omega - \omega_0)^2}{2!} + \cdots$$

$$= F(\omega_0) + \omega_0 F'(\omega_0)x + \omega_0^2 \frac{F''(\omega_0)}{2!}x^2 + \cdots \qquad (13.05–20)$$

$$= f_0 + f_1 x + f_2 x^2 + f_3 x^3 + f_4 x^4 + \cdots$$

in which

$$f_n = \omega_0^n \frac{F^{(n)}(\omega_0)}{n!}. \qquad (13.05–21)$$

The function F must of course be regular at ω_0. Now we equate (13.05–17) and (13.05–20), within an error $\Delta(\omega)$, and require that the series for Δ begin with as high a power of x as possible. This we accomplish by multiplying through by the denominator of R, collecting terms in like powers of x, and of these powers of x setting as many coefficients equal to zero as we can.

We assume for the present that $F(\omega_0) \neq 0$ and set $c_0 = 1$, which involves no loss of generality. Then the resulting simultaneous equations in terms of the c's and d's are

c_1	c_2	c_3	$c_4 \cdots$	d_0	d_1	d_2	d_3	$d_4 \cdots$	
0	0	0	$0 \cdots$	f_0	0	0	0	$0 \cdots$	$= 1$
-1	0	0	$0 \cdots$	f_1	f_0	0	0	$0 \cdots$	$= 0$
0	-1	0	$0 \cdots$	f_2	f_1	f_0	0	$0 \cdots$	$= 0$
0	0	-1	$0 \cdots$	f_3	f_2	f_1	f_0	$0 \cdots$	$= 0$

$$(13.05–22)$$

in which the rule of formation is evident. Since the c's and d's must be related to the a's and b's (which are what we really want) by (13.05–19), we introduce these relations and finally obtain the simultaneous equations

a_0'	a_2'	a_4'	$a_6' \cdots$	b_0'	b_2'	b_4'	b_6'	$\cdots$	
1	1	1	$1 \cdots$	0	0	0	0	$\cdots$	$= 1$
0	0	0	$0 \cdots$	f_0	f_0	f_0	f_0	$\cdots$	$= 1$
0	-2	-4	$-6 \cdots$	f_1	$(f_1 + 2f_0)$	$(f_1 + 4f_0)$	$(f_1 + 6f_0)$	$\cdots$	$= 0$
0	-1	-6	$-15 \cdots$	f_2	$(f_2 + 2f_1 + f_0)$	$(f_2 + 4f_1 + 6f_0)$	$(f_2 + 6f_1 + 15f_0) \cdots$		$= 0$

$$(13.05–23)$$

The number of equations is of course equal to the total number of (unknown) a's and b's, and those not present in a particular problem are to be taken as zero in (13.05–23). Here the f's are known, so that the a's and b's can be found by solution of these simultaneous equations.

If $F(\omega_0) = 0$, then we must set $c_0 = 0$. For network problems the zero must be at least double, so we also have $F'(\omega_0) = 0$ and set $c_1 = 0$. Then we set $c_2 = 1$ (if the zero is only double) and obtain a similar set of equations. Alternatively, we may divide both sides by the leading power of x, which procedure then presents us with exactly the same problem as that above.

If the degrees of the numerator and the denominator of the approximating function are markedly different, the work can sometimes be shortened by dealing with the *reciprocal* functions. That is, we use $1/R$ to approximate $1/F$, a procedure which, for approximation in the Taylor sense, leads to exactly the same result as does approximation of F with R. If the numerator of R is but a constant (say unity), and if the series for $1/F$ is easily obtained, for example, then the d's can be obtained by merely equating the denominator of R to the series for $1/F$, term by term in powers of x—a procedure which replaces the simultaneous equations (13.05–22). Then the b's are obtained in the usual fashion by substituting for the d's through (13.05–19). The illustrative problem above might well have been solved in this manner.

Although it may be possible to develop short cuts, the procedure given above is straightforward and can readily be applied to the maximal approximation at ω_0, with an even function of frequency, of any function $F(\omega)$ that is regular at the point ω_0. The result must be independently tested for realizability, a property not in any way related to this approximation process.

If the focus point ω_0 is the origin, then transformation to the variable x is unnecessary. The approximation is expressed by

$$R = \frac{a_0 + a_2\omega^2 + a_4\omega^4 + \cdots}{b_0 + b_2\omega^2 + b_4\omega^4 + \cdots} = f_0 + f_2\omega^2 + f_4\omega^4 + \cdots + \Delta(\omega)$$

$$(13.05\text{–}24)$$

in which

$$f_n = \frac{F^{(n)}(\omega_0)}{n!}.$$

$$(13.05\text{–}25)$$

The function $F(\omega)$ that is to be approximated must in this case be an even function, else the approximation cannot proceed beyond the first odd power of ω that has a nonzero coefficient. If $F(0) = f_0 \neq 0$, then we set $a_0 = 1$ and obtain the simultaneous equations (13.05–26). If $F(0) = 0$, we have $a_0 = 0$ and may divide through by the leading power of ω, which reduces the problem to exactly the same sort of thing.

a_2	a_4	a_6	$a_8 \cdots b_0$	b_2	b_4	$b_6 \cdots$	
0	0	0	$0 \cdots f_0$	0	0	$0 \cdots = 1,$	
-1	0	0	$0 \cdots f_2$	f_0	0	$0 \cdots = 0,$	
0	-1	0	$0 \cdots f_4$	f_2	f_0	$0 \cdots = 0,$	(13.05–26)
0	0	-1	$0 \cdots f_6$	f_4	f_2	$f_0 \cdots = 0,$	
$\cdots$							

which are in essence the same as those of (13.05–22). Again the work may sometimes be shortened by using the reciprocal functions.

To illustrate this point, as well as approximation at the origin, consider the approximation of $F = e^{-\omega^2}$ with a resistance function whose numerator is a constant (say unity), a form chosen to insure a simple L-C ladder realization. We have

$$R = \frac{1}{b_0 + b_2\omega^2 + b_4\omega^4 + \cdots + b_{2n}\omega^{2n}} = e^{-\omega^2} + \Delta(\omega). \quad (13.05–27)$$

In terms of reciprocals, we have

$$\frac{1}{R} = b_0 + b_2\omega^2 + b_4\omega^4 + \cdots + b_{2n}\omega^{2n} = e^{\omega^2} + \bar{\Delta}(\omega) \quad (13.05–28)$$

in which $\bar{\Delta}$ is the error in the approximation of the reciprocal, still small near the origin, and starting with the same power of ω as Δ does. Evidently we can write the values of the b's immediately, for they are the coefficients of powers of ω in the first $(n + 1)$ nonzero terms of the power series for e^{ω^2} about the origin. That is

$$b_{2m} = \frac{1}{m!} \quad (13.05–29)$$

and we obtain

$$R(\omega) = \frac{1}{1 + \omega^2 + \omega^4/2! + \omega^6/3! + \cdots + \omega^{2n}/n!} \quad (13.05–30)$$

as the approximating function. The quality of approximation is shown in Fig. 13.05–C which exhibits the error, and by Fig. 13.05–D which shows the function $e^{-\omega^2}$ and the approximating functions R_n, for $n = 1, 2,$ and 3. It here requires only a low-order approximating function to obtain an extremely good match at all frequencies, in marked contrast to the previous example (cf. Fig. 13.05–B). The explanation is that the function

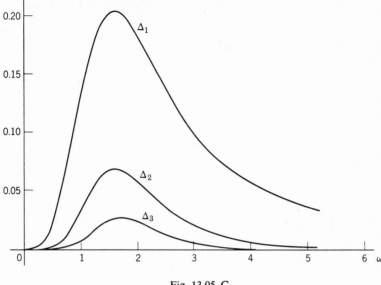

Fig. 13.05–C

$e^{-\omega^2}$ behaves more nearly as rational functions do (much more so than does the function $1/\sqrt{\omega}$), at least in that it falls off as rapidly. The error shown in Fig. 13.05–C is very small numerically at high frequencies for this reason, but in fractional, or percentage, terms it is actually extremely

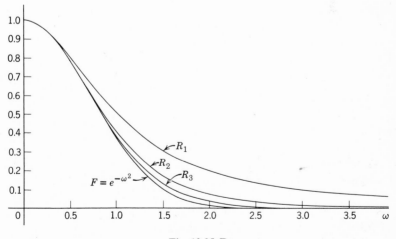

Fig. 13.05–D

large, since $e^{-\omega^2}$ falls off much *more* rapidly than a rational function does. Fortunately our interest, in network problems, is often limited to the numerical size of errors.

13.06 Taylor approximation, continued

When the approximating function is *odd* in frequency (as for reactance, susceptance, or angle of immittance), the principles involved in Taylor or maximal approximation are unchanged, but there are some differences in details. An odd rational function can be of either odd or even order (in contrast to the even order required of all even rational functions). If the order is odd, the function must have a zero at the origin and a pole at infinity, or a pole at the origin and a zero at infinity; if the order is even the function must have zeros at both the origin and infinity, or poles at both points. All of these zeros and poles (at the origin and infinity) must be of odd order. These restrictions arise from the requirement that the function be an odd function of frequency, and are easily demonstrated by considering the behavior required of odd rational functions at the origin and infinity, and the number of zeros and poles to be distributed in the finite plane and at infinity.

We have then to decide whether the approximating function should have a zero or a pole at the origin, a problem that does not generally arise in the case of even functions. In each problem we must generally try both possibilities to decide which is best. In other words, the approximating function must be the quotient of an even polynomial and an odd polynomial, and we have to decide which of the two is to be the numerator. We can avoid the necessity of two discussions, however, by simply observing that one situation is the reciprocal of the other in effect. Accordingly we write, for example,

$$X(\omega) = \frac{a_1\omega + a_3\omega^3 + a_5\omega^5 + \cdots}{b_0 + b_2\omega^2 + b_4\omega^4 + \cdots} \qquad (13.06\text{–}1)$$

as the approximating function (of order N) for the datum function $F(\omega)$, and in each problem consider the approximation both of F and of $1/F$ by $X(\omega)$. The function $X(\omega)$ has a zero at the origin; and it has a pole at infinity if N is odd, a zero at infinity if N is even. The zero at the origin may be of order $1, 3, 5, \cdots$ depending on the values found for the a's, some of which may turn out to be zero. (If b_0 should turn out to be zero, this would reduce the function to one of lower order, implying an unusual ability to approximate on the part of that lower order; a similar situation arises if the last a vanishes in the odd-order case.) Generally the order N is determined by economic considerations. We may write complete numerator and denominator as implied in (13.06–1), or (as in the even function case) we may specify the locations of some of the zeros (e.g., for the purpose of improving the general trend of the error over a large band); this specification changes the general procedure described below only by reducing the number of unknowns.

The general procedure is essentially as it is with even approximating functions. We convert $X(\omega)$ to the corresponding function of $x = (\omega - \omega_0)/\omega_0$,

$$
\begin{aligned}
X(\omega) &= \frac{a_1\omega_0(1 + x) + a_3\omega_0^3(1 + x)^3 + \cdots}{b_0 + b_2\omega_0^2(1 + x)^2 + b_4\omega_0^4(1 + x)^4 + \cdots} \\
&= \frac{c_0 + c_1x + c_2x^2 + c_3x^3 + \cdots}{d_0 + d_1x + d_2x^2 + d_3x^3 + \cdots}
\end{aligned}
\tag{13.06-2}
$$

in which the c's and d's are the appropriate linear combinations of the a's and b's respectively. With the notation of (13.05–18), these are now

$$
\begin{aligned}
c_0 &= a_1' + a_3' + a_5' + a_7' + \cdots, \\
c_1 &= a_1' + 3a_3' + 5a_5' + 7a_7' + \cdots, \\
c_2 &= 3a_3' + 10a_5' + 21a_7' + \cdots, \\
c_3 &= a_3' + 10a_5' + 35a_7' + \cdots, \\
c_4 &= 5a_5' + 35a_7' + \cdots, \\
&\quad\cdot \quad\cdot \quad\cdot \quad\cdot \quad\cdot \quad\cdot \quad\cdot \quad\cdot
\end{aligned}
\tag{13.06-3}
$$

and a set identical to (13.05–19) except for the exchange of d's for c's and b's for a's. The set (13.06–3) thus corresponds to that of (13.05–19). We again expand the function to be approximated about ω_0, as indicated in (13.05–20) and (13.05–21). By the same process as before we obtain (13.05–22) which becomes the following set of equations for the a's and b's in the case where $F(\omega_0) \neq 0$. (We have set $c_0 = 1$, since one of the coefficients is arbitrary.)

a_1'	a_3'	a_5'	$a_6' \cdots$	b_0'	b_2'	b_4'	b_6'	$\cdots$
1	1	1	$1 \cdots$	0	0	0	0	$\cdots = 1$
0	0	0	$0 \cdots$	f_0	f_0	f_0	f_0	$\cdots = 1$
-1	-3	-5	$-7 \cdots$	f_1	$(f_1 + 2f_0)$	$(f_1 + 4f_0)$	$(f_1 + 6f_0)$	$\cdots = 0$
0	-3	-10	$-21 \cdots$	f_2	$(f_2 + 2f_1 + f_0)$	$(f_2 + 4f_1 + 6f_0)$	$(f_2 + 6f_1 + 15f_0)$	$\cdots = 0$

$$\tag{13.06-4}$$

The number of equations in a particular problem is equal to the number of unknowns; superfluous a's and b's are to be taken as zero. Solution of (13.06–4) gives the coefficients of the approximating function, from which the error can be computed. If $F(\omega_0) = 0$, then we have c_0 (and possibly more c's) equal to zero; we can set the first nonzero c equal to unity and proceed to solve the equations—or, alternatively, first divide through by the leading power of x, which reduces the problem to one of the original kind. If $F(\omega)$ has a pole of the allowed kind at ω_0, then $d_0 = 0$, and we may use the Laurent expansion for $F(\omega)$, but otherwise proceed in the same fashion. In some cases, use of the reciprocals may again shorten the work. In any case one must also investigate the approximation of F with the reciprocal of (13.06–1), for completeness. If the focus point ω_0 is the origin, the work simplifies again, for transformation to the variable x is not necessary.

To illustrate the maximal approximation of an odd function, let $F(\omega) = \sin \omega$, and take $\omega_0 = 0$. Then we must use the form (13.06–1) for the approximating function (its reciprocal is inappropriate). In it we set $a_1 = 1$ (one coefficient is arbitrary) and then see immediately that we must have $b_0 = 1$. The simultaneous equations for the remaining coefficients are those indicated in (13.06–5).

a_3	a_5	a_7	a_9	b_2	b_4	b_6	b_8	
1	0	0	$0 \cdots$	-1	0	0	$0 \cdots$	$= -1/3!$
0	1	0	$0 \cdots$	$1/3!$	-1	0	$0 \cdots$	$= 1/5!$
0	0	1	$0 \cdots$	$-1/5!$	$1/3!$	-1	$0 \cdots$	$= -1/7!$
0	0	0	$1 \cdots$	$1/7!$	$-1/5!$	$1/3!$	$-1 \cdots$	$= 1/9!$

$$\cdots \quad \cdots \quad \cdots \quad \cdots \quad \cdots \quad \cdots \quad \cdots \quad \cdots \quad \cdots$$

$$(13.06\text{--}5)$$

Solution of these equations for various values of N, the order of $X(\omega)$, is straightforward, though accompanied as usual with arithmetical difficulties for large N. The first four results, all of which are realizable, are given below.

$$N = 1 \qquad X = \omega$$

$$N = 2 \qquad X = \frac{\omega}{1 + \frac{1}{6}\omega^2} = \frac{6\omega}{6 + \omega^2}$$

$$N = 3 \qquad X = \frac{\omega - \frac{7}{60}\omega^3}{1 + \frac{1}{20}\omega^2} = \frac{60\omega - 7\omega^3}{60 + 3\omega^2}$$

$$N = 4 \qquad X = \frac{\omega - \frac{31}{294}\omega^3}{1 + \frac{3}{49}\omega^2 + \frac{11}{5880}\omega^4}$$

$$= \frac{5880 - 620\omega^3}{5880 + 360\omega^2 + 11\omega^4}$$

$$(13.06\text{--}6)$$

Graphic evidence of the nature of the approximation and the improvement with increasing N is given in Fig. 13.06–A. The error is of course

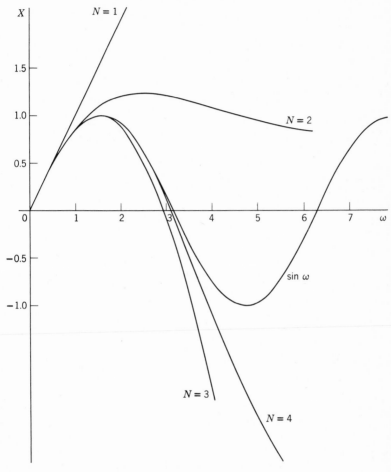

Fig. 13.06–A

very small at very low frequencies, the band of negligible error increasing with N. The function is such that a very large N is required for good approximation of even the first cycle of the sine function; but Taylor approximation, by its very nature, concentrates on excellent approximation at one point, in this case the origin. (For good approximation over a band, one might better specify the zeros of X to agree with those of the sine function, and possibly match at other points also—but then the approximation is made in a different sense.) An interesting idea (which we shall not develop here) is that the sine function may be considered a rational function of "infinite order," for as N increases without limit, presumably the sine function is better and better approximated. This idea we have encountered before (§ 3.27) and we shall meet it again.

The preceding discussion applies to the approximation of reactance and susceptance functions. If angle is to be approximated, the transcendental tangent function is involved, leading generally to complications in forming the series for the angle of the rational function. The work can often be simplified, however, by approximating the *tangent* of the desired angle with a rational function. This is equivalent, and if the series for this tangent is easily obtained, is no more difficult than approximation for reactance or resistance or square of magnitude (Problem 13-67).

We have discussed maximal approximation of both even and odd functions of frequency by rational functions, i.e., by functions potentially realizable as resistance (conductance), magnitude (squared), reactance (susceptance), and (tangent of) angle at the driving points of networks. All of these are real at real frequencies. It is also possible to approximate *complex* functions in maximal fashion, through exactly the same procedure, by rational functions potentially realizable as complete driving-point immittances. In this case we merely write a rational function of p for the approximating function and equate derivatives at the appropriate point to those of the function to be approximated. For example, if we wish to approximate

$$F(p) = 1 - e^{-p} \tag{13.06-7}$$

we may write

$$Z(p) = \frac{a_0 + a_1 p + a_2 p^2 + \cdots}{b_0 + b_1 p + b_2 p^2 + \cdots} \tag{13.06-8}$$

and proceed exactly as before, except that now we work with the complex variable p, in the vicinity of some point p_0.

This point must generally be the origin (or infinity), else difficulties arise in making the coefficients real. Hence if the frequency of primary interest is not zero (or infinity), it may be better to work in terms of resistance or reactance or the like, as previously outlined. Because real and imaginary parts, magnitude and angle, are closely related (Chapter 8), one might expect that it would be possible to work with, say, the real part alone, or with the complete (complex) function, and not get radically different answers. In a sense this is true, but if we are given a definite order of immittance function to work with, the two procedures will give somewhat different results. For example, concentration on the real part of some function $F(p)$ by the methods of § 13.05 leads to an even function of ω that is a maximal approximation to the real part; when the corresponding immittance function is obtained, we usually find that the approximations to the imaginary part of F and to $F(p)$ itself and to its magnitude and angle are not maximal, and that better results for any one of these could be obtained by concentration on that part alone. Similarly, such concentration on any one part usually leads to poorer results for the others.

On the other hand, if we follow the procedure above, that connected with (13.06–8), we find that maximal approximation in terms of p leads to functions that give the same degree of approximation also to the real and imaginary parts, and to the magnitude and angle, but that none of these in general is as good an approximation for that part as could be obtained by concentration on that part alone. Working "in the complex" (or simultaneous resistance and reactance approximation, to put it another way) spreads the available approximation between real and imaginary parts, so to speak, neither being approximated as well as it could be if given individual attention, but each attaining a degree of approximation that is an average of the maximal degree of approximation and the degree obtained if it is neglected and the other part given all the attention. In some cases the requirements laid down for the network may make such approximation "in the complex" desirable; in many cases it is more important, or essential, to approximate one part (e.g., the resistance) primarily.

13.07 The Padé table

From the discussion of the two preceding sections we see that any specific function that is to be approximated at a certain point generates a set of rational functions, each of which is a maximal approximation at that point, to the best of its ability. This set of functions may conveniently be laid out in tabular form. For example, if we wish to approximate $F(\omega)$ at ω_0 with an even function of frequency (i.e., for resistance, conductance, or square of magnitude), we use

$$H_{nm} = \frac{a_0 + a_2\omega^2 + a_4\omega^4 + \cdots + a_{2m}\omega^{2m}}{b_0 + b_2\omega^2 + b_4\omega^4 + \cdots + b_{2n}\omega^{2n}} \quad (13.07\text{–}1)$$

as the approximating function. And we can obtain a variety of solutions depending on the choice of m and n. These can be arranged in a table, as in Table 13.07–A, which we call the even-function *Padé table* (PA 3) for $F(\omega)$ at ω_0. Each H here represents a rational function, (13.07–1), that requires some labor to obtain. The entries in such a table will change as ω_0 is changed, of course, and will be entirely different for different functions F. This table is a convenient summary of Taylor (maximal) approximations for any given situation; in it there will be many entries that are not realizable in network form, as well as those that are of interest.

Table 13.07-A

If the approximating function is to be odd (as for reactance, susceptance, tangent of angle), then the entries in the table are

$$H_{nm} = \frac{a_1\omega + a_3\omega^3 + a_5\omega^5 + \cdots + a_{2m+1}\omega^{2m+1}}{b_0 + b_2\omega^2 + b_4\omega^4 + \cdots + b_{2n}\omega^{2n}} \qquad (13.07\text{--}2)$$

or

$$H_{nm} = \frac{a_0 + a_2\omega^2 + a_4\omega^4 + \cdots + a_{2m}\omega^{2m}}{b_1\omega + b_3\omega^3 + b_5\omega^5 + \cdots + b_{2n+1}\omega^{2n+1}}, \qquad (13.07\text{--}3)$$

depending on whether numerator or denominator is to be the odd polynomial. In this case the entries are double, or one may say there are really two odd-function Padé tables for $F(\omega)$, approximated at ω_0.

If the approximating function is not restricted to even or odd character, i.e., if the whole immittance is approximated, then we use

$$H_{nm} = \frac{a_0 + a_1 p + a_2 p^2 + \cdots + a_m p^m}{b_0 + b_1 p + b_2 p^2 + \cdots + b_n p^n} \qquad (13.07\text{--}4)$$

and build up the table for $F(p)$, approximated at p_0, with these entries. This last case is evidently general, and the two previous cases are very special, restricted by the requirement that the approximating function be odd or even.

A useful example is the Padé table for the *exponential function*. It is advantageous to construct this first in terms of an arbitrary variable x; for by giving x various forms (functions of frequency), several different

tables can in effect be extracted therefrom, as we shall see. We confine
ourselves to maximal approximation at the origin and write

$$H_{nm} = \frac{a_0 + a_1 x + a_2 x^2 + \cdots + a_m x^m}{b_0 + b_1 x + b_2 x^2 + \cdots + b_n x^n} = \frac{P_{nm}(x)}{Q_{nm}(x)}. \quad (13.07\text{-}5)$$

By the usual process, with $b_0 = 1$ and hence $a_0 = 1$, we obtain the
simultaneous equations

a_1	a_2	a_3	a_4		b_1	b_2	b_3	b_4		
1	0	0	$0 \cdots$		-1	0	0	$0 \cdots$	$= 1$	
0	1	0	$0 \cdots$		-1	-1	0	$0 \cdots$	$= {}^1\!/_{2!}$	
0	0	1	$0 \cdots$		$-{}^1\!/_{2!}$	-1	-1	$0 \cdots$	$= {}^1\!/_{3!}$	$(13.07\text{-}6)$
0	0	0	$1 \cdots$		$-{}^1\!/_{3!}$	$-{}^1\!/_{2!}$	-1	$-1 \cdots$	$= {}^1\!/_{4!}$	

in which those a's and b's not appropriate to a particular H are to be
taken as zero in finding H. The solution of these equations for large m
and n is not only laborious but arithmetically difficult (large numbers that
are approximately equal often have to be subtracted, with an attendant
loss of accuracy). But an ingenious device can be used to overcome this
difficulty (PA 3), with the following result (Prob. 13-39).

$$P_{nm}(x) = 1 + \frac{m}{m+n} \times \frac{x}{1!} + \frac{m(m-1)}{(m+n)(m+n-1)} \times \frac{x^2}{2!} + \cdots$$

$$+ \frac{m(m-1)(m-2)\cdots 1}{(m+n)(m+n-1)\cdots(n+1)} \times \frac{x^m}{m!}, \quad (13.07\text{-}7)$$

$$Q_{nm}(x) = P_{mn}(-x).$$

From these equations the entries in the Padé table for e^x, approximated
at the origin, are readily written down; for values of m and n up to 5,
the results are shown in Table 13.07–B.

By giving x various functional values we can obtain several useful Padé
tables from this one. For example, if we write $x = -\omega^2$, we obtain the
table for (maximal) approximation of $e^{-\omega^2}$ at the origin. The function
(13.05–30) evidently represents the first column of Table 13.07–B, and
other approximating functions for $e^{-\omega^2}$ can be read immediately from this
table. We can similarly equate x to any even power of ω, with either
sign, and obtain Padé tables for the corresponding exponential functions.
(In fact, x may be taken to be any rational function of ω^2 with real
coefficients and a sort of Padé table will result, but it may be incomplete

Table 13.07-B. The Padé Table for e^x, Approximated at the Origin

	$m=0$	$m=1$	$m=2$	$m=3$	$m=4$
$n=0$	$\dfrac{1}{1}$	$\dfrac{1+x}{1}$	$\dfrac{1+x+\frac{1}{2}x^2}{1}$	$\dfrac{1+x+\frac{1}{2}x^2+\frac{1}{6}x^3}{1}$	$\dfrac{1+x+\frac{1}{2}x^2+\frac{1}{6}x^3+\frac{1}{24}x^4}{1}$
$n=1$	$\dfrac{1}{1-x}$	$\dfrac{1+\frac{1}{2}x}{1-\frac{1}{2}x}$	$\dfrac{1+\frac{2}{3}x+\frac{1}{6}x^2}{1-\frac{1}{3}x}$	$\dfrac{1+\frac{3}{4}x+\frac{1}{4}x^2+\frac{1}{24}x^3}{1-\frac{1}{4}x}$	$\dfrac{1+\frac{4}{5}x+\frac{3}{10}x^2+\frac{1}{15}x^3+\frac{1}{120}x^4}{1-\frac{1}{5}x}$
$n=2$	$\dfrac{1}{1-x+\frac{x^2}{2!}}$	$\dfrac{1+\frac{1}{3}x}{1-\frac{2}{3}x+\frac{1}{6}x^2}$	$\dfrac{1+\frac{1}{2}x+\frac{1}{12}x^2}{1-\frac{1}{2}x+\frac{1}{12}x^2}$	$\dfrac{1+\frac{3}{5}x+\frac{3}{20}x^2+\frac{1}{60}x^3}{1-\frac{2}{5}x+\frac{1}{20}x^2}$	$\dfrac{1+\frac{2}{3}x+\frac{1}{5}x^2+\frac{1}{30}x^3+\frac{1}{360}x^4}{1-\frac{1}{3}x+\frac{1}{30}x^2}$
$n=3$	$\dfrac{1}{1-x+\frac{x^2}{2!}-\frac{x^3}{3!}}$	$\dfrac{1+\frac{1}{4}x}{1-\frac{3}{4}x+\frac{1}{4}x^2-\frac{1}{24}x^3}$	$\dfrac{1+\frac{2}{5}x+\frac{1}{20}x^2}{1-\frac{3}{5}x+\frac{3}{20}x^2-\frac{1}{60}x^3}$	$\dfrac{1+\frac{1}{2}x+\frac{1}{10}x^2+\frac{1}{120}x^3}{1-\frac{1}{2}x+\frac{1}{10}x^2-\frac{1}{120}x^3}$	$\dfrac{1+\frac{4}{7}x+\frac{1}{7}x^2+\frac{2}{105}x^3+\frac{1}{840}x^4}{1-\frac{3}{7}x+\frac{1}{14}x^2-\frac{1}{210}x^3}$
$n=4$	$\dfrac{1}{1-x+\frac{x^2}{2!}-\frac{x^3}{3!}+\frac{x^4}{4!}}$	$\dfrac{1+\frac{1}{5}x}{1-\frac{4}{5}x+\frac{3}{10}x^2-\frac{1}{15}x^3+\frac{1}{120}x^4}$	$\dfrac{1+\frac{1}{3}x+\frac{1}{30}x^2}{1-\frac{2}{3}x+\frac{1}{5}x^2-\frac{1}{30}x^3+\frac{1}{360}x^4}$	$\dfrac{1+\frac{3}{7}x+\frac{1}{14}x^2+\frac{1}{210}x^3}{1-\frac{4}{7}x+\frac{1}{7}x^2-\frac{2}{105}x^3+\frac{1}{840}x^4}$	$\dfrac{1+\frac{1}{2}x+\frac{3}{28}x^2+\frac{1}{84}x^3+\frac{1}{1680}x^4}{1-\frac{1}{2}x+\frac{3}{28}x^2-\frac{1}{84}x^3+\frac{1}{1680}x^4}$

and may contain spurious entries.) With that we exhaust the possibilities of the table for real functions of ω, i.e., for functions potentially suitable for resistance, conductance, and square-of-magnitude realization.

Another potential use of the table for e^x is to obtain functions of p itself, by substituting for x some rational function of p with real coefficients. (Again powers of p are the most useful functions to use.) The results are of little direct value for driving-point immittance functions, for they yield few p-r functions. Yet useful functions can be derived from them. If the function is even, one of the cases mentioned above results. If the function is odd, certain other interesting cases arise. For then, by virtue of (13.07–7), we have for the entries on the principal diagonal

$$H_{nn} = \frac{P_{nn}(x)}{Q_{nn}(x)} = \frac{P_{nn}(x)}{P_{nn}(-x)}. \tag{13.07–8}$$

Since x is an odd function of p, at real frequencies ($p = j\omega$) x is purely imaginary—hence numerator and denominator of H are then conjugate, and the magnitude of H is unity. Moreover, the angle of H is twice the angle of P_{nn}. And this angle, with proper choice of x as a function of p, is a maximal approximation to the odd powers of frequency. If we set $x = p$, i.e., make the table for e^p, then the polynomial $P_{nn}(p)$ is that polynomial whose real-frequency angle is maximally linear with frequency at the origin. In fact, with $x = (-1)^r p^{2r+1}$ we obtain in P_{nn} that polynomial whose real-frequency angle is in maximal agreement at the origin with ω^{2r+1}.

These agreements are easily demonstrated by considering the degree of approximation of e^x given by H_{nn}, in particular of the angle, and the number of terms a polynomial of degree n could be expected to match. By the discussion of § 8.14 the determination of a p-r rational function, the tangent of whose real-frequency angle is prescribed, requires first the determination of that polynomial whose angle has this prescribed tangent. For maximal approximation (i.e., at a point), approximation of tangent and of angle itself amount to the same thing, so we have immediately in the Padé table for e^x a good start toward a tabulation of those p-r functions whose real-frequency angles are in maximal agreement at the origin with the odd powers of ω. There is a scale factor of two, due to the fact that the angle of H_{nn} is twice that of P_{nn}, which can be removed by using the substitution $x = 2(-1)^r p^{2r+1}$ rather than the substitution given above—or it can be temporarily ignored and taken care of in the final frequency denormalization of the design. There is also the step of obtaining, from the polynomial P_{nn}, the p-r rational function whose angle is that desired, to be carried out by the methods of § 8.14.

The exponential function has served as a useful illustration of the construction and use of a Padé table. For arbitrary functions it is not as easy to obtain a general formula for the entries in the Padé table (nor is the table likely to be as widely useful as that for the exponential function), although for functions satisfying a certain differential equation there is another useful device (PE 1). In theory, of course, the simultaneous-equation approach will always lead to a solution and the table can be constructed, but the calculations may become difficult for large m and n.

With this we conclude our discussion of approximation (in the Taylor sense) of functions in general. There is a fairly important special (degenerate) case whose discussion we postpone to § 13.10; we turn now to the third type of approximation envisioned in Fig. 13.02–A.

13.08 Chebyshev approximation

We have discussed approximation by several different means: by trial and error (as by matching at specified points), which usually leads to an error curve of a generally oscillatory nature; by minimization of the mean-square error, which gives more or less the same sort of error function; and by Taylor approximation, which gives substantially zero error in the vicinity of the point of maximal approximation. To the engineer whose system prescribes tolerable limits of error that are constant over the approximation band (a common case) these approximations appear inefficient. It seems probable that an approximation of the form given in the third curve of Fig. 13.02–A exploits the allowed limits of error in the most efficient manner. For here all the maxima of the error (in magnitude) reach the limiting value, which presumably gives the greatest width of approximation band attainable for a given limit of error, or for a prescribed bandwidth gives the minimum peak error. This sort of approximation, that "distributes" the error evenly or uniformly through the approximation band, is another type, of considerable engineering importance, which we must discuss. It too has an extensive mathematical background.

This kind of approximation takes its name from the mathematician P. L. Chebyshev, who was led to consider the matter of approximation by an engineering problem in the construction of steam engines. In mathematical terms he phrased the problem thus:

> to determine the parameters of the approximating function so that the maximum value of the magnitude of the error is minimized.   (13.08–1)

He sought, in other words, so to fix the available parameters that the largest error (in magnitude, signs being ignored) that occurred in the approximating band was reduced to the smallest possible value. If we attack the approximation problem with this end in mind, using trial-and-error methods, we can reasonably expect to get a series of error curves like those of Fig. 13.08–A. In the first approximation (*a*), there is a salient

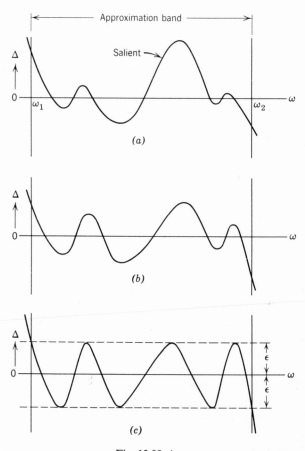

Fig. 13.08–A

"bump" of error which we endeavor to reduce by readjusting our parameters. In the next approximation (*b*), this hump is thus appreciably reduced in magnitude, but in consequence the other humps have become larger. Finally we reach in (*c*) a situation where all the humps are of equal magnitude, which is probably the best we can do.

Intuitively this seems to be a very reasonable behavior of the error

curve. We shall not attempt any rigorous mathematical discussion of the theory of Chebyshev approximation, but shall assume that in general

minimization of the maximum value of $|\Delta|$ (by adjusting the available parameters) results in an error curve in which all the peaks are equal in magnitude. (13.08-2)

This is generally true, though the theory is complicated. In addition, the number of oscillations or "ripples" of the error curve should be as large as possible, consistent with the complexity of the approximating function and the nature of the function to be approximated, for maximum efficiency of approximation. In our work here we shall accordingly consider as synonymous the two terms *Chebyshev approximation* (approximation in the Chebyshev sense, i.e., approximation that minimizes $|\Delta|_{max}$) and *equal-ripple approximation* (approximation that makes all the humps of the error curve equal in magnitude).

Chebyshev's first application of these ideas was to the simple case of approximation of a constant by a polynomial (CH 1). Simple though it is, we shall find this case of great interest in network synthesis. He later extended his theory to the approximation of a constant by a general rational function, a case also of importance to us, and gave a start towards a general theory (CH 2). The general theory becomes complicated and seems not yet to be completely understood. Fortunately, we can solve many network approximation problems without it.

Chebyshev's work was entirely mathematical; that is to say, he used only the processes of mathematical analysis to obtain his results. These are, of course, completely valid, but there is at least one other approach, and it is more likely to interest the engineer because it makes use of a physical analogy, with attendant simplification in the thinking required. We do not yet have the tools we need for this approach (Chapter 14) nor for another (related) one, so we must postpone the discussion of these methods of obtaining Chebyshev approximations. But the fact that we do not discuss them here at length, as we have done with Taylor approximation, does *not* mean that Chebyshev approximation is comparatively unimportant; if anything, the converse is true. (Taylor approximation, in fact, can be thought of as but a special case of Chebyshev approximation.)

We can point out even here, however, one method of obtaining a Chebyshev approximation. That is simply the application of trial-and-error methods, as implied in Fig. 13.08-A. And in fact, if the function to be approximated is not a simple one, this may well be the only method we have. One might begin by matching the function at a series of convenient (perhaps equally spaced) points. Then from examination of the resulting error curve, revised values to be specified can usually be found easily, and the process repeated until an equal-ripple approximation is obtained. An example of this was given in § 13.03, and Fig. 13.03–C corresponds to Fig. 13.08–A.

We must note again that the shortness of our discussion of trial-and-error methods of obtaining a Chebyshev approximation does not mean that they are unimportant. On the contrary, they are extremely important. But we have already discussed these methods in some detail (§ 13.03); the only thing left is practice: a large number of problems must be worked, exercise in finding such approximations is essential, and this is something the individual must do for himself.

In Chebyshev (or equal-ripple) approximation we have a very widely used engineering method. For simple functions the approximation can be obtained, for example, by analytical methods that depend on a physical analogy (Chapter 14), methods we shall discuss later and in Volume II; for complicated functions we generally have to resort to trial-and-error methods. The resultant error curve resembles a sinusoid in the approximation band in that it has a succession of loops, alternately positive and negative, all of equal magnitude. The resemblance ends there, however, as the zeros are usually not equally spaced (frequently they tend to crowd together near the ends of the approximation band) and the loops themselves are not sinusoidal. In Fig. 13.03–C, for example, the dashed curve (almost equal-ripple) has unequally spaced zeros. Another example is given in Fig. 13.08–B, which shows the error function for an actual

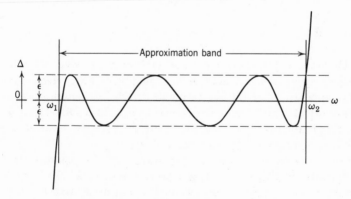

Fig. 13.08–B

Chebyshev approximation. For the present we content ourselves with having the general idea of approximation in the Chebyshev sense and the ability to achieve such approximations by "cut-and-try" methods.

13.09 Weighted approximation

In our discussion of various methods and kinds of approximation, it is only in § 13.08 that we have paid much attention to the nature of the limits of error, or tolerances, within which we have to work. These data, as well as the limits of the approximation band, are laid down by the requirements of the system of which the network is to form a part. In many cases the error limits are constant over the approximation band; here the Chebyshev approximation naturally suggests itself as appropriate. In other cases these limits may vary: it may be that an excellent approximation is important at some frequency, or in some narrow band of frequencies, while in the rest of the approximation band a cruder approximation will suffice. If the requirements are stricter in some parts of the approximation band than in others, then our remarks about the efficiency of the equal-ripple approximation must be modified.

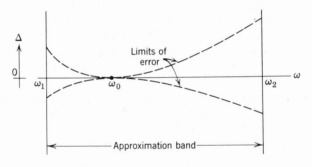

Fig. 13.09–A

For example, if the limits have the general form shown in Fig. 13.09–A, Chebyshev approximation is certainly inappropriate. Here, in fact, maximal approximation (at ω_0) may well be the best solution. A more common sort of limit variation is shown in Fig. 13.09–B. Here neither type of approximation is indicated, for both certainly waste the space available for fluctuation of the error.

What is required here is a *weighting* of the approximation, so that the error is made smaller in the central part of the band. In least-mean-square-error approximation one can introduce a mathematical weighting function in the integral to be minimized, toward this end: the error is thus weighted more heavily in the regions of severe requirements than elsewhere, though its distribution is only crudely controlled. [One might say, in fact, that in ordinary least-mean-square error approximation the error is weighted by the derivative of the approximating function, as evidenced in (13.04–4).] Taylor approximation, being made at a single point, is not subject to this treatment. Chebyshev approximation, however, can be modified to include the use of a weighting function. We shall be content with the trial-and-error approach to weighted Chebyshev approximation, which follows the methods of § 13.03 with the aim of making all the loops of the error curve tangent to the limit curves. As with constant limits, this presumably makes the most efficient use of the available parameters, resulting in the greatest bandwidth for given limits, or the least complicated network for a given bandwidth and limits. A typical result is the solid curve of Fig. 13.09–B.

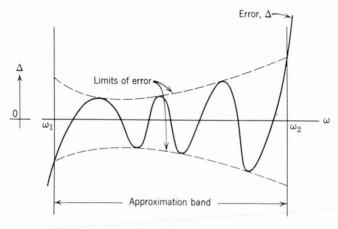

Fig. 13.09–B

In such an approximation the parameters are in effect determined with the aid of a weighting function, and the result is a more general form of Chebyshev approximation. With practice, simpler problems of this sort can be solved quickly, even though a succession of trials is the only approach available. The computations for more complicated ones can often be arranged in systematic form as an iterative process, to be carried out largely by automatic computing machines. Even without their aid, the method is in wide use and must be considered as one of the approximator's more valuable tools.

13.10 Some special cases

Our discussion of approximation has led us through various sorts and methods of approximation to a consideration of the nature of the limits (tolerances) of error prescribed, which may well influence the technique used (§ 13.09).   We have so far given no particular attention to the nature of the function to be approximated, though this may be expressed as an analytic function of frequency over the whole band, or it may be given simply as a set of points that outline an empirical curve without analytic expression.   Again, it may be expressed by analytic functions, but by different ones in each of several parts of the approximation band.

To trial-and-error methods it makes no difference how the data are expressed, for only numerical values are used.   The nature of the approximation can be controlled and desired results obtained whether a formal functional relation is given for the function to be approximated, or a series of such functions, or simply a series of points, to be joined perhaps by straight lines.   A least-mean-square-error approximation can in theory also be made in any case, though the integrals are usually difficult to evaluate.   But in the application of the theory of Taylor approximation we may encounter difficulty, for it is concerned with formal functional behavior at a single point (implying regular behavior as we go away from that point, according to the power series used).   It cannot therefore be expected to anticipate or even roughly follow irregularities in data that are away from the point of maximal approximation.   Yet in many cases the method is still extremely useful, and we shall soon discuss this.   There remains Chebyshēv approximation, which is always appropriate and useful, even if we must use trial-and-error methods to obtain it.

Our approximation of the function $(\sqrt{\omega})^{-1}$ by a resistance function (§§ 13.03–4–5) illustrates the case of analytic data over the whole approximation band.   In contrast, Fig. 13.01–A(a) shows a function to be approximated that is expressed only by a series of straight-line segments. We can proceed to approximate this by trial and error in various ways, even in the Chebyshev sense, ending up perhaps with the approximation shown by the dashed curve.   Least-mean-square-error approximation can also be applied, in theory.   But Taylor approximation is not useful here: the resulting approximation, very good at the point of maximal approximation, will (regardless of where that point is chosen) at best only tend to follow the analytic function (in this case a straight line) used as data, as frequency departs from this point; when a "break" occurs and the function to be approximated changes its analytic expression, then the approximation will probably depart widely.   That there are limitations on the utility of Taylor approximation is thus made evident (and the power of trial-and-error methods demonstrated once more).   A simpler case is given in Fig. 13.01–A(b), where a nonzero constant is to be approximated below a certain frequency, and above it zero is to be approximated.

When irregularities such as these occur in the data, trial-and-error methods, least-mean-square-error approximation, and Chebyshev approximation are not in principle affected thereby; in contrast, Taylor approximation, being concerned with a single point, is. Yet by the use of appropriate constraints we can in simple cases still make good use of Taylor approximation when the data are only piecewise analytic in nature, i.e., when the data are a series of analytic expressions, each valid over part of the approximation band. Since in these cases the segments of the datum function are usually straight lines, we are thus led to consider Taylor approximation of a straight line or, more generally, of a rational function.

The approximation of a rational function by a rational function, by whatever method performed, presents certain anomalies. If the order of the approximating function used equals or exceeds that of the function approximated, then the result is naturally exactly the function to be "approximated." If the order of the function used is less than that of the function given, however, then approximation proceeds much as in the general case. But we have rational functions to approximate only, as a rule, when the datum function is a piecewise collection thereof. To the trial-and-error approach this presents no new problems. To Taylor approximation it does, and this we must discuss.

Consider, for example, the approximation problem of Fig. 13.01–A(b), restated in Fig. 13.10–A. A resistance (or conductance) function is to

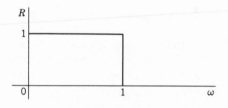

Fig. 13.10–A

approximate a constant (normalized to 1 Ω) from zero frequency up to a change-over frequency (normalized to 1 radian per sec) and thereafter to approximate zero. [This high-frequency behavior may be required by the system, or it may be simply a way of insuring that the network have a capacitor at its terminals, to absorb parasitic capacitance (§ 12.05)]. If we consider only the band $0 < \omega < 1$, regardless of the method of approximation we use, we obtain $R = 1$, an exact solution here. This is only natural, for the approximation of a simple rational function by another rational function need not be an approximation at all. To obtain the desired high-frequency behavior we must also consider the region $\omega > 1$, which presents difficulties only to the Taylor method. For a final impedance function of order N, we have

$$R(\omega) = \frac{a_0 + a_2\omega^2 + \cdots + a_{2N}\omega^{2N}}{b_0 + b_2\omega^2 + \cdots + b_{2N}\omega^{2N}} \qquad (13.10\text{--}1)$$

in which if the approximation is to be maximal at the origin the coefficients are to be determined by these conditions: (a) $R(0) = 1$, and (b) at the origin as many derivatives of $R(\omega)$ equal zero as possible. To obtain zero resistance at high frequencies, we must apply the *constraint* that at least two of the zeros of $R(\omega)$ lie at infinity. Then

$$R(\omega) = \frac{a_0 + a_2\omega^2 + \cdots + a_{2M}\omega^{2M}}{b_0 + b_2\omega^2 + b_4\omega^4 + \cdots + b_{2N}\omega^{2N}} \qquad (13.10\text{--}2)$$

in which $M < N$ and the number of zeros at infinity is $2(N - M)$; at sufficiently high frequencies $R(\omega)$ certainly approximates zero.

We return now to the origin, at which we want maximal approximation of the constant unity. One constant in (13.10–2) is arbitrary (we can divide numerator and denominator through by any one) so we take $b_0 = 1$. Then

$$R(\omega) = \frac{a_0 + a_2\omega^2 + \cdots + a_{2M}\omega^{2M}}{1 + b_2\omega^2 + b_4\omega^4 + \cdots + b_{2N}\omega^{2N}} \qquad (13.10\text{--}3)$$

$$= 1 + 0 + 0 + 0 + \cdots + \Delta$$

which we wish (as indicated) to equal unity in as many terms of the power series in ω as possible. By cross multiplication and equating of coefficients (as in § 13.05) we find that the series for Δ can be made to start with the term in ω^{2N}, and that the conditions for this Taylor approximation are:

$$
\begin{aligned}
a_0 &= 1, & 0 &= b_{2M+2}, \\
a_2 &= b_2, & 0 &= b_{2M+4}, \\
a_4 &= b_4, & 0 &= b_{2M+6}, \\
&\cdots\cdots\cdots\cdots \\
a_{2M} &= b_{2M}, & 0 &= b_{2N-2}.
\end{aligned}
\qquad (13.10\text{--}4)
$$

The last coefficient of the denominator, b_{2N}, is arbitrary (it may conveniently be used as a frequency scale factor); if we could set it equal to zero we should have a perfect "approximation," but then we should have no zero at infinity. Conditions (13.10–4) state that the numerator of $R(\omega)$ should be the same as the first $(M + 1)$ terms of the denominator, and that the only other nonzero term of the denominator should be the highest, $b_{2N}\omega^{2N}$. Then we have

$$R(\omega) = \frac{1 + a_2\omega^2 + a_4\omega^4 + \cdots + a_{2M}\omega^{2M}}{1 + a_2\omega^2 + a_4\omega^4 + \cdots + a_{2M}\omega^{2M} + b_{2N}\omega^{2N}}$$

$$= \frac{1}{1 + \dfrac{b_{2N}\omega^{2N}}{1 + a_2\omega^2 + \cdots + a_{2M}\omega^{2M}}} \tag{13.10–5}$$

and, near the origin,

$$R(\omega) = 1 - \underbrace{b_{2N}\omega^{2N} + a_2 b_{2N}\omega^{2N+2} + \cdots}_{\text{error}} \tag{13.10–6}$$

so that the quality of approximation there is indicated by the fact that the first N terms of the series (in ω^2) for the error are zero. Function (13.10–1), with which we began, has $(2N + 1)$ parameters, with which it is possible in general to match not only $(2N + 1)$ terms but *all* of the terms of the series for the function to be approximated, because the latter is rational and of lower order. On applying the constraint that $R(\omega)$ have at least two zeros at infinity, we find that the best we can do is to match N terms in the series. The effect of the constraint is thus to reduce the quality of the "maximal" approximation, which is not at all surprising. Because of the special nature of the function to be approximated, the coefficients in $R(\omega)$ are not completely determined, but we can arbitrarily specify either its poles or its finite zeros, i.e., either its numerator or its denominator. Then from the condition

$$\text{denominator} = \text{numerator} + b_{2N}\omega^{2N}, \tag{13.10–7}$$

$R(\omega)$ is fixed except perhaps for b_{2N}.

With the constraint that $R(\omega)$ have zeros at infinity, a maximal approximation of a constant at the origin is independent of the remaining zeros (alternatively, is independent of the poles). This gives us a wide range of solutions of the problem, of which perhaps the simplest is obtained by placing *all* the zeros of $R(\omega)$ at infinity. This choice not only simplifies the function $R(\omega)$ but insures that realization in a simple form, a ladder network of series inductors and shunt capacitors terminated in a single resistor, is possible (§ 9.11). Then

$$R(\omega) = \frac{1}{1 + b_{2N}\omega^{2N}}. \tag{13.10–8}$$

In (13.10–8) we have a good approximation of zero at high frequencies, and (subject to the constraint) maximal approximation of unity at the origin. The only control over intermediate-frequency behavior that we have is in b_{2N}; to determine a suitable value for this arbitrary constant we look again at the data given in Fig. 13.10–A. Perhaps as good a choice as any is that which at the change-over point $\omega = 1$ makes $R(\omega)$ pass through the mean value, i.e., makes $R(1) = \frac{1}{2}$. This is $b_{2N} = 1$; with it

$$R(\omega) = \frac{1}{1 + \omega^{2N}}. \tag{13.10–9}$$

The function to be approximated and the approximations achieved in (13.10–9) are shown in Fig. 13.10–B for several values of N. The approximation can be considered good only for rather large values of N—but if

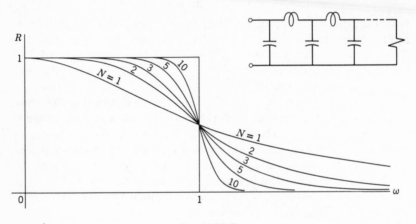

Fig. 13.10–B

we consider the irregular nature of the data, this is only reasonable. This particular result is of use in filters (to be discussed in Volume II) and in amplifier networks, and is frequently called "maximally flat." The names Norton, Bennett, Butterworth, and Landon are associated with it (NO 3, BE 3, BU 1, LA 2). It is useful because of its simplicity, even though the quality of approximation achieved is not extreme; in particular, the network realization shown in Fig. 13.10–B that uses N reactive elements and one resistor is easily obtained. The poles are extremely easy to find; they are equally spaced on the unit circle, being the roots of

$$p^{2N} + (-1)^N = 0.$$

Since the numerator of the resistance function becomes an arbitrary polynomial once the constraint of zeros at infinity has been applied, the number of possible maximal approximations is immense—and we can probably use this freedom in locating the finite zeros of $R(\omega)$ to improve the quality of approximation. For example, a zero value of $R(\omega)$ somewhat above $\omega = 1$ will evidently improve the approximation there, and very likely will stiffen the curve so that the approximation is also better below $\omega = 1$. To illustrate, let us move a zero from infinity and place it at some real frequency ω_1. For realizability, such zeros in a resistance function must be of even order and occur in conjugate pairs, so that at least four zeros must be brought in; if the function is still to vanish at infinity, the minimum value of N is now three. We now have, using (13.10–7),

$$R(\omega) = \frac{(\omega^2 - \omega_1{}^2)^2}{(\omega^2 - \omega_1{}^2)^2 + b_{2N}\omega^{2N}} \qquad (13.10\text{–}10)$$

in which we are still free to set ω_1, N, and b_{2N}, not to mention the use of additional finite zeros. The various possibilities can be adequately investigated only by a series of trials; we shall content ourselves here with one by way of example. We take $N = 3$ (the lowest and simplest order permitted) and still require $R(1) = \frac{1}{2}$ (which determines b_{2N}) in order to have a good comparison. For ω_1 we take the value 1.3 as being sufficiently close to unity to have a pronounced effect. Then

$$R(\omega) = \frac{(\omega^2 - 1.3^2)^2}{(\omega^2 - 1.3^2)^2 + (1 - 1.3^2)^2\omega^6}$$

$$= \frac{(\omega^2 - 1.69)^2}{(\omega^2 - 1.69)^2 + 0.4761\omega^6}. \qquad (13.10\text{–}11)$$

This function is certainly realizable, though not in as simple a form as before; a one-resistor realization may require mutual inductance, and to avoid this we may have to use a surplus factor. The improvement in the

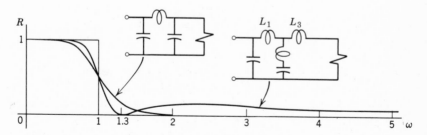

Fig. 13.10–C

approximation is shown in Fig. 13.10–C, which gives the behavior of function (13.10–9) for $N = 3$ as well as that of the new function (13.10–11).

The curve is stiffened in the vicinity of $\omega = 1$, exactly as expected, with a better approximation from $\omega = 0$ up to a point just above ω_1. Thereafter the approximation is not as good as before, the inevitable price of the improvement at lower frequencies. Also shown (in schematic form) are one-resistor realizations of these two functions. In the second case it is possible that L_1 or L_3 will be negative; if so we may choose to fall back on our other realization methods (Chapter 10).

One interesting possibility among the great number remaining in the construction of $R(\omega)$ that is maximally flat at the origin is that illustrated in Fig. 13.10–D. Here the function is presumed to be of order great

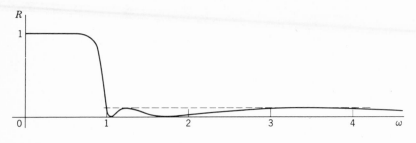

Fig. 13.10–D

enough that we can bring a number of zeros in from infinity, and they are so distributed that an equal-ripple approximation is obtained above $\omega = 1$. Analytic methods for determining this approximation we do not yet have, but presumably by trial and error, extending the work above, we could obtain it.

This example has made it clear that through the use of supplementary constraints Taylor approximation can sometimes be applied even in cases where the function to be approximated is not analytic over the whole approximation band. An important special case is that of rational-function approximation, with relaxation of the requirement of maximal approximation to permit constraints at appropriate points away from the matching point. A sort of pseudo-maximal approximation results, one that is maximal within the limits imposed by the constraints. What constraints to apply depends on the problem in hand. Arbitrariness in the approximating function may appear, as above, because the Padé table for approximation of a rational function by rational functions can well be expected to contain anomalies.

The discussion of approximations of this nature could be prolonged indefinitely. But treatment of such problems is usually a matter of common-sense application of ideas already developed, with sufficient trials to obtain a clear idea of what constraints to apply and what they can do. A few more examples follow in outline.

The "block" to be approximated may be moved up in frequency as in Fig. 13.10–E; we may have to approximate zero in both a high-frequency

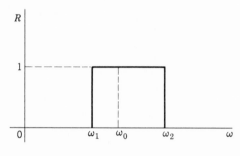

Fig. 13.10–E

band and a low-frequency band, and a constant (unity) in an internal band. To apply Taylor approximation we can place the matching point ω_0 in this internal band as shown, and apply constraints by requiring zeros at both the origin and infinity—and nowhere else. [If we are looking for a resistance-function (even-function) approximation, these constraints also insure that we can realize the network in the simple L-C ladder form, with one resistor and without mutual inductance.] We can write, simply by extension of (13.10–5),

$$R(\omega) = \frac{a_{2M}\omega^{2M}}{a_{2M}\omega^{2M} + b_{2N}(\omega^2 - \omega_0^2)^N}$$

$$= \frac{1}{1 + b[(\omega^2 - \omega_0^2)^N/\omega^{2M}]}$$

(13.10–12)

which is even, has $2M$ zeros at the origin and $2(N - M)$ zeros at infinity and no others, and has the value unity at ω_0. Nearby we have

$$R(\omega) = 1 + b'(\omega - \omega_0)^N + \cdots,$$

(13.10–13)

i.e., the first N terms of the series are matched. This approximation is maximal, subject to the restraint that an even function be used (for an equal approximation is automatically made at $-\omega_0$, which in effect uses up about half the parameters available). The function is realizable if b is positive. Even when the order of the impedance function N is fixed (N cannot be odd), we have still to decide how the $2N$ zeros are to be distributed between the origin and infinity, just where in the block to locate ω_0, and what value to give the constant b. These questions are best answered by trial; one of the many possible solutions, for example, is

$$R(\omega) = \frac{\omega^6}{\omega^6 + 0.08771(\omega^2 - 1)^6}$$

$$= \frac{1}{1 + 0.08771[\omega - 1/\omega]^6} \qquad (13.10\text{-}14)$$

which has its 12 zeros equally divided between the origin and infinity, is maximally flat (at the value unity) at unit frequency, and passes through the value 0.5 at $\omega = 0.5$. Its behavior is shown in Fig. 13.10–F. This

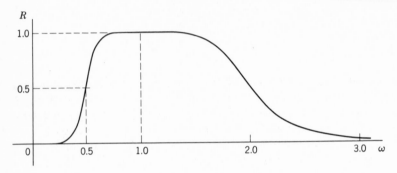

Fig. 13.10–F

equal distribution of zeros evidently results in a curve that is rather lop-sided on an arithmetic frequency scale (though the curve is symmetric on a logarithmic frequency scale); experimentation with the distribution of zeros would be necessary to make the curve more nearly rectangular. Vacuum-tube amplifiers provide an important application (Problem 13-87). There is also the possibility of placing some zeros at internal frequencies, even of obtaining Chebyshev approximation of zero in bands above and below the "block." The numerator of R (or its denominator) is in fact arbitrary, much as was indicated in (13.10–7) for the previous example (Problem 13-79).

It may be required to approximate the block of Fig. 13.10–E by an *odd* function so as to achieve approximately constant reactance (or angle) in an internal band of frequencies. (For the low-band case of Fig. 13.10–A this is impossible, since odd functions must have zeros or poles at the origin, except in the special case where the value zero is to be approximated; the approximation of zero by an odd function is discussed more generally in § 14.17.) We encounter some differences here, for by following the procedure of § 13.06, in particular by solving equations (13.06–4) for various N, we find that *all* the parameters, the coefficients in both numerator and denominator, can be used in the approximation and there is no longer any arbitrariness in numerator or denominator. The first six results are, for maximal approximation of the constant unity at unit frequency,

$$X_1 = \omega,$$

$$X_2 = \frac{2\omega}{1 + \omega^2},$$

$$X_3 = \frac{3\omega + \omega^3}{1 + 3\omega^2},$$

$$X_4 = \frac{4\omega + 4\omega^3}{1 + 6\omega^2 + \omega^4}, \qquad \text{(13.10–15)}$$

$$X_5 = \frac{5\omega + 10\omega^3 + \omega^5}{1 + 10\omega^2 + 5\omega^4},$$

$$X_6 = \frac{6\omega + 20\omega^3 + 6\omega^5}{1 + 15\omega^2 + 15\omega^4 + \omega^6},$$

or their reciprocals. These functions are all realizable (as driving-point reactance or susceptance). The appearance of the binomial coefficients, i.e., of the coefficients in the expansion of $(1 + \omega)^N$,

$$P(\omega) = (1 + \omega)^N$$

$$= 1 + N\omega + \frac{N(N-1)}{1 \times 2}\,\omega^2 + \frac{N(N-1)(N-2)}{1 \times 2 \times 3}\,\omega^3 + \cdots$$
$$\text{(13.10–16)}$$

suggests that the solution is in general

$$X_N = \frac{\mathbf{Od}\,P(\omega)}{\mathbf{Ev}\,P(\omega)}$$

$$= \frac{N\omega + \dfrac{N(N-1)(N-2)}{1 \times 2 \times 3}\,\omega^3 + \cdots}{1 + \dfrac{N(N-1)}{1 \times 2}\,\omega^2 + \dfrac{N(N-1)(N-2)(N-3)}{1 \times 2 \times 3 \times 4}\,\omega^4 + \cdots.}$$
$$\text{(13.10–17)}$$

That this is indeed true is readily seen from the form

$$X_N = \frac{(1 + \omega)^N - (1 - \omega)^N}{(1 + \omega)^N + (1 - \omega)^N} = \frac{1 - [(1 - \omega)/(1 + \omega)]^N}{1 + [(1 - \omega)/(1 + \omega)]^N}, \quad (13.10\text{--}18)$$

for this function is odd and in the vicinity of $\omega = 1$ has the expansion

$$X_N = 1 + (-\tfrac{1}{2})^{N-1}(\omega - 1)^N + \cdots. \quad (13.10\text{--}19)$$

Evidently N terms of the series are correctly matched, and since there are but N parameters available in (13.06–1) the approximation is truly maximal. This empirical method of obtaining the general solution (13.10–17) or (13.10–18) is not entirely satisfactory, even though it was successful here; there exists a more logical derivation, one more readily understood with the tools available in Chapter 14 (see § 14.18). There is no reduction in the quality of the approximation, as there was in (13.10–12), because there is here no automatic simultaneous approximation at $-\omega_0$; the function there approximates -1, but that is a different function. Some of the results are shown in Fig. 13.10–G for even values

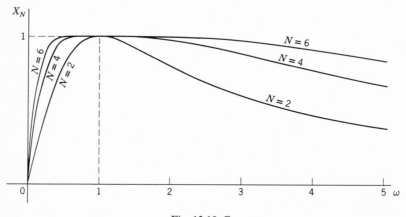

Fig. 13.10–G

of N; for odd values of N the functions rise at high frequencies and do not approximate zero. The flatness sought at unit frequency is evidently achieved, but there is little tendency to follow the outline of the rectangle. By sacrificing some of the flatness at unit frequency, we can improve the approximation of zero at low and high frequencies, though not as easily as with the resistance (even) function approximation. If it is the *angle* of an immittance that is to approximate a constant, we can use all these results, interpreting them as the tangent (except for a multiplier) of the immittance's angle rather than as reactance (susceptance).

For another example of this sort of problem, consider the function of Fig. 13.10–H. This line cannot be approximated very well near the

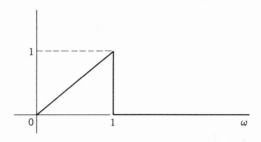

Fig. 13.10–H

origin by an even function but if we seek a reactance (susceptance) of this sort with, for example, unit slope at the origin, maximal linearity there, and (by way of constraint to approximate zero above unit frequency) a certain number of zeros at infinity, we can write

$$X(\omega) = \frac{a_1\omega + a_3\omega^3 + \cdots + a_{2M+1}\omega^{2M+1}}{b_0 + b_2\omega^2 + \cdots + b_{2N}\omega^{2N}}. \qquad (13.10\text{–}20)$$

On application of the principles of Taylor approximation at the origin to the function ω we find

$$X(\omega) = \omega\,\frac{1 + b_2\omega^2 + \cdots + b_{2M}\omega^{2M}}{1 + b_2\omega^2 + \cdots + b_{2M}\omega^{2M} + b_{2N}\omega^{2N}}, \qquad (13.10\text{–}21)$$

in which the b's are arbitrary. This is exactly the function (13.10–5) multiplied by ω, and all the discussion as to arbitrariness of numerator (denominator) and quality of approximation given in connection with (13.10–5) is equally applicable here. In fact, maximal approximation of ω^n at the origin and of zero at high frequencies, be n odd or even, is made by the product of (13.10–5) and ω^n. The zeros of the function may all be at infinity (the simplest case) or some may be moved in to internal frequencies to improve the approximation of zero there.

If we seek an immittance function whose *angle* is maximally linear at the origin, we cannot obtain it directly from (13.10–5), though we can obtain it by the methods of § 13.06—but we have already discovered a family of such functions in the Padé table for e^p (§ 13.07). Additional functions can be obtained by prescribing more zeros (or poles) of the tangent function at infinity, not to mention internal frequencies.

In the preceding examples we have illustrated the approximation of functions that are piecewise rational by applying Taylor approximation at one point, subject however to constraints in the form of prescribed zeros at other points. The effect of these constraints is to give approximations to the datum functions that are often very useful; the fact that they are not maximal approximations (because some parameters are used to satisfy the constraints rather than in the Taylor-approximation mechanism) need not detract from their utility.

Another device is to apply Taylor approximation simultaneously at several points. When the datum function is composed of a series of segments, each with its own analytic expression, this method may give a good approximation over a wide band of frequencies in spite of the irregular character of the datum function. For example, suppose we need a resistance function to approximate the function of Fig. 13.10–I and that

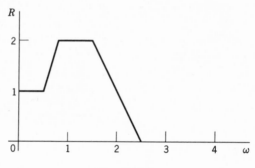

Fig. 13.10–I

we wish to realize this with an impedance function of order four. We may write

$$R(\omega) = \frac{a_0 + a_2\omega^2 + a_4\omega^4 + a_6\omega^6 + a_8\omega^8}{b_0 + b_2\omega^2 + b_4\omega^4 + b_6\omega^6 + b_8\omega^8} \qquad (13.10\text{–}22)$$

and choose to utilize our nine parameters in the following fashion: three for Taylor approximation at the origin, four for Taylor approximation at $\omega = 1$, two for zeros at infinity (a sort of Taylor approximation of zero there). We might write a set of nine simultaneous equations, but the problem is sufficiently special to enable us to say immediately, taking $b_0 = 1$,

$$\text{for the zeros at infinity:} \quad \begin{aligned} a_6 &= 0, \\ a_8 &= 0, \end{aligned} \qquad (13.10\text{–}23)$$

and for unit value and flatness at the origin:

$$a_0 = 1,$$
$$a_2 = b_2, \qquad (13.10\text{--}24)$$
$$a_4 = b_4.$$

For value two and flatness at $\omega = 1$, proceeding as in the other examples then gives us the equations

b_2	b_4	b_6	b_8	
1	1	2	2	$= -1$
2	4	12	16	$= 0$
1	6	30	56	$= 0$
0	4	40	112	$= 0$

$$(13.10\text{--}25)$$

whose solution leads us to

$$R(\omega) = \frac{1 - 4\omega^2 + 6\omega^4}{1 - 4\omega^2 + 6\omega^4 - 2\omega^6 + \frac{1}{2}\omega^8}. \qquad (13.10\text{--}26)$$

This approximating function may be compared with the datum function in Fig. 13.10–J. There are of course countless other possibilities for $R(\omega)$ which can be investigated if (13.10–26) is not satisfactory.

One can proceed thus to apportion the "maximal" approximation

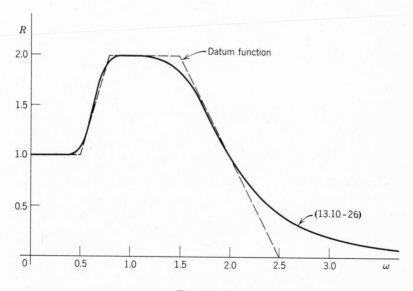

Fig. 13.10-J

between a number of points; each Taylor subapproximation gives some of the equations necessary to determine the parameters, by the same sort of calculation as with the truly maximal approximation, where all the equations come from a single point. For irregular functions (composed, e.g., of a succession of straight lines, as above) this may be a useful method —but it can equally well be applied to a datum function that is analytic, and may well increase the width of the useful approximation band. As the number of points used increases, the number of derivatives matched at each one decreases (for a given network order) and the quality of the approximation at each point is diluted.

It is possible indeed to regard almost any sort of approximation as a limiting case of this distribution (among various points) of the available parameters. If only one is assigned to each point, the point-matching technique (§ 13.03) results; if these points are properly chosen (a difficult task in general), the Chebyshev or equal-ripple approximation results. The extensions are many and they offer one way of looking at approximation in a unified fashion.

13.11 In retrospect

The examples of § 13.10, interesting though they are, have led us into somewhat specialized territory. We have explored the general subject of approximation in this chapter, and discussed some of its aspects in detail —perhaps in too much detail, so that we are lost therein. It is important that we stop here to review our accomplishments to date, both in the matter of approximation and in the general problem of one-terminal-pair network synthesis.

Approximation problems arise in network synthesis because the data for synthesis problems are often given in nonrealizable form. (For example, the ideal resistance function of Fig. 13.10–A is not rational and therefore not realizable.) We must then set up a rational function of appropriate form: an odd or even function of ω, or an ordinary rational function of p, as the case may be—and then proceed to determine the coefficients so that we have both a good approximation to the behavior desired and a realizable function. The conditions for realizability we have discussed in previous chapters: § 8.16 gives the conditions for the separate parts of an immittance function (resistance, conductance, reactance, susceptance, magnitude, angle), whereas for immittance functions as a whole positive reality is both necessary and sufficient. To obtain a good approximation to the behavior desired, we have now available the various methods discussed in §§ 13.03 through 13.10. We may approximate simply by a succession of trials, improving the function each time by the application of common sense. Or, in contrast, we may apply the mathematically elegant technique of Padé approximation. The former gives us approximations whose quality we judge by examination of the error curves; the latter leads to approximation in the Taylor sense, i.e., to approximations that are maximal in a very precisely defined sense. There are other methods of obtaining approximations—and there are other senses of approximation, notably the equal-ripple or Chebyshev sense, which is efficient, practical, and therefore important. We must postpone its discussion, however, until we have additional tools. But even without it, we find ourselves now in a good position to solve (completely) many network-synthesis problems.

Of the general *properties* of the one-terminal pair, we acquired detailed knowledge in Chapters 4, 5, and 8. *Approximation* we have studied in this chapter, enough to be able already to solve approximation problems in several ways. The resulting function must of course be realizable (it must be tested for realizability, for this quality is independent of successful approximation); we can then proceed to the *realization* or synthesis proper (on paper), by the methods of Chapters 6, 7, 9, and 10. The three divisions of synthesis (§ 1.01) have thus received a good deal of attention, and the fourth, if we wish to call it such—the matter of building the concrete network and making it work—we have also discussed a little in Chapter 12.

What is lacking, what we must yet consider before turning our attention to the two-terminal pair, are certain additional matters concerning techniques of approximation. In the remaining chapters of this volume we shall investigate the use of an analogy (based on potential theory) and certain examples useful in various ways for illustration. We turn next to the potential analogy.

13.12 References

Approximation in general: BE 2, CE 1, HI 1, HO 4, LA 1, LA 4, WI 4 (a bibliography).
Trial-and-error techniques: BO 3, LI 1, TR 1.
Padé (maximal) approximation: theory: BE 1, FR 5, PA 3, PE 1, WA 2; examples: BE 3, BU 1, FI 2, LA 2, LY 1, NO 3, ST 3, TH 3, TU 2.

PROBLEMS

13-1. (*a*) Determine the coefficients a and b in (13.03–16) and calculate and plot the function; compare it with the function it approximates. Calculate and plot the function (13.03–17).

(*b*) Determine the reactance associated with the resistance function defined by (13.03–15) by the method of § 8.09. Compare the result with that of (*a*) above.

13-2. Solve each of the following approximation problems by trial-and-error methods; the initial trial may be based on matching at conveniently spaced points in the approximation band, for example. Carry the improvement to the stage where the error in the approximation band is essentially of the equal-ripple type. Insure that each result is realizable and then complete the synthesis by realizing the networks. Give also the dual problems and their solutions.

(1) A resistance function is to be constant, at unit value, from $\omega = 0$ to $\omega = 1$, dropping off thereafter, and remaining below 0.1 for $\omega > 1.4$. Let the

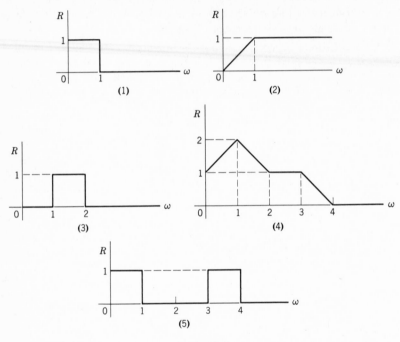

Prob. 13–2

order of the corresponding impedance function be two, and solve the problem (a) with all the zeros of the resistance function at infinity, (b) with the zeros of the resistance function placed wherever they will do the most good in reducing the error. Compare the results. Repeat for impedance functions of orders three, four, and five.

(2) A resistance function is to be linear with frequency from $\omega = 0$ to $\omega = 1$ and constant thereafter. The error is to be kept small at all frequencies. Let n, the order of the corresponding impedance function, be 2 and solve the problem (a) with all the zeros of the resistance function at the origin, (b) with the zeros of the resistance function placed wherever they will do the most good. Compare the results. Repeat for $n = 3, 4, 5$.

(3) A resistance function is to be of the form illustrated, with values no greater than 0.05 for $\omega < 0.8$ and for $\omega > 2.3$. Start with a low order function

and place zeros of the resistance function only at the origin and at infinity. Then investigate the improvements obtainable by increasing the order, and by relaxing the requirement on the zeros.

(4) A resistance function is to follow the requirements illustrated, with error not very great at any frequency. Increase the order as necessary to obtain a good approximation and investigate the effect of placing the zeros in positions (*a*) for maximum ease of realization and (*b*) for maximum reduction of error. Are these compatible?

(5) A resistance function is to be of the form illustrated, with values less than 0.07 for $1.2 < \omega < 2.6$ and $\omega > 4.3$. Increase the order as necessary to obtain a good approximation and investigate the effect of placing the zeros in positions (*a*) for maximum ease of realization and (*b*) for maximum reduction of error. Are these compatible?

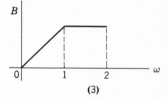

(1)

13-3. Solve the following approximation problems by the general method indicated in Prob. 13-2. In each case start with a low value of *n*, the order of the final immittance function, and investigate the benefits obtained by increasing *n*. Insure that each solution is realizable and complete the synthesis by finding a network realization. Find (*A*) impedance functions whose *magnitude* meets the various requirements laid down in Prob. 13-2 for resistance functions, (*B*) admittance functions whose magnitude meets the various requirements laid down in Prob. 13-2 for resistance functions.

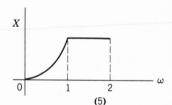

(3)

13-4. In the same general fashion as in Prob. 13-2 solve the approximation problems outlined below, and their duals.

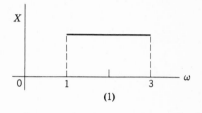

(5)

(1) A reactance function is to be constant over a band of frequencies; no requirements other than realizability are placed on the function at other frequencies. Consider the two possibilities of sign, as well as the magnitude, for the reactance scale factor.

(2) An admittance function is to be constant as to angle for $1 < \omega < 3$ with no requirements at other frequencies. Utilize the results of (1) above as far as possible and discuss the effect on the

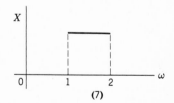

(7)

Prob. 13-4

realization of the choice of value at which the angle is nominally constant; realize for the cases $\pm 30°$, $\pm 60°$, $\pm 90°$.

(3) A susceptance function is to follow the form illustrated for $0 < \omega < 2$,

with no requirements thereafter, and another susceptance function with behavior the negative of this.

(4) An impedance function is to have the character shown in (3) as to angle. Discuss the realization of various values of angle attained at $\omega = 1$, both as to magnitude and sign.

(5) A reactance function is to be proportional to ω^5, then constant, and not restricted thereafter, as shown; a reactance function is to have the negative of this behavior.

(6) An impedance function is to follow the character of (5) as to angle; discuss the realization for various values of angle attained at $\omega = 1$, both as to magnitude and sign.

(7) A reactance function is to have the nature shown; there are no requirements for $0 < \omega < 1$ and $\omega > 2$, though it is preferable that the reactance take low values in both regions. A reactance function is to have the negative of this behavior.

(8) An admittance function is to follow the character of (7) as to angle. Discuss realization for various values of the constant approximated, both as to magnitude and sign.

13-5. By trial-and-error methods solve the approximation problems for which data are given below.

(1) Resistance and reactance are to be as illustrated, with error uniformly

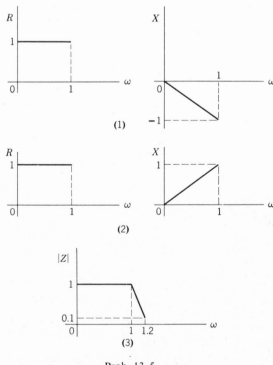

Prob. 13-5

distributed in $0 < \omega < 1$; at higher frequencies reduce resistance and reactance to zero as rapidly as possible. Discuss the variety of solutions obtainable.

(2) Data are as in (1), except that reactance is increasing rather than decreasing. Discuss and explain the difficulty that arises here.

(3) Magnitude of impedance is to be as shown in $0 < \omega < 1.2$ and to remain below 0.1 for $\omega > 1.2$. Angle of impedance is to vary linearly with frequency in $0 < \omega < 1$, at any rate that is convenient.

13-6. The bridged-T constant-resistance equalizer network (§ 11.02) is often designed by trial-and-error methods. In such problems it is often convenient

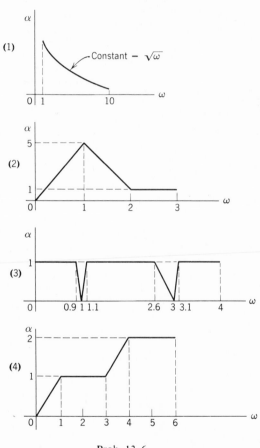

Prob. 13-6

to assume from the beginning a network configuration, on the basis of useful resonances and other distinguishing characteristics. In each of these problems make use of this, and other suggestions of § 13.03, to solve the problem. In each case $\alpha = \ln |1 + z_1|$, and an arbitrary constant may be added to the data, but it should be kept as small as possible.   Use simple networks at first, and increase the order to obtain better approximations.   The data are given pictorially.

13-7. (a) Explain why the choice of the form (13.03–4) and the requirement of matching $F = 1/\sqrt{\omega}$ at three points will inevitably lead to an unrealizable resistance function.   (*Suggestion:* Consider R^{-1} and $\bar{F}^{-1}$.)

(b) If $R = (b_0 + b_2\omega^2 + \cdots + b_{2n}\omega^{2n})^{-1}$ and the coefficients are determined by matching at $(n + 1)$ points, show that the same behavior will result when n is even but not when n is odd.

(c) When n is even, explain how a realizable resistance function can be obtained by relaxing the requirement that $(n + 1)$ points be matched.

13-8. Consider the problem of finding a resistance function $R(\omega)$ to approximate a given function $F(\omega)$ by the method of specifying the values of R at certain frequencies $\omega_1,\ \omega_2,\ \omega_3,\ \cdots$, i.e., by matching at points.   Show that if

$$R(\omega) = \frac{a_0 + a_2\omega^2 + a_4\omega^4 + \cdots + a_{2n}\omega^{2n}}{b_0 + b_2\omega^2 + b_4\omega^4 + \cdots + b_{2n}\omega^{2n}}$$

a_0 may be taken as unity without loss of generality, and that the equations for the a's and b's are linear.   Set up these equations for $n = 1, 2, 3$.   Show that in general the solutions do not depend linearly on the specified values $R(\omega_1)$, $R(\omega_2)$, $R(\omega_3)$, $\cdots$, or on their reciprocals, but if $a_2, a_4, a_6, \cdots$ are set equal to zero, then the b's do depend linearly on the reciprocals of these specified values of resistance.   Discuss the tabulation, once for all (for chosen n and matching frequencies) of the values of the b's in terms of the specifications, and the application of such a tabulation to this approximation problem in general.

13-9. When the point-matching technique is used in solving an approximation problem, under certain conditions expressions for the coefficients in the network function may be set up, once for all, that give their values in terms of the values the function is to take at these points; i.e., the simultaneous equations need be solved only once and these expressions may be used in each succeeding approximation.   Explain, justify, and illustrate this statement.   In particular, under what conditions is it valid?   Under what conditions may a resistance function be written immediately in terms of the frequencies at which the matching is made and the values required there?

13-10. Once a rough approximation has been obtained, the succeeding work may be organized on the basis of reducing the error at selected points by a minimization of the squares of these errors.   Discuss and illustrate the orthogonal-function approach to this (LI 1).

13-11. Solve the following network-design problems.   In each case the order of the function is to be small enough to be reasonable, yet large enough to give a good approximation in the band $1 < \omega < 4$.

	Network Function of Importance	Function to Be Approximated
(a)	Magnitude of impedance	$1/\sqrt{\omega}$
(b)	Reactance	$1/\sqrt{\omega}$
(c)	Reactance	$-1/\sqrt{\omega}$
(d)	Reactance	$\sqrt{\omega}$
(e)	Resistance	$\sqrt{\omega}$
(f)	Magnitude of impedance	$\sqrt{\omega}$

13-12. The function $F = (\omega)^{-1/2}$ is to be approximated in the range $1 < \omega < 4$ by the driving-point resistance of a network to be designed. The network is to use only R and C elements. Set up the appropriate form of function for the resistance (cf. Probs. 7-37, 8-127) and find network realizations for several reasonable values of n, the order of the impedance.

13-13. Design networks whose driving-point resistance functions approximate the data given below. At each point the maximum magnitude of error tolerable is 7% of the nominal resistance value.

(a)			(b)	
Frequency (kcps)	Resistance (ohms)		Freqency (cps)	Resistance (ohms)
1	550		0	5000
2	200		100	5000
3	100		200	5300
4	150		300	7000
5	350		350	8000
6	550		400	8000
			450	6200
			500	3800
			600	1200

13-14. A network is to be designed such that the magnitude of its driving-point impedance approximates the form shown. If the network is to be of order n (contain n reactive elements), how many parameters are available for use in making the approximation? Discuss in a general way how these parameters are restricted if the result is to be physically realizable. Obtain solutions for $n = 1, 2, 3, 4, 5$, and show how increasing n improves the approximation.

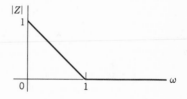

Prob. 13–14

13-15. Suppose that it is desired to design a ladder type of network (Fig. 9.11–A), in which each intermediate box contains only an inductor or a capacitor (some of which may be short or open circuits) and the final element is a resistor. The criterion is that the input resistance function approximate a given function $F(\omega)$ in the least-mean-square-error sense in the band $\omega_1 < \omega < \omega_2$.

(a) Write the general form of the function $R(\omega)$, the driving-point resistance. In particular, what form must its numerator have?

(b) Show (generally, not just for this particular problem) that if the approximation attained is reasonably good, then

$$\Delta = R - F \cong \left(\frac{1}{F} - \frac{1}{R}\right) F^2,$$

i.e., the error is closely equal to the difference between the reciprocal functions, multiplied by F^2.

(c) Show now, making use of (b), that for this particular problem the coefficients in the function $R(\omega)$ may be obtained on an approximate least-mean-square-error basis by the solution of simultaneous linear algebraic equations.

Explain why the equations for the coefficients are not nonlinear in this case, and why they would be so in general (if the network form were not restricted as it is).

(d) Give the actual equations to be solved in (c). What difficulty may arise if $\omega_1 = 0$? If $\omega_2 \to \infty$? What difficulty may arise if $\int_{\omega_1}^{\omega_2} \omega^r F(\omega)\, d\omega$ and $\int_{\omega_1}^{\omega_2} \omega^s F^2(\omega)\, d\omega$ are not simple integrals? How can these be surmounted?

(e) Illustrate the process by designing the networks specified below. Calculate and plot the error in each case.

F	ω_1	ω_2	Order of $Z(p)$	Number of Zeros of $Z(p)$ at Origin
(1) $\omega^4 e^{-\omega}$	0	∞	4	4
(2) $\tanh \omega$	0.5	2	5	2
(3) $e^{\sqrt{\omega}}$	1	3	4	2
(4) $e^{-\sqrt{\omega}}$	1	3	4	0
(5) See figure	0	∞	5	5
(6) See figure	0	∞	5	5

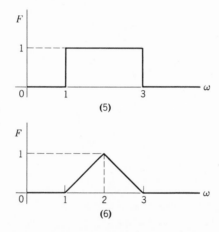

Prob. 13–15

(f) Extend this method, in general terms, to the approximation of reactance (susceptance) and of tangent of angle. What difficulty arises in extending it to square of magnitude of immittance?

13-16. A network is to be designed according to the principles of § 11.04. In particular, the network of Fig. 11.04-A is ideally to have a transmission characteristic (11.04-3) that descends linearly to zero at unit frequency and thereafter remains zero, like the function of the figure for Prob. 13-14. Solve the approximation problem

(a) by point-matching and subsequent improvement toward an equal-ripple error curve;

(b) by least-mean-square-error methods (cf. Prob. 13-15);

(c) by making a maximal approximation at the mid-point of the sloping line segment.

Constraints that insure desirable network configurations may be applied, and network orders of one, two, three, four, five should be considered. Plot the error in each case, find the element values of the networks, and discuss the possibility of compensating for parasitic dissipation in the inductors and capacitors.

13-17. A convenient method for rapid solution of some not too severe approximation problems encountered in the design of impedance simulating or balancing networks (§ 11.03) can be based on the circular property of many simple impedance-function loci (VA 4). It consists essentially of plotting the data in an impedance plane, sketching in arcs of circles as approximations, and realizing these circles by simple networks, connected in series. The following exercises illustrate the procedure.

(a) Sketch the loci (frequency being a parameter and running from 0 to ∞) in a complex plane of the impedance of all possible combinations of two and three elements. Which of these are circles or arcs of circles? What happens to these loci when a resistor is added in series to the network? Illustrate.

(b) A network is required to simulate the following measured transmission-line data.

Frequency (kcps)	Impedance (ohms)
0.1	$1000 - j800$
0.2	$800 - j500$
0.5	$650 - j250$
1.0	$610 - j130$
2.0	$605 - j65$
5.0	$600 - j30$
10.0	$600 - j10$

Sketch the locus, draw in an approximating circular arc of the most appropriate type in your compilation of (a), and find the element values of the corresponding simulating network. Discuss the quality of approximation obtainable (1) if only frequencies above 200 cps are important, (2) if the approximation band extends down to 100 cps.

(c) A network is required to simulate the following line data.

Frequency (kcps)	Impedance (ohms)
0.1	$800 - j600$
0.2	$600 - j400$
0.5	$500 - j200$
1.0	$480 - j150$
2.0	$470 - j100$
5.0	$450 - j130$
10.0	$400 - j200$
15.0	$300 - j350$

What is the essential difference in the approximation problem here, compared with that of (b)? Show how a graphical construction using two circular arcs will quickly determine the element values of a suitable R-C network of order two. Determine the element values and discuss the quality of approximation.

(d) A network is required to simulate the impedance of a pair of wires in a telephone cable, which is closely $600/\sqrt{f}\ \underline{/-45°}$ in the approximation band, $0.1 < f < 5$ kcps, f being in kcps throughout. What is the novelty in this problem? By graphical construction determine the element values of R-C networks of orders one, two, three whose impedances simulate that of the cable pair.

(e) The formula given in (d) is quite accurate for frequencies below 5 kcps. At high frequencies the cable-pair impedance approaches the value $100\ \Omega$ (purely resistive). Sketch in a smooth curve to complete the locus from 5 kcps to high frequencies, taking $100 + j0$ as the 100-kcps value. Discuss the quality of the high-frequency impedance simulation of the networks of (d).

13-18. Explain, from the point of view of weighting, how the use of powers of the error greater than the second tends to reduce large errors at the expense of small errors.

13-19. The frequency band of approximation may well extend to infinity. In (13.04–2) this would make $\omega_2 \rightarrow \infty$, so that E becomes zero, regardless of the parameter values, in general. Explain how this difficulty may be circumvented and the least-square method still used in this case.

13-20. Derive (13.04–4). If the a and b parameters enter only linearly into G, show that the corresponding set of equations is linear in these parameters and write these equations out. If in addition G is the sum of *orthogonal* functions of ω, i.e.,

$$G = a_0\phi_0(\omega) + a_1\phi_1(\omega) + \cdots + a_r\phi_r(\omega)$$

and

$$\int_{\omega_1}^{\omega_2}\phi_m(\omega)\phi_n(\omega)\,d\omega = 0, \qquad m \neq n,$$

show that the solutions for the a's may be written immediately, and give these solutions. How do the solutions change if r is now increased?

13-21. Explain why it is reasonable to make the approximation that leads from (13.04–7) to (13.04–8), derive the latter, and obtain the solution (13.04–9). (Cf. Prob. 13-15.)

13-22. Write out (13.05–19) completely for polynomials (in ω) of degree 8, 10, 12.

13-23. Derive (13.05–23). Discuss the possibility that in some problems the determinant of the coefficients of the unknown a's and b's vanishes. What does this imply, and what action must then be taken?

13-24. Show that the *percentage* or *fractional* error in the problem associated with Fig. 13.05–C actually becomes larger and larger without limit as ω increases.

13-25. Show that an odd rational function of order N can be of either odd or even order and must fall in one of the four following categories.

Behavior at the Origin	Behavior at Infinity	Nature of N
Zero of odd order	Pole of odd order	Odd
Zero of odd order	Zero of odd order	Even
Pole of odd order	Pole of odd order	Even
Pole of odd order	Zero of odd order	Odd

13-26. Construct additional entries in the appropriate Padé table, i.e., find additional functions $R(\omega)$, for the first illustrative problem of § 13.05. For all those that are realizable and correspond to impedance functions of order three or less, compute and plot the error as a function of frequency. Discuss the family of curves.

13-27. Explain, for the first example of § 13.05, how the values of the c's given in (13.05–16) can be used to obtain the b's for *any* choice of ω_0. Show also that if ω_0 is given any value not equal to 2, the curve of Fig. 13.05–A still represents the error, provided it is centered at the new ω_0, and both horizontal and vertical scales are suitably altered. Plot this curve for $\omega_0 = 1, 2, 2.5, 3, 4$, and compare the results.

13-28. Obtain network realizations of the various approximations to the function $\omega^{-1/2}$ as a resistance given in this chapter.

13-29. Design several networks whose driving-point resistance approximates, near the origin, the function $(1 + \omega)^{-1/2}$. Could the approximation problem here be solved by first obtaining a corresponding function of p, and then approximating that function in terms of p?
Repeat for driving-point reactance, using the function $\omega(1 + \omega)^{-1/2}$.

13-30. In finding maximal approximations at a frequency ω_0 (not zero) one may wonder why it should not be possible to write the approximating function directly in terms of $x = [(\omega/\omega_0) - 1]$ in the beginning, then determine the parameters for maximal agreement at $x = 0$, and only then obtain the function of ω by substitution for x. This procedure would avoid the cumbersome expressions in (13.05–12) and (13.05–13), for example. Explain why this is not possible, and why the approximating function must first be written as a function of ω, and then converted to a function of x.

13-31. Justify the equating of coefficients of like powers of x in the Taylor-approximation process, after multiplying through by the denominator of the approximating function (as is done, e.g., in § 13.05).

13-32. Explain why straightforward calculation of the value of the approximating function and of its derivatives at a point of maximal approximation, ω_0, and equating of these to the required values does not lead to simple equations for determining the parameters. What is the advantage of the method discussed in § 13.05?

13-33. Show that if a function $G(\omega)$ is approximated in the Taylor sense at a point ω_0, by a function $S(\omega)$, then $F = G^{-1}$ is approximated in the same fashion by $R = S^{-1}$. Solve the problem of maximal approximation of $\omega^{-1/2}$ at $\omega = 2$ by the function (13.05–3) by using reciprocal functions. Compare your results with (13.05–16).

13-34. The function $F(\omega) = f_0 + f_1\omega + f_2\omega^2 + \cdots$ near the origin is to be approximated there by an even function of ω. Explain why $f_1, f_3, f_5, \cdots$, f_{2m-1} must all be zero if a Taylor approximation to $2m$ terms is to be made. What can you say in general about the nature of functions to be maximally approximated at the origin by even (or odd) functions of frequency? Why is the situation different if the approximation is to be at $\omega_0 \neq 0$? Illustrate by discussing the design of a network whose driving-point resistance is to approximate, at the origin, (a) $\exp(-\omega^2)$, (b) $\exp(-\omega)$.

13-35. Although approximation in the Taylor sense is technically not possible at a point at which the function to be approximated has a pole, nevertheless we may accomplish this in effect by inserting a pole in the approximating function, dividing out the corresponding factor(s), and then proceeding with the Taylor process. Illustrate this with the following examples.

(a) Approximation of $\cot^2 \omega$ at the origin with a function suitable for realization as the square of the magnitude of a driving-point impedance.

(b) Approximation of $\tan \omega$ at $\omega = \pi/2$ with a function suitable for realization as a driving-point reactance.

13-36. Derive the simultaneous equations that determine the a's and b's in (13.06–1) when $\omega_0 = 0$. Explain their use when F has a simple zero at the origin, and when it has a multiple zero there. (See Prob. 13-35 for the procedure when F has a pole at the origin.)

13-37. Approximate the function $\sin^2 \omega$ at $\omega = \pi$ with an even function of order six, intended to represent a driving-point resistance. Do this (a) by setting $c_0 = 0$, $c_1 = 0$ and using (13.05–22) and (13.05–19), (b) by dividing through by x^2 and using (13.05–23) with appropriate change of symbols. What difference is there in the two approaches?

13-38. Find the nine entries in the upper left corner of the Padé table for the exponential function, by solving the appropriate simultaneous equations, (13.07–6). Compare the work required here (and for higher entries) with that of Prob. 13-39.

13-39. Find the general expressions for the entries in the Padé table for the exponential function, (13.07–7), by the following device (PA 3). Let $F(y)$ be a polynomial of degree r. Show (by repeated integration by parts) that

$$\int_0^1 e^{yx} F(y)\, dy = \left[\frac{F(1) \cdot e^x}{x} - \frac{F(0)}{x} \right] - \frac{1}{x} \int_0^1 e^{yx} F'(y)\, dy$$

$$= e^x \left[\frac{F(1)}{x} - \frac{F'(1)}{x^2} + \cdots + (-1)^r \frac{F^{(r)}(1)}{x^{r+1}} \right]$$

$$- \left[\frac{F(0)}{x} - \frac{F'(0)}{x^2} + \cdots + (-1)^r \frac{F^r(0)}{x^{r+1}} \right]$$

and hence that

$$e^x = \frac{F^{(r)}(0) - F^{(r-1)}(0) \cdot x + \cdots + (-1)^r F(0) \cdot x^r}{F^{(r)}(1) - F^{(r-1)}(1) \cdot x + \cdots + (-1)^r F(1) \cdot x^r} + c_{r+1} x^{r+1} + c_{r+2} x^{r+2} + \cdots$$

$$= \frac{P_{nm}(x)}{Q_{nm}(x)} + c_{r+1} x^{r+1} + \cdots.$$

Now let $F(y) = y^n(1 - y)^m$, $m + n = r$. Show then that the numerator of the rational function is

$$P_{nm}(x) = 1 + \frac{m}{m + n} \cdot \frac{x}{1!} + \frac{m(m - 1)}{(m + n)(m + n - 1)} \cdot \frac{x^2}{2!} + \cdots$$

$$+ \frac{m(m - 1)(m - 2) \cdots 1}{(m + n)(m + n - 1) \cdots (n + 1)} \cdot \frac{x^m}{m!}$$

and that the denominator is

$$Q_{nm}(x) = P_{mn}(-x).$$

Verify, from these formulas, the entries of Table 13.07–B and extend it by one row and one column.

13-40. Let $f(p)$ be a function regular at the origin.

(a) If the Padé table for $f(p)$, constructed at the origin, is to have the symmetry property $R_{mn}(p) = [R_{nm}(-p)]^{-1}$, i.e., the functions on the principal diagonal are of the form $(A + pB)/(A - pB)$ and two corresponding functions off the principal diagonal differ only by changing of the sign of p and inversion, what equation must $f(p)$ satisfy?

(b) Show that the exponential function e^p satisfies this equation, and verify the symmetry property in its Padé table.

(c) Show that any rational function of p whose magnitude is unity on the imaginary axis also satisfies this equation. Is the converse statement true? Construct Padé tables for the functions below, verify the symmetry property, and point out how the table is abnormal.

$$(1) \ \frac{1 - p}{1 + p} \qquad (2) \ \frac{2 + 2p + p^2}{2 - 2p + p^2} \qquad (3) \ \frac{2 - p^2 - p^3}{2 - p^2 + p^3}.$$

(d) Find expressions for the even part of $f(p)$ in terms of the odd part, and expressions for the odd part of $f(p)$ in terms of the even part, if $f(p)$ is to have the property discussed above. Find $f(p)$ if

$$\mathbf{Ev}\, f(p) = \cos p \qquad \mathbf{Ev}\, f(p) = p^2 \qquad \mathbf{Ev}\, f(p) = \frac{1 + p^2}{1 - p^2},$$

$$\mathbf{Od}\, f(p) = \sinh p \qquad \mathbf{Ev}\, f(p) = \sin p^2 \qquad \mathbf{Ev}\, f(p) = \frac{1}{1 - p^2}.$$

$$\mathbf{Od}\, f(p) = p$$

(In general, of course, the odd and even parts of a function are not necessarily related.)

(e) Show that if $f(p)$ has a Maclaurin series, $a_0 + a_1 p + a_2 p^2 + \cdots$, in which $a_0 = 1$, and $f(p)$ is to have the property under discussion, then in each pair of coefficients (a_1, a_2), (a_3, a_4), (a_5, a_6), $\cdots$ either member may be specified arbitrarily, and the function is then determined, provided a convergent series results. Discuss the meaning of the Padé table if the series does not converge.

13-41. Show that all the entries on the principal diagonal of the Padé table for e^p can be realized as *transmission* functions by the networks associated with (11.02–4). Show that if this type of network is specified, then the transmission phase (angle) characteristic is maximally linear at the origin. Plot this phase characteristic versus frequency and find these networks for the principal-diagonal entries in Table 13.07–B. Plot also their slopes versus frequency and discuss possible uses for these networks.

13-42. Each of the functions sin ω, cos ω, sinh ω, cosh ω, may be written as the sum of two exponential functions. One might then think that the Padé tables for approximation of these functions at the origin could be constructed from Table 13.07–B by suitable addition of entries from two corresponding tables. Show that this *cannot* be done in general and explain the nature of the approximations obtained by such additions. Relate this to the discussion that concludes § 13.06. Could the Padé table for tan ω and tanh ω be obtained by dividing entries from tables for the sin (sinh) and cos (cosh) functions?

13-43. Explain why the substitution of $-\omega^2$ for x in Table 13.07–B yields the Padé table for $e^{-\omega^2}$ at the origin. Explain why the same is true if the substitution for x is ω^{2n}. Explain why the substitution for x of an arbitrary rational function of ω^2 (with real coefficients) generally does not yield a complete Padé table. Explain why it is not possible to substitute for x functions of ω other than rational functions, if the results are to have any network applicability —and why, if the coefficients in the rational functions are to be real, they must be even functions.

13-44. Suppose that $H(p)$ is a rational function of p that maximally approximates the function $F(p)$ at the origin. In the power series for the error, the first term with a nonzero coefficient is the p^r term, i.e.

$$H(p) = F(p) + \varepsilon_r p^r + \varepsilon_{r+1} p^{r+1} + \cdots$$

near the origin. Show that **Re** $F(j\omega)$ is approximated by **Re** $H(j\omega)$ with an error also commencing in general with the ω^r term, and that similar statements can be made for the imaginary part, the magnitude, and the angle, i.e., that all four "parts" are approximated to the same degree that $H(p)$ itself is. If **Re** $F(j\omega)$ *alone* is to be approximated, can the degree of approximation be improved without raising the order of the corresponding function $H(p)$?

13-45. Construct the first part of the Padé table for the function $F(p) = 1 - e^{-p}$, the point of (maximal) approximation being at the origin. Compare these rational functions with $F(p)$ at real and imaginary frequencies in real part, imaginary part, magnitude, and angle, particularly as to degree of approximation achieved. Realize, as driving-point impedances, those that are realizable. If any one of the four parts alone is to be approximated, at the origin, with a rational function of ω, can the degree of approximation be improved without raising the order of the approximating function?
Repeat for the function $F(p) = (1 - e^{-p})/p$.

13-46. Approximate the function $F(p) = 1 - e^{-\pi p}$ with a rational function of order N, potentially suitable for realization as a driving-point impedance, in maximal fashion at the point $p = j1$. Do this for various values of N, compare the parts of these functions with those of F, and obtain network realizations where possible.

13-47. Discuss the maximal (complex) approximation of e^p at the point $j\pi$ with rational functions of p, potentially realizable as immittance functions. Repeat for sin p, at $p = j\pi$.

13-48. Discuss, with illustrations, the maximal approximation in terms of

p of the function $\exp[1/(p - 1)]$ both at the origin and at infinity. In the latter case, use the change of variable $s = p^{-1}$.

13-49. In the systems of simultaneous equations developed in §§ 13.05 and 13.06 for determining the coefficients in a maximal approximation, considerable use is made of the binomial coefficients, i.e., the coefficients in the expansion of $(1 + x)^n$. Point out exactly where these appear in both the odd-function and the even-function cases. Look up and verify the algebraic formula for the coefficient of the mth power of x in the expansion of $(1 + x)^n$ and explain why this is useful in Padé approximation. Look up and explain the use of the *Pascal triangle* in computing these coefficients.

13-50. Find maximal (Taylor) solutions to the following network-synthesis problems: Desired property: resistance to approximate $e^{-\omega^2}$; (a) point of most importance is zero frequency, (b) point of most importance is $\omega = 1$. In each case construct the appropriate Padé table through functions corresponding to networks of order five. (Cf. Prob. 13-43 and §§ 13.05, 13.07.) Of the realizable functions which are the best (1) as to quality of approximation, (2) as to practicability?

Apply your results to the design of networks (of the sort discussed in §11.04) for which the magnitude of transmission is to be in maximal agreement with the function $e^{-\omega^2}$ (a) at zero frequency, (b) at $\omega = 1$.

Which of your functions are realizable as squared magnitudes of immittance?

13-51. Find Chebyshev solutions (using trial-and-error methods) to Prob. 13-50, the approximation band being (a) $0 < \omega < 1$, (b) $0.5 < \omega < 2$.

13-52. Obtain networks whose input resistance maximally approximates the function $\omega^4 e^{-\omega^2}$ at the origin. Do this first with a numerator that contains one term only and then more generally. What advantage does the first class of functions have? Plot and discuss the errors, for resistance functions of orders up to ten. Could your results be applied to the design of a network the square of the magnitude of whose impedance is to approximate $\omega^4 e^{-\omega^2}$?

13-53. Design resistance functions of orders two, four, six, eight to approximate the function $\omega^2 e^{-\omega^2}$ maximally at $\omega = 1$. Plot the errors against frequency. Do your approximating functions have zeros at the origin? If not, could the over-all approximation be improved by specifying zeros at the origin, as constraints? Discuss. Realize your best functions.

13-54. Construct the even-function Padé table for the function ω^{-1}, the point of approximation being $\omega = 1$, through functions of order ten. Apply this to the solution of the problem of designing a network whose driving-point impedance approximates, in magnitude, the reciprocal of the square root of frequency (cf. Prob. 11-21). Which of your functions can be realized as R-C networks?

13-55. Construct the Padé table for maximal approximation of $\sin \omega$ at the origin, including all entries of order five or less. From each entry that gives information, determine an approximate value of π and tabulate these; compare with the true value. Obtain network realizations of the functions (13.06–6).

13-56. Approximate the function $\sin \omega$ with odd functions of orders three, four, and five according to the following scheme: (a) prescribe as many zeros as possible, at the correct frequencies; (b) determine the remaining parameters for maximal approximation at the origin (subject to the prescriptions of zeros). Plot the results and compare with Fig. 13.06–A.

13-57. Approximate the function sin ω with odd functions of orders three, four, and five according to the following scheme: (a) prescribe as many zeros as possible, at the correct frequencies; (b) prescribe that the approximating function equal ± 1 at each maximum of $|\sin \omega|$ as far as is possible and reasonable; (c) determine any remaining parameters for maximal approximation at the origin. To what extent are such approximations Taylor approximations?

13-58. A resistance function is desired to have the behavior $\cos^2 \omega$ for frequencies from 0 to 2π. Obtain approximating functions, (a) of order four, (b) of order six, (c) of order eight, by each of the following procedures, and compare their merits: (1) maximal approximation at $\omega = 0$ without other specification; (2) maximal approximation at $\omega = 0$, except that certain zeros are specified; (3) approximations obtained by matching at points and successive improvements.

13-59. It is desired to design a network whose driving-point conductance is an approximation to the function $[(\sin \omega)/\omega]^2$. Obtain approximations to this conductance in each of the following ways; compare and discuss the errors of each case, with particular reference to the locations of the zeros of the function: (a) maximal approximation at the origin; (b) maximal approximation at $\omega = \pi$; (c) maximal approximation at the origin, subject to the requirement of zero conductance at $\omega = \pi$.

Functions suitable for similar treatment are $[J_0(\omega)]^2$ and $[J_1(\omega)/\omega]^2$.

13-60. Construct an even-function Padé table for the approximation of each of the following functions at the origin, determining the first 16 entries. Which functions are realizable as driving-point resistances? As driving-point conductances? As driving-point-immittance squared magnitudes? For the realizable cases plot the error and find realizations.

(a) $\cosh \omega$ (b) $\operatorname{sech} \omega$ (c) $\sin^2 \omega$ (d) $\cos \omega$ (e) $\tanh^2 \omega$

(f) $\sqrt{1 + \omega^2}$ (g) $(1 + \omega^2)^{-1/2}$ (h) $\dfrac{1}{\omega} \displaystyle\int_0^{\omega} e^{-u^2}\, du$ (i) $\dfrac{\sin \omega}{\omega}$

(j) $\dfrac{\tan^{-1} \omega}{\omega}$ (k) $\omega^4 e^{-\omega^4}$ (l) $\omega^6 e^{-\omega^2}$

13-61. A network is to be designed, by the method of § 11.04, to provide a maximally "Gaussian" transmission characteristic (VA 1) in the vicinity of ω_0, i.e., the transmission function $|E_2/I_0|$ is to approximate the function $\exp\{-K[(\omega - \omega_0)/\omega_0]^2\}$ in the Taylor sense at $\omega = \omega_0$. Discuss the construction of the appropriate Padé table and illustrate, taking $K = 3$. Which functions are realizable in ladder-network form (Fig. 9.11–A) without the use of Type-C and Type-D sections? If zeros of the resistance (better, even part of impedance) function are to lie only at the origin and infinity, how must the approximation procedure be modified? Illustrate with error curves and network realizations, using one, two, three, four, and five reactive elements.

13-62. Each of the following functions is to be approximated in maximal fashion at $\omega_0 = 1$, (a) with an even function of frequency that is to be realized as a driving-point resistance or conductance or square of magnitude of immittance, (b) with an odd function of frequency that is to be realized as a driving-point reactance, susceptance, or tangent of angle of immittance. In the cases where these can be done, carry out the approximation for functions of orders up to five and discuss your results. Obtain network realizations where possible.

(1) $-\omega^{-1/2}$ (2) $+\sqrt{\omega}$ (3) $-\sqrt{\omega}$ (4) $+\omega^{3/2}$ (5) $-\omega^{3/2}$

(6) $+\omega^{-3/2}$ (7) $\sqrt{\omega}(1 + \omega)$ (8) $\dfrac{\sqrt{\omega}}{(\omega - 1)^2}$ (9) $\dfrac{(\omega - 1)^2}{\sqrt{\omega}}$

(10) $\sin(\pi\omega)$ (11) $\cos(\pi\omega)$ (12) $\sin^2(\pi\omega)$ (13) $\cos^2(\pi\omega)$

(14) $\omega^6 e^{-\omega^6}$ (15) $\tan(\pi\omega)$ (16) $\tan\left(\dfrac{\pi\omega}{2}\right)$ (17) $\tanh\omega$

(18) $\sinh\omega$ (19) $\cosh\omega$ (20) $[\ln\omega]^2$ (21) $e^{\sqrt{\omega}}$

13-63. Approximate the function $-\cot\omega$ in maximal fashion at the origin with a function suitable for realization as a driving-point reactance, of order five. Obtain a realization.

13-64. Construct a Padé table for the approximation of $\omega e^{-\omega^2}$ at the origin. Does it contain odd, even, or mixed functions? Explain. Which functions are realizable as driving-point reactance (susceptance)? Which as angle of immittance? Plot the error versus frequency for these and find network realizations.

Repeat for each of the following functions.

(a) $\sin\omega$ (b) $\tan\omega$ (c) $\tanh\omega$ (d) $\sinh\omega$ (e) $J_1(\omega)$

(f) $-\csc\omega$ (g) $\pm(\cos\omega)/\omega$ (h) $\omega^3 e^{-\omega^2}$ (i) $\cot\omega$ (j) $\omega\cos\omega$

13-65. Consider the problem of maximal approximation of the straight line $F = 1 + k(\omega - \omega_0)$ at the point ω_0 with an even function of ω (TU 2). Here k may be positive or negative; such a network might be of use in frequency-modulation receivers.

(a) If k is prescribed, build up the appropriate Padé table.

(b) If k is not prescribed, but may be chosen to improve the linearity, determine the values that k may have when an even function of order four with all of its zeros at infinity is used. (Although the equations are now not linear in k, those unknowns that appear linearly may be eliminated, leaving a simple nonlinear equation that determines k.) Repeat with the zeros all at the origin. Repeat with zeros not prescribed, but located to improve the linearity. In each case plot the function, and compare results.

(c) Discuss the procedure for the general case. Build up a table showing the values of k for each entry in the Padé table, if k is not prescribed but is used to improve linearity.

(d) Obtain network realizations of those functions found that may be realized as driving-point resistances.

(e) Obtain network realizations of those functions found that may be realized as squared magnitudes of immittance.

13-66. Show that if a rational function is to be obtained, such that its angle is in maximal agreement with some prescribed function of frequency at some point ω_0, it makes no difference whether (a) the angle of the rational function is actually made to agree with the data in value and a certain number of derivatives, or (b) the tangent of the angle of the rational function is made to have similar maximal agreement with the tangent of the datum angle; i.e., the two are equivalent.

13-67. Consider the problem of designing a p-r rational function

$$F(p) = \frac{a_0 + a_1 p + \cdots + a_m p^m}{b_0 + b_1 p + \cdots + b_n p^n}$$

such that its real-frequency angle approximates some desired function $D(\omega)$.

(a) Explain the procedure to be used to determine the a's and b's if the approximation is to be made by matching the desired angle exactly at certain prescribed points. Convert the general transcendental equation into a purely algebraic one, and indicate the difficulties of solution.

Now make use of the general ideas of § 8.14 to simplify the procedure to the following:

Determine a polynomial $Q(p) = A + pB = c_0 + c_1 p + \cdots + c_r p^r, r = m + n$, such that $[(pB)/(jA)]_{p=j\omega} = \tan D$ at the prescribed frequencies. (The equations to be solved here for the c's are linear.) From $Q(p)$ a number of rational functions with the same real-frequency angle can be obtained.

Explain the above and discuss the conditions under which one of these functions is the desired p-r result.

(b) Suppose the approximation is to be in the Taylor sense at a frequency ω_0. Set up the formal procedure that leads to a series involving the a's and b's that can be equated term by term to that for $D(\omega)$. Discuss the practical difficulties of solution of the problem in this fashion.

Develop a procedure, corresponding to that outlined under (a), that makes use of an auxiliary polynomial $Q(p) = A + pB$, and determines it by equating terms in the series for (pB/A) and for $\tanh (jD)$ near $p = j\omega_0$. Explain and justify each step. (This reduces the problem to the type discussed in the text under resistance and reactance approximation.)

13-68. Obtain p-r rational functions whose angles $\beta(\omega)$ are maximal approximations of those desired according to the list below (cf. Prob. 13-67). Realize these in network form. Where the degree of the auxiliary polynomial Q is not equal to n, explain the difference. Plot versus frequency and compare $D(\omega)$, the desired angle, and the angle achieved, in each case. The point of approximation is denoted ω_0; n is the order of the final resulting immittance function.

$D(\omega)$	ω_0	n	Additional Requirements
ω	0	3	
ω^3	0	3	
$\sin \omega$	0	4	
$\tanh \omega$	0	3	
$e^{-\omega}$	1	3	$\beta = 0$ at the origin and at infinity
$e^{-\omega}$	1	3	$\beta = \pi/2$ at the origin
			$\beta = 0$ at infinity
$45°$ (constant)	1	4	$\beta = 0$ at the origin and at infinity
$\dfrac{\omega}{1 + \omega^2}$	0	5	
ω^{-4}	1	3	$\beta = \pi/2$ at the origin
			$\beta = 0$ at infinity
$k(\omega - \omega_0)$	1	various	
$\sin^{-1} k(\omega - \omega_0)$	1	various	

13-69. Use the Padé table for the exponential function to obtain a table of p-r rational functions whose real-frequency angles are maximally linear with frequency at the origin (with unit slope), according to the procedure outlined below.

(1) Set $x = 2p$. Show that $H_{nn} = e^{2p} + (p^{2n+1})$, in which the parentheses indicate a series beginning with the power of p shown, and hence (by taking the logarithm) that the real-frequency angle of P_{nn} is given by $\beta_{nn} = \omega + (\omega^{2n+1})$, and that this angle is maximally linear at the origin, within the capabilities of a polynomial of degree n.

(2) Write $P_{nn} = A + pB$ and give a formula for this polynomial for any n. Show, at least for the first few, that these polynomials are Hurwitz.

(3) From P_{nn} find the rational function that is p-r and has a real-frequency angle that is maximally linear at the origin. Show that it can be realized as a driving-point impedance by an L-C network in series with a resistor, and give also the dual realization. Discuss the use of these functions as impedance functions in the networks of § 11.02.

13-70. An alternative proof of the fact that the polynomials forming the numerators of the principal-diagonal functions in the Padé table for e^p have real-frequency angles that are maximally linear at the origin is outlined below. Fill in the details.

$$H_{nn} = \frac{A + pB}{A - pB} = \frac{1 + T}{1 - T} = e^p + \Delta, \qquad T = pB/A.$$

$$T = \frac{H_{nn} - 1}{H_{nn} + 1} = [\tanh (p/2)](1 + \Delta_1).$$

When $p = j\omega$, $\overline{H_{nn}} = 2 \tan^{-1} (T/j) = \omega + \Delta_2$.

13-71. Show that the angle of a function H_{nm} from Table 13.07–B, with $x = p = j\omega$, is linear with frequency at the origin, within an error starting with a term in ω^{m+n+1}. If a rational function of the same degrees in numerator and denominator as H_{nm} is designed to have maximally linear angle at the origin, with what power of ω does the error begin?

Obtain such rational functions for $m = n = 1$, $m = 2$ and $n = 0$, $m = 0$ and $n = 2$, and show that the corresponding p-r function (with maximally linear angle) is the same as that obtained from H_{22}, with proper adjustment of the frequency scale.

13-72. Obtain a reasonable number of realizations of driving-point immittance functions that have (at the origin) maximally cubic real-frequency angles.

13-73. Plot the zeros and poles of the functions on the principal diagonal of the Padé table for e^p, for $n = 1, 2, 3, 4, 5$. Discuss their apparent behavior as n gets larger, and relate this, in a general way, with the nature of the zeros and the singularities of the exponential function.

The loci of the zeros and poles of the functions in Padé tables for other functions provide many interesting exercises of similar nature.

13-74. Consider the Taylor approximation of a rational function by a rational function, at the origin. Let the function to be approximated, of order S, be written in factored form,

$$F = K \frac{(\ )(\ ) \cdots}{(\ )(\ ) \cdots}$$

and the approximating function, of order N, be written

$$R = K' \frac{(\ )(\ ) \cdots}{(\ )(\ ) \cdots}.$$

In the absence of additional constraints, and if $S \leq N$, what will be the relations between K and K', between the zeros of F and those of R, between the poles of F and those of R? Are any of the zeros or poles of R arbitrary? Explain. If now $S > N$, how are the answers to these questions changed? Illustrate by finding the function R, both for $N = 2$ and for $N = 6$, given $F = (1 + \omega^2)/(1 + \omega^4)$.

Discuss these same questions, when constraints are required.

13-75. Consider the approximation, in the Taylor fashion at the origin, of $(1 + c\omega^2 + \omega^4)$ by $(1 + a_2\omega^2)/(1 + b_2\omega^2 + b_4\omega^4)$. In general, how many terms in the Taylor series can be made to agree? Are any coefficients arbitrary? For what values of c are the answers to these questions changed? Why?

13-76. Consider the maximal approximation of ω^{-2} at $\omega_0 = 1$ with a resistance function. What difficulties arise in determining the a's and b's of a resistance function whose denominator and numerator each contain two terms? Of a resistance function of any complexity? What is the reason for this behavior? What can you do to obtain an approximating function in spite of this?

13-77. Consider the resistance-function approximation of the "block" of Fig. 13.10–E by applying Taylor approximation at ω_0. Suppose the approximating function is to have the form

$$R = \frac{\omega^2}{b_0 + b_2\omega^2 + b_4\omega^4 + b_6\omega^6 + b_8\omega^8},$$

i.e., the zeros are constrained to lie two at the origin and six at infinity. What values for the b's are obtained by straightforward Padé approximation? Explain the anomaly.

If a five-element network realization is desired (only one element a resistor), how can suitable values for the b's be determined? Illustrate with an actual design.

13-78. If the block of Fig. 13.10–E is approximated by an even function with zeros only at the origin and infinity, the resulting function is *probably* (*not certainly*) realizable as a *simple L-C ladder network with but one resistor*. Explain the italicized words.

13-79. (*a*) Verify (13.10–6).

(*b*) Show that in (13.10–13) $b' = b2^N\omega_0^{N-2M}$.

(*c*) Expand the remark of the text to explain fully why the approximation (13.10–12) is indeed maximal.

(*d*) Show that the numerator can be arbitrarily selected in fact, and that

$$R = \frac{(\text{numerator})}{(\text{numerator}) + b_{2N}(\omega^2 - \omega_0^2)^N}$$

is a maximal approximation of the constant unity at ω_0. Note the possibility of arbitrary selection of the zeros, and the parallel to (13.10–7). Can the denominator (instead of the numerator) be arbitrarily selected?

(*e*) Verify the reasoning used above by applying (13.05–23) to this problem and showing by particular examples that if $R(\omega)$ is to have zeros at infinity, then the numerator (of degree $2M$) can be arbitrarily chosen without affecting the quality of approximation at ω_0.

13-80. (*a*) Plot curves of the function (13.10–12) with $N = 6$ and $R(\omega_0/2)$ = 0.5, for all the various possible distributions of zeros between the origin and infinity. Which is the most nearly rectangular? Do any of them have true symmetry about ω_0 on an arithmetic frequency scale? On a logarithmic frequency scale? Explain.

(*b*) Realize each of these resistance functions.

13-81. Set up a resistance function of order $2N$ that is maximally flat at ω_0, with zeros at the origin, at one internal frequency below ω_0 and one above ω_0, and at infinity. Discuss the freedom you have in choosing such a function.

Illustrate by taking $N = 6$ and obtaining an approximation of the block of Fig. 13.10–E (determining the arbitrary quantities by trial). Realize the network.

13-82. Which of the even-function approximations obtained for resistance purposes, in the text of this chapter and in its problems, are also suitable for realization as the square of the magnitude of an immittance? Explain. Realize them.

13-83. Show that the constraint of placing zeros at the origin, or at infinity, as in (13.10–12), for example, is equivalent to requiring a flat approximation of zero at the origin (infinity) of a certain quality.

13-84. Find the element values of the networks of Fig. 13.10–B for $N = 1, 2, 3, 4, 5$. Discuss the possibility of obtaining literal formulas for these elements, for arbitrary N (cf. Prob. 9-9).

13-85. Find the element values of the networks of Fig. 13.10–C and compare them.

13-86. Obtain the element values of a network of order five whose driving-point resistance has the form shown in Fig. 13.10–D (which is not to scale). Plot the resistance characteristic carefully.

13-87. An important application of the one-resistor network (§ 11.04) is in vacuum-tube interstage network design, where the first tube is a pentode (substantially a current source). The peculiar physical requirements imposed by the vacuum tubes are listed in Prob. 11-26.

For amplifiers the approximation problem may be resolved by requiring maximally flat transmission at the nominal center of the approximation band, i.e., the block of Fig. 13.10–E is to be approximated in the Taylor sense.

(*a*) Show that Probs. 9-12 and 9-13 deal with exactly this situation. In what way are Probs. 11-24 through 11-28 related? Probs. 13-77 through 13-81?

(*b*) Give a complete discussion of the maximally flat solution of the approximation problem for interstage networks when the frequency ω_0 is high enough that both the plate-cathode and grid-cathode parasitic capacitances must be resonated by inductors, in order to obtain reasonable values of impedance. The two "tuned circuits" so constituted are to be connected (1) by electromagnetic coupling of the inductors, (2) by a capacitor, without electromagnetic coupling. What arbitrariness is there in the solution? What limits the gain obtainable at the frequency ω_0? Illustrate by carrying out the design of such an interstage network in both forms, to operate between tubes for which C_{gk} = 15 $\mu\mu$f, C_{pk} = 20 $\mu\mu$f, ω_0 corresponds to 5 mcps, and at 4.5 mcps the transmission magnitude (squared) is to be half of its maximum value. Discuss your work and results.

13-88. Derive the functions of (13.10–15) by the method there indicated. Verify (13.10–19). Explain why each function is realizable and find network realizations of each as both reactance and susceptance. Repeat for their reciprocals and for the negatives.

Realize networks, each of which has for the tangent of its angle one of the functions of (13.10–15). Repeat for the reciprocals and for the negatives. What angle is approximated at $\omega = 1$? Repeat for angles of 30° and 60°.

13-89. Derive (13.10–21) by Taylor approximation of ω at the origin, and show the connection between this function and (13.10–5). Show more generally that maximal approximation of ω^n at the origin (n being any positive integer), subject to the constraint of zeros at infinity, can be obtained in a similar fashion from (13.10–5). Illustrate the results with plots of the functions for the following cases:

n	Order of Approximating Function (Resistance or Reactance)	Number of Zeros at Infinity
1	8	7
1	8	5
1	8	3
2	8	6
2	8	4

Finite zeros should be placed in the general region $1 < \omega < 2$ to improve the approximation of zero for $\omega > 1$, if that is possible.

13-90. Explain why odd functions obtained as maximal approximations of a constant (13.10–18) can be used immediately to obtain an immittance function whose angle approximates a constant, but this is not true if the angle is to approximate, for example, $K\omega$ at the origin in the Taylor sense.

13-91. Determine immittance functions of various orders whose angles are linear at the origin and flat (at 90° value) at high frequencies, by using approximately half the available parameters to satisfy each of the two requirements. Explain how a simple change in frequency scale will convert a design with a given slope at the origin into one with any other slope there.

13-92. Derive (13.10–25) and (13.10–26) and verify the curve of Fig. 13.10–J. Show how (13.10–26) could also be obtained, more directly, by immediately writing

$$R = \frac{2}{1 + \dfrac{(\omega^2 - 1)^4}{b_0 + b_2\omega^2 + b_4\omega^4}}$$

and determining the b's for flatness (and unit value) at the origin.

13-93. Consider the problem of approximating the rectangle of Fig. 13.10–E with a function realizable as a driving-point reactance. The function (13.10–17) is quite flat at unit frequency, but slow to drop off at high frequencies. By relaxing one term in the Taylor approximation, and substituting therefor the requirement that $X(2) = K$, endeavor to improve the approximation of the rectangle. You may, e.g., take N as 4 or 6, and determine the functions for $K = 0.9, 0.8, \cdots$. Plot your results and discuss them as to the improvement made and as to realizability. Repeat, relaxing two terms and instead specifying $X(0.5)$ and $X(2)$. What conclusions do you reach? Does raising the order of the zero at the origin, or at infinity, help? For example, determine the parameters in

$$X = \frac{\omega^3}{b_0 + b_2\omega^2 + b_4\omega^4 + b_6\omega^6}$$

for maximal flatness at $\omega = 1$. Discuss.

Attempt the same improvement by specifying zero value for X at frequencies above or below $\omega = 1$, or both. Discuss.

13-94. Verify the curves of Fig. 13.10–G by calculating X_N from the formula

$$X_N = \tanh (N \tanh^{-1} \omega)$$

which must of course be reconciled with (13.10–17) and (13.10–18). Add those for odd values of N. Realize those functions for $N = 1, 2, 3, 4, 5, 6$. Are all three kinds of elements necessary? Discuss the symmetry of these curves on arithmetic and on logarithmic frequency scales.

13-95. Find and realize immittance functions whose real-frequency angle is maximally constant at unit frequency, using (13.10–18). The problem is to be investigated for functions of various orders and for approximations to various angles, e.g., 30°, 45°, 60°.

13-96. Investigate the design of networks whose driving-point reactance is maximally linear with frequency at $\omega = 1$ at the value 1, with slope $+2$. The reactance is also to approach zero at both low and high frequencies. Take 4, e.g., as the order of the function $X(\omega)$; obtain the function and plot its behavior. Is it realizable? Suppose that good linearity is more important than matching the prescribed value of slope. Can the linearity be improved by using some other value of slope? Illustrate.

13-97. Investigate, along lines similar to those of Prob. 13-96, the design of networks the angle of whose immittance is maximally linear with frequency at $\omega = 1$.

13-98. Design a series of networks, of increasing complexity, whose driving-point resistance is flat (constant) at the value 2 near the origin, and linear (with slope -2) about the value 1 at $\omega = 1$. Each of the networks is to consist of a simple L-C ladder (series L, shunt C) terminated in a resistor. In the approximation the available parameters are to be distributed approximately equally between Taylor approximations at the origin and at $\omega = 1$.

13-99. Repeat Prob. 13-98 with the change that at $\omega = 1$ the resistance behavior is to approximate $3e^{-\omega^2}$.

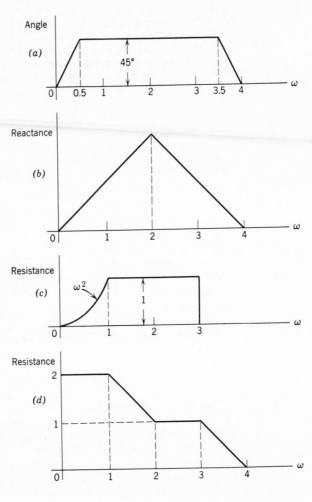

Prob. 13–100

13-100. Each of the sketches illustrates a problem to be solved by multiple-point Taylor approximation, the details of which are given in Table 1. Find suitable approximating functions and network realizations. Discuss the difficulties encountered, and *if necessary* make reasonable modifications in the distribution of parameters or order of the function.

Table 1

	Frequency	Character or Value to Be Approximated	Number of Parameters to Be Used for This Purpose
(a)	0	Linear	2
	1	Flat (constant)	2
	3	Flat (constant)	2
	∞	Zero	2
(b)	0	Linear	3
	1	Linear	3
	3	Linear	3
	∞	Zero	1
c)	0	Parabolic	3
	2	Flat (constant)	3
	∞	Zero	2
(d)	0	Flat (constant)	2
	1.5	Linear	4
	2.5	Flat (constant)	4
	∞	Zero	2

13-101. Discuss, with illustrative examples, the following idea: Approximation by point-matching (cf. § 13.03) is a process of *interpolation*; approximation in the Taylor sense (§ 13.05) is a process of *extrapolation*. (Due to W. H. Kautz.)

13-102. Obtain, by a succession of trials, Chebyshev approximations in each of the following problems.

	Function to Be Approximated	Nature of Approximating Function	Order of Approximating Function	Constraints	Approximation Band
(a)	$\sqrt{1 + \omega^2}$	Resistance	6	All zeros at infinity	$0 < \omega < 2$
(b)	$-\omega^{-1/2}$	Reactance	6	Zero at infinity	$1 < \omega < 4$
(c)	$\exp{[-(\omega - 1)^2]}$	$|Z|^2$	8	Zero at origin and infinity	$\frac{1}{2} < \omega < 2$
(d)	$\tan^{-1} \dfrac{\omega}{\sqrt{1 - \omega^2}}$	$\underline{Z}$	9	$-90°$ at infinity	$0 < \omega < 1$

For the first trial, match at appropriate points. Plot the resulting error, revise the values stipulated at these points, recalculate the error in this second trial, revise the values again, etc.   Observe the process of equalization of the "humps" of the error curve as you proceed (cf. Fig. 13.08–A).   Is there arbitrariness in the final value of these maxima and minima?   Realize the networks.

13-103. The function $(4 - \omega)$ is to be approximated with a resistance function in the band $1 < \omega < 3$ within limits of error outlined by $\pm[0.10(\omega - 2)^2 - 0.05(\omega - 2)^3]$. All of the zeros of resistance are to be at infinity.   Determine suitable functions, of orders two, four, six, and eight (a) by Taylor approximation, (b) by (weighted) Chebyshev approximation obtained by trial and error methods.   Compare the errors and efficiency of approximation.   Realize the best result.

13-104. A method of approximation that is sometimes useful is to adapt the Fourier-series expansion technique, as described below. (Cf. Prob. 8-56, BR 7, GU 8.)

(a) Let $\omega = \tan \phi/2$ define a new variable, ϕ.

(b) Expand the desired function $F(\omega)$, re-expressed as a function of ϕ, in a Fourier series, using only odd or only even terms as appropriate.

(c) Take a reasonable number of terms of the series, express this partial sum as a function of ω, and use this as the approximating function.

Explain the relationship between ϕ and ω, in particular pointing out the range of ϕ corresponding to the imaginary axis of the p plane.   Determine $e^{j\phi}$, $\cos \phi$, $\sin \phi$, as functions of ω.   Repeat for $e^{j2\phi}$, $\cos 2\phi$, $\sin 2\phi$, etc.   Explain how to determine the coefficients in $F = \Sigma a_n \cos n\phi$ or $F = \Sigma b_n \sin n\phi$ as appropriate. In what sense, and over what frequency range, is the approximation made?

What form, in each case, will the truncated series take as a function of ω? Point out the very special (restrictive) character of the denominator obtained. In what way does this limit the ability of the method?   Discuss the possibility of relaxing this restriction by considering the datum function to be the quotient of two functions, and approximating each of the two separately, by this method.

Illustrate the method with examples, the data for which may be taken from other problems in this chapter.

13-105. A method of approximation that is simple, yet may be useful in special cases, consists in the use of basic units made up of one real zero and one real

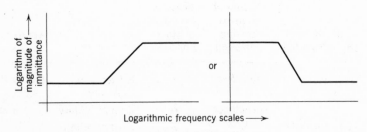

Prob. 13–105

pole, both finite and not zero (BR 6).   The procedure is reminiscent of some of the ideas of § 8.09 and of § 13.03.   It deals only with magnitude, and approximates the curve of the logarithm of the desired magnitude (on a logarithmic frequency scale) with broken-line units like those shown, each of which in turn is approximated by the behavior of one real "pole-zero pair," as mentioned above.

(*a*) Let $F(p) = (p - p_1)/(p - p_2)$ in which $p_1 = -\sigma_2$, $0 < \sigma_1 < \sigma_2$. Normalize the frequency scale by taking the distance between p_1 and p_2 as unit frequency and introduce a parameter representing the location of the point midway between them. Determine formally, and plot (on a logarithmic frequency scale), the logarithm of the magnitude of $F(j\omega)$. On this superimpose a broken-line unit that agrees asymptotically at high and low frequencies, and at the mid-point of the rising portion agrees in value and slope. Determine the maximum difference between the behavior of the pole-zero pair and of the broken-line unit. Determine the "corner" frequencies, the "mid-point" frequency, the vertical separation of the horizontal asymptotes.

(*b*) Sketch the associated angle characteristic for both the pole-zero pair and the broken-line unit, for several values of the parameters. What is the maximum value of the angle of $F(j\omega)$ in terms of the parameters?

(*c*) Show that $F(p)$ is always realizable as a driving-point immittance function. Under what conditions is $F(p)$ realizable, within a constant multiplier, as the transmission characteristic of the network of Fig. 11.02–A?

(*d*) Discuss the realizability of $F_1(p)F_2(p)$, in which each "F" represents such a pole-zero pair (the same, or different), in each of the two forms of (*c*), in general.

(*e*) Solve each of the following problems by using one pole-zero pair. Use the broken-line approximation and graphical methods to determine the parameters, keeping the error as small as possible. Realize each result in both forms. (Constant multipliers in F, or additive constants in $\log |F|$, may be used.)

(1) The logarithm of F is to approximate the square root of frequency between $\omega = 1$ and $\omega = 10$. Repeat for the *negative* of $\sqrt{\omega}$.

(2) Repeat (1) for an approximation band from $\omega = 1$ to $\omega = 3$ and compare the quality of approximation.

(3) The logarithm of F is to approximate $(1 + \omega^2)^{-1}$ at all frequencies.

(4) The logarithm of F is to approximate ω^3 from $\omega = 0$ to $\omega = 1$.

(*f*) Solve the same problems, using more than one pole-zero pair to improve the approximations. Where possible, obtain realizations in both forms. Where neither is possible, obtain realizations for the *individual* pairs in the second (bridged-T) form. (These networks may then be used in a "cascade" or "tandem" connection to realize the complete transmission function; cf. Probs. 10-98, 11-19, 11-20.)

13-106. A method of approximation that is sometimes useful (BA 2) utilizes the same basic idea as did § 8.09: to use a series of segments of straight lines to approximate the desired function. These lines must be further approximated here, of course, by rational functions. (Cf. also the ideas of § 13.03.)

The method uses a plot of the logarithm of F on a logarithmic frequency scale, F being the desired behavior for a resistance, conductance, or square-of-magnitude-of-immittance function. This is then approximated with a series of straight-line segments, drawn on the curve. We then think of these as a set of semi-infinite lines, as in § 8.09, and approximate each with a convenient function, $\left[1 + \left(\dfrac{\omega}{\omega_0}\right)^{2n}\right]$, that follows it fairly closely. The resulting function, if the work is carefully done, may be a useful and realizable rational-function approximation to the data.

(a) Plot the logarithm of $\left[1 + \left(\dfrac{\omega}{\omega_0} \right)^{2n} \right]$ on a logarithmic frequency scale, together with the pair of semi-infinite (asymptote) lines, as indicated in the figure. What are the slopes of the lines? Why are logarithmic scales used for both coordinates in this method? Determine the maximum departure of the curve representing the rational function from the straight-line "curve."

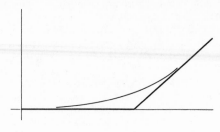

Prob. 13-106

(b) The method requires that we approximate the datum curve (logarithm of desired behavior on a logarithmic frequency scale) with a series of straight-line segments, to be approximated in turn with rational functions of the form above. What restriction does this impose on the slopes of the line segments used? Show how the straight-line approximations joining the points given in Table 2 can be approximated by several of the polynomials given in (a) above, give the values of ω_0 and of n for each, and sketch both the straight-line "curve" and the resulting rational-function smooth curve in each case.

Table 2

(a)		(b)		(c)	
ω	F	ω	F	ω	F
0	1	0	2	0	2
1	1	1	2	1	2
4	0.5	2	1	3	3
∞	0.5	4	1	9	1
		8	2	27	2
		∞	2	∞	2

How should the straight lines be drawn (with respect to the datum curve) in order to reduce the error caused by the departure of the smooth curve from the straight lines?

(c) Each of the following functions F represents a desired behavior for a driving-point resistance (conductance). Using the method outlined above, obtain approximations, and then network realizations, for each problem.

(1) $F = 1$, $0 < \omega < 1$,
$F = 0$, $2 < \omega$;
F to drop linearly with ω for $1 < \omega < 2$; approximation band is $0 < \omega < \infty$; immittance is to be of order five.

(2) $F = e^{\omega^2}$, $0 < \omega < 1$,
$F = e$, $1 < \omega$; approximation band is $0 < \omega < \infty$, immittance is to be of order four.

(3) $F = e^{\omega}$; approximation band is $1 < \omega < 3$. Obtain results for immittance functions of order one, two, three, four, and five.

(4) $F = (1/\omega) + \omega$; approximation band is $0.5 < \omega < 2$; immittance is to be of order three.

(*d*) Repeat (*c*), interpreting F as a desired behavior for square of magnitude of impedance (admittance). What additional restriction is now imposed the slopes of the initial and final (low-frequency and high-frequency) lines?

(*e*) Explain how the use of the particular function $\left[1 + \left(\dfrac{\omega}{\omega_0}\right)^{2n}\right]$ makes the calculation of immittance from resistance (conductance) or from squared magnitude of immittance a fairly simple process.

(*f*) If the method is to be extended to reactance (susceptance) or (tangent of) angle, then all real-frequency zeros and poles must first be removed from the data (by suitable multiplication by appropriate factors). Explain how this could be done, and illustrate by solving the following problems:

(1) A network is desired to have a driving-point reactance that approximates the function $\sin \omega$ in the range $0 < \omega < 2$, with an immittance function of order five.

(2) The requirement is that the angle of the driving-point impedance be a good approximation of the function $[(\pi/2) \tanh \omega]$ over the entire frequency range, with an immittance function of order three or less.

13-107. The emphasis, in these problems for Chapter 13, has of course been on the approximation problem. For practical completeness, pick out one or more of the preceding problems and investigate carefully the effect of incidental dissipation in the L and C elements of the realization, and discuss what can be done, if necessary, to reduce these effects. Discuss also compensation for parasitic capacitance.

14.

The Potential Analogy

Similia similibus curantur.
—(Medical proverb)

Approximation by rational functions is a process that can be carried out in a vast number of ways, of which we have found some in Chapter 13. One method of great interest and importance, which we have not discussed, is approximation by *analogy*, the utilization of our understanding of other, related physical problems. In particular, we can find in the mathematical physics of two-dimensional potential problems a fascinating and extremely useful analogy.

14.01 Origins of the analogy

Our network functions are functions of a complex variable, which we have called $p = \sigma + j\omega$. Perhaps the most striking property of such a function $F(p) = x(\sigma, \omega) + jy(\sigma, \omega)$, the property that principally makes it useful, is its obedience to the Cauchy–Riemann equations (3.10–6),

$$\frac{\partial x}{\partial \sigma} = \frac{\partial y}{\partial \omega},$$

$$\frac{\partial x}{\partial \omega} = -\frac{\partial y}{\partial \sigma}.$$

(14.01–1)

By differentiation and combination of these equations we can show that

$$\frac{\partial^2 x}{\partial^2 \sigma^2} + \frac{\partial^2 x}{\partial \omega^2} = 0$$

and

(14.01–2)

$$\frac{\partial^2 y}{\partial \sigma^2} + \frac{\partial^2 y}{\partial \omega^2} = 0,$$

i.e., that both the real and imaginary parts of a well-behaved function of a complex variable obey Laplace's equation in two dimensions. But

832

Laplace's equation is a fundamental one in mathematical physics, hence in many engineering problems. In fact, the development of the theory of functions of a complex variable in the nineteenth century was greatly stimulated by these practical applications.

As function theory developed, the inverse point of view began to be useful also: the use of corresponding physical problems, in concrete form, to assist at least in the numerical part of the solution of problems in function theory. Even in nineteenth century literature we can find instances of this (§ 14.21) and the current literature is voluminous.

Since there are many physical situations in which Laplace's equation appears—in electrostatics, magnetostatics, elasticity, hydraulics, e.g.— there are many possible analogies that we can study. From these we select, as most illuminating and useful for our purposes here, the electrostatic field in two dimensions. (The flow of electric current in conducting matter, both solid and liquid, is also extremely useful, particularly for the realization in concrete form of analog devices for computation; cf. § 14.20.) Its first application to network-synthesis problems was apparently made by Bode (BO 7) about 1940. But we must begin by stating the relevant parts of electrostatic-potential theory.

14.02 Electrostatics in two dimensions

Without reviewing the experimental basis for the theory of the electrostatic field we shall suppose the following. When electric charge is distributed in space and does not move, a static electric field exists. This field is a vector function of the observer's position in space—and it is conservative; i.e., an electric *potential* exists. This potential is a scalar function of position and satisfies Laplace's equation. The lines of force that describe the electric field can be thought of as representing electric *flux* emanating from the electric charge, and there is a (scalar) flux function connected with these lines. All of these ideas have exact expression in the mathematical theory of electrostatics, which we shall find very useful. We shall study it, however, only as we need it.

Our interest is clearly in two-dimensional electrostatics, for we have only the two dimensions of our p plane to relate by analogy to the dimensions of electrostatic problems. In two-dimensional electrostatics all quantities are independent of one space coordinate, say the z coordinate in the rectangular-coordinate system (x, y, z). Electric charge is found only in infinitely long filaments, bearing a certain charge per unit length in the z direction, the charge density. Very often the charge is distributed on the surface of (cylindrical) conductors; the charge density of a filament is then infinitesimal, the number of filaments is infinite, but the density of charge on the conductor is a reasonable, nonzero number that may be a function of x and y. The important property of a conductor is that the potential is constant everywhere in it, and that the electric charge is automatically distributed (on the *surface*) to be consistent with this equipotential property. The function that describes the charge distribution, and the resulting potential and flux functions, may be quite complicated: they depend, of course, on the shape of the trace of the conductor in the x-y plane.

We begin our mathematical study with the simplest case, that of a single filament of charge, of density q coulombs per meter (in the z direction). Whether this is an isolated charge filament or the charge exists on the surface of a conductor of infinitely small cross section does not matter; its trace is denoted in Fig. 14.02–A by a small circle at the point $(x_0,\ y_0)$. The electric field is entirely radial, by symmetry; its strength E_r is easily determined by applying Gauss's theorem (of electrostatics) to an imaginary right circular cylinder of radius r meters, 1 meter long in the z direction (Fig. 14.02–B). The charge enclosed is simply q, and the total flux crossing the cylinder is $(2\pi r)(\varepsilon E_r)$, in which ε is the permittivity of the (uniform) medium in which we find ourselves. By equating these we obtain

$$E_r = \frac{q}{2\pi\varepsilon r} \quad \text{volts per meter.} \tag{14.02–1}$$

The electric potential V in which we are primarily interested is obtained by integration, since its gradient is by definition essentially the electric field. Here, with the conventional negative sign,

$$\frac{dV}{dr} = -E_r = \frac{-q}{2\pi\varepsilon r} \quad \text{volts per meter,} \tag{14.02–2}$$

for V depends only on r, by symmetry. Hence

$$V = -\frac{q}{2\pi\varepsilon} \ln{(r/r_0)} \quad \text{volts} \tag{14.02–3}$$

in which r_0 is some arbitrary radial distance at which we consider the potential zero. (By its definition as an integral, potential is always arbitrary to the extent of an additive constant.) The amount of flux emanating in an angle θ (Fig. 14.02–B) is proportional to θ because the field depends only on r (is independent of θ), and in fact

$$\text{flux in an angle } \theta = 2\pi r\varepsilon E_r \frac{\theta}{2\pi} = \frac{q}{2\pi}\theta \quad \text{coulombs per meter per radian.} \tag{14.02–4}$$

In the potential function V and the flux function (14.02–4) we also have in essence the real and imaginary parts of a function of a complex variable, i.e., two functions that satisfy the Cauchy–Riemann equations in the x-y

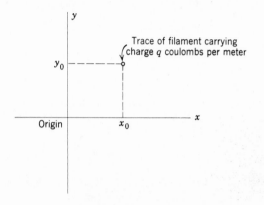

Fig. 14.02–A

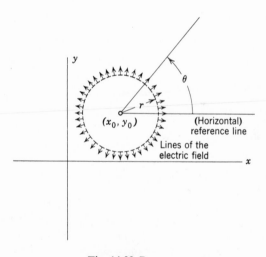

Fig. 14.02–B

plane. But they differ in dimensions, and one has a negative sign, so we define a flux function

$$\Phi = -\frac{q}{2\pi\varepsilon}\,\theta \quad \text{volts} \tag{14.02–5}$$

that is proportional to the flux actually found in an angle θ (measured from the positive real axis) but that has the same dimensions as the potential function V. If we then use the polar coordinates r and θ that are evidently most appropriate to the symmetry of the situation, we can write

$$W = V + j\Phi = -\frac{q}{2\pi\varepsilon}\ln{(r/r_0)} - j\frac{q}{2\pi\varepsilon}\theta$$

$$= -Q\ln\left(\frac{r}{r_0}e^{j\theta}\right) \quad \text{volts,} \qquad (14.02\text{-}6)$$

in which $Q = q/(2\pi\varepsilon)$ volts represents the strength of the charged filament more conveniently than does q. Finally, if we measure distances in units of r_0 for simplicity, we have

$$W = V + j\Phi = -Q\ln{(re^{j\theta})} = -Q\ln{(z - z_0)} \qquad (14.02\text{-}7)$$

in which both polar and rectangular coordinates are given (Fig. 14.02–C). In W we have a function of the complex variable $z = x + jy$ that expresses

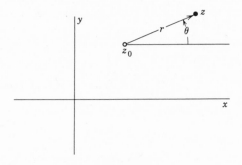

Fig. 14.02–C

in a single function both the potential and flux functions; it is appropriate to call it the *complex-potential function*. It is simpler to deal with the complex potential than with the real potential V, for the complex potential also contains the flux function, and is generally more useful. Hence we shall use W from now on. By its logarithmic nature, W is not single-valued, and this is quite consistent with the physical situation: each time we encircle the charge filament at z_0 the flux Φ changes in value by $2\pi Q$ volts, proportionally to the amount of flux cut which is the total flux radiating from the filament. The potential function V, on the other hand, is single-valued. This multivalued property will not trouble us.

When the electrostatic situation is complicated by the addition of more (isolated) filaments of charge, cutting the x-y plane at various points, the resultant complex-potential function is obtained simply by superposition, for the mathematics is linear. That is, for N filaments

$$W = \sum_{k=1}^{k=N} [-Q_k \ln (z - z_k)] + \text{constant} \quad \text{volts}, \quad (14.02\text{--}8)$$

in which $Q_k = q_k/(2\pi\varepsilon)$ volts represents the strength of the charged filament that cuts the x-y plane at $z_k = x_k + jy_k$, and the additive constant is arbitrary (and may be complex). This immediately suggests an alternative method of expressing the potential function (and one that will prove useful), in that it is in the form of a sum of logarithms, i.e., the logarithm of a product. If we suppose potential and charge normalized, in other words, measured now in units of some reference potential, so that W and Q_k lose their dimensions, we can write

$$W = \ln \prod_{k=1}^{k=N} (z - z_k)^{-Q_k} + \text{constant} \quad (14.02\text{--}9)$$

or

$$e^W = K \prod_{k=1}^{k=N} (z - z_k)^{-Q_k}, \quad (14.02\text{--}10)$$

in which K is arbitrary. Electric charge can be either positive or negative, so that we have in this *exponential-potential function* e^W, in the cases where the Q_k are integers (they will usually be so), simply a *rational* function of z. For example, the two charged filaments of Fig. 14.02–D,

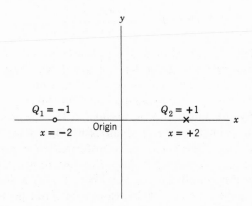

Fig. 14.02–D

in which the small circle denotes the trace of a negatively charged filament and the small cross that of a positively charged filament, lead to

$$e^W = K \frac{(z + 2)}{(z - 2)}. \quad (14.02\text{--}11)$$

The exponential function then has the advantage of having the familiar rational-function form and the additional advantage that it is not multiple-valued—there is no ambiguity in its imaginary part.

The term "trace of a charged filament" being awkward, we shall from now on simply talk of *charges*, represented by small circles when negative and by small crosses when positive, and measured in normalized units that have neither dimensions nor name. Another example is given by

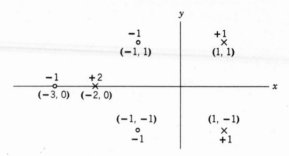

Fig. 14.02–E

Fig. 14.02–E, with three unit negative charges and three positive charges, of which one is of two units. Here

$$e^W = K \frac{(z + 3)(z^2 + 2z + 2)}{(z + 2)^2(z^2 - 2z + 2)}. \qquad (14.02\text{–}12)$$

The physics of such electrostatic-potential problems is often made clearer by drawing some of the lines of the electric field, i.e., flux lines, determined by the equation $\Phi = constant$, and some of the curves of constant potential, i.e., equipotential lines or simply "equipotentials," determined by the equation $V = constant$. The members of these two families of curves intersect at right angles, forming a network of curvilinear squares (suggestive of the conformal transformation or mapping that they really form), which we call a *field map*, *flux plot*, or *equipotential diagram*. When we put arrowheads on the flux lines of such a diagram, we shall point them in the direction of increasing potential (rather than in the direction of the electric field) in order to obtain a right-handed system in the curvilinear coordinates. The diagram for a single negative charge at the origin (Fig. 14.02–F) is not complicated, for here we have from (14.02–7)

$$V = |Q| \ln r,$$
$$\Phi = |Q|\theta, \qquad (14.02\text{–}13)$$

in which r and θ have their usual polar-coordinate meanings. The curves shown here (and in succeeding drawings) are not drawn for equally spaced values of V or of Φ, but spaced simply to give a convenient general idea of the field. The arrowheads shown correspond to the positive directions for these two coordinates and to the directions of increasing potential and increasing flux function (direction of "positive" flux cutting). Although neither V nor Φ has dimensions or units now, we have no difficulty in giving them numerical values, from (14.02–13). The flux function Φ

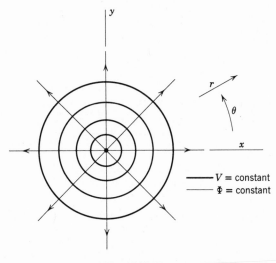

Fig. 14.02–F

in particular can be thought of as an angle measured in radians (or in degrees if more convenient), both here where it is proportional to θ and in general because it is the imaginary part of a logarithm, or simply the angle of e^W. Because of its multiple-valued nature, the numerical values given Φ are somewhat arbitrary; we shall usually take the simplest ones; here, those from 0 to 2π radians.

This diagram makes clear one additional fact: not all the charge is shown, for every flux line must have an end as well as a beginning. A single negative charge cannot exist alone but must always be accompanied by positive charge of the same amount, in order that all the flux lines may terminate. In the case of the negative charge at the origin of Fig. 14.02–F, the positive charge is presumably at a great distance, symmetrically distributed around a circle (cylinder), or we may simply say it is at infinity. From the potential function

$$V = -Q \ln r \qquad (14.02\text{–}14)$$

this is also evident, for the potential becomes negatively infinite at the origin (where the negative charge is located) and also positively infinite at infinity (where the positive charge is located). Evidently in general terms, since each unit of negative charge must be accompanied by a unit of positive charge to terminate the flux lines, the net (total) charge (including that at infinity, if any) must be zero,

$$\sum_{k=1}^{N} Q_k = 0. \tag{14.02-15}$$

In the case of the pair of charges of Fig. 14.02–D, all the charge is in the finite plane and the flux plot (Fig. 14.02–G) shows the entire trajectory of the flux lines, which happen here to be arcs of circles. (The equipotentials are circles too.)

An interesting variation occurs in the equipotential diagram when the two charges are of the *same* sign, say negative. Then, for example,

$$e^W = \frac{(z + 2)(z - 2)}{4}. \tag{14.02-16}$$

The equipotentials are still very closely circles near the charges (see Fig. 14.02–H). But as we move out on a flux line they change shape, as they must because potential increases in leaving *either* charge. There is a sort of figure-of-eight curve for the equipotential at which a marked change in shape occurs (this is zero potential with the choice of multiplier made here). For higher potentials the curves tend again to become circles, since at great distances the effect of the two charges is substantially that of a two-unit negative charge at the origin. The peculiar behavior at the origin of the x-y plane here, where the zero equipotential crosses itself and the nature of the equipotentials changes from a pair of separate curves for a given potential to a single curve, is described by the mathematical term *saddle point* (GU 3). At such a point, as Fig. 14.02–H shows, for the flux line(s) that leave the charges horizontally, going toward the origin, a sharp turn occurs in some of the normally smooth flux lines. The behavior can be more clearly understood perhaps by temporarily invoking another analogy, that with the gravitational potential, which is simply altitude on the earth's surface. Then the diagram is a (contour) map, equipotentials are contour lines of constant altitude, and flux lines are the paths of steepest ascent or descent. Figure 14.02–H then shows the terrain near two mountain peaks; the origin is the center of the mountain pass between them, whose shape is that of the saddle of a riding horse. When more than two peaks are adjacent the terrain becomes more complicated because of the additional "valleys," but the term "saddle point" is still used.

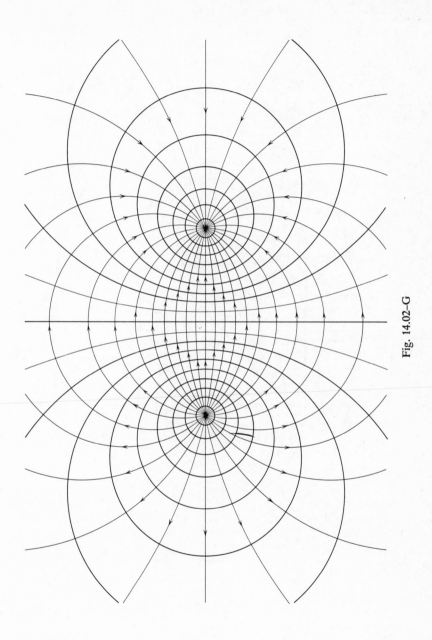

Fig. 14.02–G

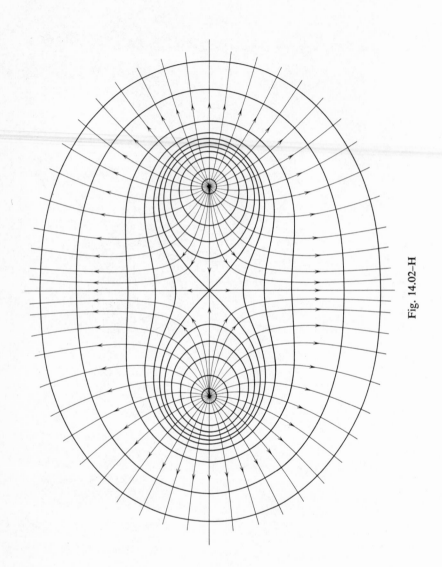

Fig. 14.02–H

Fig. 14.02–I

The flux plot for the charge distribution of Fig. 14.02–E, given in Fig. 14.02–I, shows additional saddle points and some of the complexities of more complicated diagrams.

14.03 Analogies

It is apparent now that there exists a formal analogy between network immittance functions and two-dimensional potential functions in the exponential form. We have only to look at the exponential-potential function (14.02–10): this is a rational function, and if we change the symbol for the complex variable from z to p, it may well be an impedance or admittance function. To be sure, if we are to identify e^W with a positive-real Z or Y, then the charge distribution must be subject to certain restrictions; none of the functions (14.02–11) or (14.02–12) or (14.02–16) is p-r, for example, though each represents a perfectly good electrostatic-potential problem. Before discussing these restrictions, however, let us specifically state the analogy. We shall henceforth use $p = \sigma + j\omega$ in place of $z = x + jy$ as the electrostatic position complex variable, as well as for the network complex frequency variable. Because of the directness of the analogy, a single complex-plane diagram will serve for both situations. We can think of any rational function as the exponential-potential function e^W of an electrostatic charge distribution; its zeros and poles are the traces of the charges, as in § 14.02. If the same rational function is now regarded as an immittance function $Z(p)$, we can in fact write down the details of the analogy as direct equalities:

$$Z(p) = e^{W(p)},$$

$$\ln Z(p) = W(p),$$

$$\ln |Z| + j\overline{Z} = V + j\Phi, \tag{14.03–1}$$

$$\ln |Z| = V,$$

$$\overline{Z} = \Phi.$$

In words, we have not only analogy but direct equality between

immittance function *and* exponential-potential function,

logarithm of immittance function *and* complex-potential function,

logarithm of magnitude of

immittance function *and* electric-potential function,

angle of immittance function *and* flux function.   (14.03–2)

Those important points of the p plane marked O and X are now subject to two interpretations, depending on the point of view:

Point	Immittance Interpretation	Electrostatic Interpretation	
O	zero (of order m)	negative charge (of strength m units)	(14.03–3)
X	pole (of order n)	positive charge (of strength n units)	

The multiplier of the rational function is not particularly important; it represents merely the level or scale of impedance or admittance on the one hand and an additive constant in the complex potential on the other.

It is interesting to note here that the relation (3.11–3) has a vivid analogical interpretation. Although it may not seem obvious that the number of zeros of a rational function is the same as the number of poles, it is almost certainly obvious that the total electric charge is zero—else some flux lines would lack either end or beginning, and they always terminate on charge. Hence (14.02–15) is analogous to (3.11–3). This is an instance of the utility of this analogy in understanding the mathematics of functions of a complex variable.

Our ultimate interest is in the steady-state behavior of the networks we synthesize, hence in the variation of the potential W on the imaginary axis. The potential here depends, of course, on the distribution of electric charge throughout the plane, which is another way of indicating the need for the complex frequency variable and investigations throughout the plane, even when we are interested only in steady-state behavior. And here, on the imaginary axis, we have in potential terms the same sort of relation between real and imaginary parts on the one hand and even and odd parts on the other, as before. Starting from (14.03–1), we have in general

$$\ln Z(p) = W(p),$$

$$\mathbf{Ev} \ln Z(p) = \tfrac{1}{2} \ln [Z(p)Z(-p)] = \tfrac{1}{2}[W(p) + W(-p)], \quad (14.03\text{–}4)$$

$$\mathbf{Od} \ln Z(p) = \tfrac{1}{2} \ln [Z(p)/Z(-p)] = \tfrac{1}{2}[W(p) - W(-p),]$$

from which, when $p = j\omega$, we obtain

$$\ln |Z(j\omega)| = \tfrac{1}{2}[W(j\omega) + W(-j\omega)] = V,$$

$$\overline{Z(j\omega)} = \frac{1}{j} \times \frac{1}{2} [W(j\omega) + W(-j\omega)] = \Phi. \quad (14.03\text{–}5)$$

When our interest is in the magnitude of an immittance function, in its angle, or in its complex value in general, then in the electrostatic potential, the flux function, or both, we have analogical representations that are often of great value in helping us to visualize where the zeros and poles ought to be to give the desired behavior.

When our interest is in a resistance (conductance) or reactance (susceptance) function, on the other hand, we have found that it is the even and odd parts of $Z(p)$ itself, and not of its logarithm, that are important. To apply this potential analogy we must then take for our exponential-potential function the modified functions

$$[Z(p) + Z(-p)] \quad and \quad [Z(p) - Z(-p)] \quad (14.03\text{-}6)$$

rather than $Z(p)$ itself. Because the addition or subtraction is no longer in terms of the logarithm, because we are dealing only with *parts* of $Z(p)$, the analogous charge distributions no longer correspond exactly to the pole diagram of $Z(p)$. The poles (positive charges) are the same (except possibly for imaginary ones) with the addition of symmetrically located ones in the right half plane, but the zeros (negative charges) are usually quite different. This does not, however, invalidate the analogy; it merely requires that we study a different charge distribution, one with the required symmetry. For example, the impedance function

$$Z(p) = \frac{p^2 + p + 1}{p + 1} \quad (14.03\text{-}7)$$

has for its even and odd parts

$$\mathbf{Ev}\, Z(p) = \frac{1}{1 - p^2}, \quad (14.03\text{-}8)$$

$$\mathbf{Od}\, Z(p) = \frac{-p^3}{1 - p^2}. \quad (14.03\text{-}9)$$

In each part a symmetrically located pole in the right half plane is added (Fig. 14.03–A) but the zeros of the parts are quite different from the zeros

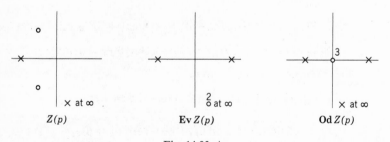

Fig. 14.03–A

of $Z(p)$. The pole at infinity in $Z(p)$ has no counterpart in $\mathbf{Ev}\, Z(p)$, though it does in $\mathbf{Od}\, Z(p)$; and this is natural, for a pole on the imaginary axis implies nonminimum-reactance character, and such a pole belongs really to the reactance, or odd part. When zeros or poles (negative or positive charges) are not simple (of unit strength), we shall indicate their orders (strengths) by numbers at the symbols, as for the second-order zero at infinity in **Ev** Z and the third-order zero at the origin in **Od** Z in Fig. 14.03–A. A more complicated example is

$$Z(p) = \frac{3p^2 + 3p + 3}{p^3 + 4p^2 + 6p + 4} \tag{14.03–10}$$

the diagrams for which are given in Fig. 14.03–B. The symmetry of the diagrams for even and odd parts is characteristic and merely a graphical expression of their innate symmetrical nature.

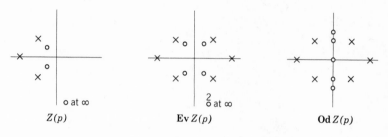

$$Z(p) \qquad \text{Ev}\,Z(p) \qquad \text{Od}\,Z(p)$$

Fig. 14.03–B

Although the analog for an immittance function $Z(p)$ itself contains in the potential and flux functions direct analogs of its magnitude and angle, it is sometimes convenient to construct analogs in which attention is concentrated on one of these two aspects. Such diagrams resemble those for even and odd parts, and are readily suggested by (14.03–4) and (14.03–5). When the magnitude is of primary interest we use the function $[Z(p)Z(-p)]$; when the angle is of primary interest we use $[Z(p)/Z(-p)]$, exactly as in § 8.13 and § 8.14. The convenience of these diagrams in comparison with that for $Z(p)$ alone lies in their symmetry, which makes it easier to visualize and compute the quantities of interest when $p = j\omega$. (The factors of 2 are easily compensated for in scale adjustments.) In the former case the imaginary axis is a flux line ($\Phi = 0$), in the latter an equipotential ($V = 0$), as is illustrated in Figs. 14.02–H and 14.02–G respectively for the function ($p + 2$). Such diagrams for the functions (14.03–7) and (14.03–10) are given in Figs. 14.03–C and 14.03–D.

It is appropriate now to consider when a charge diagram is analogous to a physically realizable network. Any rational function whatever gives a meaningful charge distribution, but only certain rational functions lead to realizable networks. The diagram for a whole immittance function (as opposed to that for one of its parts), to begin with, must be that of a positive-real function. Unfortunately, positive reality is not a quality that is readily apparent from a pole-zero diagram, and hence not from the analogous charge distribution diagram. We can translate our definitions

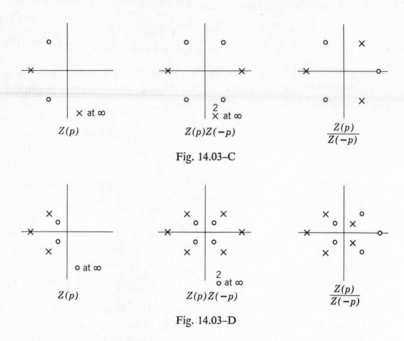

Fig. 14.03–C

Fig. 14.03–D

of a p-r function (4.05–3) into electrostatic terms without difficulty. The rectangular form becomes

    (*a*) the positive half of the real axis must be a flux line (and the arbitrary constant in the complex potential chosen so that on it $\Phi = 0$)

and

    (*c*) in the right half plane the flux function must lie between the values $-\pi/2$ and $+\pi/2$,   (14.03–11)

and the polar form becomes

    (*b*) in the right half plane the flux function must not exceed in magnitude that of a single unit charge located at the origin.   (14.03–12)

Either of these (equivalent) restrictions is sufficient to make the exponential-potential function p-r and hence realizable as a driving-point immittance function. But neither gives us a means of ready determination of positive reality. Nor does the electrostatic form of the test for positive reality (5.13–5), which becomes

1. the positive-real axis must be a flux line (and the arbitrary constant in the complex potential chosen so that on it $\Phi = 0$);

2(a). if there is charge at infinity it must be a unit (positive or negative) charge; alternatively, the net (total) charge at finite points must be, at most, of unit magnitude;

2(b). no charges may lie in the right half plane;

2(c). if there are charges on the ω axis they must be of unit value (positive or negative) and the flux line $\Phi = 0$ (or $\Phi = \pm 2\pi,\ \pm 4\pi,\ \cdot\ \cdot\ \cdot$) must emanate therefrom horizontally to the right;

3. on the ω axis the flux function must obey the condition $-\pi/2 \leq \Phi \leq +\pi/2$. 　　　　　　　　(14.03–13)

Given a complete flux plot, to be sure, we can readily determine whether the analog function is p-r; but the construction of the plot may be laborious, and we find once more that in general to test for p-r character requires work.

If our concern is only with the magnitude of an immittance function, and we have chosen to work with the diagram for $[Z(p)Z(-p)]$, we have again no ready method of determining whether a given charge diagram (with even-function symmetry) corresponds to a realizable immittance function. Exactly (in analog fashion) as in § 8.13, we must first discard the right-half-plane charges (and half of those on the imaginary axis and at infinity) and then examine the flux plot for what is left, i.e., for $Z(p)$, as above. There is no apparent short cut.

When our interest is confined to the angle (rather than the magnitude), however, the situation is quite different. If the diagram for $[Z(p)/Z(-p)]$ is used for obtaining a satisfactory flux- (angle-) function behavior on the imaginary axis, then appropriate symmetry is the only requirement. The appropriate symmetry here is *odd symmetry*, i.e., each left-half-plane charge is accompanied by a charge of the same strength but opposite sign, located at the image point in the origin (in addition to the usual symmetry between upper and lower halves of the plane). There will be no charges on the ω axis here, for such charges are canceled in the ratio $[Z(p)/Z(-p)]$, though odd symmetry in general permits such (symmetrical) charges and requires charges of odd numbers of units at both the origin and infinity. If the diagram for this function has odd symmetry of this sort, then the flux function can be realized as the angle of an immittance, with the possible exception that certain sharp steps of π radians may be necessary (§ 8.14). If we choose to set up an analog directly for the tangent function rather than the angle itself, then there is not even this exception. The only requirement now is odd symmetry in the general form: charges may also appear on the imaginary axis and there must be a charge at the origin, and one at infinity, both of an odd number of units. The rational function so represented, $T(p)$, is always realizable as the (generalized) tangent of an immittance angle (§ 8.14). In such an application of the analogy for approximation purposes it is often convenient to focus attention on the magnitude of the tangent itself (now analogous to potential) by considering the function $[T(p)T(-p)]$, which eliminates the now irrelevant flux (on the imaginary axis), exactly as when the magnitude of $Z(p)$ is of primary interest. The condition for realizability then is a restricted form of even symmetry. *Even symmetry* in general requires that each left-half-plane charge be accompanied by a charge of the same strength and sign, located at its image point in the origin (in addition to the usual symmetry between upper and lower halves of the plane); i.e., it is essentially equivalent to quadrantal symmetry. Charges at the origin and at infinity, however, must be of an even number of units. Here we have the added stipulation that when $T(p)$ is formed from $[T(p)T(-p)]$ an odd function should result.

When resistance (conductance) is of primary interest, then it is the even part of the immittance with which we deal. The appropriate diagram then represents **Ev** $Z(p)$ and the charges must be located with quadrantal symmetry. There can be no positive charge on the imaginary axis, and the strength of negative charges there must be a multiple of two units. Any such charge distribution, interpreted as the even part, will lead to a realizable immittance function (§ 8.11).

When reactance (susceptance) is of primary interest, then it is the odd part of the immittance that is represented by the analog. The diagram then represents **Od** $Z(p)$ and the charge distribution must have odd symmetry. Further, if positive charges appear on the imaginary axis, they must be of unit strength and the flux line $\Phi = 0$ (or $\Phi = \pm 2\pi, \pm 4\pi,$ $\cdot\ \cdot\ \cdot$) must emanate therefrom horizontally to the right. These conditions suffice for the physical realizability as an immittance of the function obtained by taking this as the odd part (§ 8.12). It may at times be convenient to set up the analog for $[X(p)X(-p)]$ rather than for $X(p)$ or **Od** $Z(p)$ alone.

The analogies, which we have now specifically set up, are more than formal: they are useful. In *analysis* they provide ready insight into the behavior of given networks, exactly as does the pole-zero diagram itself, but here the consideration of line lengths and angles is replaced by consideration of electric potential and flux, which may add clarity. We could stop here to look at many of the subjects we have discussed in previous chapters in this new light. But it is *synthesis* that is our primary objective, and so we pass on to the use of the analogy in solving the approximation part of synthesis problems. The applications outlined above will be discussed later in detail when we consider actual approximation.

14.04 The rôle of the conductor

It is not surprising that in electrostatics a great deal of attention is paid to situations in which *conductors* appear. They have the peculiar property of automatically "generating" an equipotential region (the volume occupied continuously by conducting material) and a corresponding distribution of charge on the surface of the conductor. Such a remarkable property naturally gives the conductor an important rôle in electrostatics, and consequently, by analogy, in approximation by this method. In our diagrams of the p plane a conductor appears only as its trace in that plane, for in two-dimensional problems a conductor extends indefinitely above and below the plane in the form of a cylinder, and the trace is a right section thereof. This section may be of any shape, open or closed, two-dimensional (solid) or one-dimensional (curvilinear); both smooth curves and collections of segments may serve for the latter or the boundaries of the former. The charge on a conductor distributes itself automatically (on the surface) in a fashion consistent with the equipotential property. In two dimensions we have then an infinite number of charge filaments, each of infinitesimal strength, with a certain charge density that is a function of σ and ω, in other words, of p. The terms "charge distribution," and the like, and "conductor" will refer, from here on, to the traces thereof in the p plane, consistent with our use of the term "charge"; continuous charge will be measured in the same sort of normalized units as is concentrated charge. In the p plane we see a continuous charge distribution on a conductor, in place of the discrete or lumped charges we have been discussing.

Since flux lines terminate (or begin) on charges, we have a discontinuity in the flux function at the surface of a conductor, though the potential is continuous. This is illustrated in Fig. 14.04–A, which shows a (magnified) portion of the surface of a conductor. The flux lines coming from the left (for example) terminate on the (positive) surface charge, whose density is ρ charge units per unit length along the conductor. Along a normal to the conductor (the direction n in Fig. 14.04–A) the potential V varies as shown in Fig. 14.04–B in the immediate vicinity of the surface, increasing until the charge is reached, and then remaining constant inside the conductor. In the tangential, t, direction, V remains constant within and on the surface of the conductor. The flux function Φ is constant along a normal, outside the conductor, since the flux lines are perpendicular to the conductor surface (which is an equipotential). Inside the conductor there is no flux, for this is a field-free region. But on the surface Φ varies (in the t direction) proportionately to the charge density, to express the number of lines that terminate on the surface charge, thus giving rise to the discontinuity in Φ. We have in fact the relation

$$\frac{\partial \Phi}{\partial t} = \rho \qquad (14.04\text{-}1)$$

on the surface, which shows how Φ varies in the t direction. The discontinuity in Φ is evident in that Φ does not vary in the interior of the

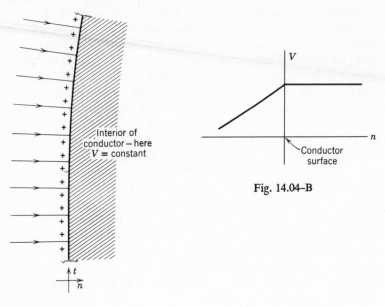

Fig. 14.04–B

Fig. 14.04–A

conductor, and yet has a variety of values on the surface, depending on where it is evaluated. (In the interior its value is indeterminate.) It is interesting to note that the rate at which V varies in the immediate vicinity of the surface (outside the conductor) is given by one of the Cauchy–Riemann equations as

$$\frac{\partial V}{\partial n} = \frac{\partial \Phi}{\partial t} = \rho. \qquad (14.04\text{-}2)$$

Equipotentials in the immediate vicinity of the conductor tend to follow the shape of the conductor's surface, which is itself an equipotential, and the flux lines are of course perpendicular thereto. Figure 14.04–C shows a flux plot which illustrates this for a solid conductor; Fig. 14.04–D does the same for a conductor that is infinitesimally thin, a mere sheet or plate of conducting material.   This is conveniently regarded as a limiting case, when the conductor thickness shrinks to zero; from such a point of view it is easy to account for the two layers of surface charge, one on each side;

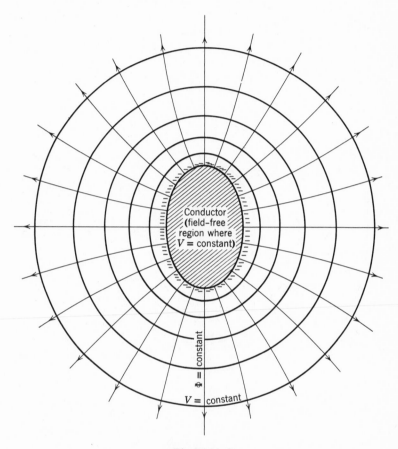

Fig. 14.04–C

the discussion of conductor surface properties applies to each side independently.   At great distances the effect is substantially the same, of course, whether a given amount of charge is distributed on either of these conductors or simply lumped at a point in the same general region.

The conductor in Fig. 14.04–C need not be solid; exactly the same conditions will prevail, both inside and outside the innermost equipotential, if the conductor is only a thin shell coincident with this equipotential.   In these particular figures the equipotential curves and the flux lines are drawn for equal increments of potential and of flux, and the "other" charge is taken to be at infinity.   That is, we may think of the positive charge on which the flux lines terminate as being symmetrically

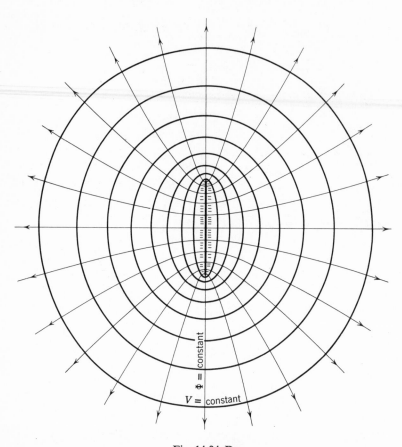

Fig. 14.04–D

distributed on a circular conductor centered on the conductor shown, but of infinitely great radius, which gives these plots their symmetry.   If part or all of this positive charge were near the conductor shown, we should naturally find a radically different distribution of the surface charge and a completely different field map.

By using a conductor, we can easily create a region of constant potential. It may of course be a matter of lengthy calculation to obtain the resulting complex-potential function, to make a flux plot, and to determine the density of the charge distributed on the conductor's surface. And it is not apparent here how $W(p)$ or even e^W in such a situation is analogous to network functions, for which we have found lumped (rather than distributed) charge to be appropriate. But the property of automatically generating an equipotential region is what interests us, for this is extremely useful in certain approximation procedures, in spite of these difficulties.

14.05 Approximation of a constant

A constant is probably the simplest function that one may wish to approximate, and even though it is itself a rational function, this problem often arises in network synthesis. We may need, for example, a resistance function that approximates a constant at low frequencies and then (due perhaps to the inevitable capacitance in the network) approaches zero at high frequencies. We shall discuss this problem as an excellent first illustration of the utility of the potential analogy in obtaining a solution to the approximation problem of the Chebyshev (equal-ripple) type. Figure 14.05–A shows the ideal resistance function, constant at the value

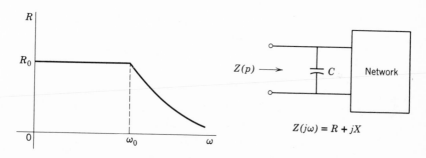

Fig. 14.05–A

R_0 from zero frequency to some frequency that marks the upper end of the approximation band, and then descending toward zero because of the capacitance C. We shall assume for the present that this is purely a *low-band* problem, i.e., that a good approximation is important in the band $0 < \omega < \omega_0$ but that no requirements other than a drop toward zero are laid down for higher frequencies. There are many solutions to this approximation problem (see § 13.10, e.g.); here we shall seek a Chebyshev approximation, as in Fig. 14.05–B, in which the resistance and frequency scales have been normalized and ϵ measures the (equal) ripples in the resistance function.

It is natural to think immediately of the use of a conductor in approximating a constant, for this automatically produces a region where V is constant. In the p plane the approximation band for this problem is the imaginary axis from $\omega = -1$ to $\omega = +1$, and if we put down a thin conductor there, much as in Fig. 14.04–D but carrying positive rather than negative charge, the exponential potential on the imaginary axis will immediately vary in the general fashion shown in the curve of Fig. 14.05–A. This does not solve our approximation problem in any sense, for the infinite number of charge filaments, infinitesimal though they are, are not

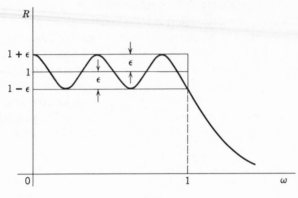

Fig. 14.05–B

realizable by a finite network of lumped elements. We might proceed to calculate the complex potential anyway, and then manipulate it in some fashion to obtain a finite-network approximation (this procedure is indeed of some value, as we shall see later), but this is not the direct approach we want here. Rather we must somehow find a set of lumped charges that gives approximately constant potential on the approximation band, and moreover an approximation in the Chebyshev sense. These charges must also have the symmetry required of even functions for we must evidently identify the corresponding exponential potential function with Ev $Z(p)$ to solve our problem.

It seems eminently reasonable, however, that this first natural step of placing a conductor on the approximation band be closely related to the Chebyshev solution (as well as others), because it gives the ideal potential function that we wish to approximate. We cannot immediately *quantize* the distributed charge on the conductor, i.e., replace it by discrete lumped charges whose average effect may be more or less the same, because the approximate equivalence would hold only at some distance. In the approximation band we should find a wild sort of behavior, with a succession of poles in the resistance function that are not physically admissible (§ 14.03) and in any event give an approximation to a constant of only the crudest sort. In Fig. 14.04–C we can find a hint of a better procedure that is still very closely related to this ideal-potential situation. A conductor of hollow form that *encloses* the approximation band is equally good for making it an equipotential; in fact, its entire interior is an equipotential region. But this region of constant potential can equally well be thought of as due to the charge distribution on the conductor, and we can replace the conductor by this same continuous distribution of charge in space, imagining it to be fixed there by some mechanism we need not consider. If now we quantize *this* charge distribution (replace it by suitably lumped charges), we can reasonably expect to find a good approximation to a constant potential on the approximation band, perhaps even a Chebyshev approximation. And at great distances (at high frequencies) there should be very little difference in the two cases. To be sure, the approximation will be poor in the vicinity of the lumped charges, but by this device we have placed them at a distance from the approximation band where our main interest lies.

We must now decide on the shape and location of this new conductor C whose distributed charge is to be the basis of the approximation. Any closed conductor whatever will give rise to a constant potential in its interior, and presumably the corresponding quantized charge will give rise to an approximately constant potential on the approximation band. But the nature of the approximation will certainly depend greatly on the nature of C; some approximations will be very crude, some may be excellent though of different kinds—in fact, it may be possible to generate all approximations by suitable choices of C. We must certainly require symmetry in the four quadrants because of the quadrantal symmetry required of the quantized charge distribution, which is to be identified with $\text{Ev}\, Z(p)$. A conductor such as that of Fig. 14.05–C could be considered, for example. But of all such possibilities one seems natural to the problem, so natural that we ought to try it first: namely, one of the closed equipotentials of the field that is set up by a thin conducting plate coincident with the approximation band, i.e., the situation from which we started. If we construct the flux plot for this situation, much as in Fig. 14.04–D, then choose an equipotential from this family and put down a conductor coincident with it, carrying the same total charge as did the plate, there will be no change in $W(p)$ or in the flux plot exterior to this equipotential. Within it, of course, the potential will now be constant at the value of V on this equipotential. It remains to be seen whether quantization of the charge carried by this new conductor can be so made that these lumped charges alone will actually give us the Chebyshev approximation we seek, with symmetry appropriate for even functions.

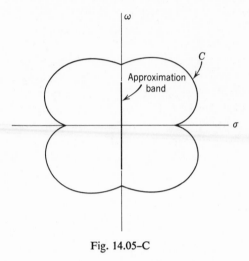

Fig. 14.05–C

Quantization of the charge distribution requires the replacement of each unit of positive (negative) distributed charge by a single unit of lumped positive (negative) charge. The logical location for the single charge is probably at the "center of charge" of the section of conductor that carries

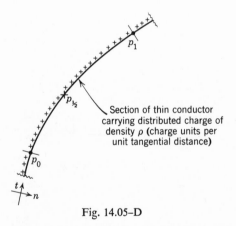

Fig. 14.05–D

the unit distributed charge. In Fig. 14.05–D, for example, starting at the point p_0 and moving on the surface of the conductor with a tangential distance coordinate t, we may locate p_1 so that the total charge in the section from p_0 to p_1 is unity,

$$\int_{p_0}^{p_1} \rho \, dt = 1, \qquad (14.05\text{-}1)$$

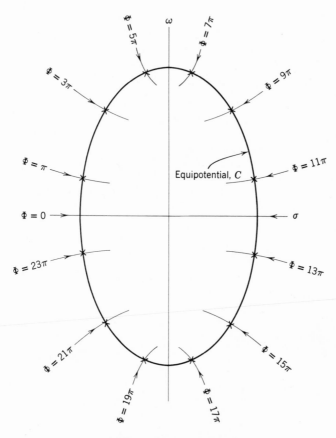

$Q/2$ = an even number
Drawn for $N = 3$, $Q = 4N = 12$

Fig. 14.05–E

and then determine the center of charge (centroid) $p_{1/2}$ so that half of this charge lies on each side thereof,

$$\int_{p}^{p_{1/2}} \rho \, dt = \int_{p_{1/2}}^{p_1} \rho \, dt = 1/2. \qquad (14.05\text{-}2)$$

A unit charge of the appropriate sign located here (as indicated by the **x**) we shall call a *quantization* of this unit of distributed charge; we have yet to see in what sense the two are equivalent. The actual determination

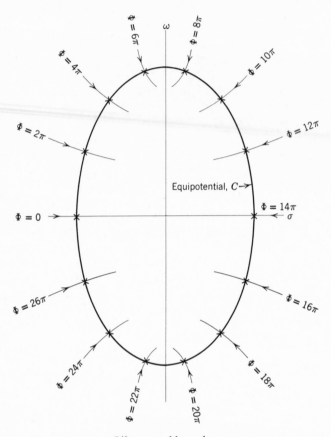

$Q/2 =$ an odd number

Drawn for $N = 3$, $Q = 4N + 2 = 14$

Fig. 14.05–F

of the position of $p_{1/2}$ is extremely simple in terms of the flux plot, since 2π units of flux terminate on each unit of positive charge. Thus the increase in Φ between p_0 and $p_{1/2}$ is π, as it is between $p_{1/2}$ and p_1. If we start from a suitable reference point p_0 at which we call the value of Φ zero, then the first quantization point is where the $\Phi = \pi$ line reaches the conductor, the second where the $\Phi = 3\pi$ line reaches it, etc. Thus the "odd π lines" ($\Phi = \pi$, 3π, 5π, $\cdot$ $\cdot$ $\cdot$) of the flux plot give these quantization points by their intersections with the chosen equipotential. The reference point must of course be chosen so that the resulting set of lumped charges has the proper symmetry, in this problem even symmetry, without any charge on the ω axis. The total distributed charge Q on the chosen conductor must be of an integral number of units for the quantization to terminate correctly in a set of discrete unit charges; furthermore, Q must be even so that the set will have even symmetry, and within this restriction two possibilities can arise (Figs. 14.05-E, -F). If $Q = 2 \times$ (an even number) $= 4N$, N being a positive integer, then N charges will have to lie within each quadrant and none will be on the real axis (Fig. 14.05-E). If $Q = 2 \times$ (an odd number) $= 4N + 2$, N being a positive integer or possibly zero, then N charges will have to lie in each quadrant and two will be on the real axis (Fig. 14.05-F). It is often convenient to take the origin of flux as a part of the real axis (which is usually a flux line because of the necessary vertical symmetry of charge location); then on at least a part of the real axis $\Phi = 0$. In the first of the two cases above, p_0 is then on the real axis and the quantized charges lie at the intersections of the odd π lines with the chosen equipotential, as above (as in Fig. 14.05-E, e.g.). In the second case, however, two charges must lie on the real axis to obtain the required symmetry, p_0 is itself the location of a charge, and we must use the *even* π lines ($\Phi = 0$, 2π, 4π, $\cdot$ $\cdot$ $\cdot$) to locate the quantized charges on the equipotential (as in Fig. 14.05-F, e.g.). In any given approximation problem it is a simple matter of inspection to determine how the group of quantized charges should be shifted along the equipotential to give the required symmetry.

The discussion up to this point has presented a plausible method that makes good use of the potential analogy to obtain an approximation to the desired constant. It remains to be seen exactly what sort of approximation it yields and to discuss the details of its application to the low-band constant-resistance problem we have set up and to other problems in which it may be useful.

14.06 The complex-potential plane

We can unequivocally determine the approximation this procedure yields, in any given case, by simply forming the rational function that represents the exponential potential of the quantized charges, and then computing the potential on the approximation band. But it would be much more satisfactory to determine the character of the approximation in more general terms, and this we shall now attempt to do.

What makes it difficult to calculate the potential on the ω axis in situations such as those of the foregoing figures is the more or less irregular positioning of the charges with respect to this axis. There is a definite regularity of spacing along the equipotential C, however, in units of Φ. We may combine this observation with the fact that conformal mapping with the object of transforming rather complicated contours into simpler shapes is very useful in solving two-dimensional potential problems in general. The particular transformation that is likely to be useful here is that from the p plane to the plane of W, the complex potential of the original situation in which a thin conductor occupies the approximation band. For the curve C is an equipotential, i.e., **Re** $W(p) = V = $ constant thereon, and the quantized charges occur thereon at equal intervals of **Im** $W(p) = \Phi$. In this W plane the charges consequently ought to lie on a line parallel to the imaginary axis with a regularity of spacing that may make our calculation simple.

We are concerned here with two different potential problems, which must not be confused, though they are interrelated. The first is that of a thin conductor that occupies the approximation band and is positively charged; the associated negative charge is all at infinity. This we call the *prototype* situation. The complex potential of this situation we call $W(p)$; its flux plot could be, for example, that of Fig. 14.04–D with the directions of the field (flux) lines reversed because the conductor is here positively charged. There is another complex-potential function, quite different, which is that of the lumped charges which we locate on an equipotential of the first problem; this we wish to calculate in the end, for it represents our approximation, but not until we have discussed the first function, $W(p)$, and the transformation (mapping) it defines.

Since $W(p)$, aside from its multivalued nature, is analytic everywhere except where charge is present, i.e., everywhere except on the approximation band and at infinity, this transformation will map the entire p plane into a new, W plane with singular behavior only in the mapping of the approximation band and of the point at infinity and in the ambiguity ever-present in the value of Φ. The general nature of this mapping is not hard to see; it is not even necessary actually to calculate $W(p)$, which might be a difficult task. For in the flux plot of $W(p)$, Fig. 14.06–A, we have the mapping in the p plane of the lines $V = $ **Re** $W = $ constant and $\Phi = $ **Im** $W = $ constant, i.e., of lines parallel to the axes in the W plane. For convenience we take the potential of the approximation band to be zero; then the equipotentials represent negative values of potential that tend to $-\infty$ as we go outward. We also take the horizontal flux line on the negative-real axis as the origin of Φ so that $W = 0$ at the origin on the left side of the conducting plate: $W(0^-) = 0$. Because of the surface charge on the conductor, whose total amount we take as $+1$ for convenience (the potential is linear with respect to the charge and can be easily adjusted in magnitude later as necessary), we have $W(0^+) = 0 \pm j\pi$; at the origin on the right side of the plate the potential is still zero, but the flux function has the value π, if we go around the top of the conductor to get there since π lines must then be cut, or the value $-\pi$ if we go around the bottom and so cut flux in the opposite sense.

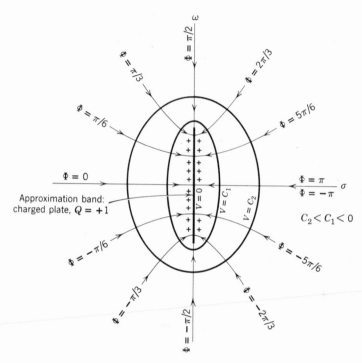

Fig. 14.06–A

Figure 14.06–A shows these and several other typical flux lines and equipotentials. In keeping with the physical situation here and the multivalued nature of flux functions in general, the value of W at the origin on the right side of the plate depends on the direction chosen for going around the plate; if we make additional complete trips around the plate in the appropriate direction, we can make $W(0^+) = 0 + j\pi + j2M\pi$ in which M is any positive (or negative) integer. The behavior of W is of this sort at any point. We shall call the values of Φ between $-\pi$ and $+\pi$, such as those shown in Fig. 14.06–A, the *principal values* and consider now what the multivalued nature of W means in the mapping.

To every point in the p plane corresponds a principal value of $W(p)$; this is the complex potential corresponding to the potential problem of Fig. 14.06–A. Thus the entire p plane is mapped into a semi-infinite strip of the W plane, extending infinitely to the left from the imaginary axis and bounded above and below by the lines $\Phi = \pi$ and $\Phi = -\pi$ respectively (Fig. 14.06–C). An excursion along the outside surface of the conductor in the p plane, following the path $ABCDE$ of Fig. 14.06–B,

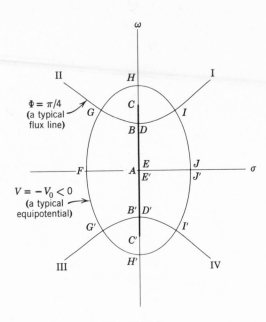

Fig. 14.06–B

corresponds in the W plane to following the line $V = 0$ as Φ increases from 0 to π, i.e., the path $ABCDE$ of Fig. 14.06–C, on the imaginary axis of the W plane, any two points bearing the same designation being in correspondence. Similarly, the paths marked $AB'C'D'E'$ in the two figures correspond. An excursion of the same sort along a typical equipotential $V = -V_0$ (a negative potential) is marked $FGHIJ$ and $FG'H'I'J'$ in the two planes. In this way the entire p plane is mapped into the shaded strip of the W plane of Fig. 14.06–D(a). This leaves a vast expanse of the W plane that is not accounted for! The remainder of its left half, however, contains merely repetitions of the mapping of the p plane. Since we can add to Φ at any point of the p plane any multiple of 2π by encircling the conductor the appropriate number of times in the appropriate direction, repeated excursions on the paths described above will show this repeated mapping in the manner indicated in Fig. 14.06–D(b) and (c). The roman numerals show the locations of the substrips that map the corresponding quadrants of the p plane in the manifold mapping. Note that contiguous portions of the repeated mappings correspond to contiguous portions of the p plane; traveling along the line $\Phi = \pi$ out from $V = 0$, for example, we see the IV quadrant on the right and the I quadrant on the left in both planes.

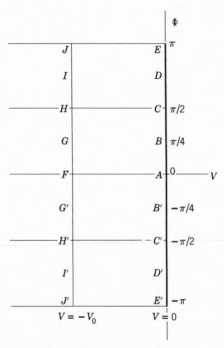

Fig. 14.06–C

It remains to explain the right half of the W plane. Here the potential V is positive—and there are no points at positive potential in the p plane. If we move in the p plane from a great distance, say along the line $\Phi = 0$ (the negative real axis) in the direction of increasing potential, we arrive at the conductor, where $V = 0$. We can go no further in the direction of increasing potential, and the same is true of an approach along any flux line; we cannot, that is, so long as we regard the conductor as an impenetrable barrier (of charge), where the flux lines stop. From another, more imaginative point of view, we may see in the barrier a sort of Looking

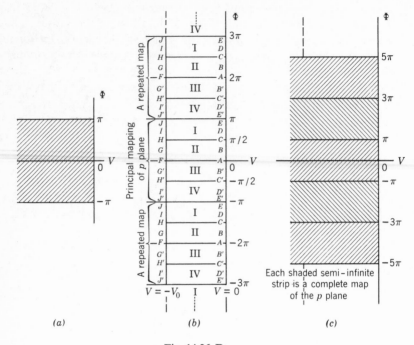

Fig. 14.06–D

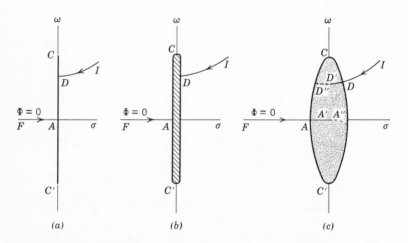

Fig. 14.06-E. Stages in the development of the *p* plane's other sheet.

Glass with a whole world of interesting things within it, between the surfaces of the thin conductor.

Suppose we look more closely at the conductor as we approach it. It is very thin, but with the magnifying power of our imagination it expands (Fig. 14.06–E) to an appreciably thick metal plate, as in Fig. 14.06–E(b). The flux lines that come up to it really end on surface charge—but we shall not at all change the flux plot outside the conductor if we imagine the lines to continue on into the interior (no longer a conductor), provided we construct this imaginary world so that it receives them properly and does not change the plot at the boundary. Our line $\Phi = 0$ goes on from the point A, then, along the line A-A'-$A'' \cdots$, Fig. 14.06–E(c), until somewhere in Looking-Glass World it terminates on positive charge. The path A-A'-$A'' \cdots$ must be in the region of positive potential, increasing, very likely, all the way to positive infinity by the time this charge is reached. Here, then, is an explanation of how the right half of the W plane maps back to the p plane: it does so in the interior of the region covered by the conductor, conventionally an infinitely thin line (CC' in Fig. 14.06–B) but imaginatively a whole new world reached by following flux lines up to the conductor and then right on through its surface into another world much like Alice's. This is the *Riemann-surface* method of interpreting the mapping defined by multivalued functions. It looks on the p plane as being constructed of two *sheets* joined together along the line CC' (and only there) in such a fashion that one cannot cross this line, but is automatically shunted on to the other surface if one tries to.

Figures 14.06–F and –G attempt to show this double p plane and the path we must follow in it if we move along a flux line. It is impossible to show the nature of the junction on the line CC'; we have to be content with imagining it to provide paths from the left half of the plane to the right half of the new sheet (and conversely), and from the right half of the plane to the left half of the new sheet (and conversely). How this is done without intersection we cannot depict, but we can *imagine* it done by the Riemann surface. Figure 14.06–G shows a model that may aid the imagination. The line CC' is a *branch cut* and each of the two sheets represents one of the two branches of the function of W inverse to $W(p)$ that p is. This is evidently a more sophisticated view than that taken in § 4.14, where the branch cut was regarded simply as an insurmountable barrier; here we look on it as an entrance to another, novel part of the p domain. In this second sheet the flux plot is evidently exactly the same as in the basic p plane, except that the direction of all flux lines is reversed. That is, the situation is much that of Fig. 14.04–D, and in the second sheet we may look on the conductor $C'C$ as bearing *negative* charge and being the *origin* of all the flux lines (which terminate on positive charge at

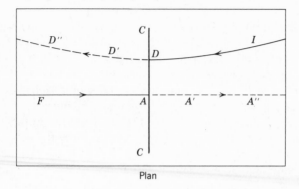

Plan

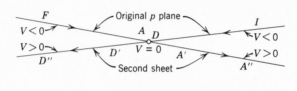

Elevation

Fig. 14.06–F.   Two sheets of the p plane.

infinity), if we wish.   On closer examination of the conductor, approached from the second sheet, we find that the flux lines come through the branch cut from the other sheet, and originate in negative charge at infinity thereon.   Because of this symmetry between the two planes, we see that the right half of the W plane contains another series of semi-infinite strips,

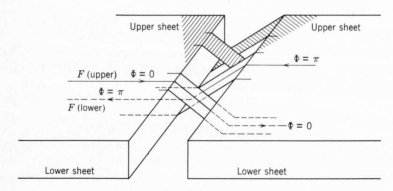

Fig. 14.06–G

each of which maps the whole p plane (actually the lower sheet of the p plane).

This is shown in Fig. 14.06–H in which the same lines as those of Fig. 14.06–B, but in the second sheet, are mapped in the (right half of the) W

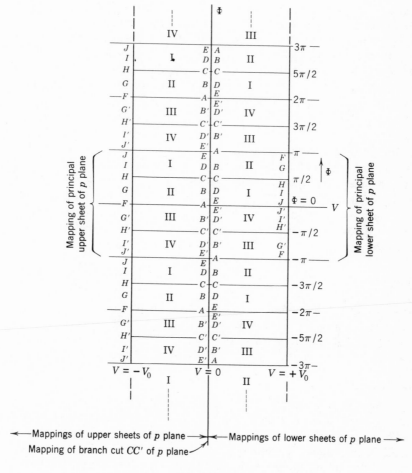

Fig. 14.06–H

plane. The same notation is used, but we must remember that the point G, for example, in the right half of the W plane is a mapping of the point G in the lower p plane, situated directly under the original point G.

The concept of the Riemann surface will be useful in demonstrating the utility of our proposed method of approximating a constant by quantization of charge on an appropriate equipotential. It is not difficult to imagine the Riemann surface, though it is extremely difficult to portray it. The two sheets of the p plane, joined together in a mystic fashion that permits passage from one sheet to the other without interference, map one to each half of the W plane, where passage from one to the other is extremely simple, requiring only that one cross the imaginary axis. Whenever we cross the line $V = 0$ in the W plane we accordingly pass from one sheet to the other in the p-plane mapping. Travel entirely within either the right or the left half of the W plane, as on the lines $V = -V_0$ or $V = +V_0$ for example, seems to correspond to travel entirely on one sheet of the p plane. Yet on second thought, this is not entirely satisfactory. For example, the line EJ in the original sheet of the p plane can be interpreted either as the flux line $\Phi = \pi$ or the line $\Phi = -\pi$, or any of a host of others. Just as the left and right halves of the W plane represent two different mappings of the p plane, which is conveniently interpreted to mean that the p plane has two sheets, so ought the vertically repeated mappings of the p plane in the W plane to correspond to different sheets of the p plane. And so, in the Riemann surface, they do. We arbitrarily take the line of junction (transition from one of these p-plane sheets to another) that is the branch cut, as the positive half of the real axis, the line $E\text{-}J \cdot \cdot \cdot$. Then we see that vertical travel in the W plane as on $V = -V_0$, which we had previously thought took us in the p plane merely around and around the conductor on the line $FGHIJJ'I'H'G'FGH$, actually takes us from one sheet to another every time we cross a line $\Phi = \pm \pi \times$ (an odd number). With this in mind the mapping becomes completely one-to-one, i.e., single-valued. Each of the shaded strips in Fig. 14.06–D(c) corresponds to one sheet of the p plane, with junctions along the positive half of the real axis; following the contour $V = -V_0$ then takes one along a sort of spiral staircase that mounts (or descends) indefinitely.

Each of these sheets is really two, according to our previous discussion, one corresponding to each half of the W plane, so that the Riemann-surface representation of the p plane is really quite complicated. The W plane is an ordinary single plane. The p plane, because of the vertical multiplicity of mapping to the W plane, and the horizontal double mapping, is a doubly infinitely sheeted surface. In any one sheet of the p "plane" there are two branch cuts, one coincident with the conductor's position, CC', and the other coincident with the positive half of the real axis, as in Fig. 14.06–I(a). A path such as $G\text{-}B \cdot \cdot \cdot$ takes us through one branch cut to the lower sheet, that on which V is positive, somewhat as in Fig. 14.06–I(b), in which the branch cuts have been opened up to emphasize their nature of portals to other sheets. Coming from the lower sheet to the upper is illustrated by the path $\cdots D'\text{-}I'$. Mounting the staircase to values of Φ greater than the principal values can be done by following the path $I\text{-}J \cdots$; descending to lower values by following $K\text{-}L \cdots$, for example. All of these correspond to simpler paths in the

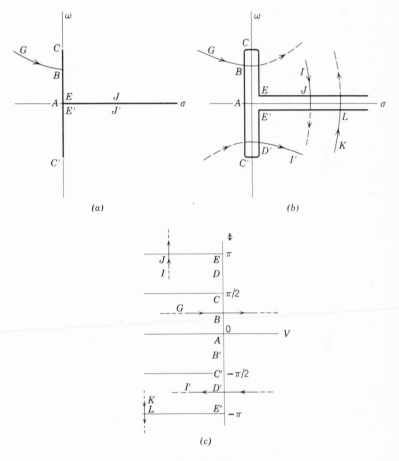

Fig. 14.06–I

W plane, shown with the same markings in Fig. 14.06–I(c). We make no attempt to portray such a complicated structure as this p "plane," but do take satisfaction in the fact that with it all the multivalued nature of our mapping can be explained and in fact removed. Fortunately, when we come actually to apply the mapping, we shall find it possible to cut the ties that bind one sheet of the Riemann surface that is the p plane to its neighbors and to sew together the edges into one single plane—in which we can do our work of approximation in safety.

This mapping we expect to be of help to us in calculating the complex potential in the p plane due to the quantized charges. But we must first decide how these lumped charges on the single-sheeted real p plane are to be transformed to the W plane, and how the complicated Riemann-surface p plane of the inverse transformation is related to the real p plane.

The complex potential, $W(p)$, of the situation in which the approximation band is occupied by a thin conductor deliberately placed there with positive charge (the negative charge being all at infinity for simplicity) thus defines a mapping of the p plane. The mapping is extremely complicated but it is the periodicity in this complication that makes easy our calculation of a new potential function, that due to the quantized charge rather than the distributed charge on the conductor. This new potential will surely give us some sort of approximation to a constant in the approximation band. Let us see just what it is.

14.07 Charge and potential in the w plane

Our purpose in discussing the W plane of § 14.06 is to develop a simple method of calculating the complex potential of charge arrays such as those of Figs. 14.05–E and –F. In such a plane these charges ought to arrange themselves in a symmetrical, periodic fashion that would make the calculation simple. It remains first to find exactly how charges map in this transformation, and how potential calculated in the new plane is related to potential in the p plane; and second, actually to calculate the potential functions of the quantized charges.

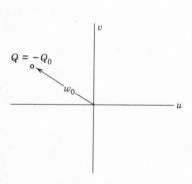

Fig. 14.07–A

To avoid confusion let us adopt a new symbol for the complex-potential function generated by the conductor on the approximation band, carrying a total charge of $+1$, the complementary charge of -1 being all at infinity. This is the transformation function described in § 14.06, and we now call it $F(p) = w = u + jv$. It is exactly the same as $W(p)$ in § 14.06, except for normalization (scale change) to the unit-charge case.

We may start by setting up a potential problem in the w plane. Since this plane is one-sheeted, i.e., an ordinary plane, there is no particular difficulty in calculating the potential due to, say, a negative charge of strength $-Q_0$ at $w = w_0$ (Fig. 14.07–A). The potential (on assuming the complementary positive charge to be at infinity) is clearly

$$W_w = Q_0 \ln (w - w_0) + \text{constant.} \qquad (14.07\text{–}1)$$

The field map consists of circles centered on the charge, and their radii, much as in Fig. 14.02–F. This flux plot we can map to the p domain without difficulty, since with the Riemann-surface concept the mapping is one-to-one and not multivalued. The various sheets of the p domain will have different flux plots, since the various semi-infinite strips of the w plane contain sections of the plot that are different. But the flux lines and equipotentials, changed in shape though they are in the transformation, remain mutually orthogonal and are still lines of constant real part and constant imaginary part of a function of the complex variable in the p domain (because the transformation is conformal). In symbols, the equipotentials in the w plane are

$$V_w = \text{Re } W_w(w) = \text{constant} = \text{Re } W_w[F(p)] = \text{Re } W_p(p) \qquad (14.07\text{–}2)$$

and the flux lines are

$$\Phi_w = \text{Im } W_w(w) = \text{constant} = \text{Im } W_w[F(p)] = \text{Im } W_p(p) \qquad (14.07\text{–}3)$$

in which $W_p(p)$ is this new function of the p domain. Then

$$W_p(p) = W_w(w) = Q_0 \ln (w - w_0) + \text{constant} \qquad (14.07\text{–}4)$$

represents the complex potential of a potential problem in the p domain, and the charge distribution for this consists evidently merely of a charge at p_0, the (unique) mapping of w_0, with a complementary charge at infinity. Near p_0 in the p domain, and near w_0 in the w plane, we have

$$
\begin{aligned}
W_p(p) &= Q_0 \ln [F(p) - F(p_0)] + \text{constant} \\
&= Q_0 \ln [F'(p_0) \times (p - p_0) + \cdot \cdot \cdot] + \text{constant} \qquad (14.07\text{–}5) \\
&= Q_0 \ln (p - p_0) + Q_0 \ln F'(p_0) + \cdot \cdot \cdot + \text{constant}
\end{aligned}
$$

in which the dots indicate the negligible portion of the Taylor-series expansion. Since the transformation is regular, the first term eclipses the others and we find in the p domain the same charge, $-Q_0$, at p_0. The entire potential problem is thus mapped into the p domain, and the potential computed there is $W_p(p)$. At any two corresponding points (in p and w) the complex potentials are identical (if the constants are suitably adjusted). This will continue to be true if additional charges are present in the w plane, provided only that like charges are placed at the mappings of their locations in the p domain, because of the linearity of the mathematics of potential.

But our real interest is in the actual p plane of network theory, and not in the complicated Riemann surface, however useful the latter may be in explaining a complicated multivalued mapping of the real p plane. It can be really useful only if the Riemann surface can be related in a simple fashion to the actual p plane. And this we can do: we can identify, say, the *principal sheet* of the Riemann surface with the *actual p plane* by making suitable use of symmetry. If all sheets of the p plane carry like charge distributions, and hence all semi-infinite strips of the w plane do so also, then the flux lines that cross from one sheet to another will be indistinguishable no matter which branch cut (within each of the two series) we look at. This is evident in the w plane, for the periodicity of the charge distribution there leads to a periodicity in the flux plot, as

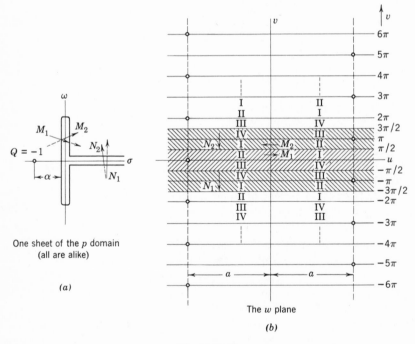

One sheet of the p domain
(all are alike)

(a)

The w plane

(b)

Fig. 14.07–B

illustrated in Fig. 14.07–B. Suppose, for simplicity, a unit negative charge at $\sigma = -\alpha$ in the principal sheet of the p domain, and repeated on every sheet. (The complementary positive charge is at infinity.) In the w

plane there is then a double infinity of unit negative charges, located at

$$w = -a \pm j2N\pi$$

and $$(N = 0, 1, 2, \cdots) \qquad (14.07\text{–}6)$$

$$w = +a + j\pi \pm j2N\pi$$

in which $a = |F(-\alpha)|$. The first set of charges (those in the left half of the w plane) are mappings of the charges in the upper of the pairs of sheets (corresponding to negative potentials in the original potential problem); the second set (in the right half of the w plane) are mappings of the charges in the lower of the pairs (corresponding to positive potential)—they are "offset" vertically a distance π since the point $(-\alpha, 0)$ where the charge is located in the lower sheet of the principal pair, directly under the corresponding point in the upper sheet, is on the line $v = \pi$ rather than $v = 0$ because of the way that flux line of the original diagram comes through the branch cut (Fig. 14.06–F). So it is with all the other charges on lower sheets.

The flux plot in the w plane is surely periodic, from the periodicity of its charges. The periodicity is vertical, and the period is 2π in v. More than that, there is a sort of inner periodicity, for the flux plot between $v = -\pi/2$ and $v = +\pi/2$, for example, is exactly that between $v = \pi/2$ and $v = 3\pi/2$ except that these two strips are rotated 180° about their central point with respect to each other. The strips in Fig. 14.07–B(b) with like shading have identical flux plots, and the two sorts differ only by this rotation. This is evident merely by inspection of the charge locations and is verified by examination of the quadrant numbers mapped from the p plane, which are similarly rotated in one strip compared to the next.

Because of this periodicity of the flux plot, it is evident that conditions at the branch cuts in the p domain are also periodic. A typical crossing from upper sheet to lower of a pair is shown as M_1 in Fig. 14.07–B; the crossing from lower to upper at the same point is M_2. Looking at these in the w plane we see that conditions at the head of the arrow M_1 are the same, because of the inner periodicity, as those at the head of M_2. It would accordingly make no difference in the flux plot if we were to cut the "ramps" (Fig. 14.06–G) that join upper and lower sheets at M_1 and M_2 and simply sew together the two parts of the upper sheet, and also the two parts of the lower sheet. The same applies at any junction between upper and lower sheets of a pair, i.e., anywhere on the v axis in the w plane. Furthermore, an exactly similar argument applies at the other series of branch cuts: conditions at the head of N_1 (descending) and the head of N_2 (ascending) are identical, as evidenced by their symmetrical locations in the w plane. Consequently we find, to our relief, that the tremendously complicated nature of the p domain is really no handicap at all to our use of the mapping to the w plane. If we make all sheets of the p domain identical as to charge distributions and hence make the charge distribution in the w plane appropriately periodic, the sheets become in effect independent, and may be cut apart and sewed up into single ordinary planes, the flux plot for any one of which is the corresponding one among the infinite number of identical ones of the w plane.

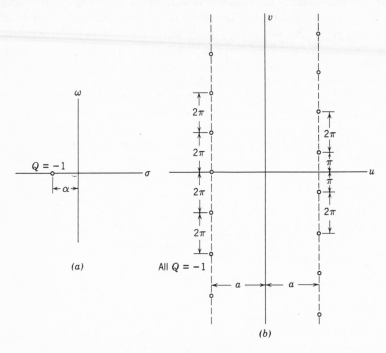

Fig. 14.07–C

It is not difficult to verify this conclusion in a purely formal manner by calculating the complex potential both for a single such charge in an ordinary one-sheeted p plane and for the w plane with its periodic charge. For the ordinary p plane, Fig. 14.07–C(a), we have

$$e^{W_p} = K_p(p + \alpha) \tag{14.07–7}$$

as the exponential potential, K_p being arbitrary. In the w plane, Fig. 14.07–C(b), we have a more complicated situation. Yet it is not at all difficult to find the potential here if we recall the discussion of § 3.27, in particular Fig. 3.27–B. Except for horizontal displacement and the vertical scale, the two vertical strings of charges look exactly like the diagrams for the zeros of the sinh and cosh functions. Our mapping converted an ordinary plane into an infinite sequence of mappings; it is only reasonable then that the exponential-potential function be converted from an ordinary rational function into an "infinite-order rational function" which we have found (§ 3.27) that circular and hyperbolic functions may be regarded as being. For the left-half-plane string of charges we accordingly write (with the usual arbitrary constant, here K_L)

$$e^{W_L} = K_L \sinh (Aw + B) \qquad (14.07–8)$$

in which the (complex) constants A and B are inserted to take care of the vertical scale and the horizontal shift respectively. These constants are easily determined from the conditions (a) that at $w = -a + j0$ the argument of the sinh function be zero (this is its principal zero), and (b) that the vertical increment in w from one zero to the next, $j2\pi$, correspond to the increment in the argument of the sinh function from one zero of the function to the next, $j\pi$. Formally we have

$$(a) \quad A(-a + j0) + B = 0,$$
$$(b) \quad A(j2\pi) \qquad = j\pi, \qquad (14.07–9)$$

which immediately yield

$$A = {}^1/_2, \qquad B = a/2. \qquad (14.07–10)$$

Thus for the left-half-plane string of charges we have

$$e^{W_L} = K_L \sinh \left(\frac{w + a}{2} \right) \qquad (14.07–11)$$

whose zeros evidently are exactly the locations of the negative unit charges in the left half of the w plane.

The right-half-plane string of charges, offset as it is, suggests the cosh function. We write

$$e^{W_R} = K_R \cosh (Aw + B) \qquad (14.07–12)$$

and require that the argument be $j\pi/2$ at $w = +a + j\pi$ (the principal zero) and that the increment of the argument be $j2\pi$ in w from one zero to the next:

$$A(a + j\pi) + B = 0 + j\pi/2,$$
$$A(j2\pi) \qquad = j\pi, \qquad (14.07–13)$$

from which

$$A = {}^1/_2, \qquad B = -a/2, \qquad (14.07–14)$$

so that

$$e^{W_R} = K_R \cosh\left(\frac{w - a}{2}\right) \qquad (14.07\text{–}15)$$

whose zeros evidently are exactly the locations of the negative unit charges in the right half of the w plane. We now have, for the w plane,

$$e^{W_w} = K_w \sinh\left(\frac{w + a}{2}\right) \cosh\left(\frac{w - a}{2}\right) \qquad (14.07\text{–}16)$$

which is easily converted (Problem 14-24), by the algebra of hyperbolic functions, to

$$e^{W_w} = \frac{K_w}{2}(\sinh w + \sinh a). \qquad (14.07\text{–}17)$$

By comparing this with (14.07–7) we see that the two can be made identical if we take $K = K_p = K_w/2$ (as we certainly may, since this is in effect the arbitrary constant of potential in each case) and further

$$p = \sinh w \qquad (14.07\text{–}18)$$

and, consistently, $\alpha = \sinh a$. Then

$$e^{W} = K(p + \alpha) = K\left(\sinh w + \sinh a\right) \qquad (14.07\text{–}19)$$

represents the exponential potential both in the ordinary p plane of one sheet and in the ordinary w plane with periodic mappings of the p plane's charge. An unexpected by-product here is relation (14.07–18) which evidently is the formal statement of the relation we have written as $w = F(p)$, i.e., $F(p)$ is actually $\sinh^{-1} p$ which clearly exhibits the multi-valued nature of the transformation. (We shall discuss this in more detail later.) Notice that in place of (14.07–18) we might equally well have written $p = \omega_0 \sinh w$, since this would amount only to revising the arbitrary constants. This would mean merely a scale change in the p plane, and we choose to retain (14.07–18) as written, noting that in it the p plane is normalized so that the point $p = 0 + j1$ corresponds to $w = 0 + j\pi/2$, i.e., that the conductor (or the approximation band) in the original problem which led to this transformation extends from $-j1$ to $+j1$ in the p plane.

From (14.07–19) we see that the potentials are the same in the two cases, at corresponding points, from the mathematical argument just given. The conclusion is the same as it was for the previous pictorial discussion.

We may extend these results to any number of charges, located as we wish, in the p plane, because of the linearity of the mathematics involved. The result, of great importance in our work, is the following.

If all the charge in the p plane is mapped (with the same strengths) to the w plane with the required periodicity, i.e., is repeated in each mapping of the p plane in the w plane, then the potentials are the same (except possibly for the arbitrary constant) at any two points in the two planes that are mappings of each other. (14.07–20)

With this we can now return to the calculation of the potential of charge distributions such as those of Figs. 14.05–E and –F, and shall find this easy to make.

14.08 Approximation of a constant, continued

Since we began our search for an even function that suitably approximates the desired resistance function of Fig. 14.05–A, we have followed a twisting road that has led us through some strange regions. But their utility will soon be evident, for we can now calculate the potential of our lumped charges in the (real, one-sheeted) p plane. These came into being by our quantization of the charge distribution on some equipotential of the field produced by a charged conductor on the approximation band. This (positive) charge of Q units (the complementary negative charge $-Q$ is for the present all at infinity) we quantized in the "center-of-charge fashion," with due regard also to the symmetry required of even functions in the p plane.

Since the charges lie (in the p plane) on an equipotential of the problem that gave rise (through its complex potential) to the w plane, at equal intervals of flux, their positions in the w plane follow a pattern of strict regularity: they lie on the line $u = -V_0/Q$ at equal intervals in v. Here $-V_0$ is the potential on the chosen equipotential in the flux plot of the charged conductor; it is divided by Q to adjust the potential to that for a unit charge on the conductor, the situation to which the w plane applies. The interval in v between charges is $2\pi/Q$, since a total flux of 2π is to be divided up into Q intervals. For the required quadrantal symmetry of the end result, Q must be an even integer, and there are two different possibilities, according as $Q/2$ is even or odd, as mentioned in § 14.05. If $Q = 2 \times$ (an even integer) $= 4N$, then the quantized charges lie at

$$u = -V_0/Q, \qquad v = \frac{\pi}{4N}, \frac{3\pi}{4N}, \frac{5\pi}{4N}, \cdot \cdot \cdot, \frac{4N-1}{4N}\pi,$$

$$-\frac{\pi}{4N}, -\frac{3\pi}{4N}, -\frac{5\pi}{4N}, \cdot \cdot \cdot, -\frac{4N-1}{4N}\pi, \qquad (14.08-1)$$

in the fashion of Fig. 14.05–E (in which $N = 3$). If $Q = 2 \times$ (an odd integer) $= 4N + 2$, then the positions are

$$u = -V_0/Q, \qquad v = 0, \frac{\pi}{2N + 1}, \frac{2\pi}{2N + 1}, \frac{3\pi}{2N + 1}, \cdots, \frac{2N\pi}{2N + 1}, \pi,$$

$$-\frac{\pi}{2N + 1}, -\frac{2\pi}{2N + 1}, -\frac{3\pi}{2N + 1}, \cdots, -\frac{2N\pi}{2N + 1}, \quad (14.08\text{–}2)$$

in the fashion of Fig. 14.05–F (in which $N = 3$).

In the discussion of § 14.07 we concluded that charge in the p plane must be mapped to the w plane with the full periodicity of the mapping. Consequently these charges must be repeated indefinitely, both above and below the positions just given; they must also be repeated in the right

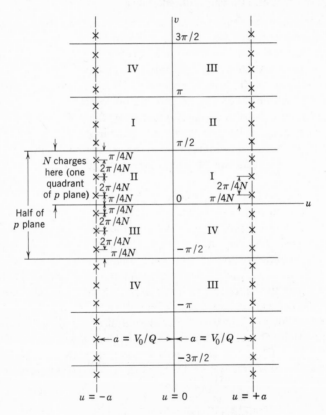

$$Q/2 = \text{an even integer} = 2N$$
$$\text{Drawn for } N = 3, Q = 12$$

Fig. 14.08–A

half of the w plane, since this too turned out to contain mappings of the p domain, all sheets of which are now identical (Fig. 14.06–H). The positions in the right half plane of any one charge are offset or staggered as in Fig. 14.07–B—but because of the symmetry of the p-plane charge distribution, when the right-half-plane charges are laid down, they appear to form simply a replica of the left-half-plane charges, but on the line $u = +V_0/Q$. Figures 14.08–A and –B in which a has been written for V_0/Q, show the complete w-plane charge distributions.

We can now write the exponential potential almost immediately, making use of our experience in § 14.07 with the hyperbolic functions.   For the case where $Q/2$ is *even* (Fig. 14.08–A) we write

$$e^{-W} = K \cosh (Aw + B) \cosh (Cw + D) \qquad (14.08\text{-}3)$$

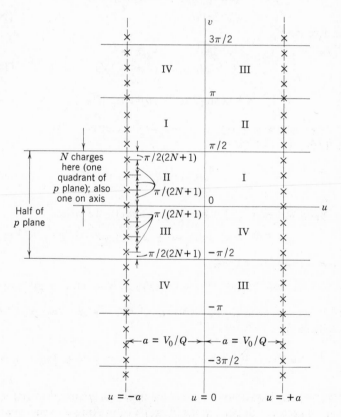

$Q/2 =$ an odd integer $= 2N + 1$

Drawn for $N = 3, Q = 14$

Fig. 14.08–B

in which the first cosh function represents the contribution of the left-half-plane charges and the second that of the right-half-plane charges and K is arbitrary. The subscript q is added to the symbol for the complex potential to emphasize that we are now discussing the *quantized* situation. (Since we are dealing here with positive charges, the hyperbolic functions appear in the denominator of the exponential-potential expression rather than the numerator; to avoid unnecessary fractions we write e^{-W_q} instead of e^{W_q}.) We must have

$$A(-a + j\pi/4N) + B = 0 + j\pi/2,$$
$$A(j2\pi/4N) \qquad = j\pi, \tag{14.08-4}$$

and

$$C(a + j\pi/4N) + D = j\pi/2,$$
$$C(j2\pi/4N) \qquad = j\pi, \tag{14.08-5}$$

which give us

$$A = 2N, \qquad C = 2N,$$
$$B = 2Na, \qquad D = -2Na. \tag{14.08-6}$$

Thus

$$e^{-W_q} = K \cosh\,[2N(w + a)]\cosh\,[2N(w - a)] \tag{14.08-7}$$

whose zeros are exactly the locations of the charges. This can be transformed (Problem 14-24) to

$$e^{-W_q} = \frac{K}{2}(\cosh 4Nw + \cosh 4Na). \tag{14.08-8}$$

For the case where $Q/2$ is *odd* (Fig. 14.08–B) we write

$$e^{-W_q} = K \sinh\,(Aw + B)\sinh\,(Cw + D) \tag{14.08-9}$$

and find, by similar reasoning,

$$e^{-W_q} = K \sinh\,[(2N + 1)(w + a)]\sinh\,[(2N + 1)(w - a)], \tag{14.08-10}$$

whose zeros are exactly the locations of the charges and which can be transformed (Problem 14-24) to

$$e^{-W_q} = \frac{K}{2}[\cosh\,(4N + 2)w - \cosh\,(4N + 2)a]. \tag{14.08-11}$$

These are the expressions for the exponential potential in the w plane. They have been developed, in the interests of making our first application of the potential analogy a careful one, in detailed terms. The resulting equations tend somewhat to obscure the real effect of quantization on an equipotential of the prototype problem (in which charge is distributed on a conductor that occupies the approximation band). The effect becomes much clearer if we rewrite (14.08–8) and (14.08–11) in terms of the total charge on the prototype conductor, Q, and then in terms of the prototype-situation complex potential $W = Qw$ and the potential of the equi-potential chosen for quantization, $-V_0$. We obtain

for $Q/2$ even,

$$e^{W_q} = \frac{2/K}{\cosh Qw + \cosh Qa} = \frac{2/K}{\cosh W + \cosh V_0} \qquad (14.08\text{–}12)$$

and for $Q/2$ odd,

$$e^{W_q} = \frac{2/K}{\cosh Qw - \cosh Qa} = \frac{2/K}{\cosh W - \cosh V_0}. \qquad (14.08\text{–}13)$$

These forms exhibit with startling clarity both the manner of quantization and the nature of the approximation achieved. The two denominators

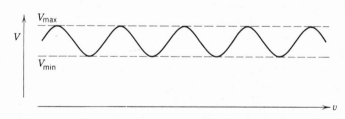

Fig. 14.08–C

vanish (thus locating the quantized charges) when $V = -V_0$ and Φ is a multiple of π (odd or even depending on whether $Q/2$ is even or odd)—which is of course the quantization principle on which we have based our work. Since $V = 0$ on the prototype conductor, W is purely imaginary there and $\cosh W$ becomes a sinusoid; *we have accordingly, in the quantized exponential potential, an approximation of the Chebyshev or equal-ripple type.* In later applications we shall again encounter equations like

(14.08–12) and (14.08–13) which by their very nature show that quantization on an equipotential of the prototype situation automatically results in a quantized exponential-potential function that has the Chebyshev approximation property.

Alternatively, in terms of the mapping function w which is purely imaginary on the mapping of the approximation band, the same property is evident in (14.08–8) and (14.08–11), for the hyperbolic functions there become merely sinusoids on the approximation band. This is also evident on mere inspection of the charge distribution in the w plane, in fact: in Figs. 14.08–A and –B the potential must oscillate repeatedly along the imaginary axis, with maxima at points directly opposite the charges and minima at points halfway between the maxima (Fig. 14.08–C) —this follows from the symmetry and infinitely repetitive character of the charge distribution.

It remains to rewrite these expressions in terms of p and finally of ω to find out exactly what approximation this procedure gives. For this it is appropriate first to investigate the p-w transformation in more detail. The details of the approximation will be developed in § 14.10.

14.09 The transformation $p = \sinh w$

We have found, almost by accident, the formal relation between p and w in (14.07–18). It is interesting to verify this by an independent derivation, based on the general nature of the transformation. The p plane is, in effect, cut on the heavy lines of Fig. 14.06–I(a) and then opened out and distorted so that the four quadrants become the semi-infinite strip of the w plane $[u < 0, \ -\pi < v < \pi]$, i.e., the principal mapping (Fig. 14.06–H). In Fig. 14.09–A this process is indicated in several stages: (a) cutting the p plane (making the branch cuts), (b) opening these cuts up somewhat, followed by bending (c) that forces the entire p plane over to the left as in (d), and finally (e) the straightening out of the compressed p plane into the semi-infinite strip of the w plane. This point of view is very helpful in following the mapping of any given point of the p plane as it is transformed. It too presents a mystery as to what is found when we open the cuts, i.e., as to what the rest of the w plane contains. This question we shall answer here by developing the transformation in a purely formal manner.

The device needed to formalize the sequence of distortions of Fig. 14.09–A is the Schwarz-Christoffel transformation (3.24–9). This is a convenient method of developing a transformation that maps one series of line segments into another, for it expresses exactly the bending that takes place in the two planes. In our case we wish to map the path $J'E'D'C'B'ABCDEJ$ from its p-plane shape of Fig. 14.09–B(a) to the

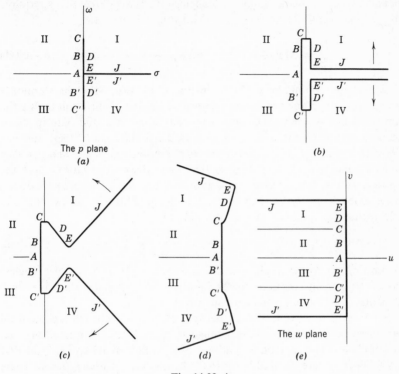

Fig. 14.09–A

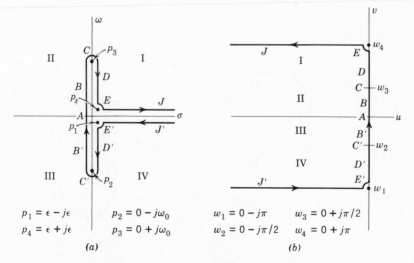

$p_1 = \epsilon - j\epsilon$ $p_2 = 0 - j\omega_0$ $w_1 = 0 - j\pi$ $w_3 = 0 + j\pi/2$

$p_4 = \epsilon + j\epsilon$ $p_3 = 0 + j\omega_0$ $w_2 = 0 - j\pi/2$ $w_4 = 0 + j\pi$

(a)   *(b)*

Fig. 14.09–B

boundary of a w-plane infinite rectangle, Fig. 14.09–B(b). This requires that expression (3.24–9) be written with four factors, as

$$\frac{dw}{dp} = K(p - p_1)^{a_1}(p - p_2)^{a_2}(p - p_3)^{a_3}(p - p_4)^{a_4}, \qquad (14.09\text{–}1)$$

in which the p points lie as shown in Fig. 14.09–B(a); the corresponding points in the w plane are to lie as shown in Fig. 14.09–B(b), on taking the limit $\epsilon \to 0$. As mentioned in § 3.24, the mapping of the path in the w plane remains a straight line so long as the p-plane path does, and has "corners" (i.e., changes its direction) at the points p_1, p_2, p_3, and p_4. We must choose a_1, a_2, a_3, and a_4 so that these direction changes have the correct values. The relative directions (angles) of the w-plane lines are determined from those of the p-plane lines by (14.09–1), which states, in effect, that increments in w and in p are related by

$$\Delta w = (\Delta p)(K)(p - p_1)^{a_1}(p - p_2)^{a_2}(p - p_3)^{a_3}(p - p_4)^{a_4}. \qquad (14.09\text{–}2)$$

A limiting process is implied, to be sure, but as far as directions (angles) go in straight-line motion, (14.09–2) is correct and states that five components go to make up the w-plane directions.

Starting from a point well to the right, J', we move in the p plane until we come to the first point of change in direction, p_1. For clarity, we accomplish the change on a quadrant of an infinitesimal circle, as in Fig. 14.09–B(a). Here we find [Fig. 14.09–C(a)] that Δp undergoes an angle

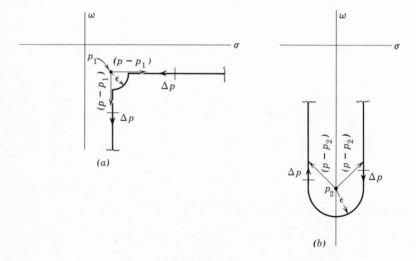

Fig. 14.09–C

change of $+\pi/2$ radians, $(p - p_1)$ an angle change of $-\pi/2$ radians; the remaining three factors of (14.09-2) do not change in angle since they are measured from distant points. In the w plane we wish Δw to change from a left-right motion to an upward motion at the corresponding point w_1 in Fig. 14.09-B(b), i.e., that Δw undergo an angle change of $+\pi/2$ radians. Then (14.09-2), only angles being considered, becomes

$$+\pi/2 = (+\pi/2) + a_1(-\pi/2) + a_2(0) + a_3(0) + a_4(0) \quad (14.09\text{-}3)$$

so that we must have

$$a_1 = 0. \quad (14.09\text{-}4)$$

This result could have been predicted, for the bend at p_1 and the bend at w_1 are both right-angled and both in the positive (counterclockwise) sense, so that no factor $(p - p_1)^{a_1}$ is necessary in (14.09-1); conditions are the same at these two points.

At the point p_2 we wish no change in direction at all in the w plane, but the angle of Δp decreases by π radians and that of $(p - p_2)$ by 2π radians, as in Fig. 14.09-C(b); the other factors undergo no change in angle. Hence we need

$$0 = (-\pi) + a_1(0) + a_2(-2\pi) + a_3(0) + a_4(0) \quad (14.09\text{-}5)$$

and

$$a_2 = -\tfrac{1}{2}. \quad (14.09\text{-}6)$$

Similar analysis at p_3 and p_4 leads to

$$a_3 = -\tfrac{1}{2}, \qquad a_4 = 0, \quad (14.09\text{-}7)$$

so that (14.09-1) becomes

$$\frac{dw}{dp} = K(p - p_2)^{-1/2}(p - p_3)^{-1/2}$$
$$= \frac{K}{\sqrt{p^2 + \omega_0{}^2}} \quad (14.09\text{-}8)$$

which is the differential equation defining the transformation of Figs. 14.09-A and -B. It is easily integrated, to give

$$w = K \sinh^{-1}(p/\omega_0) + K' \quad (14.09\text{-}9)$$

or

$$p = \omega_0 \sinh\left(\frac{w - K'}{K}\right). \quad (14.09\text{-}10)$$

The appearance of the unknown constant of integration K' and of the scale-factor constant K is only natural, since our method of developing the transformation has as yet injected no information on relative scales nor on correspondence of any two particular points. To make, say, the two points A in Fig. 14.09–B correspond, i.e., origin map to origin, we set $K' = 0$; for K we take the value unity, a choice of w-plane scale that insures that the two points C', for example, then correspond. (These two constants K' and K merely translate, and rotate and magnify, the w plane and do not affect the basic nature of the transformation; these choices are the simplest ones.) We also normalize the p plane so that the points $\pm j\omega_0$ become $\pm j1$, in the usual fashion. Thus we obtain

$$p = \sinh w \qquad (14.09\text{--}11)$$

for our transformation, exactly as (14.07–18).

The details of this mapping are given in part in Fig. 14.06–H. To be a little more precise, we now write specifically

$$\sigma + j\omega = \sinh (u + jv)$$
$$= \sinh u \cos v + j \cosh u \sin v \qquad (14.09\text{-}12)$$

from which

$$\sigma = \sinh u \cos v,$$
$$\omega = \cosh u \sin v. \qquad (14.09\text{--}13)$$

Mapping of a few important lines will suffice to give us the needed details. The imaginary axis of the w plane is $[u = 0, v = v]$; then

$$\sigma = 0,$$
$$\omega = \sin v, \qquad (14.09\text{--}14)$$

i.e., the segment of the p-plane imaginary axis where the approximation band lies is mapped repeatedly on the imaginary axis of the w plane, as we expected. The imaginary axis of the p plane is $[\sigma = 0, \omega = \omega]$; then *either* $\sinh u = 0$, which gives $u = 0$, $v = v$, and $\omega = \sin v$ and covers the approximation-band segment just as above, *or* $\cos v = 0$, which gives

$$v = \pm \frac{\pi}{2}, \qquad \pm 3\frac{\pi}{2}, \qquad \pm 5\frac{\pi}{2}, \cdots,$$
$$u = u, \qquad (14.09\text{--}15)$$
$$\omega = \pm \cosh u, \mp \cosh u, \pm \cosh u, \cdots.$$

The parts of the imaginary axis above $\omega = +j1$ and below $\omega = -j1$ are mapped, in repetitive fashion, exactly as expected, on the horizontal lines $v = \pm(\text{odd multiples of } \pi/2)$. The real axis of the w plane is $[v = 0, u = u]$; then

$$\omega = 0,$$
$$\sigma = \sinh u, \qquad (14.09\text{--}16)$$

i.e., it maps to the p-plane real axis with, of course, a functional relation (distortion) between values of u and of σ. Inversely, the real axis of the p plane is $[\omega = 0, \sigma = \sigma]$ and then $\sin v = 0$, which gives

$$v = 0, \qquad \pm \pi, \qquad \pm 3\pi, \cdots,$$

$$u = u, \qquad\qquad\qquad\qquad (14.09\text{--}17)$$

$$\sigma = \sinh u, \mp \sinh u, \pm \sinh u, \cdots.$$

The p-plane real axis is mapped repeatedly, with alternate orientations, exactly as expected (Fig. 14.09–D).

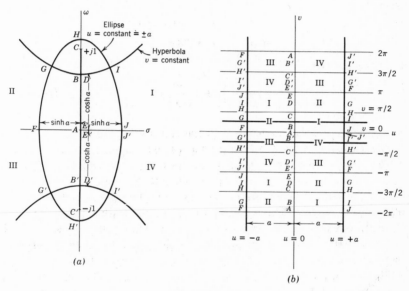

Fig. 14.09–D

One other interesting mapping is that of a line parallel to the imaginary axis of the w plane, say $u = -a$. (This is the locus of our quantized charges and is therefore especially important.) From (14.09–13) we have, on it,

$$u = -a, \qquad \sigma = -\sinh a \cos v,$$

$$v = v, \qquad \omega = \cosh a \sin v, \qquad (14.09\text{--}18)$$

and consequently

$$\left(\frac{\sigma}{\sinh a}\right)^2 + \left(\frac{\omega}{\cosh a}\right)^2 = 1. \qquad (14.09\text{--}19)$$

This is the equation of an *ellipse* of semiaxes sinh a and cosh a, as shown in Fig. 14.09–D. All of the equipotentials in preceding figures such as 14.04–C and –D, 14.05–E and –F, 14.06–A and –B are ellipses, then, of eccentricities that depend on a. The approximation band itself is an ellipse for which $a = 0$, i.e., a line segment; for large values of a the ellipses are substantially circles (at great distances the charge on the approximation-band conductor could be lumped at the origin without much change). Because of the periodicity of the mapping a line $u = +a$ maps to the p plane on exactly the same ellipse.

Horizontal lines in the w plane (flux lines of the original problem) become curves in the p plane that are orthogonal to these ellipses. They are given by

$$v = b, \qquad \sigma = \sinh u \cos b,$$
$$u = u, \qquad \omega = \cosh u \sin b, \qquad (14.09\text{--}20)$$

and consequently

$$-\left(\frac{\sigma}{\cos b}\right)^2 + \left(\frac{\omega}{\sin b}\right)^2 = 1. \qquad (14.09\text{--}21)$$

These are hyperbolas, orthogonal to the ellipses (Fig. 14.09–D).

This (Schwarz–Christoffel) approach to the mapping and the mathematics thereof changes nothing in the previous development. They do give precise formulas that will be useful, but the transformation is still exactly the same. One should note once more that the periodicity of the mapping is exactly that required to permit a flexible point of view. Instead, for example, of considering the semi-infinite strip between $v = \pi$ and $v = -\pi$ for $u < 0$ as the principal mapping (as the potential problem originally indicated), we could take the infinite strip between $v = +\pi/2$ and $v = -\pi/2$, utilizing both halves of the w plane. This strip contains all four quadrants of the p plane and is just as good a principal mapping as any other, if we look on this simply as a transformation. An excursion $ABCH \cdots$ in the p plane, with the first quadrant on the right and the second quadrant on the left, in the w plane follows (for example) the imaginary axis up from the origin to the point C. Here one can turn either to the right or the left and move horizontally; in each case there continues to be a mapping of the first quadrant on the right and of the second quadrant on the left. Each successive horizontal strip of height π is rotated 180° about its center, in order that these relative orientations of quadrants be preserved. Still other combinations of the mappings of the four quadrants could be taken as fundamental mappings if we wished. In other words, there is much arbitrariness in the location of the branch cuts.

14.10 Approximation of a constant, continued

We now have the explicit mathematical apparatus necessary to complete our calculation of the details of the potential of the quantized charges in the p plane. The two cases, $Q/2$ even and $Q/2$ odd, must still be treated separately. It is convenient now to let $n = Q/2$; then n is the number of charges in each half of the p plane.

When n is *even*, we have $Q/2 = n = 2N$ and, from (14.08–12),

$$e^{-W_q} = \frac{K}{2}(\cosh 2nw + \cosh 2na)$$

$$= K(\cosh^2 nw + \cosh^2 na - 1)$$

$$= K \sinh^2 na \left(1 + \frac{\cosh^2 nw}{\sinh^2 na}\right) \qquad (14.10\text{–}1)$$

$$= K_e \left(1 + \frac{\cosh^2 nw}{\sinh^2 na}\right), \qquad n \text{ even}$$

in which the arbitrary constant multiplier has been redefined as $K_e = K \sinh^2 na$. The object of the algebraic development above (which uses the formula for the double-argument cosh function) is to get the exponential potential into the form

$$e^{-W_q} = \text{constant} \times (1 + F) \qquad (14.10\text{–}2)$$

in which F is to exhibit clearly the equal-ripple property in the approximation band, by some sort of sinusoidal behavior.

When n is *odd*, we have $Q/2 = n = 2N + 1$, and, from (14.08–13),

$$e^{-W} = \frac{K}{2}(\cosh 2nw - \cosh 2na)$$

$$= K(\cosh^2 nw - \cosh^2 na)$$

$$= K(\cosh^2 nw - 1 - \sinh^2 na) \qquad (14.10\text{–}3)$$

$$= -K \sinh^2 na \left(1 - \frac{\cosh^2 nw - 1}{\sinh^2 na}\right)$$

$$= K_0 \left(1 - \frac{\cosh^2 nw - 1}{\text{sing}^2 na}\right), \qquad n \text{ odd}$$

in which, again, the arbitrary constant multiplier has been redefined.

Since we know how to write the exponential potential as a rational function of p (its poles are the locations of the quantized charges on the ellipse, its zeros are all at infinity), our principal interest here is in an explicit formula for the potential on the imaginary axis, i.e., at real frequencies, in order to evaluate the worth of this approximation procedure. Because of symmetry we need concern ourselves only with one mapping, say $H'C'B'ABCH$ in the left half plane in Fig. 14.09–D. There we have, in the approximation band, $u = 0$ and $\omega = \sin v$ by (14.09–14). Hence there

$|\omega| < 1$
(approximation band)

$$
\begin{aligned}
\cosh nw &= \cosh (nj \sin^{-1} \omega) \\
&= \cos (n \sin^{-1} \omega) \\
&= \cos [n(\pi/2 - \cos^{-1} \omega)] \qquad (14.10\text{–}4) \\
&= \pm \sin (n \cos^{-1} \omega) \qquad n \text{ odd,} \\
&= \pm \cos (n \cos^{-1} \omega) \qquad n \text{ even,}
\end{aligned}
$$

and

$$
\begin{aligned}
e^{-W_q} &= K_0 \left[1 + \frac{\cos^2 (n \cos^{-1} \omega)}{\sinh^2 na} \right] \qquad n \text{ odd,} \\
&= K_e \left[1 + \frac{\cos^2 (n \cos^{-1} \omega)}{\sinh^2 na} \right] \qquad n \text{ even.}
\end{aligned}
\qquad (14.10\text{–}5)
$$

Outside of the approximation band, i.e., for $|\omega| > 1$, we have $v = \pm\pi/2$ and $\omega = \pm \cosh u$ by (14.09–15). Hence there

$|\omega| > 1$

$$
\begin{aligned}
\cosh nw &= \cosh [n(u \pm j\pi/2)] \\
&= \cosh (nu) \cos (n\pi/2) + j \sinh (nu) \sin (n\pi/2) \\
&= \pm j \sinh (n \cosh^{-1} \omega) \qquad n \text{ odd,} \qquad (14.10\text{–}6) \\
&= \pm \cosh (n \cosh^{-1} \omega) \qquad n \text{ even,}
\end{aligned}
$$

and

$$
\begin{aligned}
e^{-W_q} &= K_0 \left[1 + \frac{\cosh^2 (n \cosh^{-1} \omega)}{\sinh^2 na} \right] \qquad n \text{ odd,} \\
&= K_e \left[1 + \frac{\cosh^2 (n \cosh^{-1} \omega)}{\sinh^2 na} \right] \qquad n \text{ even.}
\end{aligned}
\qquad (14.10\text{–}7)
$$

In (14.10–5) and (14.10–7) we have, finally, explicit statements of the results of this particular approximation procedure. These differ, as between the cases n odd and n even, only in their multipliers, which are arbitrary and to be evaluated as may be convenient. Here, on the imaginary axis, the exponential potential is purely real (from the symmetry of the charge distribution, all points of the imaginary axis are flux lines) as an even-part function should be and can be identified directly with **Ev** $Z(j\omega)$ or with the resistance function $R(\omega)$.

In the approximation band, where ω varies from 0 to 1, $\cos^{-1}\omega$ varies from $\pi/2$ to 0 and $n\cos^{-1}\omega$ from $n(\pi/2)$ to 0; accordingly $\cos^2(n\cos^{-1}\omega)$ oscillates between 1 and 0. Hence the quantity in brackets in (14.10–5) oscillates in equal-ripple fashion between the upper limit $[1 + (\sinh^2 na)^{-1}]$ $= \coth^2 na$, and the lower limit 1. These are, however, reciprocals of the exponential potential that we have identified with $\mathbf{Ev}\,Z(p)$, i.e. (on the ω axis), with the resistance function, $R(\omega)$. Consequently the resistance function itself that we have obtained oscillates in the approximation band between the limits 1 and $\tanh^2 na$, in Chebyshev fashion. Notice that this is true whether n be odd or even; the only difference of any consequence between the two cases is that at the origin for n odd the potential is maximum (the bracketed expression is unity) and the first oscillation is downward, while for n even the potential is minimum (the bracketed expression is $\coth^2 na$) and the first oscillation is upward (Fig. 14.10–A).

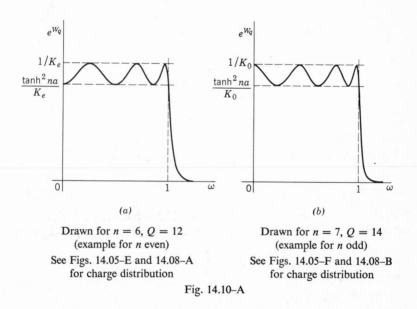

(a)

Drawn for $n = 6$, $Q = 12$
(example for n even)
See Figs. 14.05–E and 14.08–A
for charge distribution

(b)

Drawn for $n = 7$, $Q = 14$
(example for n odd)
See Figs. 14.05–F and 14.08–B
for charge distribution

Fig. 14.10–A

Outside of the approximation band, where (14.10–7) applies, the quantity in brackets rises steadily from the value $\coth^2 na$, since as ω increases from unity, $\cosh^{-1}\omega$ does so also, and so does $\cosh(n\cosh^{-1}\omega)$. Hence the exponential potential (resistance) drops steadily, in this region, from the value $\tanh^2 na$ to zero, whether n be odd or even.

For the two examples we have been considering, this behavior is shown in Fig. 14.10–A, the curves of which are easily calculated from (14.10–5) and (14.10–7). The method of approximation originally proposed in

§ 14.05, and developed at some length thereafter, has led indeed to a Chebyshev or equal-ripple approximation in the approximation band. To complete the discussion of this problem, we have only to evaluate the constant multipliers and set down in recapitulation the important steps.

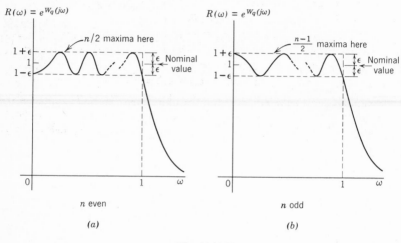

Fig. 14.10–B

The multipliers are probably most lucidly expressed in the form that leads to Fig. 14.10–B, for the equal-ripple behavior can then be clearly stated:

in the approximation band the resistance function oscillates between the limits $(1 + \epsilon)$ and $(1 - \epsilon)$;   (14.10-8)

thereafter it drops steadily toward zero. The expressions for K_e and K_0 should evidently be the same, and are found by writing (with $K_e = K_0 = K$)

at a maximum (of potential or of resistance)
$$(1 + \epsilon) = \frac{1}{K(1 + 0)},$$

(14.10–9)

at a minimum
$$(1 - \epsilon) = \frac{1}{K[1 + (1/\sinh^2 na)]},$$

which yield

$$K = \frac{1}{1 + \epsilon}$$ (14.10–10)

and

$$\frac{1}{\sinh^2 na} = \frac{2\epsilon}{1 - \epsilon}.$$ (14.10–11)

The expression for the resistance (exponential potential) function corresponding to Fig. 14.10–B is thus

$$R(\omega) = e^{W_q(j\omega)} = \frac{1+\epsilon}{1 + \dfrac{2\epsilon}{1-\epsilon}[\cos^2(n\cos^{-1}\omega)]} \qquad \begin{array}{l} -1 < \omega < +1, \\ \text{i.e., } |\omega| < 1 \end{array}$$

$$(14.10\text{–}12)$$

$$= \frac{1+\epsilon}{1 + \dfrac{2\epsilon}{1-\epsilon}[\cosh^2(n\cosh^{-1}\omega)]} \qquad |\omega| > 1.$$

Because of the (even) symmetry these hold as indicated for both positive and negative values of ω. Within the approximation band (considering both positive and negative values of ω) there are n maxima of resistance (potential), one corresponding to each left-half-plane pole (positive charge), which produces a potential maximum in its vicinity (this is most evident in the w plane). (The right-half-plane charges act in concert with those in the left half plane and merely reinforce the behavior.) The approximation-band behavior is truly equal-ripple; the fact that the peaks and valleys are not equally spaced but cramped toward the upper end in no way detracts from this quality: the unequal spacings are necessary to obtain this sort of behavior, and may be thought of as due to the changing vertical increment of distance between charges on the upper part of the ellipse. The rate of falling off beyond the approximation band is determined by both n and a; the behavior here is a monotonic approach to the value zero at high frequencies.

Since the expressions for $R(\omega)$ and for the quantized exponential potential have all their zeros at infinity, their functional behavior is concentrated in the denominator polynomials. In the forms shown in (14.10–12), which so clearly show the equal-ripple property of the approximation, the parts of the polynomials in brackets are the commonest of those polynomials that are called *Chebyshev polynomials* (Problem 14-35). In the later sections of this chapter, as we generalize this mode of approximation, we shall encounter similar rational functions with Chebyshev behavior, but it is only in this particular case (where all the zeros are at infinity) that such simple functions are obtained.

With these observations, the experiment of approximation using the potential analogy in the fashion suggested first in § 14.05 is complete. Since the result is a specific useful technique (as well as an indication of more general techniques that we shall discuss later), it is well to look back and evaluate it carefully, both as to principles and as to results, recapitulating the important points.

14.11 Recapitulation

In spite of the length of the development leading up to the results shown in Figs. 14.10–A and –B, the ideas that form the heart of the technique are simple and easily stated. We set them down here both to emphasize the essential part of the technique and to have them clearly in mind for future use.

Since the function to be approximated is a *constant*, the use of a conductor in the potential analogy is natural. An infinitesimally thin conductor is placed on the approximation band, charged with $Q = 2n$ units of (positive) charge that distributes itself according to the laws of electrostatics, all of the complementary charge $(-Q)$ being at infinity. This is the *prototype* situation; from it the solution is derived by quantizing the Q units of positive charge on an equipotential of the prototype problem at equal intervals of flux, with due regard for the symmetry required in the final result, the negative charge (which is already lumped) being left untouched—this is the *quantized* situation. The resulting rational function (which has these new points as poles and zeros only at infinity) gives a Chebyshev approximation to a constant in the approximation band, the size of the error ripple being determined by the choice of equipotential in the prototype problem. Formally, this function is

$$e^{W_q} = \frac{\text{constant}}{\cosh W \pm \cosh V_0} = \frac{\text{constant}}{1 \pm \epsilon \cosh W} \qquad (14.11\text{–}1)$$

in which the constants differ, and $\epsilon = \text{sech } V_0$. It is clear from the fashion in which the prototype potential W appears in this equation, since in the approximation band $W = 0 + j\Phi$, that Chebyshev or equal-ripple approximation is obtained on quantization. The equation is fairly general, as we shall see. In the particular case we have been treating, it can be expanded into the forms of § 14.10 which lead to certain Chebyshev polynomials (Problem 14-35); in general, we should expect to find rational functions, appropriate to each case, with Chebyshev properties. In these few sentences is stated what is important in the process; the rest is detail, detail that is necessary for demonstration of the character of the approximation and for obtaining precise formulas for actual designs, but is secondary to the basic principles of this (potential-analogy) method of obtaining a Chebyshev approximation to a constant.

An actual design procedure, once the technique has been developed, can also be set down in a brief space. The product na is determined by the desired fractional error ripple ϵ, according to (14.10–11). The significance of this quantity na should not be overlooked: since $n = Q/2$ and $a = V_0/Q$, we have $na = V_0/2$. That is, $2na$ is in fact the negative of the potential on that equipotential of the prototype situation which is chosen for the quantization. More convenient forms of the relation between ϵ and na and V_0, obtained by manipulation of (14.10–11), are

$$\epsilon = \operatorname{sech} 2na = \operatorname{sech} V_0 \qquad (14.11\text{–}2)$$

and

$$na = \tfrac{1}{2} \operatorname{sech}^{-1} \epsilon$$

$$= \frac{1}{2} \ln (2/\epsilon) - \frac{\epsilon^2}{8} + \cdots. \qquad (14.11\text{–}3)$$

Since logarithm tables are usually more convenient to work with, na being fairly large as a rule and ϵ small, the second form in (14.11–3) is useful to determine na; the first term in the expansion is generally entirely adequate. The choice of n is dictated either by cost or by a requirement on the rapidity of falloff. In the latter case some computations with (14.10–12) at a frequency somewhat above unity will indicate (ϵ being fixed) how large an n is necessary. Then a is calculated from na, and the left-half-plane pole positions from

$$p = \sinh (-a + jv) = - \sinh a \cos v \pm j \cosh a \sin v \qquad (14.11\text{–}4)$$

in which v takes the values given in (14.08–1) or (14.08–2). The right-half-plane pole positions are the reflections of these points in the origin, the zeros are all at infinity, and hence the rational function $\mathbf{Ev}\, Z(p)$ is now determined except for the multiplier. Realizability of the corresponding impedance function $Z(p)$ is assured by the properties of $\mathbf{Ev}\, Z(p)$, according to § 8.16. The numbers (14.11–4) are not only the left-half-plane poles of $\mathbf{Ev}\, Z(p)$ but also (all) the poles of $Z(p)$. That is, this particular approximation method makes it unnecessary in the next step, that of determining $Z(p)$ from $R(\omega)$, to factor the denominator of $\mathbf{Ev}\, Z(p)$ in order to extract the left-half-plane poles—the job is already done! It remains to determine the numerator of $Z(p)$. This can be accomplished by using (8.11–10), in which all the c's except c_0 are zero [all of the zeros of $R(\omega)$ are at infinity] and the b's are the coefficients in the polynomial whose zeros are the points determined by (14.11–4). The value of c_0 is determined by the value wanted for $Z(0) = R(0)$; this is either $(1 + \epsilon)$ or $(1 - \epsilon)$ according as n is odd or even (Fig. 14.10–B). Finally, this function $Z(p)$ is to be realized. Since all the zeros of $\mathbf{Ev}\, Z(p)$ lie at infinity, a simple L-C ladder network terminated in a resistance (Fig. 14.11–A) is a possible realization, this follows from (9.11–6) and the fact that the "resonances" are to occur only at infinity. Accordingly, we can immediately develop the function $Z(p)$ in a continued fraction in p (by division, inversion, division, $\cdots$) whose coefficients are the element values. There will be n reactive elements and one resistor, whose value is $R(0)$. The element values must be adjusted (denormalized) for actual resistance and frequency scales, and (if the job requires it) consideration given to parasitic effects.

This problem's discussion has been lengthy but is worth the effort. Its practical value is evident with the point of view of § 11.04: it becomes the

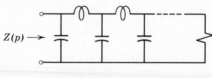

Fig. 14.11–A

problem of designing a low-pass filter, for then the transmission is proportional in magnitude to $R(\omega)$, as shown for example by (11.04–3): signals of frequencies in the approximation band are transmitted more or less uniformly; those of higher frequencies are attenuated. This is an important type of network in practice, which will be given more attention in Volume II.

The dual problem, that of designing a network whose input *conductance* is approximately constant (in the Chebyshev sense) in a low band and thereafter falls off steadily, differs only in that words and symbols are changed to their duals. Its practical application as a low-pass filter is in the situation where the source is a voltage generator rather than a current generator (§ 11.04).

The value of this discussion in adding to our knowledge of *approximation*, our main interest here, is also great. It has shown how useful the potential analogy can be, at least in approximating a constant, and may point the way to other applications. We ought now to examine it critically and list the aspects of this example that are restrictive or limiting, in order to define the general utility of this procedure. On reflection we see that there are four aspects of this work that are very special and require discussion, in that they might well have been different:

1. all the zeros of the resistance function are placed at infinity;
2. the approximation band is centered on the origin;
3. an even function is used as the approximating function;
4. the function approximated is a constant.   (14.11–5)

Any or all of these restrictions may hinder the application of this technique in general. Even in this particular problem we ought to consider the possibility of placing zeros at finite points; the band of importance can be *internal*, extending from some frequency ω_1 to another, ω_2, rather than confined to low frequencies; it may be an odd function, say a reactance, rather than an even one that we have to generate; and it may not be as simple a function as a constant that we have to approximate. Our next steps accordingly will be to investigate how well these four restrictions can be removed.

14.12 Arbitrary zeros

The first of the four special qualities of the previous development is that all the zeros of the resistance function (the even part of the impedance function) are placed at infinity. Such a disposition of the zeros is not at all necessary (though it does simplify the work); the principles are still valid no matter where the zeros lie. On the other hand, the positions of the poles in the p plane are not so readily calculated and simple equations such as (14.11–4) are not obtainable in the general case of arbitrary zeros. Hence we shall begin our generalization with a specific example.

Suppose a network is to be designed so that its driving-point resistance function approximates a constant in a low-band, Chebyshev fashion subject to the requirement that the zeros of resistance lie at prescribed frequencies. All but the first of the four special qualities in (14.11–5) thus still hold. And to keep the calculations reasonably simple, let us consider an impedance function of order three, whose resistance function is then of order six. Let the six zeros (arbitrarily prescribed) lie

$$\text{two at } (0 + j\omega_1),$$
$$\text{two at } (0 - j\omega_1), \quad\quad\quad (14.12\text{–}1)$$
$$\text{two at infinity,}$$

the approximation band running from the origin to unit frequency. [Zeros on the imaginary axis must be of even order and occur in conjugate pairs, of course, as they do in (14.12–1).] The approximation problem is then to find a rational function that has these prescribed zeros, is even, has real coefficients, is finite and positive (or zero) at all points on the imaginary axis, and approximates a constant in equal-ripple fashion in the interval $0 \leq \omega \leq 1$. Such a function meets the requirements and is realizable as a driving-point resistance function.

The method used previously is still valid—all we need do is apply the same principles, with care and patience in working out those details that are different and verifying the continuing soundness of the process. We start by placing a thin conductor on the approximation band (Fig. 14.12–A). It must bear a charge of $+6$ units, since there are six poles to be determined; the six negative charges are shown in their prescribed positions. The next step is to construct, at least in the mind's eye, the flux plot for this situation, so that we may quantize the positive charge. This time the flux plot is evidently considerably more complicated; the equipotentials are not curves as simple as ellipses, for example. Since the actual numerical work will probably have to be done more accurately than any graphical procedure can do it, the flux plot's principal value is to aid in visualizing how the quantization process operates. For this a rough

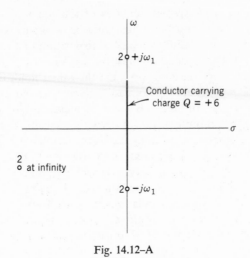

Fig. 14.12–A

sketch will suffice, and the time and effort spent in making a careful drawing can hardly be justified—especially since each change in the pre-scribed zeros will change the plot. (It is only in the relatively simple case where all the zeros are at infinity that an accurate flux plot is readily drawn.) Furthermore, it is necessary to distort the plot by expanding it in certain regions, in order to make its interesting features clearly visible.

Such a plot is shown in Fig. 14.12–B, of which several features are noteworthy. It has quadrantal symmetry, generated by the symmetry of the charge distribution, as required. The approximation band (conduc-tor) itself is an equipotential, let us say again at potential *zero*; the flux function we once more take to be zero at the origin on the left side of the conductor, and thus we fix the arbitrary constant of the complex potential. Equipotentials near the approximation band have an almost elliptical character, but as the potential drops and we go further from the conductor their shape changes: the ellipses of Fig. 14.09–D(a) and 14.06–A are distorted by being forced in along the imaginary axis by the negative charge which comes in from infinity to the prescribed points $\pm j\omega_1$. At points remote from the imaginary axis the distortion is less pronounced, but in the parts of the imaginary axis between the ends of the conductor $(\pm j1)$ and the negative charge $(\pm j\omega_1)$ there is a great change, for *all*

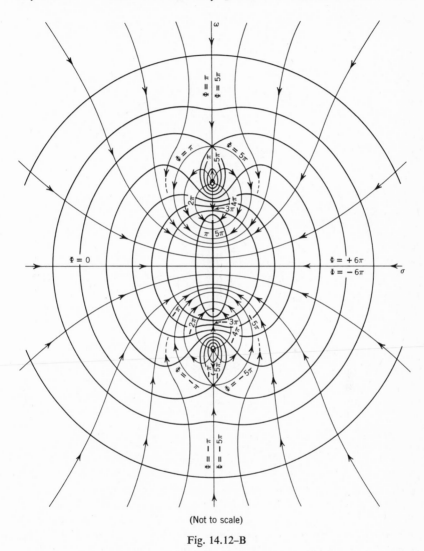

(Not to scale)

Fig. 14.12–B

equipotentials from $V = 0$ to $V = -\infty$ must cross the ω axis in this interval. Near the points $\pm j\omega_1$ the equipotentials must be substantially circles, since here the influence of the negative (lumped) charge is predominant. This requires a transition between the two kinds of equipotentials, which is effected by a pair of saddle points (§ 14.02) much as in Figs. 14.02–H and 14.02–I.   (Cf. Fig. 14.12–C.)

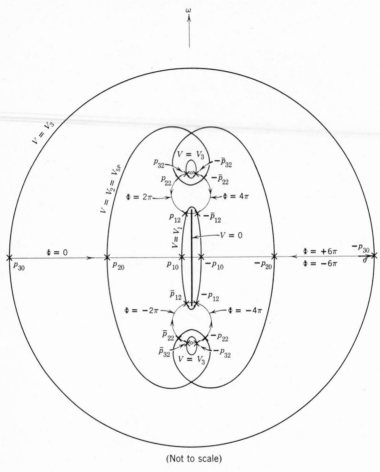

(Not to scale)

Fig. 14.12–C

There is one particular equipotential, that for $V = V_{sp}$, whose shape partakes of both natures.   For $V > V_{sp}$ the equipotentials are essentially distorted ellipses, the distortion being most evident near the ω axis.   For $V < V_{sp}$ the equipotentials have three parts or branches: one part is a distorted ellipse that encircles both the approximation band and the negative charge at the finite points, the other two parts are distorted circles that encircle these negative charges.   In the transitional equipotential, that for $V = V_{\mathrm{sp}}$, these three branches are continuously connected, as the diagram shows. On the ω axis (as we move up from the origin, e.g.) the potential varies from zero (on the conductor) down continuously to $-\infty$ at the location of the prescribed negative charge; thereafter it rises to a maximum at the saddle point and then falls off steadily towards the value $-\infty$ at infinity. On the σ axis (as we move to the left from the origin, e.g.) the potential drops continuously from zero toward the value $-\infty$ at infinity. A study of Fig. 14.12–B will indicate in detail how the potential varies throughout the p plane. It should be noted again that for values of potential between zero and V_{sp} there is one closed equipotential, while for values of V less than V_{sp} there are three: the equipotential for $V = V_{\mathrm{sp}}$ is a single curve that yet has three distinct parts.

The course of the flux lines is as usual perpendicular to the equipotentials. Flux lines for values of Φ between 0 and π come from infinity directly in to the conductor; for values of Φ between π and 3π they run from the prescribed negative charge to the positive charge on the conductor. In the other three quadrants perfectly symmetrical lines occur. The part of the ω axis above the conductor and below the negative charge is a flux line, on which $\Phi = 3\pi$; the part of the ω axis above the negative charge is also a flux line, on which $\Phi = \pi$ if approached from the left, and $\Phi = 5\pi$ if approached from the right. This multivalued property is characteristic of Φ, of course, for the difference between these two values corresponds to making a circuit of the negative charge and hence cutting $2 \times 2\pi = 4\pi$ lines. The value of Φ is everywhere indeterminate in the sense that it can be changed by various multiples of 2π simply by following a closed path that encircles charge and returns to the starting point. The values shown in Fig. 14.12–B are those obtained, for example, with the chosen origin of flux, by not crossing the ω axis above the negative charge at $+j\omega_1$, nor below that at $-j\omega_1$, nor crossing the positive real axis (nor, of course, the conductor), a strictly arbitrary rule.

Only those lines that interest us most are drawn in Fig. 14.12–C, which is again but a rough sketch and is deliberately not drawn to scale in order to bring out the important behavior clearly. These are the even-π lines and a few equipotentials, those for V_1 (near the conductor), V_2 (the saddle-point equipotential), and V_3 (a distant equipotential). Because our method is to quantize on equipotentials at their intersections with appropriate flux lines (the even-π lines here, because $Q/2$ is an odd number), and the choice of the equipotential is determined by the magnitude of the error ripple in the approximation band, we can look on these flux lines as loci of positions of the positive charges, on which they move as the ripple is varied. For a rather large ripple, quantization on $V = V_1$, for example, the locations of the quantized charges would be p_{10}, p_{12}, and $\bar{p}_{12}$ in the left half plane, and the corresponding points in the right half plane; for a moderate ripple, corresponding to quantization on $V = V_2$, the left-half-plane points would be p_{20}, p_{21}, $\bar{p}_{21}$ and these would be accompanied by their negatives; for a small ripple ($V = V_3$), the points would be p_{30}, p_{32}, $\bar{p}_{32}$ and their negatives. For the impractical case of a 100% ripple (this would correspond to $\epsilon = 1$ in § 14.10 and would give the resistance function poles on the imaginary axis) the quantization points lie on the conductor and are the starting points of the loci; as the ripple decreases the points move smoothly out on these even-π flux lines (against the arrowheads) toward the (prescribed) negative charges, wherever they lie (at infinity or at finite points), reaching them in the limit of no ripple at all. The fact that the equipotentials may have either one or three separate branches offers no obstacle; this is simply required by the fact that all the negative charge is no longer at one point.

The foregoing discussion contains all that it is necessary to say about the principle by which the required rational function is determined. Its zeros are those prescribed, its poles are those obtained by quantization on an equipotential at appropriate values of Φ, and its multiplier is simply a scale factor. We must, however, append a mathematical discussion to indicate how the poles may be found with good numerical accuracy, to demonstrate that the approximation is still truly Chebyshev in character, and to evaluate the exact behavior of the resulting rational function both within and outside the approximation band.

Let us begin by calculating the complex potential W for the prototype problem, that described in Fig. 14.12–A, to which corresponds the flux plot of Fig. 14.12–B. Because part of the charge is distributed (on the approximation-band conductor), e^W is not rational and cannot be written by inspection; nor is the w plane of § 14.07 and § 14.09 any longer the complex-potential plane, because some of the negative charge has moved in from infinity to complicate the function. This w plane is still of use, however, because of its intimate relation to the approximation-band conductor. The charge distribution of Fig. 14.12–A, transformed to the plane of w [defined, as before, by (14.09–11)] is shown in Fig. 14.12–D. It requires only a slight extension of the reasoning of § 14.07 to show that the complex potential will again be invariant, i.e., it will be the same (within a constant) at corresponding points in the two planes (those of p and w) provided we are careful to place charge at *every* mapping of each p-plane charge location in the w plane. We need then concern ourselves no further with the multivalued nature of the mapping.

The (prescribed) negative charges, which lie in the p plane at the points $\pm j\omega_1$, then lie in the w plane at the points

$$w = \pm \cosh \omega_1 \pm j(2m + 1)\frac{\pi}{2} \qquad (m = 0, 1, 2, 3, \cdots) \quad (14.12\text{–}2)$$

in accordance with the discussion of § 14.07. At each of the points in the two infinite sets defined by (14.12–2) there must be *two* units of negative charge, to agree with the *p*-plane situation. There is in addition negative

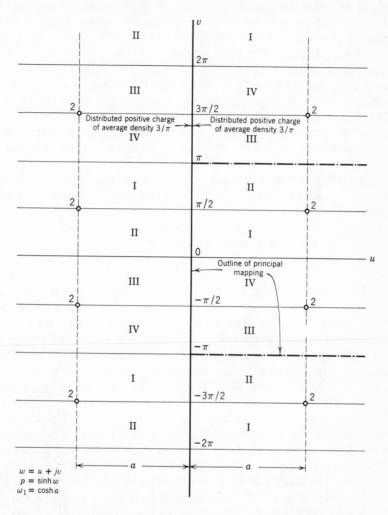

Fig. 14.12–D. The charge distribution of Fig. 14.12–A transformed to the *w* plane.

charge at infinity, in amount two units for each mapping of the *p* plane, and consequently infinite in amount; it is convenient to think of this as being two units at each "infinite end" (both left and right) of each horizontal strip of the *w* plane of height 2π, in accordance with Fig.

14.07–B.   This charge at infinity must not be forgotten when the potential is calculated.

The positive charge is distributed, in the p plane, on the outside surface of the approximation-band conductor; in the w plane it must also be distributed on a conductor (also at zero potential) which evidently occupies the imaginary axis—and that from negative infinity to positive infinity by virtue of the periodicity of the mapping.   In Fig. 14.12–D we thus find a conductor on the imaginary axis, carrying a distributed charge on each of its surfaces whose total amount, in any part of height 2π, is six units (on each side).   The average density of the surface charge on the conductor is accordingly $3/\pi$ (without dimensions since we have normalized all of our quantities).   This charge is not uniformly distributed; it will be most intense at points opposite the negative charges ($v + \pm\pi/2$, $\pm3\pi/2$, $\cdot$ $\cdot$ $\cdot$) and least intense at points midway ($v = 0$, $\pm\pi$, $\pm2\pi$, $\cdot$ $\cdot$ $\cdot$). The genesis of this conductor and its distributed charge is neatly explained by the cut-and-bend point of view of the transformation's development expressed in § 14.09.

In order to obtain numerical values for the quantization points (Fig. 14.12–C) we must calculate the potential W for the prototype problem. This is difficult to do in Fig. 14.12–A, and it is not as easy in (the equivalent) Fig. 14.12–D as it was in § 14.08—because of the prescribed negative charge at finite points.   There is symmetry in Fig. 14.12–D, however, that, with the aid of the method of electrostatic images, makes the calculation simple.   The conductor effectively divides the w plane into two parts, quite independent (in potential) of each other, because of the shielding effect of the conductor.   We can accordingly consider the two half planes independently, and while considering one of them we can replace the bounding conductor, if we wish, by any situation in the other half plane which will retain the boundary condition imposed by the conductor, without altering conditions in the half plane under consideration. This boundary condition is that the imaginary axis be at constant potential (zero potential with our choice of the arbitrary constant of potential). Since the entire p plane is mapped repeatedly in both halves of the w plane, it matters not which half we use; we arbitrarily take the right half, and the horizontal semi-infinite strip bounded by $v = \pi$, $u = 0$, and $v = -\pi$ as the principal mapping of the p plane (cf. Fig. 14.12–D).   The boundary conductor, viewed from points within the right half plane, acts much like a mirror; it is merely a larger apparatus for terminating flux lines which we could, if we chose, follow on into the conductor's Looking-Glass World again (§ 14.06).   Exactly the same conditions will obtain on the v axis, in fact, if we imagine the conductor removed and the flux lines to pass on into the left half plane in symmetrical (mirror-image) fashion;

they will then terminate on double *positive* charges at the points $u = -a$, $v = \pm\pi/2, \pm 3\pi/2, \cdots$.

Thus we develop here the situation of Fig. 14.12–E: the conductor is gone; only lumped charges remain; and these are the same in the right half plane (which we do not disturb), but in the left half plane they are

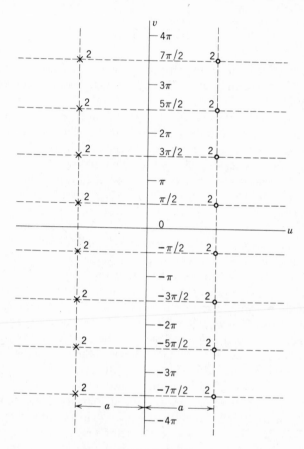

Fig. 14.12–E

quite different. The left half plane is no longer a region whose potential is that of Fig. 14.12–D; it is simply a hypothetical region in which symmetrical charge is introduced in order to retain the boundary condition $V = 0$ on the v axis in the absence of the conductor. That it does so is evident by inspection of Fig. 14.12–E, for the v axis "bisects" the charge distribution in such a fashion that its potential is constant (at the value zero, say) by mere symmetry.   The potential in Fig. 14.12–E is easily calculated now, for all the visible charge is lumped, and this will be exactly the potential in the right half of the w plane of Fig. 14.12–D—hence in the p plane which is repeatedly mapped there.   We write immediately, on the basis of experience and in accordance with Fig. 3.27–B

$$\left[\frac{\cosh\,(w - a)}{\cosh\,(w + a)}\right]^2 \tag{14.12-3}$$

as the contribution to the exponential potential of the two vertical series of lumped charges, the power 2 being necessary because the charges are of strength 2.

But this is not all; the negative charge at infinity, two units per mapping of the p plane, i.e., two units per horizontal strip of height 2π, also contributes to the potential.   In the equivalent situation of Fig. 14.12–E the flux lines from this negative charge run from the right on across the v axis (instead of terminating on the conductor that is in Fig. 14.12–D) to terminate on the image charge, which is at infinity to the left.   Since the first contribution (14.12–3) already satisfies the boundary condition of zero potential on the v axis, we need merely superpose a contribution to the potential that also meets the boundary condition and corresponds to this charge at infinity.   This corresponds to the extremely simple case of charge uniformly distributed on the conductor in Fig. 14.12–D, or of flux lines uniformly distributed vertically in Fig. 14.12–E, for which the complex potential is simply proportional to $-w$.   In fact, this is merely the situation in our first problem in which the w plane is essentially the complex-potential plane—or we may say the charge on the conductor is uniformly distributed in the w plane because the conductor is of infinite length and there is no other charge at finite points to cause any concentration of charge on the conductor.   Since we have two units of charge per horizontal strip of height 2π, the actual component of complex potential due to this charge must be $-2w$.   (The negative sign is required because potential is to drop as we go to the right.)   The correctness of the factor 2 can be established by calculating the flux crossing the v axis from the right: it is $2 \times 2\pi$ units for each increment of 2π in v, as it should be.   The contribution to the exponential potential is accordingly e^{-2w}, which can be verified in a different fashion by taking the limit of (14.12–3) as a approaches infinity.

On combining these contributions we have

$$e^W = Ke^{-2w}\left[\frac{\cosh\,(w - a)}{\cosh\,(w + a)}\right]^2 \tag{14.12-4}$$

in which the value to be given K is that value which will make the potential zero on the v axis and also make the origin of the flux function agree with the plot of Fig. 14.12–B.   Both of these conditions are satisfied by $K = 1$, since at a point just to the right of the origin in Fig. 14.12–C the complex potential has the value $W = 0 \pm j6\pi$ and hence $e^W = +1$.   We have then

$$e^W = e^{-2w} \frac{\cosh^2 (w - a)}{\cosh^2 (w + a)} \qquad (14.12\text{–}5)$$

for the exponential potential in the right half of the w plane.   It is evident that when $u = 0$ the magnitude of e^W is unity (the fraction is then the quotient of two conjugate complex numbers) and the boundary condition of zero potential there imposed by the conductor *is* fulfilled.

In (14.12–5) we have the exponential potential for the prototype problem, that of Fig. 14.12–A and –D, expressed in terms of w.   It can readily be developed into a function of p in the following fashion.   We have, as the fundamental relation connecting p and w (14.09–11),

$$p = \sinh w \qquad (14.12\text{–}6)$$

from which we readily derive

$$\cosh w = \pm \sqrt{p^2 + 1}$$

and

$$(14.12\text{–}7)$$

$$e^w = p \pm \sqrt{p^2 + 1}.$$

Multiple values are no longer any surprise, but we have found that with careful description of corresponding regions there are in fact no multiple values at all.   There can be no ambiguity in the choice of signs in (14.12–7) then, because the correspondence between the planes is one-to-one.   By correlating points in the semi-infinite strip that we have taken as the principal mapping of the p plane (bounded by $u = 0$, $v = +\pi$, and $v = -\pi$) with points in the p plane itself, we find that both square roots are to be taken with the positive sign, or more precisely, that what we need to use in (14.12–7) for the function $\sqrt{p^2 + 1}$ is the p-r branch thereof.   The situation is exactly that of § 4.14, and much like that of Fig. 4.14–E(b), and the discussion there applies here: we choose that branch whose real part is positive on the positive half of the real axis of the p plane, and thereafter move continuously to any point we wish, being careful not to cross the branch cut—which in this case is naturally the ω axis from $-j1$ to $+j1$, since this is occupied by a charged conductor that we could not cross without introducing a discontinuity in the flux function. We have then the following relations:

$$\sinh w = p,$$
$$\cosh w = \sqrt[+]{p^2 + 1}, \qquad (14.12\text{--}8)$$
$$e^w = \sqrt[+]{p^2 + 1} + p,$$
$$e^{-w} = \sqrt[+]{p^2 + 1} - p.$$

No ambiguity exists here, and the last relation is derived from the one immediately above it. It is to be understood from here on that the symbol $\sqrt{p^2 + 1}$ represents the p-r branch. Now (14.12–5) becomes

$$
\begin{aligned}
e^W &= e^{-2w} \left(\frac{\cosh w \cosh a - \sinh w \sinh a}{\cosh w \cosh a + \sinh w \sinh a} \right)^2 \\
&= e^{-2w} \left(\frac{\cosh w - \tanh a \sinh w}{\cosh w + \tanh a \sinh w} \right)^2 \\
&= (\sqrt{p^2 + 1} - p)^2 \left(\frac{\sqrt{p^2 + 1} - mp}{\sqrt{p^2 + 1} + mp} \right)^2, \qquad (14.12\text{--}9)
\end{aligned}
$$

in which we have for simplicity written

$$m = \tanh a. \qquad (14.12\text{--}10)$$

The relations between the three parameters ω_1, a, and m are given in (14.12–11), in which all square roots are positive. Sometimes one is more convenient than another; all of the three are (equivalent) parameters defining the finite locations of the prescribed negative charge.

$$\omega_1 = \cosh a = \frac{1}{\sqrt{1 - m^2}},$$
$$a = \tanh^{-1} m = \cosh^{-1} \omega_1, \qquad (14.12\text{--}11)$$
$$m = \tanh a = \sqrt{1 - \frac{1}{\omega_1^2}}.$$

In (14.12–9) we have an expression for the potential of the prototype problem. It may easily be checked by calculating its value on the approximation band, the points at which it vanishes (it does not become infinite), the flux emanating therefrom—and thus verifying its obedience to the boundary conditions. A further check is obtained by allowing the negative charge at the points $\pm j\omega_1$ to recede to infinity. Then we find

$$e^W \to (\sqrt{p^2 + 1} - p)^6 = e^{-6w} \qquad (14.12\text{--}12)$$

which is the exponential potential of our first problem (§ 14.06), since w is by definition proportional to the complex potential there. (It is e^{-6w} because we have chosen here to work in the right half of the w plane; were we in the left half, we would have e^{+6w} in exact agreement with previous work in which $w = W/6$ for this particular numerical case.) To obtain the six points of quantization, we write the six equations

$$W = -V_0 + j2m\pi \qquad (m = 0, 1, 2, 3, 4, 5) \qquad (14.12\text{--}13)$$

exactly as in § 14.05 and § 14.08, $-V_0$ being the potential chosen to give the desired error (ripple) in the approximation band. In terms of the exponential potential, (14.12–13) is in effect the single equation

$$e^W = e^{-V_0} \qquad (14.12\text{--}14)$$

which can be expected to have six roots. If we make use now of (14.12–9) we obtain in fact an algebraic equation of degree six, on eliminating the radicals (Problem 14-56); a simpler and more enlightening method of obtaining the equation will, however, be given below. We shall first verify the Chebyshev character of the approximation in the approximation band.

In our previous problem we examined the locations of the quantized charges in the w plane and found there, because of the symmetry and periodicity of their locations, that the potential was easily calculated and the nature of the approximation quickly determined. The basic reason for this is that w is proportional to W, the complex potential of the prototype problem, so that the quantization points lie on vertical lines ($V = $ constant) at equal spacings (equal increments of flux). In the present problem, although the same w is no longer proportional to W, we have yet been able to calculate the potential for the prototype case without difficulty in (14.12–5) and (14.12–9). But what we really want is the potential for the quantized case that represents our ultimate result. This we can again obtain from the W plane. But the mapping represented by the W plane is more complicated now, because of the prescribed negative charges. We note in Fig. 14.12–B that the part of the W plane corresponding to points in the immediate vicinity of the approximation band will present a mapping not greatly different from the previous one. But for values of V less than V_{sp} the equipotentials have three branches, appearing on the p plane as three distinct curves—and this suggests that the W plane has three sheets (in the Riemann-surface representation).

That this is true can be demonstrated by considering how the p plane must be broken up by branch cuts in order to remove the multivalued nature of the flux function and obtain a one-to-one mapping. Since any circuit of charge on an equipotential alters Φ but not V, there must be a branch cut emanating from each of the negative charges as well as from the conductor, e.g., the three branch cuts of Fig. 14.12–F, that connect the charges at finite points with the charge at infinity. (There is a fourth branch cut, coincident with the approximation-band conductor, whose purpose is exactly as it was before.) By prohibiting the crossing of these lines, the complex potential is made single-valued. By interpreting them

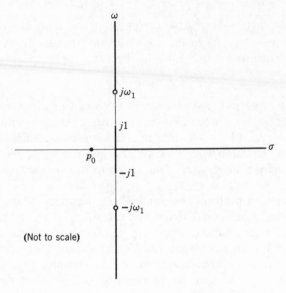

Fig. 14.12–F.   Branch cuts in the p plane.

as transitions to other sheets of the p plane, on the other hand, the single valued property of $W(p)$ is retained, without restriction on freedom of movement in the p plane.

But we now have a W plane considerably more complicated than in our previous problem because there is here more than one point at which W has some given, precise value. Take, for example, the point p_0 in Fig. 14.12–G, near the approximation band, at which $W = -V_0 + j0$. Let us follow the equipotential on which $V = -V_0$, which is a single curve in this case, up to the point p_1, at which $W = -V_0 + j4\pi$ (cf. Fig. 14.12–B); the path is shown in Fig. 14.12–G by a dot-dash line. We now continue on this line, up and around the two units of negative charge at the point $j\omega_1$ (Fig. 14.12–G) and return to the point p_1. We have of course moved to another sheet by virtue of crossing the branch cut—and the value of W on our second arrival at p_1 is $W = -V_0 + j0$ because we have encircled the charge. But this is the *same* as the value of W at p_0. This means that the plane of W is multisheeted, and that the corresponding path in that plane also moves from one sheet to another.

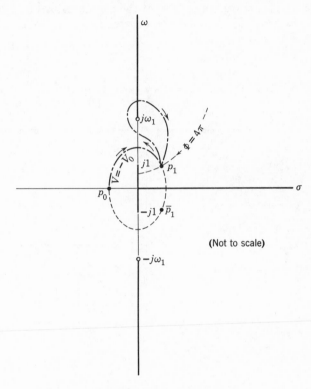

Fig. 14.12–G

A closer analysis shows that the W plane has three sheets (the point $\bar{p}_1$ also maps to the same value of W) and that these are connected conveniently on the branch cuts shown in Fig. 14.12–H; on any one of these there is contact between two sheets while the third remains aloof. Fortunately, when we proceed to quantize the distributed positive charge, it will lie with such a symmetry in this three-sheeted W plane that we can still quickly calculate the new complex potential. The loci will be vertical lines at the chosen value of V, as before, and the vertical spacings will again be equal, with the value 2π.

A careful examination of the way in which the charges map from the p plane to that of W shows that all three sheets carry exactly the same charge and hence that the flux crossing any branch cut is the same on both descending and ascending ramps. This permits us, as in § 14.07, to cut the sheets apart and sew them up into a single sheet, an ordinary plane (of W) in which the potential is unchanged from that of the manifold W "plane." This is true regardless of the chosen value of V, be it greater or less than V_{sp}, be the quantized charges on a one-branch equipotential

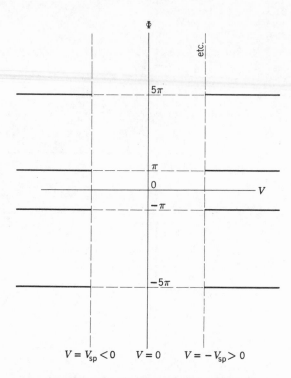

Fig. 14.12–H.   Branch cuts in the W plane.

in the p plane or on one with three separate parts. Fortunately, it is not necessary to verify this in detail, for we shall be able to check the validity of our work later in a purely formal manner. In any case, after quantization, the W plane (in one-sheet form) carries the charges shown in Fig. 14.12–I. The equipotential chosen for quantization is that on which the potential is $-V_0$, V_0 being a positive number. The negative charge is all at infinity, for the potential at the points $\pm j\omega_1$ in the p plane is (negatively) infinite, which causes these charges to map to infinity in the W plane.

This situation then is exactly the same in principle as that of Figs. 14.08–A and –B, and the calculation of the new complex potential proceeds as it did there. We shall retain the symbol W for the complex potential of the prototype problem, and use W_q for that of the quantized problem, as before. Then we have

$$e^{W_q} = \frac{K}{\sinh\left[(W + V_0)/2\right]\sinh\left[(W - V_0)/2\right]}$$

$$= \frac{2K}{\cosh W - \cosh V_0}.$$

(14.12–15)

The prescribed negative charge, located at the points $\pm j\omega_1$ in the p plane, does not explicitly appear, for in the W plane it is at infinity (in both

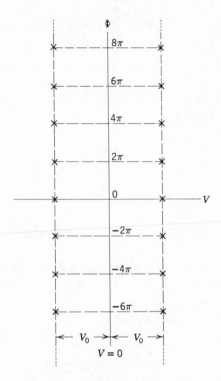

Fig. 14.12–I

prototype and quantized situations) but its effect is expressed in the W function. In (14.12–15) we have the exponential potential for the quantized, or final, situation. This function should correspond then to the charge distribution of Fig. 14.12–J and should have the desired properties: Chebyshev approximation to a constant in the approximation, band

and falling off to zero at the prescribed points $\pm j\omega_1$, and infinity. We shall next verify these properties in a formal way.

To begin with, the function (14.12–15) should be rational (as a function of p), with the zeros and poles shown in Fig. 14.12–J. As a function of

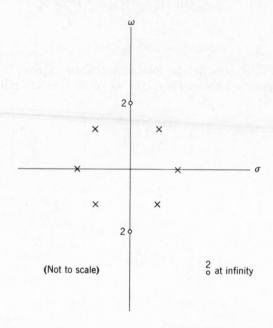

(Not to scale) $\overset{2}{\text{o}}$ at infinity

Fig. 14.12–J.   The quantized charge distribution in the p plane.

W, or of w, it is not rational, but in the plane of p it *is*. The prototype exponential potential e^W is given as a function of p by (14.12–9) which, upon multiplication and division by $(\sqrt{p^2 + 1} - mp)^2$ and performance of the multiplications required, becomes

$$e^W = \frac{A + pB\sqrt{p^2 + 1}}{[(1 - m^2)p^2 + 1]^2} \qquad (14.12\text{–}16)$$

in which

$$A = a_6 p^6 + a_4 p^4 + a_2 p^2 + a_0, \qquad (14.12\text{–}17)$$

with

$$a_6 = 2m^4 + 8m^3 + 12m^2 + 8m + 2,$$
$$a_4 = m^4 + 8m^3 + 18m^2 + 16m + 5, \qquad (14.12\text{–}18)$$
$$a_2 = 6m^2 + 8m + 4,$$
$$a_0 = 1,$$

and B is an even polynomial of degree four whose explicit coefficients we do not need. By writing the reciprocal of (14.12–9), making use of the last two relations in (14.12–8), and then performing operations similar to those above, we obtain

$$e^{-W} = \frac{A - pB\sqrt{p^2 + 1}}{[(1 - m^2)p^2 + 1]^2} \qquad (14.12\text{–}19)$$

in which A and B are the same polynomials as before, and the radical sign is taken to mean the p-r branch as hitherto. With (14.12–16) and (14.12–19) we can readily rewrite (14.12–15) as an explicit function of p,

$$e^{W_q} = \frac{2K}{\dfrac{A}{[(1 - m^2)p^2 + 1]^2} - \cosh V_0} \qquad (14.12\text{–}20)$$

which is clearly a rational function of order six, as it should be. Its zeros are the roots of

$$[(1 - m^2)p^2 + 1]^2 = 0 \qquad (14.12\text{–}21)$$

which are $p = \pm j(1 - m^2)^{-1/2} = \pm j\omega_1$, each double as prescribed; its poles are the roots of

$$A - (\cosh V_0)[(1 - m^2)p^2 + 1]^2 = 0 \qquad (14.12\text{–}22)$$

or of

$$\cosh W = \cosh(-V_0) = \cosh V_0 \qquad (14.12\text{–}23)$$

which is equivalent. The roots of the latter are those values of p for which (in the prototype problem) $W = -V_0 + j2m\pi$, m taking all integer values, positive and negative. But these are exactly the points chosen for quantization, of which there are only six; the other values of m correspond merely to periodic recalculation of the same points. Consequently our derived exponential potential is rational, with the corresponding zeros and poles. As to its multiplier, that is most readily evaluated by considering the function's behavior at real frequencies.

For $p = j\omega$, the general behavior of the complex potential is readily calculated from (14.12–9). In the approximation band, $|\omega| < 1$, the radical $\sqrt{p^2 + 1}$ is real and the exponential potential has unit, constant magnitude. In terms of the complex potential, we have there

$$W = 0 + j\Phi \qquad (p = j\omega, |\omega| < 1) \qquad (14.12\text{–}24)$$

in which the flux function Φ varies from zero to 3π as we traverse the left side of the approximation-band conductor from the origin up to the point $+j1$ (Fig. 14.12–B). (On the right side the variation is from 6π to 3π, because of the multivalued nature of Φ, but we shall see that this difference is of no consequence to us.) Figure 14.12–K displays the behavior of V, Φ, and e^V. On leaving the approximation band and continuing up the ω axis, the potential drops and the exponential potential

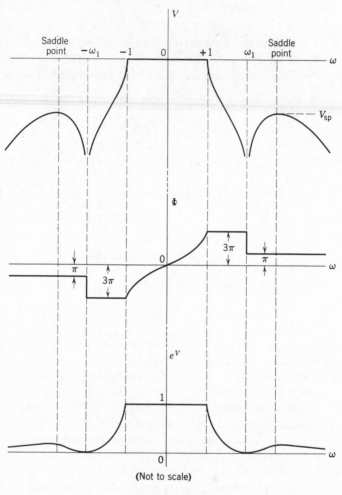

(Not to scale)

Fig. 14.12–K

reaches zero at $j\omega_1$, the location of the prescribed negative charge; there-after the potential rises until the saddle point is reached and then drops slowly off toward the value zero (for the exponential potential) at infinity. Since flux lines lie on the part of the ω axis above the approximation band, the function Φ remains constant for $|\omega| > 1$, except for the discontinuity of 2π at the negative charge; this corresponds to a small detour around the negative charge (which causes the discontinuity since it terminates flux lines) to the left; we cannot pass directly through the charge but must detour slightly to the left (which gives the variation in Φ shown) or to the right (which would cause Φ to jump from 3π to 5π, a difference again to be expected and of no consequence to us).

With the aid of Fig. 14.12-K we can now sketch the behavior of the rational function that is the result of our approximation process, using (14.12-15). In the approximation band, cosh W becomes simply cos Φ, by (14.12-24), and hence varies from the value $+1$ at the origin through three half cycles of a cosine wave. The wave is, of course, distorted in that the cycles are compressed more and more near the upper end of the approximation band (where the flux density increases because of the proximity of the negative charge), but the amplitude variation, between

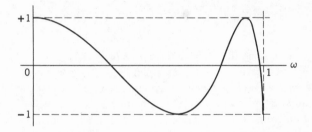

Fig. 14.12–L. The behavior of cosh W in the approximation band.

$+1$ and -1, is preserved, as in Fig. 14.12–L. It follows that the exponential potential (14.12–15) of the quantized charge distribution varies in the approximation band between the limits $2K(1 - \cosh V_0)^{-1}$ and $2K(-1 - \cosh V_0)^{-1}$; since both parentheses are negative and we wish this rational function to be positive here (it is to represent a resistance function), we give to K a negative value. The limits of the oscillation are then $2|K|(\cosh V_0 - 1)^{-1}$ and $2|K|(\cosh V_0 + 1)^{-1}$; we determine the magnitude of K by requiring that these limits be $(1 + \epsilon)$ and $(1 - \epsilon)$ respectively, in order to make the equal-ripple behavior an approximation of unity, with error oscillating between $\pm\epsilon$. Then we obtain (as before)

$$\epsilon = \text{sech } V_0 \qquad (14.12\text{–}25)$$

and also

$$2K = -\frac{1 - \epsilon^2}{\epsilon}. \qquad (14.12\text{–}26)$$

The first of these two equations gives us the specific relation between the equipotential chosen for quantization (that on which $V = -V_0$) and the error ripple obtained, ϵ. Using the second we can rewrite (14.12–15) as

$$e^{W_q} = \frac{(1 - \epsilon^2)}{1 - \epsilon \cosh W}$$

$$= \frac{(1 - \epsilon^2)}{1 - \epsilon \dfrac{A}{[(1 - m^2)p^2 + 1]^2}} \qquad (14.12\text{–}27)$$

in the second line of which we have rewritten the function as an explicit function of p; the first of these two forms is convenient for verifying the general behavior. The equation whose roots determine the points of quantization (the poles of e^{W_q}) can now be written in its most convenient form,

$$A - \frac{1}{\epsilon}[(1 - m^2)p^2 + 1]^2 = 0 \qquad (14.12\text{–}28)$$

in which the polynomial A is defined by (14.12–17) and (14.12–18).

For a given location of the prescribed negative charges (i.e., for a given value of m) and for a given error ripple ϵ, (14.12–28) can be solved numerically to find the points of quantization, i.e., the poles of e^{W_q} (or of the resistance function). The calculation may be tedious, but is straightforward (Appendix A). Actual finding of all the zeros of the denominator of the quantized exponential potential is not necessary for realization as a driving-point resistance function; the denominator of the associated driving-point impedance function can be obtained merely by factoring or splitting the denominator polynomial into two parts, one with the left-half-plane zeros and one with the right-half-plane zeros, of which the first is the denominator of the driving-point-impedance function. If the individual poles of e^{W_q} are wanted, the calculation may sometimes be recast in a slightly more convenient form (cf. Problems 14-56, -57). It is only in the very simplest cases that the points of quantization can be determined directly, as by (14.11–4).

On examining the ω-axis behavior of W (Fig. 14.12–K), we can verify by inspection the Chebyshev nature of the approximation to unity in the approximation band, where (14.12–27) oscillates between $(1 + \epsilon)$ and $(1 - \epsilon)$. Here (14.12–24) applies, in fact, and

$$e^{W_q} = \frac{1 - \epsilon^2}{1 - \epsilon \cos \Phi}. \qquad (14.12\text{–}29)$$

Above the approximation band we have

$$\cosh W = \cosh (V + j\Phi) = - \cosh V \qquad (14.12\text{–}30)$$

(since either $\Phi = \pi$ or $\Phi = 3\pi$) and

$$e^{W_q} = \frac{1 - \epsilon^2}{1 + \epsilon \cosh V}. \qquad (14.12\text{–}31)$$

By the nature of the behavior of V (Fig. 14.12–K) we see that e^{W_q} drops to zero at $j\omega_1$, rises to a maximum at the saddle point (which is a saddle point in *both* the W and W_q fields), and drops again toward zero at infinity. Exact calculations are conveniently made in the w plane (Problem 14-65), or by using (14.12–9), and the result is shown in Fig. 14.12–M

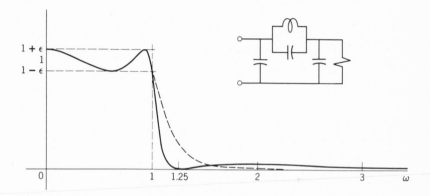

Drawn for $\epsilon = 0.1$, $\omega_1 = 1.25$, or $m = 0.6$, $a = 0.6931$

Fig. 14.12–M.　The result of the quantization procedure.

(drawn for $\omega_1 = 1.25$). The solid curve represents the exponential potential e^{W_q} (which for $p = j\omega$ is real), i.e., the rational function of p (14.12–27) which is the end result of our approximation procedure. The dashed curve shown for values of $\omega > 1$ gives the behavior of the corresponding curve obtained by the methods of § 14.11, i.e., the result of leaving all six negative charges at infinity and quantizing on the ellipse that gives the same ripple. The effect of bringing in four units of negative charge is exactly as expected: much steeper falloff just above the approximation band and somewhat greater values above a frequency of about 1.55; in the approximation band itself the change is minor and is not shown. A network realization of this new function as a driving-point resistance (it is clearly so realizable—cf. § 8.16) must take the finite zeros into account, as by a Brune network; it happens that the form shown in Fig. 14.12–M (§ 9.06) requires no negative elements and is therefore a very practical realization.

We have now completed the task proposed at the beginning of this section: to apply the same general principles in this particular case of finite negative charge at two symmetrically located points, and obtain by quantization a rational function with these prescribed zeros and Chebyshev approximation to a constant in the approximation band. The procedure does give exactly the results expected, and it can speedily be generalized to take care of an arbitrary array of prescribed zeros (negative charges), for there will be no difference in principle.

Suppose the zeros of the resistance function desired (which is to approximate unity in the Chebyshev fashion in the approximation band) are prescribed at the points $\pm j\omega_1$, $\pm j\omega_2$, $\cdots$, ∞, with multiplicities respectively $2n_1$, $2n_2$, $\cdots$, $2n_\infty$, the n's being integers. (These zeros must be of even order and lie in conjugate pairs, except for those at infinity, if the function is to be realizable as a driving-point resistance.) Let $Q = 2n$ be the total number of zeros, i.e., the order of the desired resistance function, so that $Q = 2n = 4n_1 + 4n_2 + \cdots + 2n_\infty$. We then place a (zero-potential) conductor on the approximation band, extending from $-j1$ to $+j1$ as before, and deposit on it Q units of positive charge. Under the influence of the $2n_1$ units of negative charge that we also put down at $+j\omega_1$ and at $-j\omega_1$, of the $2n_2$ units at $\pm j\omega_2$, $\cdots$, and finally of the $2n_\infty$ units at infinity, the positive charge will distribute itself on the conductor and a prototype static field will be set up. Its complex potential W we can immediately write in exponential form, for we need merely superpose in W, or multiply in e^W, the various contributions; it is given by

$$e^W = \left(\frac{\sqrt{p^2 + 1} - m_1 p}{\sqrt{p^2 + 1} + m_1 p} \right)^{2n_1} \times \left(\frac{\sqrt{p^2 + 1} - m_2 p}{\sqrt{p^2 + 1} + m_2 p} \right)^{2n_2}$$

$$\times \cdots (\sqrt{p^2 + 1} - p)^{2n_\infty}, \quad (14.12\text{–}32)$$

in which

$$m_1 = \tanh a_1 = \sqrt{1 - \omega_1^{-2}},$$

$$m_2 = \tanh a_2 = \sqrt{1 - \omega_2^{-2}}, \text{ etc.} \quad (14.12\text{–}33)$$

and $\sqrt{p^2 + 1}$ is understood to mean the positive-real branch of the function. This gives the prototype potential, $W(p)$. The plane of W is now extremely complicated in its mapping, but as before we simply write, for quantization on the equipotential $V = -V_0$,

$$W = -V_0 \pm j2r\pi \quad (r = 0, 1, 2, \cdots) \quad \text{if } n = Q/2 \text{ is } odd$$

$$(14.12\text{–}34)$$

or

$$W = -V_0 \pm j(2r + 1)\pi \qquad (r = 0, 1, 2, \cdots) \qquad \text{if } n = Q/2 \text{ is } even.$$
$$(14.12\text{–}35)$$

Then, by considering the one-sheeted W plane obtained by cutting and sewing, we obtain

$$e^{W_q} = \frac{\text{constant}}{\cosh W - \cosh V_0} \qquad n \text{ odd,} \qquad (14.12\text{–}36)$$

$$= \frac{\text{constant}}{\cosh W + \cosh V_0} \qquad n \text{ even,} \qquad (14.12\text{–}37)$$

as the exponential potential for the quantized situation. As before, it is readily seen as a function of p to be rational, have the prescribed zeros, and for its poles the roots of (14.12–34) or (14.12–35).

The behavior of W on the ω axis is still substantially that of Fig. 14.12–K, except that the behavior at ω_1 and the saddle point occurs a number of times, as, e.g., in Fig. 14.12–N. The important property,

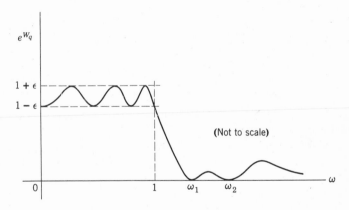

Fig. 14.12–N

$V = 0$ in the approximation band, is unchanged; and Φ is always some odd multiple of π (when n is odd) or some even multiple of π (when n is even) for $\omega > 1$. Hence we have

$$\cosh W = \cosh (0 + j\Phi) = \cos \Phi \qquad \text{for } p = j\omega, \ |\omega| < 1, \quad (14.12\text{–}38)$$

and

$$\cosh W = \cosh \left[V + j \begin{pmatrix} 2r + 1 \\ \text{or} \\ 2r \end{pmatrix} \pi \right] = (-1)^n \cosh V$$
$$\text{for } p = j\omega, \ |\omega| > 1. \quad (14.12\text{–}39)$$

By considering the behavior of (14.12–36) and (14.12–37) in the approximation band, with the use of (14.12–38) we can evaluate the constants, much as we did to obtain (14.12–27). We find that

$$\epsilon = \text{sech } V_0 \tag{14.12–40}$$

and

$$e^{W_q} = \frac{1 - \epsilon^2}{1 + (-1)^n \epsilon \cosh W} \tag{14.12–41}$$

which, at real frequencies, becomes

$$e^{W_q} = \frac{1 - \epsilon^2}{1 + (-1)^n \epsilon \cos \Phi} \quad \text{for } p = j\omega, \ |\omega| < 1, \tag{14.12–42}$$

$$= \frac{1 - \epsilon^2}{1 + \epsilon \cosh V} \quad \text{for } p = j\omega, \ |\omega| > 1. \tag{14.12–43}$$

The desired equal-ripple behavior is obtained in the approximation band; thereafter, as V decreases, the function drops off, reaching zero at each prescribed frequency (ω_1, ω_2, $\cdot$ $\cdot$ $\cdot$) with minor maxima between, as in Fig. 14.12–N.

By operating on (14.12–32) in the same manner as with (14.12–9) we obtain

$$e^W = \frac{A + pB\sqrt{p^2 + 1}}{[(1 - m_1)^2 p^2 + 1]^{2n_1}[(1 - m_2^2)p^2 + 1]^{2n_2} \cdots} \tag{14.12–44}$$

in which A and B are even polynomials in p of degree $Q = 2n$ and $(Q - 2) = 2(n - 1)$ respectively. Again we also find that the only change in (14.12–44) necessary to obtain e^{-W} is that of the sign following A, so that

$$e^{W_q} = \frac{1 - \epsilon^2}{1 + (-1)^n \epsilon \dfrac{A}{[(1 - m_1^2)p^2 + 1]^{2n_1}[(1 - m_2^2)p^2 + 1]^{2n_2} \cdots}} . \tag{14.12–45}$$

The equation of quantization, the equation whose roots are the poles of e^{W_q}, is thus

$$A + (-1)^n \frac{1}{\epsilon} [(1 - m_1^2)p^2 + 1]^{2n_1}[(1 - m_2^2)p^2 + 1]^{2n_2} \cdots = 0. \tag{14.12–46}$$

It is again an algebraic equation whose solution is a laborious but straightforward numerical task (Appendix A) which can often be accelerated by first obtaining approximate roots through the use of an "average" value of m (Problem 14-72). It usually suffices to factor the left side of (14.12–46) into two polynomials (Appendix A) of which that with the left-half-plane zeros is the denominator of, for example, the associated driving-point impedance function. If the actual points of quantization are desired, they can be obtained by additional factoring of this polynomial, or by direct solution of (14.12–46), for which a change of variable (Problem 14-74) is sometimes convenient.

The design procedure for a function of order Q, given the set of pre-scribed zeros (the numbers ω_1, ω_2, $\cdots$ with the associated multiplicities n_1, n_2, $\cdots$, n_∞) and the desired ripple ϵ, is simply to write down the function (14.12–45), which has the desired properties. For its realization as a driving-point resistance function $R(\omega)$ (it is so realizable, by § 8.16) we must

1. find the left-half-plane roots of (14.12–46) and from them form the denominator of the driving-point impedance function $Z(p)$, a process which may be performed in one step by the polynomial-factoring method (Appendix A);
2. determine the numerator of $Z(p)$ by using (8.11–10) in which the c's are determined by writing out the numerator of $R(\omega)$ to have the pre-scribed zeros, the b's having been determined in step 1 above; the remaining constant is determined by requiring that $R(0) = (1 + \epsilon)$ if n is odd, $(1 - \epsilon)$ if n is even;
3. realize the network from its driving-point impedance function $Z(p)$ by any one of the methods of Chapters 9 and 10;
4. adjust the resistance and frequency scales, i.e., denormalize the element values. (14.12–47)

The network realization, in this case, will of course be moderately compli-cated, though in particular the one-resistor realization can usually be made without the use of the Type-C and Type-D sections of Chapter 9. Again with the point of view of § 11.04, we can visualize filtering applications for this sort of network, which we shall discuss in Volume II.

We have, up to now, considered the zeros of $R(\omega)$ to be prescribed, i.e., that the negative charges in the analog are given and not to be changed. It may be that we are given only some general requirements on the behavior of $R(\omega)$ once past the approximation band. In that case we have to determine the appropriate locations for the zeros, generally by trial. For example, the requirement may take the form sketched in Fig. 14.12–O, in which the solid lines show the (unrealizable) behavior desired, and the dashed lines outline the tolerable errors. The sort of function we have been discussing would be well suited to this problem, but the locations of the zeros, very likely in the vicinity of ω_1, ω_2, and at infinity, would have to be determined by a succession of trials, making for each a plot of the resulting $R(\omega)$ and improving the function at each step on the basis of the information gained thereby (cf. § 13.03). (Through skillful

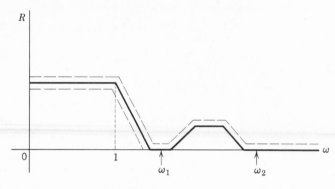

Fig. 14.12–O

use of the w plane and the function W, this sort of calculation can be greatly shortened over the extended task it may first seem.) If, in addition, we are not told the order of the final impedance function, n, but simply asked to keep it as low as possible, a series of trials must be made for different values of n until a suitable value is determined. The best procedures for this are learned chiefly by experience.

One interesting case is that in which the requirement is simply that of Fig. 14.12–P: Chebyshev approximation to unity in the approximation

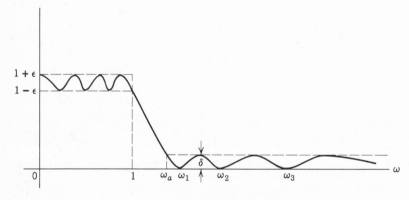

Fig. 14.12–P

band, and also Chebyshev approximation to zero at frequencies above ω_a in the sense shown. Here we do not know the locations of the zeros

$(\omega_1, \omega_2, \omega_3, \cdot\cdot\cdot)$ but we can find them by an extension of our quantization method—in fact, all we need do is to start with *two* conductors, one in the low approximation band and one in the high approximation band (for we have two approximation bands here), on the first of which the positive charge is distributed and on the second of which the negative charge is distributed, as in Fig. 14.12–Q. We now make the flux plot, for which

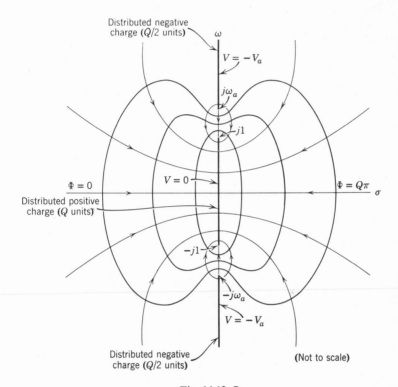

Distributed negative charge ($Q/2$ units)

ω

$V = -V_a$

$j\omega_a$

$-j1$

$\Phi = 0$

$V = 0$

$\Phi = Q\pi$ σ

Distributed positive charge (Q units)

$-j1$

$-j\omega_a$

$V = -V_a$

Distributed negative charge ($Q/2$ units)

(Not to scale)

Fig. 14.12–Q

a few curves are sketched in Fig. 14.12–Q. On the assumption of a positive charge $Q = 2n$ on the low approximation band conductor (hence $-Q/2 = -n$ on each of the high approximation band conductors), a certain potential difference V_a will exist between the conductors; we take the low band conductor to be at zero potential and the others at potential $-V_a$. We draw an equipotential, say that for $V = -V_0$, and quantize the positive charge thereon as before. And the negative charge we also quantize in the same fashion, on the equipotential $V = -V_a$, i.e., in the high band. That this process gives the desired Chebyshev behavior in both bands we can predict by glancing at the W plane, the plane of the complex potential of the prototype (three-conductor) problem. Figure 14.12–R shows a part of this plane, which is of course quite complicated.

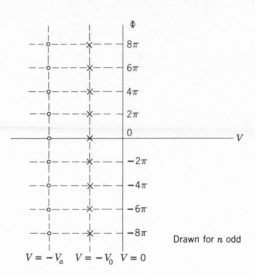

Fig. 14.12–R

The quantization suggested places the lumped positive and negative charges as shown, in parallel vertical, infinite sets. Since the low approximation band maps to the vertical line $V = 0$ and the high approximation band to the vertical line $V = -V_a$, both being infinite, the exponential potential in the quantized case will have exactly the desired behavior (Fig. 14.12–P), merely from symmetry and periodicity. The points of quantization will appear in the p plane on the equipotentials $V = -V_0$ and $V = -V_a$ of Fig. 14.12–Q, as in Fig. 14.12–S.

We do not have the mathematical equipment (the theory of elliptic functions) necessary to verify formally the double-Chebyshev nature of this approximation, though we shall do so in Volume II. A careful analysis shows that the negative charges in Fig. 14.12–R are double charges (because of the nature of the mapping), as is indicated in Fig. 14.12–S and is required for a resistance function. The analysis, using elliptic functions, also develops formulas for the locations of the positive and negative charges that obviate the need for root finding (given a table of elliptic functions), expressions for the error ripples ϵ and δ, and for the quantized potential function so that it may readily be plotted. For the present we content ourselves with this brief discussion, and the fact that the behavior of Fig. 14.12–P can always be obtained, if necessary, by locating the zeros by trial, i.e., by a trial-and-error approximation process

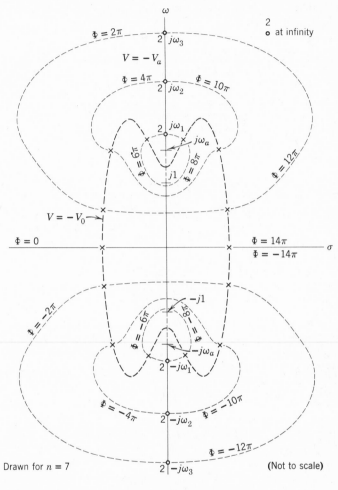

Fig. 14.12–S

—to which various numerical, graphical, and analog methods can be applied.

In all of the foregoing we have assumed that the zeros of the resistance function are to lie on the ω axis (including infinity). There is no reason that the zeros cannot lie off this axis, on the σ axis or in the complex parts of the plane, if this is desired. For efficiency in shaping the resistance characteristic, this is not usually done. Zeros off the axis do have the effect of making the ripples in the approximation band more evenly spaced, in other words, of "uncompressing" the oscillations, because they correspond to moving negative charge to points such that the flux density on the prototype conductor becomes more nearly uniform. Then, of course, the resistance function does not fall to zero at real frequencies, though it can be made to drop down appreciably. The formulas we have developed are still generally applicable, except that the parameter m becomes greater than unity, or complex (Problem 14-67).

Our discussion of the incorporation of arbitrary (prescribed) zeros in the construction of a resistance (even) function that approximates a constant in the Chebyshev sense in a low band is now substantially complete. We need, once the resistance function is set up, to continue to the network realization proper, by finding the corresponding impedance function and developing it into a network schematic. This we have already discussed (Chapters 9, 10), along with various practical matters (Chapter 12) that often play important rôles in a synthesis. The actual realization may be a lengthy process, since it is advisable to explore the possibility of various equivalent (but different) realizations that may offer practical advantages.

The problem of finding a *conductance* function with these properties is exactly dual and requires no further comment.

We have now removed the first of the four restrictions listed in (14.11–5); we are able to incorporate zeros that are entirely arbitrary in the design, except that they must have symmetry and be of even order if they lie on the ω axis. Our next step will be to remove the second restriction, that the approximation band be centered on the origin.

14.13 High bands and frequency transformations

We now turn to the problem of approximating a constant (still with an even function) with arbitrarily prescribed zeros, in an approximation band that is no longer centered on the origin, no longer a low-band problem. This discussion will remove the second restriction listed in (14.11–5).

After the low-band case the next simplest is the high-band case, in which the (Chebyshev) approximation is to be made in the band $\omega > \omega_0$ (Fig. 14.13–A). Because of the inevitable symmetry, we now seem to have two approximation bands, the one shown and a symmetrical one at negative frequencies (Fig. 14.13–B). Since these both run to infinity, and since we have long since become accustomed to thinking of infinity as a single point, there must be some grounds for regarding this as still a one-approximation-band problem.

This point of view can be vividly reinforced by imagining the p plane to be wrapped (with some shrinkage in the vertical direction) on a right circular cylinder, whose axis is parallel to the σ axis, so that the upper

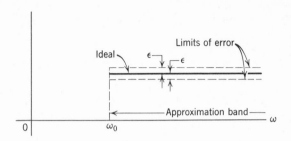

Fig. 14.13–A

end of the upper approximation band and the lower end of the lower approximation band join (at infinity) on the far side of the cylinder. Then we have indeed a single approximation band "centered on infinity"; and by rotating the cylinder we can move it back into view, much as in the low-band case.

By the more precise means of conformal mapping and analytic transformation we can actually accomplish this change, and indeed transform the high-band problem into a low-band one. This is a perfectly general transformation, and it will make the conversion for *any* high-band problem, thus making it unnecessary for us to study the high-band problem itself. The transformation simply interchanges the origin and infinity, as

$$p' = \frac{K}{p}, \qquad (14.13\text{–}1)$$

in which $p' = \sigma' + j\omega'$ is the variable of the new mapping. If we give to the constant K the real positive value $\omega_0\omega_0'$, then in

$$\frac{p'}{\omega_0'} = \frac{\omega_0}{p} \qquad (14.13\text{–}2)$$

Fig. 14.13–B

we have an eminently suitable mapping. It maps right half plane to right half plane, imaginary axis to imaginary axis, and left half plane to left half plane, in either direction of transformation, in a straightforward, single-valued way (though not without distortion, of course); in fact, it is a special case of the mapping of Fig. 5.14–D. Points far from the origin in one plane are moved close thereto, and the reverse, in the particular

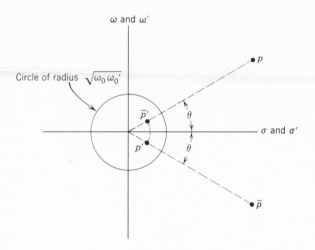

Fig. 14.13–C

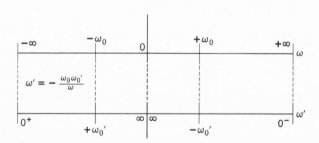

Fig. 14.13–D

manner shown in Fig. 14.13–C. A typical right-half-plane point p is first transformed to its image point in the circle, $\bar{p}'$, and then reflected in the real axis to its mapping p' in the new plane. Similarly, $\bar{p}$ maps to $\bar{p}'$. The imaginary axes of the two planes in particular are related by the scheme shown in Fig. 14.13–D, in which the frequency scales have been compressed to finite extent (as in the frequency patterns of § 6.07) for convenience. It is clear that the approximation band of Fig. 14.13–A occupies the ω' axis from $-\omega_0'$ to the origin, and that its complement at negative frequencies (Fig. 14.13–B) occupies the ω' axis from the origin to $+\omega_0'$. Consequently (for a constant remains a constant in the transformation, and it matters not how the frequency scale is distorted) the problem is transformed, in the p' plane, into the low-band problem of the preceding sections.

Although it would be perfectly possible to develop, in the p plane, a similar theory of quantization to give Chebyshev approximations, it is entirely unnecessary. We need merely transform the data of the p plane (the location of the approximation band, i.e., the value of ω_0, and of the prescribed zeros, none of which can now be at infinity, though some may be at the origin) to the p' plane. The problem then becomes simply that of approximating by an even function a constant in the Chebyshev sense in the band $-\omega_0' < \omega' < \omega_0'$ with the prescribed ripple (the same in both planes), with prescribed zeros [transformed according to (14.13–2)]. (For the constant ω_0' we can conveniently take the value unity, i.e., normalize the p' plane as usual.) The solution of this problem we have discussed at length. It remains, after the solution is obtained in the p' plane, only to transform this solution back to the p plane. But even this work can be abridged: we can actually complete the design in terms of p'

Table 14.13–A

p' Design		p (Final) Design
(Here $\omega_0' = 1$, and unity is the nominal value, approximated within $\pm\epsilon$ in the approximation band)		(Here ω_0 is the lower end of the approximation band, and R_0 is the nominal value, approximated within $\pm100\epsilon\%$ in the approximation band)
L'	$\longrightarrow$	$C = \dfrac{1}{R_0 L' \omega_0}$
C'	$\longrightarrow$	$L = \dfrac{R_0}{C' \omega_0}$
R'	$\longrightarrow$	$R = R_0 R'$

to the point where we have a schematic diagram of a network, with element values (L', C', R'), the real frequency variable being ω'. To transform back to the domain of p we need merely change each symbol on the schematic diagram according to Table 14.13–A. Then, just as the p' design provides a driving-point resistance whose value oscillates between $(1 + \epsilon)$ and $(1 - \epsilon)$ in the band $0 < \omega' < 1$, with appropriate zeros at higher frequencies, so does the p design provide a driving-point resistance whose value oscillates between $(1 + \epsilon)R_0$ and $(1 - \epsilon)R_0$ in the band $\omega_0 < \omega < \infty$, though the curve has of course been distorted along the frequency scale, with the prescribed zeros. (Denormalization has also been accomplished in the transformation.) That this is so can easily be verified by noting that $Z'(p)$, the driving-point impedance of the network designed in the p' domain, becomes $R_0 Z'(\omega_0/p)$ under the transformation of Table 14.13–A, with the effect of converting the low approximation band into the high approximation band desired. If, for example, all the zeros of the resistance function are prescribed to be at the origin (in the p plane), they fall at infinity in the p' plane and the resulting network has

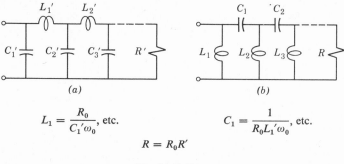

$$L_1 = \frac{R_0}{C_1' \omega_0}, \text{ etc.} \qquad\qquad C_1 = \frac{1}{R_0 L_1' \omega_0}, \text{ etc.}$$

$$R = R_0 R'$$

Fig. 14.13–E

the form shown in Fig. 14.13–E(a); on transformation it becomes finally that of Fig. 14.13–E(b).

When zeros are prescribed at frequencies between the origin and ω_0, it may be necessary (as when negative inductance is used in the Brune synthesis) to modify the network further in order to obtain a convenient form. But the fact that p' is a p-r function of p and that $R_0 Z'(\omega_0/p)$ is then p-r guarantees realizability in the final, p domain also.

With this device of a particular *frequency transformation*, as this sort of transformation is also called, we can now dismiss the high-band problem. There is always an "equivalent" low-band problem which we can solve, for resistance or conductance; we have then only to transform the low-band network into a high-band network for our solution. We shall find other frequency transformations useful from time to time also (e.g., Problem 14-96).

14.14 Internal bands

We consider next the situation in which the approximation band is purely internal, running from some frequency ω_1 to some higher frequency ω_2. For the usual reasons of symmetry we have here a two-band problem (Fig. 14.14–A); the two bands are related by considerations of symmetry

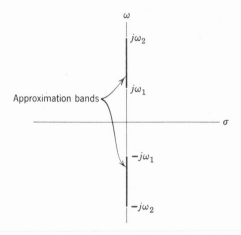

Fig. 14.14–A

but cannot be considered as two parts of one band in as simple a fashion as in § 14.13. It is quite possible to transform this into a one-band problem, however, and such a procedure is indeed useful, though not always necessary.

We still consider the approximation of a constant in the approximation band, with an even function, subject to the arbitrary prescription of the zeros of the function. These zeros must be of even order if they lie on the ω axis (outside the approximation bands); if they are off the ω axis their orders are arbitrary, but the usual quadrantal symmetry must always be preserved.

We begin, in the now familiar fashion, by placing (thin) conductors on the approximation bands, both carrying the same distributed charge, as is evidently required for symmetry. By symmetry also we see that their two potentials will be the same, and we call this common potential zero, i.e., we take $V = 0$ on both conductors. The negative charge we place at the prescribed zeros (which may include the origin and infinity). This is the prototype situation, and our first task is to find the corresponding potential, $W(p)$, as a preliminary to quantization. Because of the linearity of the potential problem, we may consider each symmetrical tetrad or pair of zeros, in conjunction with the approximation-band conductors, separately and superpose the results, exactly as in § 14.12.

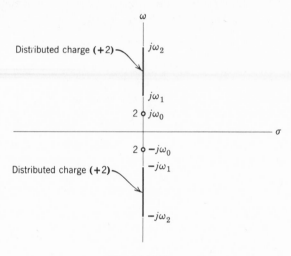

Fig. 14.14–B

In Fig. 14.14–B is shown a pair of prescribed zeros on the ω axis, each of order two, at $\pm j\omega_0$. Complementary to these four units of negative charge, in the analog, the four units of positive charge are distributed, two on each conductor. The flux plot has the general form shown in Fig. 14.14–C, and is moderately complicated, though no more so than that of Fig. 14.12–B, for example. Fortunately we need construct only rough sketches, for general guidance, as before. To obtain the exact potential function we may look for a transformation that will take us to the plane of W, thus solving the prototype problem. We may expect the required transformation to be more complicated than the one we used for the one-band problem, since the geometry with two bands is more complicated. This is true; in fact, if we develop a transformation in the fashion of § 14.09 we are led to elliptic functions. The discussion of these we postpone to Volume II, for it happens that this particular problem can be solved by reducing it to a one-band problem—a reduction that can be accomplished simply by "squaring" the p plane, i.e., by taking p^2 as a new variable. (Cf. § 14.18, however.)

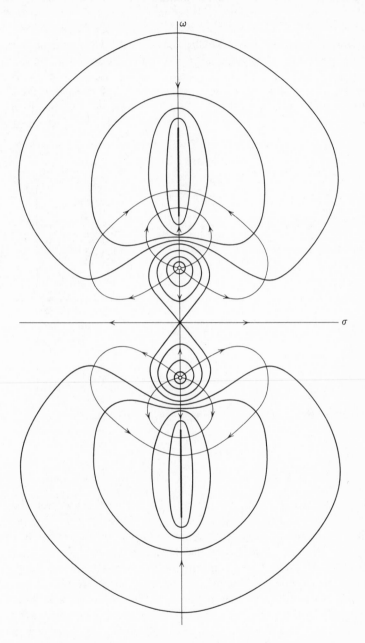

Fig. 14.14–C

Suppose we imagine a transformation of the p plane brought about by folding the two halves of the imaginary axis together to the left, as in Fig. 14.14–D(a). The left half of the p plane will finally be lost to sight on another sheet; the visible sheet, Fig. 14.14–D(b), will be a mapping of the right half of the original p plane, and the negative half of the real axis is a natural branch cut. Because of the symmetry of the problem, the flux plot in the upper half of the p plane is the image in the real axis of that in the lower half (Fig. 14.14–C). Consequently, the flux descending on one ramp of the branch cut in Fig. 14.14–D(b) is identical to that

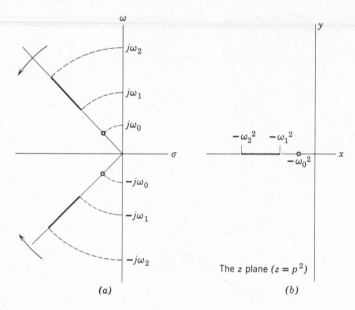

(a)   (b)

Fig. 14.14–D

mounting the other, and we may cut the connection between sheets and sew together the two parts of the upper sheet to give a single plane—all without altering the flux plot therein. In this process the conductor, and the lumped charges, are to be thought of as being "bisected," and when the two halves, one from each ramp, are sewn together, to form the single plane, the original conductor and lumped charge are restored, with the same charge as in one half of the p plane. We can now think of the plane of Fig. 14.14–D(b) as an ordinary plane in which we have a single conductor, carrying a total charge of $+2$ units, and a lumped charge of -2 units. For formal purposes, such a transformation can be generated by squaring the variable, for this has exactly the effect illustrated in Fig. 14.14–D. To be sure, in addition to the bending desired (accomplished by the doubling of the angle in the squaring) there is also a distortion in the radial (magnitude) scale, of the nature of squaring. But this is necessary and need not disturb us; what is important is that in the new plane of Fig. 14.14–D(b) we have again a one-band problem, and this we can easily solve.

We denote the new plane that of $z = x + jy$, with

$$z = p^2. \tag{14.14–1}$$

Then the coordinates of the conductor ends and the lumped charge are those shown in Fig. 14.14–D(b). It is convenient now to shift the origin to the center of the conductor, and to rotate the plane through an angle of 90°, to give a more familiar configuration. The linear change of variable

$$z' = -j\left(z + \frac{\omega_1^2 + \omega_2^2}{2}\right) = x' + jy' \tag{14.14–2}$$

will do just this, giving the situation of Fig. 14.14–E. Except for the lack of symmetry between upper and lower halves of the plane, this is the

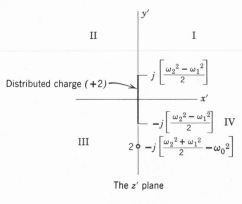

The z' plane

Fig. 14.14–E

problem discussed at length in previous sections. We can solve it rapidly, with the same techniques. On normalizing the plane and invoking the sinh transformation, in other words, by using

$$z' = \left(\frac{\omega_2^2 - \omega_1^2}{2}\right)\sinh w, \tag{14.14–3}$$

we transform the problem to that of Fig. 14.14–F(a), in which the value of a is determined by substituting in (14.14–3) the appropriate expressions. The conductor now occupies the entire imaginary axis, effectively isolating the two halves of the plane by its shielding action. The periodicity of the mapping gives us the infinite vertical sets of negative charges shown; these lack symmetry about the u axis because there is no lumped charge on the upper half of the y' axis in the z' plane. We may use the method of images, as in § 14.12, removing the conductor and adding symmetrical image charges in, say, the left half plane to keep the v axis at constant potential, as in Fig. 14.14–F(b). The potential is unchanged in the right half plane, and it is easily calculated.

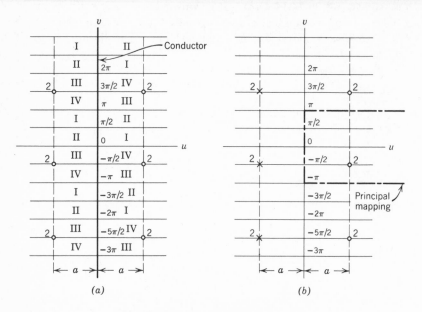

Fig. 14.14–F. The w plane ($w = u + jv$).

From Fig. 14.14–F(b) we can write the potential immediately, on the basis of our previous experience. We write $e^{W/2}$ for simplicity (or take the lumped charge as unit charge temporarily),

$$e^{W/2} = K\,\frac{\cosh\left[\dfrac{w - (a + j\pi/2)}{2}\right]}{\cosh\left[\dfrac{w - (-a + j\pi/2)}{2}\right]} \qquad (14.14\text{–}4)$$

by recognizing that the central point of the right-hand set of zeros, regarded as a cosh function, is at $(a + j\pi/2)$, and that the vertical distance between adjacent zeros is 2π, with similar conditions in the left half plane. Alternatively, we could write for the numerator $\cosh(Aw + B)$ and determine A and B as was done in § 14.08, with a similar calculation for the denominator. The value to be given the arbitrary constant K we shall determine when we return to the p plane. On expanding, much as in § 14.12, we obtain

$$e^{W/2} = K \frac{\cosh\dfrac{w - j\pi/2}{2}\cosh\dfrac{a}{2} - \sinh\dfrac{w - j\pi/2}{2}\sinh\dfrac{a}{2}}{\cosh\dfrac{w - j\pi/2}{2}\cosh\dfrac{a}{2} + \sinh\dfrac{w - j\pi/2}{2}\sinh\dfrac{a}{2}}$$

$$= K \frac{\coth\dfrac{w - j\pi/2}{2} - \tanh\dfrac{a}{2}}{\coth\dfrac{w - j\pi/2}{2} + \tanh\dfrac{a}{2}}. \tag{14.14-5}$$

By using formulas from § 3.26 we find that

$$\coth\frac{w - j\pi/2}{2} = \sqrt{\frac{\cosh(w - j\pi/2) + 1}{\cosh(w - j\pi/2) - 1}}$$

$$= \sqrt{\frac{-j\sinh w + 1}{-j\sinh w - 1}} \tag{14.14-6}$$

in which that branch is taken which is positive on the line $v = \pi/2$ in the principal mapping. We can now transform this back to the p plane by successive use of (14.14-3), (14.14-2), and (14.14-1), to obtain

$$\coth\frac{w - j\pi/2}{2} = \sqrt{\frac{-j\dfrac{2z'}{\omega_2{}^2 - \omega_1{}^2} + 1}{-j\dfrac{2z'}{\omega_2{}^2 - \omega_1{}^2} - 1}}$$

$$= \sqrt{\frac{\dfrac{-(2z + \omega_1{}^2 + \omega_2{}^2)}{\omega_2{}^2 - \omega_1{}^2} + 1}{\dfrac{-(2z + \omega_1{}^2 + \omega_2{}^2)}{\omega_2{}^2 - \omega_1{}^2} - 1}}$$

$$= \sqrt{\frac{-2z - 2\omega_1{}^2}{-2z - 2\omega_2{}^2}}$$

$$= \sqrt{\frac{p^2 + \omega_1{}^2}{p^2 + \omega_2{}^2}}, \tag{14.14-7}$$

in which that branch is to be taken that is positive on the ω axis at high frequencies. We have then, finally,

$$e^{W/2} = K \frac{\sqrt{\dfrac{p^2 + \omega_1^2}{p^2 + \omega_2^2}} - \tanh \dfrac{a}{2}}{\sqrt{\dfrac{p^2 + \omega_1^2}{p^2 + \omega_2^2}} + \tanh \dfrac{a}{2}}$$

$$= K \frac{\sqrt{\dfrac{p^2 + \omega_1^2}{p^2 + \omega_2^2}} - \sqrt{\dfrac{\omega_1^2 - \omega_0^2}{\omega_2^2 - \omega_0^2}}}{\sqrt{\dfrac{p^2 + \omega_1^2}{p^2 + \omega_2^2}} + \sqrt{\dfrac{\omega_1^2 - \omega_0^2}{\omega_2^2 - \omega_0^2}}}. \qquad (14.14\text{--}8)$$

The evaluation of the constant $\tanh (a/2)$ implied by the second line can be made by inspection (for it is at $p = \pm j\omega_0$ that e^W is to vanish), or by similar successive transformation; in it the positive value of the square root is clearly to be taken.

The prototype-potential expression (14.14–8) is easily checked by sketching the behavior of $\sqrt{(p^2 + \omega_1)/(p^2 + \omega_2^2)}$ for $p = j\omega$ (Fig. 14.14–G). With the proper choice of branch, the function is real and

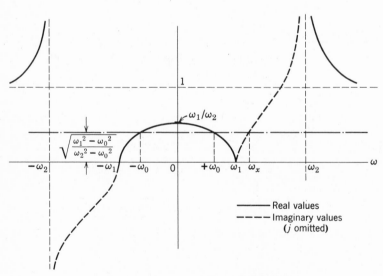

Fig. 14.14–G. Sketch of $\sqrt{\dfrac{-\omega^2 + \omega_1^2}{-\omega^2 + \omega_2^2}}$.

positive for $0 < \omega < \omega_1$ and for $\omega_2 < \omega$; and is imaginary for $\omega_1 < \omega < \omega_2$; it has the sort of symmetry shown (*even* for regions where it is real, *odd* where imaginary). All of this can be summarized, if we wish, in the statement that the p-r branch is chosen. The numerator of (14.14–8) is formed by subtracting a (real, positive) constant from this function, the denominator by adding the same constant to it. On drawing in this constant, we find the two intersections expected (at $\pm \omega_0$) and note that there are no others (at ω_x one function is imaginary, the other real). The numerator of (14.14–8) consequently has, on the ω axis, the requisite zeros (which are simple) and only those; the denominator has none there. On searching through the rest of the p plane we find there are no other zeros, and no infinities or other singularities except for the branch points at $\pm j\omega_1$ and $\pm j\omega_2$. The action of these branch points is to change the character of the function $\sqrt{(p^2 + \omega_1^2)/(p^2 + \omega_2^2)}$ between purely real and purely imaginary; this gives to numerator and denominator of (14.14–8) constant magnitude at all points in the approximation bands, i.e., on the conductors, which gives the requisite constant potential there. Finally, by examining the change in angle of e^W as we pass over the surface of the conductor, the total flux emanating therefrom is found to be correct.

The verification above also shows that equation (14.14–8) is still valid if $\omega_0 > \omega_2$, i.e., if the prescribed zero lies above the approximation band —and also if ω_0 has either of the special values infinity or zero, in which case the zero doubles. This makes it unnecessary to repeat the analysis for these cases. The value to be given K is in magnitude unity (for the potential V to be zero on the two conductors). Its angle is determined by the choice of origin for the flux function Φ, which cannot conveniently be taken on either conductor in this case, since we should like to keep K real. If we take the origin of the plane (or the real axis just to the right of the origin) as the point where we wish Φ to be zero, then K should be either $+1$ or -1, depending on whether $\omega_0 < \omega_1$ or $\omega_0 > \omega_2$. Fortunately, we need not make the decision between these, for the form (14.14–8) must be squared to give us the solution to the problem posed in Fig. 14.14–B. We have then finally,

$$e^W = \left[\frac{\sqrt{\dfrac{p^2 + \omega_1^2}{p^2 + \omega_2^2}} - \sqrt{\dfrac{\omega_1^2 - \omega_0^2}{\omega_2^2 - \omega_0^2}}}{\sqrt{\dfrac{p^2 + \omega_1^2}{p^2 + \omega_2^2}} + \sqrt{\dfrac{\omega_1^2 - \omega_0^2}{\omega_2^2 - \omega_0^2}}} \right]^2 \qquad (14.14–9)$$

as the exponential potential for the prototype problem. In its use the p-r branch of the radical function is to be taken, with branch cuts drawn, say as in Fig. 14.14–H, based on the sort of analysis made in § 14.12.

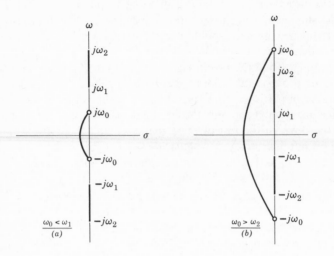

Fig. 14.14–H. Branch cuts in the p plane.

The process of quantization is carried out exactly as before. We first form a complete prototype exponential function, taking into account all the prescribed zeros (negative charges) by using (14.14–9) repeatedly. This will be

$$
e^W = \left[\frac{\sqrt{\dfrac{p^2 + \omega_1^2}{p^2 + \omega_2^2}} - \sqrt{\dfrac{\omega_1^2}{\omega_2^2}}}{\sqrt{\dfrac{p^2 + \omega_1^2}{p^2 + \omega_2^2}} + \sqrt{\dfrac{\omega_1^2}{\omega_2^2}}} \right]^{2n_0} \times \left[\frac{\sqrt{\dfrac{p^2 + \omega_1^2}{p^2 + \omega_2^2}} - \sqrt{\dfrac{\omega_1^2 - \omega_{01}^2}{\omega_2^2 - \omega_{01}^2}}}{\sqrt{\dfrac{p^2 + \omega_1^2}{p^2 + \omega_2^2}} + \sqrt{\dfrac{\omega_1^2 - \omega_{01}^2}{\omega_2^2 - \omega_{01}^2}}} \right]^{2n_1}
$$

$$
\times \left[\frac{\sqrt{\dfrac{p^2 + \omega_1^2}{p^2 + \omega_2^2}} - \sqrt{\dfrac{\omega_1^2 - \omega_{02}^2}{\omega_2^2 - \omega_{02}^2}}}{\sqrt{\dfrac{p^2 + \omega_1^2}{p^2 + \omega_2^2}} + \sqrt{\dfrac{\omega_1^2 - \omega_{02}^2}{\omega_2^2 - \omega_{02}^2}}} \right]^{2n_2} \cdots \left[\frac{\sqrt{\dfrac{p^2 + \omega_1^2}{p^2 + \omega_2^2}} - 1}{\sqrt{\dfrac{p^2 + \omega_1^2}{p^2 + \omega_2^2}} + 1} \right]^{2n_\infty}
$$

$$(14.14\text{–}10)$$

which provides for $4n_0$ zeros at the origin, $2n_1$ each at $\pm j\omega_{01}$, $2n_2$ each at $\pm j\omega_{02}, \cdots$, and $4n_\infty$ at infinity. (If it is desired to have zeros off the ω axis, appropriate similar expressions are to be used for their contributions.) It is not necessary, of course, to have zeros at the origin, or at infinity (the numbers n_0 and n_∞ may be zero); it is also possible to have zeros of order 2, 6, 10 and the like at these points, rather than zeros of order 4, 8, 12, etc., as implied (Problem 14-92)—but these possibilities are not in general as useful. An exception is the case where zeros of order $2(2m + 1) = 2, 6, 10, \cdots$ and the like exist at *both* the origin and infinity; this case is useful and to it the development that follows applies except for certain changes in sign (Problem 14-93).

The total positive charge is now a multiple of four; specifically, it is

$$Q = 4n_0 + 4n_1 + 4n_2 + \cdots + 4n_\infty$$
$$= 4n \qquad\qquad (14.14\text{--}11)$$
$$= 2m$$

of which $m = 2n = Q/2$ units are on each conductor, and $n = m/2 = Q/4$ are on each side of each conductor. The total negative charge is the same in magnitude, distributed as prescribed. Without discussing in detail the (now extremely complicated) nature of the plane of W, we can show how the quantization process proceeds (exactly as before in essence). For Φ we have taken the value zero on the positive-real axis. In mounting to the upper conductor, skirting the negative charges to the right as required by the branch cuts, the value of Φ increases in steps to

$$[\tfrac{1}{4}(4n_0) + \tfrac{1}{2}(2n_1) + \tfrac{1}{2}(2n_2) + \cdots]2\pi = (n_0 + n_1 + n_2 + \cdots)2\pi = \Phi_0$$
$$(14.14\text{--}12)$$

at the lower end of the conductor. Here the summation of n's is of course over only those values that correspond to prescribed negative charges *below* the conductor. In traversing the right side of the conductor the value of Φ now drops an amount $n(2\pi)$ to attain the value

$$[(n_0 + n_1 + n_2 + \cdots) - n]2\pi \qquad (14.14\text{--}13)$$

at the upper end of the conductor. Hence, in the W plane the mapping of the upper conductor is to that portion of the Φ axis ($V = 0$) between the two values of Φ given by (14.14–12) and (14.14–13) (Fig. 14.14–I). Quantization on the equipotential $V = -V_0$ now proceeds exactly as before, except that the central horizontal line, which was $\Phi = 0$, is now $\Phi = (\Phi_0 - n\pi)$. If n is odd, a quantized charge lies on this line, Fig. 14.14–I(a); if n is even, no charge lies there, Fig. 14.14–I(b). By encircling the conductor we find the usual vertical periodicity of mapping that insures that we are dealing with infinite vertical sets of quantized charges; the nature of the Riemann surface again requires that there be

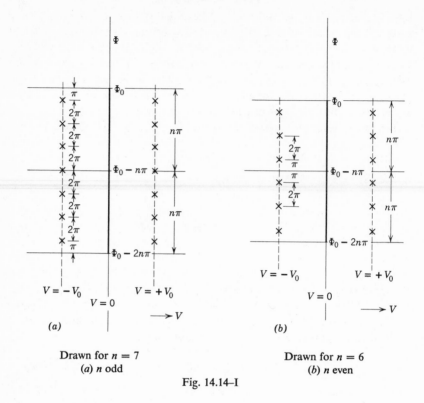

Drawn for $n = 7$ Drawn for $n = 6$
(a) n odd   (b) n even

Fig. 14.14–I

a symmetrical set of charges on $V = +V_0$. The quantized exponential potential is

$$e^{W_q} = \frac{K_0}{\sinh\left[(W - j\Phi_0 + jn\pi + V_0)/2\right] \sinh\left[(W - j\Phi_0 + jn\pi - V_0)/2\right]}$$

for n odd,

$$(14.14\text{–}14)$$

$$= \frac{K_e}{\cosh\left[(W - j\Phi_0 + jn\pi + V_0 - j\pi)/2\right] \cosh\left[(W - j\Phi_0 + jn\pi - Vo - j\pi)/2\right]}$$

for n even.

Both of these, after the usual manipulation, have the same expression, valid for both odd and even values of n,

$$e^{W_q} = \frac{\text{constant}}{\cosh W + \cosh V_0}. \qquad (14.14\text{–}15)$$

From the symmetry of the situation, we need not consider the lower conductor.

We can easily verify the behavior and the nature of the result of this quantization procedure, the function (14.14–15). Below and above the approximation band, i.e., for $0 < \omega < \omega_1$ and for $\omega_2 < \omega$, we have in the prototype problem $\Phi = $ (multiple of 2π); in other words, the flux function is constant (except for the steps of 2π occurring at the prescribed zeros) at multiples of 2π, while V varies (cf. Fig. 14.14–C). In the approximation band, i.e., for $\omega_1 < \omega < \omega_2$, V is constant at the value zero and the flux function varies between the limits discussed above. We have then, for $p = j\omega$, and $\omega_1 < \omega < \omega_2$,

$$e^{W_q} = \frac{\text{constant}}{\cos \Phi + \cosh V_0} = \frac{1 - \epsilon^2}{1 + \epsilon \cos \Phi} \qquad (14.14\text{–}16)$$

in which $\epsilon = \text{sech } V_0$ as usual and the constant has been evaluated in order to make the limits of the exponential-potential oscillation there $(1 + \epsilon)$ and $(1 - \epsilon)$. Outside of the approximation band, i.e., for $p = j\omega$ and $0 < \omega < \omega_1$ and $\omega_2 < \omega$,

$$e^{W_q} = \frac{\text{constant}}{\cosh V + \cosh V_0} = \frac{1 - \epsilon^2}{1 + \epsilon \cosh V}. \qquad (14.14\text{–}17)$$

Figure 14.14–J shows, for a specific case, the real-frequency behavior in both the prototype case and the quantized case, and makes even clearer the relation between the two.

The function (14.14–15) which with the appropriate evaluation of the constant becomes

$$e^{W_q} = \frac{1 - \epsilon^2}{1 + \epsilon \cosh W} \qquad (14.14\text{–}18)$$

is the solution to the immediate problem. By manipulating (14.14–10) in a fashion similar to that previously employed, i.e., by removing the radicals from the denominator of each factor by multiplying and dividing by each numerator, by multiplying out the numerator of e^W, by forming e^{-W}, we find again that $\cosh W$ is a rational function of p, hence that e^{W_q} is rational in p. It vanishes at the prescribed points in the prescribed manner and it becomes infinite at the roots of the quantization equation

$$\cosh W + \cosh V_0 = 0,$$

or

$$1 + \epsilon \cosh W = 0,$$

$$(14.14\text{–}19)$$

which are $Q = 4n = 2m$ in number. (The rationality could be proved by careful investigation of these facts alone.) Approximate locations of these roots and a clear idea of the quantization process can be obtained

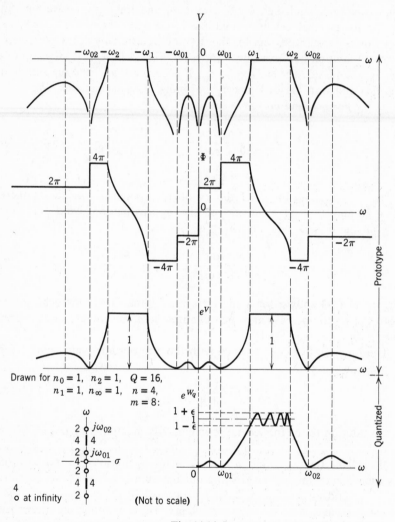

Fig. 14.14–J

from a flux plot for the prototype situation. The roots in effect move out from the conductors on loci that are the appropriate flux lines, stopping when they reach the equipotential $V = -V_0$; Fig. 14.14–K illustrates the "motion." That rational function that has for its poles and zeros the points marked X and O in Fig. 14.14–K (and four zeros at infinity) and a

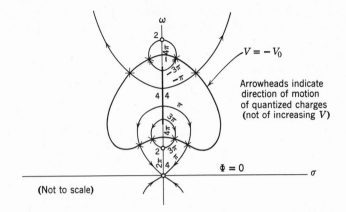

Fig. 14.14–K. The quantization process for the example of Fig. 14.14–J (only the upper half of the plane is shown here).

suitable multiplier (say one that gives the value $1 - \epsilon$ at $p = j\omega_1$) is the end result. It has the desired equal-ripple behavior in the approximation band and falls off outside to the prescribed zeros. It is evidently realizable as a driving-point resistance (conductance) function, by inspection.

The design procedure, given the prescribed zeros, and the desired ripple ϵ, is simply to

1. formulate and solve the quantization equation (14.14–19);
2. determine the impedance (admittance) function that has for its poles the left-half-plane roots of (14.14–19), has a numerator such that the corresponding resistance (conductance) function has the prescribed zeros, and has an appropriate multiplier (as in § 8.11);
3. realize a corresponding network. (14.14–20)

The details of these steps are sufficiently like those of previous design processes to require no further comment. It is not necessary actually to obtain the individual roots of the quantization equation; all that is needed is the polynomial whose zeros are the left-half-plane roots, for this is the denominator of the immittance function. Nevertheless, a good deal of numerical calculation is required, which cannot be avoided. In step 3 we have generally a number of possibilities; in a one-resistor realization, for example, the zeros may be "removed" in various sequences that lead to rather different networks (cf. Chapter 9, particularly § 9.11, and Problems 9-8 and 14-94).

The prescription of the zeros may be dictated by certain requirements of the system in which the network is to operate. Then again, these zeros may not be exactly prescribed, and it may be a part of the approximation procedure to determine, perhaps simply by trial, where they should lie to achieve a given end. The example of Fig. 14.14–L is a case in point.

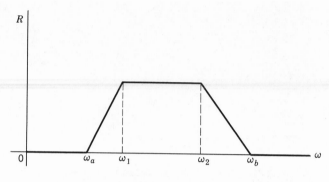

Fig. 14.14–L

Within prescribed limits of a certain amount, zeros can be located in the regions $0 < \omega < \omega_a$ and $\omega_b < \omega$ in various ways to meet the requirement; perhaps zeros at the origin and at infinity will suffice, with the corresponding simplicity in the design. How many zeros are necessary, and where they should go, is best determined by trial. The interesting solution suggested by Fig. 14.14–M is one possibility; we do not have

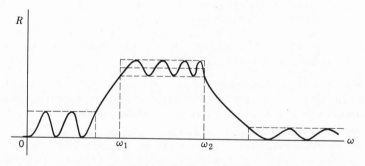

Fig. 14.14–M

the mathematics necessary to obtain this solution exactly, but given sufficient patience, a designer can achieve it by trial (aided, perhaps, by an analog computer of the sort mentioned in § 14.20). Wherever possible, however, the designer may choose to distribute the zeros between the origin and infinity, to insure simplicity in the final network [cf. (9.11–6)].

With this discussion of the approximation of a constant (by an even function, with arbitrarily prescribed zeros) in an internal band, we have gone far to remove the second restriction in (14.11–5). We shall not discuss the manifold possibilities in cases where additional approximation bands are required. The transformations become more complicated, and the mathematics more transcendental, even though the basic idea remains the same: deposition of positive charged conductors on the approximation bands, construction of the flux plots (with negative charges at the prescribed or otherwise determined zeros), and quantization of the positive charge on one of the equipotentials. This is the essence of Chebyshev approximation of a constant, regardless of the number or location of the approximation bands.

14.15 Taylor and Chebyshev approximation

There is an important connection between the approximation of a constant (or indeed of any function) in the fashion we have been discussing, and approximation of the same in the Taylor sense. Taylor approximation of a constant, which we have discussed in a purely algebraic fashion (§§ 13.05, 13.10) can be effected equally well by means of the potential analogy: all that is necessary is to allow the approximation band in our Chebyshev-approximation work to shrink to zero width, with the requirement that the error ripple ϵ simultaneously approach zero. Quantization on an equipotential of the prototype problem then gives Taylor approximations.

That this should be true is not surprising. As the bandwidth and ripple size of a Chebyshev approximation decrease we can easily visualize the approximating function as becoming flatter and flatter in the approximation band, and this is exactly what Taylor approximation of a constant requires. Furthermore, we have found the zeros of the approximating function to be arbitrary in both Taylor (§ 13.10) and Chebyshev approximation of a constant with an even function. It is entirely reasonable, then, to expect Taylor approximation to be a limiting case of Chebyshev approximation. So it is, not only here, but in general. We first consider the precise nature of the relation in this approximation of a constant by an even function.

The Chebyshev approximation is given in the internal-band case by

$$
\begin{aligned}
e^{W_q} &= \frac{\text{constant}}{\cosh W + \cosh V_0} \\
&= \frac{.\,1 - \epsilon^2}{1 + \epsilon \cosh W}
\end{aligned}
\tag{14.15–1}
$$

according to (14.14–15) and (14.14–18), in which W is the complex potential in the prototype case: positively charged conductors on the approximation bands and negative charges at the prescribed points. The number of crossings of the nominal value (the constant approximated within $\pm\epsilon$) in the approximation band is equal to m, the positive charge on the prototype conductor (see, e.g., Fig. 14.14–J), and the size of the error ripple is $\epsilon = \operatorname{sech} V_0$. If we now let both the approximation-band width $(\omega_2 - \omega_1)$ and the error ripple ϵ approach zero, we can evaluate the nature of the resulting approximation. In (14.14–10) we can rewrite a typical factor, say the second one, by multiplying and dividing by the denominator, as

$$\left[\frac{\dfrac{p^2 + \omega_1^2}{p^2 + \omega_2^2} - \dfrac{\omega_1^2 - \omega_{01}^2}{\omega_2^2 - \omega_{01}^2}}{\left(\sqrt{\dfrac{p^2 + \omega_1^2}{p^2 + \omega_2^2}} + \sqrt{\dfrac{\omega_1^2 - \omega_{01}^2}{\omega_2^2 - \omega_{01}^2}}\right)^2}\right]^{2n_1}$$

$$= \left[\frac{(p^2 + \omega_{01}^2)(\omega_2^2 - \omega_1^2)}{(p^2 + \omega_2^2)(\omega_2^2 - \omega_{01}^2)\left(\sqrt{\dfrac{p^2 + \omega_1^2}{p^2 + \omega_2^2}} + \sqrt{\dfrac{\omega_1^2 - \omega_{01}^2}{\omega_2^2 - \omega_{01}^2}}\right)^2}\right]^{2n_1}$$

$$\tag{14.15–2}$$

Similar expressions can be written for all the factors in (14.14–10); each one exhibits zeros at the prescribed points—and apparently poles at $\pm j\omega_2$, though the latter are actually removed by the factor that contains the radicals. If we proceed now to the limit of zero bandwidth, if $(\omega_2 - \omega_1) \to 0$, then each of the factors in e^W will vanish. Each of the factors in e^{-W}, however, will become infinite. And in e^{W_q} we shall find the expected limit, provided ϵ is made properly to approach zero. In particular, we obtain

$$e^{W_q} = \lim_{\substack{(\omega_2 - \omega_1) \to 0 \\ \epsilon \to 0}} \frac{1 - \epsilon^2}{1 + \epsilon \cosh W}$$

$$= \lim \frac{1}{1 + \dfrac{\epsilon}{2}(e^W + e^{-W})}$$

$$\tag{14.15–3}$$

$$= \lim \frac{1}{1 + \dfrac{\epsilon}{2}\dfrac{1}{(\omega_2^2 - \omega_1^2)^{2n_0 + 2n_1 + \cdots + 2n_\infty}}\left[\dfrac{(p^2 + \omega_2^2)4\omega_2^2}{p^2}\right]^{2n_0}}{}$$
$$\times \left[\dfrac{(p^2 + \omega_2^2)4(\omega_2^2 - \omega_{01}^2)}{p^2 + \omega_{01}^2}\right]^{2n_1} \cdots [(p^2 + \omega_2^2)4]^{2n_\infty}$$

$$= \lim \frac{1}{1 + \dfrac{\epsilon}{(\omega_2{}^2 - \omega_1{}^2)^m} \dfrac{(p^2 + \omega_2{}^2)^m}{p^{4n_0}(p^2 + \omega_{01}{}^2)^{2n_1}(p^2 + \omega_{02}{}^2)^{2n_2} \cdots}}$$

$$(14.15\text{-}3)$$

in which m is defined by (14.14–11). In order to have a meaningful result, it is evidently necessary that ϵ approach zero in a certain way, at such a rate that

$$\frac{\epsilon}{(\omega_2{}^2 - \omega_1{}^2)^m} = K \qquad (14.15\text{-}4)$$

remain constant. With this proviso we finally obtain, writing ω_0 as the limit of ω_1 and of ω_2,

$$e^{W_q} = \frac{1}{1 + K \dfrac{(p^2 + \omega_0{}^2)^m}{p^{4n_0}(p^2 + \omega_{01}{}^2)^{2n_1}(p^2 + \omega_{02}{}^2)^{2n_2} \cdots}}. \qquad (14.15\text{-}5)$$

That this is indeed that even function that is maximally flat (at unit value) at ω_0 becomes evident on expansion in a Taylor series about $p = j\omega_0$; we obtain

$$e^{W_q} = 1 + \varepsilon_m(\omega - \omega_0)^m + \cdots \qquad (14.15\text{-}6)$$

as that series. This is as flat as the order of the function, $2m$, will permit, because of the requirement (constraint) of even symmetry; the m crossings of the nominal value in the Chebyshev approximation have been transformed into the matching of m terms in the Taylor series for the function approximated. It is exactly the function obtained by the methods of § 13.10 (Problem 13-79), in fact.

A similar treatment of the low-band case of § 14.12 leads to the function

$$e^{W_q} = \frac{1}{1 + (-1)^n K \dfrac{p^{2n}}{(p^2 + \omega_{01}{}^2)^{2n_1}(p^2 + \omega_{02}{}^2)^{2n_2} \cdots}} \qquad (14.15\text{-}7)$$

which is maximally flat (at unit value) at the origin, with prescribed zeros ($2n_1$ each at $\pm j\omega_{01}$, $2n_2$ each at $\pm j\omega_{02}$, $\cdots$). In both (14.15–5) and (14.15–7) zeros prescribed at infinity (if any) do not specifically appear, but will be taken care of by an appropriate difference in degree between numerator and denominator.

High-band and multiband cases yield similar results: Taylor approximation to a constant, with an even function and arbitrarily prescribed zeros, is similarly a limiting case (as bandwidth and ripple approach zero in a certain way) of the corresponding Chebyshev approximation. In the prototype-potential problem the approximation-band conductors are replaced by lumped charges (at the points of maximal flatness) equal in strength to those on the conductors; the prescribed negative charges are unchanged. The flux plot will not differ greatly in general appearance, except in the immediate vicinity of the approximation bands, where equipotentials that are substantially ellipses in the Chebyshev case become substantially circles in the Taylor case. "Quantization" (no longer strictly an appropriate term in Taylor approximation, since the positive charge is already lumped, but still convenient) takes place on an equipotential of the prototype problem in both cases. In the Taylor case, since the approximation band becomes a point and the positive charge lumped, the potential there will become infinite, and the symbol V_0 loses its meaning. At the same time there is no longer a ripple magnitude ϵ to consider; in its place there is a constant, K in (14.15–5) and (14.15–7), to be evaluated to suit the conditions of the problem. It has no effect on the flatness (on the number of derivatives matched) but acts somewhat like a frequency scale factor, exactly as in (13.10–8) and (13.10–10). Once it is chosen (probably by trial, or by meeting some requirement as to rate of falloff), a "quantization" equation can be written by setting equal to zero the denominator of (14.15–5) or of (14.15–7), or the corresponding expression for some other case.

The approximation procedure for maximally flat resistance (conductance) functions can be carried out in potential-analogy fashion, then, if desired. The procedure is to

1. locate lumped positive charges at the point(s) of maximal approximation of the constant, and lumped negative charges at the prescribed zeros, all with due regard to symmetry, and of multiplicity appropriate to the problem (or network complexity desired);
2. "quantize" on an appropriate equipotential, by solving the algebraic equation obtained by setting the denominator of (14.15–5) or (14.15–7) or other appropriate expression equal to zero. (14.15–8)

We may equally well look on step 2 as forcing a motion of the positive charges out along appropriate flux lines of the plot for the prototype problem, step 1. The stopping point is determined by selecting a value for K that gives the desired shape of curve as the point of maximal flatness is left behind; there is, of course, no longer a "ripple" to determine the end of the motion. These steps taken, we have a suitable rational resistance (conductance) function for realization in network form by the usual processes.

This view of Taylor approximation as a limiting case of Chebyshev approximation is usually valid in general, not simply for the case of approximating a constant with an even function. We can understand this in a general way by considering what happens in an arbitrary case of

Chebyshev approximation, as both approximation-band width and ripple size approach zero. We shall assume that Chebyshev approximation implies an error function $\Delta(\omega)$ (§ 13.02) that oscillates in the approximation band between equal maxima $(+\epsilon)$ and equal minima $(-\epsilon)$, and that there will be one crossing of the zero line for each available parameter in the approximating function. That the best approximation is obtained when there is one crossing (one zero of error) in the approximation band for each available parameter seems reasonable in that we could not expect more (from a point-matching point of view, if n parameters are available for adjustment, only n crossings can be forced in general), and if fewer are present, then the approximation is probably not as good as it might be, for if we could introduce additional crossings we might widen the approximation band, or decrease the ripple size, or do both. These ideas are generally valid, though there are exceptions, into which we shall not

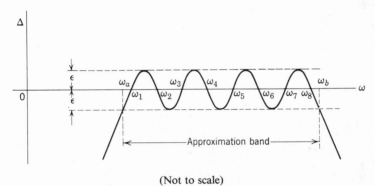

(Not to scale)

Drawn for $n = 8$, 8 zeros of error in approximation band.

Fig. 14.15–A

inquire. Figure 14.15–A shows such an error function for an internal-band case, the approximating function having eight available parameters $(n = 8)$. The n zeros of error occur at $\omega_1, \omega_2, \cdots, \omega_n$, and all of the $(n + 1)$ maxima of $|\Delta|$ are equal to ϵ.

Before proceeding to the limit we set up a sequence of differences of $\Delta(\omega)$ that will approach, on division by the proper power of the increment in ω, its derivatives in the limit. These are given in Table 14.15–A in which the values of $\Delta(\omega)$ at the matching points (the zeros of Δ) are indicated by the symbols $\Delta_1, \Delta_2, \cdots$ even though these values are all zero. All of the values of the differences of $\Delta(\omega)$ shown in Table 14.15–A are thus actually zero. If now we allow ω_a and ω_b (the limits of the

Table 14.15-A

ω	Δ	First Difference	Second Difference	Third Difference	Fourth Difference	Fifth Difference	Sixth Difference	Seventh Difference
ω_1	Δ_1							
		$\Delta_2 - \Delta_1$						
ω_2	Δ_2		$\Delta_3 - 2\Delta_2 + \Delta_1$					
		$\Delta_3 - \Delta_2$		$\Delta_4 - 3\Delta_3 + 3\Delta_2 - \Delta_1$				
ω_3	Δ_3		$\Delta_4 - 2\Delta_3 + \Delta_2$		$\Delta_5 - 4\Delta_4 + 6\Delta_3 - 4\Delta_2 + \Delta_1$			
		$\Delta_4 - \Delta_3$		$\Delta_5 - 3\Delta_4 + 3\Delta_3 - \Delta_2$		$\Delta_6 - 5\Delta_5 + 10\Delta_4 - 10\Delta_3 + 5\Delta_2 - \Delta_1$		
ω_4	Δ_4		$\Delta_5 - 2\Delta_4 + \Delta_3$		$\Delta_6 - 4\Delta_5 + 6\Delta_4 - 4\Delta_3 + \Delta_2$		$\Delta_7 - 6\Delta_6 + 15\Delta_5 - 20\Delta_4 + 15\Delta_3 - 6\Delta_2 + \Delta_1$	
		$\Delta_5 - \Delta_4$		$\Delta_6 - 3\Delta_5 + 3\Delta_4 - \Delta_3$		$\Delta_7 - 5\Delta_6 + 10\Delta_5 - 10\Delta_4 + 5\Delta_3 - \Delta_2$		$\Delta_8 - 7\Delta_7 + 21\Delta_6 - 35\Delta_5 + 35\Delta_4 - 21\Delta_3 + 7\Delta_2 - \Delta_1$
ω_5	Δ_5		$\Delta_6 - 2\Delta_5 + \Delta_4$		$\Delta_7 - 4\Delta_6 + 6\Delta_5 - 4\Delta_4 + \Delta_3$		$\Delta_8 - 6\Delta_7 + 15\Delta_6 - 20\Delta_5 + 15\Delta_4 - 6\Delta_3 + \Delta_2$	
		$\Delta_6 - \Delta_5$		$\Delta_7 - 3\Delta_6 + 3\Delta_5 - \Delta_4$		$\Delta_8 - 5\Delta_7 + 10\Delta_6 - 10\Delta_5 + 5\Delta_4 - \Delta_3$		
ω_6	Δ_6		$\Delta_7 - 2\Delta_6 + \Delta_5$		$\Delta_8 - 4\Delta_7 + 6\Delta_6 - 4\Delta_5 + \Delta_4$			
		$\Delta_7 - \Delta_6$		$\Delta_8 - 3\Delta_7 + 3\Delta_6 - \Delta_5$				
ω_7	Δ_7		$\Delta_8 - 2\Delta_7 + \Delta_6$					
		$\Delta_8 - \Delta_7$						
ω_8	Δ_8							

approximation band) to approach each other, the various matching points ω_1, ω_2, $\cdot\cdot\cdot$, ω_n will of course approach the same limit as ω_a and ω_b, say ω_0, which may be anywhere in the original approximation band. The value of $\Delta(\omega_0)$ will be zero. The value of the derivative $\Delta'(\omega)$ at this point will be the limit of the quotient of the first difference of Δ and the corresponding increment of ω; since the first difference remains zero throughout the limiting process, the value of the derivative will be zero, provided that ϵ also approaches zero sufficiently rapidly. (If ϵ were not also infinitesimal, if the loops of the curve did not drop to infinitesimal size, then we should have a meaningless series of oscillations in a band of zero width.) The value of the second derivative $\Delta''(\omega_0)$ will similarly be zero, for the second difference of Δ remains zero throughout the limiting process; and so will the values of the first $(n - 1)$ derivatives also be zero in the limit—provided that ϵ approaches zero at the proper rate (neither too fast nor too slowly). Consequently, the end result will be an error function whose behavior in the vicinity of ω_0 will be

$$\Delta(\omega) = \Delta^{(n)}(\omega_0) \frac{(\omega - \omega_0)^n}{n!} + \cdot\cdot\cdot. \qquad (14.15\text{–}9)$$

This is a Taylor-approximation error function, for the first n terms of the Taylor series for the error about the point of maximal approximation are zero.

So it is in general (though the argument above leaves something to be desired in rigor): a Chebyshev approximation with n zeros of error in the approximation band becomes, in the limit of zero approximation-band width and zero ripple, a Taylor approximation of quality n (n terms of the Taylor series are matched). We shall not discuss the exceptions, for certain difficult aspects of approximation theory are involved (BE 2, CH 2). The process, be it noted well, is not reversible. We can easily contract a Chebyshev approximation to obtain a Taylor approximation; we cannot obtain a Chebyshev approximation from a Taylor approximation (except by using the latter as a first step in a trial-and-error process). The fundamental reason for this is that Taylor approximation is also the limit of an indefinite number of *other* approximations, e.g., those obtained by specifying n equally spaced points of matching in the approximation band and determining the corresponding approximating function. As the width of the approximation band is decreased, the n matches being retained at equally spaced points, a similar limiting process leads again to the Taylor approximation. The points of match could be specified in some other manner; the variety is endless, hence we cannot hope to be able to extract from a Taylor approximation a Chebyshev approximation, or any other one.

In Chapter 13 (§ 13.05) we discussed the relation between the quality of Taylor approximation obtained and the number of parameters available in the approximating function: in general, if n parameters are available, one can match the approximating (rational) function to the function to be approximated in the first n terms of the Taylor series about the point of maximal approximation, and no further.   Similarly, one can generally obtain a Chebyshev approximation with n zeros of error in the approximation band, and no more.   Exceptions can be found, but we shall not discuss them here (Problems 14-117, -118).

When symmetry conditions or other constraints are imposed, the quality of approximation that one can obtain is correspondingly reduced. A requirement of even symmetry reduces the quality of approximation by about 50%, for only half of the zeros and poles can be used in the approximation; the remaining zeros and poles are then fixed by the symmetry requirement.   (The multiplier may or may not play a significant rôle in the approximation.)   Alternatively, about half the coefficients in the numerator and denominator polynomials must be zero, for no odd powers can appear.   If, for example, we are to approximate with a rational function of order ten, which contains 21 parameters (10 zeros, 10 poles, and a multiplier *or* 21 independent coefficients), a requirement that the function be even reduces the number of parameters to 11 (5 zeros, 5 poles, and the multiplier *or* 11 independent coefficients).   In general, we should be able to match 11 terms in the Taylor series, or obtain a Chebyshev approximation with 11 zeros of error.   Anomalies can occur, however, as discussed in § 13.10, if the function to be approximated is rational, and also if it is even.   If we are to approximate a constant, we have seen that the zeros are arbitrary, which reduces the number of useful parameters to six.   Furthermore, the multiplier here cannot contribute to the number of terms matched (or to the number of zeros of error) for it is of the same nature as the function approximated and serves only as a scale factor. We are left then with *five* as a measure of the quality of approximation— and this is exactly the quality we achieve.   The Chebyshev approximation, in the low-band case, is summarized in Fig. 14.15–B: in the approximation band, $0 < \omega < 1$, there are five zeros of error.   The most general corresponding Taylor approximation (§ 13.10) is

$$\frac{1 + a_2\omega^2 + \cdots + a_{10}\omega^{10}}{1 + a_2\omega^2 + \cdots + a_{10}\omega^{10} + K\omega^{10}}$$

$$= \frac{1}{1 + \dfrac{K\omega^{10}}{1 + a_2\omega^2 + \cdots + a_{10}\omega^{10}}} = 1 + K'\omega^{10} + \cdots$$

$$(14.15–10)$$

in which the last expression, valid near the origin, shows that ten terms of the Taylor series are matched. Ten, rather than five, are matched because the symmetry of the function approximated is *also* even, and the contiguous image of the approximation band at negative frequencies therefore also contributes an equal quality of approximation, gratuitously. In Fig. 14.15–B we see that there are also five zeros of error in the band

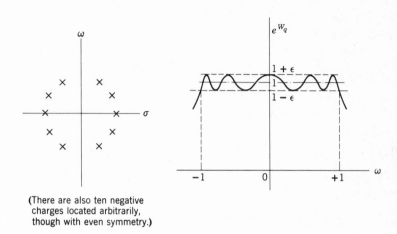

(There are also ten negative charges located arbitrarily, though with even symmetry.)

Fig. 14.15–B

$-1 < \omega < 0$, making a total of ten zeros of error, in agreement with the ten terms matched in (14.15–10). The anomaly is due to the fact that the function approximated is *even* and any approximation at positive frequencies with an even function is therefore automatically repeated at negative frequencies; in general this will not happen.

Another illustration can be found in Fig. 14.14–J. The approximating function is of order 16 and contains 33 parameters (16 zeros, 16 poles, and the multiplier *or* 33 independent coefficients). The requirement of even symmetry reduces this number to 17; the fact that the function approximated is also rational (which makes the zeros arbitrary) reduces it further to 9; and since the multiplier is of no help, the effective number of parameters is only 8. The Chebyshev approximation of Fig. 14.14–J has consequently eight zeros of error in the approximation band. The Taylor approximation obtained by concentrating the positive charge at two points (instead of distributing it on two conductors) is

$$\frac{1}{1 + K \dfrac{(\omega^2 - \omega_0^2)^8}{\omega^4(\omega^2 - \omega_{01}^2)^2(\omega^2 - \omega_{02}^2)^2}} = 1 + K'(\omega - \omega_0)^8 + \cdots$$

$$(14.15\text{–}11)$$

in which $\pm j\omega_0$ are the points of maximal approximation, K is arbitrary (to be determined by some requirement, as on rate of falloff), and the last development, valid near $\omega = \omega_0$, indicates that eight terms are matched in the Taylor series. Because the function to be approximated is also even, a similar approximation occurs at negative frequencies, in both cases. In the low-band Taylor-approximation case this additional approximation gratuitously reinforces that of primary interest, as in (14.15–10); in the internal-band case here it does not, and the quality of the approximation is measured by 8 and not by 16.

This discussion of obtainable quality of approximation points out what can be expected in general. When the function to be approximated is rational (as well as the approximating function) or when it behaves substantially as certain rational functions in or near the approximation band, anomalies can occur, not only to reduce the expected quality of approximation but to increase it (Problems 14-117, -118). Symmetry conditions may also introduce anomalies, as indicated, and as will be seen later (§ 14.17). With this brief discussion we leave the matter, to return to it when necessary or appropriate, or for the approximator to consider in the light of any particular approximation problem.

14.16 Constant magnitude of immittance

In the discussion of the approximation of a constant by an even function, we have so far assumed that this function is to represent a driving-point resistance or driving-point conductance. The requirements for the realizability of such a function are simple (§ 8.16) and we can readily insure its realizability, as we have done; in fact, by suitably locating the zeros, as at the origin or infinity or both, we can even insure realizability in certain simple network forms (§ 9.11). But among the even functions that one must deal with in one-terminal-pair problems are also the *magnitude* (of impedance or admittance) functions. Approximation to a constant magnitude of immittance is not as simple a matter, and requires some separate discussion.

The principal reason that this even-function approximation problem must be treated differently is that realizability is not readily predicted (§ 8.13). It is not possible, in general, to determine by examination of an even function proposed as the (square of the) magnitude of a driving-point immittance, whether or not it is realizable—the corresponding immittance function must actually be found, and tested for positive reality, as in Example 1 of § 8.13. Some necessary conditions can be laid down (§§ 8.16, 14.03) but sufficient conditions are not available. From this stems the added complexity of the design work for magnitude-of-immittance problems.

One may profitably examine more closely the rôle of the zeros in even-function approximation of a constant. Since we are approximating an even rational function (the constant) with an even rational function, a perfect solution exists, namely the constant itself (§13.10). This is not likely to be satisfactory, however, and we apply constraints in requiring that some zeros be present. We generally, in a low-band problem for example, want some zeros at infinity, and perhaps elsewhere too. We have found in both Taylor and Chebyshev approximation that these zeros are then arbitrary in the sense that they may be prescribed at will without altering the quality of approximation that can be obtained: in Taylor approximation the number of terms matched at the point of approxima-tion is not affected (§§ 13.10, 14.15), nor in Chebyshev approximation is the number of ripples. As far as *approximation* goes, the same is true when we consider the magnitude of an immittance, but here *realization* has a strong effect on the solution of the approximation problem. If we seek a resistance function we may put all the zeros at infinity, or we may use zeros of order 4, 6, 8, $\cdot$ $\cdot$ $\cdot$ at real frequencies—but such zeros we cannot have if the function is to represent the (square of the) magnitude of a driving-point immittance function. The rôle of the zeros is evidently different here, and their proper location may be the key to realizability of the derived immittance function. We must then pay more attention here to the locations of the zeros.

We deal not with the magnitude function $|Z|$ itself, since that is not analytic, but rather as in § 8.13 with the function $F(p) = Z(p)Z(-p)$ which reduces, at real frequencies, to the square of the magnitude of $Z(j\omega)$. For realizability it is necessary and sufficient that $Z(p)$ be p-r. Accordingly, we must so design the function $F(p)$ in solving the approx-imation problem that when $Z(p)$ is extracted from it (§ 8.13), $Z(p)$ will be p-r. This limits us, for example, to double zeros on the ω axis (and we may sometimes have double poles there also). In potential-analogy terms, the requirements on $Z(p)$ for realizability are certain matters of symmetry, certain requirements as to charges on the ω axis, and primarily a restriction on the flux that crosses the ω axis (§ 14.03). It is not at all clear in the function $F(p) = Z(p)Z(-p)$ whether these requirements will be met in the derived function $Z(p)$. On the ω axis, for instance, the flux function for $F(p)$ is merely a constant (or series of constants) which is of no help to us: the flux function for $Z(p)$ simply is not present, since we dismissed it in considering $F(p)$ instead of $Z(p)$, our primary interest being in the *magnitude* of the immittance. Hence it is always necessary, once a tentative solution to the approximation problem, an $F(p)$, has been found, to extract $Z(p)$ from it and to test this function $Z(p)$ either analytic-ally (§ 5.13) or in its potential analog (§ 14.03) for positive reality. Unless the zeros have been properly placed, the result will not be p-r. Exactly what regions the zeros may lie in is not clear, and it generally becomes necessary to resort to a series of trials to obtain a satisfactory solution.

One thing we can say, in following the approximation procedure that uses a prototype conductor and subsequent quantization of charge: if all the zeros of $F(p)$ are prescribed at points off the ω axis, then if we make V_0 large enough (i.e., if we make the approximation-band error ripple small enough) the derived function $Z(p)$ will be p-r. For if the quantized positive charges (poles) move far enough out on their flux-line trajectories, they will be close enough to their ultimate destinations (the negative charges or zeros) so that the bulk of the flux lines will be confined to the immediate vicinity of these positive-negative-charge (pole-zero) combinations. There will be only a limited amount of flux to cross the ω axis in the plot for $Z(p)$, and since the symmetry requirements presumably have also been met, $Z(p)$ will meet the requirements of § 14.03 and be p-r. Just how far the motion must be carried can be determined only by trial, and this procedure is not likely to give us a good solution, unless the zeros are carefully placed, for small approximation-band ripples generally imply a rather poor rate of falloff outside the band (GO 1).

Evidently it is rather important that the zeros be properly located, both to insure realizability and to give the best performance. Unfortunately, there seems to be no way of finding the best locations for the zeros but by trial. The necessary succession of trials may be a tedious job, but with experience one may develop a feeling for this sort of problem that is an invaluable aid. We shall not discuss this approach further.

A very different attack can be based on the relations between the various parts of an immittance function discussed in Chapter 8. If the *magnitude* of $Z(j\omega)$ is prescribed at all frequencies, the corresponding *angle* can be determined, without ambiguity (§§ 8.07, 8.13). And when we deal with a prescribed angle-of-driving-point immittance function, the situation is quite different, for the realizability question can be answered almost by inspection (§ 8.16). We might then convert the magnitude data into the corresponding angle function and then proceed to approximate the latter. This seems to be a suspiciously simple way around the fundamental obstacle (of predicting realizability of a given magnitude function)—and there is indeed another obstacle. In order to find the angle function, whether by analytic or graphical means (§§ 8.07, 8.09, 8.13), we must know the magnitude function *at all frequencies*. If it is desired to approximate a constant magnitude in a certain band (low or high or internal) and no further data are given, except for the general requirement of a falling off toward zero outside the approximation band(s), then we must settle on some definite behavior outside the approximation band in order to find the angle function. What particular behavior we choose will affect the nature of the angle function, perhaps radically—and in turn the nature of the final approximation to constant magnitude will be affected by the nature of the angle function as well as the method and range of approximation thereto. These effects, depending as they do on integrals over the entire ω axis, are not readily predicted and may indeed produce some surprising errors. Without experience and sound judgment obtained thereby, the designer will probably not find a good method here, then. Further conversion to the corresponding resistance (conductance) or reactance (susceptance) function, which may then be approximated, will merely introduce additional possibilities for error, though it does offer another possibility. These techniques, aside from the unpredictability of their efficacy, lead to the objectionable necessity of approximating over the whole ω axis (instead of the approximation band alone) and of approximating a function other than a constant (in, say, the corresponding angle function). We shall not develop them further here, though there are some interesting possibilities (Problems 14-120, -121, -122, -146).

There is at least one other avenue of considerable interest, based on the potential analogy, though developed therefrom in a different way. Consider first the low-band case, in which we seek a (realizable) magnitude-of-driving-point immittance function that approximates a constant from the origin up to unit (normalized) frequency, thereafter dropping off. Such a function we have already found in the prototype exponential-potential function for the resistance (conductance) function problem. If we use but one zero and place it at infinity for simplicity, the prototype exponential potential is, by (14.12–32) or (14.12–7),

$$e^W = \sqrt[+]{p^2 + 1} - p. \tag{14.16-1}$$

The genesis and the behavior of this are shown again in Fig. 14.16–A. (In what follows it is to be understood that $\sqrt{p^2 + 1}$ means the p-r branch, though we shall no longer bother to indicate this specifically.) If we now take as analogs the exponential-potential function and the immittance function $Z(p)$ itself [rather than using $Z(p)Z(-p)$], then e^V represents $|Z|$. And the behavior of e^V is exactly that desired (Fig. 14.16–A). Moreover the function (14.16–1) is positive-real! To be sure, it is not rational, but the fact that it is p-r offers some hope for successful approximation thereof. As a matter of fact, this function gives the ultimate in rate of falling off after the region of constancy, if it is required that the function approach zero at infinity, fall off monotonically (steadily), and be p-r. More than that, the function (14.16–1) provides (in normalized form) the maximum obtainable value of constant magnitude of impedance in the approximation band, if it is required that the network realization commence with a capacitor (e.g., to provide for parasitic capacitance in vacuum-tube circuits). In terms of this capacitance C and

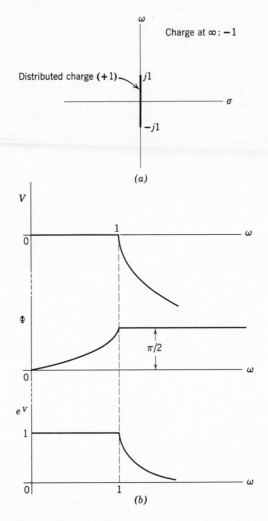

Fig. 14.16–A. (a) The prototype-potential problem.
(b) Real-frequency behavior of the prototype-potential function $W = V + j\Phi = \ln(\sqrt{p^2 + 1} - p)$.

an approximation band $0 < \omega < \omega_0$, this maximum obtainable magnitude of impedance is $2/(C\omega_0)$ ohms (Problems 14-137, -138, -139).

To investigate this approach, let us attempt the realization of the function (14.16–1) regarded as a driving-point impedance function, in spite of its irrationality. Since it has a real-frequency zero (at infinity) we proceed by the fundamental process of susceptance reduction (§ 8.01) and remove the pole of admittance at infinity. We have

$$Y(p) = \frac{1}{Z(p)} = \frac{1}{\sqrt{p^2 + 1} - p} = \sqrt{p^2 + 1} + p \qquad (14.16\text{–}2)$$

in which (14.12–8) has been used. The pole at infinity is evidently simple, for $Y(p)$ can be written (for large values of p) as

$$Y(p) = p\sqrt{1 + 1/p} + p$$
$$= p[1 + 1/(2p) + \cdots] + p = 2p + \tfrac{1}{2} + \cdots. \qquad (14.16\text{–}3)$$

The term to be removed corresponds to a 2-farad capacitor, Fig. 14.16–B(a), and we have

$$Y(p) = 2p + Y_1(p) \qquad (14.16\text{–}4)$$

in which the "reduced" admittance function is

$$Y_1(p) = Y(p) - 2p = \sqrt{p^2 + 1} - p. \qquad (14.16\text{–}5)$$

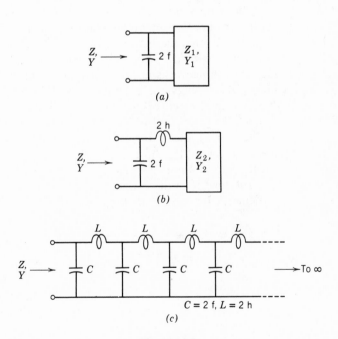

(a)

(b)

$C = 2\text{ f}, L = 2\text{ h}$

(c)

Fig. 14.16–B

This function now has a zero at infinity, i.e., the impedance function $Z_1(p)$ has a pole at infinity; we proceed to remove it in similar fashion. Since

$$Z_1(p) = \frac{1}{Y_1(p)} = \frac{1}{\sqrt{p^2 + 1} - p} = \sqrt{p^2 + 1} + p, \quad (14.16\text{-}6)$$

we find ourselves in exactly the same mathematical position as above, and we can remove a 2-henry inductor, Fig. 14.16-B(b);

$$Z_1(p) = \sqrt{p^2 + 1} + p = 2p + Z_2(p). \quad (14.16\text{-}7)$$

Now

$$Z_2(p) = Z_1(p) - 2p = \sqrt{p^2 + 1} - p$$

and

$$(14.16\text{-}8)$$

$$Y_2(p) = \frac{1}{Z_2(p)} = \frac{1}{\sqrt{p^2 + 1} - p} = \sqrt{p^2 + 1} + p.$$

We have come full circle and find in $Y_2(p)$ exactly the same admittance function as in $Y(p)$, the function from which we started. The process can be continued indefinitely, with no effective reduction, regardless of the number of cycles [a "cycle" being the removal of a capacitor and an inductor, as in Fig. 14.16-B(b)]. Evidently the presence of the radical in the p-r immittance function does not preclude realizability, though it does make necessary (by this method) an infinite number of elements; we can say, for theoretical purposes, that the infinite network of Fig. 14.16-B(c) is a realization of the driving-point impedance function (14.16-2). We shall encounter such infinite networks again in Volume II and find that they have a definite place in two-terminal-pair theory also. Here we merely observe that this infinite network offers a theoretical solution to the problem of realizing the function (14.16-2).

It is also interesting to note the mathematical equivalent of our C-L ladder-network development of the function (14.16-2). For a ladder network in general, the input immittance functions are readily written in continued-fraction form, for this is the mathematical equivalent (§§ 6.10, 7.10). Here in particular, from Fig. 14.16-B(c),

$$Y(p) = \sqrt{p^2 + 1} + p = 2p + \cfrac{1}{2p + \cfrac{1}{2p + \cfrac{1}{2p + \cfrac{1}{2p + \cfrac{1}{\ddots}}}}} \quad (14.16\text{-}9)$$

so that we have in fact made use of a continued-fraction expansion of the datum admittance function in order to realize it. This technique is not new (we used it in canonic development of L-C, R-C, and R-L driving-point immittance functions) and it is interesting to note its applicability here. As a matter of fact, all the realizations discussed in Chapter 9 are in ladder-network form (though some negative elements occur) and consequently could be developed by a continued-fraction expansion (DA 1). And many other driving-point immittance functions can be realized by this technique (FR 2).

Our aim here, however interesting the infinite-network realization may be, is to find an approximate realization that may be useful—and the infinite network is not practical. But we have not yet performed the approximation, for the infinite network is an *exact* realization of a constant magnitude in the approximation band. The approximation is evidently to be performed by the act of making the network finite: by truncating it in some manner, by cutting it at some point, and perhaps affixing a termination of some sort. Mere cutting off of the network will surely not give a very good solution, for we should then have only an L-C network (in the third canonic form of Fig. 6.10–D) with zeros and poles confined to the imaginary axis—and consequently a magnitude whose variation with frequency would be a succession of alternating zero and infinite values, a poor approximation to a constant in the approximation band. Short-circuiting at the severed end would not affect this general property, but perhaps by affixing a simple termination we can improve matters. The simplest possibility is a resistor, and the simplest value for its resistance is 1 Ω, since the nominal low-frequency value of the magnitude of the impedance is just that. This idea leads to the succession of networks of Fig. 14.16–C, with the behavior there shown. The approximation is much better than the purely L-C truncated network without the terminating resistor gives, but is still not excellent, and hardly Chebyshev in character. As one might expect, the approximation follows the function approximated quite closely at high frequencies, where the first capacitor predominates. At low frequencies the pronounced oscillations are indicative of the behavior of the truncated network without the terminating resistor.

A somewhat disturbing thought occurs here, that perhaps by moderate adjustment of the element values (in any of the networks) we can improve the approximation. But the number of possibilities, even say in the case of Z_3, is too great to discuss here. What it amounts to is that we make use of the potential analogy and the truncated continued-fraction development with resistance termination to obtain a suggested schematic diagram, the network configuration. Then, realizability being thus assured, we

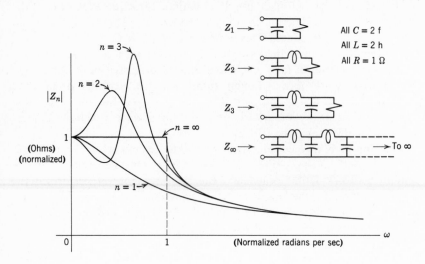

Fig. 14.16–C

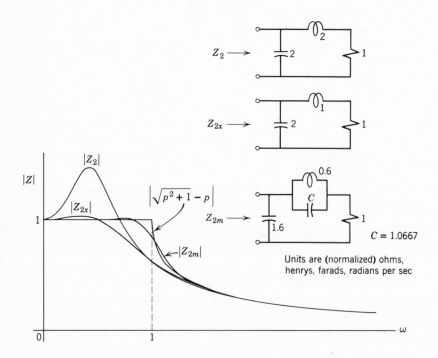

Fig. 14.16–D

apply the trial-and-error method of approximation to "optimize" the element values within the constraint of using this schematic diagram. A complete discussion of the possibilities of this we shall not attempt here. To illustrate what can be done, however, Fig. 14.16–D shows in Z_{2x} the effect of terminating the infinite network (with the 1 Ω resistor) not after the first inductor (as in Z_2 of Fig. 14.16–C) but after *one half* of the first inductor, i.e., at a point midway in the second step of the development, midway in the first series element. The result is a definite improvement, as Fig. 14.16–D shows, the large oscillation being essentially suppressed. The third curve shows the result of a different technique of improvement, to be discussed next.

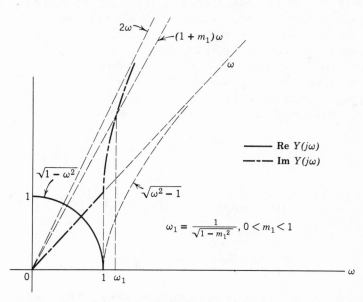

Fig. 14.16–E

One other possibility should be considered. In the discussion of realization methods for L-C driving-point immittance functions (Chapter 6) we first noted that many additional realizations could be obtained by removing not "all" of a pole but only a "part" thereof (§ 6.13). The number of elements used is increased (in comparison with a canonic form) but the vast number of possibilities offered is fascinating. So it is here: by removing only a *part* of the pole at infinity in the foregoing development we can obtain a tremendous number of other possibilities. For example, starting again from (14.16–2) which approaches $2p$ at high frequencies, by (14.16–3), we can remove not all of the pole at infinity, but only a portion, say $(1 + m_1)$ instead of 2, m_1 being a real positive number between zero and one. Then we obtain

$$Y_1(p) = Y(p) - (1 + m_1)p = \sqrt{p^2 + 1} - m_1 p,$$

$$0 < m_1 < 1, \quad (14.16\text{–}10)$$

which is still p-r, has still a pole at infinity, but has also zeros at $\pm j\omega_1 = \pm j(1 - m_1{}^2)^{-1/2}$. Figure 14.16–E shows graphically how this removing of only part of the pole at infinity shifts the zero that appeared at infinity in Y_1 of the previous development (where all the pole at infinity was removed) down to the frequency ω_1. Removing $2p$ means subtracting 2ω from $\mathbf{Im}\ Y(j\omega)$, leaving $\mathbf{Re}\ Y(j\omega)$ untouched, and the result will vanish only at infinity, since it is only there that $\mathbf{Im}\ Y(j\omega)$ reaches the line 2ω. But if $(1 + m_1)\omega$ is removed, the zero is moved in from infinity, for this line crosses $\mathbf{Im}\ Y(j\omega)$ at ω_1, the zero. This is clearly a simple zero in $Y_1(p)$ with positive derivative (from the way in which the curves cross) and can presumably be removed as a pole of $Z_1(p) = [Y_1(p)]^{-1}$. (Since these functions are not rational, it requires some extension of our previous work to show that this is true.) We find

$$Z_1(p) = \frac{1}{Y_1(p)} = \frac{1}{\sqrt{p^2 + 1} - m_1 p} = \frac{\sqrt{p^2 + 1} + m_1 p}{(1 - m_1{}^2)p^2 + 1}$$

$$= \frac{2m_1 p}{(1 - m_1{}^2)p^2 + 1} + \frac{\sqrt{p^2 + 1} - m_1 p}{(1 - m_1{}^2)p^2 + 1} \quad (14.16\text{–}11)$$

$$= \frac{\left(\dfrac{2m_1}{1 - m_1{}^2}\right) p}{p^2 + \omega_1{}^2} + \frac{1}{\sqrt{p^2 + 1} + m_1 p}.$$

The pole at $j\omega_1$ (together with its mate at $-j\omega_1$) has been extracted by the device of observing the amount necessary to subtract from the numerator of $Z_1(p)$ in order that the remainder have a zero there, so that the pole is entirely removed; the straightforward calculation of the residue gives, of course, the same result. It is clear that the term removed corresponds to a realizable parallel L-C combination of the usual form, with the element values (L_2, C_2) shown in Fig. 14.16–F. It is also clear from (14.16–11) that the remaining impedance is not substantially different from that from which we started. In fact, we have

$$Y_2(p) = \sqrt{p^2 + 1} + m_1 p = (1 + m_1 p) + (\sqrt{p^2 + 1} - p) \quad (14.16\text{–}12)$$

so that we could resume the original development and continue to infinity in the manner of Fig. 14.16–F. The interesting possibility is that we may obtain a better result by terminating (with a resistor) somewhere in the novel part of this network, somewhere between the vertical dashed lines where the impedance presented by the infinite network is different from that previously presented. We might terminate midway between these lines, for example, using only "half" of the L_2-C_2 network; the result is shown in Fig. 14.16–D (as Z_{2m}), for illustration. Here again, the value of m_1 must be determined by trial, and we have once more to explore the possibilities of modifying all the element values in other ways. The

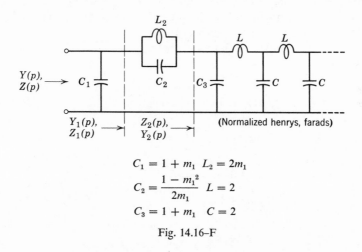

$$C_1 = 1 + m_1 \quad L_2 = 2m_1$$
$$C_2 = \frac{1 - m_1^2}{2m_1} \quad L = 2$$
$$C_3 = 1 + m_1 \quad C = 2$$

Fig. 14.16–F

infinity of other possibilities here, some of which may be better, we do not discuss. The modifications shown in Fig. 14.16–D as Z_{2x} and Z_{2m} are illustrative of what can be done; only experience can give the feeling for the effects of element-value changes that is necessary for a good understanding and efficient prosecution of this trial-and-error method of approximation.

The basis of the improvement obtained by Z_{2m} in Fig. 14.16–D over that of the third case of Fig. 14.16–C (which uses the same number of elements) is the alteration of the impedance presented (to the right) by the infinite network of Fig. 14.16–B(c) at any element, and that presented by the infinite network of Fig. 14.16–F at a point between the vertical dashed lines, which are rather different. If one of these impedances more closely resembles that of the resistor which replaces the infinite network (i.e., if the resistor provides a more accurate termination), then the driving-point impedance of the terminated (finite) network should be closer to $Y(p)$, which we seek—for $Y(p)$ is the same in both cases, when the infinite networks are used. Not only is a variety of possibilities afforded by variation of the element values from those obtained by simply truncating these networks (a matter for investigation by trial), but another series of possibilities is offered by continuation of the process by which the $Y(p)$ realization of Fig. 14.16–B(c) was changed into that of Fig. 14.16–F, the removal of only a part of a pole. Some of these may present impedance even closer to that of a resistor at various intermediate points, and hence offer, in terminated form, better finite-network approximations to $Y(p)$. We may proceed as before by removing only a part of the pole at infinity in $Y(p)$, i.e., by removing $C_1 = (1 + m_1)$ instead of $C = 2$; and then, instead of removing all of the pole at ω_1 as in (14.16–11) and Fig. 14.16–F, we may remove only part of it.

The analytic development is first, as before,

$$Y(p) = \sqrt{p^2 + 1} + p = (1 + m_1)p + (\sqrt{p^2 + 1} - m_1 p)$$
$$= C_1 p + Y_1(p). \tag{14.16–13}$$

Then we write

$$Z_1(p) = \frac{1}{\sqrt{p^2 + 1} - m_1 p} = \frac{\sqrt{p^2 + 1} + m_1 p}{(1 - m_1^2)p^2 + 1}$$
$$= \frac{\left(\dfrac{m_1 + m_2}{1 - m_1^2}\right) p}{p^2 + \omega_1^2} + Z_2(p) \tag{14.16–14}$$

in which

$$\omega_1^2 = \frac{1}{1 - m_1^2} \tag{14.16–15}$$

and we have extracted not the whole of the pole at $j\omega_1$, but only a part of it. If the new parameter m_2 is equal to m_1, the whole of the pole is removed; if $0 < m_2 < m_1$, as we now assume, only a part of it is removed (Figs. 14.16–G, –H). The advantage of this partial extraction is, just as before, that it creates a new zero in the remaining impedance Z_2 (or a pole in Y_2) at an internal frequency ω_2 (Fig. 14.16–G). In developing Y_2 we can accordingly remove this pole (or a part of it), as well as the pole at infinity (or part of it). The number of possibilities rises rapidly, and we shall only indicate briefly how the development may be made. We have

$$Z_2(p) = \frac{\sqrt{p^2 + 1} - m_2 p}{(1 - m_1^2)p^2 + 1} \tag{14.16–16}$$

and

$$Y_2(p) = \frac{(1 - m_1{}^2)p^2 + 1}{\sqrt{p^2 + 1} - m_2 p} = \frac{[(1 - m_1{}^2)p^2 + 1](\sqrt{p^2 + 1} + m_2 p)}{(1 - m_2{}^2)p^2 + 1}$$

$$= \frac{\left[\dfrac{2m_2(m_1{}^2 - m_2{}^2)}{(1 - m_2{}^2)^2}\right] p}{p^2 + \omega_2{}^2} + \left(\frac{1 - m_1{}^2}{1 - m_2}\right) p + Y_3(p), \qquad (14.16\text{--}17)$$

in which

$$\omega_2{}^2 = \frac{1}{1 - m_2{}^2},$$

and $Y_3(p)$ has no poles at $\pm j\omega_2$ or at infinity.   Figure 14.16–H shows (in L_3, C_3, and $C_3{}'$) the removal of the poles of Y_2.   If these are only

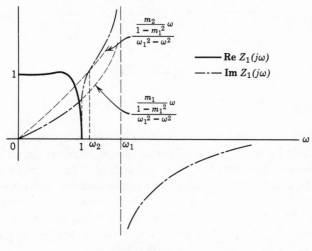

Fig. 14.16–G

partially removed, zeros can be created in Y_3 and removed as poles of Z_3 in the next step, with attendant variations in the impedance.   The process can be carried on indefinitely, though the complexity increases rapidly, and the number of parameters to be determined by trial soon becomes large.   Nevertheless, these possibilities should not be overlooked, for the quality of approximation improves.

The most interesting feature of the foregoing development is its novel approach to the approximation problem.   Normally, and logically, we solve the approximation problem first and obtain a realizable function—

and then proceed to its realization. But here this sequence is reversed. The realization is made first (and requires an infinite network because a nonrational function cannot be realized with a finite number of our network elements). Then the approximation is made, by the process of truncating the infinite network and substituting, for the infinite part discarded, some simple termination (here a resistor). The quality of approximation cannot be predicted, nor is it necessarily good. This

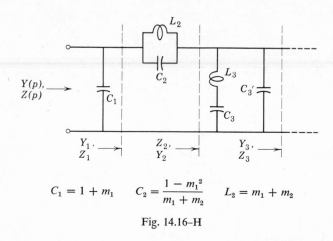

$$C_1 = 1 + m_1 \qquad C_2 = \frac{1 - m_1{}^2}{m_1 + m_2} \qquad L_2 = m_1 + m_2$$

Fig. 14.16–H

method does, however, give an excellent starting point for a series of trials, to be made by moderate variations of the values of the elements given by this process. In cases where the magnitude of a driving-point immittance is involved, and hence whether a given approximating function is realizable is not evident but requires a good deal of calculation to determine, this method has its advantages. It is an imaginative approach, this of realization first and approximation second, but not without merit; we shall find further use for it in Volume II.

Networks whose driving-point immittance functions approximate a constant are of use in vacuum-tube amplifiers where the performance is essentially proportional to the driving-point impedance of a two-terminal interstage network (§ 11.05). Curves illustrating to some extent the possibilities obtainable by this method are available (BO 2), but the fact remains that, even in the low-band case, a good deal of approximation by trial is still required after the general schematic diagram and approximate element values have been obtained by the process of truncating an exact realization in infinite-network form.

For the internal-band case we can obtain immediate results by a frequency transformation of any low-band design (Problem 14-96). The number of elements is essentially doubled thereby, introducing further possibilities for "tinkering" to obtain improvement. If one is willing to investigate further, a fresh start from the appropriate internal-band function corresponding to (14.16–1) will indicate a vast number of other possibilities, not obtainable by frequency transformation.

We have now completed our discussion of the approximation of a constant with an even function. If the result is to be realized as a driving-point resistance (conductance), the procedure is straightforward, though perhaps lengthy. If the realization is to be as the magnitude of a driving-point immittance, the difficulty of predicting realizability forces us to use different methods—and here the process of trial and error becomes very important. It lacks the elegance of the other methods but we may be forced to use it in cases where realizability is not apparent and we must, in effect, work from a schematic diagram to insure realizability.

To complete the discussion of approximation of a constant, we must next consider the possibility of approximating it with an *odd* function.

14.17 Odd-function approximation of a constant—I

Of the four restrictions listed in (14.11–5), we have now effectively removed three: using even functions we have been able to approximate an arbitrary constant, taking account of arbitrarily prescribed zeros, in low, internal, and other approximation bands. The next step is to discuss the use of *odd* functions in approximation of a constant, for it may well be necessary (AN 1) to find a network whose reactance (susceptance) or angle must approximate a constant in some band of frequencies—and these are odd functions of frequency. With these parts of an immittance function we do not have the difficulty of § 14.16, for realizability of the associated immittance function is evident from the reactance (susceptance) or (tangent of) angle functions themselves (§ 8.16).

If the approximation band is a low band, centered on the origin, the constant to be approximated must be *zero*, for no other finite constant meets the requirement of odd symmetry. (True, it may be required to approximate infinity, but then it must be "$+\infty$" on one side of the origin and "$-\infty$" on the other that is approximated; such a problem is best handled by considering its reciprocal, i.e., approximating zero and then inverting the result.) This alters the application of our potential-analogy method of approximation somewhat, but not greatly. We begin by placing a prototype conductor on the approximation band as before. But its (distributed) charge must now be *negative*, in order to obtain zeros on or near it after quantization—as we must if the quantized exponential potential is to approximate zero. There must in fact be a zero at the origin in the final result, since it is to be an odd function, and this further requires that the total amount of (negative) charge be an odd integer. We accordingly place a charge $Q = -(2m + 1)$ on the approximation-band conductor; the complementary charge of $+(2m + 1)$ units we place for the moment at infinity, and this is the prototype situation. Quantization proceeds more or less as before, except that it takes place *on* the conductor; i.e., we take $V_0 = 0$ and do not move the lumped charges out on the flux lines of the prototype problem, but keep them on the approximation band, in order that it be zero and not some constant unequal to zero that is approximated. And since we wish the quantized charges to be single units (in the interests of efficient approximation) and not the double units that would result from merely following our previous process with $V_0 = 0$, their locations are determined in a slightly different manner.

The function Φ represents the flux emanating from, say, the right side of the conductor. If we look now at the charge distributed on the conductor, its value is determined by 2Φ, since there are two infinitesimal layers of charge, one on each of the right and left surfaces of the conductor, and these are only an infinitesimal distance apart. The charge, which can be considered as the source of the field, can consequently be thought of as a simple layer of infinitesimal thickness on the ω axis, of density ρ (charge units per unit ω) such that the total charge q between the origin and some point ω is given by

$$q = \int_0^\omega \rho \, d\omega = 2 \left(\frac{\Phi}{2\pi} \right) \qquad (14.17\text{--}1)$$

(for each unit of charge emanates 2π units of flux). Alternatively, we may adopt the Riemann-surface point of view, cut the ramps joining the two sheets at the branch cut (the approximation band), and sew them together with a charge distribution that will give the same exterior potential. To quantize we merely determine sets of adjacent points between which the total charge is unity and place a quantized (unit) charge at the center of charge of each interval (cf. § 14.05), being careful to obtain the necessary over-all symmetry. Since the number of quantized charges is odd, there will be one at the origin, and the others will be at the points where

$$q = 1, 2, 3, \cdots, n$$

or $(14.17\text{--}2)$

$$\Phi = \pm\pi, \pm 2\pi, \pm 3\pi, \cdots, \pm n\pi.$$

Figure 14.17–A shows both the prototype problem and curves illustrating the quantization process. The charge at the origin is the quantization of that part of the prototype distributed charge that lies in the region $-\omega_{1/2} < 0 < +\omega_{1/2}$, i.e., the unit of distributed charge that is

centered on the origin; the charge at $j\omega_1$ is the quantization of the prototype charge that lies in $\omega_{1/2} < \omega < \omega_{3/2}$, etc. An alternate process is to
look at the charge density function, $\rho = dq/d\omega$, and to quantize at centers
of area under the curve, since area here represents charge; this is also
shown in Fig. 14.17–A. Either viewpoint leads to (14.17–2) as the

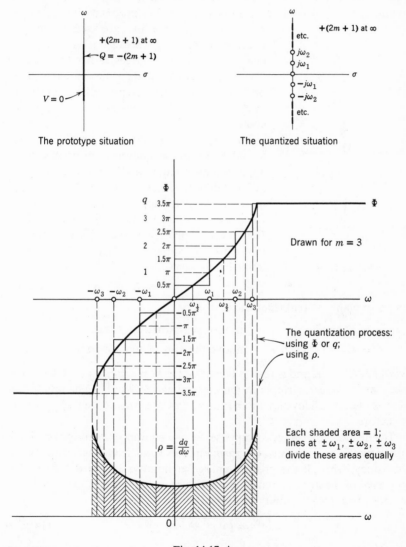

Fig. 14.17–A

equation of quantization, which evidently can also be written in any of the following forms.

$$e^W = \pm 1 \quad \text{or} \quad \cosh W \pm 1 = 0,$$
$$e^{2W} = 1 \quad \text{or} \quad \cosh^2 W - 1 = 0. \tag{14.17-3}$$

The second form is that corresponding to our previous version [see, e.g., the denominators of (14.12–36, –37)], in which ϵ is now unity (corresponding to $V_0 = 0$ or to quantization *on* the approximation band) and

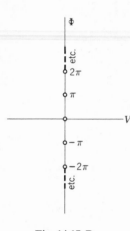

Fig. 14.17–B

both odd and even π lines are used in the quantization in order to "spread out" the quantized charges into single charges rather than double. The quantized charge distribution can evidently be looked on as the "step-function" approximation to the original distributed charge, also shown in Fig. 14.17–A.

The rational function with these zeros (obtained by the above quantization process on the approximation band) and the prescribed poles (all at infinity) is then the result of the approximation, and it approximates zero in the Chebyshev fashion in the approximation band. For in the W plane we have, after quantization, the situation shown in Fig. 14.17–B, which immediately gives us

$$e^{W_q} = K \sinh W. \tag{14.17-4}$$

In the p plane, at real frequencies, this is

$$e^{W_q} = K' \sin \Phi \qquad \text{in the approximation band}$$
$$= K'(-1)^m \cosh V \qquad \text{above the approximation band,} \tag{14.17-5}$$

in which $K' = jK$ and is real. The constant K' is arbitrary and determines the size of the error ripple in the approximation band. The approximation is clearly Chebyshev in character, and the general behavior is much as before.

To illustrate the process, suppose we use an approximating function of order five ($n = 2$). For an approximation band from the origin to unit frequency, with all the positive charge at infinity, and zero taken as the potential of the approximation-band conductor, the prototype exponential is, from Fig. 14.17–C and (14.12–8)

$$e^W = (\sqrt{p^2 + 1} + p)^5. \tag{14.17-6}$$

The flux plot is that of Fig. 14.04–D, the equipotentials being ellipses and the flux lines the orthogonal hyperbolas. The behavior of the complex potential on the ω axis is shown in Fig. 14.17–C, which also shows the quantization process. The equation of quantization is here

$$\cosh W = \cos \Phi = \pm 1 \qquad (14.17\text{–}7)$$

all of whose roots are in the approximation band. This is readily solved by rewriting it as

$$\cos (5 \sin^{-1} \omega) = \pm 1 \qquad (14.17\text{–}8)$$

whose roots are the p-plane points

$$p = 0,\ 0 \pm j \sin (\pi/5),\ 0 \pm j \sin (2\pi/5). \qquad (14.17\text{–}9)$$

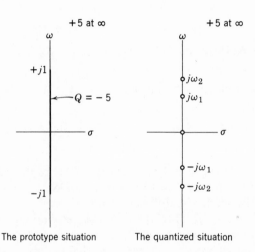

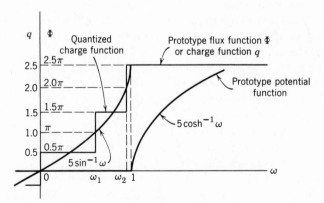

Fig. 14.17–C

The result of this approximation procedure is thus

$$e^{W_q} = Kp(p^2 + \omega_1{}^2)(p^2 + \omega_2{}^2), \qquad (14.17\text{--}10)$$

whose real-frequency behavior is shown in Fig. 14.17–D. For plotting purposes the alternative forms

$$
\begin{aligned}
e^{W_q} &= K' \sin (5 \sin^{-1} \omega), & 0 < \omega < 1 \\
&= K' \cosh (5 \cosh^{-1} \omega), & 1 < \omega & \qquad (14.17\text{--}11) \\
&= K'\omega(\omega^2 - \omega_1{}^2)(\omega^2 - \omega_2{}^2), & \text{for all } \omega
\end{aligned}
$$

are convenient. This illustration is easily generalized to the case $Q = -(2m + 1)$, the complementary charge still being kept at infinity, to

$$
\begin{aligned}
e^{W_q} &= -jK'p(p^2 + \omega_1{}^2)(p^2 + \omega_2{}^2) \cdots (p^2 + \omega_m{}^2), \\
\omega_r &= \sin [r\pi/(2m + 1)], \qquad (14.17\text{--}12)
\end{aligned}
$$

in which K' is real but otherwise arbitrary, with the special forms for real frequencies,

$$
\begin{aligned}
e^W &= K' \sin [(2m + 1) \sin^{-1} \omega], & 0 < \omega < 1, \\
&= K' \cosh [(2m + 1) \cosh^{-1} \omega], & 1 < \omega, \\
&= (-1)^m K'\omega(\omega^2 - \omega_1{}^2)(\omega^2 - \omega_2{}^2) \cdots (\omega^2 - \omega_m{}^2), & \text{all } \omega.
\end{aligned}
$$
$$(14.17\text{--}13)$$

These functions evidently are closely related to the odd-order Chebyshev polynomials met in § 14.10 (Problem 14-35), which is not surprising in view of the similarity of the problems.

The function (14.17–11) is realizable as the tangent of the angle of a driving-point immittance, as the third form in (14.17–13) shows (§ 8.16). If it is desired to design a network whose angle approximates zero in a low band and then tends to ±90°, such a network can be designed by assigning a suitable sign and numerical value to K', taking this function as the tangent of the immittance angle and determining the corresponding immittance function by the methods of § 8.14, and proceeding to a network realization in the most appropriate fashion. The zeros and poles of the immittance function will lie on an ellipse, the principal difference from the results of § 14.09 being that here both zeros and poles of the immittance function lie on the ellipse, in alternating fashion.

The function (14.17–11) is not, however, realizable as a driving-point reactance (susceptance) function, because of the multiple pole at infinity. Real-frequency poles are not allowed in such functions unless they are simple and have residues (in ω) that are real and negative—and infinity is included in the category of real frequencies (§ 8.16). We shall discuss how it may be modified, in a moment.

The general approximation obtained above is made with a rational function of order $(2m + 1)$. Of the $[2(2m + 1) + 1]$ parameters generally available in such a function, one is used in requiring a zero at the origin, one in requiring a pole at infinity, one (the multiplier) is of no help in improving the quality of approximation, and of the $4m$ remaining, half

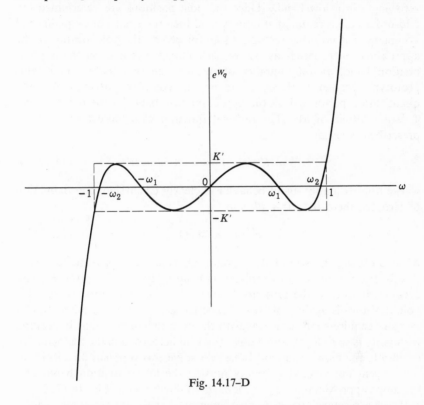

Fig. 14.17–D

must be expended in assuring odd symmetry, leaving only $2m$. Of these we have used m in placing the poles at infinity, so that the approximation is only of quality m, i.e., there are m zeros of error in the approximation band. To be sure, the zero at the origin contributes one more, so that $(m + 1)$ is a better measure of the quality, the number of zeros of error. Moreover, the m parameters expended above in placing poles at infinity cannot be used to improve the quality of approximation, for it is an odd rational function (zero) that we are approximating, and the poles are thus arbitrary in the approximation process, exactly as with even-function approximation of a constant.

We are free, then, to place the poles at points other than infinity, if we wish. They can be anywhere, so long as quadrantal symmetry is pre-served (the coefficients in the result must be real, and odd symmetry is required) and a pole of odd order is kept at infinity, and the result will be realizable as the tangent of a driving-point immittance angle (§ 8.16). This leads to an infinite variety of possibilities for the approximation of a zero angle in a low band. Once the pole positions are determined (an odd-order pole is required at infinity, and the others must have quadrantal symmetry, but no other restrictions are placed on the pole locations), the approximation proceeds as before: a conductor is laid on the approx-imation band, an odd number of negative charges placed on it, this prototype problem solved to obtain its complex potential W, and quantization performed on the approximation band (at the points where Φ is a multiple of π). The rational function with these zeros and the prescribed poles is

$$e^{W_q} = K \sinh W = -jK' \sinh W \qquad (14.17\text{–}14)$$

whose approximation-band behavior is clearly Chebyshev approximation of zero, for there $W = 0 + j\Phi$ and

$$e^{W_q} = K' \sin \Phi, \qquad (14.17\text{–}15)$$

K' determining the size of the ripple. Outside the approximation band this function increases (or decreases, depending on the sign given K') and becomes infinite at the prescribed poles. The determination of suitable pole positions is again a matter of experience or trial, or of other supple-mentary requirements, as it was with the even functions. One interesting possibility is so to locate these poles (by trial here, though the mathematics of elliptic functions when available will solve this problem directly) that the tangent approximates infinity outside the approximation band, and the angle approximates 90°, in the fashion illustrated in Fig. 14.17–E.

If it is a reactance (susceptance) function that we are designing, we are still free to locate the poles provided that we are careful about those on the ω axis. We need one at infinity, which must be simple, and the function must be positive at high frequencies. If any others are placed on the ω axis, they too must be simple, and the function must be positive just below the pole and negative just above it (in the manner of the pure reactance functions of Chapter 6, because of the requirement on the residue). This necessitates that we have zeros between two such poles, so that for the sort of problem we are discussing here, such poles will not be used. Except for the pole required at infinity, and this prohibition of other real-frequency poles, the location of the poles of a reactance (sus-ceptance) function is arbitrary and the number of possibilities infinite.

The function (14.17–11) can be made realizable as a driving-point reactance (susceptance) function simply by repeating the approximation with all poles but one moved away from infinity and off the ω axis. If they are very close to this axis the function will still be realizable, but one can naturally expect unrealistic element values for pole positions very close to

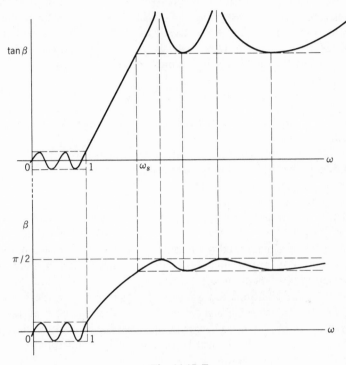

Fig. 14.17–E

the axis, since the function becomes unrealizable when the poles are *on* the axis. In designing a reactance (susceptance) function that approximates zero in a low band, then, it is well to place the poles (apart from that at infinity) well away from the ω axis. The number of possibilities is infinite and we shall not explore the matter further. The actual network design, of course, requires the determination of the associated immittance function (§ 8.12) and its realization.

Maximal (Taylor) approximation of zero requires simply the compression of the approximation band to a point. In the prototype situation, then, the $(2m + 1)$ negative charges are lumped at the origin, the positive charges are located at the prescribed pole positions, and the result is immediately

$$e^{W_q} = \frac{Kp^{2m+1}}{1 + b_2 p^2 + b_4 p^4 + \cdots + b_{2m} p^{2m}} \qquad (14.17\text{-}16)$$

in which the zeros of the denominator are the prescribed (finite) pole positions. No "quantization" is necessary, just as no motion out from the conductor was necessary in the Chebyshev case. The quality of approximation is now $(2m + 1)$ instead of $(m + 1)$, for the collapse of the approximation band into a point gives us the gratuitous aid of the negative half of the approximation band, exactly as in § 14.15. Near the origin, we have

$$e^{W_q} = (-1)^m K' \omega^{2m+1} + \cdots \qquad (14.17\text{-}17)$$

(with $K' = jK$) which shows that $(2m + 1)$ terms of the Taylor series are matched.

High-band approximation with odd functions involves only a simple frequency transformation of a low-band design (Problems 14-96, -144) and requires no further comment here.

If the approximation band is internal, approximation of a constant with an odd function may take on quite a different character (§ 14.18). But if the constant to be approximated is zero, we have still an odd rational function to approximate, and the anomalies we have encountered are still present: only half (approximately) of the parameters can be used in the approximation, for most of the poles and the multiplier are arbitrary. Chebyshev approximations are obtained by quantizing on the prototype conductors (each of which may now carry either an odd or an even number of units of negative charge) in the presence of positive charges at the prescribed poles (which must include the origin and infinity). (If it is desired to approximate infinity, as for an angle to approximate 90°, a suitable approximation to zero can be made and then inverted.) Realizability must of course be considered, and the poles located consistently with the nature of the problem, as reactance (susceptance) or angle approximation.

14.18 Odd-function approximation of a constant—II

The constant to be approximated in an *internal* band need not be zero, however, and in general it will not be. Then we are approximating an even rational function (the nonzero constant) with an odd rational function, and the possibility of a perfect solution no longer exists. Consequently, some of the anomalies disappear. In particular, we shall find that now neither poles nor zeros are arbitrary (if the approximation is to be most efficient), in that all zeros and all poles may be put to work to achieve the best quality of approximation within the constraint of odd symmetry. This makes this particular approximation problem both more interesting and somewhat more difficult (exactly as we found in § 13.10).

We may begin by attempting the solution of this approximation problem by the methods we found so successful when the approximating function was even. Suppose, for example, that our function is to be of order eight, and that we wish three of the eight zeros to be at the origin, five at infinity. (The number of zeros at each of these points must be odd, for the function is to be odd.) Let the approximation band extend from ω_1 to ω_2 and place a conductor on it, positively charged with four units of charge, the other four units of positive charge being of necessity on a symmetrical conductor in the lower half plane (Fig. 14.18–A). As before, we now quantize the positive charge and imagine the lumped charges to move out on appropriate flux lines of the prototype problem until the appropriate equipotential is reached, say that on which $V = -V_0$. Looking for the moment only at the upper conductor, we see that the appropriate flux lines here are those on which $\Phi = +\pi/2, -3\pi/2, +5\pi/2, +9\pi/2$, as Fig. 14.18–A shows. (The positive real axis has been taken as the zero flux line, and the values of Φ shown are those associated with branch cuts on the negative real axis and on the imaginary axis for $|\omega| > \omega_1$; in the exponential-potential function the choice of branch cuts is of course immaterial.) These are chosen, as before, to give symmetry; they are equally spaced (fluxwise) around the conductor at intervals of 2π, so that equal vertical spacings result in the W plane and the series is oriented to place the left-half-plane and right-half-plane quantized charges at symmetrical positions in the p plane. In the W plane we have again vertical series of equally spaced positive charges, for which we obtain as the quantized exponential potential

$$e^{W_q} = \frac{\text{constant}}{\cosh\,[W - j(\pi/2)] - \cosh V_0}. \qquad (14.18\text{–}1)$$

This function behaves, at real frequencies, exactly as we wish, approximating a constant in the Chebyshev fashion in the approximation band, and falling off outside. Our difficulties arise in the conversion of this function to the rational function we ultimately want.

To begin with, the points in the lower half plane at which the function (14.18–1) becomes infinite must be where $V = -V_0$ and $\Phi = +5\pi/2$, $+\pi/2, -3\pi/2, -9\pi/2$. These are also shown in Fig. 14.18–A. They definitely do not suit us because they are not symmetrical with respect to the first (upper-half-plane) set of points; any rational function with these eight poles would have some nonreal coefficients. More than that, we find on calculation that (14.18-1) is not even rational. Consequently, this method of finding Chebyshev approximations, that works so nicely in the case of even functions, fails completely, for our purposes, when odd

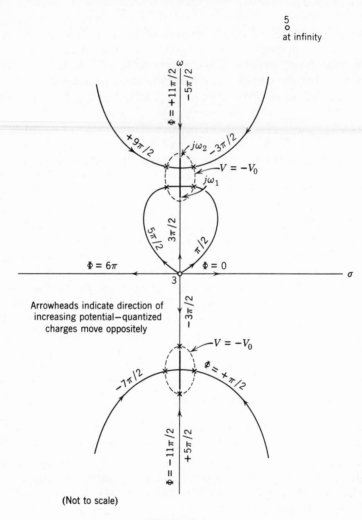

Fig. 14.18-A

functions are used. The cause is basically in the odd symmetry (as between upper and lower halves of the plane) of the flux function (which leads to complications in the Riemann surface representation of the W plane). It can also be said to arise from the impossibility of finding symmetrical paths for the quantized charges to follow in their journey from the prototype conductors to the lumped negative charges: that at the origin can receive only three positive charges, and there is no way in which an odd number of charges can approach with the quadrantal symmetry we need. Similar difficulties arise whenever the number of charges at the origin (or at infinity) is odd, as it inevitably is with odd functions.

We need now to find a way to circumvent these difficulties caused by odd symmetry. One approach would be simply to form a rational function with the prescribed zeros, the four upper-half-plane poles of Fig. 14.18–A, and four symmetrically located lower half plane poles (rather than the lower-half-plane poles of Fig. 14.18–A). This cannot be expected to give us truly Chebyshev approximation, but might yield a fairly good approximation thereto. This method may sometimes be of use, but does not, of course, solve the problem of finding true Chebyshev approximations. There seems to be no method of predicting the error function it does yield, other than by actual computation of the behavior of the rational function so constructed.

The principal difficulty is caused by the fact that the origin (and infinity) have an odd number of negative charges and therefore must ultimately (for infinitesimal ripple ϵ) receive an odd number of quantized positive charges. It is this odd-number requirement that causes the method to fail. In order to restore quadrantal symmetry in the trajectories it would be necessary to quantize on a finer scale, say in *half-unit* charges rather than in full units. The general principles of quantization do not depend on the strength of the lumped charges, so that we can easily carry out such a novel quantization process—and we can now have quadrantal symmetry, since the origin (and infinity) will receive an *even* number of such half-unit positive charges, each unit of negative charge attracting two half-unit positive charges. The disadvantage of such a procedure is that it leads to an array of (satisfactory) integral negative charges and of (unsatisfactory) half-integral positive charges, the exponential potential of which is not a rational function. But the trajectories followed by quantized positive charges need not always be independent paths that do not meet. In the even-function case it is possible to have, say, two zeros at the origin and two at infinity, and in such a case the trajectories must be as shown in Fig. 14.18–B. The charges must approach the origin along the real axis (the imaginary axis is also a possibility, but of no interest here). In order to reach it they first follow the curved paths to the points SP (which are saddle points of the prototype field) where two charges join momentarily to form a double charge, then follow the real axis, one to the origin and one to infinity on each side. This sort of behavior occurs whenever

the charge at the origin (or infinity) is twice an odd integer and in it lies
the key to the resolution of our difficulty with odd functions.

Half-unit charges imply square roots in the exponential potentials and
consequently are not admissible.   But if four half-unit charges follow the
trajectories of Fig. 14.18–B, there is one point at which they merge and

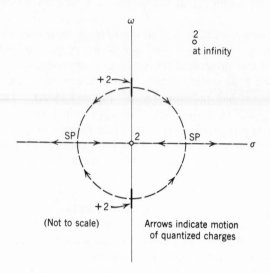

(Not to scale)   Arrows indicate motion
                      of quantized charges

Fig. 14.18–B

become two *unit* charges (at the points SP).   If we can force the positive
charge, quantized in half units, all to follow trajectories like these and if
the mergings occur simultaneously, then there will be one value of V_0
(i.e., of ϵ) for which the result is a rational function.   For this to occur
it is necessary that the trajectories fall in a highly cooperative pattern, for
in general there will not be enough saddle points SP and even if there are
enough, they will not all be reached simultaneously.   It is at this point
that the zeros of the function can be put to work.   For the zeros are the
terminal points of the trajectories—and their locations have tremendous
influence on the nature of these paths.   Of all the possible positions the
set of zeros of a function can take, there may be some that will give us sets
of trajectories, all of the character of those in Fig. 14.18–B.   And if one
(or more) of these solutions is such that the quantized half-unit positive
charges all reach saddle points simultaneously, our difficulty is resolved.
There is indeed such a solution, and its existence shows why the zeros are
no longer fully arbitrary, when it is an *odd* function that approximates the
constant: by making use of these zeros in a certain way, the quality of

approximation can be greatly improved and all the parameters of the function exploited.

In a general way we can see that the zeros should be on the real axis. For if they are located there, as in Fig. 14.18–C, all of the positive half-unit

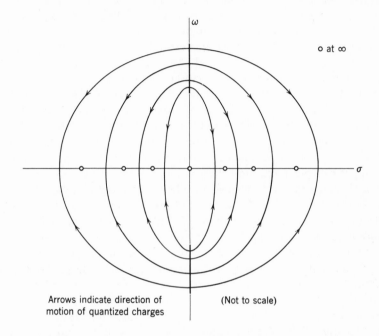

Arrows indicate direction of   (Not to scale)
motion of quantized charges

Fig. 14.18–C

charges will be enticed down to saddle points that lie between the negative charges (zeros). If the positive charges all reach the real-axis saddle points simultaneously (for the same value of V_0, i.e., of ϵ), then at that moment an odd rational function is formed that approximates a constant in the internal approximation band in Chebyshev fashion. There will be one maximum of error in the approximation band for each half unit of positive charge on one side of the prototype conductor (in the W plane there is a maximum of potential at each approximation-band point that is opposite a quantized charge). Consequently, the number of zeros of error in the approximation band will be twice this number, i.e., four times the number of units of positive charge on one side of the prototype conductor, or the total number of full units of positive charge on both prototype conductors. But this is the order of the function. Since the total number of parameters in a function is one more than twice its order, and since the multiplier is of no help and half the zeros and half the poles are fixed by the requirement of odd symmetry, the number of parameters available is equal to the order of the function and no greater. Hence this approximation uses all the parameters available and cannot be improved in quality. In Fig. 14.18–C the order of the approximating function is taken to be 8; of its 17 parameters, 1 is the multiplier, 4 zeros and 4 poles are determined by symmetry when the other 4 zeros and 4 poles are located, and only 8 parameters are available for approximation. There will be 4 maxima of error and 8 zeros of error in the approximation band, the highest quality approximation obtainable.

A little consideration of Fig. 14.18–C shows that zero locations off the real axis will reduce the quality of approximation obtained, and that all the zeros should be simple as well as real. Then the half-unit charges from the lower half plane contribute to the Chebyshev ripples in the (upper-half-plane) approximation band also, in that they make those from the upper half plane into unit charges and hence give a useful result. The zeros, then, are not arbitrary but must be located to give a flux plot of the sort shown in Fig. 14.18–C, with the added stipulation that the prototype potential be the same at all the saddle points. There is then but one solution for a given approximation band and order of approximating function, and only one value of ϵ. Since we are no longer free (as with even functions) to locate the zeros arbitrarily, it is not surprising that we are not free to specify ϵ either. Nor, for the same reason, have we any control over the rate of falloff outside the approximation band.

It remains only to calculate the positions required for the zeros. Given their locations, the approximation procedure will be substantially as before, except that V_0 has one definite value and is not arbitrary. We can start by giving the negative-charge (zero) positions literal values, carrying these symbols through the quantization process, and finally requiring that the equation of quantization have only real, double roots. This procedure will give us both the points of quantization (poles) *and* the required zeros, and the value of V_0 or ϵ, so that the problem is solved. Unfortunately, the algebra becomes involved, and calls for the solution of nonlinear simultaneous equations. For example, suppose we use an approximating function of order four. One zero will be at the origin and one at infinity (as required) and two zeros at some real points $\pm a$ (Fig. 14.18–D). The value of a is to be such that, on half-unit quantization, the positive charge distributed on the conductors will move on the flux lines as shown, two pairs reaching the points $(\pm b, 0)$ and the other two pairs the points $(\pm c, 0)$ simultaneously. Not only are b and c unknown; the "prescribed" zero position a is also unknown. We can determine all of these unknowns by following the quantization procedure below. For the exponential potential of the prototype problem we have, following (14.14–10) with forms and exponents appropriate to single charges at the origin, infinity, and $(\pm a, 0)$,

$$e^W = \left[\frac{+\sqrt{\dfrac{p^2 + \omega_1{}^2}{p^2 + \omega_2{}^2}} - \dfrac{\omega_1}{\omega_2}}{+\sqrt{\dfrac{p^2 + \omega_1{}^2}{p^2 + \omega_2{}^2}} + \dfrac{\omega_1}{\omega_2}} \right]^{1/2} \left[\frac{+\sqrt{\dfrac{p^2 + \omega_1{}^2}{p^2 + \omega_2{}^2}} - 1}{+\sqrt{\dfrac{p^2 + \omega_1{}^2}{p^2 + \omega_2{}^2}} + 1} \right]^{1/2}$$

$$\times \left[\frac{+\sqrt{\dfrac{p^2 + \omega_1{}^2}{p^2 + \omega_2{}^2}} - +\sqrt{\dfrac{a^2 + \omega_1{}^2}{a^2 + \omega_2{}^2}}}{+\sqrt{\dfrac{p^2 + \omega_1{}^2}{p^2 + \omega_2{}^2}} + +\sqrt{\dfrac{a^2 + \omega_1{}^2}{a^2 + \omega_2{}^2}}} \right] . \quad (14.18\text{–}2)$$

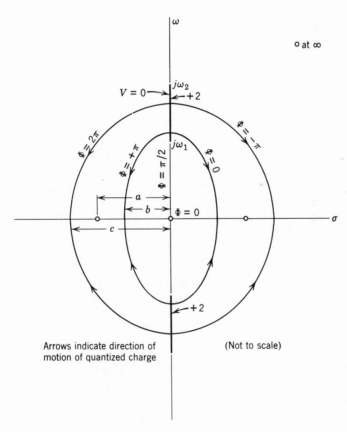

Arrows indicate direction of motion of quantized charge

(Not to scale)

Fig. 14.18–D

Quantization (in half-unit charges) is to be at the points determined by (cf. Fig. 14.18–D)

$$V = -V_0, \qquad \Phi = 2\pi, \pi, 0, -\pi, \qquad (14.18\text{-}3)$$

in which V_0 is unknown, but must be that value that corresponds to the points $(\pm b, 0)$, $(\pm c, 0)$ where the charges "join up," which they are to do simultaneously. For convenience we square (14.18–2) and work in terms of e^{2W}; this brings us, in effect, back to an even-function approximation problem with zeros prescribed, two at the origin, two at infinity, and two each at $(\pm a, 0)$, and the requirement that a and V_0 be selected for (simultaneous) junction of the upper-half-plane and lower-half-plane quantized (unit) charges. On rationalizing and multiplying out, we obtain

$$e^{2W} = \frac{A + B\sqrt{\dfrac{p^2 + \omega_1{}^2}{p^2 + \omega_2{}^2}}}{C} \qquad (14.18\text{-}4)$$

in which A, B, and C are even polynomials in p, and

$$e^{-2W} = \frac{A - B\sqrt{\dfrac{p^2 + \omega_1{}^2}{p^2 + \omega_2{}^2}}}{C}. \qquad (14.18\text{-}5)$$

The equation of quantization (14.18–3) can be written

$$\begin{aligned}
\cosh 2W &= \cosh\,[2(-V_0 + jm\pi)], \qquad m = -1, 0, +1, +2 \\
&= \cosh 2V_0
\end{aligned} \qquad (14.18\text{-}6)$$

which evidently, from consideration of (14.18–4) and (14.18–5), will be simply the algebraic equation in p,

$$A - KC = 0, \qquad (14.18\text{-}7)$$

in which $K = \cosh 2V_0$. The eight roots of (14.18–7) are the points of quantization. We require now that (14.18–7) take the form

$$A - KC = \text{constant} \times (p^2 - b^2)^2(p^2 - c^2)^2, \qquad (14.18\text{-}8)$$

i.e., that the roots be real and double. On multiplying out and equating coefficients of like powers of p we obtain a set of five simultaneous equations containing five unknowns: the "prescribed" zero position a, the quantization positions b and c, the constant K (i.e., V_0), and the constant on the right-hand side of (14.18–8). These will not be linear, but can be solved, if only by trial, for the values of these unknowns.

For the quantized exponential potential we have

$$e^{W_q} = \frac{K_1}{[\sinh(W + V_0)\sinh(W - V_0)]^{1/2}}$$

$$= \frac{K_2}{[\cosh 2W - \cosh 2V_0]^{1/2}} \qquad (14.18\text{–}9)$$

$$= \frac{K_3}{[1 - \delta \cosh 2W]^{1/2}}$$

in which the K's are arbitrary constants and $\delta = \operatorname{sech} 2V_0$. This displays the desired Chebyshev approximation of a constant in the approximation band, where $W = 0 + j\Phi$ and $\cosh 2W = \cos 2\Phi$. The maximum value is $K_3(1 - \delta)^{-1/2}$ and the minimum is $K_3(1 + \delta)^{-1/2}$. If we choose the scale

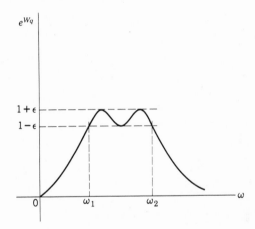

Fig. 14.18–E

so that these values are $(1 \pm \epsilon)$, as in Fig. 14.18–E, we find that ϵ, which of course is not arbitrary, is given by

$$\epsilon = e^{-2V_0}. \qquad (14.18\text{–}10)$$

The equation of quantization (14.18–6) agrees with the denominator of (14.18–9), and e^{W_q} so given will be rational if these quantization points are double, as described. The actual odd rational function that represents the solution has the zeros and poles determined by satisfying (14.18–8), and a multiplier fixed to give the approximation-band limits $(1 \pm \epsilon)$.

The difficulties of algebraic computation encountered in this method of determining the appropriate odd function [cf. the discussion about

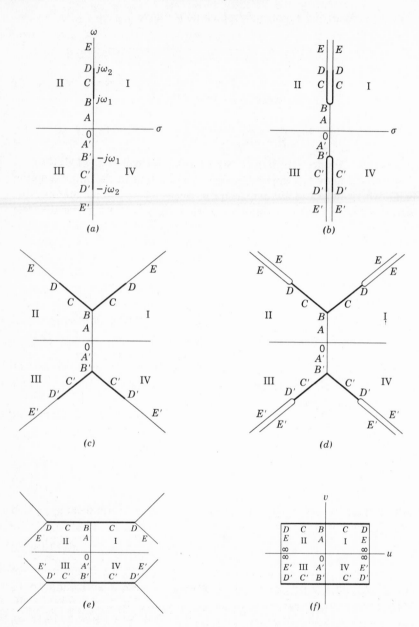

Fig. 14.18–F

(14.18–8)] increase rapidly with the order of the function; even for the low-order example above the method is hardly satisfactory. The discussion does clarify the rôle of the zeros here, however, and shows that the problem can be solved. Fortunately, there are other ways to do this, and in particular we can develop a geometrical approach that will lead to a straightforward solution.

We have seen that it is desirable to place the zeros on the real axis. How they should be spaced there is a question difficult to answer by algebraic methods. But an extension of the method used in § 14.09 can provide a transformation that is very useful. If there is a transformation that will change the field map of Fig. 14.18–C into one in which the (unknown) curves become regular because of symmetry, we may be able to find a comparatively simple, direct solution. Here two conductors are involved (rather than one, as in § 14.09), which suggests the transformation of the problem into an infinite parallel-plate-capacitor problem; we need, in other words, to cut, bend, and stretch the plane so that the two conductors become parallel and of infinite extent. In such a transformed picture the flux lines will be parallel lines, the location of the zeros a simple matter of symmetry, and quantization equally simple.

We begin by cutting the ω axis from infinity in to the lower edge of the approximation band, on the line $\infty EDCB$ in Fig. 14.18–F(a) with a symmetrical cut in the lower half plane, as in Fig. 14.18–F(b). We proceed to open these cuts up, as in Fig. 14.18–F(c). If we continued this to the point where the cut lines became horizontal, we should have again the transformation of § 14.09: the conductors would be parallel, but not infinite. To improve this situation, we make the four additional cuts of Fig. 14.18–F(d), and open these up in Fig. 14.18–F(e). Finally we compress the length of the line(s) $DE\infty$ and bend the set to form the rectangle of Fig. 14.18–F(f). The conductors have become parallel, but seem still to be finite. But since the whole of the p plane is mapped into the rectangle of the new w plane of Fig. 14.18–F(f), we expect a periodicity that will in effect make the conductors of infinite extent by repeating them indefinitely, much as in § 14.09. Since such a repetition would fill only a horizontal strip of the w plane, as shown in Fig. 14.18–G(a), there is probably an additional periodicity in the vertical direction, to complete the w plane, Fig. 14.18–G(b). That the periodicities of Fig. 14.18–G are correct can be established by taking an imaginary excursion along the ω axis, in the p plane, like that described at the end of § 14.09. By considering the parts (quadrants) of the p plane one has on the right and on the left during such an excursion, one can rapidly establish the correctness of the quadrant mapping indicated by the Roman numerals in Fig. 14.18–G.

The formal expression of such a mapping must be rather complicated, because of the double periodicity, and the nature of the Riemann surface involved difficult to visualize. We can again find the necessary function,

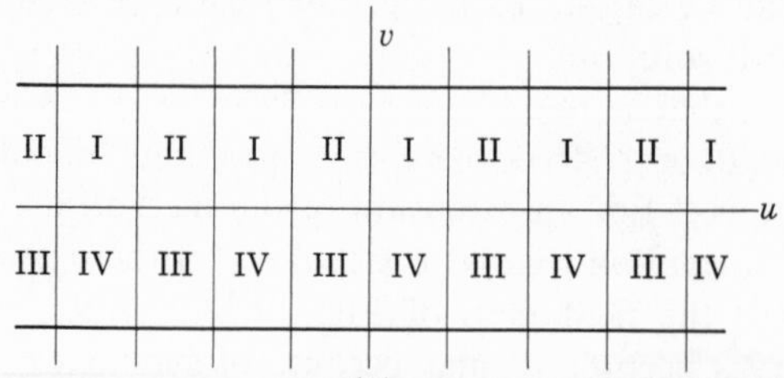

v

II	I	II	I	II	I	II	I	II	I
III	IV	III	IV	III	IV	III	IV	III	IV

—*u*

(a)

v

II	I	II	I	II	I	II	I	II	I
III	IV	III	IV	III	IV	III	IV	III	IV
IV	III	IV	III	IV	III	IV	III	IV	III
I	II	I	II	I	II	I	II	I	II
II	I	II	I	II	I	II	I	II	I
III	IV	III	IV	III	IV	III	IV	III	IV
IV	III	IV	III	IV	III	IV	III	IV	III
I	II	I	II	I	II	I	II	I	II
II	I	II	I	II	I	II	I	II	I
III	IV	III	IV	III	IV	III	IV	III	IV

—*u*

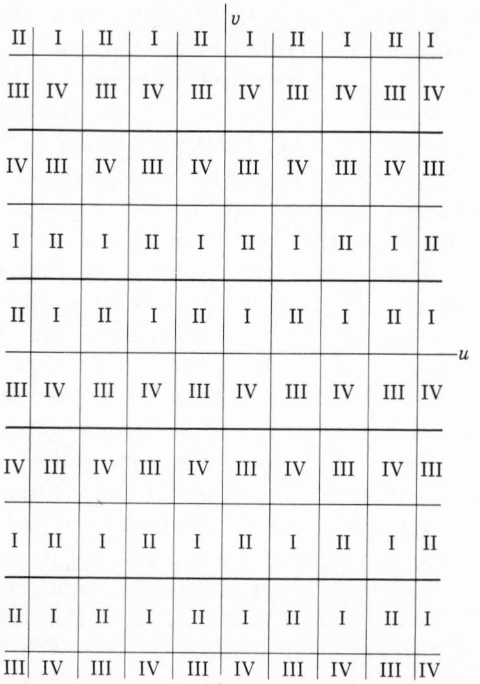

(b)

Fig. 14.18–G

however, by the Schwartz–Christoffel transformation. We have to map the ω axis of the p plane to a rectangular boundary in the w plane in the fashion shown in Fig. 14.18–H. The indentations at the corners of the rectangle are made inward, and those at the corresponding points in the

p plane to the left, so that we get the correspondence between left half plane and interior of rectangle that we wish. Following the method of § 14.09 we write for the appropriate form of (3.24–9)

$$\frac{dw}{dp} = H(p + j\omega_2)^{a_1}(p + j\omega_1)^{a_2}(p - j\omega_1)^{a_3}(p - j\omega_2)^{a_4}, \quad (14.18\text{–}11)$$

in which H is a constant (to be determined). We mount the ω axis from a point below E', until we come to the first critical point, D'. Here Δp

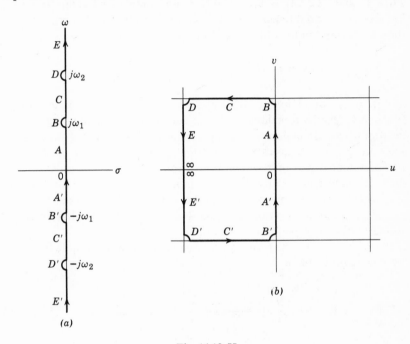

Fig. 14.18–H

is to undergo no change in direction, but at the corresponding point D' in the w plane Δw is to change from a downward to a left-right motion, i.e., to undergo an angle change of $+\pi/2$ radians. Now $(p + j\omega_2)$ undergoes an angle change of $-\pi$ radians in following the indentation at D' in the p plane, and the other factors in (14.18–11) undergo no change in angle. Thus (14.18–11), only angles being considered, becomes

$$+\frac{\pi}{2} = a_1(-\pi) \qquad (14.18\text{–}12)$$

so that we must have

$$a_1 = -\tfrac{1}{2}. \qquad (14.18\text{–}13)$$

Exactly the same behavior occurs at the other three critical points, so that all four of the a's (exponents) in (14.18–11) must have the value $-\frac{1}{2}$. Hence (14.18–11) becomes

$$\frac{dw}{dp} = \frac{H}{\sqrt{(p^2 + \omega_1^2)(p^2 + \omega_2^2)}}, \tag{14.18–14}$$

which is the differential equation that defines the transformation of Figs. 14.18–F and –G. It is appreciably more complicated than (14.09–8), because of the double periodicity (in contrast to the single periodicity of the transformation of § 14.09), and the function

$$w = H \int \frac{dp}{\sqrt{(p^2 + \omega_1^2)(p^2 + \omega_2^2)}} \tag{14.18–15}$$

is not to be found in the simpler tables of integrals. It is an *elliptic* function (of which functions double periodicity is an outstanding characteristic) whose discussion we again postpone to Volume II. Nevertheless, since its use seems necessary for straightforward solution of the odd-function-approximation-to-a-constant problem, we shall give a few formulas, sufficient for numerical calculation, without derivation or proof. The calculations of any approximation work will be checked carefully anyway, by computation of the actual behavior of the function obtained, so that verification will always be obtained.

In order to obtain the form usually treated in works on elliptic functions we now rewrite (14.18–15) as

$$w = \frac{H}{\omega_2} \int \frac{\left(\dfrac{1}{\omega_1}\right) dp}{\sqrt{\left(1 + \dfrac{p^2}{\omega_1^2}\right)\left(1 + \dfrac{\omega_1^2}{\omega_2^2}\dfrac{p^2}{\omega_1^2}\right)}}. \tag{14.18–16}$$

The form (14.18–16) can be found in tables of integrals involving elliptic functions and leads to

$$w = \frac{H}{\omega_2} \operatorname{tn}^{-1}\left(\frac{p}{\omega_1}, k\right) \tag{14.18–17}$$

with

$$k = \sqrt{1 - \omega_1^2/\omega_2^2}. \tag{14.18–18}$$

The symbol tn represents the appropriate elliptic function, which appears in inverse form, exactly as the inverse form appeared in (14.09–9). The argument is twofold because it is necessary to specify the relation between the sides of the rectangle of the w-plane map, i.e., a sort of "eccentricity" that corresponds to the approximation-band width, and this is usually done by the parameter k, defined by (14.18–18). On giving H the convenient value ω_2 and inverting (14.18–17), we have finally

$$p = \omega_1 \operatorname{tn} (w, k). \qquad (14.18–19)$$

This function, it can be shown, accomplishes exactly the mapping of Figs. 14.18–F and 14.18–G.

In this mapping we can now determine simply by symmetry conditions where to place the zeros (negative charges) so that the pairs of positive charges, when quantized as half units and moved out on their flux lines to the appropriate equipotential, will simultaneously join, on the real axis, to form unit positive charges. The important features of the mapping are that the entire p plane is mapped into a finite rectangle and that this mapping is repeated, both horizontally and vertically, throughout the w plane. We need only place the zeros (negative charges) in one rectangle so that the pattern of this rectangle, repeated indefinitely, forms one infinite pattern with complete regularity from one zero to the next, in other words, place them (on the real axis) at equal spacings. Then surely all the positive charges will join up at points on the real axis midway between the negative charges and the junctions will occur simultaneously.

Figure 14.18–I shows an example of this, for an odd function of order eight. In Fig. 14.18–I(a) one zero is placed at the origin, and one at infinity, as we must do; of the remaining six, three go on the left-half-plane real axis, at intervals equal to one-quarter of the horizontal distance between the lines $BAA'B$ and $DEE'D$, as shown; and the other three must of course be symmetrically located in the right half plane. (For the prototype situation and quantization in the p plane, see Fig. 14.18–C.) The periodicity of the mapping now requires (cf. § 14.07) that this pattern be repeated, throughout the w plane, as indicated in Fig. 14.18–I(b). The approximation-band conductors occupy the positions BCD, and are also shown in Fig. 14.18–I(b). Because of the periodicity, these are now not only parallel but infinite in extent (as well as in number). It is clear, simply by symmetry, that our quantization procedure will divide up the two units of positive charge that appear on each surface of each conductor (and therefore on each side of each horizontal distance K of conductor in the w plane) into four half-unit charges, that the flux lines on which they move will be vertical lines, at spacings of $K/4$ and midway between the vertical lines on which the negative charges lie, and that they will all reach the real axis simultaneously and thus give unit positive charges at points midway between the (equally spaced) negative charges. With this condition our goal is attained: we have a rational function which is odd, is the desired Chebyshev approximation to a constant in the approximation band, and makes full use of all the parameters of the function. The

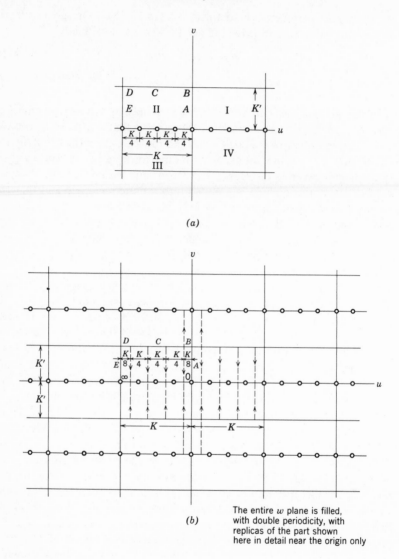

(a)

(b)   The entire w plane is filled,
with double periodicity, with
replicas of the part shown
here in detail near the origin only

Fig. 14.18–I

quantized charge distribution demonstrates, in fact, simply by its symmetry in the w plane (Fig. 14.18–J) that Chebyshev behavior is attained, and a count of the number of ripples and zeros of error obtained verifies that the approximation is the most efficient. In the p plane (Fig. 14.18–C) this symmetry is not evident; the advantage of the transformation is that it distorts the p plane so that location of the zeros (and poles) there, to obtain the sort of behavior shown in Fig. 14.18–K, becomes a simple matter.

It remains only to give the necessary formulas for determining the p-plane positions of the zeros and poles, and the (unique) error ripple ϵ

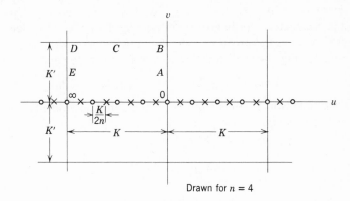

Drawn for $n = 4$

Fig. 14.18–J

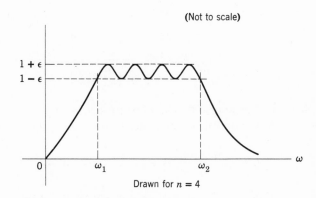

(Not to scale)

Drawn for $n = 4$

Fig. 14.18–K

that is obtained for a given approximation band and order of approximating function. The development of the necessary elliptic-function theory will be given in Volume II; the formulas below are stated without derivation in order to make it possible to find these odd-function approximations to a constant—for without these formulas this is practically impossible.

Let

$$F(p) = Dp \frac{(p^2 - p_2^2)(p^2 - p_4^2) \cdots (p^2 - p_{2n-2}^2)}{(p^2 - p_1^2)(p^2 - p_3^2) \cdots (p^2 - p_{2n-1}^2)} \qquad (14.18\text{--}20)$$

be the odd function we seek. $F(j\omega)$ will be purely imaginary, and $\text{Im } F(j\omega) = F(j\omega)/j$ is to approximate a real constant in the approximation band $\omega_1 < \omega < \omega_2$ (as in Fig. 14.18–K). Its zeros and poles are real and alternate according to the foregoing discussion; we have given it simple zeros at the origin and at infinity in keeping with the same. In the w plane (Fig. 14.18–J) these zeros and poles are located at the points

$$\pm m(K/2n) + j0, \qquad m = 0, 1, 2, \cdots, 2n \qquad (14.18\text{--}21)$$

and at the additional points required by the double periodicity. The first and the last points of the sequence (14.18–21) map to the origin and infinity in the p plane, the others to

$$p_m = \pm \omega_1 \, \text{tn}\left(\frac{m}{2n} K, k\right) \qquad (14.18\text{--}22)$$

which lie, of course, on the real axis of the p plane. The numerical values required can sometimes be obtained from elliptic-function tables such as SP 1. These tables give values of two other elliptic functions, sn and cn, whose quotient is the function we need:

$$\text{tn}\left(\frac{m}{2n} K, k\right) = \frac{\text{sn}\left(\dfrac{m}{2n} K, k\right)}{\text{cn}\left(\dfrac{m}{2n} K, k\right)}. \qquad (14.18\text{--}23)$$

Such tables must of course be two-dimensional, because the value of the parameter k or an equivalent parameter θ to be determined from

$$k = \sqrt{1 - \frac{\omega_1^2}{\omega_2^2}} = \sin \theta, \qquad \cos \theta = \frac{\omega_1}{\omega_2}, \qquad (14.18\text{--}24)$$

must be specified as well as that of the argument proper. This may require two-way interpolation. But the values p_m can easily be calculated with sufficient accuracy from a variety of expansions in more familiar functions. One useful pair of such expansions (SP 1, HA 1), with the necessary preliminary formulas, is given in the design procedure that follows.

Let

$$t = \frac{1}{2} \times \frac{1 - \sqrt{\omega_1/\omega_2}}{1 + \sqrt{\omega_1/\omega_2}}. \qquad (14.18\text{--}25)$$

Then calculate

$$q = t + 2t^5 + 15t^9 + 150t^{13} + 1707t^{17} + 20910t^{21} + \cdots \quad (14.18\text{–}26)$$

of which a few terms generally suffice. For (extremely) large approximation-band widths this calculation becomes difficult, and may be replaced by the calculation of

$$t' = \frac{1}{2} \times \frac{1 - [1 - (\omega_1^2/\omega_2^2)]^{1/4}}{1 + [1 - (\omega_1^2/\omega_2^2)]^{1/4}}, \quad (14.18\text{–}27)$$

of

$$q' = t' + 2t'^5 + 15t'^9 + 150t'^{13} + 1707t'^{17} + 20910t'^{21} + \cdots, \quad (14.18\text{–}28)$$

and finally of the parameter q from

$$\log_{10} q = \frac{1.8615228}{\log_{10} q'} \quad (14.18\text{–}29)$$

instead of from (14.18–26). In terms of the value of the parameter q, the pole and zero positions in the p plane are given by

$$p_m = \pm \omega_1 \frac{1 + 2q + 2q^4 + 2q^9 + 2q^{16} + \cdots}{1 - 2q + 2q^4 - 2q^9 + 2q^{16} - \cdots}$$

$$\times \frac{\sin \psi - q^2 \sin 3\psi + q^6 \sin 5\psi - q^{12} \sin 7\psi + \cdots}{\cos \psi + q^2 \cos 3\psi + q^6 \cos 5\psi + q^{12} \cos 7\psi + \cdots} \quad (14.18\text{–}30)$$

in which

$$\psi = \frac{m}{4n} \pi \text{ radians} \quad or \quad \frac{m}{n} 45°, \quad m = 0, 1, 2, \cdots, (2n - 1), 2n. \quad (14.18\text{–}31)$$

Of these $(2n + 1)$ values, the first (that for $m = 0$) gives zero, and the last (that for $m = 2n$) gives infinity, corresponding to the zeros at the origin and infinity. The intermediate $(2n - 1)$ values give, in succession, the (real) zeros and poles of (14.18–20). The mid-value, that for $m = n$, is a sort of center, about which the other values give symmetric results; in fact, the two values of p_m for $m = n + m'$ and $m = n - m'$ have p_n for their geometric mean. This symmetry simplifies the calculation of the set of values p_m. It also leads to a symmetry of the approximating function, on a logarithmic frequency scale, about the geometric mean of ω_1 and ω_2. Finally, the multiplier D should have the value that makes (14.18–20) satisfy $F(j\omega_1) = F(j\omega_2) = j(1 - \epsilon)$, to agree with Fig. 14.18–K.

Equation (14.18–30) will give sufficiently accurate values for most practical cases. (For designs in which the approximation-band width is enormous, alternate formulas will be given in Volume II.) We have then, in (14.18–20), the desired odd function, with the real-frequency behavior (apart from a factor j) shown in Fig. 14.18–K.

The relation between the ripple ϵ that is obtained for given approximation bands and orders of approximating function is given by

$$\epsilon = 4q^{2n} - 16q^{6n} + \cdots. \tag{14.18–32}$$

The curves of Fig. 14.18–L give the information necessary for making a choice for n in any particular problem; more accurate calculations can be made by (14.18–32).

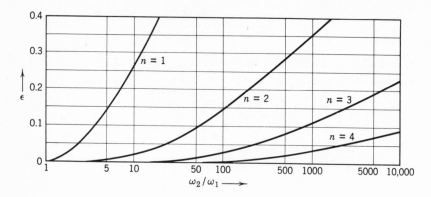

Fig. 14.18–L

By way of illustration, suppose an odd function is desired to approximate a constant within 3% in an approximation band the ratio of whose limiting frequencies is 100. In Fig. 14.18–L we find that for this bandwidth a choice of $n = 3$ will give slightly better than the required error (or the bandwidth could be increased slightly without exceeding the allowable 3% error). With this choice, the calculations, made according to the formulas above, are summarized below.

With $n = 3$, $\omega_2/\omega_1 = 100$, and ω_1 as the unit of (normalized) frequency, we find

$$t' = \frac{1}{2} \times \frac{1 - (1 - 0.0001)^{1/4}}{1 + (1 - 0.0001)^{1/4}} = \frac{1}{2} \times \frac{1 - (1 - 0.000025 + \cdots)}{1 + (1 - 0.000025 + \cdots)}$$

$$= 6.2503 \times 10^{-6}, \tag{14.18–33}$$

$$q' = 6.2503, \qquad q = 0.43883, \qquad \epsilon = 0.028565 \text{ (i.e., } 2.86\%),$$

$$\frac{1 + 2q + 2q^4 + 2q^9 + \cdots}{1 - 2q + 2q^4 - 2q^9 + \cdots} = 10.0000, \qquad \psi = 15°, 30°, 45°, 60°, 75°,$$

$$p_1 = 1.1731,$$
$$p_2 = 3.6174, \qquad p_4 = 27.644,$$
$$p_3 = 10.0000, \qquad p_5 = 85.245.$$

$$(14.18\text{--}33)$$

The end result is the function

$$F(p) = -157.20p \; \frac{(p^2 - 13.086)(p^2 - 764.18)}{(p^2 - 1.3761)(p^2 - 100.00)(p^2 - 726.68)} \quad (14.18\text{--}34)$$

in which the constant has been determined so that $F(j1) = j(1 - \epsilon)$. A convenient check is to evaluate $F(j100)$ which should of course give the same value. The actual behavior of this function at real frequencies is given in Fig. 14.18–M. (For large bandwidths it is convenient to plot

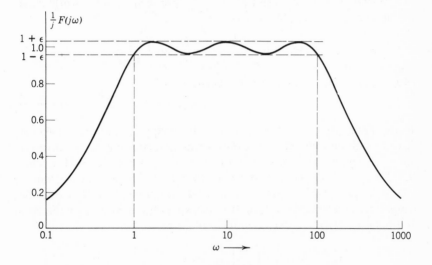

Fig. 14.18-M

the function on a logarithmic frequency scale in order to display the approximation band on a reasonable scale; this also exhibits the symmetry about the geometric mean frequency $\omega_0 = \sqrt{\omega_1 \omega_2}$.)

Both frequency and magnitude scales are of course easily altered to fit any particular problem. From this function we can obtain a driving-point immittance function whose reactance (susceptance) approximates any real constant (positive or negative) within 2.9% simply by taking $F(p)$ as the odd part of the impedance (admittance) and calculating the immittance itself by the methods of § 8.12. From the same function we can also obtain a driving-point-immittance function whose angle approximates any constant (positive or negative) β_0 within a tolerance ϵ' determined by the trigonometric relation

$$\frac{\tan(\beta_0 + \epsilon')}{\tan(\beta_0 - \epsilon')} = \frac{1 + \epsilon}{1 - \epsilon} \qquad (14.18\text{–}35)$$

by taking $F(p)$ as the generalized tangent of the angle and calculating the immittance itself by the methods of § 8.14.

The problem of approximating a constant in Chebyshev fashion in an internal band with an odd function, as for reactance (susceptance) or angle, is thus solved. In the limiting case of zero bandwidth, the discussion as to the rôle of the zeros still applies and the results above should agree (§ 14.15) with those obtained by Taylor approximation in § 13.10. That they do so is easily seen by letting ω_2 approach ω_1 in the work above. We obtain, instead of (14.18–15),

$$w = H \int \frac{dp}{p^2 + \omega_1{}^2} = \frac{H}{\omega_1} \tan^{-1}\left(\frac{p}{\omega_1}\right) \qquad (14.18\text{–}36)$$

which leads, with $H = \omega_1$ for convenience, to

$$p = \omega_1 \tan w \qquad (14.18\text{–}37)$$

as the appropriate transformation. This mapping can be interpreted directly without difficulty, since only a trigonometric function is involved. Alternatively, we can consider it a limiting case of Fig. 14.18–H in which the segments DCB and $D'C'B'$ recede to infinity, i.e., K' becomes infinite and K approaches $\pi/2$ in Fig. 14.18–I. Figure 14.18–N shows this (singly periodic) mapping, and the corresponding locations of the zeros and poles of $F(p)$. These lie in the p plane at

$$p_m = \pm\omega_1 \tan\left(\frac{m\pi}{4n}\right), \qquad m = 0, 1, 2, \cdots, 2n. \qquad (14.18\text{–}38)$$

These positions can be computed without difficulty. The resulting exponential potential function is thus proportional to $\tan(2nw)$, as the charge (pole-zero) diagram Fig. 14.18–N(c) shows. In the p plane, with the multiplier adjusted to give unit value for $F(j\omega_1)/j$, the function is

$$F(p) = \tan\left[2n \tan^{-1}\left(\frac{p}{\omega_1}\right)\right] \qquad (14.18\text{–}39)$$

which becomes, at real frequencies,

$$F(j\omega) = j \tanh\left[2n \tanh^{-1}\left(\frac{\omega}{\omega_1}\right)\right]. \qquad (14.18\text{–}40)$$

With the aid of the equation

$$\tanh^{-1} x = \frac{1}{2}\ln\left(\frac{1+x}{1-x}\right), \qquad (14.18\text{–}41)$$

this is readily converted to

$$F(j\omega) = j\left[\frac{1-\left(\frac{1-x}{1+x}\right)^{2n}}{1+\left(\frac{1-x}{1+x}\right)^{2n}}\right]. \qquad (14.18\text{–}42)$$

This is exactly the result obtained in (13.10–18), with the identification of $x = \omega/\omega_1$ with the normalized frequency there, and recognition that the

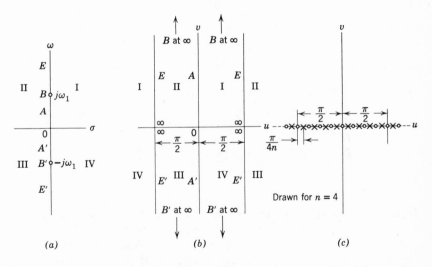

Fig. 14.18–N. (a) and (b) The mapping $p = \omega_1 \tan w$. (c) Location of charges in the w plane.

order of the function $F(p)$ is $2n = N$. In § 13.10 this function was shown to be maximally flat (at unit value) at unit frequency, which merely verifies this alternative approach through the potential analogy. This last has the advantage of giving the poles and zeros of $F(p)$ in the form (14.18–38), which the approach of § 13.10 implies but does not give as directly.

In all of the discussion above it has been assumed that zeros were desired at both the origin and infinity. An odd function that approximates a constant in an internal band can equally well have *poles* at both extreme frequencies (in which case the function F above is simply inverted), or a zero at one and a pole at the other. To obtain the corresponding function it is merely necessary to change the horizontal scale in Fig. 14.18–J or Fig. 14.18–N so that in the horizontal set(s) of alternating zeros and poles the mappings of the origin and of infinity are correspondingly occupied. The increments of the argument of the tangent function in (14.18–38) or of ψ in (14.18–31) are then simply $\pi/2N$, in which N is the order of the approximating function and may now be odd as well as even. Both Fig. 14.18–L and (14.18–32) apply to the determination of ϵ, with N in place of $2n$; in the former, interpolating curves can be sketched in for the odd values of N, while the latter applies directly. With the same substitution of N for $2n$, (14.18–39) and (14.18–42) are also valid.

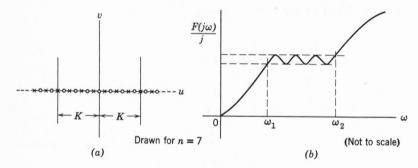

Fig. 14.18–O. (*a*) The pole-zero diagram in the *w* plane. (*b*) The real-frequency behaviour.

Figure 14.18–O illustrates the possibilities for $N = 7$ for the Chebyshev case; the Taylor case is simply a collapsed version of this.

A final matter of interest is that these odd-function internal-band approximations to a constant lead in general to *R-C* or *R-L* network realizations. In fact, any odd rational function of p whose zeros and poles are all simple and lie on the real axis in alternating fashion (subject to appropriate behavior at the origin and infinity), whether it be taken as the odd part or the generalized tangent of angle of a driving-point immittance function, leads to an immittance function that can be realized with only two kinds of elements, by the methods of Chapter 7. If a constant positive susceptance or negative reactance, positive angle of admittance or negative angle of impedance, is approximated, an *R-C* realization can usually be found; if the signs are reversed, an *R-L* realization can usually be found (Problem 14-182).

In this and the previous section, we have completed our discussion of the approximation of a constant by an odd function. In the internal-band case the odd property makes it possible to utilize the zeros of the function in a fashion not possible with even functions, to improve the approximations. The zeros cannot be specified arbitrarily if the best approximation is desired; if they are specified, some reduction in the quality of approximation must be accepted—and the potential analogy does not appear then to give a true Chebyshev approximation, by the quantization methods we have used thus far.

14.19 Recapitulation

We began the consideration of *approximation* in Chapter 13, which discussed the matter in a general way and developed some techniques, particularly that of Taylor approximation. The present chapter has been more specialized, concerning itself with exploitation of the analogy between complex-variable theory and two-dimensional potential theory. The physics of the latter can be a very useful guide to approximation procedures. We have developed this in some detail, using the physics of the two-dimensional electrostatic field as our analog guide (though many other physical situations are described by the same mathematics and could therefore be used instead).

This analogy is admirably suited to the development of methods of approximating a *constant* because of the existence in it of the *conductor*. The conductor automatically creates a region of constant potential, and it is on this fact that the methods of this chapter are based, together with the fact that the distributed charge (nonrational functions) of the con-ductor can often be replaced, in effect, by lumped charges (rational functions) whose effect is a Chebyshev approximation to that of the distributed charge, in certain regions. This is made vividly clear by transformation to the plane of W, the complex potential of the prototype situation, that in which conductors occupy the approximation band(s). Quantization, i.e., the replacement of the distributed charge by a set of lumped charges located on an equipotential of the prototype problem at equal separations in terms of flux, leads to an infinite set of equally spaced charges in the W plane whose potential W_q is therefore a Chebyshev approximation to a constant (subject to certain symmetry requirements). In more mathematical terms, the exponential potential of the prototype situa-tion, e^W, gives way to that of the quantized situation, expressed usually by

$$e^{W_q} = \frac{\text{constant}}{1 \pm \epsilon \cosh W} \tag{14.19-1}$$

which is rational in p and in which ϵ is the error ripple in the approximation band. Since this band is occupied by a conductor in the prototype problem, taken for convenience to be at zero potential, there $W = 0 + j\Phi$ and the Chebyshev behavior becomes obvious; outside the approximation band, the real part of W is no longer zero, and appropriate variation occurs. The location of the approximation band (or bands) usually suggests appropriate conformal transformations that may aid the calculations. The analogy may be exploited further to suggest computing devices for performing these calculations (§ 14.20) but for accurate results digital computation is usually necessary.

We have found it possible to apply this technique to all variations of the problem of approximating a constant: wherever the zeros may be (if the problem is such that they may be arbitrarily prescribed), wherever the approximation band(s) may lie, and whether the approximating function be odd or even. It remains, however, to apply the technique to the approximation of a function that is not a constant. That is, of the four restrictions noted in (14.11–5), only the first three have been removed. To approximate a function that is not a constant is evidently a different sort of problem, at least from the point of view of the potential analogy, for the primary weapon of the arsenal, the conductor, is evidently no longer applicable. Some problems can be reduced by artifices to the approximation of a constant. And many can be handled through the use of charge distributed on nonconducting surfaces of appropriate shapes. The results are not usually true Chebyshev approximations, though they may be very close thereto. But the discussion of these techniques is itself a lengthy matter, and we postpone it to Volume II.

For the present, then, we shall be content with the techniques developed in Chapters 13 and 14 which, on reflection, give us a fairly strong arsenal. With these techniques (and some extensions developed in the problems) we can, in fact, handle a tremendous variety of approximation problems. That part of Volume II that concerns itself with approximation will extend our abilities.

The reader who is familiar with filter theory (an aspect of network synthesis to be discussed in Volume II) will have noted a number of resemblances between that theory and the material of this chapter. To filter theory we are indebted for the original development of many of these ideas (DA 1)—they are more logically developed for the newcomer, however, in the fashion of this chapter. The relation to filter theory will be explained in Volume II.

14.20 Analog computation

As does any method of precise approximation, the potential analogy method requires a good deal of numerical computation. In contrast to the other methods developed in Chapter 13, however, the potential analogy by its very identification with physical "apparatus" offers a novel method of carrying out the necessary calculations. In place of abstract discussion of conductors, equipotentials, and flux lines, we can physically set up an apparatus in which the prototype potential exists, actually measure and map the field, and thus determine, for example, the points of quantization. The apparatus will be an analog computer, and it may take any physical form to which Laplace's equation applies. Generally the electric analogy, in which a two-dimensional field is set up either in a basin or tank containing an electrolyte or in a dry conducting medium such as a sheet of resistive material, has been found most useful. Many analog computers have been successfully built (see the references in § 14.21).

Such computers are inherently limited in accuracy by difficulties of measurement as well as of production of truly symmetrical and two-dimensional fields. Because of this we shall not discuss this method of calculation. The analog computer is not to be underrated, especially as a means of finding at least approximate solutions to involved problems and as an aid to visualization sometimes even more powerful than the paper-and-pencil analog concept, but it is not capable of yielding the accuracy justifiably necessary for precise network synthesis. For this, digital computation, either by hand (with the use of a slide rule in the less critical cases or of a desk calculator in the more critical cases) or by digital computers, is required. Nor is it the province of this book to discuss the digital computer, which has become the basis of a separate industry, though one may have to resort to it to avoid prohibitive expenditure of design time in complicated network-synthesis problems.

14.21 References

Potential theory (general): AP 1, GU 3, KE 1, SC 2, WE 4.

Of historical interest: GA 2, KE 2, KL 2, LU 1.

Applications of potential theory to network theory: BE 4, BO 7, CH 4, DA 2, DI 1, HA 3, HU 4, SC 5, SC 7.

Approximation of a constant (specifically): even functions: BO 6, FA 1, MA 9, TR 2, TR 3, TR 4, WH 4; magnitude of immittance: BO 3, GO 1, WH 2; odd functions: DA 3, MA 8, OR 1, OR 2, SA 3, WE 5, WE 6.

Chebyshev approximation by other methods: BE 2, BO 10, CA 2, CH 1, CH 2, CO 1, DA 4, HE 2, KI 4, LA 1, SA 2, SH 2.

Analog computers: BO 8, BO 9, CH 4, DO 1, FA 2, GI 2, HA 2, HA 4, HU 2, KL 1, LI 2, LU 1, MA 7, MA 9, MO 4, SC 3, SC 4, SO 1, WE 4.

Miscellaneous: SA 2.

PROBLEMS

14-1. Draw the equipotentials and flux lines in the immediate vicinity of a unit (line) charge. If the observer makes one circuit of the charge, how much do the real and the imaginary parts of the complex potential change? Explain this in both physical and mathematical terms. Where, by the way, do the flux lines begin and end?

Repeat this discussion for each of the following situations (rough plots suffice). Be sure to discuss the various possibilities as to circuits of charges.

(*a*) unit negative charges at $(0, 1)$ and $(0, -1)$;
(*b*) unit positive charges at $(1, 0)$ and $(-1, 0)$;
(*c*) unit negative charge at $(-1, 0)$, unit positive charge at $(1, 0)$;
(*d*) unit positive charge at $(-1, 0)$, unit negative charge at $(1, 0)$;
(*e*) unit negative charges at each of the points $p = -1 \pm j2$;
(*f*) unit positive charges at each of the points $p = 2 \pm j4$.

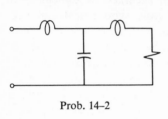

Prob. 14-2

14-2. Make a sketch of the charge diagram for the analog to the driving-point impedance function $Z(p)$ of the network shown, and rough in the flux plot.

Repeat for the impedance of an *L-C* network of order three with a pole at the origin, and for the impedance of an *R-C* network of order three with a pole at the origin.

14-3. Derive (14.01–2) from (14.01–1) and discuss the assumptions made in the process.

14-4. Make a list of physical two-dimensional problems in which Laplace's equation appears and for each make a table of analogous quantities for the rational functions of network theory.

14-5. Derive (14.02–3) from Laplace's equation. Explain carefully why the origin of the electrostatic potential is never determined, why the potential always contains an arbitrary additive constant.

Show that (14.02–3) and (14.03–4) are conjugate functions, apart from constant multipliers, and explain carefully why flux lines and equipotentials intersect at right angles, both in this case and in general.

14-6. Construct from plaster or with the use of layers of cardboard, properly cut and mounted on top of each other, a model of the "mountain pass" of Fig. 14.02–H. Mark on it the equipotentials and flux lines and explain the term "saddle point" with its aid.

The construction may profitably be repeated for a more complicated situation, say that of unit negative charges at each of the four points $p = \pm 1 \pm j1$.

14-7. Show that the equipotentials in Fig. 14.02–G are arcs of circles given by

$$\frac{z}{2} = \coth V + (\operatorname{csch} V)e^{j\psi}$$

and that the flux lines are also arcs of circles, given by

$$\frac{z}{2} = -j \cot \Phi + (\csc \Phi)e^{j\psi}$$

in which ψ represents an angle (parameter) that varies to trace out the curves.

If the origin of the plane is to be at zero potential, and the value of Φ there π, what value must K in (14.02–11) have? Show then on a sketch the value of Φ on all parts of the x and y axes and on some typical curved flux lines. Discuss.

14-8. Discuss the numerical construction of Fig. 14.02–H. Show in particular that for any given complex potential W, the corresponding points are given by $z = \pm 2\sqrt{1 + e^W}$ and construct some of the equipotentials and flux lines. On a similar sketch mark the lines $\Phi = 0$, $\Phi = \pi/2$, $\Phi = 3\pi/2$. How much flux cuts a circle centered on the origin of radius 5? 3? 1?

14-9. Explain in detail the analogy between the flux plots of this chapter and maps associated with the gravitational field, on the assumption that the force of gravity is constant and the earth's "radius" is large in the area of interest.

14-10. Discuss the numerical construction of Fig. 14.02–I. Point out the difficulties in comparison with the construction of Fig. 14.02–H (Prob. 14-8) and explain how they could be surmounted. Mark enough flux lines with the corresponding values of Φ that the values on those remaining can be readily interpolated. How much flux cuts a very large circle centered on the origin?

14-11. Explain by means of a flux plot how the net (total) electric charge is zero in the analogs for each of the functions below. What does this mean about the numbers of zeros and of poles?

(a) $p^3 + 3p^2 + 3p + 1$ (b) $\dfrac{1}{p}$ (c) $\dfrac{p-1}{p+1}$ (d) $\dfrac{p^2 + 6p + 25}{p^2 + 2p + 5}$.

Which of these are realizable as driving-point immittance functions? Realize them, both as impedances and as admittances.

14-12. Verify that (14.04–2) is obtained from one of the Cauchy-Riemann equations. What result does the other one give?

14-13. Explain why the complex potential at great distances from charge distributions is substantially independent of the detailed nature of these distributions. For example, consider the following distributions of negative charge (the complementary positive charge being all at infinity in each case):

(a) Q units of negative charge lumped at the origin;

(b) Q units of negative charge distributed on a circular conductor of radius r_0 at or near the origin;

(c) Q units of negative charge on an ellipse near the origin;

(d) Q units of negative charge on a square conductor centered on the origin.

14-14. Discuss the value of the flux function Φ at a point such as $(1, 1)$ when the segment of the imaginary axis from $(0, -1)$ to $(0, +1)$ is occupied by a thin conducting plate carrying Q units of negative charge. Give its value as one repeatedly encircles the plate, say on a circle of radius $\sqrt{2}$, centered on the origin, and explain. Correlate this with the integral theorems of Cauchy. How is the situation changed if the Q units of negative charge are lumped at the origin instead of being distributed on a conductor?

14-15. Construct the flux plot of Fig. 14.04–D, the plate running from $(0, -1)$ to $(0, +1)$. Explain why this is the same as that of Fig. 14.04–C, outside the conductor, if the conductor is a suitable ellipse, properly placed.

14-16. State each of the properties of driving-point immittance functions discussed in Chapter 5 in electrostatic-analog terms. Explain fully how (4.05–3) is translated into (14.03–11) and (14.03–12), and how (5.13–5) is translated into (14.03–13). In the latter case the electrostatic analog contains an additional (not necessary) requirement. What is this, and why is it natural to include it?

Explain also the translation of the conditions for realizability of proposed magnitude, angle, tangent of angle, resistance (conductance), and reactance (susceptance) functions (§ 14.03).

14-17. Look carefully through Chapter 3 and find examples of theorems, etc., in the theory of functions of a complex variable that are vividly clear in analog terms. (The various theorems of Cauchy are outstanding examples, but there are others.) See also Prob. 8-121, etc. Explain each.

14-18. Solve Probs. 3-47a, c, d, f, h, l, 8-27, 8-37a, b, 8-38a, b, 8-39 (in part) by use of the potential analogy. Note how, once the proper analog has been set up, this is essentially a matter of inspection. Why is the solution so simple thus, in contrast to methods that use the integral relations? Can you solve the other parts of Prob. 3-47 and of Probs. 8-37, 8-38, 8-39 thus with equal ease?

14-19. Consider the electrostatic analog of a polynomial, defined by equating the exponential potential to the polynomial. Where are the negative charges? The positive charges? Show that the electric field is generally zero where the derivative of the polynomial is zero, explaining the exceptions. In what way are zeros of the derivative related to saddle points of the field? From the foregoing demonstrate (as by considering components of electric field in appropriate directions) that the zeros of the derivative of a polynomial all lie within any closed curve that also encloses all the zeros of the polynomial.

As a corollary, demonstrate that the nth derivative of a Hurwitz polynomial is also a Hurwitz polynomial.

Show further that if N/D is a reactance function, so also is the quotient of the nth derivatives of N and of D. Verify the same property of R-C and of R-L driving-point-immittance functions. (RE 5.)

14-20. Test the following functions for positive-real character by considering the $\pm \pi/2$ flux lines in the analogous flux plot.

$$(a)\ K\frac{p + a}{p + b} \qquad (b)\ K\frac{p + c}{p^2 + ap + b} \qquad (K, a, b, c \text{ real and positive}).$$

Perform the same test by comparison with the flux plot of a unit charge at the origin. Discuss the utility of these potential-analog tests for positive reality in comparison with that of (5.13–5).

14-21. Construct the diagrams of Fig. 14.03–B from (14.03–10). Show, by examination of these diagrams only, that $Z(p)$ is p-r, and realize this impedance function.

14-22. Make flux plots for the following functions (to be taken as exponential-potential functions):

$$(a)\ \sqrt{p} \qquad (b)\ \sqrt{1 + p} \qquad (c)\ \sqrt{1 + p^2} \qquad (d)\ \sqrt{1 + p^2}/p.$$

Notice that in the electrostatic analog, such functions are scarcely more complicated than rational functions. Contrast this with the difficulties that arise in the analytical treatment of multivalued functions. In particular explain how the multiple values appear in the analog; what is the corresponding behavior in the case of a rational function?

14-23. Consider the function

$$F(p) = \left(\frac{p + a}{p + 1}\right)^n.$$

In terms of the flux plot of its analog explain why $F(p)$ can be p-r only for restricted values of the (real) constant a, n being fixed. What, in physical terms relevant to the analog, does this imply as to a need for "clustering" of the positive and negative charges?

Derive an equation from which, for any n, the allowable values of a can be determined.

14-24. Derive the following formulas, used in the text, from the definitions of the hyperbolic functions *sinh* and *cosh* in terms of the exponential function.

(*a*) $\sinh x \sinh y = \frac{1}{2}[\cosh (x + y) - \cosh (x - y)]$,

(*b*) $\sinh x \cosh y = \frac{1}{2}[\sinh (x + y) + \sinh (x - y)]$,

(*c*) $\cosh x \cosh y = \frac{1}{2}[\cosh (x + y) + \cosh (x - y)]$,

(*d*) $\cosh 2x = 2 \cosh^2 x - 1$,

(*e*) $\sinh 2x = 2 \sinh x \cosh x$,

(*f*) $\sinh^{-1} x = \cosh^{-1}\sqrt{x^2 + 1} = \ln [x + \sqrt{x^2 + 1}]$,

(*g*) $\tanh^{-1} x = \frac{1}{2} \ln \left(\frac{1 + x}{1 - x}\right)$,

(*h*) (14.14-6).

14-25. Construct Fig. 14.05–E to scale, on the assumption that the chosen equipotential is an ellipse, $p = \sinh (V + j\Phi)$ in which $V = 0.7$. Explain fully how the locations of the lumped charges are determined.

Consider the mapping of the p-plane charges of Fig. 14.05–E to the w plane (Fig. 14.08–A). Discuss the repetitions of the principal mapping (that on $u = -a$ for $-\pi < v < \pi$); show how each repetition is laid down and in particular how the right-half-plane charges appear, identifying them one by one with particular charges in the left half of the p plane: for example, which right-half-plane charge is another mapping of that at $(-a, \pi/4N)$? Repeat for Figs. 14.05–F and 14.08–B.

14-26. In Fig. 14.06–A, if one follows the flux line $\Phi = 0$ in from the left to the conductor's left surface, and then proceeds straight through the conductor to the right surface, what value will Φ then have? Explain.

14-27. By invoking the concept of the Riemann surface explain the p-plane mapping of the right half of the W plane of § 14.06. Show that the p plane is doubly infinitely sheeted, whereas the W plane is single sheeted. Where, in the Riemann surface, do the flux lines terminate, i.e., if we pass through the Looking Glass where do we find the positive charge?

14-28. Derive (14.07–8) by working with the complex potential W, summing over the individual charges, and using § 3.27. Repeat for (14.07–15).

Verify that the zeros of (14.07–11) and (14.07–15) are the locations of the appropriate charges in the w plane.

14-29. Sketch, in the w plane, the mapping by the transformation of § 14.09 of lines $\sigma = $ constant and $\omega = $ constant.

14-30. In the w plane of § 14.09 draw the line $v = +3\pi/4$.   Sketch its mapping in the p plane, and its repetitions in the w plane.   Explain the w-plane mapping of the other three semibranches of the hyperbola.

14-31. Show mathematically how in the limit at large distances (14.09–18) and (14.09–20) become the equations for the equipotentials and flux lines of a charge lumped at the origin.   Illustrate on the flux plot of a charged conductor on a segment of the ω axis.   Explain the situation physically.

14-32. Develop the transformation of §14.09 by applying the Schwarz-Christoffel transformation to the transformation *from w to p* (Fig. 14.09–B), i.e., in the reverse sense to that of § 14.09, by determining dp/dw and hence p as a function of w.

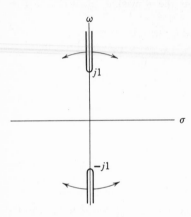

Prob. 14–33

14-33. Develop a transformation, using the Schwarz-Christoffel principle, by the following distortion of the p plane: cut the ω axis from $+j1$ to $+\infty$ and from $-j1$ to $-\infty$, open and bend the parts cut as shown, to compress the p plane into an infinite horizontal strip: $-\infty < u < +\infty$, $-\pi < v < \pi$.   Show that this is the same as the transformation of § 14.09.   What part of the w plane contains the principal mapping of the p plane?

If the principal mapping of the p plane in the w plane is to be bounded by the lines $v = -\pi$ from $u = -\infty$ to $u = 0$, $u = 0$ from $v = -\pi$ to $v = 0$, $v = 0$ from $u = 0$ to $u = +\infty$, and $v = +\pi/2$ from $u = +\infty$ to $u = -\infty$, what similar cutting and bending process should be applied to the p plane?

14-34. In (14.09–10) the two constants K and K' affect scale and orientation of the transformation only, not its fundamental properties.   Show this by giving them arbitrary values (e.g., $K = -j2$, $K' = 3 + j4$) and discussing the resulting mapping.

14-35. The commonest *Chebyshev polynomials* (those encountered in § 14.10) may conveniently be defined by

$$C_n(\omega) = \cos{(n \cos^{-1} \omega)},$$

the question of multiple values being resolved, as in § 14.10, by taking $\cos^{-1}(1)$ to be zero.   Although these polynomials appear (in the quantized exponential potential) only in the simplest case, where all the zeros of the resistance or other function are at infinity, they are nevertheless of considerable interest.   Some of their properties are to be developed here.   [Instead of *Chebyshev*, which represents English transliteration of the Russian name Чебышёв, spellings beginning *Tch-* and *Tsch-* are common, representing respectively French and German transliterations.   There are also other polynomials that bear this name (CH 1, CH 2, JA 5, MA 2).   Their more general use in approximation will be developed in Volume II.]

(*a*) Show that $C_n(\omega)$ is a polynomial in ω of degree n, even or odd according as

n is even or odd. Determine, from trigonometric formulas, the polynomials C_0, C_1, C_2, C_3.

(b) Derive the following recurrence relation, as from the trigonometric formula for the cosine of the sum of two angles suitably applied to C_{n+1} and to C_{n-1}:

$$C_n = 2\omega C_{n-1} - C_{n-2}.$$

Using this, verify the polynomials C_2 and C_3 obtained in (a), and extend the table through C_{10}.

(c) Let $\psi = \cos^{-1}\omega$, so that $e^{j\psi} = \omega + j\sqrt{1 - \omega^2}$. By expanding $e^{jn\psi} = (\omega + j\sqrt{1 - \omega^2})^n$ and taking real parts (or odd parts), or by using the formula $\cos x = \frac{1}{2}(e^{jx} + e^{-jx})$, obtain alternate verifications of all the results of (a) and (b).

(d) By expanding $e^W = (\sqrt[+]{p^2 + 1} + p)^n = e^{nw}$, using $p = \sinh w$ and $\sqrt[+]{p^2 + 1} = \cosh w$, formulas discussed at length in the text, and the fact that $\cosh x = \text{Ev } e^x$, again obtain alternate verifications of the results of (a) and (b). How is this approach related to that of (c)?

(e) Show that the hyperbolic-function form implied in (14.10–12) is another expression for these polynomials, comparable to the trigonometric-function form with which this problem starts.

(f) Plot curves of the polynomials $C_n(\omega)$ for $-1 < \omega < 1$ and for $-2 < \omega < 2$. Of the various formulas developed, which are most convenient for obtaining points for the plots? What is the salient characteristic of the polynomials' behavior?

(g) For what values of ω do the polynomials $C_n(\omega)$ vanish? (Answer both in terms of the basic definition and of your plots.) Express your answer clearly by deriving the following factored form,

$$C_n(\omega) = 2^{n-1}\left(\omega - \cos\frac{\pi}{2n}\right)\left(\omega - \cos\frac{3\pi}{2n}\right) \cdots \left[\omega - \cos\frac{(2n-1)\pi}{2n}\right].$$

For the low-band approximation problem of § 14.11 show that the more general formulas (14.12–36) and (14.12–37) are valid, and derive the Chebyshev-polynomial formulas (14.10–12) therefrom, using the proper prototype-potential function. Why, in more general cases where the zeros are not all at infinity, do these polynomials *not* appear?

14-36. Show from (14.10–11) that ϵ in (14.10–8) and (14.10–12) is related to the potential of the equipotential chosen for quantization, $-V_0$, by $\epsilon = \text{sech } V_0$, exactly as in the later applications of this method of approximation.

14-37. The formulas of § 14.10 show the exponential potential, for the symmetric charge distributions discussed there, to be real when $\sigma = 0$ and hence identifiable directly with $R(\omega)$. Show by a sketch of the flux plot why this is so.

14-38. Calculate and plot to scale the curves of Fig. 14.10–A. For a nominal resistance of 100 Ω at low frequencies, and a tolerable error of $\pm 10\%$, obtain network realizations. Can these be predistorted to allow for an average dissipation of $d = 0.01$?

14-39. Show, by solving (14.11–1) for na and then developing in series, that

$$na = \frac{1}{2}\ln\frac{2}{\epsilon} - \frac{1}{8}\epsilon^2 - \frac{3}{64}\epsilon^4 - \frac{1}{48}\epsilon^6 + \cdots.$$

Evaluate the error made in using only the first term to determine na (as suggested in § 14.11), for various values of ϵ. Draw a curve, on semilogarithmic coordinate paper, from which na can be read for values of ϵ from 0.001 to 1.

14-40. Derive (14.11–1) from (14.10–11). Alternatively, show first from (14.10–9) that $\tanh^2 na = (1 - \epsilon)/(1 + \epsilon)$ and from this obtain (14.11–1) with the aid of the formula $\tanh^2 (x/2) = (\cosh x - 1)/(\cosh x + 1)$, which is also to be demonstrated.

14-41. For the type of network whose design is summarized in § 14.11, plot, for fixed values of n, the resistance at a frequency 20% above the upper end of the approximation band as a function of the error ripple ϵ. Explain how these curves could be used to determine n, given the error tolerance permitted in the approximation band and a requirement on rate of falloff beyond the approximation band.

14-42. Design networks whose driving-point resistances meet the following requirements, using the method of § 14.11.

Nominal Resistance in Approximation Band	Approximation Band	Tolerable Departure of Resistance in Approximation Band	Falloff Requirement on Resistance
600 Ω	0–35 kcps	±5%	Down to 100 Ω at 70 kcps
75 Ω	0–1 mcps	±5%	Down to 0.22 Ω at 1.5 mcps
50 Ω	0–5 mcps	±1%	Down to 5 Ω at 6 mcps

Plot the transmission, $|E_{\text{out}}/I_{\text{in}}|^2$, as a function of frequency, for these networks used as two-terminal pairs in the fashion of § 11.04.

Discuss the possibility of predistortion to compensate for (approximately uniform) dissipation corresponding to an average reactive-element Q at the upper edge of the approximation band of 200, of 100, of 50, in each problem.

14-43. For the special low-band case of even-function approximation of a constant with all zeros at infinity, show that the poles of the Chebyshev approximation can be obtained from those of the Taylor approximation by the following geometrical construction. Here the Chebyshev approximation band is $0 < \omega < 1$ and $\epsilon = \text{sech } V_0 = \text{sech } na$. The order of the approximating function is $2n$.

1. Draw the circle that is the locus of the poles of the Taylor approximation (§ 13.10) with a radius $\omega_0 = \cosh a$. Mark the locations of the poles on it.

2. Draw the ellipse tangent to the circle at $\pm j\omega_0$, with real intercepts $\pm \sinh a$. (This may be derived from the circle by multiplying the *abscissae* of its points by $\tanh a$.)

3. Move the poles from the circle on horizontal lines to the ellipse. These new positions are those required for the Chebyshev approximation.

Verify all the statements above, both for n odd and for n even. Illustrate with careful sketches for $n = 5$ and $n = 6$, $\epsilon = 0.1$.

14-44. Describe, giving formulas as necessary, how points would be calculated to form a basis for an accurate drawing of Fig. 14.12–B. In particular, give equations (in p) whose roots trace out the π lines (both odd and even) as the parameter ϵ (contained therein) is varied from 1 to 0. How may points on other lines be found?

14-45. Give the value attained by Φ in Fig. 14.12–B on the ω axis at a point $p_1 = j\omega_1$ between $\omega = 1$ and $\omega = 1.25$ when one starts from a point $p_0 = -\omega_1$ on the negative σ axis and reaches p_1 by each of the following paths:

(a) a straight line from p_0 to p_1;
(b) a circle from p_0 through $\bar{p}_1$ and on to p_1;
(c) a series of straight lines: p_0 to $p_0 - j2\omega_1$, to $-p_0 - j2\omega_1$, to p_1;
(d) a series of straight lines: p_0 to $p_0 + j2\omega_1$, to $-p_0 + j2\omega_1$, to p_1;
(e) a series of straight lines: p_0 to $p_0 - j2\omega_1$, to $-p_0 - j2\omega_1$, to $\bar{p}_1$, then on

to p_1 clockwise on a circle through p_1 and $\bar{p}_1$, centered on the origin. Explain the discrepancies.

14-46. Find the numerical locations of the saddle points in Fig. 14.12–B. (Consider the possibility of using an equation in p, of using one in w, and of using one in $z = e^w$, and decide which is the most convenient.) Are these points still saddle points in the electric field associated with the quantized charge distribution (for which the complex potential is W_q? Where do the saddle points in the W_q field come, in general, with respect to the W (prototype, before-quantization) field?

14-47. Draw rough sketches similar to Fig. 14.12–C for each of the situations given in Table 1, showing a few typical equipotentials and those flux lines that are the loci of the quantized charge positions. Indicate clearly where the quantized charges lie for small, intermediate, and large values of ϵ.

A resistance function is to approximate a constant from $\omega = 0$ to $\omega = 1$, subject to the conditions given in Table 1. In each case give the equation whose roots determine the locations of the poles of Ev $Z(p)$.

Table 1

Zeros of Resistance (Prescribed)

Order of Final Impedance Function	At Infinity	Finite
4	4	Two at $+j2$
4	None	Four at $+j2$
5	2	Two at $+j1.5$, two at $+j2$
5	2	Four at $+j1.25$
6	None	Two at $+j1.5$, two at $+j2$, two at $+j2.5$
6	4	Two at $+j1.5$, two at $+j2$
6	8	Two at $+j1.5$
4	4	Two at $-1 + j0$
4	4	One at $-1 + j1$

Select a value of ϵ and carry through to completion the network-synthesis problem in one of the above cases.

14-48. Make a rough flux plot for the charge distribution of Fig. 14.12–D, not forgetting the charge at infinity. Do the same for the charge distribution of Fig. 14.12–E and compare the plots.

14-49. Verify that if the *left* half of the w plane in Fig. 14.12–D is considered, exactly the same result is obtained for the complex potential in the p plane.

14-50. Explain, with the aid of the Riemann-surface concept and a corresponding change in point of view of the p-plane potential problem, the p-plane significance of the potential in the left half of the w plane of Fig. 14.12–E.

14-51. Make a flux plot in the w plane of the transformed prototype problem of § 14.05. From this plot determine the complex potential, show that it can be written, as a function of p, as

$$W = Q \ln (\sqrt[+]{p^2 + 1} - p).$$

Show that the equations for quantization,

$$W = -V_0 + j[0, 2\pi, 4\pi, \cdots, (Q - 1)2\pi], \qquad Q/2 \text{ odd},$$

$$= -V_0 + j[\pi, 3\pi, 5\pi, \cdots, \pi + (Q - 1)2\pi], \qquad Q/2 \text{ even},$$

are the same in effect as (14.11–4).

14-52. Show that the limit as $a \to \infty$ of (14.12–3) is e^{-2w}, as stated in the text just before (14.12–4), and explain the physical change that corresponds to this limitless increase in a, and hence why e^{-2w} *should* have this limit.

14-53. Show that (14.12–5) represents a complex-potential function that satisfies Laplace's equation and meets the boundary conditions of the problem; in particular, verify not only the potential on the v axis, but the amount of flux emanating therefrom, and the locations and amounts of lumped charges, and the behavior at infinity. Repeat for (14.12–9), in the p plane. If the *other* square root were used in (14.12–9), of what problem would (14.12–9) be the exponential potential?

14-54. Derive the formulas of (14.12–7) and (14.12–8), explaining carefully the choice of branch for the square roots. Then derive (14.12–9) and (14.12–11).

14-55. Consider the function $F(p) = \sqrt[+]{p^2 + 1}$. Is it odd, even, or neither? Using your result, determine whether the function e^W as given by (14.12–9) is odd, even, or neither. Check your result by examining the associated flux plot. As a further check, write the exponential potential that results when the length of the conductor is reduced to zero so that all the positive charge is concentrated at the origin, the negative charge being untouched, and examine its symmetries.

14-56. The equation (14.12–13), which determines the points of quantization in the associated problem, has six roots (as can be seen from the flux plot). It may be cast in algebraic form as a polynomial set equal to zero in various ways, of which (14.12–28) is reached in the simplest fashion.

(*a*) Show that this form may also be obtained from (14.12–9) by performing the squaring operations, cross multiplying, collecting terms to obtain an equation in form $A + pB\sqrt{p^2 + 1} = 0$, and finally multiplying this by $A - pB\sqrt{p^2 + 1} = 0$ to eliminate the radical. Contrast the labor required by the two methods.

(*b*) An alternative procedure is first to "rationalize" (14.12–9) by multiplying numerator and denominator of the right side by $(\sqrt{p^2 + 1} - mp)^2$ and then to collect terms and remove the radical as in (*a*). Show that this involves even more labor and leads to an algebraic equation in p of degree ten. What are the four extraneous roots of this equation?

14-57. Calculate the polynomial B in (14.12–16). By letting $m = 1$ obtain a check on both B and A, using the expansion of $\sqrt{p^2 + 1} - p$ to the appropriate power. An equation whose roots determine the points of quantization may be obtained in terms of B, rather than of A, as in (14.12–22). Show that this equation is

$$\frac{pB\sqrt{p^2 + 1}}{[(1 - m^2)p^2 + 1]^2} = \sinh(-V_0) = -\sinh V_0.$$

Discuss its utility in comparison with that of (14.12–22).

14-58. Starting from the point p_0 at which $\Phi = 0$ in Fig. 14.12–G, follow the indicated path up to p_1, then around the negative charge at $j\omega_1$ and back to p_1, and verify the two values given for W at p_1 in the text, using Fig. 14.12–B. By following a similar path, obtained by reflecting this one in the σ axis, obtain the values of W at $\bar{p}_1$, on first and second arrivals there. Explain how your results indicate that the W plane has three sheets, and trace out the corresponding paths therein, using Fig. 14.12–H. Trace out the rectangular path defined by the following points in the W plane in succession, both on the sheets of the W plane and in the p plane, correlating the two:

$$(\tfrac{1}{2}V_{\mathrm{sp}}, 0), \quad (\tfrac{1}{2}V_{\mathrm{sp}}, 6\pi), \quad (2V_{\mathrm{sp}}, 6\pi), \quad (2V_{\mathrm{sp}}, 0), \quad (\tfrac{1}{2}V_{\mathrm{sp}}, 0).$$

Explain now why the three sheets of the W plane carry identical charge distributions, after quantization, and how this depends on the symmetry of the quantized charges in the p plane. How do the three charges that lie one above the other, at the "same point" in the W plane, correlate to the charges in the p plane?

14-59. Derive (14.12–15) from Fig. 14.12–I.

14-60. Verify (14.12–18) by calculating the a's. Determine also the polynomial B in (14.12–16). Verify (14.12–19) by the method indicated there; explain why the only difference between (14.12–16) and (14.12–19) is in the sign before the square root.

14-61. Show that (14.12–15), regarded as a function of p, is rational, of order six, by finding its singularities and its zeros and showing that these are finite in number and that each is of finite order; do this without invoking the explicit function-of-p relations, such as (14.12–16), but use only the flux plot. Explain the statement in the two sentences immediately following (14.12–23).

14-62. Sketch, in a complex-number plane, the loci of the complex potential W and the exponential potential e^W, as p moves along the positive ω axis from the origin to infinity in Fig. 14.12–B. Show what happens in each of the possible cases, starting on the left side and on the right side of the approximation-band conductor; show also the effect of passing around the negative charge to the left and to the right. Explain the physical meaning of these various possibilities. Explain the sharp corners in Fig. 14.12–K: why are the derivatives not continuous? Explain why the multiple-valued nature of Φ is of no consequence in the approximation problem treated in § 14.12.

14-63. Derive (14.12–25) and (14.12–26).

14-64. Show that the saddle points in the problems discussed in § 14.12, and in similar situations, are saddle points in both the prototype (W) and quantized (W_q) fields.

14-65. Consider the numerical calculations necessary for obtaining data to draw the solid curve of Fig. 14.12–M (and that of Fig. 14.12–L). One method is to use (14.12–9) to calculate the prototype exponential potential, and then to use the results in (14.12–29) and (14.12–30). An alternative is to use (14.12–5) to calculate the prototype exponential potential, in which case one finds

$$\Phi = -2v - 4\tan^{-1}(m\tan v) \quad \text{in the approximation band } (\omega = \sin v),$$

and

$$e^W = -e^{-2u}\frac{\sinh^2(u-a)}{\sinh^2(u+a)} \quad \text{beyond the approximation band } (\omega = \cosh u).$$

The calculations are performed with v and u as the independent variables and then transformed to ω points by the formulas given. To what do these reduce in the case of the dashed curve (when all negative charge is at infinity)?

Derive these formulas and compare the work required by the two methods. Which method do you prefer?

14-66. Find the element values for the network of Fig. 14.12–M, taking $\epsilon = 0.1$, $\omega_1 = 1.25$; find also the element values in two other realizations of the same driving-point resistance function.

14-67. Derive formulas for the prototype exponential potential, similar to the factors of (14.12–32), for (a) two units of positive charge on the approximation-band conductor and two units of negative charge on the σ axis at $\pm\sigma_1$; (b) four units of positive charge on the approximation-band conductor and four units of negative charge symmetrically located in the four quadrants at p_0, $\bar{p}_0$, $-p_0$, and $-\bar{p}_0$, p_0 being complex. What kind of numerical value does the parameter m take in each case?

Show that in the appropriate limit, the formula for (a) reduces to the appropriate part of (14.12–32); do the same for (b).

Discuss, with numerical illustrations, how positioning the negative charges as in (b) has the effect of making the spacing of the maxima of error in the approximation band more nearly equal, after quantization has been performed. To what does this correspond in the prototype-potential problem?

14-68. Explain the need for the *two* equations (14.12–34) and (14.12–35), and derive (14.12–36) and (14.12–37). Verify that the exponential potential given by these last two equations is rational and has the prescribed zeros and appropriate poles.

14-69. Show that in the prototype problem for the general case of arbitrarily prescribed zeros of § 14.12, the flux function Φ is, on the ω axis for $|\omega| > 1$, constant at multiples of π except for discontinuities at the zeros. Show that these multiples are odd when $Q/2$ is odd, even when $Q/2$ is even.

14-70. Verify (14.12–40) and evaluate the constants in (14.12–36) and (14.12–37) to obtain (14.12–41).

14-71. Show that in general the polynomials A and B in (14.12–44) have the properties there stated. Obtain the equations whose roots are the points of quantization for the cases given in Table 2. Sketch the behavior of the resistance function obtained versus frequency.

Table 2

Prescribed Zeros of the Resistance Function (*All* Its Zeros Are Listed Here)		Tolerable Error (Departure from Unity) in the Approximation Band, $0 < \omega < 1$
Locations (Values of ω)	Orders	
(a) $\quad +2$	2	
$\quad\quad -2$	2	$\pm 5\%$
$\quad\quad \infty$	2	
(b) $\quad +1.25$	2	
$\quad\quad -1.25$	2	
$\quad\quad +2$	2	$\pm 3\%$
$\quad\quad -2$	2	
(c) $\quad +1.25$	4	
$\quad\quad -1.25$	4	$\pm 1\%$
$\quad\quad \infty$	2	

14-72. The equation of quantization (14.12–46) must in general be solved numerically, a process that is expedited by having a knowledge of approximate values of the roots (Appendix A) to start with. Show that if *all* the prescribed zeros lie at a single pair of points $\pm j\omega_0$ (a very special case) the equation may readily be solved exactly. [*Suggestion:* Reconsider (14.12–32), (14.12–34), and (14.12–35).] Discuss the possibility of using this solution, with an "average" value of m, to give a starting point (set of approximate roots) in the general case. Discuss also the possibility of using a rough (freehand-sketch) flux plot with appropriate flux lines, as a practical source of approximate roots.

14-73. Realize networks with driving-point resistances that meet the following requirements, using no more elements than necessary. In each case give schematic diagrams and a plot of resistance versus ω. (Discuss alternative realizations, once the approximation problem is solved, from the point of view of practicality.)

(a) Resistance is to be constant at the value 75 $\Omega \pm 1\%$ in the band from zero to 176 kcps, to be zero at 220 kcps, and zero at high frequencies.

(b) Resistance is to be constant at the value 600 $\Omega \pm 2\%$ in the band from zero to 3 mcps, to be zero at 3.1, 3.2, 3.5, and 4 mcps, and at high frequencies.

14-74. (a) Show that a rational equation of quantization like (14.12–46), or the corresponding expression in other problems, can be obtained from (14.12–32) by making the substitution $x = \sqrt{p^2 + 1}/p$ and using (14.12–34) or (14.12–35). Carry this out for the first case discussed in § 14.12 and compare the two equations of quantization (one in p, one in x) and discuss the relative amounts of labor required in each method of obtaining the points of quantization in the p plane. Is the polynomial-splitting method (Appendix A) applicable when the change of variable to x is used?

(b) The quantization equation (14.14–19) can also be obtained by such a change of variable, rather than by forming cosh W by the process indicated in the text just before (14.14–19). The appropriate substitution here is

$$x = \sqrt{\frac{p^2 + \omega_1{}^2}{p^2 + \omega_2{}^2}},$$

to be used in (14.14–10). Give a discussion of this method similar to that called for in (a), using the example of Fig. 14.14–J for illustration.

14-75. Design a network whose driving-point resistance function meets the requirements shown, using no more elements than necessary. Show how the use of the w plane for the trials can expedite the process. (Cf. Prob. 14-65.)

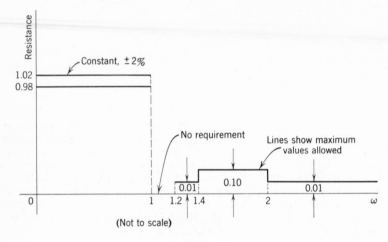

Prob. 14–75

14-76. Solve completely the network-synthesis problem outlined by Fig. 14.12–O, assuming that the nominal value of resistance at low frequencies is unity, the limits are ± 0.02 for $0 < \omega < 1$, and the dotted lines remain at a distance of 0.02 from the solid ones and that the "break points" of the characteristic are at $\omega = 1$, 1.3, 1.6, 2, 2.5, 3.

14-77. In § 14.12 the even-π (or odd-π) flux lines are shown to be loci on which the points of quantization move out from the conductor toward the negative charges as ϵ varies from 1 to 0. Show that it is possible to take a purely algebraic view of this "motion" as outlined below, and that exactly the same equations must be solved and the same numerical values result. (Cf. also Prob. 14-104.)

(a) Obtain the points in the approximation band where these π lines terminate.

(b) Form a rational function whose *poles* are the prescribed zeros of $R(\omega)$ and whose *zeros* are the terminal points of the appropriate π lines on the approximation band. Show here that this function has the general behavior of oscillation between 0 and 1 in the approximation band if the multiplier is properly chosen, and rises to infinity at each of the prescribed zeros of $R(\omega)$ if these are on the ω axis. Where are the maxima in the approximation band, and the minima, in terms of the terminal points of the π lines?

(c) Add to this rational function a constant K. What is the new behavior as a function of ω?

(d) Form a new rational function by inverting that of step (c) and then multiplying by a constant K'. Sketch this last function's behavior and show that it is the same as that obtained by the methods of § 14.12. Evaluate K and K' in terms of ϵ.

With this point of view "adding a constant" takes the place of "motion on the π lines." Illustrate your discussion with actual sketches and equations for these specific cases: (1) order of (low-band) resistance function is six, all zeros at infinity; (2) order of resistance function is eight, two zeros at $+j1.25$, four zeros at infinity.

14-78. For each of the following approximation-to-a-constant problems make a sketch of the loci of the motion of the quantized charges, similar to that of Fig. 14.14–K, and correlate it with the flux plot for the prototype problem. The function is to be realized as a driving-point resistance or conductance.

Approximation Band	Number and Location of Zeros
$0 < \omega < 1$	6, all at infinity
$0 < \omega < 1$	8, all at infinity
$0 < \omega < 1$	10, 2 each at $+j2$, $+j4$, ∞
$1 < \omega < 2$	16, 8 at the origin, 8 at infinity
$1 < \omega < 2$	16, 4 at the origin, 2 at $+j0.5$, 2 at $+j3$, 1 at $-2 + j3$

Explain how the "add a constant" (algebraic) view of Prob. 14-77 applies equally well to both low-band and internal-band problems, illustrating with sketches for the foregoing problems.

14-79. Verify the details of the mapping of Figs. 14.13–C and –D as described in § 14.13, and the transformation formulas of Table 14.13–A and Fig. 14.13–E.

Show that Chebyshev approximation of a constant remains Chebyshev approximation of the same constant, with the same limits of error, when the low-band-designed network is transformed to a high-band network.

Plot the behavior of the reactance of an inductor (and of a capacitor) on the ω' scale of Fig. 14.13–D and that of the corresponding element in the transformed network on the corresponding ω scale; from these curves alone demonstrate the same fact.

If the network designed in the p' domain happens to be realized with a Brune network that includes a negative inductance, the transformed network will include a negative capacitance. Show that the driving-point impedance of the transformed network is still p-r (because p and p' are p-r functions of each other) and suggest a more attractive schematic. With this possibility in mind, discuss the advisability of making the p' design in the dual Brune form (Fig. 9.06–B).

14-80. Discuss the compensation in the p' domain of parasitic dissipation in the p domain, in the frequency transformation of § 14.13. In particular, how does the horizontal movement of zeros and poles in the p domain due to uniform dissipation appear in the p' domain? How should predistortion be made in the p' domain? Illustrate with a numerical example.

14-81. Design networks to meet the following specifications:

(a) Resistance to be constant within $3 \pm \%$ of the nominal value 300 Ω at all frequencies above 10 kcps, descending to zero at zero frequency (where the resistance function is to have six zeros).

(b) Conductance to be constant within $\pm 1\%$ of the nominal value 72^{-1} mhos at all frequencies above 1 mcps, with zero value at the frequencies 0.7, 0.5 mcps (two zeros at each), and the origin (four zeros there).

14-82. Set up the transformation required for the solution of the problem of § 14.14 by the "bending" technique of § 14.09 and obtain the differential equation for the new variable w by the Schwarz-Christoffel transformation. Verify, by consulting a table of integrals, that elliptic functions are required to give the relation between p and w.

14-83. Show that the value of a in Fig. 14.14–F is given by

$$\cosh a = \frac{[(\omega_2{}^2 + \omega_1{}^2)/2] - \omega_0{}^2}{(\omega_2{}^2 - \omega_1{}^2)/2}.$$

Verify the evaluation of $\tanh a/2$ in (14.14–8) by both of the methods there suggested.

14-84. Explain the choice of branch to be made in (14.14–6) and in all the subsequent formulas that involve square roots, in § 14.14. Make use of the mappings and of flux considerations in the analogs.

14-85. Verify Fig. 14.14–G from the analog, by flux considerations. The figure is drawn for passage to the right of the conductors; show that passage to the left changes the figure slightly but has no effect on any of the associated reasoning. Verify that (14.14–8) has only the proper zeros and singularities, has constant magnitude in the approximation bands, and that its change in angle over each approximation band corresponds to the flux emanating therefrom in the analog.

14-86. Sketch the locus of e^W as given by (14.14–9) in a complex-number plane as ω varies from zero to infinity.

14-87. Derive the expression to be used in (14.14–10) for (a) a pair of zeros at prescribed points on the σ axis; (b) a tetrad of prescribed complex zeros. (Cf. Prob. 14–67.)

14-88. In §§ 14.12 and 14.14 the flux function is evaluated on the ω axis by passing charge (distributed and lumped) sometimes on the right and sometimes on the left. In developing the end results, the rational-function approximations that come from quantizing, does it make any difference, in any case, on which side the passage is made? Explain.

14-89. Show that (14.14–10) leads indeed to a rational function of p for $\cosh W$. Illustrate by obtaining the quantized exponential potential for the case shown in Fig. 14.14–J, taking specific numerical values for the important frequencies, if desired. Make a plot, to scale, of Fig. 14.14–J.

14-90. Obtain networks that meet the following requirements, the driving-point resistance being an approximation of a constant in an internal band:

Zeros (All Prescribed)	Approximation Band	Resistance in Approximation Band
(a) 4 at the origin 4 at infinity	$1 < \omega < 2$	$1 \pm 0.05 \ \Omega$
(b) 4 at the origin 4 at $+j1$ 4 at infinity	$2 < \omega < 4$	$1 \pm 0.1 \ \Omega$

14-91. Discuss completely the *Chebyshev* solution of the approximation problem for all the vacuum-tube interstage networks of Prob. 13-87. Give qualitative sketches of the transmission (gain) characteristics showing clearly the number of ripples obtainable, outline the design procedure, and carry it through for at least one specific case. What are the limitations on the ripple ϵ, or (if there are none) what is the effect on the characteristic of varying ϵ? What limits the value of (nominally constant) gain in the approximation band?

14-92. In (14.14–10) and the subsequent discussion it is assumed that the total positive charge used in finding the resistance (conductance) function is a multiple of four. Then the number of positive charges on each prototype conductor is even, and the charge on each side of each conductor is integral. This has the advantage that the loci (or trajectories) of quantization (on which the positive charges move out from the conductors) fan out symmetrically into each quadrant, avoiding the ω axis. It is possible, however, to use an odd number of positive charges on each prototype conductor. Then, with symmetrical quantization, one quantized charge travels along the ω axis from the approximation band to the origin (or to infinity), there to meet, at a saddle point, its mate from the lower half of the plane. The two charges now move off on the real axis until they take up their final positions. Discuss this possibility in detail for the following cases.

(*a*) Three units of charge on each prototype conductor; negative charge prescribed of two units at a point above the approximation band and one unit at a point on the real axis, with other charges only as required by symmetry. Discuss the variations that occur here if the single units of negative charge are both at the origin, or both at infinity, instead of on the real axis.

(*b*) Same as (*a*) except that the two-unit charge is at a point *below* the approximation band.

(*c*) Five units of charge on each prototype conductor; negative charge prescribed of two units at one point above the approximation band, two units at another point above the approximation band, one unit at a point on the real axis. What changes occur if the charges lie *below* rather than above the approximation band?

(*d*) Same as (*c*) except that the negative charges lie, one unit each, at the points $-a + j(0, b, 2b)$.

What characteristic of the final resistance-frequency function differs markedly from those obtained in § 14.14? Is there a limitation on the size of the ripple that can be obtained?

Is it possible, in such cases, to prescribe negative charge at points both above *and* below the approximation band? Explain.

Is it possible, when the total positive charge used is a multiple of four, to "rotate" the quantization picture, so that two charges leave the approximation band on the ω axis, one going to the origin and one to infinity? If so, under what conditions? What characterizes the shape of the final resistance (conductance) curve?

Could such a technique as that just described be applied in a low-band resistance (conductance) problem? In a high-band problem? Explain.

14-93. Develop the theory and formulas that follow (14.14–10) for the case where the number of zeros at the origin is $2(2m + 1)$, i.e., twice an odd integer, and the number of zeros at infinity is in the same category. Point out, in particular, the necessary changes of sign in (14.14–15) and subsequent formulas. Illustrate by an example formed from Fig. 14.14–J by removing two of the zeros at the origin and two of those at infinity.

14-94. A network whose driving-point resistance approximates a constant in an internal band in the Chebyshev fashion is to have a driving-point impedance function of order six, with the zeros of the resistance function divided equally between the origin and infinity. Give the schematic form of a network realization that uses only one resistor.

Give the schematic forms of all other reasonable realizations in the same category, obtained by varying the sequence of removing zeros of the resistance in the synthesis.

Complete this tableau of schematic diagrams by doing the same for the other possibilities of dividing the zeros of the resistance between the origin and infinity.

14-95. In both § 14.12 and § 14.14 the exponential potential for what might be called a basic component in the solution takes the form

$$e^W = \frac{\sqrt{F(p)} - K}{\sqrt{F(p)} + K}$$

in which K is a (real) constant and $F(p)$ takes various forms. Show that if F is the ratio (or product) of two reactance functions, a solution of a prototype-potential problem results. Find these reactance functions for the following cases.

Kind of Approximation Band	Positive Charge on (Each) Conductor	Location of Negative Charge
Low	Two units	Two units at infinity
Low	Two units	One unit each at $\pm j\omega_1$
Internal	Two units	Various

What relation between the two reactance functions changes at the edges of the approximation band(s)?

Discuss briefly why the solution of more complicated problems is not possible with such functions.

14-96. Show that the frequency transformation

$$\frac{p}{\omega_0} = K\left(\frac{s}{\omega_0} + \frac{\omega_0}{s}\right), \qquad p = \sigma + j\omega, \ s = \Sigma + j\Omega,$$

transforms a low band in the p plane into an internal band in the s plane. Determine the relations between the (low) approximation band in the p plane, $0 < \omega < \omega_0$, and the (internal) approximation band in the s plane, $\Omega_a < \Omega < \Omega_b$, the frequencies ω_0, Ω_a, and Ω_b being prescribed. What are convenient values to give K and ω_0?

Determine the corresponding schematic-diagram transformation and give element value formulas in terms of (prescribed) ω_0, Ω_a, Ω_b, and nominal value of resistance, R_0.

Discuss the complete mapping of the p plane on the s plane, pointing out the various parts of the s plane into which the p plane maps.

Show that to map a given point p_0 to the s plane it is necessary to solve a quadratic equation. Explain the multiplicity of solutions. Expand the solutions in series useful for small and for large values of p where a small number of terms suffice, and illustrate their application.

If the internal approximation band in the s plane is narrow, in what way does the transformation simplify? Estimate the error in simply translating the p-plane diagrams to appropriate positions in the s plane. Illustrate by plotting the exact transformations to the s plane of circles and ellipses in the p plane and comparing with circles and ellipses centered there on $\pm j\omega_0$, both for narrow s-plane approximation bands where the error is negligible, and for bandwidths in which it is appreciable. (Cf. also Prob. 15-17.)

14-97. Certain problems of the class discussed in § 14.14 may be solved by transforming a previously designed low-band approximation (or network) into an internal-band approximation (or network) by the frequency transformation

$$p = \frac{\omega_0}{2} \left(\frac{s}{\Omega_0} + \frac{\Omega_0}{s} \right)$$

in which s is the new frequency variable (of the internal-band problem), Ω_0 is a reference frequency or scale factor in the s plane, and p is the (unnormalized) frequency variable in the original (low-band) problem (Prob. 14-96).

(a) What limitations are imposed on the nature of an internal-band approximation that comes from a low-band function through this transformation? Illustrate with sketches (charge distribution and real-frequency behavior) of functions that can be so derived and others that cannot. Show also schematic diagrams of network realizations (without element values) and compare them also in this light.

(b) If this method is acceptable, determine formulas that convert the internal-band problem data (frequencies of approximation-band limits and locations of prescribed zeros) into corresponding data for the low-band problem. Also, obtain formulas that will convert the schematic diagrams of the network solution of the low-band problem into the appropriate internal-band network.

14-98. Consider a network of internal-band nature, designed by frequency transformation of a low-band network (Probs. 14-96, 14-97). In the former, the presence of individual incidental dissipation shifts all zeros and poles a distance d to the left (§§ 12.02, 12.03). Show that to a first approximation this corresponds to a similar shift in the prototype low-band network. Under what conditions is this approximation a good one? In a wide-band (or heavily dissipative) case is it possible to show the effect of uniform dissipation in the internal-band network in the low-band prototype? Explain. Illustrate by calculating and plotting the actual pole-zero motion in the internal-band network corresponding to a uniform motion in the low-band prototype.

14-99. Describe qualitatively, with sketches, the potential analog for Chebyshev solution of the approximation problem in each of the following cases.

(a) A resistance is to be constant (at the same value) in the bands $0 < \omega < \omega_1$ and $\omega_3 < \omega < \infty$, and to be zero at $\omega = \omega_2$, a point that lies between the two bands.

(b) A resistance is to be constant (at the same value) in the bands $1 < \omega < 2$ and $4 < \omega < 6$, and to be zero at the origin, at $\omega = 3$ and at infinity.

Outline a method of solution of the approximation problem.

14-100. Discuss the finding of a network whose driving-point resistance is to approximate constants, in the Chebyshev sense, in three bands (within ±0.1 in each) according to the illustration shown.

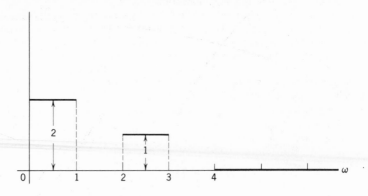

Prob. 14–100

14-101. A resistance function is to have $2r$ zeros at the origin, $2s$ zeros at infinity, and to be maximally flat at $\omega = 1$. Set up the electrostatic problem for the potential-analogy method of solution and draw a flux plot that shows how the poles are determined. Verify that the results are the same as when the algebraic method of Chapter 13 is used by obtaining from the flux plot the equation whose roots are the pole locations. Of what Chebyshev approximation is this a limit?

Explain the solution of Probs. 13-87 and 14-91 in this light.

14-102. Determine a driving-point resistance function that is flat (at unit value) at both the origin and $\omega = 3$, with two zeros each at $\omega = 1$, $\omega = 2$, $\omega = 4$, $\omega = 5$, and infinity. Distribute the flatness available equally between the two points $\omega = 0$ and $\omega = 3$, and determine the constant to give the value 0.5 at $\omega = 0.75$. Perform the approximation both algebraically (as in Chapter 13) and in terms of the potential analog, verifying that both approaches give the same result. In the latter case illustrate the "quantization" process with a flux plot. Complete the network realization.

If Chebyshev approximation, rather than Taylor approximation, were required in the vicinity of the origin and of $\omega = 3$, how would the work change?

14-103. Maximal approximation of a constant at some frequency, with an even function, is obtained, from the potential-analogy point of view, by placing negative charges at the prescribed zeros, positive charges at the points where maximal approximation is desired, and then quantizing—or better, since the positive charge is already lumped, *distributing*—the positive charge on equi-potentials of this prototype situation, on appropriate flux lines.

Explain how this is simply the limiting procedure of Chebyshev approximation (§ 14.15). What determines which equipotential is to be used here for "quantizing," since there is no ϵ? Correlate this with the effect, in Chebyshev approximation, of the choice of ϵ on the rate of falling off outside the approximation band.

The following algebraic procedure accomplishes the same result. Write a function with poles at the positions of the prescribed zeros, zeros at the point(s) where maximal approximation is desired, and an arbitrary multiplier; add to this a constant of appropriate magnitude and sign; the reciprocal of the resulting function is the desired function. Correlate this algebraic procedure with the potential-analogy procedure, showing that they are identical. Explain in particular how the addition of the constant moves the positive charges out on flux lines to their final positions. Plot the function used in the algebraic procedure versus ω and show how the addition of a constant changes it to the reciprocal of the desired function without affecting the quality of the Taylor approximation. Correlate the motion of the zeros here with that of the positive charges in the analog.

Illustrate with the following examples.

Order of (Even) Approximating Function	Point of Maximal Approximation (of Unity)	Locations of Prescribed Zeros
8	0	8 at ∞
8	0	4 at ∞, 2 at $+j3$
8	$+j1$	4 at the origin, 4 at ∞
9	$+j2$	2 at $+j1$, 2 at $+j3$

If Chebyshev, rather than Taylor approximation is desired, what should be the behavior of the function to which a constant is added? (Cf. Probs. 14-77, 14-104.)

14-104. The Chebyshev "add a constant" approach of Prob. 14-77 can be expedited (and perhaps illuminated) by utilizing the *exponential-potential* plane, i.e., the plane of e^W rather than the plane of W. To show this, consider the low-band approximation of a constant with an even function, all the zeros being at infinity by prescription.

(*a*) Sketch the prototype potential-analogy situation and show the quantization procedure in both the p plane and the w plane, defined by $p = \sinh w$. (Here the w plane is the complex-potential plane, normalized for unit charge on the prototype conductor.)

(*b*) Develop the mapping to the exponential-potential plane, defined (for unit charge on the conductor) by

$$z = e^w, \quad \text{i.e., } p = \frac{1}{2}\left(z - \frac{1}{z}\right).$$

Show in particular that the approximation band of the p plane maps to the unit circle centered on the origin of the z plane, and that the p plane is two-sheeted, one sheet mapping to the exterior of the unit circle, one to its interior. What is the mapping relation between the planes of w and of z? Explain the quantization procedure graphically in the z plane.

(*c*) Set up the prototype problem in the z plane. Show that the circular conductor can be replaced, as far as conditions outside the unit circle go, by a lumped charge at the origin. With what interpretation of conditions of the two sheets of the p plane will this replacement also have no effect on the conditions *inside* the unit circle?

Write the exponential-potential function for the z-plane problem thus revised (lumped charge at the origin and at infinity, no conductor, no other charge). Show that on addition of a constant to the reciprocal of this function the lumped charge at the origin will move out on appropriate radii. Plot the "quantized" potential along the unit circle for various values of the constant (various values of the amount of radial motion), deriving and using the expression

$$e^{V_q} = |e^{-W} + K| = K^2 + 2K \cos 2n\theta + 1.$$

Here V_q represents the potential after adding the constant K (whose sign is to be discussed) to the prototype potential function e^W, and θ is the central angle in the z plane in polar coordinates. Show that after the charge has passed the unit circle we have exactly the points of quantization determined previously by quantization in the p plane (using the w plane as a guide). Develop a formula for the amount of radial motion necessary to obtain a given error ripple ϵ.

Show also that by starting with charge appropriately quantized on the approximation band in the p plane (at locations determined by the flux function of the prototype problem which must there equal appropriate multiples of π), as in Prob. 14-77, the same result is obtained by adding a constant. Correlate this procedure with that in the z plane above, and with plots of the exponential potential versus w as the constant is added in.

Discuss completely what happens to this procedure in the limiting case (Chebyshev becomes Taylor approximation) and how the procedure of Prob. 14-103 results. What relation then exists between the p and z planes? These procedures can be extended to the cases of arbitrarily prescribed zeros, and of high and internal bands. Give a brief discussion of the important changes necessitated by such new features. In particular, point out what the prototype situation is, in the z plane, when zeros of a low-band resistance problem problem are prescribed at points other than infinity. Is there then any change *in principle* in the method?

14-105. Go back and interpret the procedure of resistance (conductance) reduction (Chapters 8, 9) in terms of the potential analogy and the process of adding (subtracting) a constant. (Cf. Prob. 9-44.)

Discuss also the addition of a constant to a proposed $|Z|^2$ function, in order to insure a p-r result for $Z(p)$, in this light. (Cf. Prob. 8-103.)

14-106. It has been pointed out that in even-function approximation of a constant, the zeros of the approximating function are entirely arbitrary as far as quality of approximation goes. This problem considers briefly the possibility of prescribing *poles* of the approximating function.

Let it be required to find an even function of order ten that is to approximate unity in Chebyshev fashion in a low band, $0 < \omega < 1$; it is to have simple poles at the prescribed points ($\pm \alpha$, 0).

Show that if all the zeros are to be at infinity, and maximal quality of approximation is to be obtained, the prescription on the poles cannot in general be met. What is the exceptional case?

Show now that if it is permitted to place some of the zeros at certain points, the prescription on the poles can be met without sacrifice of quality of approximation. What is the minimum number of zeros that must be moved from infinity, and where must they be placed? Consider all cases that may arise for values of α between zero and infinity. (Both algebraic and graphic, or potential-analogy, discussions are to be given.) Comment on the realization as driving-point resistance of the resulting function, particularly if only one resistor is to be used.

If it is required that all the zeros remain at infinity, and yet that the approximating function have the prescribed poles, can such a function be found by sacrificing some quality of approximation? Consider first the case of Taylor approximation at the origin, and then try to extend your results to the Chebyshev case.

Discuss the application of all of the above to the case of Taylor approximation at the origin. Why are the problems simpler here?

Discuss in a general way the extensions of the ideas developed above to cases in which more than two poles are prescribed, including the possibility of prescribed complex poles. What is the maximum number of poles that can be prescribed, in terms of the order chosen for the approximating function?

Apply all of the foregoing to the problem of approximating an even polynomial in a low band with an even rational function. What is the relation between the two problems? If Chebyshev approximation is used, are the "ripples" of the error equal on an absolute (arithmetic) or on a fractional (logarithmic) basis? What is the answer to this question when a *constant* is approximated?

Discuss the problem of approximating the *reciprocal* of an even polynomial, in the light of the foregoing. Why is this a much simpler problem?

Finally, let the (even) function to be approximated be rational, with both zeros and poles that are finite. Discuss its approximation by using all the foregoing.

(The cases discussed here are special ones in the problem of approximating a nonconstant function.)

14-107. Correlate the derivation of an even function that approximates zero in the approximation band, with prescribed poles, given in SH 2, with the potential-analogy solution to the same problem. In particular, what function in SH 2 corresponds to the prototype potential W?

Discuss HE 2 in the same light.

14-108. Show that the number of crossings of the nominal value of constant approximated by (14.15–1) is equal to the number of positive charges on the prototype conductor, i.e., to the number of charges in the general vicinity thereof after quantization.

14-109. Verify (14.15–6). Derive (14.15–7) and correlate the number of terms matched at the origin with the number of crossings of the nominal value in the Chebyshev approximation from which you start.

Show also that both (14.15–5) and (14.15–7) can be obtained by following the method of Prob. 14-104 in the limiting case of Taylor approximation (cf. also Prob. 14-77).

14-110. Make rough flux plots for each of the following approximation problems showing the loci of the motions of the quantized charges. The function to be approximated is the constant unity, and the approximating function is to be realizable as a driving-point resistance (conductance). In each case the Chebyshev and Taylor methods are to be compared, the approximation carried out, and actual network realizations obtained.

Approximation Band	Manner of Approximation	Prescribed Zeros (Each Double Unless Otherwise Indicated)
$1 < \omega < 3$	Chebyshev, $\pm 10\%$	$\omega = 0, 0.5, 4, \infty$
$\omega = \sqrt{3}$	Taylor, down to 0.5 at $\omega = 3.5$	Same as above
$2 < \omega < 3$	Chebyshev, $\pm 5\%$	$\omega = 0$ (4 zeros), ∞ (8 zeros)
$\omega = \sqrt{6}$	Taylor, down to 0.5 at $\omega = 1$	Same as above
$1 < \omega < 4$	Chebyshev, $\pm 2\%$	$\omega = 0$ (8 zeros), ∞ (8 zeros)
$\omega = 2$	Taylor, down to 0.5 at $\omega = 6$	Same as above
$0 < \omega < 1$	Chebyshev, $\pm 1\%$	$\omega = 2, 4, 8, \infty$
$\omega = 0$	Taylor, down to 0.5 at $\omega = 1.5$	Same as above

14-111. Explain how approximate values of the second and higher derivatives can be obtained from Table 14.15–A, and why they approximate zero if ϵ decreases sufficiently rapidly.

14-112. In the determination of even functions to approximate a constant, the zeros have been shown to be arbitrary; once the zeros are assigned, the poles are determined, for Chebyshev and for Taylor approximation. Discuss the possibility of arbitrarily prescribing the *poles* of the approximating function and then determining where the zeros should be to give either kind of approximation. Illustrate with examples. Does this approach have any advantages over that of the text? (*Suggestion:* Consider the reciprocal of the function of ultimate interest.)
Explain carefully the relation of this to Prob. 14-106.

14-113. How is Fig. 14.15–A and its discussion altered if n is an odd integer?

14-114. Plot carefully to a large scale in the approximation band and its vicinity the behavior of the resistance function that approximates unity within $\pm 10\%$ limits in the Chebyshev sense in the band $0 < \omega < 1$, with ten zeros at infinity and no other zeros. Repeat, changing the approximation band to $0 < \omega < 0.5$, to $0 < \omega < 0.25$, to $0 < \omega < 0.125$, and finally to the single point 0, in each case reducing the error ripple in the manner required to approach the Taylor approximation. Note the geometric development of the maximally flat approximation from the equal-ripple approximation.

14-115. Show by careful plots that if ϵ is not reduced rapidly enough in Prob. 14-114 the maximally flat behavior does not result. For example, reduce ϵ in direct proportion to the approximation-band width. In the case of the Chebyshev-polynomial approximation, using $C_n^2(\omega/\omega_0)$ in general, $C_5^2(\omega/\omega_0)$ in Prob. 14-114, in proportion to what power of the bandwidth ω_0 must ϵ vary? (C_n is defined in Prob. 14-35.)

14-116. A resistance function of order six (corresponding to an impedance function of order three) is to approximate unity in a low band, and to have all of its zeros at infinity. Determine the coefficients in the resistance function by matching at $\omega = 0$, $\omega_0/3$, $2\omega_0/3$, and ω_0, ω_0 being the upper end of the approximation band. Do this for $\omega_0 = 1, 0.5, 0.25, 0$, in each case making a careful plot, and point out how the maximally flat approximation can be approached by this procedure also (cf. Prob. 14-114).

A similar treatment of other approximation problems can be very illuminating (e.g., the approximation of $\omega^{-\frac{1}{2}}$, §§ 13.03, 13.05).

14-117. How many derivatives of the function

$$F(\omega) = \exp\left[-(\omega - 1)^5\right]$$

can be matched at the point $\omega = 1$ if an even rational function of order n (to be realized as a resistance or conductance function) is used? Consider the cases $n = 0, 2, 4, 6$. How does this number compare with the number of parameters available in the approximating function? Explain, and correlate your discussion with that of § 14.15. What are the relevant properties of the function that lead to anomalies in the approximation here?

Discuss in a general way, with illustrative sketches showing the expected number of zeros of error, Chebyshev approximation of the same function. What property of the function to be approximated would lead to similar anomalies in the Chebyshev approximation?

Give a similar discussion of the approximation of each of the following functions at the indicated points.

$\exp\left(-\omega^8\right)$ At the origin ⎱ To be approximated with
$\omega^2 \exp\left(-\omega^{10}\right)$ At the origin ⎰   even functions

$\omega \exp\left(-\omega^6\right)$ At the origin   To be approximated with
    odd functions

14-118. Suppose a nonrational function to be approximated, $F(\omega)$, has one or more of the following properties:

Taylor approximation at $\omega = 1$; $F(1) = 1, F'(1) = 0, F''(1) = 0, F'''(1) = 0,$ $F^{\mathrm{iv}}(1) = 0.$

Chebyshev approximation in the vicinity of $\omega = 1$; $F(\omega) = 1 + \epsilon C_n(\omega - \omega_1)$ $+ \epsilon_{n+1}(\omega - \omega_1)^{n+1} + \cdots.$

How do these affect its approximation in Chebyshev and Taylor sense with regard to quality of approximation achieved with an approximating function of order n? Consider both odd- and even-function approximation.

14-119. Show that the following conditions are sufficient, though not necessary, for the realizability as a driving-point immittance of the function $Z(p)$ extracted from $F(p) = Z(p)Z(-p)$ that approximates a constant in the approximation band and is designed by the methods of § 14.14 and § 14.13.

(a) None of the prescribed zeros of $F(p)$ are on the ω axis.
(b) The approximation-band error ripple ϵ is very small.

Illustrate with loci and tests in specific examples, such as

(1) $F(p)$ of order four, zeros at $p = \pm 1, \pm 2$, approximation band $1 < \omega < 2$.
(2) $F(p)$ of order eight, zeros at $p = \pm 1 \pm j1, \pm 2, \pm 3$, approximation band $0 < \omega < 1$.
What is the criterion that determines the maximum allowable ripple ϵ?

14-120. For each of the $|Z|$ functions shown calculate and plot the corresponding angle function for all ω. All of these are constant in the approximation band $0 < \omega < 1$ and approach zero at infinity, but they differ in their falling off. Discuss the effect of the manner of falling off on the associated angle function. For those cases which lead to realizable angle functions approximate the tangent of the angle function with odd rational functions of several

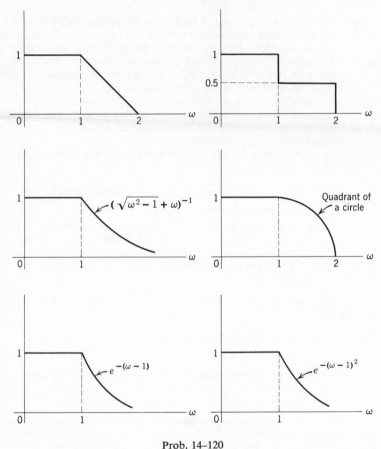

Prob. 14–120

different reasonable orders. Calculate and plot the associated magnitude functions and compare with the originals. (Appropriate methods from Chapter 8 may be used; in particular cf. § 8.09 and some of the problems.) Obtain network realizations.

14-121. Discuss the utility, to obtain constant $|Z|$ in a low band, of working with the $\overline{Z}$ function and designing maximally flat angle functions, as by $\tan \beta = K\omega^n$. Plot the associated $|Z|$ for $n = 1, 2, 3, 4, 5$. To what limit does $\beta(\omega)$ tend for large n? What is the corresponding $|Z(j\omega)|$? Explain your answer both analytically and in terms of the potential analogy.

14-122. To what $|Z(j\omega)|$ does the resistance function

$$R = \sqrt{1 - \omega^2}, \qquad 0 < \omega < 1,$$
$$= 0, \qquad\qquad 1 < \omega,$$

correspond? Answer (a) by obtaining the corresponding reactance and the whole immittance function, (b) by using the potential analogy (which furnishes the answer almost by inspection). Approximate this resistance function in the Padé manner at the origin, placing the zeros all at infinity or at various frequencies above unity, determine the corresponding $|Z|$ function, and discuss this as a method of approximating to the $|Z|$ function concerned.

14-123. Determine positive-real functions whose squared magnitude in a real-frequency low band is a Chebyshev approximation to a constant, under the following conditions. The order of the p-r function is three, its zeros are at ∞, -2, -1. What are the limitations on the error ripple ϵ? Obtain a maximally flat (at the origin) solution to the same problem, and discuss its arbitrariness.

Repeat for a function of order five with zeros at ∞, -4, -3, -2, -1.

14-124. Explain why the function

$$F(p) = (\sqrt{p^2 + 1} - p)^2,$$

whose magnitude is constant in the low band $0 < \omega < 1$ and which thereafter falls off more rapidly than does that of (14.16–1), cannot be used as the basis of a design for a $|Z|$ function.

14-125. Plot $|Z|$ versus ω for the networks obtained by truncating the infinite network of Fig. 14.16–B(c) after one element, after two, after three, with short- or open-circuit termination in each case as appropriate. Compare these results with those of § 14.16 in which a resistor termination is used.

14-126. Calculate and plot the curves of Fig. 14.16–C for verification. Continue the family by adding curves for $n = 4$ and $n = 5$. Determine the zeros and poles of the impedance function $Z_n(p)$ and plot them in the plane of p. Is there a noticeable pattern, or locus, of these as n increases? To what limit, in the light of the potential analogy, can these sets of zeros and poles be expected to tend? What generalization could be made if the method of approximation were of some other sort?

14-127. Show that (14.16–10) is p-r, both by testing and by an argument based solely on the modification made in (14.16–2), which is p-r, to get this new function.

14-128. In what way must the development of the test for positive reality (5.13–5) be modified so that it is directly applicable to functions such as (14.16–1) that contain square roots? If a real-frequency pole is removed from such a p-r function, as is done in (14.16–12), is the remaining function automatically p-r?

14-129. Obtain the expansion in (14.16–11) by actually calculating the residue at each pole and removing the poles. Show that $Y_2(p)$, given by (14.16–12), is actually realized by the network shown to the right of L_2 and C_2 in Fig. 14.16–F.

14-130. Terminate the network of Fig. 14.16–F midway between the vertical dashed lines with a 1 Ω resistor. Plot the magnitude of the input impedance of the terminated network for $m = 0.4, 0.5, 0.6, 0.7$, and discuss the qualities of approximation. What other modifications of element values may be useful?

1038   **Network Synthesis**

14-131. Plot the impedance (resistance, reactance, magnitude, angle) presented to the right by the infinite network (a) after the first inductor of the network of Fig. 14.16–B(c), (b) midway in the first inductor of the network of Fig. 14.16–B(c), (c) midway between the vertical dashed lines in Fig. 14.16–F, with $m_1 = 0.6$. On the basis of these curves explain the difference in the quality of approximation of a constant in the three curves of Fig. 14.16–D.

14-132. Plot the impedance left to be realized in Fig. 14.16–E after removal of only a fraction of the impedance of the L_2-C_2 combination, taking $m_1 = 0.6$. Do this for a number of different partial removals. Select two or three of your cases, terminate in a resistor at those points, and plot the magnitude of the driving-point impedance of the terminated network. What do you consider the optimum point of termination and terminating resistor?

14-133. Make the necessary calculations and draw Fig. 14.16–G carefully to scale, taking $m_1 = 0.7$ and $m_2 = 0.4$. Explain your construction fully. Plot $|Z|$ for a network formed by termination in a 1 Ω resistor at a point midway in the network between the second and third vertical dashed lines in Fig. 14.16–H.

Plot the admittance left to be realized in Fig. 14.16–H after removal of only *part* of the admittance of the combination L_3-C_3-C_3', taking $m_1 = 0.7$ and $m_2 = 0.4$. Do this for a number of different partial removals. Select two or three of your cases, terminate in a resistor at those points, and plot the magnitude of the driving-point impedance of the terminated network. What do you consider the optimum point of termination and terminating resistor?

14-134. Show that in (14.16–17)

$$Y_3(p) = \frac{[(1 - m_1{}^2)p^2 + 1]\sqrt{p^2 + 1} - \left[1 - \dfrac{m_1{}^2 - m_2{}^2}{1 + m_2}\right]p - (1 - m_1{}^2)p^3}{(1 - m_2{}^2)p^2 + 1}$$

and that this function is p-r and has no poles at $\pm j\omega_2$ or at infinity. Check this in the following specific (degenerate) cases both algebraically and in the schematic development of Fig. 14.16–H, by verifying the reduction to simpler cases: (a) $m_1 = m_2$, (b) $m_1 = 1$, (c) $m_1 = m_2 = 1$. Show that case (b) is similar to that developed in Fig. 14.16–E except that the removal of part of the pole at infinity is postponed one step in the ladder development.

14-135. Show how partial removal of the poles at $\pm j\omega_2$ and at infinity from Y_3 in (14.16–17) can be made to lead to a development of Z_3 in Fig. 14.16–H

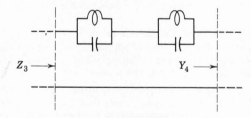

Prob. 14–135

that starts as illustrated in the accompanying figure. Give the schematic diagram of the development for several further stages, generalizing from this result.

14-136. In writing down (14.16–1) we used but one unit of positive charge on the approximation-band conductor, and placed the single unit of negative charge at infinity. Some interesting ideas are attached to this function.

(a) Show that (14.16–1) is a p-r function.

(b) Show that if more than one unit of positive charge is placed on the conductor, the exponential potential is no longer p-r, and that this property does not depend on the location of the negative charge.

(c) Show that if the single unit of negative charge is brought in from infinity and divided equally between two (positive and negative) finite frequencies, the charge on the conductor remaining one positive unit, the exponential potential is still p-r. Sketch its magnitude, angle, and real and imaginary parts versus frequency. (The realization of this function is postponed to Volume II.)

(d) If the single unit of negative charge is divided equally between four finite (symmetrically located) frequencies, is the exponential-potential function still p-r?

14-137. Discuss and verify the statement made in the text in connection with (14.16–1) that this function gives the fastest obtainable rate of falling off beyond the approximation band for a function whose magnitude is constant in the approximation band, subject to the conditions that the function be p-r, approach zero at infinity, and that the falling off be steady (monotonic). In particular, explain why the use of additional charge on the conductor and at infinity, or at various finite frequencies, is ruled out. In terms of a fixed (unavoidable) capacitance C, what is the maximum obtainable value of $|Z|$ at low frequencies, if $|Z|$ is to be constant in $0 < \omega < \omega_0$?

14-138. Demonstrate that the function (14.16–1) is the p-r function that provides the maximum obtainable value of constant $|Z|$ in the approximation band, if it is required that the network realization behave as a capacitor at high frequencies (to provide, e.g., for parasitic capacitance in vacuum-tube circuits). A suggested outline is given below (BO 3).

Let

$$Z_a(p) = 2\,\frac{\sqrt{p^2 + \omega_0^2} - p}{C\omega_0^2} = \frac{2}{C(\sqrt{p^2 + \omega_0^2} + p)} \quad \text{ohms}$$

be the denormalized form of (14.16–1), in which the approximation band runs from 0 to ω_0, and C is the actual value of the capacitance in the infinite ladder realization thereof [in the form of Fig. 14.16–B(c)].

Let $Z_b(p)$ be some other impedance, to be compared with (1), which is p-r, and approaches $(Cp)^{-1}$ at high frequencies. The value of C is the same as that in (1), to have a valid comparison.

Working in terms of logarithms, to have a tractable function in which real part corresponds to $|Z|$, form the integral

$$\oint_{C_1} \frac{\ln Z_b - \ln Z_a}{\sqrt{p^2 + \omega_0^2}}\, dp$$

in which C_1 is the usual contour made up of a large semicircle of radius R in the right half plane and the imaginary axis with suitable small semicircular indentations of radius r into the right half plane. The numerator is formed to exhibit the comparison between Z_b and Z_a; the denominator serves two purposes: (a) to insure that the integral on the large semicircle approach zero, (b) to interchange real and imaginary parts at the end of the approximation band. The indentations are at the singularities of $\ln(Z_b/Z_a)$ and at the two branch points $p = \pm j\omega_0$.

Show that the integrand is analytic in the right half plane and that the integral approaches zero as $R \to \infty$ and $r \to 0$. Show that the small semicircles contribute nothing, nor does the large semicircle. The end result, on separating real and imaginary parts and taking account of symmetry, is

$$\int_0^{\omega_0} \frac{\ln\left|\dfrac{CZ_b}{2}(\sqrt{-\omega^2 + \omega_0^2} + j\omega)\right| \, d\omega}{\sqrt{-\omega^2 + \omega_0^2}} + \int_{\omega_0}^\infty \frac{\beta + (\pi/2)}{\sqrt{\omega^2 - \omega_0^2}} \, d\omega = 0$$

in which $\beta = \overline{Z_b}$. Obtain

$$\int_0^{\omega_0} \frac{\ln\left|\dfrac{C\omega_0}{2} Z_b\right| \, d\omega}{\sqrt{-\omega^2 + \omega_0^2}} = -\int_{\omega_0}^\infty \frac{\beta + (\pi/2)}{\sqrt{\omega^2 - \omega_0^2}} \, d\omega.$$

If $|Z_b|$ is constant at the value Z_0 in $0 < \omega_0$, this gives

$$\frac{\pi}{2} \omega_0 \ln\left(\frac{C\omega_0 Z_0}{2}\right) = -\int_{\omega_0}^\infty \frac{\beta + (\pi/2)}{\sqrt{\omega^2 - \omega_0^2}} \, d\omega. \tag{2}$$

The angle of Z, β, can be negative, but $-\pi/2 \leq \beta \leq +\pi/2$ is required by positive reality. The right-hand side of (2) is therefore never positive, and for maximum Z_0, evidently $\beta = -\pi/2$. Then we have in $0 < \omega < \omega_0$, $|Z_b| = Z_0 = $ constant, and in $\omega_0 < \omega$, $\overline{Z_b} = -\pi/2 = $ constant. But this is exactly the function (1). Note that $Z_0 = 2(C\omega_0)^{-1}$ is the actual maximum value obtainable.

14-139. Problem 14-138 may also be solved by using as integrand simply $\ln(CpZ)/\sqrt{p^2 + \omega_0^2}$, assuming that $Z(p)$ approaches $(Cp)^{-1}$ at infinity, and following the same sort of contour and reasoning. Carry out this derivation of that maximum value of constant $|Z|$ obtainable and compare the two derivations. The value of $\int_0^1 [(\ln x)/(1 - x^2)] \, dx$ is $-(\pi/2) \ln 2$.

14-140. Show that for any two-terminal network whose structure commences with a capacitor C across the terminals, such as those of § 14.16,

$$\int_0^\infty \ln|C\omega Z| \, d\omega = -\frac{\pi}{2} KC$$

and determine the physical meaning (by considering high-frequency behavior) of K. Explain the meaning of this relation as a comparison of the integral of $\ln|Z|$ in the two cases: (a) Z represents the driving-point impedance of the arbitrary network considered, (b) Z represents the driving-point impedance of the capacitor alone. If the capacitance C is regarded as fixed, and the purpose of the network is to reshape the curve of $|Z|$ versus frequency, what limitations, in a general way, does C impose? (BO 3.)

14-141. A pentode vacuum tube, between whose output terminals a parasitic capacitance C exists, drives an L-C network terminated in a resistor, in the fashion of § 11.04. By application of the resistance integral (§ 8.06) show that the gain of such an amplifier is limited by the capacitance C. Determine specifically the maximum value of constant gain that can be obtained over a frequency band of width ω_0 in terms of the resistor used (BO 3). If the value of this resistor is arbitrary, is there a limit on the gain obtainable (explain both theoretically and practically)?

14-142. Apply the resistance integral (§ 8.06) to the infinite network of Fig. 14.16–B(c), and verify the result by actual calculation of the integral for this network, using (14.16–1).

14-143. The various approximations to a low-band constant magnitude of driving-point impedance of § 14.16 are all in the form of an L-C network terminated in a resistor, across whose input terminals appears a capacitor. Discuss, with illustrative examples, the obtaining of networks for this purpose by designing driving-point *resistance* (conductance) functions that approximate the ideal, the resistance of (14.16–1), at low frequencies, with zeros placed only at real frequencies to insure reasonably simple realization. Use Padé approximation (with prescription of zeros perhaps) as well as trial-and-error methods.

14-144. Apply the low-band–high-band transformation of Probs. 14-96 and 14-97 to obtain networks whose driving-point impedance approximates a constant magnitude in an internal band, starting from the various low-band networks of § 14.16. Discuss the possibility of additional alteration of element values, not possible in the low-band case, to obtain better approximations. Illustrate.

14-145. Show that

$$\int_0^\infty \frac{\ln |Z(j\omega)|}{\omega^2} \, d\omega = + \frac{\pi}{2} \cdot \frac{Z'(0)}{Z(0)}$$

in which it is assumed that $Z(p)$ is p-r. For the function (14.16–1) what is the value of this integral? Discuss its implications as to the rate of falloff obtainable beyond the band of approximation to a constant, if it is proposed to vary this falling off.

Obtain the value of

$$\int_0^\infty \frac{\ln |Z(j\omega)|}{\omega^2 - \omega_0^2} \, d\omega$$

in which $Z(p)$ is p-r and ω_0 is an arbitrary frequency. Extend the low-band discussion above to the internal-band case.

14-146. Since the realizability of a given even function as the square of the magnitude of a driving-point impedance $Z(p)$ is not readily predictable (§ 8.16), we may choose to work in terms of the corresponding *angle* function (§ 14.16). Discuss the possibility of estimating the error in the magnitude function from the error in approximating the angle function, by an appropriate integral relation (Chapter 8). That is, if $\beta = \beta_x + \Delta$, in which β_x is the angle corresponding exactly to the desired magnitude function, find an expression for the error in $\ln |Z|$ as an integral. Discuss the application of the graphical method of § 8.09 to the calculation of error in magnitude. Illustrate with examples (cf. Prob. 14-147).

14-147. In contrast to the infinite-network development of § 14.16 we may attack the low-band approximation of a constant magnitude of immittance by transferring our attention to the *angle* function, where realizability is more evident (Prob. 14-146). For the function (14.16–1) write the angle function and plot both angle and tangent thereof versus ω. Construct the Padé table (at the origin) for the tangent function, through functions of order five. [Note that the table for $(1 - \omega^2)^{-\frac{1}{2}}$ may be constructed first and modified by multiplication by ω.] Which entries appear most suitable for approximation to the desired function over the entire ω axis? Explain. Plot the associated magnitude functions and compare with the original magnitude function. Obtain network realizations.

A modification is to apply constraints that tend to improve the high-frequency approximation, while maintaining Padé approximation at the origin (with the remaining parameters) to get good low-frequency approximation. Set up an odd rational function of order five with double poles at $\omega = \pm\omega_\infty$ and a simple pole at infinity. Determine the remaining parameters by requiring maximal agreement at the origin with the desired tangent function. (This amounts to moving poles in from infinity in a certain function from the top row of the above Padé table—with the object of improving the over-all approximation.) Show by plots that although large values of ω_∞ lead to more or less useful approximations, as ω_∞ is prescribed lower and lower the approximation becomes less valuable. In particular, make plots for both the tangent and the angle for $\omega_\infty = 4, 2, \sqrt{1.6}, 1$. Select a good value, plot the associated magnitude, and obtain a network realization.

Repeat for a tangent function of order nine, obtaining the best approximation you can. (You will probably want to keep the poles at real frequencies, and double—why?)

Discuss the value of this method from the point of view of simplicity of realization of the resulting immittance functions.

14-148. Realize, in infinite-network form, those of the impedance functions below that are p-r. (Resistance and conductance, as well as susceptance and reactance, removal may be useful.)

$$\sqrt{p+1} \qquad \sqrt{p^2+1} \qquad \sqrt{p^3+1} \qquad \frac{\sqrt{p+1}}{p} \qquad \frac{\sqrt{p^2+1}}{p} \qquad p\sqrt{\frac{p^2+2}{p^2+1}}$$

14-149. Determine the input impedance Z_K of the infinite ladder network formed from two impedances Z_1 and Z_2 in the manner shown, as a function of

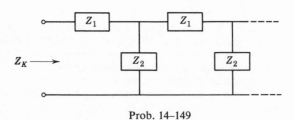

Prob. 14–149

Z_1 and Z_2. Z_K is known as the *iterative impedance* of the basic unit, the L-shaped network composed of Z_1 and Z_2 with which the network starts, i.e., the impedance formed when this small network is *iterated* or repeated indefinitely in the fashion shown.

14-150. A small-signal video (low-band) vacuum-tube amplifier is to consist of a cascade of stages, each of the (very practical) form shown. It is to have a

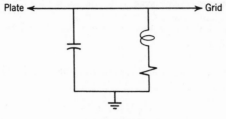

Prob. 14–150

very flat transmission characteristic as a function of frequency. The over-all transmission will be proportional to the product of the one-terminal-pair driving-point impedances (on the assumption of very large plate resistances in the tubes); cf. § 11.05. Ignore blocking capacitors.

(*a*) Explain why it is not possible to set up a flat (Chebyshev or Taylor) transmission function by the methods of this chapter and proceed directly to calculating the element values of the interstage networks.

(*b*) Consider the possibility of solving the design problem by an iterative method which may circumvent the awkward fact that the zeros of the impedance functions are not independent of the poles. Such a procedure might consist of (1) assuming a reasonable set of zeros, (2) finding the poles that are associated therewith by approximation theory, (3) finding the zeros that must be associated with these poles according to the prescribed schematic diagrams, (4) find new poles that are associated with these new zeros by approximation theory, etc., until a convergence (closed cycle) is established.

Try this procedure for a two-stage amplifier, both for Chebyshev and Taylor approximation of a constant in $0 < \omega < 1$. Repeat for three stages. (CA 6.)

14-151. A vacuum-tube amplifier is to consist of a chain of tubes between each pair of which an interstage network of the form shown is to be inserted.

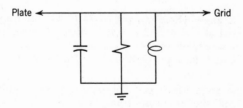

Prob. 14–151

Parasitic capacitance and internal tube resistance are to be considered, but the d-c blocking capacitors to the grids can be ignored, for only high frequencies are of interest here. Explain how to design such a cascade, using the approximation methods of this chapter for flat (constant) transmission. Note how the prescription of the schematic diagram determines where the zeros will be, and explain why you encounter no difficulty here with the question of realizability of a given $|Z|$ function. Illustrate by carrying out actual designs to meet the following requirements, giving schematic diagrams and curves of transmission obtained. What limits the maximum level of gain that can be obtained? Discuss the relation of this problem to Probs. 14-91 and 14-150, pointing out similarities and differences.

Number of Stages	Nature of Approximation	Approximation Band
2	Chebyshev, $\pm 5\%$	$1 < \omega < 3$
2	Maximally flat	$\omega = 2$
3	Chebyshev, $\pm 4\%$	$1 < \omega < 4$
3	Maximally flat	$\omega = 2$
4	Chebyshev, $\pm 3\%$	$1 < \omega < 5$
4	Maximally flat	$\omega = 2$
5	Chebyshev, $\pm 2\%$	$1 < \omega < 6$
5	Maximally flat	$\omega = 2$

The maximally flat transmissions are to be down to 50% at $\omega = 1$. All numbers refer to the square of the voltage transmission ratio.

For a given number of stages, and a given ripple ϵ in Chebyshev approximation, what is the effect on the gain-versus-frequency characteristic of widening the approximation band? What is the corresponding phenomenon in Taylor approximation?

14-152. Verify (14.17-5). Verify (14.17-6), (14.17-8), and show that nothing new to add to (14.17-9) is obtained by continuing on to values of $\Phi = 3\pi$, $4\pi, 5\pi, \cdots$.

14-153. Give the relation between e^{W_q} of (14.17-13) and the Chebyshev polynomial $C_n(\omega)$ of Prob. 14-35. If this function is to be an ordinary sine wave when plotted as a function of a new variable ϕ, what function of ω must ϕ be? What values of ω correspond to multiples of $\pi/2$ in the argument of the sine function?

14-154. Plot the angle whose tangent is (14.17-11) for ripple values in the approximation band of $\epsilon = 1°$ and $\epsilon = 10°$. Realize networks whose driving-point immittances have these angles. By what manipulation of the poles of the tangent function could the approximation to $90°$ at frequencies above unity be improved?

14-155. Plot the angle which best approximates zero within $3°$ in the low band $0 < \omega < 1$, all the $90°$ points being at infinity, for $n = 1, 2, 3, 4, 5$, n being the order of the immittance of the network realization. Realize corresponding networks.

14-156. Demonstrate that the zeros and poles of a driving-point immittance whose angle approximates zero in a low band, (14.17-13) being its tangent, lie on an ellipse in the p plane, zeros and poles alternating along the ellipse.

14-157. Demonstrate that (14.17-14) is a rational, odd function of p (with real coefficients). Sketch its real-frequency behavior for various specific cases such as the following situations of poles:

(a) at infinity (simple), at $\pm j3$ (each double);
(b) at infinity (triple), at $\pm 1 \pm j1$ (each simple);
(c) at infinity (simple), at ± 1 (each simple).

What is the relation between K' and ϵ if these functions are to be tangents of driving-point immittance angles that approximate zero within $\epsilon°$? Plot the angles and obtain network realizations.

Which of the functions above are realizable as driving-point reactances? as driving-point susceptances? Obtain network realizations.

14-158. Determine, by trial, a tangent function with the behavior shown in Fig. 14.17–E, the low-band error ripple ϵ being 4°, and the minimum angle at frequencies above ω_s being 80°. May ω_s be arbitrarily specified or not? Obtain a network realization.

14-159. Develop a design procedure for networks whose driving-point immittance angle is to approximate zero in an internal band in the Chebyshev fashion (and maximally, in the limit) and to rise to $+90°$ (or to drop to $-90°$) outside the approximation band. Do this in detail for cases where the poles of the tangent function are all at the origin and infinity (considering the possibility of various distributions between these two points). Discuss briefly also the possibility of the use of finite, nonzero poles. Illustrate with examples. In what way is the procedure different if the angle is to tend to $+90°$ below the approximation band and to $-90°$ above it? In what way must your design procedure be altered if it is driving-point reactance (susceptance) rather than angle that is to approximate zero in an internal band?

14-160. Discuss the design of a series of networks the angles of whose driving-point immittance functions approximate 90° in the band $0 < \omega < 1$. Show that mere inversion of a function such as (14.17–13) will not give a satisfactory result in that the angle changes sign repeatedly, though the tangent remains

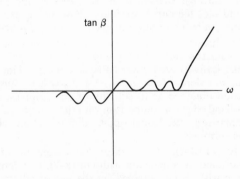

Prob. 14–160

large in magnitude. What form will the realization of such a function take? Find suitable functions by inverting *maximal* approximations of zero at the origin. Discuss the possibility of modifying these or setting up others with the behavior shown, and their use in solving the problem. Determine a function (by trial) with the Chebyshev behavior shown, all poles being at infinity, and use it to obtain a network with the property desired. How might the poles be relocated to improve the simultaneous approximation of zero angle in a high band ?

14-161. Explain the factor of two that multiplies Φ in (14.17–1), and the discussion leading up to it, in terms of the limit of approximation to a constant with an even function with quantization on $V = -V_0$, as V_0 approaches zero. What sort of approximation results if we do not modify the quantization process to give single instead of double zeros ?

14-162. For the network shown, determine **Od** $Z(p)$ and sketch its zeros and poles. If the dissipation is small, where do the zeros and poles lie? In the limit of zero dissipation, what happens to them?

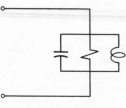

Prob. 14–162

Consider now a rational function with three zeros at the origin and one at infinity, and with poles at $\pm\epsilon \pm j\omega_0$. Let this be the driving-point reactance of a network. Determine the associated minimum-resistance driving-point impedance function, noting in particular the value of R_∞, i.e., the minimum value of $Z(\infty)$ necessary for positive reality. Obtain a realization and contrast it with that shown.

In the light of this work, discuss what happens to the network realization as $\epsilon \to 0$, bearing in mind that the reactance is realizable so long as $\epsilon \neq 0$ but not if $\epsilon = 0$. Correlate with the mention of a related fact in § 14.17.

Why does no such difficulty arise in realizing the reactance obtained in the first part of this problem?

14-163. Derive (14.18–1) from the associated prototype potential problem. Sketch and explain its real-frequency behavior. Show that the function is not rational.

14-164. Carry through the calculations necessary for the construction of Fig. 14.18–B and plot the curve carefully. Plot, to the same scale, the equal-ripple approximation to a constant obtained from the elliptic-function formulas.

14-165. Carry through the calculations for the construction of a rational function with the zeros and the four upper-half-plane poles of Fig. 14.18–A, and four symmetrically located lower-half-plane poles. Plot the real-frequency behavior of this function. Take $\omega_2/\omega_1 = 2$, $V_0 = 2.3$. Discuss the nature of the approximation obtained as to equality of error ripples, and as to effective approximation-band edges in comparison with those expected. Plot to the same scale, for comparison, the equal-ripple approximation obtained from the elliptic-function formulas.

14-166. Verify (14.18–2). Carry through the solution of the problem, by the methods indicated in connection with (14.18–2), and compare the resulting values of a, b, c with those obtained by the use of elliptic functions. Take $\omega_2/\omega_1 = 10$, and consider the use of the substitution

$$x = \sqrt{\frac{p^2 + \omega_1{}^2}{p^2 + \omega_2{}^2}}$$

and the solving of the equation $e^{2W} = e^{-2V_0}$ rather than (14.18–6).

Discuss the complexity of the equations that would have to be solved if the algebraic approach were used for an approximating function of order six, and point out the increased difficulties.

14-167. Derive (14.18–9). Explain why this function (of p) is rational in spite of the square root in its denominator.

14-168. Derive (14.18–10). Determine also the value of K_3 in terms of ϵ.

14-169. Verify the periodicities of the mapping of Fig. 14.18–G by taking the "excursion" there mentioned.

14-170. Discuss the transformation that results in Fig. 14.18–H(a) on making the indentation to the *right* rather than to the left.

14-171. Explain, in terms of Fig. 14.18–J, how the equal-ripple approximation of Fig. 14.18–K is obtained, and verify the relation between number of available parameters in the approximating function and number of zeros of error in the approximation band. Repeat for an arbitrary value of n.

14-172. Plot curves of error ripple ϵ' for approximation to a constant angle, against ϵ, the error ripple in the tangent, using (14.18–35). Do this for $\beta_0 = 30°$, $45°$, $75°$.

14-173. Show that in the sequence of values of p_m given by (14.18–30) there is geometric symmetry about p_n. Show how this gives, at real frequencies, a symmetry about the frequency $\omega_0 = \sqrt{\omega_1 \omega_2}$, on a logarithmic frequency scale. Of what sort is the symmetry?

14-174. For the multiplier in (14.18–30),

$$\frac{1 + 2q + 2q^4 + 2q^9 + 2q^{16} + \cdots}{1 - 2q + 2q^4 - 2q^9 + 2q^{16} - \cdots}$$

find a single series, $1 + 4q + \cdots$, calculating its first six terms. Explain, using the example of (14.18–33), why the quotient form given in (14.18–30) is preferable to this new series, even though it involves the calculation of two series rather than of one.

14-175. Design a network whose driving-point reactance is constant at the value $-75\,\Omega$ within 3%, in the band from 200 cps to 20 kcps.

As corollaries, give network designs for which the reactance is constant at $+75\,\Omega$, and for which the *susceptance* is constant at $+75^{-1}$ mhos and at -75^{-1} mhos respectively, with the same limits and approximation band.

14-176. Design a network whose driving-point reactance is constant at the value $-50\,\Omega$, within 1%, in the band from 100 cps to 10 kcps.

What other network-design problems can be solved with the use of your work in approximation here?

14-177. Design a network the angle of whose driving-point impedance is constant at $-45°$ (within 2%) in the band from 200 kcps to 2000 kcps.

14-178. Derive specific formulas for the angle function (of frequency) and for the error, from (14.18–39) or (14.18–40) (MA 8).

14-179. Verify (14.18–36) and derive the mapping of Fig. 14.18–N(a) and (b) therefrom. What is the relation between ω, and u and v that maps real-frequency points to the w plane? Explain the periodicity of the mapping. Then verify that (14.18–39) expresses the exponential potential for the charge distribution of Fig. 14.18–N(c). Show that the function possesses a certain symmetry about ω_1 and plot it (on a logarithmic frequency scale) for $n = 1, 2, 3, 4, 5$. Verify (14.18–41) and thus establish its identity with (13.10–18).

14-180. Design networks whose reactance is a maximal approximation to a negative constant at unit frequency and use one, two, three, four, five reactive elements. Repeat for the property of maximally constant *angle* of driving-point impedance, at $-30°$, $-45°$, $-60°$ value.

14-181. Derive the mapping of Fig. 14.18–N(*a*) and (*b*) directly by developing the Schwarz-Christoffel transformation that maps the ω axis into the rectangle $\infty E'B'A'0ABE\infty$ of Fig. 14.18–N(*b*), by making 180° "bends" at $\pm j\omega_1$ in the p plane.

14-182. The odd-function approximations of a constant of § 14.18 can in general be realized with R-C or R-L networks. Verify this by correlating this statement with Probs. 7-37, 8-127, and 13-94. Explain why even-function approximations of a constant (for driving-point resistance, e.g.) *cannot* be so realized.

14-183. Determine the p-plane positions of the poles and zeros of an $F(p)$ (in the language of § 14.18) that has a zero at the origin, a pole at infinity, is of order three, and approximates $+j1$ in the band $1 < \omega < 10$. What error ripple ϵ will it have? Verify your answer by actual calculation and plotting of $j^{-1}F(j\omega)$. Repeat for an $F(p)$ of order five.

Repeat both exercises for maximally flat approximation at $\omega = \sqrt{10}$ and plot $j^{-1}F(j\omega)$ on the same scale for comparison.

Obtain network realizations of these functions: for approximation of (*a*) constant reactance of value -1, (*b*) constant susceptance of value $+1$, (*c*) constant angle of impedance of $-45°$.

14-184. In Fig. 14.18–L. sketch in interpolating curves for $n = \frac{3}{2}, \frac{5}{2}, \frac{7}{2}$, and verify them (for the smaller values of ϵ) by (14.18–32). Explain the meaning of these curves.

14-185. Discuss the relation between the order of the approximating function and the order of the immittance function that realizes it for

(*a*) even-function approximation of a constant, to be realized as driving-point resistance (conductance);

(*b*) odd-function approximation of a constant, to be realized as driving-point reactance (susceptance);

(*c*) odd-function approximation of a constant, to be realized as driving-point-immittance angle.

14-186. Section 14.18 demonstrates that in odd-function approximation of a constant the zeros are in general not arbitrary. If one insists on prescribing some or all of the zeros, the quality of approximation must therefore suffer. Discuss and explain this with the aid of the following examples.

(*a*) In

$$X(\omega) = \frac{\omega^3}{b_0 + b_2\omega^2 + b_4\omega^4}$$

determine the b's for maximal approximation of unity at $\omega = 1$. What is the quality of approximation, measured by the number of terms matched in the Taylor series? What quality would be obtained if one were free to utilize the zeros to obtain the maximum quality of approximation? Plot $X(\omega)$ and show the positions of the zeros and poles of $F(p) = jX(p/j)$.

Explain the real-frequency behavior outside the approximation band. Is the function realizable as a driving-point reactance? susceptance? tangent of angle of a driving-point immittance?

Form a "prototype" potential analog with positive charges at $\pm j1$ and negative charges at the prescribed points (0 and ∞). Show the flux lines and equipotentials at the positions of the poles obtained above by Taylor approximation. Do these correspond to the potential-analogy method of quantization on equipotentials of the prototype problem? Explain your answer.

Repeat all of the above for the case where one zero is prescribed at the origin and three at infinity.

(b) Sketch the error function that can reasonably be expected if Chebyshev approximation is used instead of Taylor approximation. What is the quality of approximation to be expected with zeros prescribed as above, and with zeros utilized to improve the approximation?

Discuss the possibility of using a potential analog to obtain the poles of $X(\omega)$, when the zeros are prescribed as above, for Chebyshev approximation. Obtain a Chebyshev approximation by starting from the Taylor approximation and using a cut-and-try process.

(c) Repeat (a) and (b) for odd functions of order and zeros prescribed as follows:

Order of Function	Number of Zeros at Origin	Infinity
6	1	5
	3	3
	5	1
8	1	7
	3	5
	5	3
	7	1

14-187. The use of *half-unit* quantized charges in approximation of a constant with an odd function is quite successful (§ 14.18). This suggests the use of half-unit quantization in the approximation of a constant in an internal band with an even (e.g., resistance) function, which might be expected to increase the number of ripples of error in the approximation band. Discuss this possibility.

14-188. Consider the problem of approximating the function $1/\omega$ in an internal band with an even function suitable for realization as a driving-point resistance and with all of its zeros at infinity.

Explain why maximal approximation at any point in the approximation band is straightforward (except for the usual anomaly, which is also to be explained).

Attempt to obtain a Chebyshev approximation by the device of reducing this to the problem of approximating a constant in the following fashion.

1. Place conductors on the approximation bands, carrying the positive charge.
2. Place the negative charge at infinity.
3. Place a single negative charge at the origin.
4. Quantize the positive charge to obtain a rational function that approximates a constant in the approximation band.
5. Remove the zero at the origin to obtain a solution to the original problem.

Explain how this process reduces the problem to approximation of a constant. Does the quantization yield the expected result? What difficulties arise? How good an approximation can be obtained? Illustrate by numerical cases. (*Suggestion:* Some of the remarks of § 14.18 may be helpful.)

14-189. Repeat Prob. 14-188, taking as the function to be approximated $1/\sqrt{\omega}$. Compare your results with the approximations thereto made in Chapter 13.

14-190. Extend the discussion started in Probs. 14-188 and 14-189 to the approximation of ω^n, n being arbitrary.

What happens if the prescription on the zeros is removed?

14-191. What happens in the foregoing three problems if the approximating function is to be *odd*?

14-192. Consider the design of a network whose input impedance is to approximate that of a pair of wires in a telephone cable, in a rather low (but internal) band. The cable is dissipative and moderately long, so that the impedance to be approximated is essentially proportional to $1/\sqrt{p}$. The network is required to terminate the cable pair in its characteristic impedance (cf., e.g., RO 3). You may limit yourself to the magnitude (ignore the angle) of impedance here, which is to approximate in Chebyshev fashion on a fractional (logarithmic) basis, constant$/\sqrt{\omega}$ in the band $\omega_1 < \omega < \omega_2$, with $f_1 = 100$ cps, $f_2 = 4$ kcps. The network is to contain four reactive elements.

Follow, as closely as you can, the ideas of the potential analogy, taking $Z(p)Z(-p)$ to be analogous to the exponential potential. For the prototype situation put down conductors on the approximation bands, carrying positive charge. Place the negative charges, as single units, on the real axis at points to be determined (see below), and one at the origin, one at infinity. Carry out the quantization in the usual way for odd functions, by letting half-unit charges travel out from the conductors, eventually joining up on the real axis to form full unit charges. Their locations may be determined:

(*a*) graphically, by plotting e^V against σ or log σ, and making successive trials; the radical that appears in the exponential-potential expression for the basic unit of one positive charge on each conductor and one negative charge each at $p = \pm \sigma_1$ may be plotted once for all, and the curve utilized by sliding a triangle up and down on the paper, the negative-charge positions to be obtained, by trial, for equal maxima in e^V (why?);

(*b*) by using elliptic functions in the manner of § 14.18.

When the negative charges have been properly located in (*a*), the positive ones have also, i.e., quantization has been "automatically" carried out. Explain carefully. What corresponds, in (*b*)?

Now multiply exp (W_q) by p^{-1}, identify the new function with $Z(p)Z(-p)$, determine $Z(p)$, and carefully plot its approximation-band behavior. Why is it that desired? What is the error ripple? Plot the error in $\ln|Z|$ and in $|Z|$ against frequency and compare the plots. Plot the angle of $Z(j\omega)$ and compare it with $45°$. How close is it, and why should this result appear?

Complete the network realization and discuss your work in summary.

15.

Illustrations

The great end of life is not knowledge but action.
—T. H. Huxley

It is the aim of this concluding chapter of the first part of this work to look back over our treatment of the one-terminal pair, to measure our accomplishments, and to illustrate them with unifying examples.

15.01 Looking back

When we began our discussion (in Chapter 1) we planned a triple investigation that would find out (1) what networks could do, (2) how to approximate things they could not do, and (3) how actually to synthesize networks. To these we found it necessary to add a fourth topic (Chapter 12), the consideration of the practical difficulties of constructing a network from a given schematic diagram. Our treatment of this was brief, for it deals with an art best learned by experience, but the first three topics we have discussed in detail, as they apply to the one-terminal pair.

Network synthesis, as discussed in this book, is the design of a network to have certain prescribed characteristics. These we have confined to the sinusoidal steady state, i.e., to functions of ordinary frequency (though we have found it convenient, even necessary, to use the complex frequency variable p in our work). And we do not concern ourselves with the origin of these characteristics but simply accept them as prescribed requirements to be met, furnished, as it were, by a customer for whom we serve simply as a supplier of networks. They are presumably determined by the part that the network is to play in some larger communication, control, or similar system, and may be in the form of prescribed resistance (conductance), reactance (susceptance), magnitude or angle functions of frequency, or of combinations of these (Chapter 11 gives some examples). Our job is to realize them as closely as is physically and economically possible.

The first step is to decide whether the proposed characteristics are physically realizable or not. To this end we have studied the *properties* of one-terminal pairs, chiefly in Chapters 4, 5, and 8. The most notable result is the property of positive reality, which is both necessary and sufficient for physical realizability of a given function of p as a driving-point immittance. To this there are many corollaries, such as the relations between, for example, resistance and reactance. With our knowledge of these properties we can determine whether or not the requirements can be met exactly.

The second step, that of *approximation*, is to be taken in cases where the requirements cannot be met exactly. In Chapters 13 and 14 we have discussed some methods of approximation that enable us to treat a large variety of problems (though we have not exhausted the subject). The result of taking this second step is a realizable function that is at the same time a sufficiently good approximation of that originally prescribed.

The third step is that of the *synthesis proper*, the construction of a schematic diagram that shows what elements are to be used and how they are to be interconnected. For this we have a wide variety of procedures, ranging from the canonic forms of Chapters 6 and 7 that provide a straightforward synthesis where they can be used, to the more complicated and arbitrary methods of the general R-L-C case (Chapters 9 and 10).

It remains, in the fourth step, actually to construct and test the networks. Some of the difficulties to be expected here and precautions to be taken have been discussed in Chapter 12.

These same steps must be taken in the synthesis of a two-terminal pair, or of any more complicated network—and, in fact, they may be advisable in any synthesis problem whatever. In Volume II we shall consider the two-terminal pair; but before concluding this treatment of the one-terminal pair, it is appropriate to discuss some examples of synthesis that are complete in that they illustrate in one synthesis all of the steps. They are chosen to review the most important parts and to bring them together in one place. That they are in reality two-terminal-pair syntheses merely emphasizes the practical importance of the two-terminal pair; these are all cases in which the actual synthesis reduces, however, to that of one-terminal pairs, emphasizing the primary need for a clear understanding of them.

15.02 Illustration I

Our first example is the design of an equalizing network of the type shown in Fig. 11.02–A. Such (constant-resistance, bridged-T) networks are commonly used in communication systems to correct distortion because of the convenience of the constant-resistance property and the simplicity of the formal expression of their effect on transmission in the system. In fact we have, by (11.02–3), simply

$$\frac{E_1}{E_2} = 1 + \frac{Z_1}{R_0} = 1 + z_1. \qquad (15.02\text{–}1)$$

The transmission function of this network is thus essentially a driving-point immittance function, corresponding to the impedance of the normalized impedance $z(p)$ in series with a 1 Ω resistor.

Let us suppose that in a certain carrier-telephone system an equalizer is required to remove certain irregularities of transmission magnitude; these are small irregularities remaining, perhaps, after the major equalization of transmission-line and amplifier characteristics has been made. The data for this design, converted into required magnitude of the ratio E_1/E_2, are given in Table 15.02–A; R_0 is to be 600 Ω. Our concern is

Table 15.02–A

Frequency (kcps)	$\lvert E_1/E_2 \rvert$ Desired
30	1.00
35	1.60
38	1.90
40	2.00
42	1.90
45	1.60
50	1.45
54	1.55
56	1.55
58	1.45
60	1.00

only with magnitude, the angle presumably being of no importance in this problem. The data represent measurements and are only valid within $\pm 3\%$; they are to be matched with about this accuracy, subject to the use of only a reasonable number of elements. They may be multiplied by a reasonable constant, if that is helpful in the design, since only the functional nature, or shape, is of importance. The size of constant acceptable, and the exact quality of approximation, will be determined finally by conference between the system engineer and the network designer, when the latter has completed one or more syntheses and can indicate the cost of these items.

As the first step of a synthesis, we consider the realizability of the data. When these are plotted we observe a reasonably smooth nature (Fig. 15.02–A) for the function $\lvert 1 + z \rvert$. The curve appears to offer no great obstacles—yet if we proceed to approximate this in the approximation band (30 to 60 kcps) with an even function representing the (square of the) magnitude of $(1 + z)$ we shall not be able actually to insure its realizability. It will be necessary to extract the function $(1 + z)$ and to test it for positive reality (§ 8.16). Moreover, in this particular problem, we shall have to be sure that the function is not minimum-resistance, in fact that

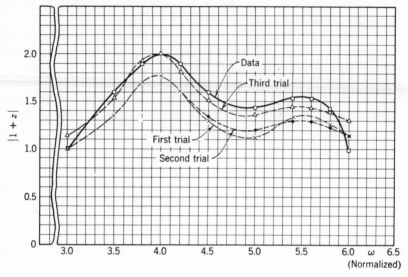

Fig. 15.02–A

1 Ω of resistance could be successfully removed from it. A very practical method of avoiding this difficulty (inherent in all problems where the data represent magnitude of immittance) is to assume a reasonable schematic form for the network and to determine element values in it by suitable approximation methods. This approach lacks technical elegance but is eminently practical in situations like this one. The design of such equalizers is in fact an art, in which experience is an invaluable aid.

The second step is approximation. We have here a synthesis problem in which the data are empirical (measured) and hence of limited accuracy. In addition, the very nature of many equalization problems, such as this one, makes the data form an irregular curve difficult of formal expression. In such cases elaborate analytical methods of approximation are entirely out of place; the appropriate technique is that of trial and error (§ 13.03). This is entirely in keeping with our decision first to assume a schematic form; we shall do so and determine its element values by trial and error. The third step, the realization in schematic form of the approximating function, is thus automatically performed in the course of carrying out the approximation.

On consideration of the data (Fig. 15.02–A) it seems reasonable that for $(1 + z)$ a network of either of the forms shown in Fig. 15.02–B is

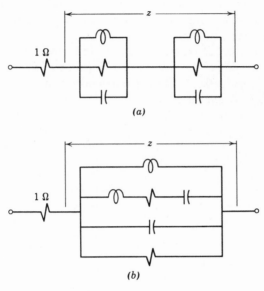

(a)

(b)

Fig. 15.02–B

suitable. [The 1 Ω resistor shown is not a part of the actual bridged-T network; it is included to aid in visualizing the behavior of (15.02–1).] Because of the two definite "humps" or "peaks" in the data, a network of less complexity is very unlikely to succeed. The first form has two damped resonant networks, each to provide one of the humps, in a rather obvious fashion. The second form is perhaps not quite as natural a form to choose, but does have certain practical advantages in design; in parallel, rather than series, connection of branches one can control the "valleys" more easily, and these are likely to present more difficulty. The use of paralleled branches is common in practice, and with the aid of suitable charts (Problem 11-5) designs can be greatly expedited.

We start, in any case, by setting up an *L-C* network (Chapter 6) with appropriate poles and zeros, and then proceed to add dissipation to these as necessary to approximate the data. A convenient normalization of the frequency scale makes $\omega = 3$ correspond to a frequency of 30 kcps. In such terms, the frequency pattern of Fig. 15.02–C is rather clearly the minimum that it is reasonable to use: the locations of the poles and the internal zero shown are suggested by the peaks and the valley of the data. The first canonic form of this L-C network leads, on adding dissipation, to the network of Fig. 15.02–B(a); the second canonic form, preferred here, leads (with dissipation) to the network of Fig. 15.02–B(b); the other two canonic forms are of no help here, because they do not place the resonances in evidence and are not adapted to simple adjustment of the damping required.

We now drop the 1 Ω resistor, which is not really part of the network, and concentrate on z, the normalized impedance which controls the behavior of the network. The second canonic form of the L-C network of Fig. 15.02–C is shown in Fig. 15.02–D, with the addition of two

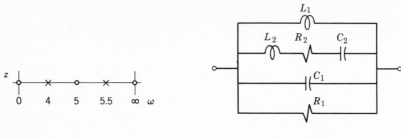

Fig. 15.02–C   Fig. 15.02–D

resistors. The shunt resistor R_1 is necessary to reduce the magnitude of the impedance at the two poles to finite height. The series resistor R_2 is necessary to raise the magnitude of the impedance at the internal zero from zero to some reasonable value. With the six elements shown in Fig. 15.02–D we ought to be able to match the data fairly closely; it remains to approximate, and to determine element values, by trial.

We set a tentative multiplier of the vertical scale by assuming (arbitrarily) that at $\omega = 3$ the network z will have a predominantly reactive impedance of about 1 Ω. Then $|1 + z|$ will be about 1.4 at $\omega = 3$, and we take this as our multiplier. At $\omega = 4$ we shall then need $|1 + z| = 2 \times 1.4 = 2.8$. At this frequency $|1 + z|$ is predominantly determined by R_1 since the reactive elements are in resonance (R_2 being neglected for the moment), and we accordingly set $|1 + R_1| = 2.8$, or $R_1 = 1.8 \, \Omega$. We now return to $\omega = 3$ and determine the admittance required of the L-C network (R_2 still being neglected) to give the assumed 1.4 value of $|1 + z|$. We have

$$|1 + z| = \left| 1 + \frac{1}{(1/1.8) - jb} \right| = 1.4 \qquad (15.02\text{–}2)$$

and readily find, either analytically or perhaps just as rapidly merely by trial, that $b = 1.4$ is satisfactory. With this we can now develop the L-C network (still neglecting R_2) in the second canonic form, as follows. We have for it

$$Y(p) = \frac{K(p^2 + 16)(p^2 + 30)}{p(p^2 + 25)} \qquad (15.02\text{–}3)$$

in which 30 has replaced $(5.5)^2 = 30.25$ as being a round number entirely close enough, the general accuracy required of the design being considered. On inserting $p = j3$ in (15.02–3) and requiring $Y(j3) = -j1.4$, we obtain $K = 0.456$. Then

$$Y(p) = \frac{0.456(p^2 + 16)(p^2 + 30)}{p(p^2 + 25)}$$

$$= \frac{8.75}{p} + \frac{0.820p}{p^2 + 25} + 0.456p \qquad (15.02\text{–}4)$$

which gives the element values

$$L_1 = 0.114 \text{ h}, \qquad C_2 = 0.033 \text{ f},$$
$$L_2 = 1.22 \text{ h}, \qquad C_1 = 0.46 \text{ f}, \qquad \text{and } R_1 = 1.8 \ \Omega. \qquad (15.02\text{–}5)$$

These are, of course, on the basis of $R_0 = 1 \ \Omega$ and $\omega = 3$ corresponding to an actual frequency of 30 kcps. For all the calculations of this first example, with its inherent lack of great precision, a 10-inch slide rule is more than adequate, and indeed some rounding off of numbers has been made in (15.02–5).

It remains to select a value for R_2, neglected so far. To do this we turn our attention to the vicinity of $\omega = 5$, the frequency of the valley, at which R_2 is to be most effective. At $\omega = 5$ the effects of L_2 and C_2 of course cancel; the admittances of the remaining elements lead to

$$|1 + z| = \left| 1 + \frac{1}{[(1/1.8) + (1/R_2)] + j0.53} \right| \qquad (15.02\text{–}6)$$

which gives the value 1.14 if $R_2 = 1$, and 1.29 if $R_2 = 2$. R_2 must not be made too large, or it will spoil the resonances by excessive damping; fortunately, the closest one, that at $\omega = 5.5$, is required to be relatively damped anyway, and at $\omega = 4$ the effect of R_2 will presumably be less important. On examining the size of the reactance of the L_2-C_2 combination at $\omega = 5.5$ (it is $+1.16 \ \Omega$) we decide that $1 \ \Omega$ is a reasonable value for R_2, for a first trial, and plan to obtain the necessary increase in $|1 + z|$ at $\omega = 5$ by subsequent readjustment as seems best.

We have now determined trial values for all the elements in Fig. 15.02–D, and the next task is that of computing $|1 + z|$ at various frequencies in the approximation band in order to determine what we actually have, account being taken of the various interactions we have hitherto neglected. We can then make changes (small ones will suffice, we hope) and thus determine the effect of varying each element, in order to arrive at a good design. This computation can be expedited by charts made for the purpose (Problem 11-5), but it is not a difficult one if properly organized in tabular form (Problem 15-3).

The computation leads to the values given in Table 15.02–B, in which

Table 15.02–B

ω	$|1 + z|$	$\left|\dfrac{1 + z}{1.40}\right|$
3.0	1.40	1.00
3.5	1.92	1.37
3.8	2.39	1.71
4.0	2.48	1.77
4.2	2.26	1.61
4.5	1.81	1.29
5.0	1.59	1.13
5.4	1.88	1.34
5.6	1.89	1.35
5.8	1.79	1.28
6.0	1.66	1.18

the last column has been divided by 1.40, the value of $|1 + z|$ at $\omega = 3$, for comparison with the data. These points are plotted in Fig. 15.02–A as crosses, connected by a light dashed curve ("first trial"). The effect of R_2 in reducing the hump at $\omega = 4$ is evident; the general shape, however, is not radically different from that desired.

This first trial is defective in several respects. If we imagine the curve moved generally up, by multiplication by a constant (or perhaps by revision of R_1), we see that neither the curvature at the low-frequency end nor that at the high meets the requirements. In addition, there is too much difference between the valley at $\omega = 5$ and the peak at $\omega = 5.5$.

To begin at the high-frequency end, we observe that if the pronounced drop in the range $5.6 < \omega < 6$ is to be obtained it will probably be necessary to add an additional zero in the prototype L-C network in the vicinity of $\omega = 6$. This would call for an additional reactive element and more or less complete recomputation of our network; we postpone its consideration for the moment. We can easily improve the fit in the range $4.5 < \omega < 5.5$ by "damping" the curve by increasing the value of R_2. We must use care here, however, for the dissipation in the L_2-R_2-C_2 branch is already large, and the "wiggle" will be completely lost if R_2 is increased too much.   We first try $R_2 = 2$, making only a few rough calculations, and find this definitely too large.   Then we try $R_2 = 1.4$, which gives (all other elements remaining unchanged) the points marked by dots in Fig. 15.02–A ("second trial").   Notice that it is not necessary to recalculate points for $\omega < 4$, as such a change in R_2 has no effect at these lower frequencies.   On readjusting the "level," i.e., multiplying by a suitable constant, this is brought up to the set of triangles ("third trial").

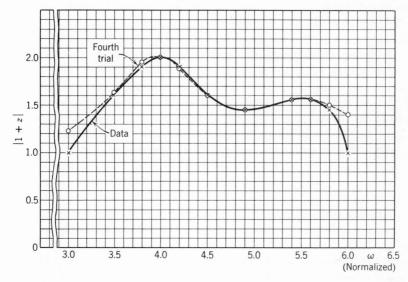

Fig. 15.02–E

A technique of considerable importance in such trial-and-error approximation is to note the effect of a small change in one element, as given here, for example, by the difference between the first and second trials, for R_2.   By a series of such calculations one can determine the effects of small element changes throughout the set, and since these effects combine more or less linearly when the changes are small, the final stages of approximation can be made easier through their use.   Here we note that this increase in R_2 of 0.4 is a little too much, for the wiggle is damped too much; an increase of about 0.3 would be better.

For our next trial we accordingly set $R_2 = 1.3$; this will probably give a fairly good fit in the range $4.5 < \omega < 5.6$.   We need also to correct the general dropping below the requirement in the upper half of the approximation band.   This is best done by reducing R_1 so that our curve more or less parallels the data, and then readjusting the multiplier to raise the whole curve. On taking $R_1 = 1.6$ (a value determined by calculation at $\omega = 4$), recomputing our points with these two changes (in R_1 and R_2), and adjusting the multiplier to give the value 2 at $\omega = 4$, we obtain the points marked by circles ("fourth trial") in Fig. 15.02–E, which also repeats the data. Except for the two end points and their immediate vicinity, this fit is within the requirements.

At this point it is appropriate to confer with the system engineer, to determine whether this solution is not acceptable, as it may be that the additional design work, network complexity, and cost required to obtain a better fit at the ends of the approximation band are not warranted. We shall assume here that the decision is to use this solution as it is.

The fourth step of synthesis remains: to correct for dissipation in the element values, and other practical matters of construction. We find, on calculation, that a Q of 50 in L_1 has no appreciable effect, and note that R_2 can be reduced to compensate for any reasonable dissipation in L_2. The Q's of the capacitors will probably be sufficiently high to be ignored. Hence we need only compute the actual element values to complete the synthesis and prepare for the construction of the network (parasitic capacitance is usually negligible at these frequencies with impedances of this order of magnitude). These are given in Fig. 15.02–F, both normalized and actual values, for the complete bridged-T network. The table of element values should, in practice, be augmented by specification on the Q's required (discussed above) and the precision needed in their realization. The latter can best be determined by computations made with individual elements slightly varied, to determine the effect on the characteristic—some of the design trials may be helpful (in differences between them) here. In addition, a final check of at least two or three points should be made from the final (actual) element values, to detect errors in the calculations.

Although an additional element would be required to improve the fit at the high-frequency end, we have not investigated one simpler possibility that may improve the fit at the low end. That is the use of a smaller value of K in (15.02–3). This would increase the magnitude of z in $(1 + z)$ and, with readjustment of damping resistors, might better adapt the stiffness of the L-C network to the data. To determine this, it would be necessary to start the design again with, say, $K = 0.25$.

We have discussed this problem sufficiently to illustrate one important type of practical network synthesis. In it the data are not extremely precise; this, and the irregular tendencies of the data, indicate that the "cut-and-try" method of approximation is the appropriate one. The art of making such designs rapidly and efficiently can only be learned by experience, which gives one the ability to make appropriate choices of configuration and element values, to decide then which element to vary, and a host of useful "tricks." One does not escape, however, the need for making a succession of trials and for doing a certain amount of computing (essential in trial-and-error approximation).

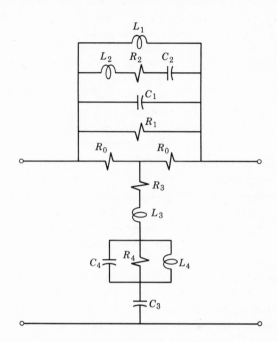

Value

Element	Normalized	Actual
L_1	0.114	1.09
L_2	1.22	11.7 mh
L_3	0.46	4.4 mh
L_4	0.033	0.315 mh
C_1	0.46	0.0123 μf
C_2	0.033	0.00088 μf
C_3	0.114	0.00304 μf
C_4	1.22	0.0325 μf
R_0	1	600 Ω
R_1	1.6	962 Ω
R_2	1.3	780 Ω
R_3	0.625	375 Ω
R_4	0.77	462 Ω

Fig. 15.02–F

15.03 Illustration II

The problem chosen for our second illustration is one to which a more sophisticated approximation technique can be applied. It too has its origin in a communication system, but one which involves a wider frequency band (as for a larger number of telephone channels, or for a television channel, or even for a combination of the two) and a different location in the frequency spectrum. The system uses a coaxial cable and the frequencies of importance run from 2 to 8 mcps. The problem is again to equalize transmission magnitude (which ideally should be constant with frequency), but this time we concern ourselves with the coaxial cable itself. The transmission magnitude of such a transmission line is in logarithmic terms closely proportional to the square root of frequency; i.e., the ratio of the magnitudes of voltages (or currents) at output and input ends of a section of line is substantially $\exp\left(-k_1\sqrt{\omega}\right)$, k_1 being a constant. We take as our problem then the design of a network whose transmission will be proportional to $\exp\left(k_1\sqrt{\omega}\right)$, so that in conjunction network and cable will form an equalized system. We also assume that for this system accuracy is very important in the center of the 2 to 8-mcps region; near the ends of this approximation band some error is tolerable and can be compensated by other apparatus.

The form the network is to take is that discussed in § 11.04 and § 11.05: a one-resistor network driven by a vacuum tube of substantially infinite internal impedance, so that the transmission function reduces merely to the driving-point resistance function and the two-terminal-pair (transmission) problem becomes a one-terminal-pair (driving-point) problem. The vacuum tubes are found in the repeaters (amplifiers), a number of which must be provided in the coaxial-cable system in any case, for amplification, for each direction of transmission. The problem then is to design a network whose driving-point resistance is proportional to $\exp\left(2k_1\sqrt{\omega}\right)$, for use as in Fig. 15.03–A, since there

$$\left|\frac{E_{\text{out}}}{E_{\text{in}}}\right|^2 = \text{constant} \times \mathbf{Re}\,Z(j\omega) \qquad (15.03\text{--}1)$$

with the usual assumptions as to linearity of vacuum-tube operation, size of internal impedance, etc.

We have to find a p-r function whose real part (at real frequencies) behaves closely as $\exp\left(2k_1\sqrt{\omega}\right)$ in the approximation band. Such a driving-point resistance function must of course be rational, so that our standard first question, that of realizability, must be answered *no*; approximation is necessary. Since the data are given in analytic-function form (in contrast to the numerical data of Illustration I), and since the center is the most important part of the approximation band as far as accuracy of approximation is concerned, we turn naturally to Taylor approximation. We write

$$\mathbf{Re}\,Z(j\omega) = R(\omega) = \frac{a_0 + a_2\omega^2 + \cdots + a_{2m}\omega^{2m}}{b_0 + b_2\omega^2 + \cdots + b_{2n}\omega^{2n}} \quad (15.03\text{--}2)$$

as the general form of the function sought and recall that realizability demands only that $R(\omega)$ remain finite and not be negative, for all values of ω, infinity included (§ 8.16). Determination of the a's and b's, once

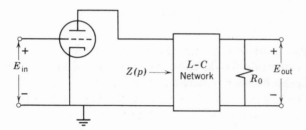

Fig. 15.03–A

m and n have been fixed, is a matter of straightforward calculation, following §§ 13.05–7, as far as approximation goes. But if the network is to be practical, not only must the zeros of the denominator of $R(\omega)$ not lie at real frequencies, and any real-frequency zeros of the numerator be of even order, but the network must be realizable in a fairly simple practical form. Mutual inductance is to be avoided if at all possible, and the number of elements must be reasonably small. In addition, because of the high frequencies involved, parasitic capacitance must be very carefully considered. Moreover, the use of the network in association with coaxial cable and vacuum tubes implies that the lower input *and* output terminals of the *L-C* network in Fig. 15.03–A will be grounded, and thus must be at the same potential. A form of network which meets these requirements of practicality is that shown in Fig. 15.03–B in which each small box is a one-terminal *L-C* pair. Both the first and the last boxes must have zeros of impedance at infinity, to assure that capacitors will be present there, since the parasitic capacitance presented by the driving vacuum tube and by the apparatus which receives the output voltage and by the wiring must be incorporated in the network. The simplest way of insuring that all these additional requirements of practicality will be met is to confine the zeros of **Ev** $Z(p)$, i.e., of the driving-point resistance function, to the origin and infinity. Then each box in Fig. 15.03–B will contain one, or at most two, reactive elements and no mutual inductance will be necessary (§ 9.11). If enough zeros are placed at infinity, the end capacitor requirement will also be met.

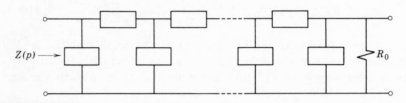

Fig. 15.03–B

To design a network we must have a numerical value for the constant k_1 in the expression for the cable transmission. This will depend on the length of cable between repeaters and on the fraction of the total equalization job that is to be performed in each stage (Fig. 15.03–A) of the repeater. A reasonable value is that given by

$$F_1(\omega) = e^{(-0.92\sqrt{f_{mc}})} \tag{15.03–3}$$

which represents the *square* of the cable transmission function's magnitude, i.e., $\exp(2k_1\sqrt{\omega})$ of the previous discussion. This corresponds closely to a 4-mile length of an actual cable between repeaters, and a division of the equalization into four stages (MO 1, p. 884). The symbol f_{mc} refers to frequency measured in megacycles per second. If we now take the center frequency of 5 mcps as the frequency at which the approximation is to be made, the function which the driving-point resistance $R(\omega)$ is to approximate is

$$F_2(\omega) = Ke^{(+0.92\sqrt{5}\sqrt{\omega})}$$
$$= Ke^{(2.06\sqrt{\omega})} \tag{15.03–4}$$

in which ω now represents normalized frequency, $\omega = 1$ corresponding to 5 mcps. The exact value of K is not specified, for only the *shape* of the transmission function is important. K should of course be as large as possible in order that the repeater amplify well. Since it amounts in our problem only to an impedance scale factor, we assign it the convenient value that makes the function to be approximated have unit value at $\omega = 1$. Then

$$F(\omega) = \frac{e^{2.06\sqrt{\omega}}}{e^{2.06}} \tag{15.03–5}$$

is the function with which we work. It is to be approximated in the Taylor sense at $\omega = 1$; we must remember, however, that the approximation band is $0.4 < \omega < 1.6$ (corresponding to the actual frequency band from 2 to 8 mcps) even though the most important part is the center.

We need the numerical values of $F(\omega_0)$, $F'(\omega_0)$, $F''(\omega_0)$, $\cdots$, $\omega_0 = 1$ being the point of approximation. Looking ahead, we realize that our final approximating function will probably have most, if not all, of its zeros at infinity because of the practical requirements previously discussed. Most of the coefficients to be determined will therefore be in the denominator. Consequently, it will simplify the work a little to work in terms of reciprocals. [Approximation of F^{-1} with the reciprocal of (15.03–2) will lead to the same result as approximation of F with (15.03–2).] We accordingly proceed to calculate the various derivatives of

$$G(\omega) = K^{-1}e^{-k\sqrt{\omega}} = K^{-1}e^{-k\sqrt{1+x}} \qquad (15.03\text{–}6)$$

in which $K^{-1} = e^{2.06}$ and $k = 2.06$. We have made the substitution

$$\omega = \omega_0(1 + x) = 1 + x \qquad (15.03\text{–}7)$$

in order to introduce the fractional frequency departure variable x, convenient in Taylor approximation when ω_0 is not zero (§ 13.05), for it is actually power series in x of which we make use, by equating coefficients. We need the coefficients in

$$G(x) = G_0 + G_1 x + G_2 x^2 + \cdots \qquad (15.03\text{–}8)$$

whose calculation is somewhat tedious but straightforward, with the results given in (15.03–9).

$$G(x) = K^{-1}e^{-k\sqrt{1+x}}$$

$$G_0 = G(0) = 1$$

$$G'(x) = K^{-1}\left(-\frac{k}{2}\right)e^{-k\sqrt{1+x}}(1 + x)^{-1/2}$$

$$G_1 = G'(0) = -k/2 = -1.03$$

$$G''(x) = K^{-1}\left(\frac{k}{4}\right)e^{-k\sqrt{1+x}}\{(1 + x)^{-3/2} + k(1 + x)^{-1}\}$$

$$G_2 = \frac{G''(0)}{2!} = \frac{k}{8}(k + 1) = +0.78795$$

$$(15.03\text{–}9)$$

$$G'''(x) = K^{-1}\left(-\frac{k}{8}\right)e^{-k\sqrt{1+x}}\{3(1+x)^{-5/2} + 3(1+x)^{-2} + k^2(1+x)^{-3/2}\}$$

$$G_3 = \frac{G'''(0)}{3!} = -\frac{k}{48}(k^2 + 3k + 3) = -0.576096$$

$$G^{\mathrm{iv}}(x) = K^{-1}\left(\frac{k}{16}\right)e^{-k\sqrt{1+x}}\{15(1+x)^{-7/2} + 15k(1+x)^{-3}$$
$$+ 6k^2(1+x)^{5/2} + k^3(1+x)^{-2}\}$$

$$G_4 = \frac{G^{\mathrm{iv}}(0)}{4!} = \frac{k}{384}(k^3 + 6k^2 + 15k + 15) = +0.429722$$

$$G^{\mathrm{v}}(x) = K^{-1}\left(-\frac{k}{32}\right)e^{-k\sqrt{1+x}}\{105(1+x)^{9/2} + 105(1+x)^{-4}$$
$$+ 45k^2(1+x)^{-7/2} + 10k^3(1+x)^{-3} + k^4(1+x)^{-5/2}\}$$

$$G_5 = \frac{G^{\mathrm{v}}(0)}{5!} = -\frac{k}{3840}(k^4 + 10k^3 + 45k^2 + 105k + 105)$$
$$= -0.331365.$$

$$(15.03\text{-}9)$$

Since a great deal depends on accurate calculation of these coefficients, it is well to check these results by an independent calculation. There are several possible methods, two of which are suggested in Problem 15-7.

We shall carry out our actual design by stipulating zeros at the origin and infinity, as suggested above—but we might first investigate the matter a little more generally, to satisfy our curiosity and to get a preliminary "feel" for what can be done in the way of Taylor approximation to our function by rational functions suitable for realization as driving-point-resistance functions. If we leave the zeros of $\mathrm{Ev}\,Z(p)$ unassigned, i.e., make use of them to aid the approximation process (and thus find out where the function would *like* the zeros to be), then we set $m = n$ in (15.03-2), for $m > n$ would make the function unrealizable. With no further restrictions, we now compute the function (15.03-2) for several values of n and study the functions and approximations obtained. We write

$$R(\omega) = \frac{a_0 + a_2\omega^2 + \cdots + a_{2n}\omega^{2n}}{1 + b_2\omega^2 + \cdots + b_{2n}\omega^{2n}} \overset{\mathrm{T}}{=} F = \frac{1}{G} \qquad (15.03\text{-}10)$$

in which the symbol $\overset{\mathrm{T}}{=}$ means that the a's and b's are to be determined by approximation in the Taylor sense at $\omega = \omega_0 = 1$, in other words, that the two power series in x, about $x = 0$, for the left and right sides of (15.03-10) are to agree in the first $(2n + 1)$ terms. One coefficient in (15.03-2) is as usual arbitrary, and we have given b_0 the value unity on this account (on the reasonable assumption that a pole at the origin would not be desirable).

Since the approximation point is not at the origin but at an internal frequency, we must transform the left side of (15.03–10) into a function of x, by using (15.03–7), as we have already done with the right side. We may take formulas from § 13.05 and merely substitute in them; it is more instructive, and just as quick, however, to recall only the *principle* and work out the mathematics as we go. On transforming from ω to x and then cross-multiplying (in which the fact that we have the series for G rather than for F is no handicap) we obtain, much as in § 13.05 (though here it is unnecessary to distinguish between coefficients a and a', or b and b', because $\omega_0 = 1$),

$$[a_0 + a_2(1 + 2x + x^2) + a_4(1 + 4x + 6x^2 + 4x^3 + x^4) + \cdots]$$
$$\times (G_0 + G_1 x + G_2 x^2 + G_3 x^3 + G_4 x^4 + \cdots)$$
$$= 1 + b_2(1 + 2x + x^2) + b_4(1 + 4x + 6x^2 + 4x^3 + x^4) + \cdots$$
$$+ \underbrace{\epsilon_{2n+1} x^{2n+1} + \cdots}_{\text{error}}. \quad (15.03\text{–}11)$$

On collecting terms and equating coefficients we obtain the set of linear simultaneous equations written with detached coefficients in (15.03–12), to be compared with (13.05–23).

a_0	a_2	a_4	$\cdots$ b_2	b_4 $\cdots$	
G_0	G_0	G_0	$\cdots -1$	$-1 \cdots$	$= 1,$
G_1	$(2G_0 + G_1)$	$(4G_0 + G_1)$	$\cdots -2$	$-4 \cdots$	$= 0,$
G_2	$(G_0 + 2G_1 + G_2)$	$(6G_0 + 4G_1 + G_2)$	$\cdots -1$	$-6 \cdots$	$= 0,$
G_3	$(G_1 + 2G_2 + G_3)$	$(4G_0 + 6G_1 + 4G_2 + G_3)$	$\cdots \ 0$	$-4 \cdots$	$= 0,$
G_4	$(G_2 + 2G_3 + G_4)$	$(G_0 + 4G_1 + 6G_2 + 4G_3 + G_4) \cdots$	$\ 0$	$-1 \cdots$	$= 0,$

$$(15.03\text{–}12)$$

Of these, only the first $(2n + 1)$ are to be used, with zero values for the higher a's and b's.

With $n = 1$ we have

a_0	a_2	b_2	
1	1	-1	$= 1,$
-1.0300	$+0.9700$	-2	$= 0,$
$+0.7880$	-0.2721	-1	$= 0,$

$$(15.03\text{–}13)$$

whose solution gives

$$R_1(\omega) = \frac{0.4164 + 0.7167\omega^2}{1 + 0.1331\omega^2}. \quad (15.03\text{–}14)$$

In Fig. 15.03–C are plotted the function to be approximated, $F(\omega)$, the approximating function (15.03–14), and, to a different scale for clarity, the error.

The fit accomplished by the function $R_1(\omega)$ is excellent in view of the low order of the function. But its realization as a driving-point resistance

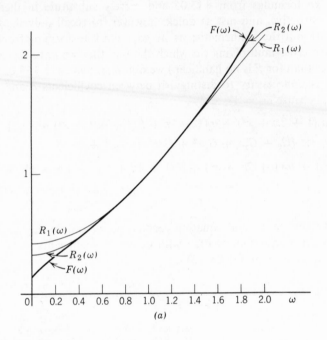

(a)

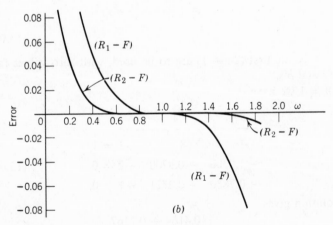

(b)

Fig. 15.03–C

function for use in the system of Fig. 15.03–A requires the use of a Brune network (Chapter 9) with its impractical mutual inductance, and the network has no capacitor at its ends. The mathematical approximation is excellent, but its realization is entirely impractical. In this we encounter the primary object lesson of this Illustration II: the practical requirements of the job are not necessarily at all consistent with the best theoretical solution. Our theory alone is not enough: it must be modified by the practical aspects of engineering.

Nevertheless, this academic solution is of interest in that it shows us what we are up against. If in (15.03–10) we set $n = 1$ and then determine all three of the parameters for maximal approximation at ω_0, we obtain the function (15.03–14) whose zeros and poles lie as shown in Fig. 15.03–D.

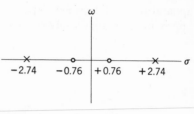

Fig. 15.03–D

For practicality we need zeros of **Ev** $Z(p)$, i.e., of $R(\omega)$, at infinity. Nature, however, acting through the approximation process, wishes the zeros to lie on the real axis.

This can be verified by repeating the above approximation process with $n = 2$. Equations (15.03–12) are then

a_0	a_2	a_4	b_2	b_4	
1	1	1	-1	$-1 = 1,$	
-1.03000	0.97	2.97	-2	$-4 = 0,$	
$+0.78795$	-0.27205	2.66795	-1	$-6 = 0,$	(15.03–15)
-0.57610	-0.03020	0.39570	0	$-4 = 0,$	
$+0.42972$	$+0.06548$	-0.26696	0	$-1 = 0,$	

and their solution gives

$$R_2(\omega) = \frac{0.3208 + 1.7528\omega^2 + 0.8528\omega^4}{1 + 1.9015\omega^2 + 0.0250\omega^4}. \qquad (15.03\text{–}16)$$

This function, and the corresponding error, are also plotted in Fig. 15.03–C; its zeros and poles are shown in Fig. 15.03–E. The fit, over the approximation band, is well nigh perfect, but the realization is subject to the same practical objections. That the mathematical process of approximation wants the zeros to lie on the real axis is again demonstrated, a situation incompatible with a practical engineering solution to the problem. Further calculations with higher values of n would probably confirm this.

We must therefore expect, in a practical solution, not to obtain as good an approximation with a function of the same order; i.e., the price we shall have to pay for requiring zeros at infinity will undoubtedly be a degradation in the quality of approximation, or the use of a function of higher order (with a consequent increase in network complexity). It is reasonable to expect that the same would be true if we had the necessary apparatus for Chebyshev approximation, since Taylor and Chebyshev approximation are closely related (§ 14.15).

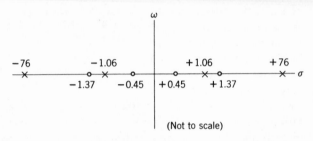

Fig. 15.03–E

In order to estimate this price, let us jump to the opposite extreme and require that *all* of the zeros of $\mathrm{Ev}\, Z(p)$ lie at infinity; the (parasitic) capacitance requirement will presumably then be met, for the network will consist of a ladder of shunt capacitors and series inductors terminated in a resistor. (Intermediate cases, where some of the zeros lie at the origin, can be taken up later if that seems advisable.) We now require that all the a's in (15.03–2) be zero except a_0. We give to a_0, rather than b_0, the value unity, and observe that (15.03–10) becomes

$$R(\omega) = \frac{1}{b_0 + b_2\omega^2 + \cdots + b_{2n}\omega^{2n}} \overset{\mathrm{T}}{=} F(\omega) = \frac{1}{G(\omega)} \quad (15.03\text{–}17)$$

or simply

$$b_0 + b_2(1 + 2x + x^2) + b_4(1 + 4x + 6x^2 + 4x^3 + x^4) + \cdots$$
$$= G_0 + G_1 x + G_2 x^2 + G_3 x^3 + G_4 x^4 + \cdots + \underbrace{\epsilon_{n+1} x^{n+1} + \cdots}_{\text{error}}.$$

$$(15.03\text{–}18)$$

The quality of approximation is reduced, in that the error series begins with the term in x^{n+1}, rather than x^{2n+1}, because we have required that all the zeros lie at infinity.   On collecting terms and equating coefficients we obtain equations (15.03–19), corresponding to (13.05–23), of which the first n are to be used, the higher b's being taken as zero.

b_0	b_2	b_4	b_6	b_8	$b_{10} \cdot \cdot \cdot$	
1	1	1	1	1	$1 \cdots = G_0,$	
0	2	4	6	8	$10 \cdots = G_1,$	
0	1	6	15	28	$45 \cdots = G_2,$	
0	0	4	20	56	$120 \cdots = G_3,$	(15.03–19)
0	0	1	15	70	$210 \cdots = G_4,$	
0	0	0	6	56	$252 \cdots = G_5,$	

Their solution is simply a numerical chore.   It is of some advantage to solve these for the b's without substituting numerical values for the G's; the solution can then be used later if necessary with zeros located at the origin, by changing the G's to other appropriate numbers.

On carrying out the solution for $n = 1, 2, 3, 4, 5$ and substituting the numerical values of the G's from (15.03–9), we obtain the functions $R_n(\omega)$ of (15.03–20), which are plotted in Fig. 15.03–F.   Note that here, as with the previous calculation where the a's were also unknown, slide-rule calculation is sufficient; there are no annoying differences of nearly equal numbers and the carrying of more significant figures is not necessary at this stage (unless several significant figures are desired in the error).

$$R_0(\omega) = 1,$$

$$R_1(\omega) = \frac{1}{1.515 - 0.515\omega^2},$$

$$R_2(\omega) = \frac{1}{1.841 - 1.167\omega^2 + 0.326\omega^4},$$

$$R_3(\omega) = \frac{1}{2.076 - 1.872\omega^2 + 1.031\omega^4 - 0.235\omega^6}, \qquad (15.03–20)$$

$$R_4(\omega) = \frac{1}{2.258 - 2.602\omega^2 + 2.127\omega^4 - 0.966\omega^6 + 0.183\omega^8},$$

$$R_5(\omega) = \frac{1}{2.39 - 3.30\omega^2 + 3.59\omega^4 - 2.54\omega^6 + 0.92\omega^8 - 0.15\omega^{10}}.$$

The first five functions are more than sufficient for us to decide how well this placing of all the zeros at infinity will work. In addition, they point out an essential difference between the functions for odd n and those for even n. Those for even n are evidently realizable; those for odd n are not (they have real-frequency poles and are negative at high frequencies). This might have been predicted, had we thought of it, for we had a similar experience in § 13.03. We need only sketch the behavior required of

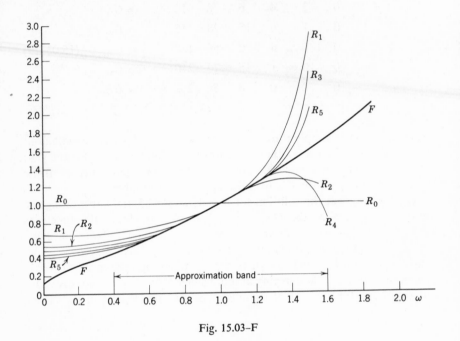

Fig. 15.03–F

$R_n(\omega)$ if it is to match $F(\omega)$ at $(n + 1)$ points and be the reciprocal of an even polynomial, to observe that the coefficient of ω_{2n} must be negative when n is odd; since Taylor approximation can be considered a limiting case of such a point-matching technique (§ 14.15), the same should be true here, as it evidently is. Unfortunately, it is just the odd-n case that interests us, for it provides shunt capacitance at both ends of the L-C network of Fig. 15.03–A; the even-n case provides it at only the input end. Once more we are confronted with the practical limitations of theory and a general lack of cooperation on Nature's part.

Since the form of network obtained when all the zeros of **Ev** $Z(p)$ are at infinity is such a practical one, we shall press its development further. From Fig. 15.03–F we note that $n = 4$ and $n = 5$ give fairly good fits at the lower end of the approximation band as well as in the middle; the difficulty comes at the high end, where even $R_5(\omega)$ departs far too much from $F(\omega)$. In discussion with the engineers concerned with the complete system, we decide that the cost of a network of four or five reactive elements (corresponding to $n = 4$ or $n = 5$) is reasonable, provided that the good match is maintained in the center of the band, and that deviations of as much as 0.1 can be tolerated at the high end if the error becomes substantially smaller when ω is about 1.5. At the low end, errors such as those of R_4 and R_5 in Fig. 15.03–F are tolerable. Capacitance must, however, be provided at both ends of the L-C network, since the parasitic capacitance of the vacuum tubes and wiring cannot be neglected.

We decide then to fix n at the value 5, which will provide a network of the form shown in Fig. 15.03–G, with the necessary capacitors. The

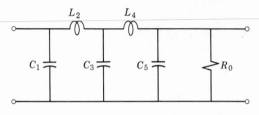

Fig. 15.03–G

function R_5 of (15.03–20) is not realizable, of course, so we must somehow alter the b's, both to make the function realizable and to improve the high-frequency error. We have, in obtaining the functions (15.03–20), used some of our parameters in locating zeros at infinity, and the rest in obtaining maximal approximation at $\omega = 1$. We shall keep the ten zeros at infinity, for the sake of the network configuration. In order to improve the error at high frequencies and to obtain a realizable function, we must then sacrifice some of the approximation at $\omega = 1$, to which six parameters have been devoted, so that the error there starts with a term in x^6. The mathematically elegant process of Taylor approximation has been found somewhat wanting in practicality, but can still be used to determine all the parameters not required to satisfy the demands of practicality. To determine the latter, some trial-and-error work is necessary.

Since our major difficulty is at the high-frequency end, we shall use one of the parameters to insure that $R(1.6)$ have a certain value. It is only reasonable to expect that to insure realizability, another parameter will have to be withdrawn from the Taylor approximation itself. We may conveniently use this to obtain a certain value for $R(0.4)$. Then the four remaining parameters can be determined by Taylor approximation at

$\omega = 1$. As to the "certain values" to be prescribed at $\omega = 0.4$ and $\omega = 1.6$, the best choices can only be determined by trial, after looking at the error over the whole approximation band for a set of realizable curves.

One simplification is suggested by the nature of the functions $R_n(\omega)$ at low frequencies. In Fig. 15.03–F we see that there is probably little difference in specifying the value of $R(\omega)$ at $\omega = 0.4$ and that at $\omega = 0$; if the latter is used, the parameter b_0 is immediately determined and we shall have one less equation in the simultaneous set to be solved. And since this is a trial-and-error process anyway, we lose nothing by the change. We accordingly proceed to set up the equations necessary, all ten zeros being at infinity, to determine the six parameters in the approximating function $R(\omega) = (b_0 + b_2\omega^2 + b_4\omega^4 + b_6\omega^6 + b_8\omega^8 + b_{10}\omega^{10})^{-1}$ from the six conditions that

$R(0)$ have a specified value,
$R(1.6)$ have a specified value,
$R(\omega)$ agree with $F(\omega)$ in the first four terms of the Taylor series about $\omega = 1$.

$$(15.03\text{–}21)$$

These are
$$b_0 = [R(0)]^{-1} \quad \text{and}$$

b_2	b_4	b_6	b_8	b_{10}	
1	1	1	1	1	$= \{G_0 - b_0\}$,
2	4	6	8	10	$= G_1$,
1	6	15	28	45	$= G_2$,
0	4	20	56	120	$= G_3$,
$(1.6)^2$	$(1.6)^4$	$(1.6)^6$	$(1.6)^8$	$(1.6)^{10}$	$= \{[R(1.6)]^{-1} - b_0\}$,

$$(15.03\text{–}22)$$

in which the four Taylor-approximation equations are obtained from (15.03–19) and the first and last equations from the first two requirements of (15.03–21). The solution of these (for which somewhat more than slide-rule accuracy is almost essential), with numerical values for the G's from (15.03–9), is

$$b_0 = [R(0)]^{-1},$$
$$b_2 = 7.23571 - 4.39063b_0 + 0.06596[R(1.6)]^{-1},$$
$$b_4 = -14.64073 + 7.56250b_0 - 0.26383[R(1.6)]^{-1},$$
$$b_6 = +12.89370 - 6.34375b_0 + 0.39574[R(1.6)]^{-1},$$
$$b_8 = -5.29302 + 2.56250b_0 - 0.26383[R(1.6)]^{-1},$$
$$b_{10} = +0.80435 - 0.39063b_0 + 0.06596[R(1.6)]^{-1}.$$

$$(15.03\text{–}23)$$

We can now calculate the b's for a set of prescribed values of $R(0)$ and $R(1.6)$, the other four parameters being determined by Taylor approximation at $\omega = 1$. With the corresponding curves we can then make a decision on the suitability of the network of Fig. 15.03–G.

In picking a set of values for these two new parameters, it is more than interesting to note how they enter into the determination of b_{10}, for it is the negative value of b_{10} in $R_5(\omega)$ of (15.03–20) that makes the function unrealizable. If b_{10} is made zero and $R(1.6)$ given the proper value (about 0.86, read from Fig. 15.03–F), we should obtain once more the function $R_4(\omega)$ of (15.03–20). The improvements desired in the error of $R_4(\omega)$ are, from Fig. 15.03–F, an increase in $R_4(1.6)$ and a decrease in $R_4(0)$. Either of these changes, made in (15.03–23), will make b_{10} *negative*, however! In other words, any attempt to improve on $R_4(\omega)$ by making such adjustments will result in an unrealizable function. To put it another way: a positive value of b_{10} requires, by (15.03–23), either an increase in $R(0)$ or a decrease in $R(1.6)$, both of which are undesirable. This is simply another manifestation of the fact that a good approximation in the odd-n case calls for an unrealizable function. Since any positive value of b_{10} can be counted on to degrade the approximation, we shall work temporarily with $b_{10} = 0$. When we have the best fit under this condition, we can raise b_{10} to a positive value in order to provide the second end capacitor required.

The requirement that $b_{10} = 0$ gives us a relation between $R(0)$ and $R(1.6)$, in the last equation of (15.03–23). We have then only one parameter and can proceed to plot a family of curves. Since this relation is much more sensitive to changes in $R(1.6)$ than in $R(0)$, we can expect to be able to improve the high-frequency error without serious degradation of the low-frequency error. Several resistance functions obtained under these conditions [$b_{10} = 0$, four terms of the Taylor series matched at $\omega = 1$, particular values given $R(0)$ or $R(1.6)$] are plotted as curves a, b, and c in Fig. 15.03–H. (Slide-rule calculation is sufficient for these.) The curve $R_4(\omega)$ in Fig. 15.03–F is another member of this family. The curve marked c, for which $R(1.6)$ was taken as 1.6, gives a not unreasonable error. Its realization will lack the capacitor C_5 of Fig. 15.03–G, however. To obtain a capacitor C_5 we must raise the value of b_{10} above zero, a nuisance as far as approximation goes, for this will surely not improve the error. On the other hand, we may be able to introduce a C_5 without excessive degradation of the error.

We retain the value 1.6 for $R(1.6)$, since this is in the region of greatest sensitivity, and allow $R(0)$ to increase as necessary. Now we must make some estimate of a reasonable value for b_{10}, for which we have no immediate guide. To get a start, suppose we allow $R(0)$ to increase by about 0.02 (about 4%) which, with $R(1.6)$ fixed, ought not to change the error curve greatly. This calls for a value of b_{10} of $0.04 \times 0.39 \times (0.5)^{-1}$ = 0.03, by the last equation in (15.03–23). Let us be somewhat more modest and try $b_{10} = 0.02$. The two functions obtained by solving (15.03–23) with $R(1.6) = 1.6$, first with $b_{10} = 0$ and then with $b_{10} = +0.02$, are

$$R_{\mathrm{I}}(\omega) = \frac{1}{2.16467 - 2.22733\omega^2 + 1.56469\omega^4 - 0.59109\omega^6 + 0.08906\omega^8}$$

and $\hspace{9cm}$ (15.03–24)

$$R_{\mathrm{II}}(\omega) = \frac{1}{\begin{aligned}&2.11347 - 2.00253\omega^2 + 1.17749\omega^4 - 0.26629\omega^6\\ &\hspace{4cm}- 0.04214\omega^8 + 0.02\omega^{10}.\end{aligned}}$$

$$\hspace{9cm} (15.03\text{–}25)$$

Curve c of Fig. 15.03–H essentially exhibits the behavior of both of these, since the differences are small. On making an accurate calculation of the

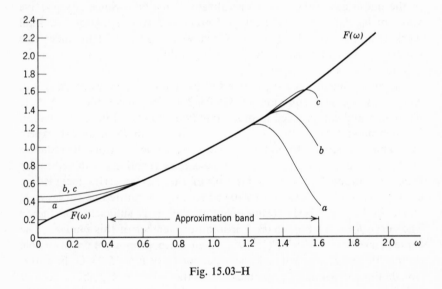

Fig. 15.03–H

error in each case we obtain the curves of Fig. 15.03–I. The effect of changing from $b_{10} = 0$ to $b_{10} = +0.02$ is not serious; there is a small deterioration at the low-frequency end of the approximation band and the expected greater deterioration near the high-frequency end. The effect of a further small increase in b_{10} can be estimated by linear extrapolation. It is clear now that a thorough study of the possibilities would require the expenditure of a large amount of time and effort. In particular, it would be interesting to find how good a Chebyshev approximation could be made, since we have found it necessary to give up some of the quality of our Taylor approximation. We do not have the necessary approximation methods (which will be discussed in Volume II) apart from trial-and-error methods, and since the value $+0.02$ for b_{10} has raised the height of the peak of error at $\omega = 1.4^+$ to about the height of

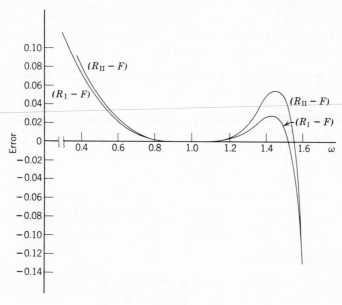

Fig. 15.03–I

the peak at $\omega = 0.4$, we shall stop here. We shall next find the network element values for both of the functions (15.03–24) and (15.03–25) as a further guide to the effect of requiring the capacitor C_5 (Fig. 15.03–G). For this the method of § 8.11 is the best. Once more we recall only the general principle (do not use the detailed formulas there) and develop the mathematics as we need it.

From (15.03–24) we obtain, on substituting p for ω/j and dividing numerator and denominator by the coefficient of the highest power of ω in the denominator,

$$\text{Ev}\, Z_\mathrm{I}(p) = \frac{11.228}{p^8 + 6.6368p^6 + 17.5683p^4 + 25.0085p^2 + 24.3049}.$$

$$(15.03\text{--}26)$$

The denominator is now to be factored into two polynomials, each of degree four, each with zeros confined to one half of the plane. The polynomial-splitting method of Appendix A gives us these, of which only the Hurwitz polynomial is of interest. We write it as the denominator of $Z_1(p)$, and an appropriate numerator with literal coefficients, to obtain

$$Z_1(p) = \frac{a_3 p^3 + a_2 p^2 + a_1 p + a_0}{p^4 + 2.0983 p^3 + 5.5200 p^2 + 5.4239 p + 4.9300}. \qquad (15.03\text{--}27)$$

The value of a_0 can be immediately obtained by equating (15.03–27) and (15.03–24), with $p = 0$; it is $a_0 = 4.9300/2.1647 = 2.2775$. We calculate next the even part of (15.03–27), whose denominator will be identical with that of (15.03–26). Its numerator is

$$(a_2 p^2 + a_0)(p^4 + 5.5200 p^2 + 4.9300) - (a_3 p^3 + a_1 p)(2.0983 p^3 + 5.4239 p).$$
$$(15.03\text{--}28)$$

On expanding this and equating it with the numerator of (15.03–26), we obtain the following simultaneous equations for the a's:

a_1	a_2	a_3	
0	$+1$	$-2.0983 = 0,$	
-2.0983	$+5.5200$	$-5.4239 = -2.2775,$	(15.03–29)
-5.4239	$+4.9300$	$0 \quad = -12.5718.$	

Their solution leads to

$$Z_1(p) = \frac{1.1990 p^3 + 2.5158 p^2 + 4.6045 p + 2.2775}{p^4 + 2.0983 p^3 + 5.5200 p^2 + 5.4239 p + 4.9300}. \qquad (15.03\text{--}30)$$

We know that the form of the network is the simple ladder of Fig. 15.03–G (though C_5 will be missing); hence a continued-fraction expansion, corresponding to the removal of poles at infinity, alternately from admittance and impedance, is all we need make. This is accomplished

Table 15.03–A

Element	Value in $Z_1(p)$	Value in $Z_{II}(p)$
C_1	0.8340 f	0.8706 f
C_3	1.5475 f	1.7413 f
C_5	0	0.5178 f
L_2	0.7138 h	0.7356 h
L_4	0.2202 h	0.3560 h
R_0	0.4620 Ω	0.4732 Ω

simply by the divide-invert-divide- · · · process (§ 5.14) shown in (15.03–31).

```
1.1990  2.5158  4.6045  2.2775)1  2.0983  5.5200  5.4239  4.9300(0.8340
                            1     2.0982  3.8403  1.8995
                            0  0         1.6797  3.5244  4.9300(0.7138
1.1990  2.5158  3.5191
0       0       1.0854  2.2775)                         (1.5475
                                        1.6797  3.5245
                                        0       0       4.9300(0.2202
                1.0854
                0       2.7775)                                (2.1647
                                                        4.9300
                                                        0
```
$$(15.03\text{–}31)$$

Space and time are saved by writing down only the necessary numbers and by "zigzagging" rather than stringing out the numbers in the usual fashion. The element values of the network are the numbers in the right-hand column, which we tabulate in the first column of Table 15.03–A. The corresponding schematic diagram is in Fig. 15.03–G. As a check (in addition to the usual checks made in connection with the arithmetic steps omitted above) we calculate $Z_I(j1)$ from the schematic with these element values, and obtain $\mathbf{Re}\, Z_I(j1) = 0.9998$, a satisfactory check against the designed value of unity.

From (15.03–25) we obtain

$$Z_{II}(p) = \frac{50}{-p^{10} - 2.1070p^8 + 13.3145p^6 + 58.8745p^4 + 100.127p^2 + 105.674}$$
$$(15.03\text{–}32)$$

which leads, on factoring the denominator, to

$$Z_{II}(p) = \frac{a_4p^4 + a_3p^3 + a_2p^2 + a_1p + a_0}{p^5 + 4.0807p^4 + 9.3794p^3 + 16.1411p^2 + 15.2226p + 10.2797}$$
$$(15.03\text{–}33)$$

The equations that determine the a's, obtained by equating $\mathbf{Ev}\, Z_{II}(p)$ and (15.03–25), are

$$a_0 = 4.8639$$

and

a_1	a_2	a_3	a_4
0	0	-1	$+4.0807 = 0,$
-1	$+4.0807$	-9.3794	$+16.1411 = 0,$
-9.3794	$+16.1411$	-15.2226	$+10.2797 = -19.8481,$
-15.2226	$+10.2797$	0	$0 = -78.5096,$

$$(15.03\text{-}34)$$

which lead to

$$Z_{11}(p) = \frac{1.1486p^4 + 4.6870p^3 + 8.9797p^2 + 11.2213p + 4.8640}{p^5 + 4.0807p^4 + 9.3794p^3 + 16.1411p^2 + 15.2226p + 10.2797}$$

$$= \cfrac{1}{0.8706p + \cfrac{1}{0.7356p + \cfrac{1}{1.7413p + \cfrac{1}{0.3560p + \cfrac{1}{0.5178p + \cfrac{1}{0.4732}}}}}}$$

$$(15.03\text{-}35)$$

the continued-fraction expansion being obtained by the sort of arithmetic process shown in (15.03–31). These element values are tabulated in the second column of Table 15.03–A. On calculating **Re** $Z_{11}(j1)$ we obtain the satisfactory check 0.9998. (Because of the higher degree, somewhat greater precision is necessary in these calculations.)

The introduction of the capacitor C_5 in the network makes the error worse, as Fig. 15.03–I shows—but it is necessary, to accommodate the inevitable parasitic capacitance. There is an advantage, however, in increasing C_5 (i.e., b_{10}) even more. The actual element values are obtained from the normalized values of Table 15.03–A by the formulas (2.09–7)

$$L_{\text{actual}} = L_{\text{norm}} \frac{R_n}{\omega_n},$$

$$C_{\text{actual}} = C_{\text{norm}} \frac{1}{R_n \omega_n}, \qquad (15.03\text{-}36)$$

$$R_{\text{actual}} = R_{\text{norm}} \times R_n,$$

in which R_n and ω_n are the actual resistance and (angular) frequency corresponding to 1 Ω and to 1 radian per sec in the normalized network. It is desirable to make R_n as large as possible, since $|E_{\text{out}}|$ is thereby maximized, by (15.03–1). That is, the K of (15.03–4) is made larger as the impedance scale is raised. But the largest possible value of R_n is determined by the fact that both C_1 and C_5 are limited by the parasitic capacitance present; increasing R_n too much will reduce one of these (C_5 in the second set of element values of Table 15.03–A) below the minimum, by the second relation in (15.03–36). Hence an additional increase in b_{10}, say from 0.02 to 0.03, which would presumably increase the value of C_5 also by about 50%, would permit a 50% higher value of R_n and hence of $|E_{out}/E_{in}|$. (There are minor changes in the other element values also, of much less importance; we notice, however, that in all probability C_1 will shortly become the limiting element, rather than C_5, if further increases are made.) It is necessary then to strike a balance between the degradation of the error and the improvement in the transmission level, the K of (15.03–4), that result from increasing the value of b_{10}. It is increasingly evident that a thorough study of this synthesis problem would involve a great deal of work, not only to find the optimum value of b_{10} here but also to consider other network configurations. We shall stop here, with the assumption that $Z_{II}(p)$ provides a satisfactory solution. The element values, with $\omega_n = 2\pi(5 \times 10^6)$ cps and R_n determined by giving C_5 the limiting value of 20 $\mu\mu$f, are shown in Fig. 15.03–J.

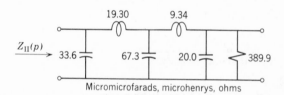

Fig. 15.03–J

The network of Fig. 15.03–J represents a more or less satisfactory solution of the problem. Its error is not excessive and it provides for parasitic capacitance. The effect of parasitic dissipation we shall not here examine, since this requires some knowledge of the two-terminal-pair properties of the network; it will not, however, be serious. A study should also be made to determine the precision necessary in realizing the elements.

The possibility of other network configurations should not be overlooked, if a thorough study is to be made. For example, Fig. 15.03–F suggests that zeros at the origin may improve the low-frequency error. Since this is a practical possibility, as we have already observed, it should be investigated. We shall only briefly start the investigation here.

If we move two of the zeros of $R(\omega)$ from infinity to the origin, (15.03-10) becomes

$$R_n(\omega) = \frac{\omega^2}{b_0 + b_2\omega^2 + \cdots + b_{2n}\omega^{2n}} \qquad (15.03\text{-}37)$$

which is to approximate G^{-1} at $\omega = \omega_0 = 1$ in the Taylor fashion. On introducing $x = (\omega - 1)$ and performing the appropriate manipulations, we obtain the following equations for the b's:

b_0	b_2	b_4	b_6	b_8	$b_{10}\cdots$	
1	1	1	1	1	$1\cdots$	$= G_0,$
0	2	4	6	8	$10\cdots$	$= G_1 + 2G_0,$
0	1	6	15	28	$45\cdots$	$= G_2 + 2G_1 + G_0,$
0	0	4	20	56	$120\cdots$	$= G_3 + 2G_2 + G_1,$
0	0	1	15	70	$210\cdots$	$= G_4 + 2G_3 + G_2,$
0	0	0	6	56	$252\cdots$	$= G_5 + 2G_4 + G_3.$

$$(15.03\text{-}38)$$

The first five solutions are

$$R_1(\omega) = \frac{\omega^2}{0.515 + 0.485\omega^2},$$

$$R_2(\omega) = \frac{\omega^2}{0.326 + 0.864\omega^2 - 0.189\omega^4},$$

$$R_3(\omega) = \frac{\omega^2}{0.235 + 1.136\omega^2 - 0.462\omega^4 + 0.091\omega^6}, \qquad (15.03\text{-}39)$$

$$R_4(\omega) = \frac{\omega^2}{0.183 + 1.345\omega^2 - 0.775\omega^4 + 0.300\omega^6 - 0.052\omega^8},$$

$$R_5(\omega) = \frac{\omega^2}{0.149 + 1.513\omega^2 - 1.112\omega^4 + 0.637\omega^6 - 0.221\omega^8 + 0.034\omega^{10}},$$

and their behavior is shown in Fig. 15.03–K. In this case it is evidently the *odd-n* curves that are realizable, a result that could again be predicted by considering the nature of the curves resulting from a point-matching technique. These are, unfortunately, the less practical ones, since their realizations do not provide the capacitors required at the two ends of the *L-C* network. The $n = 5$ case, for example, might be realized in the forms shown in Fig. 15.03–L. Since the fit is rather good for $n = 5$, it may well be worthwhile to add the additional capacitor here and examine the effect on the error, much as we did to obtain the network of Fig. 15.03–J.   We shall not do this here.

Additional possibilities lie in placing more zeros at the origin.   In the case of four zeros at the origin the odd-n cases may be expected, by

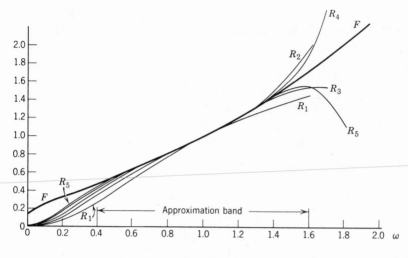

Fig. 15.03–K

extrapolation, to be both realizable and desirable from the parasitic-capacitance point of view.   Unfortunately, the functions turn out to have poles at real frequencies (below $\omega = 1$) and hence not to be realizable. There are also possibilities in shift-ing the location of the matching point, in obtaining Chebyshev approximations by a trial-and-error process starting from one of the Taylor approximations [or by more analytical methods (DA 4) which will be discussed in Volume II], and in the use of other methods (DA 2, BR 7).   Once more we observe that a large amount of work would be involved in a thorough study.

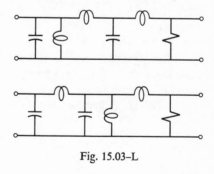

Fig. 15.03–L

Such a study is not necessary, however, for our illustration.   It has made one very important point: that mathematical approximation theory is not necessarily enough, that it must be tempered with the practical experience of the engineer, that some trial-and-error work may still be necessary, coupled even with ingenuity. Nevertheless, engineering art alone is not enough and the theory we have developed in this book is both useful and necessary.

15.04 Illustration III

As a welcome contrast to the first two illustrations, the third deals with a problem which can be solved straightforwardly with the aid of our theory. No trial-and-error work, no exercise of ingenuity, are required—which means, from one point of view, that the problem is not a particularly interesting one. Yet it is of practical importance, and it is perhaps satisfying to conclude our work with the one-terminal pair with such an example of the immediate, successful application of our theory.

The problem is the design of a four-stage vacuum-tube amplifier, in which each stage takes the form of Fig. 11.05–A; the complete amplifier

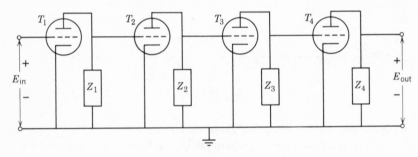

Fig. 15.04–A

is shown in Fig. 15.04–A. The uses of such amplifiers are legion: in radio receivers and transmitters, in carrier-telephone repeater amplifiers, in control systems, etc. With the usual assumptions as to linearity, negligible effect of other apparatus (bias arrangement, power supply, blocking capacitor, grid-plate capacitance, etc.), and of high internal impedance (as of pentode tubes), the amplifier's transmission function is

$$F(p) = \frac{E_{\text{out}}}{E_{\text{in}}} = (-g_{m1}Z_1)(-g_{m2}Z_2)(-g_{m3}Z_3)(-g_{m4}Z_4) \quad (15.04\text{--}1)$$

in which the g_m represent the transconductances of the vacuum tubes and the Z's the driving-point impedance functions of the four one-terminal-pair interstage networks. The band of frequencies to be transmitted in our case is 600 to 1500 kcps. In this band substantially constant (with frequency) magnitude of transmission is desired, but at lower and higher frequencies no transmission at all is wanted (Fig. 15.04–B). The angle or phase of transmission is not important. The parasitic capacitance to be expected (from tubes, wiring, etc.) is about 25 $\mu\mu$f and should be taken into account in the design. In the interests of simplicity we are limited, in each interstage network, to the use of a simple "tuned circuit," the

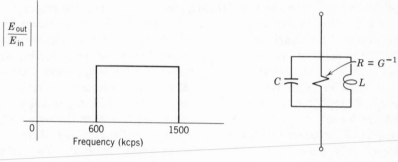

Fig. 15.04–B

Fig. 15.04–C

network of Fig. 15.04–C. (Such networks are extremely practical, since they can absorb parasitic capacitance, are easily tuned or adjusted by using variable capacitors or inductors, and already incorporate some dissipation.)

The function of interest is thus the transmission magnitude

$$
\begin{aligned}
|F(j\omega)| &= \left| \frac{-g_{m1}}{C_1 p + G_1 + (1/L_1 p)} \times \frac{-g_{m2}}{C_2 p + G_2 + (1/L_2 p)} \right. \\
&\qquad \left. \times \frac{-g_{m3}}{C_3 p + G_3 + (1/L_3 p)} \times \frac{-g_{m4}}{C_4 p + G_4 + (1/L_4 p)} \right|_{p=j\omega} \\
&= \left| \frac{-g_{m1}/C_1}{p^2 + (G_1/C_1)p + (1/L_1 C_1)} \times \frac{-g_{m2}/C_2}{p^2 + (G_2/C_2)p + (1/L_2 C_2)} \right. \\
&\qquad \left. \times \frac{-g_{m3}/C_3}{p^2 + (G_3/C_3)p + (1/L_3 C_3)} \times \frac{-g_{m4}/C_4}{p^2 + (G_4/C_4)p + (1/L_4 C_4)} \right|_{p=j\omega} \\
&= \left| \frac{(g_{m1}g_{m2}g_{m3}g_{m4})(C_1 C_2 C_3 C_4)^{-1} p^4}{p^8 + b_7 p^7 + b_6 p^6 + b_5 p^5 + b_4 p^4 + b_3 p^3 + b_2 p^2 + b_1 p + b_0} \right|_{p=j\omega},
\end{aligned}
$$

(15.04–2)

in which the subscripts on C, G, L, and g_m refer to the successive stages, and the b's represent appropriate functions of these element values. Since this function is rational, our answer to the primary question of realizability is *no*, for the function of Fig. 15.04–B is not rational—approximation is necessary. Now approximation of a constant in an internal band is a problem we have discussed in Chapter 14, and we are equipped to solve it directly, in either Taylor or Chebyshev fashion. Since Chebyshev approximation gives more rapid falling off outside the approximation band (if the transmission is held well up over the band), we shall use it. The zeros of $F(p)$ are prescribed, four at the origin and four at infinity, so that there is no arbitrariness in the work, except for the size of the approximation-band error ripple. On consultation with the "customer" for whom we are designing the interstage networks, we find that a 2% departure from the nominal value is the largest error permissible in $|F|$. We now have all the data necessary; it remains simply to apply the technique of Chapter 14, of § 14.14 in particular, to find the values of the b's in (15.04–2) and then to realize the networks. In spite of the active two-terminal-pair nature of the amplifier, there are clearly only passive one-terminal-pair networks involved. The only requirements for their realizability are that the b's in (15.04–2) be real and that the eight poles lie in the left half of the plane; we can then associate them in pairs, and obtain each $Z(p)$, and realize each network in straightforward fashion.

Once more we shall draw from our previous work only general principles and formulas as far as possible, and derive the details of our mathematics here instead of substituting in detailed formulas perhaps difficult to find and reinterpret. We recall that internal-band Cheybshev approximation of a constant with an even function is not at all difficult: we need only, in potential-analogy terms, place positively charged conductors on the approximation band(s), locate the negative charges (zeros), solve the potential problem, and quantize the positive charge. Now (15.04–2) is not a rational function. But we are concerned only with *magnitude* and can therefore equally well deal with the function

$$G(p) = F(p)F(-p) = \frac{\text{constant} \times p^8}{(p^8 + b_7 p^7 + b_6 p^6 + \cdots + b_0)}$$
$$(p^8 - b_7 p^7 + b_6 p^6 - \cdots + b_0)$$

$$(15.04\text{–}3)$$

since $G(j\omega) = |F(j\omega)|^2$, and if $F(j\omega)$ is to approximate a constant in magnitude, so also must $G(j\omega)$. The potential analog for determining the function $G(p)$ is shown in Fig. 15.04–D. Here the scale of p has been normalized so that $p = j0.6$ corresponds to a frequency of 600 kcps. The 16 positive charges are distributed equally on the two approximation-band conductors; the 16 negative charges are lumped, half at the origin and half at infinity.

We need now to determine the appropriate equipotential and find the 16 points of quantization thereon. This can be expected to lead to a 16th-degree equation, which is really only of 8th degree because of the even symmetry. Finding the roots of such an equation is a tedious job, to be avoided if at all possible. And in this case, it is possible to reduce the numerical work.

The potential problem of Fig. 15.04–D looks very much like a super-position of two low-band problems; it is not exactly that, to be sure, but

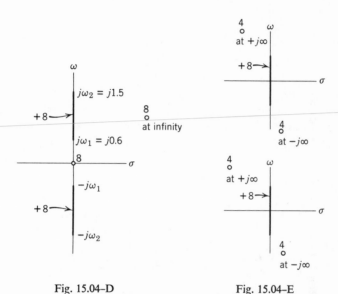

Fig. 15.04–D   Fig. 15.04–E

we can imagine the two separate low-band problems of Fig. 15.04–E to merge into each other vertically, with suitable distortion, to form that of Fig. 15.04–D. This requires a mental separation of the charge at infinity into two parts, as indicated. Such a fanciful process is not at all rigorous, but imaginative leaps have paid us dividends before. If this (frequency) transformation can be rigorously made, the dividend here will be the elimination of the root-finding job, for the location of the quantiz-ation points in the low-band problem is straightforward: they lie on a certain ellipse at easily determined points (§ 14.11). The transformation can in fact be made, and we have mentioned the possibility before (Problems 4-15, 4-32, 6-67, 14-96, 14-97). Its success depends, however, on some symmetry in the location of the zeros above and below the approx-imation band in the internal-band problem, for in the low-band problem symmetry was required between upper and lower halves of the plane.

Some of the particular point transformations needed are listed in Table 15.04–A, in which $p = \sigma + j\omega$ refers to the actual complex-frequency

Table 15.04–A

Point in p Plane (Fig. 15.04–D)	Corresponding Point in s Plane (Fig. 15.04–F)
∞	$+j\infty$
$+j\omega_2$	$+j1$
$+j\omega_1$	$-j1$
0	$-j\infty$

plane (Fig. 15.04–D) and $s = \Sigma + j\Omega$ to the artificial plane in which the "equivalent" low-band problem is to be solved (Fig. 15.04–F). It is convenient to associate the s plane with the upper plane of Fig. 15.04–E, as implied by the notation "$+j\infty$" and "$-j\infty$"; evidently the transformation has a double nature (the s plane is in fact a two-sheeted Riemann surface), but it is not necessary to consider this property. These

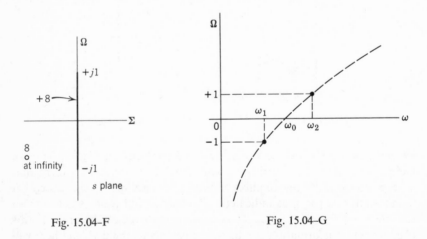

Fig. 15.04–F   Fig. 15.04–G

points are shown in a different fashion in Fig. 15.04–G which indicates the nature of the functional relation required between ω and Ω. This is strongly reminiscent of the curve of the reactance of an inductor and capacitor in series (or susceptance of a capacitor and inductor in parallel), which suggests the possible relation

$$\Omega = K_1\omega - \frac{1}{K_2\omega} \tag{15.04–4}$$

or, more generally,

$$s = K_1 p + \frac{1}{K_2 p} = K_1 \frac{p^2 + \omega_0^2}{p} \qquad (15.04\text{--}5)$$

in which $\omega_0 = (K_1 K_2)^{-1/2}$ is the point at which the Ω curve of Fig. 15.04–G crosses the ω axis. The transformation (15.04–5) has been obtained somewhat intuitively and must now be verified; this we shall do here in a purely algebraic fashion, though the mapping point of view (Problem 14-96) is equally valid, and more graphic.

In the p plane, the prototype complex potential, for the problem of Fig. 15.04–D, is given by (14.14–10) as

$$e^{W_p} = \left[- \frac{\left(\sqrt{\dfrac{p^2 + \omega_1^2}{p^2 + \omega_2^2}} - \dfrac{\omega_1}{\omega_2} \right)\left(\sqrt{\dfrac{p^2 + \omega_1^2}{p^2 + \omega_2^2}} - 1 \right)}{\left(\sqrt{\dfrac{p^2 + \omega_1^2}{p^2 + \omega_2^2}} + \dfrac{\omega_1}{\omega_2} \right)\left(\sqrt{\dfrac{p^2 + \omega_1^2}{p^2 + \omega_2^2}} + 1 \right)} \right]^4 \qquad (15.04\text{--}6)$$

in which the square root signs refer to the p-r branches of the functions. In the s plane, the complex potential for the problem of Fig. 15.04–F is, from (14.12–8),

$$e^{W_s} = (\sqrt{s^2 + 1} - s)^8 = \left(\frac{\sqrt{s^2 + 1} - s}{\sqrt{s^2 + 1} + s} \right)^4. \qquad (15.04\text{--}7)$$

The second form is introduced here for convenience in showing that (15.04–6) and (15.04–7) are identical if the relation between p and s is that of (15.04–5)—which is what is required to demonstrate the validity of the transformation. In each case the arbitrary constant of potential has been determined to make $V = 0$ on the conductors and $\Phi = 0$ on the positive real axis.

By algebraic manipulation of (15.04–6) we obtain

$$e^{W_p/4} = - \frac{\left(\dfrac{p^2 + \omega_1^2}{p^2 + \omega_2^2} + \dfrac{\omega_1}{\omega_2} \right) - \left(1 + \dfrac{\omega_1}{\omega_2} \right) \sqrt{\dfrac{p^2 + \omega_1^2}{p^2 + \omega_2^2}}}{\left(\dfrac{p^2 + \omega_1^2}{p^2 + \omega_2^2} + \dfrac{\omega_1}{\omega_2} \right) + \left(1 + \dfrac{\omega_1}{\omega_2} \right) \sqrt{\dfrac{p^2 + \omega_1^2}{p^2 + \omega_2^2}}}$$

$$= \frac{\dfrac{\omega_2 + \omega_1}{\omega_2} \sqrt{\dfrac{p^2 + \omega_1^2}{p^2 + \omega_2^2}} - \dfrac{\omega_2 + \omega_1}{\omega_2} \times \dfrac{p^2 + \omega_1 \omega_2}{p^2 + \omega_2^2}}{\dfrac{\omega_2 + \omega_1}{\omega_2} \sqrt{\dfrac{p^2 + \omega_1^2}{p^2 + \omega_2^2}} + \dfrac{\omega_2 + \omega_1}{\omega_2} \times \dfrac{p^2 + \omega_1 \omega_2}{p^2 + \omega_2^2}} \qquad (15.04\text{--}8)$$

$$= \frac{\sqrt{(p^2 + \omega_1^2)(p^2 + \omega_2^2)} - (p^2 + \omega_1\omega_2)}{\sqrt{(p^2 + \omega_1^2)(p^2 + \omega_2^2)} + (p^2 + \omega_1\omega_2)}$$

$$= \frac{\sqrt{K_1^2 \dfrac{(p^2 + \omega_1^2)(p^2 + \omega_2^2)}{p^2}} - K_1 \dfrac{p^2 + \omega_1\omega_2}{p}}{\sqrt{K_1^2 \dfrac{(p^2 + \omega_1^2)(p^2 + \omega_2^2)}{p^2}} + K_1 \dfrac{p^2 + \omega_1\omega_2}{p}}.$$

$$(15.04\text{-}8)$$

We now ask whether there is a value of the constant K_1 that will make $W_p = W_s$, s and p being related by (15.04-5). By evaluating $(s^2 + 1)$ and comparing with the square-root term in the last form in (15.04-8), we find that $K_1 = (\omega_2 - \omega_1)$ will do this, if $\omega_0^2 = \omega_1\omega_2$. Thus the transformation

$$s = \frac{1}{\omega_2 - \omega_1} \times \frac{p^2 + \omega_1\omega_2}{p} = \frac{\omega_0}{\omega_2 - \omega_1}\left(\frac{p}{\omega_0} + \frac{\omega_0}{p}\right), \qquad \omega_0 = \sqrt{\omega_1\omega_2},$$

$$(15.04\text{-}9)$$

is the formal statement of our mapping, now verified, of the internal-band problem of the p plane (Fig. 15.04-D) to the low-band problem of the s plane (Fig. 15.04-F).

In the s plane, the solution of the approximation problem can be written down almost immediately. The function F is to oscillate about a constant in the approximation band with a 2% ripple; the function $G = F^2$ is therefore to oscillate about a constant with a (very closely) 4% ripple. When the eight positive charges of Fig. 15.04-F are quantized on the equipotential $V = -V_0$, which is an ellipse, the quantized exponential potential is given (§ 14.11) by

$$e^{W_{sq}} = \frac{\text{constant}}{\cosh W_s + \cosh V_0} = \frac{\text{constant}}{1 + \epsilon \cosh W_s}, \qquad \epsilon = \text{sech } V_0.$$

$$(15.04\text{-}10)$$

Since ϵ is very small, there is no appreciable difference between the ripple in $(1 + \epsilon \cosh W_s)$ and that in its reciprocal, so that we take $\epsilon = 0.04$. Then $V_0 = \text{sech}^{-1}(0.04) = 3.91$. The points of quantization are determined (§ 14.11) by

$$W_s = -V_0 + j(\pm\pi, \pm 3\pi, \cdots). \qquad (15.04\text{-}11)$$

But W_s is eight times the potential due to a single positive charge on the conductor, which in turn is exactly the function $w = \sinh^{-1}(s)$ (14.07-18).

Hence the points of quantization are easily computed with the aid of tables of trigonometric and hyperbolic functions:

$$s = \sinh \{\tfrac{1}{8}[-V_0 + j(\pm\pi, \pm 3\pi, \cdot \cdot \cdot)]\}$$
$$= \sinh [-0.489 + j(\pm\pi/8, \pm 3\pi/8, \cdot \cdot \cdot)]$$
$$= \pm[\sinh (0.489) \cos (22.5°, 67.5°) \pm j \cosh (0.489) \sin (22.5°, 67.5°)]$$
$$= \begin{Bmatrix} \pm 0.470000 \pm j0.429356, \\ \pm 0.194680 \pm j1.036558, \end{Bmatrix} \quad \text{(eight points in all).} \qquad (15.04\text{--}12)$$

The six significant figures are not really necessary; they are carried simply for checking purposes since somewhat greater than slide-rule accuracy is necessary anyway because of the transformation yet to come. To transform these points to the p plane, we solve (15.04–9) for p, obtaining

$$p = \omega_0(Ks \pm \sqrt{K^2s^2 - 1}),$$
$$\omega_0 = \sqrt{\omega_1\omega_2} = \sqrt{0.9} = 0.948683, \qquad (15.04\text{--}13)$$
$$K = \frac{\omega_2 - \omega_1}{2\omega_0} = \frac{0.9}{2\sqrt{0.9}} = 0.474342.$$

Substitution of numerical values from (15.04–12) and carrying out the complex algebra (cf. Appendix A) gives us the left-half-plane points of (15.04–14); the right-half-plane points are of no interest.

$$p = -0.048845 \pm j0.587780,$$
$$-0.168293 \pm j0.752551,$$
$$-0.254708 \pm j1.138973, \qquad (15.04\text{--}14)$$
$$-0.126367 \pm j1.520683, \quad \text{(eight points in all).}$$

Figure 15.04–H shows to scale the positions of these points, in the s plane as well as the p plane. It is interesting to note that the locus of these points (the equipotential of the prototype problem), which is an ellipse in the s plane, is distorted to some other form in the p plane, by the presence of the negative charge at the origin and of the second conductor. [If the width of the approximation band were small in comparison with ω_0, i.e., if K were a small number, this distortion would be negligible and the transformation from s plane to p plane would be a mere vertical shift (Problem 15-17).]

Calculation of the amplifier's actual transmission function can also be simplified by using this transformation. In the low-band plane we have from (15.04–10)

$$e^{W_{sq}} = \frac{\text{constant}}{1 + 0.04 \cosh W_s} \qquad (15.04\text{--}15)$$

in general, which for $s = j\Omega$ (i.e., for the mapping of the ω axis) becomes

$$e^{W_{sq}} = |F|^2 = \frac{\text{constant}}{1 + 0.04 \cos (8 \sin^{-1} \Omega)}, \qquad |\Omega| < 1,$$

$$= \frac{\text{constant}}{1 + 0.04 \cosh (8 \cosh^{-1} \Omega)}, \qquad |\Omega| > 1,$$

(15.04–16)

on making use of the relation $W_s = 8w = 8 \sinh^{-1}(s)$. With trigono-metric and hyperbolic-function tables we can now readily plot the function

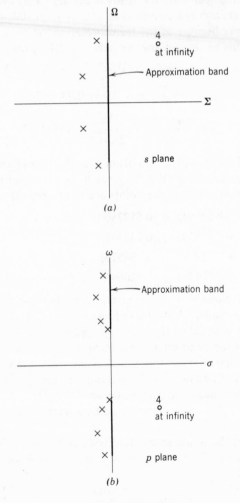

Fig. 15.04–H

$|F|$, except for the constant factor, as in Fig. 15.04–I. *Response* here is the function $|F|$ normalized to unit mean value in the approximation band. After making a careful plot of the relation

$$\Omega = \frac{\omega_0}{\omega_2 - \omega_1}\left(\frac{\omega}{\omega_0} - \frac{\omega_0}{\omega}\right) \tag{15.04–17}$$

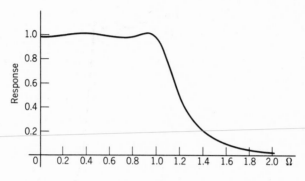

Fig. 15.04–I

obtained from (15.04–9) or from (15.04–4), as in Fig. 15.04–J, in which actual frequency values are used rather than normalized values of ω, we can transfer points from the Ω-axis plot of Fig. 15.04–I to an ω-axis plot,

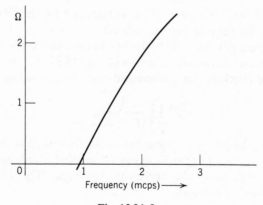

Fig. 15.04–J

as in Fig. 15.04–K, since potential is the same at corresponding points in the two planes. Only positive values of Ω need be plotted in Fig. 15.04–J, for points in the lower half of the s plane have symmetrical potentials;

these become, in the transformation, values of ω (or of actual frequency) geometrically symmetrical to those corresponding to positive values of Ω, as (15.04–17) clearly shows: substitution of ω_0/ω for ω/ω_0 merely changes the sign of Ω. This symmetry is made clear by using a logarithmic frequency scale in Fig. 15.04–K. The actual scale of the values attained

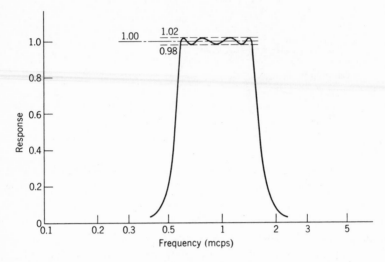

Fig. 15.04–K

by the transmission function $|F|$ is determined by the impedance scale factor, which we have not yet considered.

From the pole positions of (15.04–14) we can readily obtain the element values of the four interstage networks of Fig. 15.04–A. We first take the precaution of checking the arithmetical work by calculating the values of

$$\left| p^4 \prod_{i=1}^{8} \frac{1}{(p - p_i)} \right|_{p=j\omega} \tag{15.04–18}$$

at $\omega = \omega_1$, ω_0, and ω_2. At these points the transmission should take the same value, for they are the locations of the first, third, and fifth of the five minima that lie in the approximation band (Fig. 15.04–K). The calculation yields the values

$$3.38109, \qquad 3.38116, \qquad 3.38124, \tag{15.04–19}$$

which not only provides a satisfactory check but also could be used to establish the scale factor to be applied to Fig. 15.04–K to give the actual transmission magnitude. The element values can be obtained from

(15.04–14), for the admittance function of each interstage network (Fig. 15.04–C) is

$$Y(p) = Cp + G + \frac{1}{Lp} = \frac{C}{p}\left(p^2 + \frac{1}{RC}p + \frac{1}{LC}\right)$$

$$= \frac{C}{p}(p^2 + ap + b).$$

(15.04–20)

The two (complex-conjugate) poles associated with each stage determine only the corresponding numbers a and b; i.e., two of the elements are determined in terms of the third, which is arbitrary as far as the approximation process is concerned. In realizing the networks, we wish the impedance scale factor to be as large as possible in order to maximize the magnitude of the transmission function (15.04–1). The larger this scale factor, however, the smaller the capacitor, since capacitance values vary inversely with impedance scale. Practical limitations (parasitic capacitance present in the apparatus) set a lower limit of 25 $\mu\mu f$ on the four C values, as we have stated above. We first set all C values at 25 $\mu\mu f$ and determine the remaining element values therefrom. The necessary formulas, from (15.04–20), are

$$C = 25 \times 10^{-12}\,\text{f},$$

$$R = \frac{1}{aC} = \frac{0.04 \times 10^{12}}{a}\,\Omega,$$

$$L = \frac{1}{bC} = \frac{0.04 \times 10^{12}}{b}\,\text{h},$$

(15.04–21)

which represent actual (denormalized) element values. The numbers a and b are obtained from (15.04–14), by combining conjugate-pole factors and restoring the actual frequency scale (an actual frequency of 10^6 cps corresponds to unity on the normalized frequency scale):

$$a = -2(\text{Re}\,p)(2\pi \times 10^6),$$

$$b = |p|^2 (2\pi \times 10^6)^2,$$

(15.04–22)

in which p takes on successively the four upper-half-plane (say) values in (15.04–14). The results are given in Table 15.04–B. The numbering of

Table 15.04–B

Stage	C ($\mu\mu f$)	R (kΩ)	L (mh)
1	25	65.17	2.913
2	25	18.91	1.704
3	25	12.50	0.744
4	25	25.19	0.435

the stages, or the sequence in which they appear in Fig. 15.04–A, is of no consequence; the numbering in Table 15.04–B is upward from the origin (Fig. 15.04–H). These values should be checked once more, as by calculation of each of the four Z's at $p = j\omega_1 = j2\pi(0.6 \times 10^6)$ radians per sec, from the schematic diagram with these element values. The results are

$$p = j\omega_1, \quad |Z_1| = 63.70 \times 10^3 \ \Omega,$$
$$|Z_2| = 1.935 \times 10^3 \ \Omega,$$
$$|Z_3| = 12.38 \times 10^3 \ \Omega, \tag{15.04–23}$$
$$|Z_4| = 3.645 \times 10^3 \ \Omega,$$

which lead to

$$|Z_1 Z_2 Z_3 Z_4|_{p=j\omega_1} = 5544 \times 10^{12} \ \text{ohms}^4. \tag{15.04–24}$$

Since expression (15.04–18) is equal to $\prod_{i=1}^{4} (CZ_i)$, we multiply (15.04–24) by C^4, obtaining the value 2166×10^{-30}; this is to be compared with the denormalized value of (15.04–18), which is $3.3811(2\pi \times 10^6)^{-4} = 2169 \times 10^{-30}$, a satisfactory check. We also obtain, from (15.04–24), the actual value of transmission obtained. If the four transconductances g_m are taken to be 3000 micromhos, then from (15.04–1) and (15.04–24) we obtain

$$\left| \frac{E_{\text{out}}}{E_{\text{in}}} \right| = 449 \times 10^3 \tag{15.04–25}$$

as the "voltage amplification" attained; it is substantially constant (within 2%) in the approximation band.

The choice $C = 25 \ \mu\mu f$ is not the most practical. It assumes a parasitic capacitance of exactly 25 $\mu\mu f$, and we may be sure that the actual parasitic capacitance will vary, perhaps by as much as 30% or 40%. Such variation will certainly destroy the amplifier's characteristic, so that it is necessary to provide a means for adjusting the capacitance to the correct value. Deficiencies in the 25 $\mu\mu f$ figure can be made up by adding a small capacitor, but excesses cannot be compensated. A practical solution is to raise the nominal value of C and to use an adjustable (tuning) capacitor in the network, to be adjusted in each stage so that the total of its value and the parasitic capacitance will be the desired value. To do this we must of course drop the impedance scale factor and thus sacrifice some of the amplification; if we raise C to 50 $\mu\mu f$, for example, then (15.04–25) becomes $(449 \times 10^3) \div 16 = 28 \times 10^3$. This is still a respectable amplification and it may even be advisable to raise C to, say, 75 or 100

$\mu\mu$f to make the adjustment easier. With $C = 50$ $\mu\mu$f the element values are those of Table 15.04–C; with $C = 100$ $\mu\mu$f the R and L values would

Table 15.04–C

Stage	C ($\mu\mu$f)	R (kΩ)	L (mh)
1	50	32.58	1.456
2	50	9.46	0.852
3	50	6.25	0.372
4	50	12.59	0.218

be halved. Another adjustment of practical use would be to change the impedance scale factor in each stage so that the value of R becomes a standard value, obtainable from resistors in stock, or easily made to standard specifications. A possible series of values would be, for example, 30, 10, 6, and 12 kΩ. With corresponding readjustment of the L and C values, the shape of the transmission characteristic is unaffected, and there is little loss of amplification.

There remains one important practical matter: compensation for parasitic dissipation. We have seen in a general way how small amounts of dissipation in capacitors and inductors affect network properties (§ 12.02), and have discussed one method of compensation (§ 12.03). Those discussions are more elaborate than need be for this Illustration III, which is simple enough to permit straightforward treatment. Dissipation in the capacitors, if it is appreciable, can be compensated simply by appropriate increase in the values of the

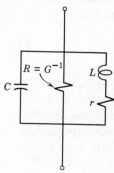

Fig. 15.04–L

R's (decreases in the values of the G's). Dissipation in the inductors has an effect which can also be readily compensated. Each interstage, in this case, takes the form shown in Fig. 15.04–L, for which

$$Z(p) = \frac{1}{Cp + G + [1/(Lp + r)]}$$

$$= \frac{p + r/L}{C\{p^2 + [(1/RC) + (r/L)]p + [(1/LC) + (r/L)(1/RC)]\}} \quad (15.04\text{–}26)$$

$$= \frac{p + r/L}{C(p^2 + ap + b)}.$$

To obtain the poles desired, it is simply necessary to determine the resistor values from

$$R = \frac{1}{C(a - r/L)} = \frac{1}{C[a - (2\pi \times 10^6/Q)]} \qquad (15.04\text{–}27)$$

in which

$$Q = \frac{L(2\pi \times 10^6)}{r} \qquad (15.04\text{–}28)$$

is the quality factor of the dissipative inductor at the convenient frequency 1 mcps. The inductor values then follow from

$$L = \frac{1}{C[b - (r/L)(1/RC)]} = \frac{1}{C[b - (2\pi \times 10^6/Q)(1/RC)]}. \qquad (15.04\text{–}29)$$

With these values the poles have the correct positions, because a predistortion technique has been applied to them. The zeros, which should lie at the origin for the correct function, have been shifted to the left an amount r/L, according to (15.04–26), a shift whose effect is generally negligible, for it merely multiplies the transmission function magnitude by

$$\prod_{i=1}^{4} \sqrt{\frac{\omega^2 + (r_i/L_i)^2}{\omega^2}} = \prod_{i=1}^{4} \sqrt{1 + (r_i/L_i\omega)^2}. \qquad (15.04\text{–}30)$$

For inductor Q's of 100 at the (approximate) band center frequency of 1 mcps this factor varies between approximate limits of 1.0001 and 1.0007 over the approximation band, so that the distortion introduced by it is indeed negligible. Graphically put, the lengths of the complex numbers from a point $j\omega$ in the approximation band (a) to the origin and (b) to the point $(-r/L)$ are not appreciably different.

On recalculating the element values with $C = 50\ \mu\mu f$ and allowing for inductor Q's of 100 at 1 mcps, we obtain the values of Table 15.04–D.

Table 15.04–D

Stage	$C\ (\mu\mu f)$	$R\ (k\Omega)$	$L\ (mh)$
1	50	36.3	1.460
2	50	9.75	0.857
3	50	6.37	0.373
4	50	13.11	0.218

As one might expect, the appreciable changes from Table 15.04–C are limited to the resistors, which are raised in resistance to compensate for the dissipation in the inductors. Again, small changes in the impedance scale factors can be applied to yield standard values of resistance.

Since Q is a number not precisely known, slide-rule accuracy generally suffices here. Also, small errors in the L and C element values can probably be tolerated since one of the two will be made adjustable and the "tuning" (LC product) of each interstage properly adjusted. That is, the fourth stage (practical adjustment) in the synthesis of the amplifier networks cannot be neglected.

The nature of this Illustration III should not be lost in the attention we have given to practical detail. In it the approximation problem is solved in straightforward fashion; all that is necessary is to perform the calculations, and no trial-and-error work is necessary. The reason is that a very simple function, a constant, is approximated here. As we saw in Illustration II, not all synthesis problems are straightforward like this one, but it is an important one.

15.05 Conclusion

In these three illustrations we have made use of many of the subjects discussed in this book. The illustrations are not exhaustive, and much of the material has not been used here because these particular examples did not need it. They have given us some idea, however, of the variety of problems we can encounter in network synthesis, and of the fact that we need many different tools in our equipment. Not the least of these is the ability to decide which particular tool to use, and a fair measure of ingenuity.

We could consider many more illustrations, both to emphasize this point and to show that all the other things we have discussed are useful in their places. But these are enough. The statement of § 1.01 that synthesis consists of three steps (background study of properties, approximation, realization or synthesis proper) has been adequately verified, and the need of a fourth step of practical realization been added. Each of these we have discussed, not completely, but yet in considerable, perhaps overlong, detail. As far as the one-terminal pair is concerned, our work is done. For the two-terminal pair we shall follow a similar path in Volume II.

PROBLEMS

15-1. Carry out the design of the equalizer of § 15.02 by writing down an even function to represent $|1 + z|^2$, determining the coefficients by matching the data at suitable frequencies, and then obtaining $z(p)$. For the order of function to use, and the frequencies at which to match, the general results of § 15.02 may be referred to. Contrast this method with that used in § 15.02 and discuss their relative merits.

15-2. Carry out the design of the equalizer of § 15.02 in the form of Fig. 15.02–B(a). Does this method offer advantages (or disadvantages) over that used in § 15.02?

15-3. Verify all the computations of § 15.02. In addition, answer the following specific questions. Why is b in (15.02–2) prefixed with a negative sign? Is this essential, or merely useful? Make a tabular form for the computation of $|1 + z|$ versus ω and discuss the advantages gained by calculating by columns (for all points) rather than by making the complete calculation at each frequency separately. Verify that an accuracy of $\pm 1\%$ in element realization is sufficient. On which elements may the accuracy requirement be relaxed further?

15-4. Add one reactive element to the design used for z in § 15.02, and obtain the best design of this complexity. In what way is it an improvement?

15-5. Discuss the statement made in § 15.02, "the effects of small element changes · · · combine more or less linearly when the changes are small." Include explanations both of the validity and utility of this.

15-6. Carry out a redesign of the equalizer of Fig. 15.02–F, adopting the suggestion, made near the end of § 15.02, of reducing the value of K.

15-7. Verify the results in (15.03–9), (a) by direct differentiation of (15.03–6); (b) by obtaining, by logarithmic differentiation,

$$G'(x) = -\frac{k}{2} \cdot \frac{G(x)}{\sqrt{1 + x}}$$

and then differentiating it; (c) by substituting (15.03–8) in $-(k/2)G(x)$ $= \sqrt{1 + x} \cdot G'(x)$, collecting terms, and equating coefficients.

15-8. Verify (15.03–12). Carry out the associated solution for $n = 3$ and plot the error of the resulting approximation. Obtain a one-terminal-pair realization.

15-9. Obtain a one-resistor realization of (15.03–14) as a driving-point resistor. Is there a requirement here of 100% coupling between inductors? What are the primary practical objections to the network? Show that a realization can be made by interpreting (15.03–14) as the square of the magnitude of a driving-point-impedance function, to be used as in Fig. 11.05–A. What are the practical objections to this solution of the problem of § 15.03? Repeat with the function (15.03–16).

15-10. In the discussion of § 15.03 there are additional possibilities for the numerator of the resistance function. Determine the maximally approximating functions of order four, i.e., with $n = 2$ in (15.03–2), taking into account all the possibilities of two, one, or none of the a's being prescribed to have zero value. Which are realizable? Discuss the quality of approximation obtained and the practicality of these functions.

15-11. Develop the idea expressed in the text after (15.03–20) to show in more detail how the nonrealizability of $R_n(\omega)$ for odd n can be predicted.

15-12. In § 15.03 many of the arithmetic calculations are omitted or merely outlined. Carry them out and verify the results there.

15-13. Verify the results obtained in § 15.03 when two zeros of Ev $Z(p)$ are placed at the origin. Develop a practical network by adding an additional capacitor in the networks of Fig. 15.03–L.

15-14. Plot a family of curves, similar to those of Figs. 15.03–F and –K, for the case where $R_n(\omega)$ has four zeros at the origin. Discuss their utility.

15-15. Show that Taylor approximation of $G = F^{-1}$ with the reciprocal of the function (15.03–2) leads to the same result as Taylor approximation of F with (15.03–2).

15-16. Plot the functions, appropriate to the problem of § 15.04, that represent Taylor-approximation solutions and verify that Chebyshev approximation gives a more rapid falling off of transmission outside the approximation band. No more than 10% drop at approximation-band edges can be tolerated.

15-17. In § 15.04 use is made of a transformation to an auxiliary low-pass plane, in order to save work. Discuss the solution of the same problem by the methods of § 14.14 and make a detailed comparison of the two techniques. What properties of the particular problem of § 15.04 make this transformation to a low-band plane possible? (Cf. Prob. 14-97.)

Discuss the simplifications made possible in the s-p transformation of § 15.04 in the *narrow-band* case, $(\omega_2 - \omega_1) \ll \omega_0$. Show in particular that the locus of the poles in the s plane (an ellipse for Chebyshev approximation) is essentially merely shifted upward to center on the point $j\omega_0$ rather than the origin, after an appropriate scale change. Show that the error made in locating the poles by this simple method of scale change and translation is about $\frac{1}{8}[(\omega_2 - \omega_1)/\omega_0]^2$ [for which a series expansion of (15.04–13) for small $|Ks|$ is useful; cf. Prob. 14-96]. What is an approximate measure of the percentage error in the locations of the poles with respect to the point $j\omega_0$?

15-18. Develop the details of the s-p transformation of § 15.04 for maximally flat approximation. Repeat the discussion of Prob. 15-17 for this case.

15-19. In the very *wide*-band case, $(\omega_2 - \omega_1) \gg \omega_0$, is there a simplification of the s-p transformation of § 15.04 analogous to that discussed in Prob. 15-17? Explain and illustrate.

15-20. In the discussion leading up to (15.04–12) various approximations are made in view of the smallness of the ripple desired. Show that these are indeed justified, and that extreme accuracy in the determination of V_0 is not necessary.

15-21. Explain in detail why the curve of Fig. 15.04–K has symmetry about the frequency 948.7 kcps. Plot the same curve on an arithmetic frequency scale and compare the two.

15-22. Verify the calculations of § 15.04 that are not completely carried out therein.

15-23. Derive (15.04–22).

15-24. Discuss the effect on the transmission characteristic of § 15.04 of small change in L (or C) values, assuming that the C (or L) values are readjusted to give the correct resonance frequency (correct value of LC). Determine also the element-value accuracies required in the realization.

APPENDIX A

Computation

There is no substitute for hard work.
—Thomas A. Edison

A.1 Introduction

A remarkable property of electric network elements is the accuracy with which the laws that describe their behavior are obeyed. It is because of this that precise calculations can be justified in network synthesis, when precise behavior is required. We have found that the arithmetical work of approximation and of realization (synthesis proper) may constitute a large part of a network synthesis; the precision to be used in these inevitable computations depends of course on the precision required of the network. In some places mental estimates suffice, many times a 10-inch (or at most 20-inch) slide rule is enough, but cases frequently occur in which six- or eight-significant-figure accuracy is required—here a calculating machine of some sort is required. The desk calculator usually suffices (all the precise examples in this book were done on one) but the automatic digital computer may be preferable; most of the computations of network synthesis are easily programmed for such a machine. The discussions that follow are intended to point out some of the most efficient arithmetical techniques for performing the commonest computations, whether by hand or by machine.

A.2 Complex-number computations

Complex numbers, because of our use of the complex frequency variable p, inevitably enter many of the computations. The ordinary arithmetic of such numbers (§ 3.08) we shall not discuss here. It should be noted that many slide rules carry scales that make rapid conversion between polar and rectangular forms a simple matter. One form may be much more appropriate for a certain computation than the other. For machine calculations the rectangular form may be preferable (reciprocation by rationalization, for example, requires no trigonometric table and is just as rapid and may be more accurate). Other devices can be developed as necessary; for example, the square root of a complex number can be obtained by solving a quadratic equation, as shown below. In $x + jy = \sqrt{a + jb}$ suppose a and b known; to find x and y we have

$$x^2 - y^2 + j2xy = a + jb, \tag{A.2-1}$$

whence come

$$
\begin{aligned}
x^2 - y^2 &= a, \\
2xy &= b,
\end{aligned}
\tag{A.2-2}
$$

and then, on eliminating y from the first equation by using the second,

$$4x^4 - 4ax^2 - b^2 = 0. \tag{A.2-3}$$

This is a quadratic equation in x^2; after finding x^2 and then x from it, we obtain y from $y = b/2x$, being careful to associate the proper signs with x and y.

A.3 Evaluation of rational functions

It is only natural that the majority of the computations we make in network synthesis deal with rational functions with real coefficients. Whenever the behavior of a driving-point immittance function (or of one of its parts) is to be examined numerically, such a rational function must be evaluated for a number of values of the independent variable, be it p or ω.

Polynomials are best evaluated by a process of division (rather than by raising the variable to powers, multiplying by coefficients, and adding). The basis is the well-known relation of algebra described below. Let

$$P(p) = a_n p^n + a_{n-1} p^{n-1} + \cdots + a_1 p + a_0 \tag{A.3-1}$$

be the polynomial, to be evaluated at $p = p_0$. On division by $(p - p_0)$ we obtain

$$\frac{P(p)}{p - p_0} = Q(p) + \frac{R(p)}{p - p_0} \tag{A.3-2}$$

in which $Q(p)$, a polynomial of degree $n - 1$, is the quotient, and $R(p)$, a constant, say b_0, is the remainder. On multiplying through by $(p - p_0)$ we obtain

$$P(p) = (p - p_0)Q(p) + R(p) = (p - p_0)Q(p) + b_0 \tag{A.3-3}$$

so that clearly

$$P(p_0) = R(p_0) = b_0. \tag{A.3-4}$$

The evaluation of a polynomial $P(p)$ for a particular value of the variable p_0 can be accomplished simply by dividing by $(p - p_0)$: the remainder is the value of $P(p_0)$. This "remainder theorem" (FI 1, RI 4) gives us the basis of the most practical method of evaluating polynomials.

When p_0 is a *real* number, the division is simply carried out; there is little more to say than to give an example. Suppose

$$P(p) = 4p^5 + 6p^4 + 2p^3 + 5p^2 + 3p + 2 \qquad \text{(A.3-5)}$$

is to be evaluated at $p = p_0 = -3$. The arithmetic of division is

$$
\begin{array}{l}
p+3)\overline{4p^5 + 6p^4 + 2p^3 + 5p^2 + 3p + 2}\ \overbrace{(4p^4 - 6p^3 + 20p^2 - 55p + 168}\\
\quad\underline{4p^5 + 12p^4} \qquad\qquad\qquad\qquad\qquad Q(p)\\
\qquad\ \ \ \underline{-6p^4 + 2p^3 + 5p^2 + 3p + 2}\\
\qquad\ \ \ -6p^4 - 18p^3\\
\qquad\qquad\ \ \underline{20p^3 + 5p^2 + 3p + 2}\\
\qquad\qquad\ \ 20p^3 + 60p^2\\
\qquad\qquad\qquad\ \ \underline{-55p^2 + 3p + 2}\\
\qquad\qquad\qquad\ \ -55p^2 - 165p\\
\qquad\qquad\qquad\qquad\quad \underline{168p + 2}\\
\qquad\qquad\qquad\qquad\quad 168p + 504\\
\qquad\qquad\qquad\qquad\qquad\quad -502 \leftarrow R(p)
\end{array}
$$

$$\text{(A.3-6)}$$

The remainder is $R(p_0) = b_0 = -502$ and hence $P(-3) = -502$. Much of the writing in (A.3-6) is repetitious and unnecessary; in practice we use synthetic (detached-coefficient) division, writing only the essential numbers and compressing the work to

$$
\begin{array}{lllllll}
3)4 & 6 & 2 & 5 & 3 & 2(\\
\ \ 4 & 12 & -18 & 60 & -165 & 504\\
\hline
& -6 & 20 & -55 & 168 & -502 \to R(-3) = P(-3) = -502.
\end{array}
$$

$$\text{(A.3-7)}$$

This computation is simple and rapid. One should be careful of signs, however, and be sure to insert zeros where coefficients are missing; these are the commonest sources of error. Round numbers are used here for simplicity of illustration; in general, the numbers involved will not be integers, and an appropriate number of significant figures will have to be carried.

When p_0 is *complex* the division indicated in (A.3-2) involves complex-number arithmetic. This can largely be avoided by using as divisor not $(p - p_0)$ but $(p - p_0)(p - \bar{p}_0)$, for if $p_0 = \sigma_0 + j\omega_0$, the divisor

$$(p - p_0)(p - \bar{p}_0) = p^2 - 2\sigma_0 p + \sigma_0^2 + \omega_0^2 \qquad \text{(A.3-8)}$$

has only real coefficients. Then we have

$$\frac{P(p)}{(p - p_0)(p - \bar{p}_0)} = Q(p) + \frac{R(p)}{(p - p_0)(p - \bar{p}_0)} \qquad \text{(A.3-9)}$$

in which the quotient $Q(p)$ is a polynomial of degree $n - 2$ and the remainder $R(p)$ is now linear in p,

$$R(p) = b_1 p + b_0. \tag{A.3-10}$$

On multiplying (A.3-9) through by $(p - p_0)(p - \bar{p}_0)$ we obtain

$$
\begin{aligned}
P(p) &= (p - p_0)(p - \bar{p}_0)Q(p) + R(p) \\
&= (p - p_0)(p - \bar{p}_0)Q(p) + b_1 p + b_0
\end{aligned} \tag{A.3-11}
$$

so that clearly

$$P(p_0) = R(p_0) = b_1 p_0 + b_0. \tag{A.3-12}$$

Once more, the remainder gives us the value desired, and it is only in its evaluation, (A.3-12), that complex numbers appear. For example, suppose the same polynomial $P(p)$, (A.3-5), is to be evaluated at $p = p_0 = -2 + j3$. The division is

$$
p^2 + 4p + 13 \overline{)4p^5 + 6p^4 + 2p^3 + 5p^2 + 3p + 2} \underbrace{(4p^3 - 10p^2 - 10p + 175}_{Q(p)}
$$

$$
\begin{array}{r}
\underline{4p^5 + 16p^4 + 52p^3} \\
-10p^4 - 50p^3 + 5p^2 \\
-\;\underline{-10p^4 - 40p^3 - 130p^2} \\
-10p^3 + 135p^2 + 3p \\
\underline{-10p^3 - 40p^2 - 130p} \\
175p^2 + 133p + 2 \\
\underline{175p^2 + 700p + 2275} \\
-567p - 2273 \leftarrow R(p)
\end{array} \tag{A.3-13}
$$

The remainder gives

$$
\begin{aligned}
R(-2 + j3) = P(-2 + j3) &= -567(-2 + j3) - 2273 \\
&= -1139 - j1701. \tag{A.3-14}
\end{aligned}
$$

In practice we write only the essential numbers and compress the work to

$$
1\ 4\ 13 \overline{)4 \quad 6 \quad 2 \quad 5 \quad 3 \quad 2(}
$$

$$
\begin{array}{r}
4 \quad 16 \quad 52 \\
\hline
-10 \ -50 \\
-10 \ -40 \ -130 \\
\hline
-10 \quad 135 \\
-10 \ -40 \ -130 \\
\hline
175 \quad 133 \\
175 \quad 700 \quad 2275 \\
\hline
-567 \ -2273 \rightarrow R(-2 + j3) = P(-2 + j3) \\
= -1139 - j1701.
\end{array} \tag{A.3-15}
$$

When p_0 is *purely imaginary* (a common case, for our principal interest is in real frequencies), $\sigma_0 = 0$ in the above computations. The principle is unchanged, but one should be careful to write zero where necessary. For example, in the evaluation of the polynomial (A.3–5) at $p = j2$, the divisor is $(p - j2)(p + j2) = (p^2 + 4)$ and the arithmetical work is

$$
\begin{array}{rrrrrrr}
1\ \ 0\ \ 4)4 & 6 & 2 & 5 & 3 & 2(\\
4 & 0 & 16 & & & \\
\hline
6 & -14 & 5 & & & \\
6 & 0 & 24 & & & \\
\hline
& -14 & -19 & & & \\
& -14 & 0 & -56 & & \\
\hline
& & -19 & 59 & & \\
& & -19 & 0 & -76 & \\
\hline
& & & 59 & 78 & \\
\end{array}
$$

(A.3–16)

$$P(j2) = R(j2) + = 59(j2) + 78 = 78 + j118.$$

In the evaluation of even (or odd) polynomials a large number of zeros occur, since alternate powers are missing. However, these can be omitted if the proper divisor is used. Since this computation usually is needed only at real frequencies, we shall illustrate this one case. The example below is given in terms of ω rather than p, for variety; in terms of p the work would be much the same. The polynomial

$$4\omega^8 - 3\omega^6 + 17\omega^4 - 30\omega^2 + 20 \tag{A.3–17}$$

is to be evaluated for $\omega = 2$. In close parallelism to the preceding example, the divisor is $(\omega - 2)(\omega + 2) = (\omega^2 - 4)$; the work, which is like that of (A.3–7), ω^2 replacing p, is

$$
\begin{array}{rrrrr}
-4)4 & -3 & 17 & -30 & 20(\\
4 & -16 & -52 & -276 & -984 \\
\hline
13 & 69 & 246 & 1004 &
\end{array}
$$

(A.3–18)

The value of the even polynomial (A.3–17) at $\omega = \pm 2$ is accordingly $+1004$.

Rational functions, being simply quotients of polynomials, are easily evaluated by dividing the results of the individual evaluations of numerator and denominator. Complex-number arithmetic may, of course, be necessary in the division.

In some cases, where great accuracy is required in the vicinity of a zero (or pole) and that zero (pole) is accurately known, it may be preferable to write the corresponding polynomial in factored form; the small factor can then be obtained to any desired accuracy, for only subtraction is involved. But in general the use of the remainder in an appropriate division offers the best method of evaluating rational functions.

A.4 Simultaneous linear equations

In both approximation and realization we have found it necessary at times to solve sets of simultaneous linear equations with real coefficients. For these the theory of determinants provides the most elegant formal method of solution. In practice, however, some method of successive elimination of the sort originally employed by Gauss is usually better. Of the many variants that have been developed we shall describe only one; it is not necessarily the best one in every case, but is easy to remember and generally applicable. It consists simply in altering each equation so that by subtraction one unknown is eliminated and the number of equations reduced by one. This is repeated until only one unknown remains, whose value is immediately given by the one remaining equation. The other unknowns are then obtained by substitution in previous equations, after which it remains only to check the solution.

Let the set of n equations be

$$a_{11}x_1 + a_{12}x_2 + a_{13}x_3 + \cdots = a_1,$$
$$a_{21}x_1 + a_{22}x_2 + a_{23}x_3 + \cdots = a_2, \qquad \text{(A.4–1)}$$
$$a_{31}x_1 + a_{32}x_2 + a_{33}x_3 + \cdots = a_3,$$
$$\cdots \cdots \cdots \cdots \cdots ,$$

in which all the a's are known, and $x_1, x_2, x_3, \cdots, x_n$ are the unknowns. We first eliminate x_1. We divide each equation by its coefficient of x_1. The result, written in detached-coefficient form, is

x_1	x_2	$x_3 \quad \cdots$	
1	a_{12}/a_{11}	$a_{13}/a_{11} \cdots = a_1/a_{11},$	
1	a_{22}/a_{21}	$a_{23}/a_{21} \cdots = a_2/a_{21},$	(A.4–2)
1	a_{32}/a_{31}	$a_{33}/a_{31} \cdots = a_3/a_{31},$	
$\cdots$	$\cdots$	$\cdots \cdots \cdots$	

By subtracting consecutive pairs of these equations we eliminate x_1 and obtain the $n - 1$ equations

x_2	$x_3 \quad \cdots$	
a_{22}'	$a_{23}' \cdots = a_2',$	
a_{23}'	$a_{33}' \cdots = a_3',$	(A.4–3)
$\cdots$	$\cdots \cdots ,$	

in which $a_{22}' = (a_{12}/a_{11}) - (a_{22}/a_{21})$, etc., are new (known) coefficients. A repetition of the process eliminates x_2, then another eliminates x_3, etc., until we have left only a simple equation in x_n alone. With the value of x_n obtained therefrom, x_{n-1} is easily found from an equation in the set immediately preceding, then x_{n-2} from the set before that, etc., until all the x's have been found. After checking these by substitution in (A.4–1), the solution is complete.

For illustration, we shall solve the set of equations (from § 15.03) written below. Here the unknowns happen to be represented by b_1, b_2, b_3, b_4; some of the coefficients are zero, which frequently happens. All of the arithmetical work is given together; the explanation follows it.

	b_1	b_2	b_3	b_4	
(1)	-1	$+4.0807$	-9.3794	$+16.1411 =$	$0,$
(2)	-9.3794	$+16.1411$	-15.2226	$+10.2797 =$	$-19.8481,$
(3)	-15.2226	$+10.2797$	0	$0 \quad =$	$-78.5096,$
(4)	0	0	-1	$+4.0807 =$	$0.$
(5)	$+1$	$+4.0807$	$+9.3794$	$-16.1411 =$	$0,$
(6)	$+1$	-1.7209	$+1.6230$	$-1.0960 =$	$+2.1161,$
(7)	$+1$	-0.6753	0	$0 \quad =$	$+5.1574.$
(8)		$+2.3598$	-7.7564	$+15.0451 =$	$+2.1161,$ (A.4–4)
(9)		$+1.0456$	-1.6230	$+1.0960 =$	$+3.0413.$
(10)		$+1$	-3.2870	$+6.3757 =$	$+0.8968,$
(11)		$+1$	-1.5522	$+1.0482 =$	$+2.9086.$
(12)			$+1.7348$	$-5.3276 =$	$+2.0118.$
(13)			$+1$	$-3.0710 =$	$+1.1597,$
(14)			$+1$	$-4.0807 =$	$0.$
(15)				$+1.0097 =$	$+1.1597.$

$$\text{Solution:} \quad \begin{cases} b_4 = & +1.1486, \\ b_3 = & +4.6870, \\ b_2 = & +8.9797, \\ b_1 = & +11.2213. \end{cases} \qquad \text{(A.4–5)}$$

Check:

$$-b_1 + 4.0807b_2 - 9.3794b_3 + 16.1411b_4 = +0.0006,$$
$$-9.3794b_1 + 16.1411b_2 - \cdots = -19.8479,$$
$$-15.2226b_1 + 10.2797b_2 + 0 + 0 = -78.5089,$$
$$0 + 0 - b_3 + 4.0807b_4 = +0.0001.$$

(A.4–6)

The arithmetical work has been grouped in one place above so that the pattern of the work can be clearly seen. We start by dividing each of the first four lines through by the number in its first column: the first line by -1, the second by -9.3794, and the third by -15.2226. (The fourth, having a zero in the first column, need not be used at this point.) This gives us the equations represented by lines 5, 6, and 7. On subtracting line 5 from line 6, and line 6 from line 7, we obtain lines 8 and 9. These are divided through, respectively, by 2.3598 and 1.0456, to give lines 10 and 11. Subtraction of line 10 from line 11 gives line 12, which on division by 1.7348 becomes line 13. Line 14 is the original equation of line 4, rewritten; it has not been necessary to write it previously because of the two zeros it contains. Subtraction of line 14 from line 13 gives line 15, from which follows the value $b_4 = 1.1597/1.0097 = 1.1486$. The value of b_3 is obtained now from line 14 (or line 13),

$$b_3 = 0 + 4.0807 \times 1.1486 = 4.6870. \tag{A.4–7}$$

Then b_2 can be obtained similarly from line 10 or line 11, and finally b_1 from line 5, line 6, or line 7. Not the least important of the steps is the substitution of the results (A.4–5) in the original equations of (A.4–4) as a check. The results, given in (A.4–6), show a satisfactory check.

In this example, four decimal places have been carried, on the assumption that corresponding accuracy is needed. This requires the use of a calculating machine, which has the advantage that products can be accumulated without writing numbers down; this is particularly convenient in making the check. (In many cases, of course, slide-rule accuracy would suffice.) Were it not for the zeros in the fourth equation (line 4), there would be a fourth line in the group lines 5–7, a third in the group lines 8–9, etc.

This example illustrates a convenient, easily recalled method for the solution of simultaneous linear equations with real coefficients. Many variations are possible. In some cases the sequence of subtraction requires attention in order to avoid differences of nearly equal numbers, with an attendant loss in accuracy; in some cases it may simply be necessary to carry a large number of significant figures to obtain the desired accuracy (or to resort to a different method). We shall not discuss the modifications necessitated by complex coefficients (they amount, in essence, merely to a doubling of the work, since each complex number is really two real numbers) nor any of the other methods of solution (§ A.10).

A.5 Root finding

One of the more irksome, yet very common, computational tasks required in network synthesis (and analysis, for that matter) is that of finding the n roots of the algebraic equation

$$P(p) = a_n p^n + a_{n-1} p^{n-1} + \cdots + a_1 p + a_0 = 0. \quad (A.5-1)$$

We shall consider only the case where the coefficients a are real; some or all of the roots may of course be complex.

The linear ($n = 1$) case requires no comment, and for the quadratic case ($n = 2$) the well-known formula for the roots is adequate. There are also algebraic formulas for the cubic ($n = 3$) and biquadratic ($n = 4$) cases, though not for higher values of n. But in practice we use a formula only for the quadratic case; for $n \geqq 3$ some method of successive approximation is generally best. We shall make no attempt at comprehensive discussion of the many methods that exist. Some are better than others in certain cases, and no one can really be said to be "best." We shall describe only one method, one that is generally practical, simple in principle, and easy to remember. It is more than adequate for our computations of network synthesis; only the professional computer who spends most of his time in this sort of work needs more, and to him the wide literature of computation is open (§ A.10).

The method is first to find an approximate value of a root (or roots) by some appropriate means and then to improve it (them) to any desired accuracy by an iterative process. We then remove (by factoring out) the corresponding polynomial to reduce the degree of the equation, then repeat the process with the reduced equation, etc., until all n roots have been found.

Approximate values of roots are often available in the network-synthesis work that leads up to equation (A.5-1). [For example, in low-band approximation problems the roots may well lie roughly on a circle about the origin of appropriate radius (§§ 13.10, 14.15); Problem 14-72 describes another example of rough root values given by the approximation process; ingenuity may suggest approximate root values in other ways, depending on the case.] When these are available, one may go directly to the formal iterative process of root improvement (§ A.7); we shall assume for the moment that we have no knowledge whatever of the roots, and hence must first find our own approximate values.

This task may be performed by a machine of the isograph sort (§ A.10), if one is available; if not, we must use paper and pencil and slide rule—and these we assume necessary here. In the following discussion the polynomial is assumed to be mixed (neither odd nor even); even (and odd) polynomials become mixed on taking p^2 (or ω^2) as the independent variable.

A.6 Approximate roots

Real roots are easier to locate than complex ones, so we shall discuss them first. If n is odd in (A.5–1), there is at least one real root, and there may be more; if n is even, there may or may not be real roots. It is usually advisable to remove the real roots before attacking the problem of finding the complex roots.

Approximate values of real roots can be obtained by plotting the polynomial (for real values of the variable). The remainder theorem (§ A.3) makes the computation of values of the polynomial straightforward; it is only necessary to choose appropriate points for (slide-rule) computation, and to observe (from the plot) the locations of the real roots. By expanding the scale, the roots can of course be obtained to any desired accuracy; but once two- or three-significant-figure accuracy has been obtained, the method of § A.7 is usually preferable.

For example, let us find approximate values of the real roots of

$$P(p) = p^4 + 7p^3 + 14p^2 + 15p + 6 = 0. \qquad \text{(A.6–1)}$$

(Equations of higher degree are treated in exactly the same fashion; it is convenient, though by no means necessary, first to divide through by the coefficient of the leading term, as has been done here.) It is clear, from the fact that all coefficients are positive, that there are no positive real roots. We accordingly consider only negative real values of p. As a start, we make up Table A.6–1, using the method of (A.3–6) and (A.3–7)

Table A.6–1

p	$P(p)$
0	+6
−1	−1
−2	−8
−3	−21
−4	−22
−5	+31

for the computations. With the round numbers of this example, and these integer values of p, no computational aid is necessary for this arithmetic; with the irregular numbers of practical examples (or with noninteger values of p), a small slide rule is sufficient, since we are looking only for approximate values. We plot (Fig. A.6–A) each point as it is

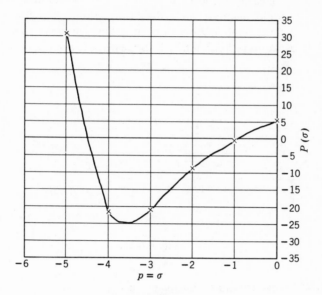

Fig. A.6–A

computed, both for checking its reasonableness and as a guide in deciding what value of p to take next. The six points of Table A.6–1 clearly show the presence of two real roots, approximately at $p = -0.9$ and $p = -4.5$, so we stop here.

An additional significant figure is easily obtained by the two sets of computations and plots given in Table A.6–2 and Fig. A.6–B. Each

Table A.6–2

p	$P(p)$
−0.9	−0.60
−0.8	−0.21
−0.7	+0.20
−4.5	−5.80
−4.6	−0.37
−4.62	+0.86

point is plotted as it is computed, as a guide to the next point needed; in the second case the third point is added simply as a check. The roots are evidently −0.747 and −4.605, the last figure being uncertain in each case. On dividing (A.6–1) by $(p + 0.747)(p + 4.605)$ we obtain a quadratic, whose roots are easily found by formula. If the equation were of higher degree we should examine the reduced equation again for real roots. We proceed thus, removing one root at a time (or more than one if we are lucky, as we were here) until all the real roots are obtained.

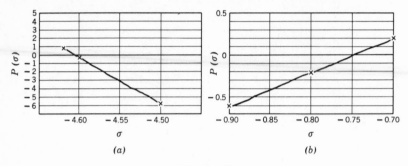

Fig. A.6–B

Complex roots are more difficult to locate, because two dimensions are involved. But approximate values can still be obtained with reasonable speed by a graphical process; it is only necessary to add the second dimension to the plot.

Approximate values of complex roots [which occur in conjugate pairs, since we assume the a's in (A.6–1) to be real] can be obtained by looking at the (conformal) map (§ 3.24) of the p plane generated by the function $P(p)$. We merely take points on suitable lines of the p plane, compute the corresponding values of $P(p)$ by the method of (A.3–15) and (A.3–16), and plot these points in the plane of $P(p)$. Looking on the curves outlined by these points as a map of the p plane, we can read the p-plane coordinates of the P-plane origin, i.e., the value of a root of $P(p) = 0$. After dividing out the factor corresponding to this root and its conjugate, we treat the reduced equation in the same fashion.

The most convenient lines of the p plane to map are its axes, and lines parallel thereto. We may start, for example, with the imaginary axis. The method of (A.3–16) makes the computation fairly easy, and we can map the points O, A, B, C, D in sequence (Fig. A.6–C), feeling our way as we go, to find suitable values of ω. (Only positive values of ω need be plotted, because of the conjugate-root property.) When the course of the line $\sigma = 0$ is plainly outlined in the P plane and it is clear that we are not getting closer to the origin, as at point D, we shift to a new line in the p plane. Some properties of functions are useful to us in estimating to what line to shift: the property of an analytic function that $P'(p)$ is independent of the direction of approach to the point in question (§ 3.10), and the properties of a conformal map that areas on, say, the left side of a curve and of its map correspond in the two planes, and that angles are preserved (§ 3.24). From Fig. A.6–C(b) it is clear that we should shift to

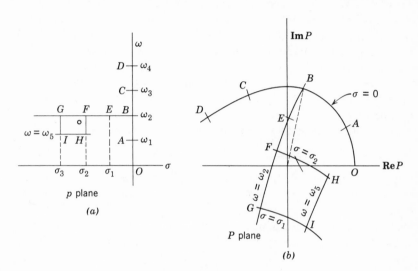

Fig. A.6–C

the left of the curve $OABCD$ (the map of the ω axis), i.e., to some line $\sigma = \sigma_1$, $\sigma_1 < 0$, in the p plane, which will map closer to the origin. Better yet, we note that lines $\omega =$ constant in the p plane will intersect our P-plane curve at right angles and that by estimating where, on the curve $\ldots ABC\ldots$, a perpendicular will pass near the origin we can move closer to the root. From B we estimate that a perpendicular to the left (the dashed line) will pass near the origin. Hence we start from B and map the line $\omega = \omega_2$ by the points E, F, G, $\cdots$, corresponding to $\omega = \omega_2$ and $\sigma = \sigma_1$, σ_2, σ_3, $\cdots$. A suitable increment for σ, i.e., a value for σ_1, can easily be determined from the approximate relation (based on the independence of the derivative of direction)

$$\left| \frac{\Delta P}{\Delta p} \right| = \frac{\overline{AB}}{\omega_2 - \omega_1} = \frac{\overline{BE}}{|\sigma_1|}. \tag{A.6–2}$$

Here $\overline{AB}$ and $\overline{BE}$ represent arc lengths; since $\overline{AB}$, $(\omega_2 - \omega_1)$, and a desired displacement $\overline{BE}$ are known, we can choose a good value for σ_1. (In practice the calculation is far simpler than any verbal discussion indicates.) We continue the mapping of the line $\omega = \omega_2$ through several points E, F, G, using the method of (A.3–15) until the origin is behind us. Then we choose additional lines to map until we reach the vicinity of the origin and have it definitely "boxed in." Because (A.6–2) is only approximate, several steps may be necessary, depending on the perversity of the equation. When we reach the stage where the P-plane origin is enclosed in a "box" of the mapping of the p-plane coordinate lines, it remains only to read off its p-plane coordinates, for $P(p) = 0$ is the condition we seek. Figure A.6–C(b), for example, indicates a root at about the location of the small circle in Fig. A.6–C(a). Usually the root can be read to two, sometimes three, significant figures from the plot. By expanding the scale the roots can be obtained to any desired accuracy, but again the method of § A.7 is preferable for more accurate work.

For example, let us find approximate values of the roots of

$$P(p) = p^4 + 6p^3 + 18p^2 + 30p + 23 \tag{A.6–3}$$

which has been found, let us assume (as by the method previously discussed), to have no real roots. This is of moderately low degree, but higher degree equations are treated in exactly the same fashion, though they may require more patience. We start by computing the points in Table A.6–3, using the method of (A.3–16). Each point is plotted in

Table A.6–3

Point	p	$P(p)$
O	0	$+23 + j0$
A	$0 + j1$	$+6 + j24$
B	$0 + j2$	$-33 + j12$
C	$-1 + j1$	$+1 + j6$
D	$-1.3 + j1$	$+0.42 + j4.04$
E	$-1.6 + j1$	$-0.49 + j2.46$
F	$-2 + j1$	$-2 + j0$
G	$-2 + j0.7$	$+0.29 - j0.71$
H	$-1.9 + j0.7$	$+0.40 - j0.04$
I	$-1.9 + j0.8$	$-0.24 + j0.14$

Fig. A.6–D(a) as it is computed; it is evident after the third point that a shift is in order. The plot is as yet too crude to make good use of

(A.6–2); with some reliance on it, however, and considering especially points O and A of Fig. A.6–D(a), and bearing in mind the probable tendency of the curves to be twisted in a counterclockwise sense, we choose an increment in σ of -1 and compute point C. Proceeding more cautiously we next compute points D, E, and F at which point a turn to

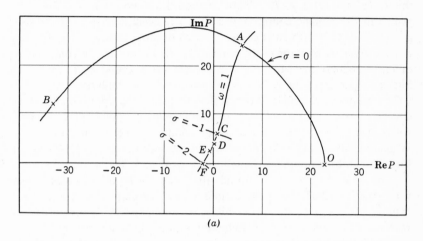

(a)

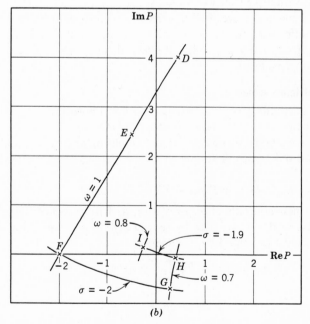

(b)

Fig. A.6–D

the left seems indicated. We proceed accordingly along the line $\sigma = -2$, taking an increment in ω of -0.3, as indicated by the relative positions of the points E, F, and the origin, bearing (A.6–2) in mind. The scale of the plot is appropriately expanded now, Fig. A.6–D(b). With points E, F, and G, the origin is well "bracketed"; an approximate root read at this stage is $-1.9 + j0.75$. With the additional points H and I we can sketch in the p-plane coordinates sufficiently accurately to read the root as $-1.91 + j0.76$ (which is correct to two decimal places). On dividing out the quadratic factor corresponding to this root and its conjugate, a quadratic equation results whose roots are easily found by formula; in higher degree cases the reduced equation would be similarly treated.

The graphical methods above suffice to give good approximate roots. (Indeed, for some purposes their results may be quite good enough; where not, they provide fine starting points for the method of § A.7.) Which root is obtained first depends on the way the plot is followed; in Fig. A.6–D, for example, we might have gone in to the origin from point B, and would then have found the other pair of complex roots, $p = -1.09 \pm j2.07$. In complicated cases the plots may contain unexpected twists and turns (after all, a Riemann surface is involved), but with patience one can ultimately obtain the roots whenever they are simple. A multiple root will manifest itself in the plots and can be found by similar methods; we shall not discuss such cases here.

When approximate values for all the roots (real and complex) have been obtained, it is a good idea to check them (§ A.8) before proceeding to their improvement.

A.7 Root improvement

Many methods have been developed for improving the accuracy of approximate roots. We shall discuss only Newton's (or the Newton–Raphson) method (WH 3), which is simple of application and easy to recall, and only cases of simple roots. It derives from the Taylor series about p_1,

$$P(p) = P(p_1) + P'(p_1)(p - p_1) + \cdots. \qquad (A.7\text{–}1)$$

If p_1 is a first approximation to a root, and if we neglect terms beyond the second in the series, then by setting $P(p) = 0$ we obtain an equation that determines a second approximation, p_2:

$$P(p_2) = P(p_1) + P'(p_1)(p_2 - p_1) = 0; \qquad (A.7\text{–}2)$$

i.e.,

$$p_2 = p_1 - \frac{P(p_1)}{P'(p_1)} \qquad (A.7\text{–}3)$$

gives us the second approximation to the root. The evaluation of $P(p_1)$

has been discussed in § A.3; it is easily accomplished by dividing by $(p - p_1)$,

$$P(p) = (p - p_1)Q(p) + R(p) = (p - p_1)Q(p) + b_1, \quad \text{(A.7-4)}$$

$Q(p)$ being the quotient and $R(p) = b_1$ the remainder, which is equal to $P(p_1)$. Evaluation of $P'(p_1)$ is equally simple, for from (A.7-4) we obtain by differentiation

$$P'(p) = Q(p) + (p - p_1)Q'(p) + 0 \quad \text{(A.7-5)}$$

which gives us

$$P'(p) = Q(p_1). \quad \text{(A.7-6)}$$

All that is necessary to obtain the value of the derivative is to evaluate the quotient $Q(p)$ at the same point. In the arithmetical work this is not at all difficult; it calls only for a second division (application of the remainder theorem) under the first one, as the examples below show.

Once $P(p_1)$ and $P'(p_1)$ are evaluated, the second approximation p_2 is computed from (A.7–3). This completes one cycle of the iterative process. The second cycle is a repetition of the first, starting from p_2 and computing a third approximation p_3 from

$$p_3 = p_2 - \frac{P(p_2)}{P'(p_2)}. \quad \text{(A.7-7)}$$

The process is continued until a satisfactory approximation to the root is obtained, indicated by the size of the remainder. We then repeat the process, either with the reduced polynomial [available immediately in the quotient $Q(p)$ in the last cycle] or with the original polynomial, starting from one of the other approximate roots. Use of the reduced polynomial calls for less work; use of the original polynomial sometimes gives greater accuracy. In this way, all of the roots are eventually determined to the desired degree of accuracy.

In the case of a *real root*, the formulas above apply exactly. For example, let us find an accurate value of one of the real roots of (A.6–1). We start from the rough value -0.9, obtained from Fig. A.6–A, rather than from the more accurate value obtainable from Fig. A.6–B, in order to illustrate clearly how Newton's method operates. We first evaluate $P(p)$ and its derivative at $p = p_1 = -0.9$. The arithmetical work, using the method of (A.3–7), is

$$
\begin{array}{rrrrl}
0.9)1 & 7 & 14 & 15 & 6 \quad (\\
1 & 0.9 & 5.49 & 7.659 & 6.607 \\
\hline
& 6.1 & 8.51 & 7.341 & -0.607 \rightarrow P(p_1) = -0.607, \\
\end{array}
$$
$$\text{(A.7-8)}$$
$$
\begin{array}{rrrrl}
1 & 0.9 & 4.68 & 3.45 & \\
\hline
& 5.2 & 3.83 & 3.89 & \longrightarrow P'(p_1) = +3.89.
\end{array}
$$

Since the quotient $Q(p)$ is contained in the coefficients resulting from the first division [it is $Q(p) = p^3 + 6.1p^2 + 8.51p + 7.341$ above], the evaluation of the derivative by (A.7–6) calls simply for the second division shown, which entails a minimum of writing. The second approximation to the root, from (A.7–3), is

$$p_2 = -0.9 - \frac{-0.607}{+3.89} = -0.9 + 0.156 = -0.744. \qquad \text{(A.7-9)}$$

Computations similar to those of (A.7–8), made with p_2, give

$$P(p_2) = +0.01309,$$

$$P'(p_2) = +4.14, \qquad \qquad \text{(A.7-10)}$$

$$p_3 = p_2 - \frac{0.01309}{4.14} = -0.744 - 0.00316 = -0.74716.$$

As a matter of interest, these and the results of two more cycles are given in Table A.7–A. Notice that the approximate root read from Fig.

Table A.7–A

Approximate Root	$P(p_i)$	$P'(p_i)$	Indicated Correction
$p_1 = -0.9$	-0.607	$+3.89$	$+0.156$
$p_2 = -0.744$	$+0.01309$	$+4.14$	-0.00316
$p_3 = -0.74716$	$+0.0000095$	$+4.13$	-0.00000230
$p_4 = -0.74716230$	-0.00000003		$+0.00000001$

A.6–B(b) agrees with this in its three figures. The number of significant figures it is necessary to carry increases with each cycle, in keeping with the increased accuracy. In the calculation of the derivative, however, and of the change to be made in improving an approximate root, slide-rule accuracy is sufficient since (A.7–3) is only approximate and usually gives the increment to two or three significant figures at best. For that matter, the derivative changes little, once we are close to the root, and really need not be recomputed from one cycle to the next.

The convergence is not always as rapid as in this example, in which the method works very well. Only one significant figure may be gained in each of the first few cycles, for example (though the speed of convergence usually increases once momentum is gained). Why this may occur we can easily see in Fig. A.7–A, which illustrates graphically how Newton's method operates. Starting from p_1, the method extends the tangent to $P(p)$ at this point, to give the next approximation p_2, according to (A.7–3). Then p_3, p_4, $\cdots$ follow in succeeding cycles. The iterative, "feedback" nature of the process is clear; successive approximate roots may oscillate about the true value, or approach it from one side. Evidently the speed of convergence will depend on the curvature of $P(p)$ in the vicinity of the root, i.e., on the locations of the other roots: not only may the convergence be slow in some cases but it is possible for the process to diverge (or become "unstable"), as we can see by imagining that we start from p_1' instead of p_1. We shall not discuss this phenomenon, nor the modifications of the method necessary in cases of multiple roots. If difficulties

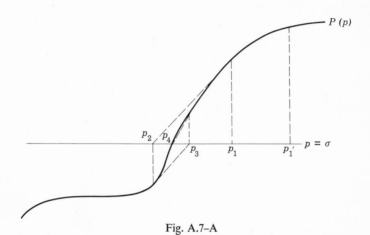

Fig. A.7–A

arise, a careful, detailed plot of $P(p)$ will usually explain them. An advantage of iterative procedures such as this is that they are self-correcting; an error does not vitiate the work, though it may well prolong it. The method can be modified by including more terms in (A.7–2) although the advantage of simplicity then disappears (DE 1, FR 8, OL 1, ST 2, WA 3); if an approximate root is first obtained by graphical methods (§ A.6), the linear improvement described here is adequate.

In the case of a *complex root* the principle of Newton's method is still valid, but it is convenient, just as in § A.3, to avoid the arithmetic of complex numbers as much as possible by using a quadratic divisor in the computation of P and P'. The computation of $P(p_1)$ is made exactly as in (A.3–13, –14, –15), from

$$P(p) = (p - p_1)(p - \bar{p}_1)Q(p) + R(p),$$
$$= (p - p_1)(p - \bar{p}_1)Q(p) + b_1p + b_0, \qquad \text{(A.7–11)}$$
$$P(p_1) = R(p_1) = b_1p_1 + b_0.$$

The computation of $P'(p_1)$ can be made in a fashion analogous to that above for the real-root case. By differentiation we obtain

$$P'(p) = (p - p_1)(p - \bar{p}_1)Q'(p) + (p - p_1)Q(p) + (p - \bar{p}_1)Q(p) + R'(p)$$
$$\text{(A.7–12)}$$

so that, with the notation $p_1 = \sigma_1 + j\omega_1$,

$$P'(p_1) = (p_1 - \bar{p}_1)Q(p_1) + R'(p_1) = j2\omega_1 Q(p_1) + b_1. \quad \text{(A.7–13)}$$

Evaluation of $Q(p_1)$ requires only a repetition of the division by $(p - p_1)(p - \bar{p}_1) = (p^2 - 2\sigma_1 p + \sigma_1^2 + \omega_1^2)$, this time into $Q(p)$. (In the arithmetical work this is again conveniently done under the first division.) It yields

$$Q(p) = (p - p_1)(p - \bar{p}_1)Q_1(p) + R_1(p)$$
$$= (p - p_1)(p - \bar{p}_1)Q_1(p) + c_1 p + c_0, \quad \text{(A.7–14)}$$

in which $Q_1(p)$ and $R_1(p)$ are the new quotient and remainder, and

$$Q_1(p_1) = R_1(p_1) = c_1 p_1 + c_0. \quad \text{(A.7–15)}$$

In terms of these results (A.7–3) becomes

$$p_2 = p_1 - \frac{R(p_1)}{j2\omega_1 Q(p_1) + R'(p_1)} = p_1 - \frac{b_1 p_1 + b_0}{j2\omega_1(c_1 p_1 + c_0) + b_1}. \quad \text{(A.7–16)}$$

Complex numbers appear only in the evaluation of the increment to be given p_1, and here slide-rule work is enough, even for very accurate root finding, since only a small number of significant figures is gained in each cycle.

The calculation of p_3 proceeds in exactly the same fashion, with succeeding cycles until the root is determined accurately enough. The graphical interpretation of this process is a motion toward the root in the p plane that may be of a spiral nature or may be fairly direct, in analogy with Fig. A.7–A. The remarks made there about convergence, etc., apply here also, with appropriate extension to two dimensions.

The reduced polynomial is immediately available in $Q(p)$ at the last stage, to be factored in similar fashion.

By way of illustration, let us improve the approximate root $p_1 = \sigma_1 + j\omega_1 = -1.09 + j2.07$ of § A.6. The divisor is

$$(p - p_1)(p - \bar{p}_1) = p^2 + 2.18p + 5.4730$$

and the arithmetical work of the first cycle is

$$
\begin{array}{llll}
1 & 6 & 18 & 30 \qquad\quad 23 \\
1 & 2.18 & 5.4730 \\
\hline
 & 3.82 & 12.527 \\
 & 3.82 & 8.3276 & 20.90686 \\
\hline
 & & 4.1994 & 9.09314 \\
 & & 4.1994 & 9.15469 \quad 22.9833 \\
\hline
 & & & -0.06155 \;\; +0.0167 \leftarrow R(p), \\
 & & & \quad\;\; b_1 \qquad\quad\;\; b_0 \\
\end{array}
$$

$$
\begin{array}{lll}
1 & 2.18 & 5.473 \\
\hline
 & 1.64 & -1.274 \leftarrow R_1(p). \\
 & c_1 & c_0
\end{array}
$$

(A.7–17)

It is unnecessary to write the divisor in the upper left corner, since it is immediately repeated in the second line [for the leading coefficient of $P(p)$ is unity]; the division of $Q(p) = p^2 + 3.82p + 4.1994$ by the (same) divisor is again conveniently carried out without rewriting $Q(p)$, just below the first division. We next calculate the correction to be applied to p_1, using the slide rule:

$$
P(p_1) = b_1 p_1 + b_0 = -0.0616(-1.09 + j2.07) + 0.0167
$$
$$
= 0.0839 - j0.127,
$$

$$
P'(p_1) = j2(2.07)[1.64(-1.09 + j2.07) - 1.274] - 0.0616
$$
$$
= -14.2 - j12.7.
$$

The correction is

(A.7–18)

$$
-\frac{P(p_1)}{P'(p_1)} = -\frac{0.0839 - j0.127}{-14.2 - j12.7} = \frac{0.152\underline{/-56.5°}}{-19.0\underline{/41.8°}}
$$

$$
= 0.00800\underline{/-98.3°} = -0.00116 - j0.00792,
$$

whence $p_2 = -1.09116 + j2.06208$. Table A.7–B shows the results of this work, and of another cycle. The value p_3 is evidently accurate to seven significant figures, should such accuracy be needed. Here again is a case of rapid convergence; the work is not always this easy.

Table A.7–B

Approximate Root	$P(p_i)$	$P'(p_i)$	Indicated Correction
$p_1 = -1.09 + j2.07$	$+0.0839 - j0.127$	$-14.16 - j12.67$	$-0.00116 - j0.00792$
$p_2 = -1.09116 + j2.06208$	$+0.000825 - j0.00191$	$-14.16 - j12.67$	$-0.000035 - j0.000104$
$p_3 = -1.091195 + j2.061976$	$+0.000009 - j0.000037$	$-14.16 - j12.67$	$-0.000001 - j0.000002$

A.8 Checking the roots

After all the roots have been found, it is essential to check them. In (A.5–1) the coefficients a are related to the roots in moderately complicated fashion, except for a_{n-1} and a_0. By writing the polynomial in factored form we can easily see that

$$\text{the sum of the roots} = -\frac{a_{n-1}}{a_n},$$

$$\text{the product of the roots} = (-1)^n \frac{a_0}{a_n},$$

(A.8–1)

which suggest a method of checking. A convenient, and generally sufficient, check is to form the sum and the product of the roots as found and compare the results with the true values, given by (A.8–1).

For example, of the four roots of (A.6–3)

$$p^4 + 6p^3 + 18p^2 + 30p + 23 = 0,$$

(A.8–2)

two were found in § A.7 to be $-1.091195 \pm j2.061976$, and the other two, obtained by applying the quadratic formula to the reduced polynomial, are $-1.908805 \pm j0.763218$. The sum of these roots is -6.000000 and their product is 23.000008; the check may be considered satisfactory.

If the check is not consistent with the accuracy expected of the roots, the work must be corrected. Trouble is sometimes caused by a cumulative loss of accuracy due to working with reduced polynomials, after removing some of the roots. In such cases the roots should be given a final improvement, one (or two) at a time, using the original polynomial (of degree n) for each.

A.9 Polynomial splitting

The process of finding the roots of an equation such as (A.5–1) amounts to factoring the polynomial $P(p)$ completely, i.e., to rewriting it in the form

$$P(p) = a_n(p - p_1)(p - p_2) \cdots (p - p_n),$$

(A.9–1)

in which $p_1, p_2, \cdots, p_n$ are the n zeros of the polynomial (roots of the equation). Factoring of a polynomial on an incomplete scale, in which the factors are less numerous and of higher degree, is a variant that is often required; we met the need for this first in Chapter 8, and shall encounter it again in Volume II. Any such partial factoring, to be sure, can be accomplished by first finding the zeros of the polynomial, as in (A.9–1), and then multiplying together the appropriate factors. But this may involve more work than is necessary, a distasteful prospect, and so we discuss now some methods of "splitting" a polynomial into factors each of which has in general more than one zero.

We limit the discussion to the case of even polynomials with real coefficients (which, in effect, includes odd polynomials, for a factor p is easily removed), for this is the case in which a saving of work is most easily accomplished; it is also rather important in network synthesis. Let

$$P(p) = a_0 - a_2p^2 + a_4p^4 - a_6p^6 + \cdots + (-1)^n a_{2n}p^{2n} \quad (A.9-2)$$

be such a polynomial, with $2n$ zeros. The minus signs have been inserted for algebraic convenience in the case we are going to discuss; it will happen there that if the sign of P is properly adjusted, both a_0 and a_{2n} in (A.9-2) will be positive. In general $P(p)$ can be factored into polynomials of lower degree in a number of ways; we shall discuss only the case of factoring into two polynomials, each of degree n, and each with all of its zeros in one half (left or right) of the p plane. Since the zeros of $P(p)$ occur in pairs, one member of each pair the negative of the other, this can be done, and it is the most useful of the various possible factorizations. We further assume that $P(p)$ has no imaginary zeros; such zeros may occur in some applications, but are then likely to require individual attention, so that it is reasonable to assume they have been removed. In addition, it is only reasonable to first remove the factors corresponding to any zeros that may be known. We write

$$G(p) = b_0 + b_1p + b_2p^2 + b_3p^3 + \cdots + b_np^n \quad (A.9-3)$$

as one of these two factors, say the one whose zeros are all in the left half plane. All the (unknown) b's will be real, and if we take the sign of $G(p)$ such that b_0 is positive, the other b's will also be positive, since $G(p)$ is a Hurwitz polynomial; in the following we assume all b's to be positive. Because the zeros of $P(p)$ that are not zeros of $G(p)$ are the negatives of the zeros of $G(p)$, the other factor is proportional to $G(-p)$. For symmetry we require that the coefficient of the highest power of p be "divided equally" between the two factors, i.e., that $b_n = \sqrt{a_{2n}}$; then the second factor is exactly $G(-p)$. We have now

$$\begin{aligned} P(p) &= a_0 - a_2p^2 + a_4p^4 - a_6p^6 + \cdots + (-1)^n a_{2n}p^{2n} \\ &= G(p)G(-p) \quad\quad (A.9-4)\\ &= (b_0 + b_1p + b_2p^2 + b_3p^3 + \cdots + b_np^n) \\ &\quad \times [b_0 - b_1p + b_2p^2 - b_3p^3 + \cdots + (-1)^n b_np^n] \end{aligned}$$

in which the $(n + 1)$ a's are known and there are exactly $(n + 1)$ unknowns, the b's. By multiplying out the last form in (A.9-4) and equating coefficients of like powers of p in the result and in the first form, we obtain the $(n + 1)$ simultaneous equations

$$b_0{}^2 \qquad\qquad\qquad\qquad\qquad\qquad\qquad\qquad = +a_0,$$
$$b_0 b_2 - b_1{}^2 + b_2 b_0 \qquad\qquad\qquad\qquad\qquad\qquad = -a_2,$$
$$b_0 b_4 - b_1 b_3 + b_2{}^2 - b_3 b_1 + b_4 b_0 \qquad\qquad\qquad = +a_4,$$
$$b_0 b_6 - b_1 b_5 + b_2 b_4 - b_3{}^2 + b_4 b_2 - b_5 b_1 + b_6 b_0 \qquad = -a_6,$$
$$b_0 b_8 - b_1 b_7 + b_2 b_6 - b_3 b_5 + b_4{}^2 - b_5 b_3 + b_6 b_2 - b_7 b_1 + b_8 b_0 = +a_8,$$
$$\text{(A.9-5)}$$

in which the rule of formation is evident; all b's with subscripts greater than n are to be taken as zero. These equations are not linear, unfortunately, and they cannot in general be immediately solved. For values of n up to 4, a straightforward method of solution is available; for $n > 4$ some method of successive approximation is required. But in most cases, solution of these equations calls for less work than does the finding of the $2n$ zeros of $P(p)$ and the recombination of half of them into $G(p)$.

Let us consider first the low values of n ($n \leq 4$). For these we can readily eliminate all but one of the unknowns, in spite of the nonlinear character of the equations (MO 3, BA 3). For $n = 4$, (A.9–5) is

$$b_0{}^2 \qquad\qquad\quad = a_0,$$
$$b_1{}^2 - 2b_0 b_2 \qquad = a_2,$$
$$b_2{}^2 - 2b_1 b_3 + 2b_0 b_4 = a_4, \qquad\qquad \text{(A.9-6)}$$
$$b_3{}^2 - 2b_2 b_4 \qquad = a_6,$$
$$b_4{}^2 \qquad\qquad\quad = a_8.$$

From these we can immediately eliminate b_0 and b_4 by using the first and last equations, to obtain

$$b_1{}^2 - 2\sqrt{a_0}\, b_2 \qquad\qquad = a_2,$$
$$b_2{}^2 - 2b_1 b_3 + 2\sqrt{a_0 a_8} = a_4, \qquad\qquad \text{(A.9-7)}$$
$$b_3{}^2 - 2\sqrt{a_8}\, b_2 \qquad\qquad = a_6.$$

Both b_1 and b_3 can be eliminated now by solving the second equation for $2b_1 b_3$, squaring the result, and subtracting four times the product of the first and third equations after solution for $b_1{}^2$ and $b_3{}^2$ respectively. The result is an equation in b_2 alone,

$$b_2{}^4 - (12\sqrt{a_0 a_8} + 2a_4)b_2{}^2 - 8(a_2\sqrt{a_8} + a_6\sqrt{a_0})b_2$$
$$+ [(a_4 - 2\sqrt{a_0 a_8})^2 - 4a_2 a_6] = 0, \quad \text{(A.9-8)}$$

whose four roots can be found by the methods of §§ A.6 and A.7. Of these we are interested only in that one which makes $G(p)$ a Hurwitz polynomial; the other roots correspond to other distributions of the zeros of $P(p)$, which give $G(p)$ one or more right-half-plane zeros while still obeying (A.9–4). Since b_3/b_4 is the negative of the sum of the zeros of $G(p)$ (cf. § A.8) and we wish all of these zeros to lie in the left half plane, we must pick that root which leads to the largest positive value of b_3/b_4. The value of b_4 is the same for all the roots, by the fifth equation in (A.9–6), and b_3 is a maximum when b_2 is a maximum, by the fourth equation there. Consequently we need only find the largest positive, real root of (A.9–8) to have the value of b_2. Then the remaining coefficients in $G(p)$ follow from the other equations in (A.9–6) and the extraction of the Hurwitz-polynomial factor $G(p)$ from $P(p)$ is complete for the case $n = 4$. For the case $n = 3$ we use the same procedure, simply setting a_8 and b_4 equal to zero in (A.9–8) and (A.9–6). For $n = 2$, we have a_8, a_6, b_4, and b_3 equal to zero; the equations can be immediately solved to give

$$G(p) = \sqrt{a_0} + \sqrt{a_2 + 2\sqrt{a_0 a_4}}\, p + \sqrt{a_4}\, p^2. \qquad (A.9\text{–}9)$$

And for $n = 1$ one can write $G(p)$ from $P(p)$ by a similar process, or simply by inspection of $P(p)$,

$$G(p) = \sqrt{a_0} + \sqrt{a_2}\, p. \qquad (A.9\text{–}10)$$

As an illustration, consider the problem of factoring the polynomial (of § 15.03)

$$P(p) = 24.305 + 25.009p^2 + 17.568p^4 + 6.637p^6 + p^8. \qquad (A.9\text{–}11)$$

In this case (A.9–8) is

$$b_2{}^4 - 94.296b_2{}^2 + 461.835b_2 - 604.527 = 0, \qquad (A.9\text{–}12)$$

of which the most positive, real root (found by the methods of §§ A.6 and A.7) is $b_2 = 5.520$. The other coefficients are computed from (A.9–6) to give the Hurwitz polynomial

$$G(p) = p^4 + 2.098p^3 + 5.520p^2 + 5.424p + 4.930. \qquad (A.9\text{–}13)$$

As a check, we multiply $G(p)$ by $G(-p)$ and obtain

$$G(p)G(-p) = p^8 + 6.638p^6 + 17.570p^4 + 25.008p^2 + 24.305, \qquad (A.9\text{–}14)$$

which is satisfactory.

For values of n greater than 4, the straightforward solution of (A.9–5) by successive elimination becomes too complicated. Instead, we may fall back on methods of successive approximation, one of which, due to Bayard (BA 3), we now describe. We first rewrite (A.9–5) in the form

$$b_0 = \sqrt{a_0},$$
$$b_1 = \sqrt{a_2 + 2b_0 b_2},$$
$$b_2 = \sqrt{a_4 + 2b_1 b_3 - 2b_0 b_4}, \tag{A.9-15}$$
$$b_3 = \sqrt{a_6 + 2b_2 b_4 - 2b_1 b_5 + 2b_0 b_6},$$
$$b_4 = \sqrt{a_8 + 2b_3 b_5 - 2b_2 b_6 + 2b_1 b_7 - 2b_0 b_8},$$

$$\cdot \quad \cdot \quad \cdot \quad \cdot \quad \cdot \quad \cdot \quad \cdot \quad \cdot \quad \cdot \quad \cdot \quad \cdot \quad \cdot$$

We then choose a set of values for the b's as a first approximation. These may be based on some rough idea of the locations of the zeros that comes from our knowledge of the synthesis work in which the problem of factoring $P(p)$ occurs. If we lack this, some set of reasonably large positive values will do. This first approximation to a solution is now improved by substituting these values in the right sides of (A.9–15) to obtain a second approximation. These values are again substituted in the right sides of (A.9–15) to obtain the third approximation, etc., until we are satisfied with the accuracy of our solution. A check, obtained by multiplying $G(p)$ by $G(-p)$, is of course the final criterion, coupled perhaps with a test of $G(p)$ to make sure that it is a Hurwitz polynomial (§ 5.14).

Theoretical questions of convergence we shall not discuss. The successive approximations usually converge, sometimes rapidly, sometimes slowly, depending on the starting point and on the nature of $P(p)$. In actual application it is soon clear whether the method is converging or not; if not, some other starting point may be chosen. If the convergence is still too slow to be satisfactory, we should shift to another method (such as one to be described below). We shall illustrate Bayard's method first by factoring

$$P(p) = 9 - 11p^2 + 5p^4 - p^6. \tag{A.9-16}$$

This is a simple problem (one for $n = 3$) which is readily solved by the first method described, using (A.9–8), but is still a good illustration of Bayard's method. By inspection, $b_0 = 3$ and $b_3 = 1$; only b_1 and b_2 remain to be found, and for them we have, from (A.9–15),

$$b_1 = \sqrt{11 + 6b_2}, \tag{A.9-17}$$
$$b_2 = \sqrt{5 + 2b_1}.$$

Starting, more or less at random, from unit values for b_1 and b_2 as a first approximation, we obtain as the second approximation $b_1 = \sqrt{17} = 4.13$,

$b_2 = \sqrt{7} = 2.65$. The third approximation is $b_1 = \sqrt{26.90} = 5.19$, $b_2 = \sqrt{13.26} = 3.64$. The results of a number of successive approximations are given in Fig. A.9–A, both numerically and graphically. The

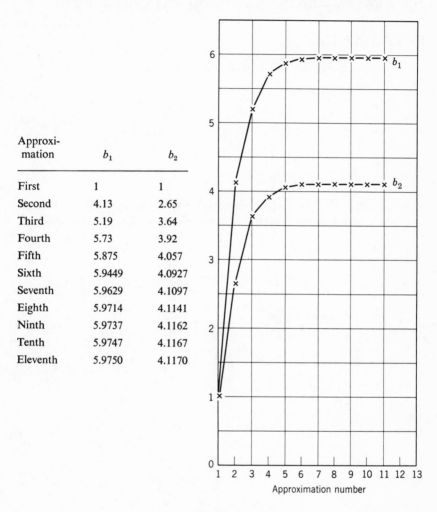

Approxi-mation	b_1	b_2
First	1	1
Second	4.13	2.65
Third	5.19	3.64
Fourth	5.73	3.92
Fifth	5.875	4.057
Sixth	5.9449	4.0927
Seventh	5.9629	4.1097
Eighth	5.9714	4.1141
Ninth	5.9737	4.1162
Tenth	5.9747	4.1167
Eleventh	5.9750	4.1170

Fig. A.9–A

first few cycles are made with a slide rule, a machine being used when it becomes appropriate. The process clearly converges, though not rapidly, and if four or five significant figures are required, the original method using (A.9–8) probably involves almost the same amount of work. On the other hand, the calculations here are simple, and easily programmed for an automatic digital computer.

For a second illustration we take (from § 15.03)

$$P(p) = 105.6735 + 100.1265p^2 + 58.8745p^4 + 13.3145p^6 - 2.1070p^8 - p^{10}$$

$$(A.9\text{--}18)$$

for which (A.9–15) is

$$b_0 = \sqrt{105.6735} = 10.2798,$$

$$b_5 = \sqrt{1} = 1,$$

$$b_1 = \sqrt{-100.1265 + 20.5596b_2},$$

$$b_2 = \sqrt{+58.8745 + 2b_1b_3 - 20.5596b_2},$$

$$(A.9\text{--}19)$$

$$b_3 = \sqrt{-13.3145 + 2b_2b_4 - 2b_1},$$

$$b_4 = \sqrt{-2.1070 + 2b_3}.$$

For a rough (first) approximation to get started, since this is a problem that arose in a low-band approximation, we may place the five zeros of

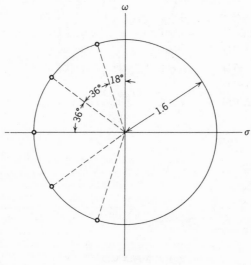

Fig. A.9–B

$G(p)$ in the vicinity of the origin, say on a circle. We choose a circle hopefully, because of its simplicity and because in the distantly related problem of maximal approximation to a constant at the origin (§§ 13.10

and 14.15) the poles lie on a circle about the origin. For the radius we use $\sqrt[10]{100} = 1.6$, to take account of the frequency scale implied by the first and last terms in $P(p)$. By spacing zeros on such a circle, as in Fig. A.9–B, we generate the polynomial

$$(p + 1.6)(p^2 + 2.6p + 2.6)(p^2 + p + 2.6)$$
$$\cong p^5 + 5p^4 + 14p^3 + 22p^2 + 22p + 10,$$

which gives us an initial set of approximate values for b_1, b_2, b_3, and b_4. Figure A.9–C shows the results of the iteration process, using (A.9–19),

Approxi-mation	b_1	b_2	b_3	b_4
First	22	22	14	5
Second	18.77	23.92	10.89	2.632
Third	19.79	20.33	8.66	4.435
Fourth	17.83	17.61	11.29	3.900
Fifth	16.18	19.53	9.40	4.525
Sixth	17.36	16.43	11.45	4.086
Seventh	15.42	19.30	9.29	4.560

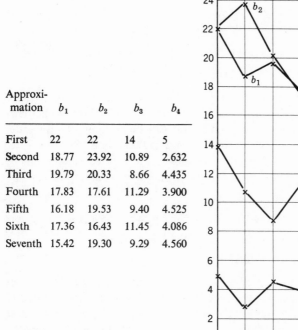

Fig. A.9–C

for the first six cycles. The process is converging—but very slowly, as comparison with the true values, to be given later, will show. If the work is done by an automatic computer, this slowness may be of no consequence; but if done by hand, and if five or six significant figures are required, the convergence is discouragingly sluggish (although an averaging process, based on such plots, may hasten it). We accordingly describe one more method which is often quite speedy.

When Bayard's method converges too slowly, we may resort to a solution of (A.9–5) by an extension of Newton's method that may be called "linearization." It depends on having an approximate solution (obtained perhaps by applying Bayard's method for a few cycles), which is improved by using only the linear terms in an expansion of (A.9–5) about the approximate solution. For its discussion, completion of the factoring of (A.9–18) will suffice.

We first write (A.9–5), or in this case (A.9–19), in the form

$$
\begin{aligned}
f_1 &= b_1{}^2 - 20.5596b_2 + 100.1265 &&= 0, \\
f_2 &= b_2{}^2 - 2b_1b_3 + 20.5596b_4 - 58.8745 &&= 0, \\
f_3 &= b_3{}^2 - 2b_2b_4 + 2b_1 + 13.3145 &&= 0, \\
f_4 &= b_4{}^2 - 2b_3 + 2.1070 &&= 0.
\end{aligned}
\tag{A.9-20}
$$

Since we do not have a true solution but only an approximate one, the functions f_1, f_2, f_3, f_4 defined by the left parts of (A.9–20) will not actually vanish, but will have nonzero values (that can be computed). In order to improve the approximate solution we differentiate the functions, treating the four b's as independent variables, and replace differentials by (small) increments denoted by Δ, to obtain the approximate relations

$$
\begin{aligned}
\Delta f_1 &= 2b_1\,\Delta b_1 - 20.5596\Delta b_2, \\
\Delta f_2 &= 2b_2\,\Delta b_2 - 2b_1\,\Delta b_3 - 2b_3\,\Delta b_1 + 20.5596\Delta b_4, \\
\Delta f_3 &= 2b_3\,\Delta b_3 - 2b_2\,\Delta b_4 - 2b_4\,\Delta b_2 + 2\Delta b_1, \\
\Delta f_4 &= 2b_4\,\Delta b_4 - 2\Delta b_3.
\end{aligned}
\tag{A.9-21}
$$

These are now to be looked on as a set of simultaneous (linear) equations in which the Δb's are unknowns, the Δf's having those values required to reduce the functions to zero. On solving for the Δb's, we apply these corrections to the approximate solution, recompute the values of the f's with the new b's, and repeat the process as necessary.

For our first set of b's, guided by the table of Fig. A.9–C, and extrapolating freely, we take

$$
\begin{aligned}
b_1 &= 15.4, \\
b_2 &= 16.4, \\
b_3 &= 9.5, \\
b_4 &= 4.1.
\end{aligned}
\tag{A.9-22}
$$

With these values (A.9–21) becomes, in detached-coefficient form,

Δb_1	Δb_2	Δb_3	Δb_4	
$+30.8$	-20.56	0	0	$= \Delta f_1,$
-19.0	$+32.8$	-30.8	$+20.56$	$= \Delta f_2,$
$+2$	-8.2	$+19.0$	-32.8	$= \Delta f_3,$
0	0	-2	$+8.2$	$= \Delta f_4.$

$$(A.9–23)$$

Since the derivatives should change little as we go along from one cycle to the next (on the assumption that say two figures are correct in our approximate solution), we solve these equations once for all, in terms of the Δf's. The method of § A.4 is convenient for this. The (slide-rule) results are

$$\Delta b_1 = 0.1095\Delta f_1 + 0.1659\Delta f_2 + 0.389\Delta f_3 + 1.139\Delta f_4,$$
$$\Delta b_2 = 0.1155\Delta f_1 + 0.248\Delta f_2 + 0.582\Delta f_3 + 1.707\Delta f_4,$$
$$\Delta b_3 = 0.0661\Delta f_1 + 0.1551\Delta f_2 + 0.454\Delta f_3 + 1.429\Delta f_4,$$
$$\Delta b_4 = 0.01613\Delta f_1 + 0.0378\Delta f_2 + 0.1108\Delta f_3 + 0.470\Delta f_4.$$

$$(A.9–24)$$

We now compute the values of the f's corresponding to (A.9–22), give to the Δf's in (A.9–24) the *negatives* of these values, and so determine the first corrections to (A.9–22). With the new b's we repeat the process

Table A.9–A

Approximation	b_1	b_2	b_3	b_4
First	15.4	16.4	9.5	4.1
Second	15.23227	16.15405	9.38784	4.08275
Third	15.22346	16.14223	9.38024	4.08085
Fourth	15.22269	16.14122	9.37947	4.08068
Fifth	15.22262	16.14113	9.37941	4.08066

until satisfied. Table A.9–A shows the work, which progresses satisfactorily rapidly. As a check we find, using the fifth set of values of b's from Table A.9–A,

$$G(p)G(-p) = -p^{10} - 2.10703p^8 + 13.31435p^6 + 58.87444p^4$$
$$+ 100.12702p^2 + 105.67429 \quad (A.9–25)$$

which indicates that these b's are correct to four decimal places. The number of cycles required by Bayard's method in this case to attain such accuracy is probably of the order of 100, but it does soon provide an excellent starting point for the application of the "linearization" method.

A.10 References

Numerical computation has interested some of the greatest mathematicians and has an enormous literature. The references following (some of which have extensive bibliographies) will provide an introduction to that part of this literature that bears on the sort of computations we have found it necessary to make in one-terminal-pair network synthesis.

Computation (general): HO 4, HI 1, JE 2, MI 5, SC 6, WH 3, WI 3.

Rational-function evaluation: the remainder theorem and related matters are discussed in nearly all algebra books, e.g., AD 1, FI 1, WE 1; see also DR 1, RI 4, SA 1, US 1, VO 1, etc.

Root finding: BR 3, DR 1, FR 4, FR 8, HI 1, OL 1, SA 1, TU 1. Newton's method: BO 11, DE 1, DO 2, HA 5, HI 1, HO 4, MI 4, SC 6, ST 2, US 1, VO 1, WA 3, WH 3, WI 3, XA 1, ZU 1. Other methods: AD 1, CO 3, DO 2, FR 6, FR 7, HI 1, HO 4, KO 2, NI 2, OL 1, RE 1, SA 4, SC 6, SH 3, US 1, VO 1, WH 3, WI 3, ZU 1. Machines (isographs): DI 2, GL 1, LO 1, LU 1, MA 10, MA 11, MO 4.

Linear equations: BO 11, DW 1, FO 3, FR 8, HA 5, HI 1, KO 2, NI 2, RE 1, RI 1, SA 4, SC 6, ST 4, ZU 1.

Nonlinear equations: HA 5, HI 1, HO 4, KO 2, SC 6, VO 1.

Polynomial splitting: BA 3, BA 4, LU 3, MO 3.

APPENDIX B

The function $F_0(\frac{\omega}{\omega_0})$ of §8.09

In § 8.09 is described a graphical method for (approximate) computation of one part (real or imaginary) of an immittance function or its logarithm from the other. It requires a table of the function (8.09–8),

$$F_0\left(\frac{\omega}{\omega_0}\right) = \frac{1}{\pi}\int_{u_0}^{\infty} \ln \coth\left|\frac{u}{2}\right| du = \frac{1}{\pi}\int_0^{x_0} \ln\left|\frac{1+x}{1-x}\right|\frac{dx}{x},$$

$$x_0 = \frac{\omega}{\omega_0} = \frac{f}{f_0}, \qquad (B-1)$$

$$u_0 = \ln x_0,$$

which is associated with the semi-infinite straight line of Fig. 8.09–D in the unit-slope ($k = 1$) case. The behavior of the function is shown in Fig. 8.09–G, and more accurately in Fig. B–A. Here the curve is drawn only for the range $0 < \omega/\omega_0 < 1$, for this can also be used in the range $1 < \omega/\omega_0 < \infty$. In the latter range we enter the scale of abcissae with the value of ω_0/ω (instead of ω/ω_0) and correct the value read from the curve according to the symmetry relation (Problem 8-66)

$$F_0\left(\frac{\omega}{\omega_0}\right) = \frac{\pi}{2} - F_0\left(\frac{\omega_0}{\omega}\right) = 1.571 - F_0\left(\frac{\omega_0}{\omega}\right). \qquad (B-2)$$

For example, with $\omega_0 = 2$, the function F_0 has the value 0.260 at $\omega = 0.8$, and the value 1.311 at $\omega = 5$. For some applications, points read from this curve will suffice, but it usually happens that in superposing the contributions of the various straight lines, near cancellations occur, and accurate values of the function F_0 are necessary.

Accurate values of the function can be computed from the series expansion (Problem 8-66)

$$F_0\left(\frac{\omega}{\omega_0}\right) = \frac{2}{\pi}\left(x_0 + \frac{x_0^3}{9} + \frac{x_0^5}{25} + \frac{x_0^7}{49} + \cdots\right), \qquad 0 < x_0 < 1 \quad (B-3)$$

1135

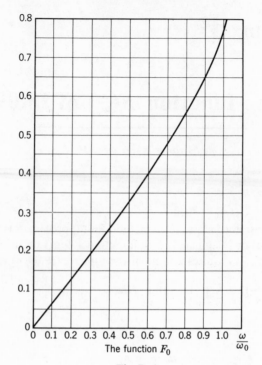

The function F_0

Fig. B–A

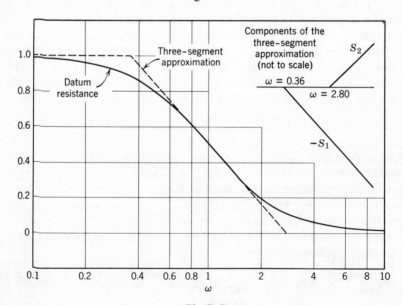

Fig. B–B

Network Synthesis

B–1. The Function $F_0(\omega/\omega_0)$ for $0 \le f/f_0 \le 1$

f/f_0	0	1	2	3	4	5	6	7	8	9
		0.00064	0.00127	0.00191	0.00255	0.00318	0.00382	0.00446	0.00509	0.00573
		0.00700	0.00764	0.00828	0.00891	0.00955	0.01019	0.01082	0.01146	0.01210
		0.01337	0.01401	0.01464	0.01528	0.01592	0.01655	0.01719	0.01783	0.01846
		0.01974	0.02037	0.02101	0.02165	0.02228	0.02292	0.02356	0.02419	0.02483
		0.02611	0.02674	0.02738	0.02802	0.02865	0.02929	0.02993	0.03057	0.03120
	0.03248	0.03311	0.03375	0.03439	0.03503	0.03566	0.03630	0.03694	0.03757	
	0.03885	0.03949	0.04012	0.04076	0.04140	0.04204	0.04267	0.04331	0.04395	
.07	0.04523	0.04586	0.04650	0.04714	0.04778	0.04841	0.04905	0.04969	0.05033	
.08	0.05160	0.05224	0.05288	0.05352	0.05416	0.05479	0.05543	0.05607	0.05671	
.09	0.05799	0.05862	0.05926	0.05990	0.06054	0.06118	0.06182	0.06245	0.06309	
.10	0.06373	0.06437	0.06501	0.06565	0.06629	0.06693	0.06757	0.06821	0.06885	0.06949
.11	0.07013[2]	0.07076	0.07140	0.07204	0.07268	0.07332	0.07396	0.07460	0.07524	0.07588
.12	0.07652	0.07716	0.07780	0.07844	0.07908	0.07972	0.08036	0.08100	0.08164	0.08228
.13	0.08292	0.08356	0.08420	0.08484	0.08548	0.08612	0.08676	0.08740	0.08804	0.08868
.14	0.08932	0.08996	0.09061	0.09125	0.09189	0.09253	0.09317	0.09381	0.09445	0.09509
.15	0.09574[3]	0.09638	0.09702	0.09766	0.09830	0.09894	0.09959	0.10023	0.10087	0.10151
.16	0.10215	0.10279	0.10344	0.10408	0.10472	0.10537	0.10601	0.10665	0.10729	0.10794
.17	0.10858	0.10922	0.10987	0.11051	0.11115	0.11179	0.11244	0.11308	0.11372	0.11437
.18	0.11501	0.11565	0.11630	0.11694	0.11759	0.11823	0.11888	0.11952	0.12016	0.12081
.19	0.12145	0.12210	0.12274	0.12339	0.12403	0.12468	0.12532	0.12596	0.12661	0.12725
.20	0.12790	0.12854	0.12919	0.12984	0.13048	0.13113	0.13178	0.13242	0.13307	0.13371
.21	0.13436	0.13501	0.13565	0.13630	0.13695	0.13759	0.13824	0.13888	0.13953	0.14018
.22	0.14082	0.14147	0.14212	0.14277	0.14342	0.14406	0.14471	0.14536	0.14601	0.14666
.23	0.14730	0.14795	0.14860	0.14925	0.14990	0.15055	0.15119	0.15184	0.15249	0.15314
.24	0.15379	0.15444	0.15509	0.15574	0.15639	0.15704	0.15769	0.15834	0.15899	0.15964
.25	0.16029	0.16094	0.16159	0.16224	0.16289	0.16354	0.16419	0.16484	0.16549	0.16615
.26	0.16680	0.16745	0.16810	0.16875	0.16941	0.17006	0.17071	0.17137	0.17202	0.17267
.27	0.17332	0.17398	0.17463	0.17528	0.17593	0.17659	0.17724	0.17789	0.17855	0.17920
.28	0.17985	0.18051	0.18116	0.18182	0.18247	0.18313	0.18378	0.18444	0.18509	0.18575
.29	0.18641[0]	0.18706	0.18772	0.18837	0.18903	0.18968	0.19034	0.19099	0.19165	0.19230
.30	0.19296	0.19362	0.19428	0.19493	0.19559	0.19625	0.19691	0.19757	0.19823	0.19888
.31	0.19954	0.20020	0.20086	0.20152	0.20218	0.20283	0.20349	0.20415	0.20481	0.20547
.32	0.20613	0.20679	0.20745	0.20811	0.20877	0.20943	0.21009	0.21076	0.21142	0.21208
.33	0.21274[3]	0.21340	0.21406	0.21472	0.21538	0.21605	0.21671	0.21737	0.21803	0.21869
.34	0.21935	0.22002	0.22068	0.22135	0.22201	0.22268	0.22334	0.22401	0.22467	0.22534
.35	0.22600[0]	0.22666	0.22733	0.22799	0.22866	0.22932	0.22999	0.23065	0.23132	0.23198
.36	0.23265	0.23332	0.23398	0.23465	0.23532	0.23599	0.23666	0.23732	0.23799	0.23866
.37	0.23933[2]	0.24000	0.24067	0.24134	0.24200	0.24267	0.24334	0.24401	0.24468	0.24534
.38	0.24601	0.24669	0.24736	0.24803	0.24870	0.24937	0.25005	0.25072	0.25139	0.25206
.39	0.25274[3]	0.25341	0.25408	0.25475	0.25542	0.25610	0.25677	0.25744	0.25811	0.25879
.40	0.25946	0.26013	0.26081	0.26148	0.26216	0.26284	0.26351	0.26419	0.26486	0.26554
.41	0.26621	0.26689	0.26757	0.26824	0.26892	0.26960	0.27028	0.27095	0.27163	0.27231
.42	0.27299	0.27367	0.27435	0.27503	0.27571	0.27639	0.27706	0.27774	0.27842	0.27910
.43	0.27978	0.28047	0.28115	0.28183	0.28251	0.28319	0.28388	0.28456	0.28524	0.28592
.44	0.28660[1]	0.28729	0.28797	0.28866	0.28934	0.29003	0.29071	0.29140	0.29208	0.29276
.45	0.29345	0.29414	0.29482	0.29551	0.29620	0.29688	0.29757	0.29826	0.29894	0.29963
.46	0.30032	0.30101	0.30170	0.30239	0.30308	0.30377	0.30446	0.30515	0.30584	0.30652
.47	0.30721[2]	0.30791	0.30860	0.30929	0.30998	0.31068	0.31137	0.31206	0.31275	0.31344
.48	0.31414	0.31483	0.31553	0.31622	0.31692	0.31761	0.31831	0.31900	0.31970	0.32039
.49	0.32109	0.32179	0.32248	0.32318	0.32388	0.32458	0.32527	0.32597	0.32667	0.32737
.50	0.32807	0.32877	0.32947	0.33017	0.33087	0.33157	0.33227	0.33297	0.33368	0.33438
.51	0.33508	0.33578	0.33648	0.33719	0.33789	0.33860	0.33930	0.34000	0.34071	0.34141
.52	0.34212	0.34282	0.34353	0.34424	0.34495	0.34565	0.34636	0.34707	0.34777	0.34848
.53	0.34919	0.34990	0.35061	0.35132	0.35203	0.35274	0.35345	0.35416	0.35487	0.35558
.54	0.35629	0.35701	0.35772	0.35844	0.35915	0.35986	0.36058	0.36129	0.36201	0.36272

and this is the basis of Tables B–1,
computation use was also made of c
order to reduce the number of points a
They tabulate the function $F_0(\omega/\omega_0)$ in ter
the "break" frequency ω_0, i.e., of $x_0 = \omega/$
variable. The range $0 \leqq x_0 \leqq 1$ is covered
B–1, with additional entries in the range 0.99
was taken of the symmetry property (B–2) to r
in the range $x_0 > 1$, so that the function is tab
terms of the *reciprocal* of x_0, i.e., in terms of $1/x_0$
range $1 \leqq x_0 \leqq \infty$ or $1 \geqq 1/x_0 \geqq 0$ in similar ste
tables used (§ 8.09) in the computation of reactance (s
ated with given resistance (conductance), of resistan
associated with given reactance (susceptance), of ang
associated with given magnitude, and of magnitude associa
angle (in radians). For convenience in the calculation of
magnitude, values are also given in Tables B–3 and B–4 of th
$F_0(\omega/\omega_0)$ multiplied by $180/\pi$, i.e., in degrees rather than in rad
this application. The tables may also be useful in other physical a
tions (FL 1, MU 1, PO 1, VA 3). Details of the methods of comput
used in forming the tables and a discussion of possible errors an e
found in the original paper from which the tables are taken (TH 1). The
superscript numbers found occasionally in the tables give the results of
independent computation (CO 2), where they differ; these differences
not important. The accuracy is ± 0.000015 in Tables B–1 and B–2,
$\pm 0.001°$ in Tables B–3 and B–4. More accurate (seven-figure) t
exist (TH 4) for the occasional circumstance in which they are neces
Still other tables, closely related, may also be consulted (Problem 8
as has been pointed out by B. A. Kingsbury of the Bell Teleph
Laboratories in unpublished work.

Use of the tables is discussed in § 8.09. By way of illustration we
here first the details of the example of Figs. 8.09–A, –B, –C, and
(following BO 3, with permission). The datum resistance functio
first plotted on a logarithmic frequency scale. (Any convenient cons
can be subtracted without affecting the computation; it is often conver
to adjust the minimum value to zero, as here.) This and a three-segr
approximation, drawn in to give as good an approximation thereto
reasonable with three lines, are shown in Fig. B–B: the break points
at (normalized) $\omega = 0.36$ and $\omega = 2.80$. (Here, as in all the follo\

* Tables B–1, B–2, B–3, and B–4 are reprinted from "Tables of phase assoc
with a semi-infinite unit slope of attenuation," D. E. Thomas, *Bell System Tech
Journal*, vol. 26, pp. 870–899, Oct. 1947, with the permission of the American Telep
and Telegraph Company, holder of the copyright.

Table B–1 (Continued)

f/f_0	0	1	2	3	4	5	6	7	8	9
.55	0.36343	0.36415	0.36487	0.36559	0.36631	0.36702	0.36774	0.36846	0.36918	0.36989
.56	0.37061	0.37133	0.37205	0.37277	0.37350	0.37422	0.37494	0.37566	0.37638	0.37710
.57	0.37782	0.37855	0.37927	0.38000	0.38072	0.38145	0.38217	0.38290	0.38362	0.38435
.58	0.38507	0.38580	0.38653	0.38726	0.38799	0.38872	0.38945	0.39018	0.39091	0.39164
.59	0.39237	0.39310	0.39383	0.39457	0.39530	0.39603	0.39677	0.39750	0.39823	0.39897
.60	0.39970	0.40044	0.40117	0.40191	0.40265	0.40339	0.40413	0.40486	0.40560	0.40634
.61	0.40708	0.40782	0.40856	0.40930	0.41004	0.41079	0.41153	0.41227	0.41301	0.41375
.62	0.41450	0.41524	0.41599	0.41674	0.41748	0.41823	0.41898	0.41972	0.42047	0.42122
.63	0.42197	0.42272	0.42347	0.42422	0.42497	0.42572	0.42647	0.42723	0.42798	0.42873
.64	0.42948	0.43024	0.43100	0.43175	0.43251	0.43327	0.43402	0.43478	0.43554	0.43629
.65	0.43705	0.43781	0.43857	0.43934	0.44010	0.44086	0.44162	0.44238	0.44315	0.44391
.66	0.44467	0.44544	0.44620	0.44697	0.44774	0.44851	0.44927	0.45004	0.45081	0.45158
.67	0.45234	0.45312	0.45389	0.45466	0.45544	0.45621	0.45698	0.45776	0.45853	0.45930
.68	0.46008	0.46086	0.46164	0.46242	0.46319	0.46397	0.46475	0.46553	0.46631	0.46709
.69	0.46787	0.46866	0.46944	0.47023	0.47101	0.47180	0.47258	0.47337	0.47415	0.47494
.70	0.47573	0.47652	0.47731	0.47810	0.47889	0.47968	0.48047	0.48127	0.48206	0.48285
.71	0.48365	0.48444	0.48524	0.48604	0.48684	0.48763	0.48843	0.48923	0.49004	0.49084
.72	0.49164	0.49244	0.49325	0.49405	0.49485	0.49566	0.49647	0.49727	0.49808	0.49889
.73	0.49970	0.50051	0.50132	0.50213	0.50295	0.50376	0.50457	0.50539	0.50621	0.50702
.74	0.50784	0.50866	0.50948	0.51030	0.51112	0.51194	0.51276	0.51358	0.51441	0.51523
.75	0.51605	0.51688	0.51771	0.51854	0.51937	0.52019	0.52103	0.52186	0.52269	0.52352
.76	0.52436	0.52519	0.52603	0.52686	0.52770	0.52854	0.52938	0.53022	0.53106	0.53190
.77	0.53274⁵	0.53359	0.53444	0.53528	0.53613	0.53697	0.53783	0.53868	0.53953	0.54038
.78	0.54123	0.54208	0.54294	0.54380	0.54465	0.54551	0.54637	0.54723	0.54809	0.54895
.79	0.54981	0.55068	0.55154	0.55241	0.55327	0.55414	0.55501	0.55588	0.55676	0.55763
.80	0.55850	0.55938	0.56025	0.56113	0.56201	0.56288	0.56377	0.56465	0.56553	0.56642
.81	0.56730	0.56819	0.56908	0.56996	0.57085	0.57174	0.57264	0.57353	0.57443	0.57532
.82	0.57622	0.57712	0.57802	0.57892	0.57982	0.58072	0.58163	0.58254	0.58345	0.58436
.83	0.58526	0.58618	0.58709	0.58801	0.58892	0.58984	0.59076	0.59168	0.59260	0.59353
.84	0.59445	0.59538	0.59631	0.59723	0.59816	0.59909	0.60003	0.60097	0.60190	0.60284
.85	0.60378	0.60472	0.60567	0.60661	0.60756	0.60850	0.60945	0.61041	0.61136	0.61231
.86	0.61327	0.61423	0.61519	0.61615	0.61711	0.61808	0.61905	0.62002	0.62099	0.62196
.87	0.62293	0.62391	0.62489	0.62587	0.62685	0.62783	0.62882	0.62981	0.63080	0.63179
.88	0.63278	0.63378	0.63478	0.63578	0.63678	0.63779	0.63880	0.63981	0.64082	0.64183
.89	0.64284	0.64387	0.64489	0.64591	0.64693	0.64796	0.64899	0.65003	0.65106	0.65210
.90	0.65313	0.65418	0.65523	0.65628	0.65733	0.65837	0.65943	0.66050	0.66156	0.66262
.91	0.66368	0.66476	0.66583	0.66691	0.66798	0.66906	0.67015	0.67124	0.67233	0.67343
.92	0.67452	0.67562	0.67672	0.67783	0.67894	0.68006	0.68118	0.68230	0.68342	0.68456
.93	0.68569	0.68683	0.68797	0.68911	0.69026	0.69141	0.69257	0.69373	0.69490	0.69607
.94	0.69724	0.69843	0.69961	0.70080	0.70199	0.70319	0.70439	0.70560	0.70681	0.70804
.95	0.70926	0.71049	0.71172	0.71297	0.71421	0.71547	0.71673	0.71800	0.71927	0.72055
.96	0.72183	0.72313	0.72443	0.72574	0.72706	0.72838	0.72971	0.73106	0.73240	0.73377
.97	0.73513	0.73651	0.73790	0.73930	0.74070	0.74213	0.74356	0.74501	0.74646	0.74794
.98	0.74942	0.75092	0.75243	0.75397	0.75552	0.75709⁸	0.75867	0.76028	0.76192	0.76358
.99	0.76527	0.76698	0.76874³	0.77053	0.77236	0.77425	0.77620	(refer to table below)		

.9960	0.77620	.9984	0.78125	.9992	0.78315
.9965	0.77720	.9985	0.78148	.9993	0.78340
.9970	0.77822	.9986	0.78171	.9994	0.78366
.9975	0.77928	.9987	0.78195	.9995	0.78392
.9980	0.78036	.9988	0.78218	.9996	0.78419
.9981	0.78058	.9989	0.78242	.9997	0.78446
.9982	0.78080	.9990	0.78266	.9998	0.78475
.9983	0.78103	.9991	0.78290	.9999	0.78505
				1.0000	0.78540

Table B–2. The Function $F_0(\omega/\omega_0)$ for $0 \leq f_0/f \leq 1$

f_0/f	0	1	2	3	4	5	6	7	8	9
.00	1.57080	1.57016	1.56952	1.56889	1.56825	1.56761	1.56698	1.56634	1.56570	1.56507
.01	1.56443	1.56379	1.56316	1.56252	1.56188	1.56125	1.56061	1.55997	1.55934	1.55870
.02	1.55806	1.55743	1.55679	1.55615	1.55552	1.55488	1.55424	1.55361	1.55297	1.55233
.03	1.55170	1.55106	1.55042	1.54979	1.54915	1.54851	1.54787	1.54724	1.54660	1.54596
.04	1.54533	1.54469	1.54405	1.54342	1.54278	1.54214	1.54150	1.54087	1.54023	1.53959
.05	1.53896	1.53832	1.53768	1.53704	1.53641	1.53577	1.53513	1.53450	1.53386	1.53322
.06	1.53258	1.53195	1.53131	1.53067	1.53003	1.52940	1.52876	1.52812	1.52748	1.52685
.07	1.52621	1.52557	1.52493	1.52430	1.52366	1.52302	1.52238	1.52174	1.52111	1.52047
.08	1.51983	1.51919	1.51855	1.51792	1.51728	1.51664	1.51600	1.51536	1.51472	1.51409
.09	1.51345	1.51281	1.51217	1.51153	1.51089	1.51026	1.50962	1.50898	1.50834	1.50770
.10	1.50706	1.50642	1.50578	1.50515	1.50451	1.50387	1.50323	1.50259	1.50195	1.50131
.11	1.50067	1.50003	1.49939	1.49875	1.49811	1.49748	1.49684	1.49620	1.49556	1.49492
.12	1.49428	1.49364	1.49300	1.49236	1.49172	1.49108	1.49044	1.48980	1.48916	1.48852
.13	1.48788	1.48724	1.48660	1.48596	1.48532	1.48468	1.48404	1.48339	1.48275	1.48211
.14	1.48147	1.48083	1.48019	1.47955	1.47891	1.47827	1.47763	1.47698	1.47634	1.47570
.15	1.47506	1.47442	1.47378	1.47314	1.47249	1.47185	1.47121	1.47057	1.46993	1.46929
.16	1.46864	1.46800	1.46736	1.46672	1.46607	1.46543	1.46479	1.46414	1.46350	1.46286
.17	1.46222	1.46157	1.46093	1.46029	1.45964	1.45900	1.45836	1.45772	1.45707	1.45643
.18	1.45579	1.45514	1.45450	1.45385	1.45321	1.45257	1.45192	1.45128	1.45063	1.44999
.19	1.44934	1.44870	1.44805	1.44741	1.44677	1.44612	1.44548	1.44483	1.44419	1.44354
.20	1.44290	1.44225	1.44161	1.44096	1.44031	1.43967	1.43902	1.43837	1.43773	1.43708
.21	1.43644	1.43579	1.43514	1.43450	1.43385	1.43320	1.43256	1.43191	1.43127	1.43062
.22	1.42997	1.42933	1.42868	1.42803	1.42738	1.42673	1.42608	1.42544	1.42479	1.42414
.23	1.42349	1.42284	1.42219	1.42155	1.42090	1.42025	1.41960	1.41895	1.41831	1.41766
.24	1.41701	1.41636	1.41571	1.41506	1.41441	1.41376	1.41311	1.41246	1.41181	1.41116
.25	1.41050	1.40985	1.40920	1.40855	1.40790	1.40725	1.40660	1.40595	1.40530	1.40465
.26	1.40400	1.40335	1.40270	1.40204	1.40139	1.40074	1.40008	1.39943	1.39878	1.39813
.27	1.39747	1.39682	1.39617	1.39551	1.39486	1.39421	1.39356	1.39290	1.39225	1.39160
.28	1.39094	1.39029	1.38963	1.38898	1.38832	1.38767	1.38701	1.38636	1.38570	1.38505
.29	1.38439	1.38374	1.38308	1.38242	1.38177	1.38111	1.38046	1.37980	1.37915	1.37849
.30	1.37784	1.37718	1.37652	1.37586	1.37520	1.37455	1.37389	1.37323	1.37257	1.37191
.31	1.37125	1.37060	1.36994	1.36928	1.36862	1.36796	1.36730	1.36665	1.36599	1.36533
.32	1.36467	1.36401	1.36335	1.36269	1.36203	1.36136	1.36070	1.36004	1.35938	1.35872
.33	1.35806	1.35740	1.35673	1.35607	1.35541	1.35475	1.35409	1.35343	1.35277	1.35210
.34	1.35144	1.35078	1.35011	1.34945	1.34878	1.34812	1.34745	1.34679	1.34613	1.34546
.35	1.34480	1.34413	1.34347	1.34280	1.34214	1.34147	1.34081	1.34014	1.33948	1.33881
.36	1.33815	1.33748	1.33681	1.33614	1.33548	1.33481	1.33414	1.33347	1.33280	1.33213
.37	1.33147	1.33080	1.33013	1.32946	1.32879	1.32812	1.32746	1.32679	1.32612	1.32545
.38	1.32478	1.32411	1.32344	1.32277	1.32209	1.32142	1.32075	1.32008	1.31941	1.31873
.39	1.31806	1.31739	1.31672	1.31604	1.31537	1.31470	1.31403	1.31336	1.31268	1.31201
.40	1.31134	1.31066	1.30999	1.30931	1.30864	1.30796	1.30729	1.30661	1.30594	1.30526
.41	1.30458	1.30391	1.30323	1.30255	1.30187	1.30120	1.30052	1.29984	1.29916	1.29849
.42	1.29781	1.29713	1.29645	1.29577	1.29509	1.29441	1.29373	1.29305	1.29237	1.29169
.43	1.29101	1.29033	1.28965	1.28897	1.28828	1.28760	1.28692	1.28624	1.28556	1.28487
.44	1.28419	1.28351	1.28282	1.28214	1.28145	1.28077	1.28008	1.27940	1.27872	1.27803
.45	1.27735	1.27666	1.27597	1.27529	1.27460	1.27391	1.27323	1.27254	1.27185	1.27116
.46	1.27048	1.26979	1.26910	1.26841	1.26772	1.26703	1.26634	1.26565	1.26496	1.26427
.47	1.26358	1.26289	1.26220	1.26150	1.26081	1.26012	1.25943	1.25874	1.25804	1.25735
.48	1.25666	1.25596	1.25527	1.25457	1.25388	1.25318	1.25249	1.25179	1.25110	1.25040
.49	1.24971	1.24901	1.24831	1.24762	1.24692	1.24622	1.24552	1.24482	1.24413	1.24343
.50	1.24273	1.24203	1.24133	1.24063	1.23992	1.23922	1.23852	1.23782	1.23712	1.23642
.51	1.23572	1.23502	1.23431	1.23361	1.23290	1.23220	1.23150	1.23079	1.23009	1.22938
.52	1.22868	1.22797	1.22726	1.22656	1.22585	1.22514	1.22444	1.22373	1.22302	1.22231
.53	1.22161	1.22090	1.22019	1.21948	1.21876	1.21805	1.21734	1.21663	1.21592	1.21521
.54	1.21450	1.21379	1.21307	1.21236	1.21165	1.21093	1.21022	1.20950	1.20879	1.20808

Table B-2 (Continued)

f₀/f	0	1	2	3	4	5	6	7	8	9
.55	1.20736	1.20664	1.20593	1.20521	1.20449	1.20377	1.20306	1.20234	1.20162	1.20090
.56	1.20019	1.19946	1.19874	1.19802	1.19730	1.19658	1.19586	1.19514	1.19442	1.19369
.57	1.19297	1.19225	1.19152	1.19080	1.19007	1.18935	1.18862	1.18790	1.18717	1.18645
.58	1.18572	1.18499	1.18426	1.18353	1.18280	1.18208	1.18135	1.18062	1.17989	1.17916
.59	1.17843	1.17770	1.17696	1.17623	1.17550	1.17476	1.17403	1.17330	1.17256	1.17183
.60	1.17110	1.17036	1.16962	1.16888	1.16815	1.16741	1.16667	1.16593	1.16519	1.16446
.61	1.16372	1.16298	1.16224	1.16149	1.16075	1.16001	1.15927	1.15853	1.15778	1.15704
.62	1.15630	1.15555	1.15481	1.15406	1.15331	1.15257	1.15182	1.15107	1.15032	1.14958
.63	1.14883	1.14808	1.14733	1.14658	1.14582	1.14507	1.14432	1.14357	1.14282	1.14207
.64	1.14131	1.14056	1.13980	1.13904	1.13829	1.13753	1.13677	1.13602	1.13526	1.13450
.65	1.13375	1.13298	1.13222	1.13146	1.13070	1.12994	1.12917	1.12841	1.12765	1.12689
.66	1.12613	1.12536	1.12459	1.12382	1.12306	1.12229	1.12152	1.12075	1.11999	1.11922
.67	1.11845	1.11768	1.11690	1.11613	1.11536	1.11459	1.11381	1.11304	1.11227	1.11149
.68	1.11072	1.10994	1.10916	1.10838	1.10760	1.10682	1.10604	1.10526	1.10448	1.10371
.69	1.10293	1.10214	1.10135	1.10057	1.09978	1.09900	1.09821	1.09743	1.09664	1.09586
.70	1.09507	1.09428	1.09349	1.09270	1.09191	1.09112	1.09032	1.08953	1.08874	1.08794
.71	1.08715	1.08635	1.08556	1.08476	1.08396	1.08316	1.08236	1.08156	1.08076	1.07996
.72	1.07916	1.07836	1.07755	1.07675	1.07594	1.07514	1.07433	1.07352	1.07271	1.07191
.73	1.07110	1.07029	1.06947	1.06866	1.06785	1.06704	1.06622	1.06541	1.06459	1.06378
.74	1.06296	1.06214	1.06132	1.06050	1.05968	1.05886	1.05804	1.05721	1.05639	1.05557
.75	1.05474	1.05391	1.05309	1.05226	1.05143	1.05060	1.04977	1.04894	1.04811	1.04727
.76	1.04644	1.04560	1.04477	1.04393	1.04309	1.04226	1.04142	1.04058	1.03973	1.03889
.77	1.03805	1.03721	1.03636	1.03551	1.03467	1.03382	1.03297	1.03212	1.03127	1.03042
.78	1.02957	1.02871	1.02786	1.02700	1.02615	1.02529	1.02443	1.02357	1.02271	1.02185
.79	1.02099	1.02012	1.01925	1.01839	1.01752	1.01666	1.01578	1.01491	1.01404	1.01317
.80	1.01230	1.01142	1.01054	1.00967	1.00879	1.00791	1.00703	1.00615	1.00526	1.00438
.81	1.00350	1.00261	1.00172	1.00083	.99994	.99905	.99816	.99726	.99637	.99547
.82	.99458	.99368	.99278	.99188	.99097	.99007	.98916	.98826	.98735	.98644
.83	.98553	.98462	.98370	.98279	.98187	.98096	.98004	.97912	.97819	.97727
.84	.97635	.97542	.97449	.97356	.97263	.97170	.97077	.96983	.96889	.96796
.85	.96702	.96607	.96513	.96418	.96324	.96229	.96134	.96039	.95944	.95848
.86	.95753	.95657	.95561	.95464	.95368	.95272	.95175	.95078	.94981	.94884
.87	.94787	.94689	.94591	.94493	.94395	.94297	.94198	.94099	.93999	.93900
.88	.93801	.93701	.93601	.93501	.93401	.93301	.93200	.93099	.92998	.92896
.89	.92795	.92693	.92591	.92488	.92386	.92284	.92180	.92077	.91973	.91870
.90	.91766	.91662	.91557	.91452	.91347	.91242	.91136	.91030	.90924	.90818
.91	.90712	.90604	.90496	.90389	.90281	.90174	.90064	.89955	.89846	.89737
.92	.89628	.89518	.89407	.89296	.89185	.89074	.88962	.88850	.88737	.88624
.93	.88511	.88397	.88283	.88168	.88054	.87938	.87823	.87706	.87590	.87473
.94	.87355	.87237	.87119	.87000	.86881	.86761	.86641	.86519	.86398	.86276
.95	.86154	.86031	.85907	.85783	.85658	.85533	.85407	.85280	.85153	.85025
.96	.84896	.84766	.84637	.84505	.84374	.84241	.84108	.83974	.83839	.83703
.97	.83567	.83428	.83290	.83150	.83009	.82867	.82724	.82579	.82434	.82286
.98	.82138	.81988	.81836	.81683	.81528	.81371	.81212	.81051	.80888	.80722
.99	.80553	.80381	.80206	.80027	.79844	.79655	.79460	(refer to table below)		

.9960	0.79460	.9984	0.78954	.9992	0.78765
.9965	0.79360	.9985	0.78931	.9993	0.78739
.9970	0.79257	.9986	0.78908	.9994	0.78714
.9975	0.79152	.9987	0.78885	.9995	0.78688
.9980	0.79044	.9988	0.78862	.9996	0.78661
.9981	0.79022	.9989	0.78838	.9997	0.78633
.9982	0.78999	.9990	0.78814	.9998	0.78605
.9983	0.78977	.9991	0.78789	.9999	0.78575
				1.0000	0.78540

1142 Network Synthesis

Table B–3. The Function $(180/\pi)F_0(\omega/\omega_0)$ for $0 \leq f/f_0 \leq 1$

f/f_0	0	1	2	3	4	5	6	7	8	9
.55	20.823	20.864	20.906	20.947	20.988	21.029	21.070	21.111	21.152	21.193
.56	21.234	21.276	21.317	21.358	21.400	21.441	21.482	21.524	21.565	21.606
.57	21.648	21.689	21.731	21.772	21.814	21.855	21.897	21.939	21.980	22.022
.58	22.063	22.105	22.147	22.189	22.230	22.272	22.314	22.356	22.397	22.439
.59	22.481	22.523	22.565	22.607	22.649	22.691	22.733	22.775	22.817	22.859
.60	22.901	22.943	22.986	23.028	23.070	23.112	23.155	23.197	23.239	23.281
.61	23.324	23.366	23.409	23.451	23.494	23.536	23.579	23.621	23,664	23.706
.62	23.749	23.792	23.834	23.877	23.920	23.963	24.006	24.048	24.091	24.134
.63	24.177	24.220	24.263	24.306	24.349	24.392	24.435	24.478	24.521	24.564
.64	24.607	24.651	24.694	24.738	24.781	24.824	24.868	24.911	24.954	24.998
.65	25.041	25.085	25.128	25.172	25.216	25.259	25.303	25.347	25.390	25.434
.66	25.478	25.522	25.566	25.610	25.654	25.698	25.742	25.786	25.830	25.873
.67	25.917	25.962	26.006	26.050	26.095	26.139	26.183	26.228	26.272	26.316
.68	26.361	26.405	26.450	26.494	26.539	26.584	26.628	26.673	26.718	26.762
.69	26.807	26.852	26.897	26.942	26.987	27.032	27.077	27.122	27.167	27.212
.70	27.257	27.302	27.348	27.393	27.438	27.484	27.529	27.574	27.620	27.665
.71	27.711	27.757	27.802	27.848	27.894	27.939	27.985	28.031	28.077	28.123
.72	28.169	28.215	28.261	28.307	28.353	28.399	28.445	28.492	28.538	28.584
.73	28.631	28.677	28.724	28.770	28.817	28.863	28.910	28.957	29.003	29.050
.74	29.097	29.144	29.191	29.238	29.285	29.332	29.379	29.426	29.473	29.521
.75	29.568	29.615	29.663	29.710	29.757	29.805	29.853	29.900	29.948	29.996
.76	30.043	30.091	30.139	30.187	30.235	30.283	30.331	30.379	30.428	30.476
.77	30.524	30.572	30.621	30.669	30.718	30.766	30.815	30.864	30.913	30.961
.78	31.010	31.059	31.108	31.157	31.206	31.255	31.305	31.354	31.403	31.453
.79	31.502	31.551	31.601	31.651	31.700	31.750	31.800	31.850	31.900	31.950
.80	32.000	32.050	32.100	32.150	32.201	32.251	32.301	32.352	32.403	32.453
.81	32.504	32.555	32.606	32.657	32.707	32.758	32.810	32.861	32.912	32.963
.82	33.015	33.066	33.118	33.170	33.221	33.273	33.325	33.377	33.429	33.481
.83	33.533	33.586	33.638	33.690	33.743	33.795	33.848	33.901	33.954	34.006
.84	34.059	34.113	34.166	34.219	34.272	34.325	34.379	34.433	34.486	34.540
.85	34.594	34.648	34.702	34.756	34.810	34.865	34.919	34.974	35.028	35.083
.86	35.138	35.193	35.248	35.303	35.358	35.413	35.469	35.524	35.580	35.636
.87	35.691	35.747	35.804	35.860	35.916	35.972	36.029	36.086	36.142	36.199
.88	36.256	36.313	36.370	36.428	36.485	36.542	36.600	36.658	36.716	36.774
.89	36.832	36.891	36.949	37.008	37.067	37.125	37.184	37.244	37.303	37.362
.90	37.422	37.482	37.542	37.602	37.662	37.722	37.783	37.844	37.904	37.965
.91	38.026	38.088	38.149	38.211	38.273	38.334	38.397	38.459	38.522	38.584
.92	38.647	38.710	38.773	38.837	38.901	38.965	39.029	39.093	39.157	39.222
.93	39.287	39.352	39.418	39.483	39.549	39.615	39.681	39.748	39.815	39.882
.94	39.949	40.017	40.085	40.153	40.221	40.290	40.359	40.428	40.497	40.567
.95	40.638	40.708	40.779	40.850	40.921	40.993	41.066	41.138	41.211	41.285
.96	41.358	41.432	41.507	41.582	41.657	41.733	41.809	41.887	41.964	42.042
.97	42.120	42.199	42.278	42.359	42.439	42.521	42.603	42.686	42.769	42.854
.98	42.938	43.024	43.111	43.199	43.288	43.378	43.469	43.561	43.655	43.750
.99	43.846	43.945	44.045	44.148	44.253	44.361	44.473	(refer to table below)		

.9960	44.473	.9984	44.763	.9992	44.871
.9965	44.530	.9985	44.776	.9993	44.886
.9970	44.589	.9986	44.789	.9994	44.900
.9975	44.649	.9987	44.802	.9995	44.915
.9980	44.711	.9988	44.816	.9996	44.931
.9981	44.724	.9989	44.829	.9997	44.946
.9982	44.737	.9990	44.843	.9998	44.963
.9983	44.750	.9991	44.857	.9999	44.980
				1.0000	45.000

Table B–3 (Continued)

f/f_0	0	1	2	3	4	5	6	7	8	9
.00	.000	.036	.073	.109	.146	.182	.219	.255	.292	.328
.01	.365	.401	.438	.474	.511	.547	.584	.620	.657	.693
.02	.730	.766	.803	.839	.875	.912	.948	.985	1.021	1.058
.03	1.094	1.131	1.167	1.204	1.240	1.277	1.313	1.350	1.386	1.423
.04	1.459	1.496	1.532	1.569	1.605	1.642	1.678	1.715	1.751	1.788
.05	1.824	1.861	1.897	1.934	1.970	2.007	2.043	2.080	2.116	2.153
.06	2.189	2.226	2.262	2.299	2.335	2.372	2.409	2.445	2.482	2.518
.07	2.555	2.591	2.628	2.664	2.701	2.737	2.774	2.810	2.847	2.884
.08	2.920	2.957	2.993	3.030	3.066	3.103	3.140	3.176	3.213	3.249
.09	3.286	3.322	3.359	3.396	3.432	3.469	3.505	3.542	3.578	3.615
.10	3.652	3.688	3.725	3.762	3.798	3.835	3.871	3.908	3.945	3.981
.11	4.018	4.054	4.091	4.128	4.164	4.201	4.238	4.274	4.311	4.347
.12	4.384	4.421	4.457	4.494	4.531	4.568	4.604	4.641	4.678	4.714
.13	4.751	4.788	4.824	4.861	4.898	4.934	4.971	5.008	5.044	5.081
.14	5.118	5.155	5.191	5.228	5.265	5.302	5.338	5.375	5.412	5.449
.15	5.485	5.522	5.559	5.596	5.632	5.669	5.706	5.743	5.779	5.816
.16	5.853	5.890	5.927	5.963	6.000	6.037	6.074	6.111	6.148	6.184
.17	6.221	6.258	6.295	6.332	6.369	6.405	6.442	6.479	6.516	6.553
.18	6.590	6.626	6.663	6.700	6.737	6.774	6.811	6.848	6.885	6.922
.19	6.959	6.996	7.033	7.070	7.106	7.143	7.180	7.217	7.254	7.291
.20	7.328	7.365	7.402	7.439	7.476	7.513	7.550	7.587	7.624	7.661
.21	7.698	7.735	7.772	7.809	7.846	7.883	7.920	7.957	7.994	8.032
.22	8.069	8.106	8.143	8.180	8.217	8.254	8.291	8.329	8.366	8.403
.23	8.440	8.477	8.514	8.551	8.589	8.626	8.663	8.700	8.737	8.774
.24	8.811	8.849	8.886	8.923	8.960	8.998	9.035	9.072	9.109	9.147
.25	9.184	9.221	9.259	9.296	9.333	9.370	9.408	9.445	9.482	9.519
.26	9.557	9.594	9.631	9.669	9.706	9.744	9.781	9.818	9.856	9.893
.27	9.931	9.968	10.006	10.043	10.080	10.118	10.155	10.193	10.230	10.267
.28	10.305	10.342	10.380	10.417	10.455	10.492	10.530	10.568	10.605	10.643
.29	10.680	10.718	10.755	10.793	10.830	10.868	10.906	10.943	10.981	11.018
.30	11.056	11.094	11.131	11.169	11.207	11.244	11.282	11.320	11.358	11.395
.31	11.433	11.471	11.508	11.546	11.584	11.622	11.659	11.697	11.735	11.772
.32	11.810	11.848	11.886	11.924	11.962	12.000	12.037	12.075	12.113	12.151
.33	12.189	12.227	12.265	12.303	12.341	12.379	12.416	12.454	12.492	12.530
.34	12.568	12.606	12.644	12.682	12.720	12.758	12.797	12.835	12.873	12.911
.35	12.949	12.987	13.025	13.063	13.101	13.139	13.177	13.215	13.254	13.292
.36	13.330	13.368	13.406	13.445	13.483	13.521	13.559	13.598	13.636	13.674
.37	13.713	13.751	13.789	13.827	13.866	13.904	13.942	13.981	14.019	14.057
.38	14.096	14.134	14.173	14.211	14.250	14.288	14.327	14.365	14.404	14.442
.39	14.481	14.519	14.558	14.596	14.635	14.673	14.712	14.750	14.789	14.827
.40	14.866	14.905	14.943	14.982	15.021	15.059	15.098	15.137	15.175	15.214
.41	15.253	15.292	15.330	15.369	15.408	15.447	15.486	15.525	15.563	15.602
.42	15.641	15.680	15.719	15.758	15.797	15.836	15.875	15.914	15.953	15.991
.43	16.030	16.070	16.109	16.148	16.187	16.226	16.265	16.304	16.343	16.382
.44	16.421	16.460	16.500	16.539	16.578	16.617	16.657	16.696	16.735	16.774
.45	16.813	16.853	16.892	16.931	16.971	17.010	17.050	17.089	17.128	17.168
.46	17.207	17.247	17.286	17.326	17.365	17.405	17.444	17.484	17.523	17.563
.47	17.602	17.642	17.681	17.721	17.761	17.800	17.840	17.880	17.919	17.959
.48	17.999	18.039	18.078	18.118	18.158	18.198	18.238	18.277	18.317	18.357
.49	18.397	18.437	18.477	18.517	18.557	18.597	18.637	18.677	18.717	18.757
.50	18.797	18.837	18.877	18.917	18.958	18.998	19.038	19.078	19.118	19.158
.51	19.198	19.239	19.279	19.320	19.360	19.400	19.441	19.481	19.521	19.562
.52	19.602	19.642	19.683	19.723	19.764	19.804	19.845	19.885	19.926	19.967
.53	20.007	20.048	20.088	20.129	20.170	20.211	20.251	20.292	20.333	20.373
.54	20.414	20.455	20.496	20.537	20.578	20.619	20.660	20.701	20.741	20.782

Table B–4.   The Function $(180/\pi)F_0(\omega/\omega_0)$ for $0 \leq f_0/f \leq 1$

f_0/f	0	1	2	3	4	5	6	7	8	9
.00	90.000	89.964	89.927	89.891	89.854	89.818	89.781	89.745	89.708	89.672
.01	89.635	89.599	89.562	89.526	89.489	89.453	89.416	89.380	89.343	89.307
.02	89.270	89.234	89.197	89.161	89.125	89.088	89.052	89.015	88.979	88.942
.03	88.906	88.869	88.833	88.796	88.760	88.723	88.687	88.650	88.614	88.577
.04	88.541	88.504	88.468	88.431	88.395	88.358	88.322	88.285	88.249	88.212
.05	88.176	88.139	88.103	88.066	88.030	87.993	87.957	87.920	87.884	87.847
.06	87.811	87.774	87.738	87.701	87.665	87.628	87.591	87.555	87.518	87.482
.07	87.445	87.409	87.372	87.336	87.299	87.263	87.226	87.190	87.153	87.116
.08	87.080	87.043	87.007	86.970	86.934	86.897	86.860	86.824	86.787	86.751
.09	86.714	86.678	86.641	86.604	86.568	86.531	86.495	86.458	86.422	86.385
.10	86.348	86.312	86.275	86.238	86.202	86.165	86.129	86.092	86.055	86.019
.11	85.982	85.946	85.909	85.872	85.836	85.799	85.762	85.726	85.689	85.653
.12	85.616	85.579	85.543	85.506	85.469	85.432	85.396	85.359	85.322	85.286
.13	85.249	85.212	85.176	85.139	85.102	85.066	85.029	84.992	84.956	84.919
.14	84.882	84.845	84.809	84.772	84.735	84.698	84.662	84.625	84.588	84.551
.15	84.515	84.478	84.441	84.404	84.368	84.331	84.294	84.257	84.221	84.184
.16	84.147	84.110	84.073	84.037	84.000	83.963	83.926	83.889	83.852	83.816
.17	83.779	83.742	83.705	83.668	83.631	83.595	83.558	83.521	83.484	83.447
.18	83.410	83.374	83.337	83.300	83.263	83.226	83.189	83.152	83.115	83.078
.19	83.041	83.004	82.967	82.930	82.894	82.857	82.820	82.783	82.746	82.709
.20	82.672	82.635	82.598	82.561	82.524	82.487	82.450	82.413	82.376	82.339
.21	82.302	82.265	82.228	82.191	82.154	82.117	82.080	82.043	82.006	81.968
.22	81.931	81.894	81.857	81.820	81.783	81.746	81.709	81.671	81.634	81.597
.23	81.560	81.523	81.486	81.449	81.411	81.374	81.337	81.300	81.263	81.226
.24	81.189	81.151	81.114	81.077	81.040	81.002	80.965	80.928	80.891	80.853
.25	80.816	80.779	80.741	80.704	80.667	80.630	80.592	80.555	80.518	80.481
.26	80.443	80.406	80.369	80.331	80.294	80.256	80.219	80.182	80.144	80.107
.27	80.069	80.032	79.994	79.957	79.920	79.882	79.845	79.807	79.770	79.733
.28	79.695	79.658	79.620	79.583	79.545	79.508	79.470	79.432	79.395	79.357
.29	79.320	79.282	79.245	79.207	79.170	79.132	79.094	79.057	79.019	78.982
.30	78.944	78.906	78.869	78.831	78.793	78.756	78.718	78.680	78.642	78.605
.31	78.567	78.529	78.492	78.454	78.416	78.378	78.341	78.303	78.265	78.228
.32	78.190	78.152	78.114	78.076	78.038	78.000	77.963	77.925	77.887	77.849
.33	77.811	77.773	77.735	77.697	77.659	77.621	77.584	77.546	77.508	77.470
.34	77.432	77.394	77.356	77.318	77.280	77.242	77.203	77.165	77.127	77.089
.35	77.051	77.013	76.975	76.937	76.899	76.861	76.823	76.785	76.746	76.708
.36	76.670	76.632	76.594	76.555	76.517	76.479	76.441	76.402	76.364	76.326
.37	76.287	76.249	76.211	76.173	76.134	76.096	76.058	76.019	75.981	75.943
.38	75.904	75.866	75.827	75.789	75.750	75.712	75.673	75.635	75.596	75.558
.39	75.519	75.481	75.442	75.404	75.365	75.327	75.288	75.250	75.211	75.173
.40	75.134	75.095	75.057	75.018	74.979	74.941	74.902	74.863	74.825	74.786
.41	74.747	74.708	74.670	74.631	74.592	74.553	74.514	74.475	74.437	74.398
.42	74.359	74.320	74.281	74.242	74.203	74.164	74.125	74.086	74.047	74.009
.43	73.970	73.930	73.891	73.852	73.813	73.774	73.735	73.696	73.657	73.618
.44	73.579	73.540	73.500	73.461	73.422	73.383	73.343	73.304	73.265	73.226
.45	73.187	73.147	73.108	73.069	73.029	72.990	72.950	72.911	72.872	72.832
.46	72.793	72.753	72.714	72.674	72.635	72.595	72.556	72.516	72.477	72.437
.47	72.398	72.358	72.319	72.279	72.239	72.200	72.160	72.120	72.081	72.041
.48	72.001	71.961	71.922	71.882	71.842	71.802	71.762	71.723	71.683	71.643
.49	71.603	71.563	71.523	71.483	71.443	71.403	71.363	71.323	71.283	71.243
.50	71.203	71.163	71.123	71.083	71.042	71.002	70.962	70.922	70.882	70.842
.51	70.802	70.761	70.721	70.680	70.640	70.600	70.559	70.519	70.479	70.438
.52	70.398	70.358	70.317	70.277	70.236	70.196	70.155	70.115	70.074	70.033
.53	69.993	69.952	69.912	69.871	69.830	69.789	69.749	69.708	69.667	69.627
.54	69.586	69.545	69.504	69.463	69.422	69.381	69.340	69.299	69.259	69.218

Table B-4 (Continued)

f_0/f	0	1	2	3	4	5	6	7	8	9
.55	69.177	69.136	69.094	69.053	69.012	68.971	68.930	68.889	68.848	68.807
.56	68.766	68.724	68.683	68.642	68.600	68.559	68.518	68.476	68.435	68.394
.57	68.352	68.311	68.269	68.228	68.186	68.145	68.103	68.061	68.020	67.978
.58	67.937	67.895	67.853	67.811	67.770	67.728	67.686	67.644	67.603	67.561
.59	67.519	67.477	67.435	67.393	67.351	67.309	67.267	67.225	67.183	67.141
.60	67.099	67.057	67.014	66.972	66.930	66.888	66.845	66.803	66.761	66.719
.61	66.676	66.634	66.591	66.549	66.506	66.464	66.421	66.379	66.336	66.294
.62	66.251	66.208	66.166	66.123	66.080	66.037	65.994	65.952	65.909	65.866
.63	65.823	65.780	65.737	65.694	65.651	65.608	65.565	65.522	65.479	65.436
.64	65.393	65.349	65.306	65.262	65.219	65.176	65.132	65.089	65.046	65.002
.65	64.959	64.915	64.872	64.828	64.784	64.741	64.697	64.653	64.610	64.566
.66	64.522	64.478	64.434	64.390	64.346	64.302	64.258	64.214	64.170	64.127
.67	64.083	64.038	63.994	63.950	63.905	63.861	63.817	63.772	63.728	63.684
.68	63.639	63.595	63.550	63.506	63.461	63.416	63.372	63.327	63.282	63.238
.69	63.193	63.148	63.103	63.058	63.013	62.968	62.923	62.878	62.833	62.788
.70	62.743	62.698	62.652	62.607	62.562	62.516	62.471	62.426	62.380	62.335
.71	62.289	62.243	62.198	62.152	62.106	62.061	62.015	61.969	61.923	61.877
.72	61.831	61.785	61.739	61.693	61.647	61.601	61.555	61.508	61.462	61.416
.73	61.369	61.323	61.276	61.230	61.183	61.137	61.090	61.043	60.997	60.950
.74	60.903	60.856	60.809	60.762	60.715	60.668	60.621	60.574	60.527	60.479
.75	60.432	60.385	60.337	60.290	60.243	60.195	60.147	60.100	60.052	60.004
.76	59.957	59.909	59.861	59.813	59.765	59.717	59.669	59.621	59.572	59.524
.77	59.476	59.428	59.379	59.331	59.282	59.234	59.185	59.136	59.087	59.039
.78	58.990	58.941	58.892	58.843	58.794	58.745	58.695	58.646	58.597	58.547
.79	58.498	58.449	58.399	58.349	58.300	58.250	58.200	58.150	58.100	58.050
.80	58.000	57.950	57.900	57.850	57.799	57.749	57.699	57.648	57.597	57.547
.81	57.496	57.445	57.394	57.343	57.293	57.242	57.190	57.139	57.088	57.037
.82	56.985	56.934	56.882	56.830	56.779	56.727	56.675	56.623	56.571	56.519
.83	56.467	56.414	56.362	56.310	56.257	56.205	56.152	56.099	56.046	55.994
.84	55.941	55.887	55.834	55.781	55.728	55.675	55.621	55.567	55.514	55.460
.85	55.406	55.352	55.298	55.244	55.190	55.135	55.081	55.026	54.972	54.917
.86	54.862	54.807	54.752	54.697	54.642	54.587	54.531	54.476	54.420	54.364
.87	54.309	54.253	54.196	54.140	54.084	54.028	53.971	53.914	53.858	53.801
.88	53.744	53.687	53.630	53.572	53.515	53.458	53.400	53.342	53.284	53.226
.89	53.168	53.109	53.051	52.992	52.933	52.875	52.816	52.756	52.697	52.638
.90	52.578	52.518	52.458	52.398	52.338	52.278	52.217	52.156	52.096	52.035
.91	51.974	51.912	51.851	51.789	51.727	51.666	51.603	51.541	51.478	51.416
.92	51.353	51.290	51.227	51.163	51.099	51.035	50.971	50.907	50.843	50.778
.93	50.713	50.648	50.582	50.517	50.451	50.385	50.319	50.252	50.185	50.118
.94	50.051	49.983	49.915	49.847	49.779	49.710	49.641	49.572	49.503	49.433
.95	49.362	49.292	49.221	49.150	49.079	49.007	48.934	48.862	48.789	48.715
.96	48.642	48.568	48.493	48.418	48.343	48.267	48.191	48.113	48.036	47.958
.97	47.880	47.801	47.722	47.641	47.561	47.479	47.397	47.314	47.231	47.146
.98	47.062	46.976	46.889	46.801	46.712	46.622	46.531	46.439	46.345	46.250
.99	46.154	46.055	45.955	45.852	45.747	45.639	45.527	(refer to table below)		

.9960	45.527	.9984	45.237	.9992	45.129
.9965	45.470	.9985	45.224	.9993	45.114
.9970	45.411	.9986	45.211	.9994	45.100
.9975	45.351	.9987	45.198	.9995	45.085
.9980	45.289	.9988	45.184	.9996	45.069
.9981	45.276	.9989	45.171	.9997	45.054
.9982	45.263	.9990	45.157	.9998	45.037
.9983	45.250	.9991	45.143	.9999	45.020
				1.0000	45.000

figures, resistance and reactance are normalized in value.) The right-hand side of Fig. B–B shows the components of the three-segment approximation, as two S functions (Fig. 8.09–D), i.e. $(-S_1 + S_2)$ forms the approximation. Between these two break points the change in the approximate resistance is 1 (normalized) ohm, so that the magnitude of the (negative) slope of the first S function is

$$k = \frac{\Delta R}{\Delta \ln \omega} = \frac{1}{\ln (2.80/0.36)} = 0.488. \qquad (B\text{–}4)$$

Since the resistance function returns to its original horizontal slope, the slope of the second S function has the value $+0.488$. It remains only to tabulate the values of the functions S_1 and S_2 (the function F_0 read from Tables B–1 and B–2 and multiplied by the appropriate k) at appropriate values of ω, and to sum them with appropriate signs. Table B–5 shows

Table B–5. Calculation of Approximate Reactance from
the Three-Segment Approximation of Fig. B–B

	$\omega_0 = 0.36$			$\omega_0 = 2.80$			
ω	ω/ω_0	F_0	S_1 $= 0.488F_0$	ω/ω_0	F_0	S_2 $= 0.488F_0$	Approximate Reactance $= -S_1 + S_2$
0.1	0.278	0.179	0.088	0.036	0.023	0.011	-0.077
0.2	0.555	0.367	0.179	0.072	0.046	0.022	-0.157
0.3	0.833	0.588	0.287	0.107	0.068	0.033	-0.254
	ω_0/ω						
0.4	0.900	0.918	0.448	0.143	0.091	0.044	-0.404
0.6	0.600	1.171	0.572	0.214	0.137	0.067	-0.505
0.8	0.450	1.277	0.624	0.286	0.184	0.090	-0.534
1.0	0.360	1.338	0.653	0.357	0.231	0.113	-0.540
1.3	0.277	1.393	0.681	0.464	0.303	0.148	-0.533
1.7	0.212	1.435	0.701	0.607	0.405	0.198	-0.503
2.5	0.144	1.479	0.722	0.892	0.645	0.315	-0.407
				ω_0/ω			
3.0	0.120	1.494	0.731	0.933	0.882	0.432	-0.299
5.0	0.072	1.525	0.745	0.560	1.200	0.586	-0.159
10.0	0.036	1.548	0.756	0.280	1.391	0.681	-0.075

this work (for the arithmetic of which a slide rule is sufficient); the resulting approximate reactance is plotted in Fig. B–C (which is a repetition of Fig. 8.09–H), where it may be compared with the exact (minimum) reactance. The maximum error in fitting the datum resistance with the three-segment approximation (Fig. B–B) is about 0.12; the maximum error in the approximate reactance (Fig. B–C) is about 0.07. These errors are of about the same size, which is usual, though no definite rule can be given.

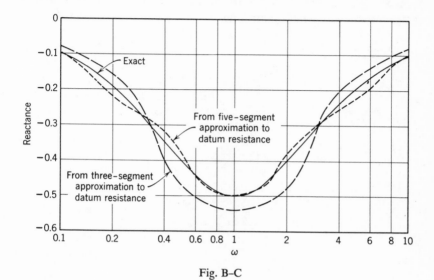

Fig. B–C

The process is repeated in a more accurate version that uses a five-segment approximation, in Fig. B–D. Here the slopes of the four S functions are

$$k_1 = \frac{0.2}{\ln (0.54/0.15)} = 0.156,$$

$$k_2 = \frac{0.6}{\ln (1.85/0.54)} - 0.156 = 0.486 - 0.156 = 0.330,$$

$$k_3 = 0.486 - \frac{0.2}{\ln (6.7/1.85)} = 0.486 - 0.156 = 0.330,$$ (B–5)

$$k_4 = 0.156.$$

It is important to note here that k_2 is not simply the slope of the third segment; this slope must be corrected by subtracting the magnitude of the slope of the second segment, k_1, since *both* $-S_1$ and $-S_2$ make up the approximating function in the region of the third segment. Similar corrections, with appropriate signs, must be applied in the computation of each k, so that the *sum* of the S functions (with appropriate signs) has the slope of the proper segment at every frequency. In the case of the first k there is no correction since no component precedes it; in the case of the last k (here k_4) the value is entirely correction, so that the sum of the S functions will thereafter be zero. Tabulation of the reactance proceeds as in the first example, except that here the contributions of four (rather than two) semi-infinite lines must be combined. The result is

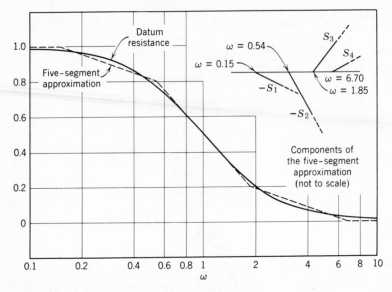

Fig. B–D

shown in Fig. B–C; the maximum errors here are about 0.03, both in fitting the datum resistance and in the approximation to the reactance, both again of about the same size.

With large scale plots and patience, one could even improve on this accuracy, though occasions on which it is necessary to go so far are rare. An example in which the resistance function has more complicated behavior can be found in the original paper (TH 1).

As an illustration of the use of the tables in inverse calculation, we start with the *reactance* (of the same immittance function) as datum, and determine the associated *resistance* with the use of a straight-line approximation and the tables. Figure B–E shows first the datum reactance, then this reactance multiplied by ω (for when the odd-function part is given it must be modified, as discussed in § 8.09), and finally a three-segment linear approximation to the latter. Use of Tables B–1 and B–2, with the additional step of multiplying by $-1/\omega$ (cf. § 8.09) gives the approximate resistance shown in Fig. B–F (together with the exact

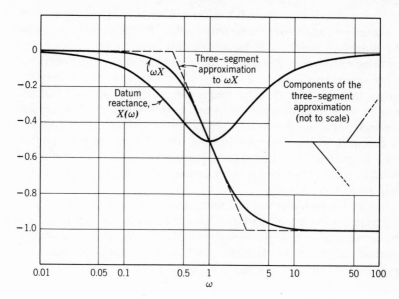

Fig. B-E

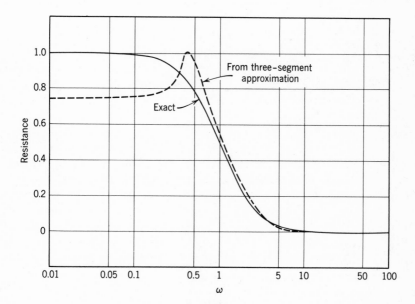

Fig. B-F

resistance). The maximum errors here are about 0.12 in fitting ωX, which is equivalent to about 0.3 in the reactance itself, and about 0.25 in the resistance, again of the same magnitude. Evidently one must consider the weighting factor ω in estimating the error to be expected in the resulting resistance. Better approximations can of course be obtained by using approximations to ωX of more complicated nature. (Comparable errors, though not at the same frequencies, can be expected if multiplication by ω is replaced by division by ω, as it may be.) The resistance obtained has zero value at infinity; to it any constant can be added, and in examples where the approximating resistance comes out negative at some frequencies it will be necessary, for a physically meaningful result, to add a constant sufficient to make the resistance equal to or greater than zero at all frequencies.

Illustrative problems will be found among those of Chapter 8.

Except for the use of the logarithm (or of logarithmic plotting paper), the determination of angle from magnitude, and the inverse computation, proceed in the same fashion. Such computations are particularly important for the two-terminal pair (Volume II).

APPENDIX C

Bibliography

I will teach thee all my original songs, my self-constructed riddles, my own ingenious paradoxes; nay, more, I will reveal to thee the source whence I get them.
— Jack Point

This bibliography is not complete; nevertheless it includes the most important sources and will lead, through the works listed and their bibliographical references, to the bulk of the literature. Some attempt at completeness has been made; relative importance is *not* proportional to length or number of entries.

Book references give city, publisher, and date of publication; journal references give abbreviated journal name, volume number, page numbers, and date; the more concise abbreviations used are

AIEE   American Institute of Electrical Engineers *Transactions*, New York.
BSTJ   *Bell System Technical Journal*, New York.
IEE   Institution of Electrical Engineers *Proceedings*, London.
IRE   Institute of Radio Engineers *Proceedings*, New York.
IRE Trans.   Institute of Radio Engineers *Transactions*, New York.
JMP   *Journal of Mathematics and Physics*, Massachusetts Institute of Technology, Cambridge, Mass.
MIT RLE   Massachusetts Institute of Technology Research Laboratory of Electronics, Cambridge.
NEC   National Electronics Conference *Proceedings*, Chicago.
PIB   Polytechnic Institute of Brooklyn (N.Y.) *Proceedings* of Symposia on Modern Network Synthesis.
RCA   *RCA Review*, Radio Corporation of America, RCA Laboratories Division, Princeton, N.J.
SEL   Electronics Laboratories of Stanford University, Stanford, Calif.

AD 1   Adams, E. P., and R. L. Hippisley, *Smithsonian mathematical formulas and tables of elliptic functions*, Washington, Smithsonian Institution, 1947 (Smithsonian Misc. Coll., vol. 74, no. 1, Pub. 2672).
AD 2   Adler, Harold, Synthesis of a finite two-terminal network whose phase angle is a prescribed function of frequency, with applications to the design of symmetrical networks, S.M. thesis (Elec. Engg.), MIT, 1948.

AL 1   Alsberg, D. A., Universal equalizer chart, *Electronics*, 24:132, 134, Nov. 1951.

AN 1   Anderson, F. B., Seven-league oscillator, *IRE*, 39:881–890, Aug. 1951.

AP 1   Appell, P., and E. Goursat, *Théorie des fonctions algébriques et de leurs intégrales*, Vol. I: *Etude des fonctions analytiques sur une surface de Riemann*, 2nd ed., Paris, Gauthier-Villars, 1929.

BA 5   Bartlett, A. C., Boucherot's constant-current networks and their relation to electric wave filters, *IEE*, 65:373–376, Mar. 1927.

BA 4   Bauer, F. L., Ein direktes Iterationsverfahren zur Hurwitz-Zerlegung eines Polynoms, *Arch. Elekr. Übertr.*, 9:285–290, June 1955 (see also *IRE Trans.*, CT-2:370–371, Dec. 1955).

BA 2   Baum, R. F., A contribution to the approximation problem, *IRE*, 36:863–869, July 1948.

BA 1   Bayard, M., Relations entre les parties réelles et imaginaires des impédances et détermination des impédances en fonction de l'une des parties, *Rev. gén. élec.*, 37:659–664, May 1935.

BA 3   Bayard, M., *Théorie des réseaux de Kirchhoff: régime sinusoïdal et synthèse*, Paris, La Revue d'Optique, 1954.

BE 4   Belgodère, P., and A. Fromageot, Application des propriétés des potentiels newtoniens aux calculs d'amplificateurs de courants modulés en fréquence, *Onde élect.*, 31:18–32, Jan. 1951.

BE 1   Bellman, R., and E. G. Straus, Continued fractions, algebraic functions and the Padé table, *Proc. Natl. Acad. Sci. U.S.*, 35:472–476, Aug. 1949.

BE 3   Bennett, W. R., Transmission Network, U.S. Patent No. 1,849,656 (29 June 1929–15 Mar. 1932).

BE 2   Bernstein, S., *Leçons sur les propriétés extrémales et la meilleure approximation des fonctions analytiques d'une variable réelle*, Paris, Gauthiers-Villars, 1926.

BL 1   Blackburn, J. F. (ed.), *Component Handbook* (Vol. 17 of MIT Rad. Lab. Series), New York, McGraw, 1949.

BO 6   Bode, H. W., A method of impedance correction, *BSTJ*, 9:794–835, Oct. 1930.

BO 1   Bode, H. W., Amplifier, U.S. Patent 2,123,178 (22 June 1937–12 July 1938).

BO 2   Bode, H. W., Relations between attenuation and phase in feedback amplifier design, *BSTJ*, 19:421–454, July 1940.

BO 7   Bode, H. W., Wave transmission network, U.S. Patent 2,342,638 (9 Oct. 1942–29 Feb. 1944).

BO 3   Bode, H. W., *Network Analysis and Feedback Amplifier Design*, New York, Van Nostrand, 1945.

BO 11   Booth, A. D., *Numerical Methods*, New York, Academic Press, and London, Butterworth, 1955.

BO 8   Boothroyd, A. R., E. C. Cherry, and R. Makar, An electrolytic tank for the measurement of steady-state response, transient response and allied properties of networks, *IEE* (I), 96:163–177, May 1949.

BO 9   Boothroyd, A. R., Design of electric wave filters with the aid of the electrolytic tank, *IEE* (IV), 98:65–93, 1951; *IEE* Monograph No. 8, 15 Sept. 1951.

BO 10   Borel, E., *Leçons sur les fonctions de variables réelles et les développements en séries de polynômes*, 2nd ed., Paris, Gauthier-Villars, 1928.

BO 5   Bothwell, F. E., Nyquist diagrams and the Routh-Hurwitz stability criterion, *IRE*, 38:1345–1348, Nov. 1950.

BO 4   Bott, R., and R. J. Duffin, Impedance synthesis without use of transformers, *J. Appl. Phys.*, 20:816, Aug. 1949.

BR 6   Bresler, A. D., On the approximation problem in network synthesis, *IRE*, 40:1724–1728, Dec. 1952.

BR 3   *Encyclopedia Britannica.* Has excellent articles on elliptic functions; equations, theory of, including root finding; etc.

BR 7   Brogle, A. P., Jr., The design of reactive equalizers, *BSTJ*, 28:716–750, Oct. 1949.

BR 5   Brotherton, Manfred, *Capacitors*, New York, Van Nostrand, 1946.

BR 4   Brune, O., Synthesis of a finite two-terminal network whose driving-point impedance is a prescribed function of frequency, Sc.D. thesis (Elec. Engg.), MIT, 1930.

BR 1   Brune, O., Synthesis of a finite two-terminal network whose driving-point impedance is a prescribed function of frequency, *JMP*, 10:191–236, 1931.

BU 1   Butterworth, S., On the theory of filter amplifiers, *Exp. Wireless*, 7:536–541, Oct. 1930.

CA 4   Carson, J. R., Electromagnetic circuit theory and the foundations of electric circuit theory, *BSTJ*, 6:1–17, Jan. 1927.

CA 6   Caryotakis, G. A., *Iterative methods in amplifier interstage synthesis*, Ph.D. thesis (Elec. Engg.), Stanford Univ., 1955; *SEL* Tech. Rpt. 86, 2 May 1955; *IRE Convention Record*, Part 2–Circuit Theory, pp. 9–16, 1955.

CA 1   Cauer, W., Die Verwirklichung von Wechselstromwiderständen vorgeschriebener Frequenzabhängigkeit, *Arch. Elektrotech.*, 17:355–388, 1926.

CA 5   Cauer, W., Das Poissonsche Integral und seine Andwendungen auf die Theorie der linearen Wechselstromschaltungen (Netzwerke), *Elek. Nachr. Tech.*, 17:17–30, Jan. 1940.

CA 2   Cauer, W., *Theorie der linearen Wechselstromschaltungen*, 2nd ed., Berlin, Akademie-Verlag, 1954 (1st ed., Leipzig, Becker und Erler, 1941, and Edwards Bros., Ann Arbor, 1948).

CA 3   Cayley, A., *An Elementary Treatise on Elliptic Functions*, London, Bell, 1895.

CE 1   Cerrillo, M. V., and E. A. Guillemin, Rational fraction expansions for network functions, *PIB*, 1:84–127, Apr. 1952.

CH 1   Chebyshev, P. L., Théorie des mécanismes connus sous le nom de parallelogrammes, in *Oeuvres*, Vol. I, St. Petersburg, 1899.

CH 2   Chebyshev, P. L., Sur les questions de minima qui se rattachent à la representation approximative des fonctions, in *Oeuvres*, Vol. I, St. Petersburg, 1899.

CH 4   Cherry, E. C., Application of the electrolytic tank techniques to network synthesis, *PIB*, 1:140–160, Apr. 1952.

CH 3   Churchill, R. V., *Introduction to Complex Variables and Applications*, New York, McGraw, 1948.

CO 3   Cornock, A. F., and J. M. Hughes, The evaluation of the complex roots of algebraic equations, *Phil. Mag.* (7), 34:314–320, May 1943.

CO 2   Corrington, M. S., Table of the integral $\dfrac{2}{\pi} \displaystyle\int_0^x \dfrac{\tanh^{-1} t}{t}\, dt$, *RCA*, 7:432–437, Sept. 1946.

CO 1   Courant, R., and D. Hilbert, *Methoden der mathematischen Physik*, 2 vols., 2nd ed., Berlin, Springer, 1931; photo. reprod. New York, Interscience Pubs., 1943; English translation as *Methods of Mathematical Physics* (Vol. 1), New York, Interscience Pubs., 1953.

DA 1   Darlington, S., Synthesis of reactance four-poles which produce prescribed insertion loss characteristics, *JMP*, 18:257–353, Sept. 1939.

DA 3   Darlington, S., Realization of a constant phase difference, *BSTJ*, 29:94–104, Jan. 1950.

DA 2   Darlington, S., The potential analogue method of network synthesis, *BSTJ*, 30:315–365, Apr. 1951.

DA 4   Darlington, S., Network synthesis using Tchebycheff polynomial series, *BSTJ*, 31:613–665, July 1952; *PIB*, 1:128–139, Apr. 1952.

DA 5   Darlington, S., A survey of network realization techniques, *IRE Trans.*, CT-2:291–297, Dec. 1955.

DE 2   DeClaris, N., An existence theorem for driving-point impedance functions, *JMP*, 35:83–88, Apr. 1956.

DE 1   Demuth, H. B., An investigation of the iterative synthesis of distributed amplifiers, *SEL* Tech. Rept. 77, 5 Aug. 1954.

DE 3   Desoer, C. A., Network design by first order predistortion technique (to be published by *IRE*).

DI 2   Dietzold, R. L., The isograph—a mechanical root finder, *Bell Labs. Record*, 16:4, Dec. 1937.

DI 1   Dietzold, R. L., Network theory comes of age, *Elec. Eng.*, 67:895–899, Sept. 1948.

DO 2   Doherty, R. E., and E. G. Keller, *Mathematics of Modern Engineering*, New York, Wiley, 1936.

DO 1   Douglas, J. F. H., The reluctance of some irregular magnetic fields, *AIEE*, 34:1067–1134, June 1915.

DR 1   Draper, C. S., W. McKay, and S. Lees, *Instrument Engineering*, Vol. II: *Methods for Associating Mathematical Solutions with Common Forms*, New York, McGraw, 1953.

DU 1   Duffin, R. J., Impedance synthesis without mutual reactance, *AIEE* Conference Paper, 24 Jan. 1951.

DU 2   Duffin, R. J., and E. Keitzer, Formulae relating some equivalent networks, *JMP*, 35:72–82, Apr. 1956.

DW 1   Dwyer, P. S., *Linear Computations*, New York, Wiley, 1951.

FA 1   Fano, R. M., A note on the solution of certain approximation problems in network synthesis, *J. Franklin Inst.*, 249:189–205, Mar. 1950; *MIT RLE* Tech. Rpt. No. 62, 16 Apr. 1948.

FA 2   Farr, H. K., and W. A. Keen, Jr., Improving field analogues through conformal mapping, *AIEE Comm. and Elec.*, 74:395–400, July 1955.

FI 4   Fialkow, A., and I. Gerst, Impedance synthesis without mutual coupling, *Quart. Appl. Math.*, 12:420–422, Jan. 1955.

FI 3   Fialkow, A., and I. Gerst, Impedance synthesis without minimization, *JMP*, 34:160–168, Oct. 1955.

FI 1   Fine, H. B., *College Algebra*, Boston, Ginn, 1904.

FI 2   Finn, D. L., The approximation of arc tangent (ω) with a linear electrical network, *NEC*, 8:435–444, 1952.

FL 1   Fletcher, A., Note on tables of an integral, *Phil. Mag.* (7), 35:16–17, Jan. 1944.

FL 2   Fletcher, A., J. C. P. Miller, and L. Rosenhead, *An Index of Mathematical Tables*, New York, McGraw, and London, Scientific Computing Service, 1946.

FO 3   Forsythe, G. E., Solving algebraic equations can be interesting, *Bull. Am. Math. Soc.*, 59:299–329, 1953.

FO 1   Foster, R. M., A reactance theorem, *BSTJ*, 3:259–267, Apr. 1924.

FO 4   Foster, R. M., Theorems regarding the driving-point impedance of two-mesh circuits, *BSTJ*, 3:651–685, Oct. 1924.

FO 2   Foster, R.M., Geometrical Circuits of Electrical Networks, *AIEE*, 51:309–317, June 1932.

FR 8   Frank, E., On the calculation of the roots of equations, *JMP*, 34:187–197, Oct. 1955.

FR 3   Frank, Philipp, and R. von Mises, *Die Differential- und Integral-gleichungen der Mechanik und Physik*, 2nd ed., Braunschweig, F. Viewig und Sohn, 1930; lithographed by Rosenberg, New York, 1943.

FR 6   Frazer, R. A., and W. J. Duncan, On the numerical solution of equations with complex roots, *Proc. Roy. Soc. London (A)*, 125:68–82, 1929.

FR 1   Frazier, R. H., *Elementary Electric-Circuit Theory*, New York, McGraw, 1945.

FR 7   Friedman, B., Note on approximating zeros of a polynomial, *Comm. on pure and applied math.*, 2:195–208, 1949.

FR 5   Frobenius, G., Ueber Relationen zwischen den Näherungsbrüchen von Potenzreihen, *J. reine angew. Math. (Crelle's J.)*, 90:1–17, 1881.

FR 2   Fry, T. C., The use of continued fractions in the design of electrical networks *Bull. Am. Math. Soc.* (2), 35:463–498, July–Aug. 1929.

FR 4   Fry, T. C., Some numerical methods for locating roots of polynomials, *Quart. Appl. Math.*, 3:89–105, July 1945.

GA 1   Gardner, M. F., and J. L. Barnes, *Transients in Linear Systems*, Vol. I, New York, Wiley, 1942.

GA 2   Gaugain, J-M., Sur les relations qui rattachent la théorie de la distribution statique de l'électricité à la théorie de la propagation, *Ann. chim. et phys.* (3), 64:174–229, 1862.

GE 1   Gewertz, C. M., *Network Synthesis*, Baltimore, Williams and Wilkins, 1933; also *JMP*, 12:1–257, Jan. 1933; also Sc.D. thesis (Elec. Engg.), MIT, 1933.

GI 2   Gilbert, E. O., and E. G. Gilbert, Capacitively coupled field mapper, *Elec. Eng.*, 72:600–605, July 1953.

GI 1   Giordano, A. B., Driving point impedances, *PIB*, 1:21–39, Apr. 1952.

GL 1   Glubrecht, H., Electrical computer for higher-order equations, *Z. angew. Phys.*, 2:1–8, Jan. 1950.

GO 1   Goldfarb, E. M., The potential analogy as applied to a driving point immittance function, Engr. thesis (Elec. Engg.), Stanford Univ. 1952,; also *SEL* Tech. Rpt. No. 56, 1 Dec. 1952.

GR 2   Green, E., *Amplitude-frequency characteristics of ladder networks*, Chelmsford, Essex, Marconi's Wireless Telegraph Co., 1954.

GR 3   Green, E. I., The story of *Q*, *Amer. Scientist*, 43:584–594, Oct. 1955.

GR 1   Grover, F. W., *Inductance Calculations*, New York, Van Nostrand, 1946.

GU 1   Guillemin, E. A., *Communication Networks*, Vol. I, New York, Wiley, 1931.

GU 2   Guillemin, E. A., *Communication Networks*, Vol. II, New York, Wiley, 1935.

GU 6   Guillemin, E. A., The effect of incidental dissipation in filters, *Electronics*, 19:130–135, Oct. 1946.

GU 8   Guillemin, E. A., Synthesis of R-C networks, *JMP*, 28:22–42, Apr. 1949.

GU 3   Guillemin, E. A., *The Mathematics of Circuit Analysis*, Cambridge, Technology Press, and New York, Wiley, 1949.

GU 4   Guillemin, E. A., A summary of modern methods of network synthesis, in *Advances in Electronics*, L. Marton (ed.), Vol. III, pp. 261–303, New York, Academic Press, 1951.

GU 5   Guillemin, E. A., *Introductory Circuit Theory*, New York, Wiley, 1953.

GU 7   Guillemin, E. A., Computational techniques which simplify the correlation between steady-state and transient response of filters and other networks, *NEC*, 9:513–532, 1953.

HA 1　Hancock, H., *Lectures on the Theory of Elliptic Functions*, New York, Wiley, 1910.

HA 2　Hansen, W. W., and O. C. Lundstrom, Experimental determination of impedance functions by the use of an electrolytic tank, *IRE*, 33:528–534, Aug. 1945.

HA 3　Hansen, W. W., On maximum gain-bandwidth product in amplifiers, *J. Appl. Phys.*, 16:528–534, Sept. 1945.

HA 4　Harries, J. H. O., The rubber membrane and resistance paper analogies, *IRE*, 44:236–248, Feb. 1956.

HA 5　Hartree, D. R., *Numerical Analysis*, Oxford, Clarendon Press, 1952.

HE 2　Helman, D., Tchebycheff approximations for amplitude and delay with rational functions, *PIB*, 5:385–402, Apr. 1955.

HE 1　Helmholtz, H. L. F., Ueber einige Gesetz der Vertheilung elektrische Ströme in körperlichen Leitern mit Andwendung auf die theorisch-elektrischen Versuche, *Annal. der Phys. und Ch.*, 89:211–233, 353–377, 1853.

HI 2　Higgins, T. J., An epitomization of the basic theory of the generalized Schwarz-Christoffel transformations as used in applied physics, *J. Appl. Phys.*, 22:365–366, Mar. 1951.

HI 1　Hildebrand, F. B., *Introduction to Numerical Analysis*, New York, McGraw, 1956.

HO 4　Householder, A. A., *Principles of Numerical Analysis*, New York, McGraw, 1953.

HO 1　Howe, G. W. O., The make and break network theorem of Helmholtz, *Wireless Engr.*, 20:319–322, July 1943.

HO 3　Hoyt, R. S., Impedance of smooth lines, and design of simulating networks, *BSTJ*, 2:1–40, Apr. 1923.

HO 2　Hoyt, R. S., Impedance of loaded lines, and design of simulating and compensating networks, *BSTJ*, 3:414–467, July 1924.

HU 3　Hurwitz, A., Ueber die Bedingungen, unter welchen eine Gleichung nur Wurzeln mit negativen reellen Theilen besitzt, *Math. Ann.*, 46:273–284, 1895.

HU 1　Hurwitz, A., and R. Courant, *Vorlesungen über allgemeine Funktionentheorie und elliptische Funktionen*, 3rd ed., Berlin, Springer, 1929; also New York, Interscience Pubs., 1944.

HU 2　Huggins, W. H., A note on frequency transformations for use with the electrolytic tank, *IRE*, 36:421–424, Mar. 1948.

HU 4　Huggins, W. H., The potential analogue in network synthesis and analysis, Cambridge, Mass., Air Force Research Labs. Report No. E5066, Mar. 1951.

IR 1　Institute of Radio Engineers, Standards on Antennas, Modulation Systems, Transmitters, 1948.

JA 1　Jahnke, E., and F. Emde, *Funktionentafeln*, 3rd ed., Leipzig, Teubner, 1938; 4th ed., New York, Dover, 1945.

JA 5　Jackson, D., Fourier series and orthogonal polynomials, *Math. Ass. of America*, 1941.

JA 2　Jacobi, C. G. J., Table of the *q* function, in *Gesammelte Werke*, Borchardt (ed.), Vol. I, pp. 363–368, Berlin, Reimer, 1881.

JA 3　Jacobi, C. G. J., Fundamenta nova theoriae functionum ellipticarum, Königsberg, 1829; also in *Gesammelte Werke*, Vol. I, pp. 49–239, Berlin, Reimer, 1881.

JA 4　James, H. M., N. B. Nichols, and R. S. Phillips, *Theory of Servomechanisms*, New York, McGraw, 1947.

JE 1   Jeans, J., *The Mathematical Theory of Electricity and Magnetism*, 5th ed., Cambridge, Cambridge Univ. Press, 1925.

JE 2   Jeffreys, H., and B. S. Jeffreys, *Methods of Mathematical Physics*, 3rd ed., Cambridge, Cambridge Univ. Press, 1956.

JO 1   Johnson, K. S., *Transmission Circuits for Telephonic Communication*, New York, Van Nostrand, 1925.

KA 1   Kang, C. L., Circuit effects on *Q*, *The Notebook*, Boonton Radio Corp., Boonton, N.J., No. 8, Winter 1956.

KE 1   Kellogg, O. D., *Foundations of Potential Theory*, Berlin, Springer, 1929; also New York, Dover, 1953.

KE 2   Kennelly, A. E., and S. E. Whiting, On an approximate measurement, by electrolytic means, of the electrostatic capacity between a vertical cylinder and the ground, *Elec. World*, 48:1239–1241, 1906.

KI 5   Kim, W. H., *A new method of driving-point function synthesis*, Univ. of Illinois Engg. Expt. Station Tech. Rpt. 1, Apr. 1956.

KI 1   King, L. V., *On the Direct Numerical Calculation of Elliptic Functions and Integrals*, Cambridge, Cambridge Univ. Press, 1924.

KI 2   Kirchhoff, G. R., Über die Auflösung der Gleichungen, auf welche man bei der Untersuchung der linearen Vertheilung galvanischer Ströme geführt wird, *Pogg. Ann.*, Vol. 72, 1847; also in *Gesammelte Abhandlungen*, Leipzig, 1882.

KI 3   Kirchhoff, G. R., Über den Durchgang eines elektrischen Stromes durch eine Ebene, insbesondere durch eine kreisförmige, *Pogg. Ann.*, Vol. 64, 1845; also in *Gesammelte Abhandlungen*, Leipzig, 1882.

KI 4   Kircherberger, P., Über Tschebyscheffsche Annäherungsmethoden, Göttingen, 1902 (inaugural-dissertation); also *Math. Ann.*, 57:509–540, 1903.

KL 2   Klein, F., *Gesammelte mathematische Abhandlungen*, Vol. III, p. 506, Berlin, Springer, 1881 and 1923.

KL 1   Klinkhamer, J. F., Empirical determination of wave-filter transfer functions with specified properties, *Philips Research Rpts.*, 3:60–80, 378–400, 1948; see also 1:250, Aug. 1946.

KN 1   Knopp, Konrad, *Funktionentheorie*, 2nd ed., Berlin, de Gruyter, 1926; *Theory of Functions* (2 vols.), New York, Dover, 1945.

KO 2   Kopal, Z., *Numerical Analysis*, New York, Wiley, 1955.

KO 1   Korman, N. I., A network theorem, *IRE*, 32:710–712, Nov. 1944.

KU 2   Kuh, E. S., Special synthesis techniques for driving point impedance functions, *IRE Trans*, CT-2:302–308, Dec. 1955.

KU 1   Küpfmüller, K., Über Beziehungen zwischen Frequenzcharakteristiken und Augsgleichsvorgängen in linearen Systemen, *Elek. Nachr. Tech.*, 5:18–32, Jan. 1928.

LA 1   Lanczos, C., Trigonometric interpolation of empirical and analytical functions, *JMP*, 17:123–199, 1938.

LA 2   Landon, V. D., Cascade amplifiers with maximal flatness, *RCA*, 5:347–362, Jan. 1941, and 5:481–497, Apr. 1941.

LA 3   Lane, C. E., Phase distortion in telephone apparatus, *BSTJ*, 9:493–521, July 1930.

LA 4   La Vallée Poussin, C. de, *Leçons sur l'approximation des fonctions d'une variable réelle*, Paris, Gauthier-Villars, 1919.

LE 1   Lee, Y. W., Synthesis of electric networks by means of the Fourier transforms of Laguerre's functions, Sc.D. thesis (Elec. Engg.), MIT, 1930; also *JMP*, 11:83–113, June 1932.

LE 2 Leroy, R., Sur la synthèse des dipôles par une méthode de récurrence, *Câbles & Transm.*, 2:101–110, Apr. 1948.

LI 2 Linvill, J. G., An experimental approach to the approximation problem for driving-point and transfer functions, S.M. thesis (Elec. Engg.), MIT, 1945.

LI 1 Linvill, J. G., The selection of network functions to approximate prescribed frequency characteristics, part of Sc.D. thesis, MIT (Elec. Engg.), 1950; pub. as *MIT RLE* Tech. Rpt. 145, 14 Mar. 1950; The approximation with rational functions of prescribed magnitude and phase characteristics, *IRE*, 40:711–721, June 1952.

LO 1 Löfgren, L., Analog computer for the roots of algebraic equations, *IRE*, 41:907–913, July 1953.

LU 1 Lucas, F., A series of papers in *Compt. rend.* (Paris), 1888–1890: 106:121–122, 195–197, 268–270, 587–589, 645–648, 1072–1074; 111:965–967.

LU 2 Lucas, F., Détermination électrique des racines réelles et imaginaires de la dérivée d'un polynôme quelconque, *Compt. rend.* (Paris), 106:195–197, 1888.

LU 3 Luke, Y. L., and D. Ufford, On the roots of algebraic equations, *JMP*, 30:94–101, 1951.

LY 1 Lynch, W. A., The role played by derivative adjustment in broadband amplifier design, *PIB*, 1:192–201, Apr. 1952.

MA5 MacColl, L. A., *Fundamental Theory of Servomechanisms*, New York, Van Nostrand, 1945.

MA 1 MacRobert, T. M., *Functions of a Complex Variable*, 3rd ed., London, Macmillan, 1947.

MA 2 Madelung, E., *Die mathematischen Hilfsmittel des Physisikers*, 3rd ed., New York, Dover, 1943.

MA 7 Makar, R., A. R. Boothroyd, and E. C. Cherry, An electrolytic tank for exploring potential field distributions, *Nature*, 161:845–846, 29 May 1948.

MA 11 Malavard, L., and J. Tissot, Sur un méthode utilisant le bassin électrique pour la détermination des racines d'une équation algébrique, *Compt. rend.* (Paris), 227:620–622, 1948.

MA 13 Malavard, L., La méthode d'analogie rhéoélectrique, ses possibilités et ses tendances, *Onde élect*., 36:762–769, Aug.–Sept. 1956; 36:829–837, Oct. 1956; 36:1046–1052, Dec. 1956.

MA 10 Marshall, B. O., Jr., The electronic isograph for roots of polynomials, *J. Appl. Phys.*, 21:307–312, Apr. 1950.

MA 3 Mass. Inst. of Tech. Dept. of Elec. Engg., *Electric Circuits*, Cambridge, Technology Press, and New York, Wiley, 1940.

MA 4 Mass. Inst. of Tech. Dept. of Elec. Engg., *Magnetic Circuits and Transformers*, Cambridge, Technology Press, and New York, Wiley, 1943.

MA 8 Matthaei, G. L., Network synthesis for a maximally-flat phase-difference characteristic, Engr. thesis (Elec. Engg.), Stanford Univ., 1950; *SEL* Tech. Rpt. 2, 31 Oct. 1950.

MA 9 Matthaei, G. L., A general method for synthesis of filter transfer functions as applied to *L-C* and *R-C* filter examples, Ph.D. thesis (Elec. Engg.), Stanford Univ., 1951; *SEL* Tech. Rpt. 39, 31 Aug. 1951; Filter transfer function synthesis, *IRE*, 41:377–382, Mar. 1953; Conformal mapping for filter transfer function synthesis, *IRE*, 41:1658–1664, Nov. 1953, and 42:1319, Aug. 1954.

MA 12 Matthaei, G. L., Some techniques for network synthesis, *IRE Convention Record*, Vol. 2, 1954, Part 2–Circuit theory, pp. 77–85; *IRE*, 42:1126–1137, July 1954; *IRE*, 43:625–626, May 1955.

MA 6   Mayer, H. F., Ueber die Dämpfung von Siebketten im Durchlässigkeitsbereich, *Elec. Nachr. Tech.*, 2:335–338, 1925.

MC 1   McLachlan, N. W., *Modern Operational Calculus*, London, Macmillan, 1948.

ME 1   Mead, S. P., Phase distortion and phase distortion correction, *BSTJ*, 7:195–224, Apr. 1928.

ME 2   Mersman, W. A., Evaluation of an integral occurring in servomechanisms, *Pacific J. Math.*, 2:627–632, Dec. 1952.

MI 4   Milne, W. E., *Numerical Calculus*, Princeton, N.J., Princeton Univ. Press, 1949.

MI 2   Milne-Thompson, L. M., *Jacobian Elliptic Function Tables*, New York, Dover, 1950.

MI 5   Mineur, H., *Techniques de calcul numérique*, Paris, Librarie Polytechnique Ch. Beranger, Paris, 1952.

MI 1   Ming, N-T., Verwirchklichung von linearen Zweipolschaltungen vorgeschriebener Frequenzabhängigkeit unter Berücksichtigung der Verluste von Spulen und Kondensatoren, *Arch. Elektrotech.*, 39:359–387, Apr. 1949.

MI 3   Miyata, F., A new system of two-terminal network synthesis, *J. Inst. Elec. Comm. Engrs. of Japan*, 35:211–218, May 1952; *IRE Trans.*, CT-2:297–302, Dec. 1955.

MO 2   Mole, J. H., *Filter Design Data for Communication Engineers*, New York, Wiley, and London, E. and F. N. Spon, 1952.

MO 4   Moore, A. D., The potential analogy in network synthesis, S.M. thesis (Elec. Engg.), Queen's Univ., Kingston, Ont., Canada, 1949.

MO 3   Moore, A. D., Synthesis of distributed amplifiers for prescribed amplitude response, Ph.D. thesis (Elec. Engg.), Stanford Univ.; *SEL* Tech. Rpt. 53, 1 Sept. 1952.

MO 5   Moore, W. C., The nature of *Q*, *The Notebook*, Boonton Radio Corp., Boonton, N.J., No. 1, Spring 1954.

MO 1   Morris, L. H., G. H. Lovell, and F. R. Dickinson, The L3 coaxial system: amplifiers, *BSTJ*, 32:879–914, July 1953.

MU 1   Murakami, T., and M. S. Corrington, Relation between amplitude and phase in electrical networks, *RCA*, 9:602–631, Dec. 1948.

NI 2   Nielsen, K. L., *Methods in Numerical Analysis*, New York, Macmillan, 1956.

NI 1   Nijenhuis, W., Impedance synthesis distributing available loss in the reactance elements, *Philips Research Rpts.*, 5:288–302, Aug. 1950.

NO 3   Norton, E. L., Filtering Circuits, U.S. Patent 1,788,538 (16 Apr. 1929–13 Jan. 1931).

NO 2   Norton, E. L., Constant resistance networks with applications to filter groups, *BSTJ*, 16:178–193, Apr. 1937.

OB 1   Oberhettinger, F., and W. Magnus, *Anwendung der elliptischen Funktionen in Physik und Technik*, Berlin, Springer, 1949.

OL 1   Olver, F. W. J., The evaluation of zeros of high-degree polynomials, *Trans. Roy. Soc. (London) (A)*, 244:385–415, 1952.

OR 1   Orchard, H. J., Synthesis of wide-band two-phase networks, *Wireless Engr.*, 27:72–81, Mar. 1950.

OR 2   Orchard, H. J., The design of network functions to have a constant phase-angle, P.O. (Great Britain) Engg. Dept. Res. Rpt. 13183, July 1950.

PA 3   Padé, H. E., Sur la réprésentation approchée d'une fonction par des fractions rationnelles, *Ann. sci. Éc. norm. sup.*, Paris (3), 9:1–93 (suppl.), 1892.

PA 1   Pantell, R. H., New methods of driving-point and transfer-function synthesis, Ph.D. thesis (Elec. Engg.), Stanford Univ., 1954; *IRE*, 42:861, May 1954; *SEL* Tech. Rpt. 76, 19 July 1954.

PA 4   Pappas, N. L., Ph.D. thesis (Elec. Engg.), Stanford Univ., 1957.

PA 2   Payne, E. B., Impedance correction of wave filters, *BSTJ*, 9:770–793, Oct. 1930.

PE 2   Pender, H., and K. McIlwain, *Electrical Engineers' Handbook*, Vol. II: *Electric Communication and Electronics*, 4th ed., New York, Wiley, 1950.

PE 1   Perron, O., *Die Lehre von den Kettenbrüchen*, 2nd ed., Leipzig, Teubner, and New York, Chelsea Pub. Co., 1929; 3rd ed., Stuttgart, Teubner, 1954.

PH 1   Phillips, E. G., *Functions of a Complex Variable*, New York, Interscience Pubs., 1947; 7th ed., Edinburgh, Oliver and Boyd, 1951.

PO 1   Powell, E. O., An integral related to the radiation integrals, *Phil. Mag.* (7), 34:600–607, Sept. 1943.

RA 1   Ragan, G. L., *Microwave Transmission Circuits* (Vol. 9 of MIT Rad. Lab. Series), New York, McGraw, 1948.

RA 2   Ramo, S., and J. R. Whinnery, *Fields and Waves in Modern Radio*, 2nd ed., New York, Wiley, 1953.

RE 2   Redheffer, R. M., Design of a circuit to approximate a prescribed amplitude and phase, *JMP*, 28:140–147, 1949; *MIT RLE* Tech. Rpt. 54, 24 Nov. 1947.

RE 1   Reed, M. B., and G. B. Reed, *Mathematical Methods in Electrical Engineering*, New York, Harper, 1951.

RE 5   Reza, F. M., A generalization of Foster's and Cauer's theorems, *IRE Convention Record*, Part 2, pp. 22–25, 1955; *Compt. Rend.* (Paris), 237:429–430, 1953.

RE 3   Reza, F. M., A supplement to the Brune synthesis, *AIEE Comm. and Elec.*, 74:85–90, Mar. 1955; *IRE Trans.*, CT-1:71–75, Mar. 1954; *IRE*, 42:349, Jan. 1954; *JMP*, 33:194–198, July 1954; *J. Appl. Phys.*, 25:807–808, June 1954; *IRE*, 42:1321, Aug. 1954.

RE 4   Reza, F. M., *RLC* canonic forms, *J. Appl. Phys.*, 25:297–301, Mar. 1954.

RI 2   Richards, P. I., A special class of functions with positive real part in a half plane, *Duke Math. J.*, 14:777–786, 1947.

RI 3   Richards, P. I., General impedance function theory, *Quart. Appl. Math.*, 6:21–29, 1948.

RI 4   Richardson, A. S., Jr., The remainder theorem and its application to operational calculus techniques, *IRE*, 38:1336–1339, Nov. 1950, and 39:287, Mar. 1951.

RI 1   Richardson, D. E., *Electrical Network Calculations: Tabular Methods of Solution*, New York, Van Nostrand, 1946.

RO 1   Rothe, R., *et al.*, *Theory of Functions as Applied to Engineering Problems*, Cambridge, Mass., Technology Press, 1933.

RO 3   Rounds, P. W., and G. L. Lakin, Equalization of cables for local television transmission, *BSTJ*, 34:713–738, 1955.

RO 2   Routh, E. J., *The Advanced Part of a Treatise on the Dynamics of a System of Rigid Bodies*, Macmillan, 1884; also numerous later editions, through: New York, Stechert, 1945.

RU 1   Russell, A., *A Treatise on the Theory of Alternating Currents*, Vol. I, 2nd ed., Cambridge, Cambridge Univ. Press, 1914.

RY 1   Ryder, J. D., *Networks, Lines and Fields*, New York, Prentice-Hall, 1949.

SA 4   Salvadori, M. G., and M. L. Baron, *Numerical Methods in Engineering*, New York, Prentice-Hall, 1952.

SA 1   Samuelson, P. A., Iterative computation of complex roots, *JMP*, 28:259–267, Jan. 1950.

SA 3 Saraga, W., The design of wide-band phase splitting networks, *IRE,* 38:754–770, July 1950.

SA 2 Saraga, W., Approximations in network design, *Wireless Engr.,* 29:208–281, Oct. 1952.

SC 6 Scarborough, J. B., *Numerical Mathematical Analysis,* 3rd ed., Baltimore, Johns Hopkins Press, and London, Oxford Univ. Press, 1955.

SC 1 Schelkunoff, S. A., *Electromagnetic Waves,* New York, Van Nostrand, 1943.

SC 2 Schelkunoff, S. A., *Applied Mathematics for Engineers and Scientists,* New York, Van Nostrand, 1948.

SC 3 Scott, R. E., An analog device for solving the approximation problem of network synthesis, *MIT RLE* Tech. Rpt. 137, 8 June 1950.

SC 4 Scott, R. E., Network synthesis by the use of potential analogs, *IRE,* 40:970–973, Aug. 1952.

SC 5 Scott, R. E., Potential analog methods of solving the approximation problem of network synthesis, *NEC,* 9:543–553, 1953.

SC 7 Scott, R. E., Potential analogs in network synthesis, *IRE Convention Record,* Part 2–Circuit Theory, pp. 2–8, 1955.

SE 2 Seely, S., W. R. LePage, and N. Balabanian, The role of analytic continuation in network synthesis, *NEC,* 9:684–689, 1953.

SE 1 Selgin, P. J., *Electrical Transmission in Steady State,* New York, McGraw, 1946.

SH 4 Shannon, C. E., and A. J. Rack, Decoding network *in* (p. 36) An experimental multichannel pulse code modulation system of toll quality by L. A. Meacham and E. Peterson, *BSTJ,* 27:1–43, Jan. 1948.

SH 3 Sharp, H. S., A comparison of methods for evaluating the complex roots of quartic equations, *JMP,* 20:243–258, 1941.

SH 2 Sharpe, C. B., A general Tchebycheff rational function, *IRE,* 42:454–457, Feb. 1954.

SH 1 Shea, T. E., *Transmission Networks and Wave Filters,* New York, Van Nostrand, 1929.

SO 1 Soroka, W. W., *Analog Methods in Computation and Simulation,* New York, McGraw, 1954.

SP 1 Spenceley, G. W., and R. M. Spenceley, Smithsonian elliptic function tables, Washington, Smithsonian Institution, 1947 (Smithsonian Misc. Col., Vol. 109, Pub. 3863).

ST 1 Starr, A. T., *Electric Circuits and Wave Filters,* 2nd ed., London, Pitman, 1948.

ST 3 Stewart, J. L., *Circuit Theory and Design,* New York, Wiley, 1956.

ST 6 Stone, H. A., Jr., Ferrite core inductors, *BSTJ,* 32:265–291, Mar. 1953.

ST 2 Stone, W. M., A form of Newton's method with cubic convergence, *Quart. Appl. Math.,* 11:118–119, Apr. 1953.

ST 5 Storer, J. E., Relationship between the Bott–Duffin and Pantell impedance synthesis, *IRE,* 42:1451, Sept. 1954.

ST 4 Stulen, F. B., and F. G. Lehman, A method of solving inhomogeneous linear simultaneous equations, *JMP,* 35:123–126, Apr. 1956.

SY 1 Synge, J. L., The fundamental theorem of electrical networks, *Quart. Appl. Math.,* 9:113–127, July 1951.

TE 2 Tellegen, B. D. H., The synthesis of passive two-poles by means of networks containing gyrators, *Philips Research Rpts,* 4:31–37, Feb. 1949.

TE 1 Terman, F. E., *Radio Engineers' Handbook,* New York, McGraw, 1943.

TH 2 Thévenin, L., Sur un nouveau théoreme d'électricité dynamique, *Compt. rend.* (Paris), 97:159–161, 1883.

TH 1   Thomas, D. E., Tables of phase associated with a semi-infinite unit slope of attenuation, *BSTJ*, 26:870–899, Oct. 1947.

TH 4   Thomas, D. E., Tables of phase of a semi-infinite unit attenuation slope, *BSTJ*, 35:747–749, May 1956, and Monograph 2550 of Bell Telephone System Tech. Pubs., New York, Bell Tel. Labs. and Amer. Tel. and Tel. Co., 1956.

TH 3   Thomson, W. E., Delay networks having maximally flat frequency characteristics, *IEE* (III), 96:487–490, Nov. 1949; Networks with maximally flat delay, *Wireless Engr.*, 29:256–263, Oct. 1952, and 29:309, Nov. 1952.

TR 3   Trautman, D. L., Jr., Amplifier synthesis through conformal representation, Ph.D. thesis (Elec. Engg.), Stanford Univ., 1949; Maximally flat amplifiers of arbitrary bandwidth and coupling, *SEL* Tech. Rpt. 41, 1 Feb. 1952.

TR 4   Trautman, D. L., Jr., Equal-ripple bandpass amplifiers, Univ. of Calif. at Los Angeles Tech. Rpt. 51–9, Aug. 1951.

TR 2   Trautman, D. L., Jr., The application of conformal mapping to the synthesis of bandpass networks, *PIB*, 1:179–192, Apr. 1952.

TR 1   Truxal, J. G., *Control System Synthesis*, New York, McGraw, 1955.

TU 1   Turnbull, H. W., *Theory of Equations*, London, Oliver and Boyd, and New York, Interscience Pubs., 1947.

TU 2   Tuttle, D. F., Jr., A problem in synthesis, *IRE Trans*, PGCT-2:6–18, Dec. 1953.

US 1   Uspensky, J. V., *Theory of Equations*, New York, McGraw, 1948.

VA 1   Valley, G. E., and H. Wallman, *Vacuum Tube Amplifiers* (Vol. 18 in MIT Rad. Lab. Series), New York, McGraw, 1948.

VA 2   van der Pol, B., and T. J. Weijers, Tchebycheff polynomials and their relation to circular functions, Bessel functions and Lissajous figures, *Physica*, 1:78–96, and 1:481–496, 1934.

VA 6   Van Valkenburg, M. E., *Network Analysis*, Englewood Cliffs, N.J., Prentice-Hall, 1955.

VA 5   Van Valkenburg, M. E., Special case of a bridge equivalent of Brune networks, *IRE*, 44:1621, Nov. 1956; *IRE*, 45:20, Jan. 1957.

VA 3   Van Vleck, J. H., The relation between absorption and the frequency dependence of refraction, Cambridge, Mass., *MIT* Rad. Lab. Rpt. 735, 28 May 1945.

VA 4   Van Wynen, K. G., Design of two-terminal balancing networks, *BSTJ*, 22:278–292, Oct. 1943.

VI 1   Ville, J., Réseaux réactifs en échelle, *Câbles & Transm.*, 3:159–176, Apr. 1949.

VO 1   von Sanden, H., *Praktische Analysis*, Leipzig, Teubner, 1914; Eng. transl. by H. Levy, New York, Dutton, and London, Methuen, 1923.

WA 1   Wall, H. S., Polynomials whose zeros have negative real parts, *Am. Math. Mon.*, 52:308–322, 1945.

WA 3   Wall, H. S., A modification of Newton's method, *Am. Math. Mon.*, 55:90–94, Feb. 1948.

WA 2   Wall, H. S., *Analytic Theory of Continued Fractions*, New York, Van Nostrand, 1948.

WE 5   Weaver, D. K., Jr., Constant-phase-difference networks and their application to filters, Engr. thesis (Elec. Engg.), Stanford Univ., 1950; *SEL* Tech. Rpt. 1, 28 Oct. 1950.

WE 6   Weaver, D. K., Jr., Design of *RC* wide-band 90-degree phase-difference network, *IRE*, 42:671–676, Apr. 1954.

WE 4   Weber, E., *Electromagnetic Fields: Theory and Application*, Vol. I: *Mapping of Fields*, New York, Wiley, 1950.

WE 7   Weber, E., *Linear Transient Analysis*, Vol. I, New York, Wiley, 1954.

WE 9   Weinberg, L., A general *RLC* synthesis procedure, *IRE Convention Record*, Part 5–Circuit Theory, pp. 2–16, 1953.

WE 3   Welsby, V. G., *The Theory and Design of Inductance Coils*, London, Macdonald and Co., 1950.

WE 1   Wentworth, G. A., *A College Algebra*, Boston, Ginn, 1902.

WE 8   Westcott, J. H., Driving-point impedance synthesis using maximally lossy elements, *PIB*, 5:63–78, 1955.

WE 2   Weston, J. D., Unification of linear network theory, *J. Inst. Radio Engrs.* (*Brit.*), 6:4–14, Jan.–Feb. 1946.

WH 2   Wheeler, H. A., Wide-band amplifiers for television, *IRE*, 27:429–438, July 1939; *also* Potential Analog for Frequency Selectors with Oscillating Peaks, Wheeler Monograph No. 15, Great Neck, N.Y., 1951.

WH 4   Wheeler, H. A., The potential analog applied to the synthesis of stagger-tuned filters, *IRE Trans.*, CT-2:86–96, Mar. 1955.

WH 3   Whittaker, E. T., and G. Robinson, *The Calculus of Observations*, London, Blackie, and New York, Van Nostrand, 1924; 3rd ed., London, Blackie, 1940.

WH 1   Whittaker, E. T., and G. N. Watson, *A Course of Modern Analysis*, New York, Macmillan (Amer. ed.), 1948.

WI 1   Wiener, N., *The Extrapolation, Interpolation and Smoothing of Stationary Time Series*, Cambridge, Mass., Technology Press, and New York, Wiley, 1949.

WI 2   Wigge, H., Einige Folgerungen aus dem Ableitungssatz von Helmholtz (Theorem von Thévenin), *Arch. Elektrotech.*, 30:754–759, Nov. 1936.

WI 3   Willers, F. A., *Methoden der praktischen Analysis*, Eng. transl. by R. T. Beyer as *Practical Analysis*, New York, Dover, 1948.

WI 4   Winkler, S., The approximation problem of network synthesis, *IRE Trans.*, CT-1:5–20, Sept. 1954.

WO 1   Wood, F. S., *Advanced Calculus*, Boston, Ginn, 1934.

XA 1   Xavier, A., *Théorie des approximations numériques et du calcul abrégé*, Paris, Gauthier-Villars, 1909.

ZO 1   Zobel, O. J., Distortion correction in electrical circuits with constant resistance recurrent networks, *BSTJ*, 7:438–534, July 1928.

ZU 1   Zurmühl, R., *Praktische Mathematik für Ingenieure und Physiker*, 2nd ed., Berlin, Springer, 1957.

Index

Accuracy in computation, 277, 754, 1071, 1103, 1110
Active network, 9
Addition of constant, *see* Constant
Admittance, 17
Admittance function, driving-point, 109, 142
Alice, 867
American Tel. & Tel. Co., 1137
Amplifier; *see also* Gain, Interstage networks, Operational amplifier
  vacuum-tube, 1043
    with approximately constant gain, 1086
Amplifier networks, 792
Analogy, 832
Analytic, *see* Function
Analytic continuation, 45, 411
Angle of immittance function, 438
  see also Real-imaginary part relations
  approximate calculation from magnitude, 407
  approximately constant, 347, 1006
  contribution of zero (pole) in one half plane, 440
  in terms of magnitude, 398
  potential analog for, 849
  properties required, 458
  use in approximating magnitude, 1041–1042
Anomalies in Taylor approximation, 794
Anti-Hurwitz, 412
Approximation; *see also* Taylor approximation, Chebyshev approximation, Error, Trial and error methods
  and realization, sequence of, 974
  band, 745

Approximation, general statements, 802
  number of parameters and quality of, 958
  of constant, using potential analogy, 896
  of nonconstant functions, 1010
  problem, 456
  quality of, 745, 958, 981, 984, 990, 1035
  with pole-zero pairs, 828
  with straight-line segments, 829
Ascending branch, 49

Balancing networks, 685, 811
Bandwidth, 713
  see also Gain
Baum, R. F., 829
Bayard, M., 382, 1126, 1128
Bennett, W. R., 792
Bilinear transformation, 72, 117–118, 483
  applications, 188
Binomial coefficients, 797, 817
Binomial theorem, 763
Bode, H. W., 382, 409, 430, 458
Bott, R., 607
Bott-Duffin partition, 632
Bott-Duffin realization process, 615–619, 623, 631, 641
Branch, 10
  of multivalued function, 909
  positive-real, 148, 910
Branch cut, 148, 150–151, 867, 912
Branch point, 38, 151, 171
  action in changing real (imaginary) character, 943
Bresler, A. D., 828

Bridged-T networks, 90, 654, 680, 1052
    use in general transmission function
        realization, 696–697
Brune, O., 108, 121, 409, 430, 504, 587,
    607
Brune cycle, formulas, 532
Brune network, 550
Brune process, 550, 584
    based on real zeros of even part, 547
    dual form, 536
    formulas, 598, 601
    standard, 534, 536
    variations in, 534, 536, 537, 599, 602–
        603
Building out of immittance, 652, 684
Butterworth, S., 792

Cable, coaxial, 693, 1062
Cable-pair immittance, 697, 812
Calculations, precision appropriate in,
    see Accuracy in computation
Canonic form, 271
    R-C, 340
    R-L, 353
Canonic realizations, 293, 298, 360
Capacitance, limitations due to, 964
    parasitic, 1080, 1095
Capacitor, 7, 706
Cauchy-Riemann equations, 37, 41, 832
Cauchy's integral formula, 43
Cauchy's integral law, 42
Cauchy's residue theorem, 60
Cauchy's theorem, 42
Cauer, W., 315, 568
Cauer canonic form, 271–273, 276
Center of charge, 858
Change from real to imaginary char-
    acter, 943
Charge, center of, 858
    filament of, 834
    loop, 12
    total equal to zero, 845
    units of, 838
    use of half units of, 987 ff.
Charges, as zeros or poles, 845
    motion of, 903, 948, 954, 962, 1024
Charts, use in design, 691, 695, 1058
Chebyshev, P. L., 782, 784, 1016

Chebyshev approximation, 784, 883,
    1009
    see also Error ripple
    limiting case as Taylor approxima-
        tion, 1034
    number of zeros of error in, 952, 955
    of a constant, 951
    of nonconstant functions, 1049, 1050
    relation to Taylor approximation,
        1018, 1030, 1032
    simultaneously in two bands, 926
    Taylor approximation as limit of, 951,
        957
Chebyshev polynomial, 895, 896, 980,
    1016–1017, 1044
Chebyshev rational functions, 895–896
Circuit, 9
Circular trigonometric functions, 81–82,
    87
Coaxial cable, *see* Cable, coaxial
Coil, *see* Inductor
Complex-number representation, 24
    see also Phasor
Complex potential function, 836
    as mapping function, 872
    principal value of, 863
Component, 10
Computation, accuracy required, *see*
    Accuracy in computation
Computers, 1011
Condenser, *see* Capacitor
Conductance, 18
    see also Even part
    approximate calculation of, from
        susceptance, 407
    in terms of susceptance, formulas,
        385, 399
    of *R-C* networks, 327
    of *R-L* networks, 354
    properties required, 457
    removal, 339
Conductor, 833, 851, 1009
Conformality, 72
Conjugate, 34
    function of also conjugate, 35
    functions, 1012
    pairs, 167
Constancy of elements, 1, 6, 703
Constant, addition of, effect, 435–436

Constant, addition of, in approximation, 1025, 1031–1032
  approximation of, 343, 1009
    using potential analogy, 896
    with prescribed zeros, 925, 949
  Chebyshev approximation of, 895, 951
  Taylor approximation of, 791, 795, 954
Constant-resistance networks, 654, 675–677
  use in general transmission function realization, 696–697
Constraints, effect of quality of approximation, 958
  in Taylor approximation, 790, 794, 795
Continued-fraction expansion, 191, 262, 270, 329, 335, 353, 665
  as realization device, 966–967
Continuity, 35
Contour of integration, deformation of, 42
Cosine function, infinite-product expansion of, 85
Coupling coefficient, 9
Critical frequencies, in L-C networks, 253
  in R-C networks, 308
  in R-L networks, 352
Cut and try, see Trial and error methods
Cutting and sewing, 938
Cylinder, mapping on, 931

Darlington, S., 550, 568, 582, 587, 607
Darlington's theorem, 583
Dasher, B. J., 365
Davis, W. R., 492
Decibel, 83, 692
Decomposition, see Partition
Delay, 683
  networks, 695–696
Denormalization, 277
Derivative, independence of direction, 36–37
Descending branch, 49
Design, see Synthesis
Desoer, C. A., 732

Determination of immittance from one part, see Immittance function
Differentiation of numerator and denominator, results of, 1014
Dissipation, correction for, 1060, 1097
  effect of, 1025, 1029
  uniform, 707
Dissipation constant, 707
Distortion, 679
Distributed character of elements, 703
Double periodicity, 995, 998, 999
Dual, graphical procedure for finding, 672
Dual networks, 260, 265, 364
Duality, 15, 351, 644, 649
Duffin, R. J., 607

Elements, network, 6, 7, 31, 703
  adjustable, 721
  number required, 253, 599, 657
Elimination of unknowns, 1108
Ellipse, 980, 1044
Elliptic functions, 87, 998
  calculation of, 1002 ff.
Energy, 108
  stored, 718
Equalizer, 679, 1052
  design, 680, 807
    charts, 691–692, 695
    examples, 1052, 1062
Equal-ripple approximation, see Chebyshev approximation
Equation of quantization, see Quantization equation
Equipotential, 838
  of several branches, 840, 902
Equivalent networks, 254, 259, 356, 364, 538, 647
Equivalent source theorems, 19
Error, 744–745
Error ripple, formulas, 919
  in Chebyshev approximation, for odd-function approximation of constant, 1004
  formulas for, 894, 897
  limits of, 919–920
  spacing of, 895, 930
  zeros of, 952, 955
Essential singularity, 50

Even function, 174
Even part, 174
  of immittance function, 542
  partition of, *see* Partition
  poles, 411
  potential analogy for, 846, 850
  relation to real part, 177
  zeros of, *see* Zeros
Even-π lines, 861
Even polynomial, factoring of, avoiding
    complex numbers, 494
  zeros of, 187
Even p-r functions, 289
Excess elements, *see* Surplus elements
Expansions, *see* Continued-fraction ex-
    pansion, Series, Taylor
Expansions of elliptic functions, 1003
Exponential function, 81
  Padé table for, 780, 814
Exponential potential function, 837
Exponential potential plane, use in
    quantization, 1031–1032
External critical frequency, 311
External zeros, poles, 253
Extrapolation, 827

$F_0(\omega/\omega_0)$ function, 405, 408, 488
Falloff rate, 897, 1018, 1030, 1039
Feedback, 689
Feedback amplifier networks, 701
Fialkow, A., 646, 670
Field map, 838
Filter, 695, 699, 792, 1010
  low-pass, 898
Flux, 833
Flux density, uniformization of, 930
Flux lines, 838
  behavior at conductor, 851
Flux linkage, node, 13
Flux plot, 838
Foster, R. M., 252
Foster canonic form, 271–273, 276
Fourier series, 99, 828
Four-terminal network, 4
Frequency, as independent variable, 2
  complex, 29
  critical, 253, 308, 352
  negative, 30
  square root of, 1050, 1062

Frequency pattern, for *L-C* networks,
    252
  for *R-C* networks, 309, 311
  for *R-L* networks, 352
Frequency transformation, 161–162,
    301, 934, 1025
  low-internal band, 1028–1029, 1087
Function, 34, 50
  see also specific functions such as
    Network function, Rational
    function.
  analytic, 37
  inverse, 35
  rational, 31–32
  regular, 37

Gain, limited by capacitance, 1041, 1081
  maximum attainable, 700
Gain-bandwidth limitations, 393, 700
Gauss, K. F., 1108
Gaussian transmission function, 818
Gauss's theorem, 834
Gerst, I., 646, 670
Gewertz, C. M., 409, 430
Gravitational field, 1013
Gravitational potential, 840
Guillemin, E. A., 121

Half-power frequencies, 734–735
Half-unit charge, 987 ff., 1049
Harmonic functions, 38
Helman, D., 1033
Helmholtz, H. L. F., 19
High approximation band, 930
High-band to low-band transformation,
    931
Hilbert transforms, 69, 385
Hose, water, 745
Hurwitz conjugate, 412, 461
Hurwitz determinant test, 225
Hurwitz polynomial, 178, 364
  derivative of also Hurwitz, 1014
  relation to reactance function, 239,
    290–291
  test for, 194
Hyperbolic trigonometric functions,
    81–82, 87

Images, method of, 906

Imaginary part, 33
  relation to odd part, 177
Imaginary-real part relations, *see* Real-imaginary part relations
Imaginary unit, *j*, 33
Imaginary zeros, poles, 169
Immittance function, 18
  see also Admittance, Angle of immittance function, Even part, Impedance, Real-imaginary part relations
  calculation of, from angle or tangent, 447
    from even part, 620
    from magnitude, 433
    from reactance, 426, 468
    from resistance, 415, 463, 480
  partitioning of, 627
  with zeros of even part confined to axes, 564
  with zeros of even part only at origin and infinity, 561, 590–591
  with zeros of even part only at real frequencies, 560
Impedance, 17
  of current source, 22
  of voltage source, 22
Impedance function, driving-point, 109, 142
Impulse function, in resistance (conductance), 474
Independent loop, 10
Independent node pair, 10
Inductor, 7, 703
  networks with only one, 606
Infinite networks, 9, 159–161, 166, 301, 367, 966, 1042
Infinite-order functions, 84
Infinity, 63
  approach of charge to, in approximation, 987
  as a point, 38–39
  behavior of immittance functions at, 172
  behavior of *L-C* network functions at, 238
  behavior of *R-C* network functions at, 307

Infinity, behavior of *R-L* network functions at, 352
Information required for specification, of *L-C* immittance function, 251, 253
  of *R-C* immittance function, 310
  of *R-L* immittance function, 354
Integration, *see also* Contour of integration
  independent of path, 40
Interlacing of zeros and poles, 236
Internal approximation band, 898
Internal critical frequency, 311
Internal zeros, poles, 253
Interpolation, 742, 827
Interstage networks, 687, 698–699, 701, 796, 823, 1027
  R-L-C ("tuned circuit") type, 1044, 1084
  shunt-peaked type, 1043
Inverse, structural, 649
Inverse networks, 260, 340, 355, 648
Inversion of *p* plane, 39, 931
Isograph, 1111, 1134
Iterative impedance, 1042
Iterative method of design, 1043
Iterative processes, 1120
  in root finding, 1111

Kautz, W. H., 827
Kingsbury, B. A., 1137
Kirchhoff, G. R., 10
Kuh, E. S., 667

L-C network, 1055
Ladder networks, 93, 159, 263, 276, 340, 355, 556, 628, 966–967
Ladder realizations, 632, 638
Lagrange's equations, 107, 154
Landon, V. D., 792
Laplace's equation, 38, 106, 832, 1012
Lattice network, 91, 654, 681
Least squares, method of, 756, 809
Left half plane, 116
Leroy, R., 568
Limits of oscillation in Chebyshev approximation, 919–920
Linear fractional transformation, *see* Bilinear transformation

Linearity, 1, 6, 703
Linearization, 1132
Loci of points of quantization, *see*
    Charges, motion of
Logarithmic function, 83
  even and odd parts of, 496
Looking Glass World, 865, 906, 1015
Loop and node methods compared, 14
Lossless, 232
Low band, 855
  to high band transformation, 935
Lumped character, 1, 6, 703

m derivation, 970 ff.
Maclaurin series, 46
Magnitude of immittance function, 431
  approximate calculation from angle,
    408
  constant, 960
  in terms of angle, 398
  maximum obtainable with capaci-
    tance, 1039–1040
  properties required of, 457
  realizability of, 1035–1037, 1041
Mapping, 872
  see also Frequency transformation
  by cutting and bending, 884
  use in root finding, 1114
Maximal approximation, 761, 767
Maximally flat functions, 792, 954
  constant, odd, 1007
Maximally linear angle, 781, 799, 821
Maximum gain attainable, 700
Maximum-minimum theorems, 78, 80
Maximum-modulus theorem, 79
Maximum power transfer, 20
Mean-square error, 757
Mean squares, method of, 756, 809
Minimum conductance, 376
Minimum (immittance) function, 380
Minimum number of elements required,
    253, 599, 657
  see also Surplus elements
  L-C networks, 253, 288, 291
  R-C networks, 340
  R-L networks, 354
Minimum reactance, 371
Minimum resistance, 376
Minimum susceptance, 371

Mirror, 906
Miyata, F., 491
Moore, A. D., 1126
Motion, of charges in approximation,
    see also Charges
  of roots of quantization equation, *see*
    Charges
  of zeros of even part, 600
Mutual inductance, 8
  in *L-C* networks, 293, 298
  need for, 608, 612, 617
  one-resistor realizations without, 584
  sign convention, 8

Natural modes, 27
Nature, perversity of, 702
Negative elements, realization of, 509
Negative pole, 507
Negative zero, 521
Neper, 83
Network, active, 9
  definition, 1, 9
Network function, 30
Network synthesis, parts of, 2, 702
Networks, *see also* specific types such as
    Balancing networks, Bridged-T
    networks, Delay networks
  equivalent, *see* Equivalent networks
  one-inductor, 606
Newton's method, 1118 ff.
Node, 10
Nondissipative, 232
Nonrational function, 145
Normalization, equations for, 22
  of elements, 277
  of frequency scale, 21
  of impedance scale, 20
Norton, E. L., 792
Norton's theorem, 19
Number of elements required, *see* Mini-
    mum number of elements re-
    quired
Nyquist's criterion, 64, 178

Odd function, 174
Odd part, 74
  of immittance, zero and pole loca-
    tions, 423
  of *R-C* and *R-L* networks, 361

Odd part, partition of, *see* Partition
potential analogy for, 846, 850
relation to imaginary part, 177
zeros, motion of, 541
Odd-π lines, 861
Odd p-r functions, 189, 234
Odd rational functions, 772
One-inductor networks, 606
One-ohm basis, 20
One-port network, 4
One-radian-per-second basis, 21
One-resistor realizations, 550, 561, 582
applications, 685
One-terminal pair, *see* Pair
Open-wire transmission line, 698
Operational amplifier, 701
Order, of *L-C* network, 291
of pole, 38, 49
of rational function, 40
of reactance function, 288
of zero, 38
Origin, approach of charge to in approx-
imation, 987
behavior of *L-C* networks at, 238
behavior of *R-C* networks at, 308
behavior of *R-L* networks at, 352
Orthogonal functions, 812

Padé approximation, 761
Padé table, 777
for exponential function, 780, 814
Pair, 4
one-terminal, 4
two-terminal, 4
Pantell, R. H., 631, 646, 670
Parallel-T network, 300, 363
Parasitic effects, 703 ff., 720
Partial-fraction expansion, 353, 664–
665
Partition, 652
of even part, 620, 626–632
of odd part, 627
Pascal triangle, 763, 817
Passive network, 9
Perfectly coupled inductors, 510, 529,
531
Periodicity, double, 995–999

Phasor (complex-number) representation, 16, 24, 89–91
Plane (complex), parts of, 116
Point matching, 746
Polar form, 34
Pole, 32, 38, 49, 62
imaginary, 168
of *L-C* networks, 235–236
of *R-C* networks, 306
of *R-L* networks, 352
order of, 49
prescription of in approximating a
constant, 1032–1034
proximity to zeros, 962, 1015
removal of part of, 275, 969 ff.
simple, 38
Polynomial, approximation of, 1033
Chebyshev, *see* Chebyshev polynomial
even, zeros of, 187
factoring of, 1124
Hurwitz, *see* Hurwitz polynomial
numerical evaluation of, 1104 ff.
splitting process, 420, 428, 436, 448,
1124
zeros of, *see* Zeros
Port, 4
P-r, 533
see also Positive-real entries
Positive-real branch, *see* Branch
Positive-real functions, 123, 144
even, 223
in potential-analogy terms, 848–849
odd, 189, 234
rational, 144
reciprocal of, 164
relation to rational functions, 289,
357, 503, 533
Positive-real square root, 148, 910
Positive reality, implications of, 163 ff.
relation to rationality, 165
sufficiency of, 246, 533, 583
test for, 182–183, 358, 365
Potential, complex, 836
as mapping function, 872
principal value of, 863
electric, 833
exponential, 837, 1031–1032
gravitational, 840

Potential, invariance in transformation, 879

Precision in computation, *see* Accuracy in computation

Predistortion, 710

Principal part, 52

Principal sheet of Riemann surface, 874

Principal value, of complex potential function, 863
    of integral, 68, 382

Prototype, 1009

Prototype potential situation, 862, 896

Q, of capacitor, 706
    of inductor, 704
    of network, 713, 720, 733

Quadrantal symmetry, 187

Quadratic form, 134
    positive (semi) definite, 136–137

Quality of approximation, *see* Approximation

Quantization, 856, 860, 1009–1010
    result of, 883

Quantization equation, 859, 879, 906, 920, 924, 949, 954, 978–979, 992, 1020
    see also Charges, motion of
    change of variable in, 1023
    solution of, 1023

Quantization process, 976

Quantized potential situation, 882, 896

R point, 311

R-C and R-L immittance functions, class, 355
    properties of even and odd parts, 500
    properties of magnitude and angle, 500

R-C networks, 1008, 1048
    real-frequency behavior, 321
    removal of, 631

R-L networks, 1008, 1048
    real-frequency behavior, 354
    removal of, 631

R-L-C one-terminal-pair realization methods, 646

Radian, 83

Radius of convergence, 45

Rational function, 164

Rational function, approximation by rational functions, 789, 794, 821
    Chebyshev type, 895–896
    number of zeros and poles, 40
    numerical evaluation of, 1107
    of infinite order, 84, 776, 877
    order of, 40
    relation to p-r functions, 289, 503, 533
    Taylor approximation of, 789, 794

Rationality, relation to positive reality, 165, 357

Reactance, 18
    approximate calculation of, from resistance, 407, 480, 484
    approximately constant, 343, 1006
    calculation of, from resistance, *see also* Real-imaginary part relations
        given in only part of spectrum, 482–486
        using Fourier series, 483
    complete determination of by resistance, 474
    in terms of resistance, formulas, 385, 399
    linear property at low frequencies, 475
    of R-C networks, 320
    of R-L networks, 354
    properties required of, 457

Reactance function, 233–234
    information necessary to determine, 251, 253
    relation to Hurwitz polynomial, 290
    result of differentiation of numerator and denominator, 1014
    slope of, 290

Reactance integral, 101, 392

Reactance removal, 275

Real-frequency behavior, of R-C immittance functions, 321, 328
    of R-L immittance functions, 354

Real-imaginary part relations, 69, 103
    approach through time response, 487
    calculations based on, *see* Angle of immittance function, Immittance function, Magnitude of immit-

tance function, Reactance function, Resistance function
evaluation of integrals, 491
Fourier-series approach, 483
Miyata's process, 491
use of potential analogy in calculation, 1014
Real part, 33
maximum and minimum of, 80
relation to even part, 177
Realizability, requirements on parts of immittance for, 457–458
simple ladder form, requirements of, 560 ff.
Realization, and approximation, sequence of, 974
general methods, 583
with only one resistor, 584
Reciprocal, 649
networks, 259–260, 326, 364
Reciprocity, 19
Rectangular form, 34
Redundant elements, see Surplus elements
Reflection of zeros (poles) from one half plane to other, 440
Regular, see Function
Remainder theorem, 1105
Removal of part of a pole, 342, 969
of zeros of even part, see Even part
Residue, 48, 58, 61
formulas for, 62–63
Resistance, 18
see also Even part
calculation of from reactance, see also Real-imaginary part relations
approximate methods, 407, 479, 484
given in only part of spectrum, 482–486
using Fourier series, 483
in terms of reactance, formulas, 385, 399
of R-C networks, 320
of R-L networks, 354
Resistance efficiency, 700
Resistance function, properties required of, 457

Resistance integral, 101, 392
Resistance removal, 334
Resistor, 3, 705
as approximate termination, 971
precision, 740
sufficiency of a single, 582
Resonance, 89–90, 712
at imaginary frequency, 314, 316
Reza, F. M., 646
Richards, P. I., 641
Richards function, 658
Riemann surface, 867
principal sheet, 874
simplification by cutting and sewing, 875
Right half plane, 116
Right-half-plane zeros, test for, 194, 226
Ripple, see Error-ripple approximation
Roots, approximate, 1023
complex, location of, 1114
number of, 102
real, location of, 1112
Routh's rule, 178, 226

S function, 1146
Saddle point, 840, 902, 987–988, 1019, 1021
Schematic diagram, 24
Schwartz-Christoffel transformation, 75, 997, 1016, 1026, 1048
as cutting and bending, 884
Section, network, 557
Sensitivity to element variations, 721, 732
Separate part, 10
Separation, see Partition
Series, Taylor, use of in approximation, 760
Sewing (of sheets), 938
Sharpe, C. B., 1033
Shea, T. E., 293
Sheet, see also Riemann surface
of Riemann surface, 867
cutting and sewing, 875
Shifting of zeros, 541
Sign of polynomial, test for, see Sturm's theorem

Significant figures, number of, *see* Accuracy in computation
Simulating networks, 684, 811
Sine function, infinite-product expansion, 85
Singing, 685
Singularities, 38, 49–50
  essential, 50
Sinh transformation, 878, 888–890
Slope, of angle (phase) function, 501
  of reactance, 723
    limitations on, 290, 518, 603
  of resistance, importance in determining reactance, 481
Slope property, of R-C networks, 306
  of R-L networks, 352
Smith, G. A., 491
Source exchanges, *see* Equivalent source theorems
Source impedances, 22
Sources, 9
Square root, "positive," 148
  positive-real, 910
  potential analogy view, 1014
Squaring of p plane, 936
Stationary points, 472
Steady state (a-c), 2
Sturm's theorem, 198, 203, 227
Sufficient conditions for realizability, 583
Sufficiency of positive reality, 246, 288, 316, 356
Superposition, 19
Surplus elements, 253, 275, 299–300
Surplus factors, 619, 623, 652, 658
  use in partitioning even part, 632
Susceptance, 18
  see also Reactance
  approximate calculation from conductance, 407
  approximately constant, 1006
  in terms of conductance, formulas for, 385, 399
  of R-C networks, 327
  of R-L networks, 354
  properties required of, 457
  removal of, 275
Susceptive, 232

Symbols, definitions of less common
  Ev, Od, 174
  Re, Im, $|\ |$, 34
  $\overset{+}{\sqrt{\ \ }}$, 148
  $\overset{-}{\ }$, 34
Symmetrical lattice network, 91
Symmetry, effect on quality of aproximation, 958
  even, 1020
  odd, 1020
  quadrantal, 187
  required of charge motion in approximation, 987
Synthesis, 1, 2, 1051–1052
System, rôle of networks in, 679

Tangent function, 237
Tangent of angle of immittance function, 438
  properties required of, 458
Taylor approximation, 761
  at several points, 800
  number of terms matched, 761, 953, 955
  potential analogy view, 954
  relation to Chebyshev approximation, 951, 957, 1006, 1018, 1030, 1032, 1034
Termination, approximate, 971
Tetrad, 187, 624
Thévenin's theorem, 19
Thomas, D. E., 1137
Time constant, 314
Tn function, 998, 1002
Tobak, M., 491
Transcendental function, 84
Transducer, 4
Transformation, *see also* Bilinear transformation, Frequency transformation, Mapping, Schwartz-Christoffel transformation
  as cutting and bending of plane, 995
  conformal, 1010
  inversion of plane, 931
  squaring, 936
Transformer, 8, 138
  coupling coefficient, 510
  equivalent networks for, 93
  ideal, 9, 93

Transmission lines, 301, 693, 697, 698, 812
Transmission networks, 678
Trial and error methods, 680, 746, 749, 969, 1060
Trigonometric functions, use in approximation, 828
Truncation of infinite network, 967, 974
Twin-T network, 300, 363
Two-port network, 4
Two-terminal network, 4
Two-terminal pair, *see* Pair
Type-A section, 557
Type-B section, 557
Type-C section, 559, 563, 599
Type-D section, 582, 604–605

Univalent, 103

Vacuum-tube interstage networks, *see* Interstage networks
Vacuum tubes, *see also* Amplifier networks for use with, 592, 1062
Ville, J., 568, 587

Water hose, 745
Weighting, 786

Zeros, 32, 38
imaginary, 168
influence in determining trajectories of charge, 988

Zeros, motion of, 541
number of, 102
in a half plane, 499
in a region, 65, 102
in right half plane, 520, 523, 566–567
of derivative of a polynomial, 1014
of even part of immittance function, 551 ff.
at origin, infinity only, 561, 590–591
confined to axes, 563
location of, 411, 584
motion of, 541
physical origin of, 556
properties, 600
real-frequency, 559
removal of, 558, 582
of even part of *R-C*, *R-L* immittance functions, 361
of *L-C* network functions, 235–236
of polynomial, tests for location, 194, 225–226
of *R-C* network functions, 306
of *R-L* network functions, 352
of symmetrical functions, 187
proximity to poles, 962, 1015
rôle in determining realizability, 961
shifting of, 970
simple, 38